RELIGIONS IN THE UK

A MULTI-FAITH DIRECTORY

Centre for
Faith and Spirituality
Loughborough University

RELIGIONS IN THE UK

A MULTI-FAITH DIRECTORY

edited by
Paul Weller

researched by
Rachelle Castle & Paul Weller

Published by the University of Derby in association with
The Inter Faith Network for the United Kingdom

First edition 1993

ISBN 0 901437 06 9

Published by University of Derby in association with The Inter Faith Network for the United Kingdom (Registered Charity number 296773).

University of Derby, Mickleover, Derby, DE3 5GX.

In association with the
Inter Faith Network for the United Kingdom,
5-7 Tavistock Place, London, WC1H 9SS.

Typset by David Bush, University of Derby.

Printed by Russell Press Ltd,
Radford Mill, Norton Street, Nottingham NG7 3HN.

CONTENTS

PREFACE

ACKNOWLEDGEMENTS

USING THE DIRECTORY

MAKING CONTACTS, ORGANISING EVENTS AND CONSULTATIONS

RELIGIOUS LANDSCAPE OF THE UK

THE BAHA'I COMMUNITY

THE BUDDHIST COMMUNITY

THE CHRISTIAN COMMUNITY

THE HINDU COMMUNITY

THE JAIN COMMUNITY

THE JEWISH COMMUNITY

THE MUSLIM COMMUNITY

THE SIKH COMMUNITY

THE ZOROASTRIAN COMMUNITY

SOME OTHER RELIGIOUS GROUPS

INTER-FAITH ACTIVITY IN THE UK

RESOURCES

INDEXES

UPDATE SHEETS

PREFACE

This directory is a resource which is designed to assist and encourage the further development of inter-religious contacts and dialogue in the UK and to facilitate the wider participation in public life of the generally accepted world religious traditions which have established communities in this country. We hope that it will be a "user-friendly" tool which will prove to be of value to a wide range of individuals and organisations.

Religious belief, identity and community are matters which relate to the deepest convictions of many. There will generally be a welcome for those who use the directory to make contact with the places of worship and religious organisations listed within it, but there is also a potential for misunderstanding. This directory will therefore only fulfill its aims if it is used sensitively.

In order to assist in the sensitive use of the names, addresses, telephone numbers and other information which it contains, the directory includes introductory materials on the beliefs and structures of the religious communities whichnit covers. It also contains keys to terms used in the titles of the organisations which are listed within it and a chapter of guidelines for making contact with and consulting religious communities, as well as advice on visiting their places of worship.

Some religious communities produce generally available and well-established directories covering organisations within their own traditions. Others have not so far done so and this directory therefore contains much information which was previously unavailable. Where information has been available on particular communities, it has never before been drawn together into a multi-faith reference of the present kind.

It was to fill this gap that the Multi-Faith Directory Research Project was established as a jointly funded and sponsored initiative between the University of Derby's Religious Resource and Research Centre and The Inter Faith Network for the United Kingdom.

The Network links seventy organisations in inter-faith activity. It exists to promote good relations between people of different faiths in the UK and to provide a public information service.

The Religious Resource and Research Centre is a joint initiative of the University of Derby and the Church of England Diocese of Derby. The Centre is involved in research and teaching in relation to the religious life of the UK. It also acts in a central service role within the University on matters of religious belief and practice.

An important principle of effective inter-faith dialogue is that the partners in dialogue should be free to define themselves. The research which lies behind this directory has tried to take into full account the concerns, perspectives and sensitivities of the religious communities with which the Project has been working. The introductory materials were therefore written in full consultation with representatives from the religious traditions which covers. The project has also drawn upon the knowledge, experience and expertise of academics working in relevant fields. What finally appears in this Directory is, therefore, the product of a lengthy and careful process of consultation, discussion and debate. It is a co-operative effort in which believers and practiioners from within religious traditions were closely involved, as well as academics.

Describing such a range of religious traditions and communities within a single volume is a challenging and sensitive task. Similarly, the gathering of data on thousands of organisations is time-consuming, exacting and not always straightforward. Because this is the first time such a directory has been attempted there are bound to be some omissions and accidental inaccuracies. We apologise for these and invite users to contact us with suggestions for any future edition.

Nevertheless, we believe that this first edition provides a more comprehensive and accurate guide than has hitherto been available and offer it in the hope that it will prove to be a useful resource in the multi-faith society of today's United Kingdom.

Paul Weller
Directory Research Project Director and Editor
University of Derby, Religious Resource and
Research Centre

ACKNOWLEDGEMENTS

The Multi-Faith Directory Research Project was funded by the University of Derby and The Inter Faith Network for the United Kingdom. The Commission for Racial Equality also made a contributory grant.

Many individuals and organisations have offered assistance to the project. Of all the acknowledgements which should be made, one of the most significant must be to **Ms Rachelle Castle** who worked as the project's Research Assistant for the two and a half years of research which lie behind this publication.

Rachelle's willingness to search out new avenues of information and knowledge and her dedication to detail have been the bedrock of the project. She has carried out much of the basic research work involved as well as handling much of the mechanics of consultation. Rachelle's work, however, has also depended upon the voluntary contributions of many individuals and organisations from within the religious communities of the UK.

In relation to the directory's introductory materials on the various religious communities, the keys to organisational names and the listings of organisations, consultative arrangements were established with representatives from the relevant religious communities.

In some cases, specific Community Consultative Panels were formed for the purpose of the project. In others, existing organisations, groups or individual consultants were approached to comment upon the original drafts. In a number of cases, individuals with particular expertise from outside of the traditions were also consulted.

Acknowledgements are due particularly to the following individuals and organisations:

THE BAHA'I COMMUNITY

Mr Hugh Adamson, Baha'i Community of the United Kingdom.

THE BUDDHIST COMMUNITY

Dharmachari Dharmadhara, Friends of the Western Buddhist Order; **Mr Anil Goonewardene,** Buddhist Society; **Sister Jotaka,** Amaravati Buddhist Centre; **Dharmachari Kulananda,** Friends of the Western Buddhist Order; **Mr Ron Maddox,** The Buddhist Society; **Revd Daiṣhin Morgan,** Throssel Hole Priory; **Revd Myokyo-ni,** The Zen Centre, London; **Dr Akong Tarup,** Kagyu Samye Ling; **Most Venerable Pandit Dr Vajiragnana,** London Buddhist Vihara; **Ms Anne Whittle,** The Buddhist Society.

Also consulted was **Professor Richard Gombrich,** University of Oxford.

THE CHRISTIAN COMMUNITY

Most Revd Father Olu Abiola, Council of African and Afro-Caribbean Churches (UK); **Mr John Adegoge,** Centre for Black and White Christian Partnership, Birmingham; **Father Michael Barnes,** Westminster Interfaith Programme; **Ms Vida Barnett,** Shap Working Party on World Religions in Education; **Ms Celia Blackden,** Roman Catholic Committee for Relations with Other Faiths of the Bishops' Conference of England and Wales; **Rt Hon David Bleakley,** Irish Council of Churches; **Prebendary Marcus Braybrooke,** World Congress of Faiths; **Revd Eric Brown,** Afro-West Indian United Council of Churches; **Mrs Jenny Carpenter,** Churches Together in England; **Revd Maxwell Craig,** Action of Churches Together in Scotland; **Revd Dr Colin Davey,** Council of Churches for Britain and Ireland; **Revd Noel Davies,** Churches Together in Wales; **Revd Basil Hazledine,** Epsom; **Rt Revd Charles Henderson,** Roman Catholic Committee for Other Faiths of the Bishops' Conference of England and Wales; **Revd Canon Dr Christopher Lamb,** Churches' Commission for Inter Faith Relations, Council of Churches for Britain and Ireland; **Revd Anne McClelland,** Richmond Inter-Faith Group; **Ms Lesley Mathias,** World Congress of Faiths; **Revd Roger Nunn,** Churches Together in England; **Mrs Gwen Palmer,** Religious Education Council for England and Wales; **Revd Canon Martin Reardon,** Churches Together in England; **Sister Margaret Shepherd, NDS,** Council of Christians and Jews; **Dr David Stevens,** Irish Council of Churches; **Rt Revd Roy Williamson,** Church of England Bishop of Southwark.

Also consulted on the Christian organisational listings were **Revd Esme Beswick**, Joint Council for Anglo-Caribbean Churches; **Rt Revd David Douglas**, International Ministerial Council of Great Britain; **Revd Carmel Jones**, New Assembly of Churches; **Revd Dr David Staple**, Free Church Federal Council.

THE HINDU COMMUNITY

A Community Consultative Panel was formed comprising: **Mr Rameshbhai Acharya**, Birmingham; **Mr Arun Chaudhary**, Loughborough; **Mr Harshad Chauhan**, National Council of Hindu Temples; **Mr Jitubhai Pancholi**, Swaminarayan Hindu Mission; **Ms Hansaben Patel**, Birmingham; **Mr Himachali Om Prakash Sharma**, Vishwa Hindu Parishad (deceased, 1992). Other Hindus consulted were **Mr Vipin Aery**, National Council of Hindu Temples; **Sri Akhandadi das**, International Society for Krishna Consciousness; **Mr Raj Bali**, Religious Resource and Research Centre Steering Committee, University of Derby; **Professor Bharadwaj**, Arya Pratinidhi Sabha; **Mr Mathoor Krishnamurti**, Bharatiya Vidya Bhavan; **Mr Thakorbhai Patel**, Vishwa Hindu Parishad; **Dr Ramabhai Shah**, Swaminarayan Hindu Mission; **Rasamandala das**, ISKCON Education Service; **Mr Om Parkash Sharma**, National Council of Hindu Temples.

Also consulted were **Mr Bob Jackson**, University of Warwick; **Dr Kim Knott**, University of Leeds; **Ms Eleanor Nesbitt**, University of Warwick. On the Hindu organisational listings the Brent Hindu Council was additionally consulted.

THE JAIN COMMUNITY

Mr Nemu Chandaria, Institute of Jainology; **Professor Padminabh Jaini**, University of California, Berkeley, USA and Trustee of the Institute of Jainology; **Mr Vinod Kapashi**, Federation of Jain Organisations in the UK; **Mr Bipin Mehta**, Institute of Jainology; **Dr Natubhai Shah**, Jain Samaj Europe.

Also consulted were: **Dr Paul Marett**, Jain Academy; **Ms Kristy Wiley**, University of California, Berkeley, USA.

THE JEWISH COMMUNITY

Rabbi David Goldberg, London Society of Jews and Christians; **Revd Jonathan Gorsky**, Council of Christians and Jews; **Rabbi Hugo Gryn CBE**, West London Synagogue of British Jews; **Rabbi Dr Julian Jacobs**, Chief Rabbi's Representative on Inter-Faith Affairs; **Mr Paul Mendel**, Council of Christians and Jews; **Professor Eric Moonman OBE**, London; **Mr Neville Nagler**, Board of Deputies of British Jews; **Mr Hayim Pinner OBE**, London; **Mr Robert Rabinowitz**, Board of Deputies of British Jews; **Mr Laurie Rosenberg**, Board of Deputies of British Jews; **Ms Marlena Schmool,** Board of Deputies of British Jews; **Rabbi Dr Norman Solomon**, Centre for the Study of Judaism and Jewish-Christian Relations, Selly Oak Colleges, Birmingham.

Also consulted was **Sister Mary Kelly** of the Sisters of Sion Study Centre for Christian-Jewish Relations.

THE MUSLIM COMMUNITY

A Community Consultative Panel was formed comprising: **Mr Javaid Bostan**, National Association of Muslim Youth; **Mr Farooq Chaudhary**, Islamic Foundation; **Maulana Mohammad Shahid Raza**, Imams and Mosques Council, UK.

Other Muslims consulted were: **Professor Kamal Abdul-Ghany**, Islamic Cultural Centre, London; **Mr Syed Faiyazuddin Ahmad**, Islamic Foundation; **Mr Nazrul Islam Bose**, Council of Mosques (UK & Eire); **Dr Mughram al-Ghamdhi**, Islamic Cultural Centre, Regent's Park Mosque, London; **Mr Mohsin Jaffer**, World Ahl ul-Bayt (AS) Islamic League; **Mr Gulam Husein Musa**, World Ahl ul-Bayt (AS) Islamic League; **Mr Syed Syediau**, World Islamic Mission (UK).

Also consulted was **Dr Jorgen Nielsen**, Centre for the Study of Islam and Christian-Muslim Relations, Selly Oak Colleges, Birmingham.

On the Muslim organisational listings: **Mr Ahmed Andrews**, Dundee, and **Mr Neil North**, Centre for the Study of Islam and Christian-Muslim Relations, Selly Oak Colleges, Birmingham; Alliance of Newham Muslim Associations; Birmingham Confederation of Sunni Mosques; Bradford Council for Mosques; Council of Birmingham Mosques; Council of Mosques and Islamic Organisations in Sheffield; Federation of Islamic Student Societies; Stoke-on-Trent Federation of Mosques; Federation of Muslim Organisations in Leicestershire; Islamic Council of Scotland; Lancashire Council of Mosques;

Manchester Council of Mosques; Muslim Education Co-Ordinating Council; Muslim Parliament of Great Britain; National Association of Muslim Youth; Sandwell Confederation of Bangladeshi Muslim Organisations; UK Islamic Mission; Union of Muslim Organisations of UK and Eire; and Young Muslim Organisation (UK) were additionally consulted.

THE SIKH COMMUNITY

A community consultative panel was formed comprising: **Sardar Mohinder Singh Chana**, Bradford; **Dr Hardial Singh Dhillon**, Religious Resource and Research Centre Steering Committee, University of Derby; **Sardar Mohinder Singh Mankoo**, Birmingham Council of Gurdwaras; **Sardar Darshan Singh Tatla**, Birmingham; **Sardar Ranjit Singh Wahiwala**. Birmingham Sikh Missionary Resource Centre. Other Sikhs consulted include: **Sardar Teja Singh Manget**, Sikh Missionary Resource Centre; and **Professor Gobind Singh Mansukhani** (deceased, 1993), Sikh Council for Interfaith Relations. **Sardar Harbans Singh** and **Sardar Indarjit Singh**, of the Sikh Council for Interfaith Relations.

Also consulted was **Ms Eleanor Nesbitt**, University of Warwick. On the Sikh organisational listings the Federation of Bradford Sikh Organisations and the Council of Sikh Gurdwaras in Birmingham were additionally consulted.

THE ZOROASTRIAN COMMUNITY

Mr Malcolm Deboo, Zoroastrian House; **Mr Jehangir Sarosh**, London Zoroastrian Community; **Dr Rashna Writer**, Birkbeck College, London.

Also consulted was **Dr Jenny Rose**, West London Institute of Higher Education.

INTER-FAITH ORGANISATIONS

Mr Peter Baker, Redbridge Council of Faiths; **Ms Vida Barnett**, Merseyside Inter-Faith Group; **Dr Peter Bell**, Leeds Concord Inter-Faith Fellowship; **Revd Jonathan Blake**, World Conference on Religion and Peace (UK & Eire Chapter) and Medway Interfaith Group; **Mr Hugh Boulter**, Reading Inter-Faith Group; **Revd Robert Boulter**, Manchester Inter-Faith Group; **Dr David Bowen**, Bradford Concord Inter-Faith Society; **Prebendary Marcus Braybooke**, World Congress of Faiths; **Revd Jean Clark**, Coventry Inter-Faith Group; **Mr Khosro Deinim**, Kirklees and Calderdale Inter-Faith Fellowship; **Ms Rosemary Eldridge**, Glasgow Sharing of Faiths Group; **Ms Jo Fageant**, Reading Inter-Faith Group; **Revd Peter Godfrey**, International Association for Religious Freedom, British Members' Group; **Rabbi David Goldberg, London Society of Jews and Christians; Mrs Ivy Gutridge**, Wolverhampton Inter-Faith Group; **Dr Mary Hall**, Multi-Faith Centre; Birmingham; **Dr Mary Hayward**, Shap Working Party on World Religions in Education; **Ms Carmen Henry,** Wellingborough Multi-Faith Group; **Mr Stanley Hope**, Rochdale Interfaith Action; **Monsignor Paul Hypher**, Peterborough Inter Faith Council; **Sister Mary Kelly**, Study Centre for Christian-Jewish Relations; **Ms Judith Law,** Waltham Forest All Faiths Group; **Revd Anne McClelland**, Richmond Inter-Faith Group; **Father Gordian Marshall**, Standing Conference of Jews, Christians and Muslims in Europe; **Mr Sirjit Singh Marway**, Medway Inter-Faith Group; **Mr Paul Mendel**, Council of Christians and Jews; **Ms Peggy Morgan**, Shap Working Party on World Religions in Education; **Mr Vince Murray**, Birmingham Inter-Faiths Council; **Mr Santokh Singh Nijran**, Nottingham Inter-Faith Group; **Mrs Gwen Palmer**, Religious Education Council; **Mr David Potter**, World Congress of Faiths; **Ms Joanne Quirke**, Walsall Inter Faith Group; **Mrs June Ridd**, Bristol Interfaith Group; **Revd Robin Ross**, Edinburgh Interfaith Association; **Mrs Doris Sadeghi**, Newham Association of Faiths; **Revd Trevor Shannon**, Shap Working Party on World Religions in Education; **Ms Janine Shrigley,** Derby Open Centre Multi-Faith Group; **Mr Hari Shukla**, Tyne and Wear Racial Equality Council Inter Faith Panel; **Revd Hilary Smart**, Walsall Inter Faith Group; **Ms Pat Stevens**, Harrow Inter-Faith Council; **Ms Caroline Wallace**, Birmingham Fellowship of Faiths; **Canon Michael Walls**, Leicester Council of Faiths; **Ms Angela Wood**, Standing Conference on Inter-Faith Dialogue in Education; **Mr S K Vadivale**, Oxford Round Table of Religions; **Mr David Yarham**, Cambridge Inter-Faith Group; **Dr Iraz Zamiri**, Cardiff Interfaith Association.

Thanks are also due to **Mr Andrew Currah** of the Manor Park Faith in the Community Project for his additional help on the listings of organisations and places of worship in Newham.

In addition to the acknowledgements above, mention should also be made of the role of the members of the project's Academic Advisory Panel for the academic expertise and guidance which they brought to bear upon the project's progress. Members of the panel were drawn from among academics associated with the work of The Inter Faith Network who have particular expertise in a range of the religious communities with which the directory is concerned, as well as University of Derby staff with particular expertise in Religious Studies, Social Science and research methodology.

This Panel therefore consisted of: **Dr John Hey**, Senior Lecturer and Subject Leader of Theology and Religious Studies, University of Derby; **Dr Kim Knott**, Senior Lecturer in the Department of Theology and Religious Studies, University of Leeds; **Revd Peter Kurti**, Deputy Head of the Religious Resource and Research Centre, University of Derby; **Ms Eleanor Nesbitt**, Senior Research Fellow, Religious Education and Community Project, Department of Arts Education, University of Warwick; **Dr Jorgen Nielsen**, Director of the Centre for the Study of Islam and Christian-Muslim Relations, Selly Oak Colleges, Birmingham; **Dr Gwen Wallace**, Reader in Policy Studies, University of Derby; **Mr Paul Weller**, Principal Lecturer and Head of the Religious Resource and Research Centre, University of Derby. **Mr Brian Pearce**, Director of The Inter Faith Network for the United Kingdom was also a member of the Panel.

Special thanks are also due to the members of The Inter Faith Network Executive Committee whose names are included in the lists above and who, as well as commenting on the introductory materials and organisational listings for their own religious community, also examined the introductory materials and organisational listings of the chapter on Inter-Religious Activity. As well as reading and commenting on the chapterc on "Making Contact, Organising Events and Consultations" those on the "Religious Landscapeof the United Kingdom" and "Using the Directory."

Thanks should also be expressed to a number of other individuals, including some members of the Network Executive Committee, who read and commented upon the introductory materials of each religious community from the perspective of its accessibility and intelligibility to an outsider to that community. Those who are not otherwise referred to above already include **Revd Michael Ipgrave**, Leicester.

Acknowledgement is especially due to the staff of the Inter Faith Network for their contributions and encouragement throughout the period of the project - to **Mr Brian Pearce**, the Network's Director, and to **Dr Harriet Crabtree**, its Assistant Director, for their support to the project team in Derby and their attention to detail in working through the drafts of the Directory.

Drafts of the introductory materials on the various religions were originated by **Ms Rachelle Castle** and **Mr Paul Weller**. Drafts of the "Religious Landscape of the UK" and "Using the Directory" were originated by **Mr Paul Weller**; drafts of "Inter-Faith Activity in the UK" by **Mr Paul Weller** and **Mr Brian Pearce**; and of the chapter on "Making Contacts, Organising Events and Consultations" by **Dr Harriet Crabtree**.

They were then circulated on a number of occasions and in different combinations, as appropriate, to the consultants indicated above. Where necessary, the original drafts were then amended in the light of the comments and guidance received.

For its listings of religious organisations, the project has also depended upon the co-operation and contributions of many individuals and organisations which have provided it with information and examined draft listings. The individuals and organisations who gave substantial help throughout the project are individually named above.

Gratitude for help and assistance should also be recorded to all the organisations which are affiliated to The Inter Faith Network; local Race Equality Councils; local Councils for Voluntary Service; Local Authority Religious Education Advisers; Local Authority Planning Departments; Superintendent Registrars in a number of cities of England and Wales; **Lee Owens** and **Sue Hodgkinson** at the Office of Population Censuses and Surveys; Local Authority Library Services and religious correspondents in the print and broadcast media, many of whom have provided the project with valuable information upon organisations and some of whom also contributed to checking the draft listings.

Acknowledgements should also be recorded to the compilers, editors and publishers of existing handbooks and directories of religious organisations and groups (which this directory is not intended to replace, but rather to complement) upon whose work the project also drew in compiling its original information for making direct contact with many of the organisations included here. Details of some of these handbooks and directories are to be found in the "Resources" chapter of this volume.

The participation and support of those listed above as well as others who cannot all be named here has saved the project from making a number of avoidable errors and has ensured that the directory is the product of a truly co-operative process of partnership. At the same time, the consultants are not responsible for any errors which might remain through the editing process.

Thanks should also be expressed to **Mr David Hopson** of UNET for computing advice and **Ms Sandy Martin** and **Mr Glen Martin** for their proof reading of the text. Also to **Revd Colin Bond**, **Mrs Gwenda Bond**, **Mr Arun Chaudhary**, **Mr Steve Connolly**, **Ms Julie Hinks**, **Mrs Margaret Pugh** and **Mr Robbie Pugh** for the practical assistance of various kinds provided at different points throughout the project in Derby.

The support of a range of past and present University of Derby staff has also been crucial to the progress of the project, including: **Mr David Udall,** former Deputy Director (Academic) and **Mr Trevor Easingwood**, former Deputy Director (Resources); **Ms Zena Hawley**, **Ms Rita Malpass and Mr Peter Mayes** of the Marketing Unit; **Mr David Bush** and **Mr Neville Wells** of the Print Unit; **Ms Sharon Keetley** and **Ms Marita Wood** of Media Services; **Ms Melanie Brailsford** and **Ms Jane Needham** of the Faculty of Education, Humanities and Social Sciences administrative staff; **Ms Debbie Miller** and **Mrs Gill Speed** of the Mickleover Reception staff; **Ms Pat Crawford**, Pro Vice-Chancellor (Finance); **Mr Michael Hall**, Pro Vice-Chancellor (Facilities); **Professor Jonathan Powers**, Pro Vice-Chancellor (Academic); **Professor Roger Waterhouse** (Vice-Chancellor).

Thanks are also due to the members of the Steering Committee of the Religious Resource and research Centre.

A final word of thanks is due to my wife **Greta Preisler-Weller** who has also contributed help to the project in the design of the directory's cover and in the distribution of publicity, and to my children **David Weller** and **Lisa Weller**, for their patience and tolerance with all the overtime I have worked on the project. For David and Lisa I hope that the directory will make one small contribution towards a society in which it might be possible for them to grow up discovering that people of various religions can live in peace and harmony with one another.

Paul Weller
Project Director

USING DIRECTORY

USING THE DIRECTORY

COVERAGE

This directory contains chapters which provide detailed coverage of the Baha'i, Buddhist, Christian, Hindu, Jain, Jewish, Muslim, Sikh and Zoroastrian communities in the UK, as well as of inter-faith activity, organisations and groups.

There are, of course, other religious traditions, communities, groups and movements than these in the UK. But in view of the large numbers of religious groups and the varieties of beliefs and practices that exist, it is impossible to be totally comprehensive and the question was not whether, but where, to draw the lines of inclusion. However, whilst restricting itself, in the main, to the communities noted above the directory does provide a chapter entitled "Some Other Religious Groups" which offer some information on a number of traditions as well as contact points which can serve as signposts for obtaining further details.

Not included, in general, are the New Religious Movements, New Age groups and Pagan organisations. However, there are some groups which are often categorised as New Religious Movements which are clearly owned and accepted by the wider religious traditions included in this directory and these are covered here and some information on Paganism is included in the chapter on "Some Other Religious Groups"..

With regard to the New Religious Movements more generally, there is an organisation called INFORM (Information Network Focus on Religious Movements) which seeks to provide an objective information service specialising in this area. Directory users who are particularly interested in this area of the religious life of the UK are therefore referred to INFORM (Houghton Street, London, WC2A 2AE, Tel: 071-955-7654).

Geographical Coverage

In general the directory covers the United Kingdom of Great Britain and Northern Ireland. There are significant multi-faith communities in the key cities of Scotland and Wales and also presences in some other areas of these countries. But the majority of religious communities other than those of the Christian tradition are to be found in England. In Northern Ireland there are very few members of religious traditions other than Christians.

In the case of the Christian Churches, there are a number of entries for bodies which are located in the Republic of Ireland since the Churches generally operate on an all-Ireland basis.

Types of Organisation Listed

In general, the directory listings cover:

- national and regional umbrella bodies for each religion (where these exist)

- significant national organisations in each religion

- most national and local inter-religious organisations

- local places of worship of each religion

- many local organisations of each religion

The listings for the Christian community have a slightly different structure. The Christian community in the UK is very large and diverse and also has highly developed regional level structures. The directory has also taken account of the existence of the *UK Christian Handbook 1994-95*, Christian Research Association, London, 1994 (forthcoming), which provides comprehensive coverage of organisations in the the Christian community.

In this directory, therefore, the Christian listings cover:

- UK and national ecumenical instruments

- UK and national Churches affiliated to these ecumenical instruments

- UK and national commissions, agencies and networks of these ecumenical instruments

- details of some other UK and national Churches and Christian organisations

- regional level ecumenical Church bodies of the UK and national Churches affiliated to the UK and national ecumenical instruments

There are some categories of organisation on which it has been difficult to locate information. For example women's groups within a number of the communities do not have as high a public profile as some other kinds of organisations within those communities and some places of worship are based in private homes. Whilst the project has made efforts to seek out all possible sources of information, it should be recognised that some sectors of religious life, even within the communities covered by the directory, will be under-represented in these pages in comparison with the actual situation on the ground.

INTRODUCTORY MATERIALS

Each of the chapters on the world religious communities in the UK contains an introduction to the religion concerned. There are some differences in approach and internal balance between these introductions because they have been produced in consultation with representatives of the communities themselves. Nevertheless, in general, a common basic format has been used as follows:

In the United Kingdom: Introduces the basic historical, ethnic, linguistic and statistical information about the community in the UK.

Origins and Development: Sketches the historical origins of the religious community in terms of its significant or founding figure or figures and outlines briefly some principal features of its global and historical development.

Sources of Beliefs and Practices: Outlines the teachings, scriptures and religious structures which are seen as authoritative within the community.

Key Beliefs: Highlights the religion's central understandings of the nature of the human and the divine or the ultimate, as well as of its basic understandings of the purpose of existence.

Traditions: Introduces the principal traditions of interpretation in the religious community.

Life: Indicates how adherents are initiated into

the religion and something of the way in which the religion shapes their everyday life in terms of ethics, family, food and similar matters.

Worship: Gives information on the buildings in which the religion's worship takes place and outlines some of the forms of public worship which occur within them.

Calendar and Festivals: Explains the dating system of the religion and the rhythm of its year, as well as highlighting some of its major days of religious significance.

Organisation and Personnel: Introduces organisational patterns of the communities in the UK and refers to some religious functionaries.

Bibliography: Provides details of a number of useful general introductions to the religion, together with a number of books and articles which particularly focus on the the life of that religion in the UK.

USING THE ORGANISATIONAL LISTINGS

General

Following the introductory material on each religion come the listings sections which give contact details for organisations and places of worship. These include addresses, telephone numbers, contact people and, where available, some details of their self-understanding and main activities.

In all but the chapter on "Some Other Religious Groups" these listings are to be found in two parts. In that chapter, there is a single section containing national contact points for the groups concerned which is also integrated with the brief introductory material on these traditions. In all other chapters the listings are organised as follows:

- In the first part of the listings, organisations operating at a UK-wide or national level are set out in alphabetical order.

- Then come the listings of local level bodies. These are grouped into sections according to the nations of the UK and the regions of

England, as set out below.

- Within these sub-sections, organisations appear by alphabetical order of town or city in which they are found and within this by alphabetical order of organisation.

- In the London region, however, where the sub-sections are formed by the London postcode areas, the organisations are first of all ordered according to the number of the postcode area in which they are located (eg N1, N2 etc in ascending order) and then within this postcode order by alphabetical order of organisation name.

Christian Listings

The exception to these general rules are the listings for the Christian Churches:

- In these listings, UK-wide and national ecumenical instruments appear first, in alphabetical order, including a note about the Churches and organisations which are affiliated to them..

- The individual Churches affiliated to one of the ecumenical instruments, and operating at a UK level or at the level of one of the nations within it, then follow in alphabetical order.

- They are followed, also in alphabetical order, by the organisations and networks affiliated to the ecumenical instruments.

- These listings are finally followed, in alphabetical order of the sector of Church life concerned, by listings of a number of Churches and organisations which are not in membership with one or more of the ecumenical instruments but representing a significant sector of Christian life in the UK.

In the case of the Christian Churches, the second set of listings is also different from the other chapters in that it does not give details of local places of worship. These would be too numerous to cover within the scope of a single volume.

With regard to England and Wales, addresses of local Christian buildings which are registered as places of worship and/or for the solemnisation of marriage can be obtained from the General Register Office of the Office of Population Censuses and Surveys *Official List of Certified Places of Worship, parts I-IV*. There are, however no comparable lists for Scotlsnd and Northern Ireland. The Christian denominations also all produce their own handbooks and directories and the *UK Christian Handbook 1994-95*, Christian Research Association, London, 1994 (forthcoming), gives comprehensive coverage of the hundreds of Christian voluntary organisations which exist.

What the directory does do is to give details of regional level Church and ecumenical bodies which can act as "signposts" to more local sources of information within the Churches. Since they are regional bodies they are also ordered slightly differently within the directory. As with the local listings of other religions, the Christian regional entries are grouped according to the nations of the UK and the regions of England. Within this, however, they are then grouped according to the Christian tradition to which they belong and only then within these groupings by alphabetical order according to town or city.

Regions

The listings of local organisations are grouped according to national and regional sub-sections as follows:

Scotland: Not further divided into regions.

Wales: Not further divided into regions.

Northern Ireland: Or Ireland, in the case of the Christian listings, since Christian Churches on the island of Ireland are organised on an all-Ireland basis.

North East England: Cleveland, Durham, Northumberland and Tyne and Wear.

Yorkshire and Humberside: Humberside, North Yorkshire, South Yorkshire and West Yorkshire

North West England: Cheshire, Cumbria, Greater Manchester, Isle of Man, Lancashire and Merseyside.

English East Midlands: Derbyshire, Leicestershire, Lincolnshire, Northamptonshire and Nottinghamshire.

English West Midlands: Herefordshire and Worcestershire, Shropshire, Staffordshire, Warwickshire and West Midlands.

East Anglia: Cambridgeshire, Norfolk and Suffolk.

South East England (North): Bedfordshire, Berkshire, Buckinghamshire, Essex, Hertfordshire and Oxfordshire.

London: Postcode areas East (E), North (N), North West (NW), South (S), South East (SE), South West (SW), West (W), and West Central (WC).

South East England (South): Channel Islands, East Sussex, Hampshire, Isle of Wight, Kent, Surrey and West Sussex.

South West England: Avon, Cornwall, Devon, Dorset, Gloucestershire, Somerset and Wiltshire.

The exception to this way of grouping the regions again occurs in the Christian regional listings. In this, London is not sub- divided into postal areas because many of the Christian regional bodies operate across wider areas then these postal zones. Outside of London, too, because regional level organisations operate on a wider basis than local areas, on occasion a single entry can be found repeated in two separate regional sections because it operates in both regions.

Entries

In each entry for an organisation, the following information may be included. However, not all entries will contain information under each heading. Some organisations have chosen only to supply particular items of information and this wish has been respected even though this does result in some unevenness of detail on each organisation. In other cases, for various reasons, it was not possible to obtain more information than is included here.

Name: Within each chapter, the entries are generally grouped together within countries or regions alphabetically according to their location, and then by organisational name.

Address: The address given is that of the organisation. In the case of a place of worship, unless otherwise indicated the address given will generally be that of the place of worship itself rather than a contact address which may be different from the place of worship. Addresses which are those of cities and also have postcodes do not generally include the county. Where postcodes are not known, the county is usually given. Where a home address (of, for example, a Secretary) rather than a public building provides the point of contact for that organisation, then this is indicated by the word "home" appearing in brackets after the address. (Some addresses not having these words may also, in fact, be home addresses, through respondents not making this clear.)

Telephone: Normally, the telephone number which appears in the listings will also be that of an organisation's office or of a place of worship. Some places of worship and organisations do not have an office telephone, or the regular contact person for that organisation is not generally present at the place of worship. In this case, the entry may well be the home telephone number of the contact person. If this is the case, it is indicated by the word "home" appearing in brackets after the telephone number.

Fax: The fax numbers given in the listings are normally those of an organisation's office or of a place of worship, unless otherwise indicated by the word "home" appearing in brackets after the fax number.

Contact: Relates to the contact person which that organisation or place of worship has designated as the principal person who handles incoming enquiries. This may be an office-holder such as a Chairperson, President or Secretary. Office holders may, of course, change (often annually) but where such changes occur, outgoing officers will usually refer callers to the relevant new person.

Office: Where possible, the nominated contact name is followed by a description of their office or role in the organisation.

Where self-descriptions have been provided by organisations, details of the organisation then follow, distinguishing between places of worship and membership groups and giving details of any special focus for their work.

KEYS TO TERMS USED IN ORGANISATIONAL TITLES

Many (but not all) of the sections of organisational listings are followed by a key to some of the terms used in the titles of organisations that are listed.

The keys are provided in order to assist directory readers from outside of the traditions concerned to understand the meaning or significance of such terms. These keys are not glossaries which attempt to provide complete coverage of generally significant terms in each religion. They relate specifically to organisational titles.

In many cases, these terms indicate something about those whom the organisation hold in great esteem, or perhaps something about the nature of the group or its place in the spectrum of that community's life. However, without further explanation, the meaning and significance of these terms might be lost for the outside reader.

For many readers this will particularly be the case if the term is not originally an English word, but it might also be the case if it is an English word and the reader does not have English as a first language, or if the English word or phrase is highly specific to the religion concerned.

By attempting to provide some explanation of the organisational terms which might be encountered by the directory user from outside of the religions concerned, the key therefore acts as a "bridge" between the more detailed introductory materials on each of the religions and the listings of their individual organisations.

To track down further information on particular concepts which are italicised within the keys, the reader should refer to elsewhere within the keys where these words appear and/or to the Keyword Index at the end of the directory which lists significant words together with their references within the text of the Introductions to the various communities.

COLLECTION AND VERIFICATION OF DIRECTORY LISTINGS

In compiling the original contact lists for researching this directory, existing published directories were utilised together with other available lists and sources.

These were then cross-checked and supplemented with lists of names and addresses provided in response to project circulars requesting information which went to Race Equality Councils; Councils for Voluntary Service; Local Authority Religious Education Advisers; Local Authority Planning Departments; Local Authority Library Services; and last, but not least, UK, national and regional religious organisations.

The aim of this research was to try and construct a grid of interlocking information-sources to ensure that as many organisations as possible would be identified.

- A standard format for directory entries was drawn up and each organisation on which the project had any information was contacted directly by post.

- They were sent a draft of the proposed directory entry on their organisation and were asked to inform the project staff if they did not wish to be included, if they wished to correct any information or if they wished to omit anything.

- Follow-up letters were sent to many of the organisations which did not respond to the original letter requesting information.

- Additional checking was conducted by telephone.

- Cross-checking of details was also carried out with Race Equality Councils, local inter-faith groups in various localities as well as with national religious bodies and individual consultants within the religious communities

and among academics based in institutions of higher education.

- New data was included as the project went on and print-outs of the listings were sent to consultants in the religious communities at a number of stages throughout the project.

- In 1993, all organisations now included in the directory were sent a draft of their proposed entry, giving them a final opportunity to correct their entry or ask for it to be omitted. This also helped to weed out many of those organisations which had become defunct since the original information on them was supplied to the project.

- The project has therefore gone to considerable lengths to try and secure the up-to-dateness and accuracy of the entries contained in the directory.

- Users will, however, appreciate that not all organisations reply to correspondence and questionnaires, not all are contactable by telephone, and that contact details can and do change with the passage of time. As a result the absolute accuracy of all entries cannot be guaranteed although every effort has been made to ensure as much accuracy as possible.

We have also sought to respect the expressed wishes of organisations which have requested that we do not include details about there their existence or certain items of information about them, even where this information might be available elsewhere in the public domain. Whilst there have not been many such requests there have been some and this might account for why a number of organisations known to directory users do not appear in the directory.

In some cases the name and general location of an organisation or place of worship is included together with reference to another organisation from which further details can be obtained.

In a few cases, where two sets of details might refer to the same organisation both sets have been included because, despite its best efforts, the directory project has been unable to positively confirm which is the correct and/or preferred contact point. In these cases, it was felt better to include both rather than none at all even if one set eventually proves to be incorrect.

The variety of information available in each organisation's entry reflects the choices made by particular organisations concerning the kind of information which they wished to have published and this accounts for the variety in the content of the entries. We were, however, able to offer free inclusion in the directory, thus ensuring that its coverage was as wide as possible.

RELIGIONS AND STATISTICS

The Lack of Accurate Figures

Many users of the directory will wish to have figures for the numerical strengths of the various religious communities. The introductory materials on each religious community make some reference to estimates of the size of these communities and, in some cases, to the relative proportions of groups within a community.

No claim is made that these are at all definitive. There are currently no entirely valid or reliable ways of producing such statistics on a national basis across the religions since details on religious affiliation have not been required in the national Census.

No UK-wide religious Census has ever taken place. In England and Wales there has been no official religious census since the 1851 Census of Public Worship, although data on religious affiliation and practice has been collected in particular contexts for a variety of specific purposes.

The only figures which are currently available are therefore based either upon extrapolations from data on ethnic background, now gathered by the national Census; from data gathered in specific and limited studies; or are figures supplied by organisations from within the religious communities themselves.

Where Census data has been used figures are still open to some question. They are partially dependent upon the particular categories of ethnicity which are offered as options in any Census or survey question and partly upon what

are, sometimes, the shifting perceptions of respondents to particular ways of describing themselves.

When figures are supplied for religious traditions it is important to establish whether these figures are for active or community membership. For example, the Christian Research Association estimates that there are around 7,023,000 practicing Christians in the UK, but probably about 37,600,000 people who would categorise themselves as Christians.

Future Possibilities for Statistics

It might be that if religion is increasingly recognised to be a key referent in individual and group identity, the Office of Population Censuses and Surveys will respond to this by including, in the future, a religious question in the national Census. However, given the concerns and prolonged public debate surrounding the recent introduction of a question on ethnicity it is unlikely that a decision could be reached on this without considerable public debate and controversy.

Issues of self-definition would also be present and would need to be taken into account in interpreting any figures on religious affiliation which might be produced by the future inclusion of a religious question in a national Census.

There are, however, some further possible sources which might yield helpful information in the relatively near future. In July of 1989 the Department of Education and Science's Circular 16/89 on "Ethnically-Based Statistics on School Pupils" (25.7.89) included a religious question alongside those on ethnicity, gender and language which was henceforth to be asked concerning all children entering schools at ages five and eleven.

This should have been implemented by all LEAs and grant-maintained schools from 1990 onwards and gives the religious options of Christian, Hindu, Jewish, Muslim, Sikh, Other (please specify), No religion, and Unclassified. On the basis of these figures it might, over a period of time, be possible to build up a reasonably accurate profile of the religious affiliation of the coming generation.

However, as with any set of statistics, even these results will need to be qualified since answering the question is voluntary; answers will be supplied by parents rather than by the children themselves and it appears that the data thus far collected is patchy.

The Directory's Figures

The figures which are included in this directory are based upon a consensus of estimates made by those who have done some work in this field. They should not therefore be treated either as definitive or as the product of new research. The directory Project has not attempted to carry out new research in this area. However, it would appear that the figures quoted would carry the most support among academics working in the field of religion and statistics.

The qualifications which apply to community figures for the UK apply even more in the case of the global estimates which are included in the individual chapters on the nine religious traditions. These generally rely on work done by David Barrett, who has done research over a number of years on the statistics for global religious communities. His most recent figures (for 1991), were published in the *International Bulletin of Missionary Research*, January 1991, p. 25.

The figures given for the different Christian denominations within the chapter on "Introducing Christianity" are taken from the *UK Christian Handbook 1994-95*, Christian Research Association, London, 1994 (forthcoming) and refer to numbers for 1992.

In these figures, the Anglican and Roman Catholic statistics are based upon the numbers of baptised members in these communities. For Baptists and Pentecostalists, the figures are double those for their official memberships on the basis that these Churches tend to have congregations and local communities which are much larger than their official membership figures. This is because many of these Churches

admit to full membership only people baptised as adults on profession of faith.

PLACES OF WORSHIP

With regard to the numbers of places of worship in each religion, in England and Wales, buildings used for religious worship may apply to become "certified" places of worship with the General Register Office, or, in the case of places of worship of the Church of England and the Church in Wales, "recorded" places of worship. The General Register Office of the Office of Population Census and Surveys maintains a record and regularly updated running totals of these "certified" and "recorded" places of worship.

The categories in which it keeps running totals are as follows: Christian (Church of England and Church in Wales); Christian Non-Conformist (which is further sub-divided into Roman Catholic, Methodist, Congregationalist, Baptist, United Reformed Church, Calvinistic Methodists, Brethren, Salvation Army, Unitarian, Quaker, Jehovah's Witnesses and Others); Jewish; Muslim; Sikh; and "other Eastern" including, for example, Hindu, Jain, Baha'i etc.

As will be noted, the categories do not exactly match the nine religious traditions with which this directory is principally concerned. However, the total numbers of "registered" and "recorded" buildings in the *Classification of Denominations and Production of Annual Statistics of the General Register Office*, as at 30th June 1993, are reported in this directory in the introductions to those religions upon which the General Register Office does keep running totals.

It should be noted that these numbers relate only to England and Wales and not to the UK as a whole and that places of worship are not legally obliged to register in this way. Therefore the true figure of places of worship is, in each case, likely to be somewhat higher than the reported figure, especially with regard to those religious traditions which have been more recently established in the UK.

In addition to these official figures from the General Register Office, the directory gives its own figures of the number of places of worship based on its research and the organisations which are recorded in the listings sections of the directory. These figures relate to the UK as a whole. Where local organisations did not specifically declare whether they were a place of worship/meditation centre, it was necessary to decide on their status on the basis of their organisational name which can give a reasonable, but not infallible, indication of their function.

It should also be noted that a small number of organisations requested not to appear in the directory. In addition, some religious traditions do not focus their corporate activity so centrally upon public places of worship. This includes, for example, the Baha'is and the Buddhists, both of which have a large number of local groups and organisations which do not meet in specifically designated buildings.

RELIGIONS AND LANGUAGES

None of the religious traditions contained in this directory has English as the language of its source materials, though in most cases there are now English translations of these. For some religions, languages other than English remain the main medium for their religious discourse and practise.

Within the introductory materials on the religious communities, terms which are of great significance in these traditions are therefore included in a Romanisation of their original languages, in italics, together with an indication in English of the approximate meaning of these terms.

Italics together with further explanation have also been used in the introductory materials with regard to terms in the English language which are specifically or strongly Christian in meaning and overtone, and which might not be readily understandable to English-speakers from outside the Christian tradition. Personal names are not italicised but the names of scriptures and of particular books within them are italicised.

Since the directory is intended for wide use and not just for specialists, the non-English italicised terms appear in the directory with Roman alphabetisation and without the use of diacritical markings, apart from apostrophes and inverted apostrophes.

Within each set of introductory materials attempts have been made to ensure consistency of usage and transliteration. However, within the listings sections there will be some considerable variation because the directory records the name of the organisation and its directory entry in the form that the organisation itself has supplied it. In addition, italics are not generally used in the listings section.

RELIGIONS, CALENDARS AND FESTIVALS

In the introductory materials for each religion some reference is made to the principal festivals of the religious tradition in question. However, since a number of religions operate on calendars that are different from the standard calendar used in British public life, it is not possible to give a regular date for the observance of all festivals and other significant religious days.

A useful resource in this regard is the *Calendar of Festivals* which is produced annually by the Shap Working Party on World Religions in Education (and which can be obtained from the National Society Religious Education Centre, 23 Kensington Square, London, W8 5HN, Tel: 071-937-4241). This can be supplemented with more detail obtainable from the book *Festivals in World Religions*, also produced by the Shap Working Party on World Religions in Education and edited by Alan Brown.

Many religious communities also publish their own calendars of festivals and significant dates. Directory users could request copies of these from relevant national organisations listed in the directory and, in some cases, from local organisations too.

The terms "AD" (Anno Domini - Latin for "in the year of our Lord", Lord being a title given to Jesus by Christians) and "BC" ("Before Christ", Christ being a title given to Jesus by Christians) were originally used by Christians to date world events in relation to the birth of Jesus.

The adoption of the conventions "CE" (Common Era) and "BCE" (Before Common Era) provides a dating system that is increasingly used (even though in origin these conventions related to a common way of describing dates which was adopted in the specific context of Jewish-Christian dialogue).

RESOURCES

The final chapter on "Resources" points the directory user to additional sources of information which may be able to fill some of the gaps within this directory and which provide a different level of detail of information than is to be found here.

Along with information about other directories, there are also some listings of organisations which are concerned with religious life in the UK and which can provide further information beyond that contained in this directory's introductory materials on the religious communities.

INDEXES

There are two indexes and a guide. The "Local Guide" lists the places were local organisations in all the local listings are to be found and indicates the region in the directory within which each place name has been located. Together with a list of these place names and regions the "Local Guide" includes an index to the page numbers for each regional section within each region so that, having located a given place and its region, the directory user can turn to the appropriate pages in the directory.

The "Topic Index" gives page references to each major section and sub-section of the Introductions to each religion and enables the directory user to find broad topic areas within these introductions.

The "Keyword Index" is based upon italicised words from the main text of the directory. In addition, it also covers some other important words in the directory and gives page reference numbers for the major sections/topics within the introductory chapters on the various religions. As

will be appreciated this is not, therefore, precisely a subject index, but as a "Keyword Index" it provides the opportunity for directory users to track down some commonly encountered words in order to locate them in a context which provides either their meaning and/or some further explanation of their significance.

FURTHER HELP

The chapter which now follows is included specifically to give users some advice on how to go about using the directory in a sensitive way for a range of purposes.

Queries about the directory and its use can be referred to the Religious Resource and Research Centre of the University of Derby (Mickleover Campus, Western Road, Derby, DE3 5GX, Tel: 0332-622222, Ext. 2102).

Further information and advice on how to make contact with the religious communities and their organisations can be obtained from The Inter Faith Network for the United Kingdom (5-7 Tavistock Place, London, WC1H 9SS, Tel: 071-388-0008).

Further details about the Religious Resource and Research Centre and The Inter Faith Network can be found in the "Resources" and the "UK Inter-Faith Organisations" chapters. The Centre contributes to a part-time taught Master's course of the University of Derby in Religious Pluralism as well as to the Univerity's undergraduate modules in Religious Studies within the BA Combined Studies and BEd degrees. The Network, together with the services provided by its office and staff, has a range of helpful publications available on matters related to inter-faith dialogue.

Finally, any directory inevitably begins to get out of date even before it is published. An update form is therefore included for sending additional entries or updated information to be included in any future edition.

MAKING CONTACTS, ORGANISING EVENTS AND CONSULTATIONS

MAKING CONTACTS, ORGANISING EVENTS AND CONSULTATIONS

USING THE DIRECTORY TO MAKE CONTACT

ARRANGING A MULTI-FAITH EVENT

ARRANGING MULTI-FAITH CONSULTANCIES OR PANELS

PRODUCING GUIDELINES

VISITING PLACES OF WORSHIP

HOSTING VISITORS TO A PLACE OF WORSHIP

USING THE DIRECTORY TO MAKE CONTACT

If you are using this Directory, it may be to get some initial assistance about how to organise events, projects, or consultations drawing together members of different religious communities. There are no hard and fast guidelines as to how to do this successfully, but some general pointers may be helpful. This chapter also includes guidance on arranging visits to places of worship.

The Importance of the Introductory Materials

The directory lists most of the key religious organisations and groups in the UK. You may already be knowledgeable about the traditions from which they come. If not, we hope that the directory's introductory material about these traditions will be helpful. Suggestions appear at the end of each chapter for further reading if you want to discover more.

The introductory material is designed to help the reader understand the basic aspects of each religious tradition, especially as it is represented in the UK. Although much is held in common within particular religious communities, no religion is monolithic. Within each religion there are many different traditions of inter-pretation and it is helpful to have a sense of these when you plan to make contact with particular groups.

The Buddhists in your neighbourhood could be either *Theravada* or they could be *Mahayana*. The Christians at the nearest church may be *Anglican* or they may be *Catholic*. They will not expect you to be an expert in their religion, but they will appreciate your efforts at least to understand where they fit in the general scheme of things.

If you are planning a multi-faith event or consultation, you will probably be hoping to ensure a certain level of representativeness. Understanding from which part of a tradition a possible speaker or participant comes can help you ensure balance and avoid later difficulties.

It is also worth bearing in mind that within any

given religious community, many ethnic backgrounds are likely to be represented. There are Pakistani Muslims and Saudi Arabian ones, Chinese Christians and English ones, Thai Buddhists and Vietnamese ones, and so forth.

Some Things to be Aware of When Making Contact

You will usually find that contacts for the different religious organisations are happy to explain more about their community, and to help with your enquiries. However, this partly depends on the time they have available.

Sometimes it is necessary to ring several times, because contact people for the various religious communities are often extremely busy. Imams, vicars, temple secretaries, women's group leaders, and others have hectic schedules and may also have full-time employment other than in the organisation in which they serve and you are contacting.

If you need information or are organising an event, allow sufficient time for the sheer logistics of getting hold of the contact people and arranging the time to speak with them. Sometimes people who are not fluent in English and in whose language you are not fluent will answer the telephone. If this happens, it might be best to offer to ring back later.

Possible Areas of Sensitivity

There are certain areas of sensitivity of which it is helpful to be aware when making contact. Sometimes, the religious outlook of the person you are talking to may make them suspicious of, or even hostile towards, multi-faith or inter-faith encounter. Diplomacy and respect for people's convictions is very important.

Where communities or their members have been the target of conversion campaigns by other religious groups, there may be particular wariness about inter-religious encounter. It is very important to explain what the context of your enquiry is and to be open about your purpose.

ARRANGING A MULTI-FAITH EVENT

If you are organising a multi-faith event, here is a checklist that may be helpful.

Check the Calendar

Check that the event you are planning does not clash with one of the key festivals of a group that you are hoping to involve. The annual *Shap Calendar of Festivals* (available from the Shap Working Party, c/o The National RE Centre, 23 Kensington Square, London, W8 5HN, Tel: 071-937-4241) is a vital resource for this.

If you are in any doubt about the significance of the festival (in other words, whether it is one that means those observing it are unlikely to be able to attend other events), then contact the relevant community to double-check details.

Fridays are difficult for observant Muslims, and especially for *imams*, because of the importance of the Friday midday prayer. If possible, avoid scheduling afternoon events during the period of *Ramadan* when practising Muslims fast from before dawn until sunset.

From late afternoon on Friday until sunset on Saturday is problematic for observant Jews in relation to events involving travel and what could be construed as "work" (though interpretations of this vary within different parts of the community).

For church-going Christians, Sundays can be difficult. However, because of the practical difficulty for many people of not being able to take time off during the working week, weekend events may prove necessary.

If you are planning a weekend event, it is important to check with members of these religions how they personally feel about attending on these days or about their participation during particular parts of the timetable.

Allow Plenty of Planning And Organising Time

A planning time of at least three months is

advisable for local events and, for national events, a lead time of at least six months will probably be needed.

Good speakers and participants are obtainable from all religious communities, but are likely to have quite full diaries and need to be booked well in advance (except for response to political or social emergencies). Participant lists also take time to draw up, and if the event involves people needing to take time off work or to arrange child care, adequate notice is needed.

Choose an Appropriate Venue

It is important not to end up with a venue which makes some of the participants uncomfortable. For example, if you are a local inter-faith group just starting up and without a strong sense of each other's views and sensitivities, it may not be wise to meet initially at one of the group's place of worship. A meeting at a member's house or on "neutral" ground might be the best way to begin.

If you are considering setting up a representative council of different religions, it will be important to rotate the venue among the religions or hold meetings on "neutral ground". It is important to discover, for any religion, just where the "sacred" area of their religious building is. There may be other parts which are not so considered.

Participants of different religions may feel comfortable about meeting in these other areas (for example in the community centre attached to a *mandir*). They may not, however, feel comfortable about any visit which would involve them in entering the sacred space where they might feel obliged to offer respect to another's sacred symbols (or might be worried about causing offence in refusing to do so for religious reasons).

In a *Gurdwara* or a *mandir* or a *mosque*, for example, the sacred area is clearly definable by the point beyond which you should not go without removing your shoes. In Christian churches, the matter may be less clear-cut because, particularly in modern and adapted buildings, meetings without a specifically religious purpose sometimes take place even in

what is the church itself, as distinct from its church hall.

The introductory materials on each religious community provide further background on the sacred buildings and their contents and significances.

Religious Observance During an Event

Members of all the different religious traditions may wish to retire for prayer or meditation at certain points during the day and time should be left within the schedule for this.

For many there are no mandatory times that should be borne in mind; however, practising Muslims pray five times a day at specific times. There is a minor amount of flexibility of time according to circumstances, but it is important to provide space for prayer at the correct times, and a sheet for covering the floor for prayer, plus a jug of water and a towel for ablutions before prayer. If there is a toilet or bathroom nearby with washing facilities this is sufficient.

Shared Religious Observance During an Event

This area is one which should be approached with great care. The least controversial option is a shared silent meditation or wordless prayer. If you are in any doubt about the feelings of the participants, it is wise to go for this choice.

When spoken prayers or readings are used, there is always the danger that people find themselves voluntarily or involuntarily joining in what appears to be lowest common denominator worship of a deity who is not recognisably the deity which they themselves worship.

Non-theists (such as Buddhists) can be put into an awkward situation by assumptions that all religions acknowledge God. Likewise, for traditions where the divine is understood wholly or partly in feminine or impersonal terms, the constant use of masculine or personal terms may prove alienating. Given these possibilities of misunderstanding and offence, it is always necessary to proceed with caution.

However, there are occasions on which people very much wish to pray together, or when civic life calls for communal celebration or mourning. In such contexts, a widely used option is what is sometimes called "serial worship". In serial worship, members of different religions pray or offer a reading relevant to the theme which others listen to, but with which they do not join in. Rather, prayer is offered individually by members of the gathering in a way which respects the integrity of their own tradition.

Because the Church of England is the established church in England, its churches have often been the venue for this kind of civic or communal worship. There are difficulties associated with this which are discussed in *Multi-faith Worship?*, Church House Publishing , London, 1992.

Catering for Multi-Faith Events

Many religious traditions have certain dietary requirements as a result of their beliefs and some of the background to these can be found in more detail by consulting the appropriate introductory material on each religion. Generally speaking, the easiest way to cater for a multi-faith event is to make it absolutely vegetarian.

Within the vegetarian dishes, make sure that at least some contain no eggs and that some of these non-egg dishes also contain no garlic or onions (since all these may be unacceptable to some Hindus, observant Jains and also some other groupings). Jains avoid eating all root vegetables (such as potatoes) because they believe that *ahimsa* or non-violence requires that you do not kill any plant: it is only acceptable to eat vegetables and fruits the removal of which leaves the plant itself alive.

Within Judaism, the *kosher* rule is widely observed, but with differing interpretations. Check in advance how your Jewish participants interpret it. Normally, it is sufficient to provide vegetarian food and disposable plates, cups and cutlery. However, for the very *Orthodox,* it may be necessary to provide separate meals which have been prepared in a *kosher* kitchen. *Kosher*

foods include *kosher* wine, bread and cheese as well as meats. Such food and drink is marked with a *hechsher* (seal) which certifies it is *kosher.*

Muslims will wish that, ideally, their food has been prepared in a kitchen where the utensils and contents have not been in contact with *haram* (forbidden) food. However, Muslims are primarily concerned to ensure that any meat served is *halal* (permitted and slaughtered according to the *Shar'iah*), and are generally happy to eat vegetarian food that has no animal fat used in its production.

If making sandwiches, avoid the use of the butter substitutes made with rendered beef fat. No animal fat should be used in any vegetarian cooking, and when cheese is used it should not be made with rennet which comes from the stomach of cows. Puddings should not include gelatine (unless it is of a vegetarian variety). Observant Jews would also wish to avoid these ingredients.

Different traditions have varying approaches to the consumption of alcohol. In Islam it is considered forbidden and there are warnings against the dangers that can arise from associating with those who drink alcohol. For Hindus and Jains, it is considered undesirable. Sikhs who have taken *amrit* are also expected to avoid alcohol.

For most Christians alcohol is not prohibited, although some groups advocate abstinence. Within Judaism, there is likewise no prohibition, and responsible use of alcohol is not frowned upon. Practice varies among Buddhists, although alcohol is viewed as dangerous in so far as it can hinder "mindfulness".

Because of the diversity of practice within religions, alcohol is often not served at a specifically inter-faith event. If you do provide alcohol at a function, it is wise to provide only wine and to set it at some distance from the non-alcoholic drinks. Fruit juice and mineral water should always be provided as an alternative.

Coffee and tea, as stimulants, are avoided by observant members of certain traditions. It is therefore important to provide juice, water or herbal tea as alternatives to morning and afternoon coffee and tea. If biscuits are provided with these refreshments, double-check that they contain no animal fats other than butter.

Relationships Between the Sexes

It is important to be aware of differing attitudes to the roles and relationships of men and women. These may vary even within one religious tradition according to how a group interprets that tradition and according to the cultural background in which their tradition has been practised.

A *Chasidic* Jewish family will have a somewhat different dynamic from a *Reform* Jewish one. *Anglicans* may differ radically one from another concerning what they believe the Bible and tradition teaches about the roles of Christian men and women. Within Islam, interpretations of the *Qur'an* and *Shar'iah* by the different legal schools mean that there is a legitimate diversity of interpretation.

However, modesty is an important concept in Islam for both women and men. Some interpret this to mean that single sex events should be the norm. Others interpret it to mean that a careful, formal, and modest manner should characterise meetings between people of different sexes in public contexts.

Within almost every religious tradition there are those who believe that women should not exercise a public leadership role, and there are those who disagree. This can lead to some awkwardness over finding women to participate in multi-faith events and panels.

Generally speaking, however, the best rule is to proceed with courtesy and care in requests for speakers and to try to accommodate requests for such things as hotel rooms in separate parts of the building for men and women, or to consider offering additional travel expenses to allow a person's husband or wife or family member to travel with them for reasons of propriety.

Consider Arranging a Creche

This will support family participation. If no creche facilities are available it can be difficult for young couples to come to events, and impossible for many women.

ARRANGING MULTI-FAITH CONSULTANCIES OR PANELS

You may be working to gain multi-faith contributions on particular issues, such as disability or sex education. If you are working locally or nationally to set up such a consultation, there are some questions worth asking at the outset:

What Kind of Input Do We Actually Want?

Depending on the project, you may be seeking to bring together:

- Religious experts (scholars or knowledgeable clergy or laity)
- Religious community leaders (who are not necessarily scholars or religious teachers themselves)
- Representative or "average" members of particular faith communities (including women and young people)
- Members of religious communities with expertise on a particular topic

Often, you will need a mixture of different kinds of participant. For example, suppose you want to determine what different religions have to say about treatment of the elderly. You might want an expert to give an overview of what the sacred texts and historical traditions have said.

Alternatively, you might include a Jew or Hindu who is an older citizen and has thought about what their religion means in the context of their own ageing. Then again, you could involve a Sikh or Christian carer who is putting their faith into practice in caring for the elderly. There are many options, and it is important to decide what you are hoping to gain from the encounter.

What Should the Composition of our Panel/Consultants be?

The scope, timetable, and financing of any project will clearly define some of the constraints. However, there are certain questions which it is important to ask at the outset:

- From which religions do we seek an input?

- Do we want all the religions represented in the UK, or just those with a substantial presence?

- Should the panel or consultants reflect the national religious composition of the UK, or of the areas with which my organisation is most involved? (Jains, for example, might be a numerically small grouping nationally, but are particularly important in a given city such as Leicester).

- Do we want input from both men and women and people of varying ages?

Questions about which religion you are seeking to involve can only be answered in the context of your particular project. People often overlook the smaller religious communities, but if you are working on an issue such as medical ethics, you may want to make a special effort to include a tradition which has a particular contribution to make to the discussion, even if that tradition is numerically not a big one in the UK.

Religious leaders bring particular knowledge and skills. It is important to note, however, that women and men under forty rarely appear in consultations drawing solely upon religious leaderships.

For some purposes, a "representative group" is sought. Complete representativeness is impossible to achieve in practice because of the diversity within and between different religious communities. There is also the question of who actually is "representative" of a given tradition. It takes a while to establish who the key figures are in a religious tradition in a particular area of the country, who is genuinely representative, and what their capacity is to relay information back to that community or to provide accurate inform-ation about what that community itself needs.

If you are looking to involve religious "leaders", the nature of these may vary very widely between traditions, as will the understanding of what a religious leader is. The role of an *imam*, for example, is not strictly comparable to that of a *vicar*. The job of a Sikh *granthi* is likewise very different. Different community structures have given rise to different types of personnel.

PRODUCING GUIDELINES

Producing Information Packs

This will depend on what kind of information is needed. If it is basic information about different religions that you need, many good resources already exist. It may not be necessary to arrange for consultants from different religions to come and help produce an entirely new pack. If the information is designed to help service provision, and you are drawing together religious community members unused to consultancy work, they will need very clear guidance on just what kind of information and assistance is needed.

Some national bodies may have staff available to respond to written requests for information or invitations to participate in various events. Many do not, and this is also true at local level. If you write asking for information and receive no reply within a couple of weeks, you may need to follow up the letter with a phone call.

Avoiding Stereotypes

It is very important to ask the groups or individuals with whom you are dealing, just what they believe and consider important. Religion is not monolithic and it is unhelpful and dangerous to operate with a stereotypical concept of, for example, a Baha'i or a Christian or a Jew (even where this is based on much research). If you are producing pamphlets or guidance for service providers working with people of a variety of religions, this cannot be stressed strongly enough. Make sure that the reader understands that there can be a wide variety of interpretation, and degrees of strictness in observance.

Some people born into religious communities may not even consider themselves any longer to be members of that community. There are, for example, ex-Christian atheists or humanists who would find it unacceptable to be asked to say what their religion was and to be treated as a practising Christian. Likewise, there may be people who are Hindu or Jewish by birth and for whom religion is still important, but who do not set particular store by ceremonial or ritual observance and may not observe the usual dietary regulations. In all cases, it is best to allow people to define their own needs.

VISITING PLACES OF WORSHIP

In the introductory materials on each religious community you will find a description of what you may see if visiting the places of worship of that religious tradition. You will also find a description of the personnel you are likely to meet and explanations of some of the key concepts found in the religious tradition concerned.

If you are making a visit to a place of worship, the likelihood is that a person of that religion will be helping to arrange the visit for you. Usually people are delighted to show others their place of worship. It is a sharing of what they hold very dear.

It is as well to think before going how you feel about such matters as joining in another's service, or receiving food that has been offered to the deities of other religions and blessed. It is quite possible to visit others' places of worship without this kind of participation, so long as you explain your reservations courteously.

The religious community you are visiting would not want you to feel ill at ease. Likewise, they would not wish to be made ill at ease by criticisms of their ways of worship or of their religion. Questions are always welcomed, but negative comparisons with the visitors' own customs are unlikely to meet with warm feelings! Whether you make your visit alone, or as a group, it is important to follow the guidelines for clothing and behaviour, so as not to cause offence. For groups, it is important not to talk loudly and disturb those at prayer. If any of your group have special needs, let the place you are visiting know in advance so that they can prepare to help. For example, although the normal custom of the place of worship in question may be to sit on the floor or to stand for worship, chairs can often be provided for elderly, infirm or disabled visitors.

Visiting Baha'i Places of Worship

There are no formal buildings for Baha'i worship in the UK. Gatherings are held at the Baha'i Centre in London and various regional Baha'i centres (for example, in Liverpool, Edinburgh and Brighton), as well as in members' homes or meeting rooms. Interested members of other religious traditions are welcome to attend *Unity Feasts* and other meetings for worship and prayer, as well as Holy Day celebrations. Those wishing to attend a Baha'i meeting should contact the secretary of the *Local Assembly* to make suitable arrangements.

Clothing

There are no special requirements, although it is appropriate to dress tidily and modestly.

Entering the Meeting

You may find a place wherever you feel comfortable.

Worship and Sacred Food

A *Unity Feast* will begin with devotional readings, prayers or songs. You may join in or not, as you wish. During prayers, a reverent silence is requested. There is no sacred food or sacrament. The feast closes with a social period during which people meet each other and share refreshments.

Visiting a Buddhist Temple

Buddhist places of devotion and worship vary considerably in style and practice. Such places may be a part of a *vihara* (a place where monks live), or may be found in a centre. In either case, the actual place of worship and devotion is the shrine room. The shrine room will contain a *Buddharupa* (statue of the Buddha) in a central position, with an incense holder, flowers and candles by its side.

Clothing

There are no particular requirements with regard to clothing except that it should be modest.

Entering the shrine room

Before entering the shrine room one should remove one's shoes as a mark of respect. Inside the room, seating is generally on the floor and it is appropriate to adopt a quiet and meditative demeanor.

Worship and sacred food

The shrine room is primarily a place for meditation and teaching. It is also the place for the performance of *puja*, which is a way of expressing one's devotion by means of offering flowers, lights, incense, food or other gifts. There is no expectation that a visitor will participate in this, although one may does so, if one wishes, in an appropriate way.

Visiting a Christian Church

Clothing

There is a wide variation between different types of churches, but as a general rule it is wise to dress tidily and avoid particularly revealing clothing. This is perhaps most strongly true in *Orthodox* as well as conservative *Catholic* and *Protestant* Churches. Men have traditionally removed their hats when entering church. If you are a male visitor of another religious tradition who normally keeps his head covered for religious reasons, it is worth explaining this fact to your hosts.

Entering the Church

Most churches have *pews* (benches with raised backs) or rows of seats, although in *Orthodox* Churches most people stand for worship. Where

there are pews or seats, find a seat and sit quietly. It is best not to sit in the front row since that prevents you seeing what the rest of the congregation are doing. Christians will not expect visitors to bow or show other forms of outward respect to the altar (or to any of the statues or *icons* that may be found in *Catholic* or *Orthodox* churches).

Worship and Sacred Food

Visitors are generally welcome to join in the prayers and hymns of the service if they wish. During services, the congregation may kneel, stand or sit depending on the part of the service. Non-Christian visitors usually sit and stand with the rest of the congregation, and kneel if they feel comfortable doing so. If you attend a *eucharist/mass/communion* service, you will not be expected to take bread or wine (and in many churches, may not be allowed to do so). If you go to a *Protestant* church where the bread and wine of the *communion* service is passed around the seated congregation, just let the plate and cup pass by to the person next to you. If you are in a church where people are going up to the altar to take *communion*, just remain in your seat. Some priests or ministers, however, will invite non-*communion* takers to come forward and receive a blessing from the *priest*. If you would like this, stand or kneel with your head bowed so the *priest* knows you wish a blessing, but it is important to be aware that the form of the blessing will be specifically Christian.

Visiting a Hindu Mandir

Clothing

Should be modest for both men and women, but head coverings are not required for either sex. Shoes are removed before going into the temple and put on the racks provided. Clean and presentable socks, stockings, or tights are therefore a good idea. Sometimes women are requested to cover their heads and they should also keep in mind that, since they will be sitting on the floor, short dresses and skirts may be unsuitable.

Entering the temple area

Walk in quietly and find a place to sit on the floor (usually carpeted). In some *mandirs* (temples), men and boys sit on one side of the room and women and girls on the other. Sit with crossed legs, or with your legs pointing to one side. It is considered disrespectful to sit with your legs forward with the feet pointing towards the sacred area at the front of the temple. In some *mandirs* guests may be expected to stand as a sign of respect during *arti*.

Worship and Sacred Food

There is no expectation that you should join in the formal prayer and worship unless you wish to. When Hindus go to the *mandir*, they usually take an offering such as food or money to give to the deities. If you are not a Hindu, this would not be expected although it would be welcomed. If offering food, it should not be cooked food and especially not if it violates the principle of *ahimsa* (not-harming). It becomes sacred when given to the deity in the course of the ceremony called *arti*.

After it becomes sacred it is called *prashada*. Often the blessed food takes the form of sweets or fruit offered on a tray. You will be offered one piece which you can either eat there and then or take home. If you take a piece, take it in cupped hands with the right hand uppermost. If you are uncomfortable for religious reasons about being given some of this sacred food to eat, let the offerer know with a quiet "No thank you". If possible, explain to your hosts in advance that you will be declining for reasons of your own personal religious position, and not out of any disrespect for them.

A note for women

In some *mandirs* women will be expected not to enter the temple during menstruation, but for other *mandirs* this would present no difficulty.

Visiting a Jain Temple

Clothing

Should be modest for both men and women.

Head coverings are not necessary for either sex. Shoes are removed before going into the temple and put on the racks provided. Clean and presentable socks, stockings, or tights, are therefore a good idea. All leather objects should be left outside when entering the temple.

Entering the Temple Area

No eating or chewing is allowed in the temple area. When Jains enter the temple they say "*Nisihi, Nisihi, Nisihi*", then offer the *Navkar Mantra*, and bow to the image in the temple if it contains one. This will not be expected of a visitor for whom a reverent silence is acceptable. Walk in quietly and find a place to sit on the floor (usually carpeted). Sit with crossed legs, or with your legs pointing to one side. It is considered disrespectful to sit with your legs forward with the feet pointing towards the sacred area at the front of the temple or to stand or sit with your back to the image.

Worship and Sacred Food

There will be no expectation that you join in the prayer unless you particularly wish to do so. You will not be offered sacred food.

A Note for Women

Traditionally, women are expected not to go into the temple during menstruation.

Visiting a Jewish Synagogue

General

You should avoid bringing non-kosher food into a synagogue.

Clothing

Dress should be modest, with arms and legs covered, and should not be formal. Women should wear a skirt or dress of reasonable length and not trousers. In an *Orthodox* synagogue, married women should cover their heads. Men and boys should cover their heads when visiting any synogogue.

Check before entering whether men and women usually sit separately at the synagogue in question. In many *Orthodox* synagogues, women will sit in a separate balcony or gallery area during worship.

Worship and Sacred Food

There is no expectation that you should join in the worship, unless you particularly wish to do so. You will not be expected to make particular gestures of respect toward any objects. No sacred food is distributed during the service, but *kiddush* (the Hebrew for sanctification) may take place after the service and visitors will be invited to join in this. A blessing will be said or sung over wine and bread to give thanks to God for these. The wine and bread will the be shared and will be offered to visitors as a sign of hospitality, although there is no compulsion to take them. Young children are usually given fruit juice..

Visiting a Muslim Mosque

Clothing

Should be modest for both men and women. For women this means an ankle length skirt or trousers, which should not be tight or transparent, together with long sleeved and high necked tops. A headscarf is essential for women. Shoes are removed before going into the prayer hall and put on the racks provided or wrapped in a plastic bag and taken into the hall. Clean and presentable socks, stockings, or tights, are therefore a good idea.

Entering the Mosque

Where women attend the mosque, men and women usually go in by separate entrances. You may be greeted by the Arabic greeting *As salaam-u-'alaikum* which means "Peace be upon you". The answer, if you like to use it, is *Wa 'alaikum-us-salaam*, or "Peace be upon you too". Do not expect to shake hands with people of the opposite sex to yourself. Before entering the prayer hall or prayer room, Muslim men and women perform *wudu* or ablutions. This is not necessary for the non-Muslim visitor who will not be joining in the prayer.

Entering the Prayer Hall

Go quietly into the hall, and sit on the floor, avoiding pointing your feet in the direction of the Qibla (the wall with the niche or alcove in it indicating the direction of Makka), unless a medical condition makes this the only possible posture. If you go as a group, and prayers are taking place, sit together toward the rear of the hall.

Worship and Sacred Food

When *salat* (Arabic) or *namaz* (Urdu), one of the five daily prayers is in progress, visitors are welcomed but simply to observe and not join in, unless one is a Muslim and wishes to join in. If you arrive at such a time, find a place near the rear wall and sit quietly observing the prayer. No sacred food will be offered to you at a mosque, nor will you be expected to make any physical gesture of respect to holy objects (except removing your shoes and acting respectfully in the prayer hall).

Note for Women

The main place of prayer is often used only by the men, and a separate room is provided for women. Where men and women pray in the same hall, they remain in separate groups. Women are expected not to come to the mosque during their menstrual period. Many Muslim women pray at home and therefore do not frequently attend the mosque. However, if you are a non-Muslim woman visiting a mosque you are likely to be as courteously welcomed and shown around as would be a non-Muslim man.

Note for Parents

Small children are not normally brought to mosques, in accordance with the request of the Prophet, except on the occasion of *Eid-al-Fitre* or *Eid-al-Adhan*.

Visiting a Sikh Gurdwara

General

No tobacco or alcohol or drugs should ever be taken into the buildings of the *Gurdwara* (not just the prayer hall). If you are a smoker, remember to leave your cigarettes outside.

Clothing

Should be modest for both men and women. This means a long skirt or trousers for women. Head covering is essential. A large clean handkerchief is adequate for men, and women are expected to use scarves. The *Gurdwara* will usually have some head coverings available for those who have not brought them, but not necessarily enough for a large group of visitors. Shoes are removed before going into the *Gurdwara* and put on the racks provided. Clean and presentable socks, stockings, or tights, are therefore a good idea.

Entering the Prayer Hall

In addition to covering your head, you may be asked to wash your hands (which Sikhs do before entering to pray). As you go in, you will see the *Guru Granth Sahib Ji* (the Sikh sacred scripture) up on a low platform, covered by a canopy. When Sikhs enter they touch the floor before this with their forehead and offer a gift such as food or money.

Visitors may also bow in similar fashion as a mark of respect, or if uncomfortable with this for religious reasons, may simply give a slight bow or stand for a few minutes before the *Guru Granth Sahib Ji* in silence as a mark of respect. No gift would be expected from a visitor though, of course, it would be deeply appreciated. If you do wish to make one, leave it with the others on the floor in front of the *Guru Granth Sahib Ji*. Seating is on the floor (usually carpeted). Men and women sometimes sit in separate groupings. Sit in a position which avoids your feet being pointed toward the *Guru Granth Sahib Ji*, or your back being turned toward it. Both those positions are considered disrespectful.

Worship and Sacred Food

If you arrive during worship, you will normally be expected to join the worshippers, but you do not have to join in unless you would particularly like to do so. At the end of the worship you may be offered *karah prashad* (holy food). In the Sikh context, this is a sweet mixture that has been blessed during the service and is given to all to signify that all are equal and united in their humanity and that there are no caste distinctions.

If you are uncomfortable, for religious reasons, about being given some of this sacred food to eat, let the offerer know with a quiet "No thank you". If possible, explain to your hosts in advance that you are declining for reasons of your own personal religious position, and not out of any disrespect to them. The same applies to *langar* (the food served in the communal kitchen at the *Gurdwara*) since this has also been blessed. Because it has been blessed, head covering should be maintained. The *langar* is a meal to which outsiders are cordially welcomed. However, it is advisable to ask only for what you are likely to eat rather than to leave any.

Visiting a Zoroastrian Place of Worship

There are no Zoroastrian fire temples in the UK. There is, however, a room for Zoroastrian worship in Zoroastrian House in London. People from outside the Zoroastrian community may, on occasion, be invited to attend a *Jashan* (festival).

HOSTING VISITORS TO A PLACE OF WORSHIP

If you are a member of a religious community, it is sometimes easy to forget how strange and complicated the proceedings in your place of worship may seem to outsiders. Making visitors feel at ease is important. If you are hosting a visit to a place of worship by people of other traditions it is helpful to think in advance about a few questions:

- What kind of service or worship or celebration would it be most appropriate for them to attend? Explain carefully the nature of the event to those attending.

- Can the suggested size of the group be accommodated comfortably whilst regular worship is taking place, or would it be better to offer a guided tour outside of the times of regular worship ?

- Will you expect visitors to join in the worship in any way ? If so, have you considered how some aspects of your worship may present difficulties of conscience for some visitors and how you will deal with such instances ?

- Will visitors be expected to express respect in any particular way to any holy item within the place of worship ? If so, you will need carefully to explain what is involved.

- Are there any rules of clothing or of hygiene which visitors must observe ? If so, make sure that these are clearly explained.

- If there are any guidelines for general behaviour within your place of worship it would be helpful to tell your visitors in advance.

- If your place of worship is regularly visited by people of other religious traditions and none you may find it helpful to create a short fact sheet about the building, its worshippers, the main forms of worship which take place, and any requirements which you may have for guests who visit or attend worship.

FURTHER HELP

If you need further advice and information on the points discussed in this chapter, The Inter Faith Network may be able to help. It can put you in touch with individuals and organisations who might be able to advise or assist with your event or consultancy.

If you are wanting to get involved in inter-faith activity locally or nationally the Network can make suggestions. Information and advice can also be obtained from the other organisations listed in the chapter on inter-faith organisations.

RELIGIOUS LANDSCAPE OF THE UK

THE RELIGIOUS LANDSCAPE OF THE UK

THE VARIETY OF RELIGIONS

Religions in the UK exhibit a considerable degree of vigour and diversity despite the impact of recent processes of secularisation on personal and social life. The UK has a greater religious diversity than any other country of the European Community. Christians form the numerically largest religious group followed by Muslims; then Hindus, Jews and Sikhs; then Buddhists; and then Baha'is, Jains and Zoroastrians; then many smaller communities.

Members of each religious community share in common many beliefs and practices, but there are also significant differences of tradition, organisation, ethnicity and language within each of the larger communities.

There are also areas of religious life which are more fluid with regard to the boundaries between religious traditions. Within this category come significant sections of the religious life of ethnically Chinese people in which, sometimes, traditions of Taoism, Confucianism and also Buddhism can be found in intermingled forms.

Finally there are also other forms of religious expression, such as that of groups which are sometimes referred to as "New Religious Movements" (NRMs) and indigenous Pagan traditions. Another area of religious life, often described as "New Age spirituality", is characterised by a concern for ecology and personal growth and draws upon spiritual practices and traditions from a variety of sources.

In addition to members of the religious communities who have an active involvement in the regular and corporate life of their communities, the UK also has a significant proportion of people whose religious life is often described as "folk religion" or "residual Christianity". Such people may turn to an active involvement in Christian religious life at times of crisis or personal significance such as birth, marriage and death or at festivals such as Christmas.

There are also, however, a large number of people who, whilst upholding strong ethical and moral values do not profess any form of religious belief or life, including humanists, some of whom may be agnostics or atheists. Not all of these, by any means, are antagonistic towards religion. Some do, however, have concerns about allowing too prominent a role for the religions in public life.

The Development of a Multi-faith Country

On the basis of the number of its adherents and of its contemporary and historical role in the wider life of the UK, Christianity is the country's principal religious tradition.

Since the coming of Christianity to Britain the older, indigenous Pagan traditions were displaced or forced underground by active persecution although some aspects which were thought to be compatible with Christianity can still be found in Christian observances and architecture.

The Jewish community has a long-standing presence although suffering intermittent expulsions and persecution until, after the seventeenth century, it became more securely established. The Jewish community extended rapidly at the end of the nineteenth and the beginning of the twentieth centuries, when there was large scale immigration to the UK from Russia and Eastern European countries.

During the nineteenth century a number of individual Parsees (Zoroastrians from India or East Africa) came to the UK, some of whom became prominent in national life, with a Zoroastrian Parsee becoming the first South Asian Member of Parliament. At the turn of this century Buddhism began to be adopted by a number of people within the indigenous population, as did the Baha'i faith.

Religious diversification increased rapidly with the migration to the UK, after the Second World War, of significant numbers of people from the New Commonwealth countries of the West Indian islands, India, Pakistan, Bangladesh and Hong Kong, and in the 1960s and 1970s of South Asians from Tanzania, Uganda and Kenya.

With these migrations came the founding of significant communities of Hindus, Muslims, Sikhs, Jains and others, and also new varieties of Christian belief and practice. During the 1970s and 1980s, various migratory and refugee movements also strengthened the Baha'i, Buddhist, Hindu, Muslim and Zoroastrian communities in the UK.

Faith and Ethnic Identity

It is important not to confuse ethnic identity with religious identity. There may be a significant overlap: for example, most people of pakistani origin in the UK are Muslim. However, most of the UK's religious communities are ethnically diverse: they have members whose original roots are from varying parts of the world.

The Christian community includes people of African, Afro-Caribbean, Chinese and South Asian background. Similarly, there are Muslims with South Asian, Middle Eastern and Far Eastern roots, just as there are Hindus with ethnic origins in the Carbbean and Fiji as well as India. Similiarly, there may be religious diversity within a common ethnic identity. Someone from Gujarat, for example, might be Hindu, or might be Christian or Muslim.

Patterns of Settlement and Presence

As a result of variable patterns of migration and of settlement, some parts of the UK have developed a more multi-faith character than others. England has the widest and proportionately greatest variety of religious communities, followed by Scotland and Wales, then Northern Ireland. In all four nations of the UK the greatest religious diversity is to be found in cities, metropolitan boroughs and some towns. The cosmopolitan nature of London as a capital city means that the religious diversity, as well as ethnic and linguistic diversity, is at its greatest there.

Seaports such as Liverpool and Cardiff often have the oldest local minority religious communities because international trade led to the settlement of seafarers from other countries. Many old industrial towns and cities of the English Midlands and North have communities which were established as a result of migration from particular areas of Commonwealth countries in response to the invitation to work in British industries during the post-Second World War labour shortage.

Local communities often exhibit a considerable degree of homogeneity in terms of ethnic, cultural and linguistic backgrounds. In some cases the bulk of the community may, for example, be Muslims from Pakistan or, in others, Muslims from Bangladesh. Even where there is religious diversity there may be common ethnic, cultural and linguistic backgrounds. For example in Preston the Muslim community is largely Gujarati and so is the local Hindu community. This homogeneity in different localities is likely to diminish slowly as people increasingly move their homes within the country.

These variations in size, concentration, ethnicity and language apply not only to the religious communities which are numerical minorities in the UK. They also apply to the Christian community. Different parts of the UK exhibit different forms of Christian religious life in both denominational, cultural, ethnic and linguistic terms.

For example, in Wales there are local Christian communities for whom Welsh is the first language of both worship and everyday life. Throughout England, Scotland and Wales, Roman Catholic Christians are predominantly concentrated in urban areas and in England the Church of England has a more widespread presence in rural areas than any other Christian Church. The Christian community is also composed of a variety of ethnic groupings with migratory origins in other continents with African and Caribbean Christianity becoming an increasingly important aspect of UK Christian life.

SIZE OF THE RELIGIOUS COMMUNITIES

Statistical Problems

Directory users will expect a directory entitled Religions in the UK to offer figures on the size of religious communities in the UK. There are, however, very great problems with statistics on UK religious communities as noted in the chapter on "Using the Directory".

Existing figures can only be estimates due to the lack of a religious question in the national Census. Those which are extrapolated from ethnic figures have limited usefulness because there is no complete match between the categories of ethnic groups and religious communities, and also because only limited work has so far been done on extrapolating figures for religious communities from the latest Census.

Statistics are also a highly sensitive matter and religious communities will naturally feel concerned if they believe that their numbers have been underestimated. The directory research project undertook no new research on religious statistics for the UK. The Project was, however, carried out in consultation with individuals from the religious communities which it covers. Efforts were also made to consult individuals, organisations engaged in academic work in the area of religious statistics.

The directory therefore reports on some widely used sets of figures and then offers a set of figures which, whilst subject to the many difficulties which have been described would, it is believed, carry a broad consensus of opinion bearing in mind that, in most cases, very approximate estimates are all that can be achieved.

In some cases, in the individual chapters, a reference is made to work being undertaken within the religious communities concerned which suggests the possibility of a significantly higher figure than the numerical estimates which are actually given.

Some Widely Used Figures

A number of figures are given in official Government publications. In *Britain 1993*, published by the Central Office of Information, figures for community membership are given in descending size as follows:

Muslims	1,000,000
Hindus	300,000
Jews	300,000
Sikhs	300,000
Jains	30,000
Baha'is	5,000

No figures for community membership are given for Buddhists, Christians, or Zororastrians who are covered in the present directory.

The Christian Research Association, in its *UK Christian Handbook 1994/1995*, which is a source that is widely used, gives community membership figures, also in descending order of size:

Christians	37,600,000
Muslims	1,100,000
Sikhs	500,000
Hindus	400,000
Jews	300,000
Others	300,000

Social Trends 23, published by the Central Statistical Office, gives 1990 figures, based upon the research of MARC Europe for adult active membership, as distinct from community membership, at the following levels, in descending order:

Christians	7,023,000
Muslims	990,000
Sikhs	390,000
Hindus	140,000
Jews	111,000
Others	23,000

The figure for "Others" is likely, therefore, to include Baha'is, Jains and Zoroastrians who are covered in the present directory.

Although *Britain 1993* and *Social Trends 23* are official publications, the figures which they give are inevitably subject to all the qualifications about statistics which have already been explained, as are the figures produced for the *UK Christian Handbook*.

Figures in This Directory

The directory estimates included in the chapters on individual religious communities are generally community figures since the directory focuses on religious communities as such. As explained above, they are not the product of new research conducted in the context of this project, but have been arrived at on the basis of wide consultation and would seem to be the figures which would attract the broadest consensus of opinion. These figures shopuld in no way br regarded as definitive but only as indicative estimates and are, as follows, in descending order of size:

Christians	37,000,000
Muslims	1,500,000
Hindus	400,000
Sikhs	400,000
Jews	300,000
Buddhists	120,000
Jains	30,000
Bahai's	6,000
Zoroastrians	6,000

RELIGIONS IN PUBLIC LIFE

The Established Church in England

In England, the Church of England is the form of religion "by law established" and the reigning monarch is its Supreme Governor. As an expression of this relationship between the Crown and the Church of England, twenty-four bishops and the two archbishops of the Church of England have seats in the House of Lords and there is Government involvement in the appointments of its bishops and its archbishops.

The Church of England thus has a special position in its relationship with the State which has many consequences for its presence within, and access to, social institutions such as hospitals, schools and universities. It is not, however, funded by the State in any direct way. Despite this public connection between the Church and State, religious belief has often, and increasingly, been seen as private matter.

Christianity in Scotland, Wales and Ireland

In Wales, Scotland and Northern Ireland religion has often been closely associated with preserving a linguistic, national or group identity in the face of perceived threats to it and the predominant forms of Christian religion are different from those in England.

In Wales, there is no established Church, since the Anglican Church in Wales was disestablished earlier this century.

In Northern Ireland there is also no religion established by law, although the Protestant Christian majority in the Province has meant that historically there has often been a de facto connection between the province and Protestant Christianity. Under the Republic of Ireland's Constitution of 1937, the Roman Catholic Christianity had a special constitutional position, but this provision was deleted in the early 1970s. Despite the political border between Northern Ireland and the Republic of Ireland and the continuing conflict in the Province, the Churches of the island of Ireland are organised on an all-Ireland basis. Regional and local bodies exist there within a common organisational framework both North and South of the border.

In Scotland, there is an established Church. This is not, however, the Scottish Church of the Anglican Christian tradition (the Episcopal Church of Scotland), but the Presbyterian Church of Scotland. Despite its established status and strong place within Scottish history the Church of Scotland has no right, corresponding to that of the Church of England, for its leaders to have seats in the House of Lords.

Diversity and Consultation

Whilst Christianity (especially in its established forms) still plays a significant role in public life of the UK by virtue of its historical position and numerical strength, other religious communities are now also beginning to have more public visibility.

For example, in recent years at many State occasions, the Church of England has facilitated the presence and participation of other Christian denominations and of representatives of other world religious traditions. This reflects a growing recognition of the increasingly multi-faith nature of religious life in the UK, a recognition which is increasingly occuring in a variety of other fields of social and political life too.

One example of this was the establishment, in 1992, by the Department of the Environment, of the Inner Cities Religious Council. It has a multi-faith membership and is designed to explore the possibilities of partnership between Government and the religious communities in tackling some of the social and economic problems of the urban areas.

Over the years, many governmental, public and voluntary bodies had developed consultative mechanisms with both the Christian and Jewish communities. Because of their presence within the society over a long period of time these communities have also been able to set up the kind of broad and widely representative bodies which have facilitated this consultation at a variety of local, regional and national levels.

Similar patterns of consultation with other religious communities are not yet as developed. This is partly because some communities have not yet been able to develop representative bodies which have found a general acceptance within their communities, particularly at the national level. This has been quite natural since many communities found that their initial energies had to be put into establishing and building up their local life and grassroots organisations.

In a whole range of areas there are increasing signs that organisations and bodies which had previously only liaised with the Christian and Jewish communities are now beginning to make efforts to consult more widely. At the same time, though, there is some significant disquiet among minority religious communities because of a concern that developments in the direction of consultation are not fast enough or sufficiently widespread. Across a wide range of religious and social institutions religious leaders and other represent- atives of minority religious communities can still find it hard to gain access to many of our public and social institutions on the same basis as many Christian leaders and representatives.

Education and Religious Diversity

In education, a variety of religious traditions are represented on every local Agreed Syllabus Conference. These are given responsibility for the syllabus of Religious Education to be used by maintained schools in the relevant Local Authority area (all Agreed Syllabi will, in future, have to be reviewed on a five yearly basis).

Representation for local religious organisations was, in addition, secured on SACREs (Standing Advisory Councils for Religious Education), which monitor the delivery of Religious Education and collective worship within the maintained sector of education under the 1988 Education Reform Act.

However, many of the minority religious communities have been greatly concerned at the way in which that Act, for the first time, explicitly specified a considerable emphasis upon Christianity in both Religious Education and collective worship, thus shifting the balance back from the broader multi-faith curricula which had been developing since the 1970s.

In terms of the structure of publicly maintained education, a significant sector of the Muslim community feels discriminated against because, as yet, the authorities have not designated any of their schools as voluntary aided schools on a similar basis to the voluntary aided schools which exist within the Jewish community and sectors of the Christian community.

RELIGIONS AND THE LAW

England and Wales, Scotland and Northern Ireland

The position of the Church of England as the established church was, in the past, buttressed by law as well as custom. For example, the Corporation and Test Act of 1661 and 1673 limited the holding of office under the Crown to communicant members of the Church of England. These Acts were repealed in 1828 and 1829, removing these particular restrictions on the participation of Roman Catholic and of nonconformist Christians in public life. But the corresponding restrictions on Jews were not fully removed until 1858. These were important steps towards recognising that participation in public life must be open not only to those Christians who do not belong to the established church but also to those of other religious traditions or none.

The legal framework for the practice of religion in the UK is clearly of importance to all religious communities. It has a bearing on the degree to which religions can operate in accordance with their own traditions. It also affects the way in which they organise themselves.

In looking at the relationship between religion and the law it is necessary, first of all, to note that the legal systems for England and Wales are distinctive from that which is operative in Scotland, and that Northern Ireland also has many provisions which are different from those which exist in the the rest of the UK.

Religious Recognition and Registration

The UK has no centralised list of religions which are officially recognised by the State and which are to be treated in accordance with this recognition. However, when a building undergoes a change of regular use, it is necessary for local authority planning permission to be obtained.

In English law, organisations which are recognised as religious are eligible for certain privileges. Firstly, they can obtain charitable status which allows the organisation to operate without being subject to most forms of national direct taxation. Secondly, religious buildings are exempt from the payment of local "rates" (property tax). Thirdly, registered religious buildings can be licensed to permit the performance within them of marriages in accordance with the religious rites of that particular organisation. Finally, buildings may register as "a place of religious worship" which is in itself a prima facie claim to the other privileges.

The registration of buildings as places of worship and their licensing for marriages is a matter for the office of the Registrar-General who, through the Director of Population Censuses and Surveys, publishes a list of registered and licensed buildings. The granting of charitable status is a matter for the Charity Commissioners but the "advancement of religion" is one of the criteria for the granting of this status.

On occasion, the courts have been called upon to adjudicate in matters of definition concerning whether a particular organisation is or is not a "religion" and also to clarify what it is which constitutes "public worship." The law itself enshrines no definitive criteria relating to these questions. However, the courts have understood certain indicators to be of importance. Chief among these have been the need to show that a group is monotheistic in belief, although this does not necessarily mean that those groups which are not monotheistic or indeed, theistic, (for example, Buddhism) are automatically regarded as not being a "religion".

Religious Slaughter and the Law

Up until the present, the response of the legal system to increased religious diversity has generally been of an ad hoc and pragmatic nature rather than seeking to provide generally applicable new frameworks for law. It has therefore often been concerned with defining permissible exceptions to generally applicable laws.

For example, the general law with regard to the slaughter of animals, including cattle, sheep and goats, is set out in the 1974 Slaughterhouses Act which imposes a general practice of pre-stunning an animal before its slaughter. Similar provisions are contained in the Slaughter of Poultry Act of 1967 which covers turkeys, chickens and other similar fowl. However, both Acts contain exemptions to allow Jews and Muslims to follow their religious traditions and requirements with regard to slaughter of animals and poultry for Jewish and Muslim consumption.

For Jews this involves the method of slaughter known as *shechita* and producing *kosher* food. For Muslims it involves *dhabh* slaughter, with the meat produced from this being known as *halal* (for details of the significance of these methods see the introductory materials on the Jewish and Muslim communities).

The Law, Religious and Racial Discrimination

With regard to Sikhs, after a long legal struggle to be allowed exemption from a 1972 Road Traffic Act requirement for motorcyclists to wear safety helmets, the Motor-Cycle Crash Helmets (Religious Exemption) Act was passed in 1976 to exempt a follower of the Sikh religion "while he is wearing a turban" from the crash helmet requirements of the 1972 Act. A similiar exemption was granted by the Employment Act 1989 to allow turbaned Sikhs to work on construction sites without a helmet or hard hat as required by new safety regulations.

Family, marriage and burial law have also been the subject of some legal and social debate involving the religious communities, raising questions about the relationship of social legislation on matters such as marriage, divorce and inheritance to religious law and practice. There has also been concern about the extent to which employers can or should provide time and facilities at work for the performance of obligatory prayers and time off for the observance of religious festivals.

At the time of writing there are legal provisions against religious discrimination in Northern Ireland but not in the rest of the UK where there are, however, legal provisions against racial discrimination. "Racial discrimination" can be judged to have occurred in relation to an "ethnic group" and one of the factors understood to be constitutive of an ethnic group is that of a shared religion. Under this provision, Jews have been judged to be an "ethnic group" in the terms of the Race Relations Act, as also have Sikhs following the case of Mandla v. Dowell Lee.

Muslims, as such, however, fall outside the scope of the Race Relations Act because they are viewed (correctly) as being a religious group and not a racial or ethnic group. However, in some circumstances a Muslim may successfully claim "indirect" discrimination has occurred by sueing as an Asian or an Arab or as a Yemen or Pakistani, relying on an ethnic or national identity and complaining that certain practices or procedures have had a detrimental effect because they unjustifiably interfere with religious observance.

There are some provisions in the common law of England and Wales against blasphemy and blasphemous libel. However, the testing of these provisions in the courts during the recent controversy over the book *The Satanic Verses* demonstrated, these laws only give protection to the Christian religion and, more particularly, to the doctrines and practices of the Church of England.

In its *Second Review of the Race Relations Act 1976,* published in 1992, the Commission for Racial Equality stated that it considered the present blasphemy laws to be unsatisfactory and recommended that consideration be given to making incitement to religious hatred an offence under English law, as well as to incorporating international obligations against religious discrimination into domestic law, thus bringing law in England and Wales, as well as Scottish law, into line with the law pertaining to Northern Ireland.

THE CHALLENGE OF THE FUTURE

The increasingly multi-faith nature of UK society is posing a large number of questions and issues across a wide area of individual and social life. As communities become more and more established so too will their case for greater recognition and representation in public and social life.

The challenge posed for all in such a society (including religious communities themseleves) is the extent to which it will be possible to evolve the common visions and structures necessary for sustaining an integrated but richly diverse community without either assimilation or fragmentation, and drawing upon the resources and distinctiveness of all for the common good. Upon whether the religious communities, social organisations and the State can rise to this challenge will depend the shape of our common future.

BIBLIOGRAPHY

Badham, P (ed), *Religion, State and Society in Modern Britain*, Edwin Mellen Press, Lampeter, 1989.

Barker, E, *New Religious Movements: A Practical Introduction*, HMSO, London, 1989.

Barley, C; Field, C; Kosmin, B; and Nielsen, J, *Religion: Reviews of United Kingdom Statistical Sources, Volume XX*, Pergamon Press, Oxford, 1987.

Bowker, J, *Worlds of Faith: Religious Belief andPractice in Britain Today*, Ariel, London, 1983.

Bradney, A G D, "Separate schools, ethnic minorities and the law", in *New Community*, Volume XIII, No 3, Spring 1987, pp 412-420.

Bradney, A, *Religions, Rights and Laws*, Leicester University Press, Leicester, 1993.

Brown, A, *Festivals in World Religions*, Longmans, Essex, 1986.

Charlton, R and Kay, R, "The politics of religious slaughter: an ethno-religious case study", in *New Community*, Volume XII, No 3, Winter 1985-86, pp 409-503.

Clarke C, Peach, C, and Vertovec, S (eds), *South Asians Overseas: Migration and Ethnicity*, Cambridge University Press, Cambridge.

Commission for Racial Equality, *Britain a Plural*

Society: Report of a Seminar, Commission for Racial Equality, London, 1990.

Commission for Racial Equality, *Schools of Faith: Religious Schools in a Multi-Cultural Society*, Commission for Racial Equality, London.

Cox, E and Cairns, J, *Reforming Religious Education: The Religious Clauses of the 1988 ERA*, Kogan Page, London, 1989.

Edwards, D, "A brief history of the concept of toleration in Britain", in Horton, J and Crabtree, H (eds), *Toleration and Integrity in a Multi-Faith Society*, University of York Department of Politics, York, 1992, pp 41-49.

Fryer, P, *Staying Power: The History of Black People in Britain*, Pluto, London, 1984.

Gibbert, A D, *The Making of Post-Christian Britain: A History of the Secularization of Modern Society*, Longman, Essex, 1980.

Halstead, M, *The Case for Muslim Voluntary-Aided Schools: Some Philosophical Reflections*, Islamic Academy, Cambridge, 1986.

Hooker, R, and Sargant, J(ed), Belonging to Britain: Christian Perspectives on a Plural Society, Council of Churches for Britain and Ireland, London, undated.

Horton, J, "Religion and toleration: some problems and possibilities", in Horton, J and Crabtree, H (eds), *Toleration and Integrity in a Multi-Faith Society*, University of York Department of Politics, York, 1992, pp 62-70.

Horton, J and Crabtree, H (eds), *Toleration and Integrity in a Multi-Faith Society*, University of York Department of Politics, York, 1992.

Hulmes, E, *Education and Cultural Diversity*, Longman, Harlow, 1989.

Inter Faith Network for the United Kingdom and Commission for Racial Equality, *Law, Blasphemy and the Multi-Faith Society*, Commission for Racial Equality, London, 1990.

James, C, *Immigration and Social Policy in Britain*, Tavistock Publications, London, 1977.

Knott, K, *Statistical Analysis of South Asians in the UK by Religion and Ethnicity*, Community Religions Project Research Paper No 8, University of Leeds, Leeds, 1981.

Lynch, J, "Cultural pluralism, structural pluralism and the United Kingdom," in Commission for Racial Equality, *Britain a Plural Society: Report of a Seminar*, Commission for Racial Equality, London, 1990, pp 29-43.

MacIntyre, *Multi-Culture and Multi-Faith Societies: Some Examinable Assumptions*, Farmington Occasional Papers, No 3, Oxford.

Murphy, T, "Toleration and the law", in Horton, J and Crabtree, H (eds), *Toleration and Integrity in a Multi-Faith Society*, University of York Department of Politics, York, 1992, pp 50-61.

Nicholls, D, *Church and State in Britain Since 1820*, Routledge and Kegan Paul, London, 1967.

Nielsen, J, *Islamic Law: Its Significance for the Situation of Muslim Minorities in Europe*, Research Papers on Muslims in Europe, No 35, September 1987.

Parekh, B, "Britain and the social logic of pluralism", in Commission for Racial Equality, *Britain a Plural Society: Report of a Seminar*, Commission for Racial Equality, London, 1990, pp 58-78.

Pearl, D, *Family Law and the Immigrant Communities*, Jordans, London, 1986.

Poulter, S, *English Law and Ethnic Minority Customs*, Butterworths, London, 1986.

Poulter, S, *Asian Traditions and English Law: A Handbook*, Trentham Books, Stoke-on-Trent, 1990.

Poulter, S, "Cultural pluralism and its limits: a legal perspective", in Commission for Racial Equality, *Britain a Plural Society: Report of a Seminar*, Commission for Racial Equality, London, 1990, pp 3-28.

Puri, G Singh, *Multi Cultural Society and Sikh Faith*, Falcon Books, New Delhi, 1992.

Rex, J, *The Concept of a Multi-Cultural Society*, University of Warwick Centre for Research in

Ethnic Relations, Coventry, 1985.

Rex, J, *Ethnic Identity and Ethnic Mobilisation in Britain*, Monographs on Ethnic Relations, No 5, Warwick University Centre for Research in Ethnic Relations, Warwick, 1991.

Rex, J, "The political sociology of a multi-cultural society", in *European Journal of Intercultural Studies*, Volume I, No 3, pp

Smart, N, "Church, Party and State" in, Badham, P (ed), *Religion, State and Society in Modern Britain*, Edwin Mellen Press, Lampeter, 1989, pp.

Thomas, T (ed), *The British: Their Religious Beliefs and Practices*, Routledge, London, 1988.

Verma, G, "Pluralism: some theoretical and practical considerations", in Commission for Racial Equality, *Britain a Plural Society: Report of a Seminar*, Commission for Racial Equality, London, 1990, pp 44-57.

Visram, R, *Ayahs, Lascars and Princes: The Story of Indians in Britain 1700-1947*, Pluto Press, London, 1984.

Wilson, B, "Old Laws and New Religions", in Cohn-Sherbok, D (ed), *The Canterbury Papers; Essays on Religion and Society*, Bellew Publishing, London, 1990, pp 210-224.

THE BAHA'I COMMUNITY

INTRODUCING THE BAHA'I COMMUNITY

BAHA'IS IN THE UNITED KINGDOM

History

Baha'is have been present in the UK since 1899. Up until 1939 most Baha'i activity centred around England, but in the years following the Second World War the Baha'i Faith was also established in Scotland, Wales and Ireland. Now around 6,000 Baha'is live in approximately 400 communities spread across the British Isles, including 179 Local Groups and 177 Local Spiritual Assemblies recorded in this directory. Totally, there are around 5,500,000 Baha'is.

Origins

Most Baha'is in the UK are of indigenous ethnic origin and most are converts from other religions or people who were previously agnostics or atheists. There are also, however, first generation immigrants from Iran and their descendants who were born of Baha'i families. Most Baha'is in the UK pray and read their scriptures in English.

ORIGINS AND DEVELOPMENT OF THE BAHA'I FAITH

The Bab

The Baha'i Faith began in Persia in the mid nineteenth century, developing out of the religious context of *Shi'a* Islam to become a new and distinctive religion. Four people were central to the development of the Baha'i Faith: the *Bab*, *Baha'u'llah*, *Abdu'l-Baha* and Shoghi Effendi.

The person known to Baha'is by the title of the *Bab* (the Gate or Door) was born in Shiraz, Persia. He was originally known by the personal name of Ali-Muhammad (1819-1850) and was a descendant of the Prophet Muhammad. In 1844 the *Bab* proclaimed himself the *Messenger of God* and heralded the coming of *One Greater* than Himself who would bring a new age of civilisation characterised by world peace. He was executed in Persia for heresy against Islam along with many early followers who were persecuted after his death. These followers were known as *Babis*.

Baha'u'llah

In 1817, Husayn Ali (1817-1892), known to Baha'is by the title of Baha'u'llah (the Glory of God) was born in Tehran, Persia. In 1863, he claimed to be the Greater One whose coming the Bab had foretold. He said he was the bringer of divine revelation who was to fulfil the promises made by the previous Messengers of other religions. Baha'u'llah was banished from Persia, and later exiled to Palestine by the Ottoman Turkish authorities in 1868. He died in Akka in 1892.

Abdu'l-Baha

After the death of Baha'u'llah his son Abdu'l-Baha (Servant of the Glory - also known among Baha'is as the Master), was appointed in his will as the authorised interpreter of Baha'i teachings. Abdu'l-Baha was born in 1841 and died in Haifa in 1921.

Shoghi Effendi

On the death of *Abdu'l-Baha*, his grandson Shoghi Effendi (1897-1957), as appointed in *Abdu'l-Baha's* will, became the *Guardian of the Faith and Interpreter of Scripture*. After the death of Shoghi Effendi in London, authority passed to the elected body called the *Hands of the Cause of God*. This was a group of twenty-seven people appointed by Shoghi Effendi to be the *Chief Stewards of the Faith*.

Universal House of Justice

In 1963 the *Universal House of Justice* was established as a guiding body for the Baha'i community and is now based at the Baha'i World Centre in Haifa in Israel.

Recent Decades

Over the past thirty years, the Baha'i Faith has experienced major expansion, especially in India, Africa, South America, the Pacific and more recently in Eastern Europe. Globally, followers are now located in two hundred and eighteen countries and dependent territories.

SOURCES OF BAHA'I BELIEFS AND PRACTICES

Baha'i Scriptures

Baha'is believe their scriptures to be the revealed message of God. These scriptures consist of the Writings of the three central figures of the Baha'i Faith: the *Bab*, *Baha'u'llah*, and *Abdu'l-Baha*. They include all documents hand-written by them; all documents signed by them; and records of their spoken words, authenticated either directly or indirectly by the speakers. The *Kitab-i-Iqan* (The Book of Certitude) contains the key doctrinal beliefs and Baha'u'llah's *Hidden Words* is a frequently used collection of ethical aphorisms.

Most of the Writings of *Baha'u'llah* and *Abdu'l-Baha* are in the form of letters known as *Tablets* and are written in Persian or Arabic. The collection and classification of Baha'i sacred writings and of their authoritative interpretations by Shoghi Effendi still continues today. There are now over sixty thousand original documents or copies kept at the Baha'i World Centre in Haifa and the Baha'i scriptures have been translated into over eight hundred and twenty languages. Foremost among these scriptures is *Baha'u'llah's 'Al-Kitab al Aqdas* (Most Holy Book, 1873) which is considered the basis for Baha'i moral principles and institutions.

KEY BAHA'I BELIEFS

Progressive Revelation

Unity and its establishment in the world is a central theme of the Baha'i religion. Followers of the religion share a conviction that there has only ever been one religion and also one God whom people have called by different names.

This God is seen as being beyond gender and as infinite and unknowable in Divine Essence, yet revealed to humanity through a series of *Messengers* sent to different places at different times. Moses, Krishna, Zoroaster, Buddha, Christ and Muhammad are all believed by Baha'is to be *Messengers* from God and are described by *Baha'u'llah* as *Manifestations of God*. There is therefore a progressive view of revelation in which each recognised *Messenger* is believed to have passed on divine law informing society how to live and behave. All *Messengers* are also believed to have promised a time when a great *Messenger* would come and bring peace to the world and Baha'is believe that *Baha'u'llah* was that *Messenger*.

One World

Baha'is believe that the future of the world lies in a single world order existing for the benefit of everyone regardless of race, religion, class or gender. This will involve the abolition of prejudices; equality for men and women; abolition of the extremes of wealth and poverty; universal compulsory education; a universal auxiliary language in addition to existing national and ethnic languages in order to facilitate international communication; and a world commonwealth with a world parliament.

Once the unity of humankind has been firmly established world peace will follow. The establishment of Baha'i communities and groups throughout the world is seen as contributing to this process and, indeed, as modelling a new world order.

Nature and Goal of Human Life

Baha'is believe that each human being has a separate rational soul which is related to, but also distinct from, the human body. The world is understood as a place where this soul, which is seen as persisting after death, can develop. Life in the world is seen as analagous to existence in the womb, and the process of death is likened to the process of birth.

Heaven is seen as a state of nearness to God and hell as being remoteness from God, each state following as a consequence of efforts, or of the lack of them to develop spiritually. Beyond this, according to Baha'i teaching, the exact nature of life after death remains a mystery.

Education and Spirituality

The importance of education and growth in knowledge is a central theme in the Baha'is

understanding of her or his place in the world and there is no dichotomy between what are often called the secular and the spiritual dimensions of life. Religion and science are viewed as complementary ways of discovering truth: science through investigation and religion through revelation.

BAHA'I LIFE

Joining the Community

A person becomes a member of the Baha'i community by applying to become a member of a Baha'i administrative body such as a *Local Spiritual Assembly* (see below). An Assembly will accept them if it is satisfied that they truly believe the tenets of the Baha'i faith and are basically informed about the central figures of the Faith as well as the existence of laws they must follow and of an administration they must obey. Being a part of the Baha'i worldwide *Administrative Order* gives individual Baha'is confidence that they can contribute in the best way to the goals of the Baha'i religion.

Teaching and Pioneering

Baha'is are forbidden to proselytise, but they are always eager to share their vision and beliefs with enquirers. This sharing of vision and belief is known among Baha'is as *teaching*. Many are also involved in what is known as *pioneering,* which is spreading the faith by means of moving where there are currently no Baha'is.

Women and Men

Men and women have equal status in the Baha'i community. Any distinctions in gender roles within the community are culture-specific rather than religious and there is a strongly held view that both men and women should receive education of equal standard. If, for any reason, education is not available to all, then women, as the first educators of the next generation, should have priority.

Diet

There are no specific dietary laws in the Baha'i Faith, although vegetarianism is encouraged. The consumption of alcohol and the taking of habit-forming drugs is forbidden, and smoking is discouraged.

TRADITIONS IN THE BAHA'I FAITH

The Baha'i community is tightly structured and organised. At each stage in the development of the Baha'i religion there have been those who have split off from the community in disputes over the succession and leadership, or who have tried to establish an alternative movement under the Baha'i name.

These groups are referred to by Baha'is as *Covenant-Breakers*, since the *Covenant* which binds Baha'is together is seen to consist of the unity of the line of authority from *Baha'u'llah* through to the *Universal House of Justice*. The sanction for such *Covenant-breaking* is expulsion. *Covenant-breaking* is viewed as being fundamentally different from simply leaving the religion or behaving in a way that falls short of Baha'i ideals.

Baha'is are thus forbidden to have social relationships with those who have attempted to establish alternative authorities and groups. None of the groups viewed as *Covenant-Breakers* has gained a major following and some of the people involved in them have subsequently gone on into the practice of other religions or philosophies.

Within the community, Baha'is are not organised into any identifiably distinct traditions of interpretation or practice. It is a part of the Baha'i self-understanding that their religion is unique among the world's religions in that not only has it survived a century and a half without splitting into sects, but that it will continue to be united in the future.

BAHA'I WORSHIP

Daily Prayers

Every Baha'i over the age of fifteen must recite daily one of three prayers known as the "obligatory" prayers. These three prayers differ in length and must be recited in differing ways. The three prayers are: a short prayer which should be recited once every twenty-four hours between noon and sunset; a medium length prayer which should be recited three times in a day – morning, noon and evening; a long and elaborate prayer which should be recited once every twenty-four hours.

In addition to making one of these obligatory prayers, Baha'is are required to read extracts from the scriptures every morning and evening. When praying, Baha'is turn in the direction of Bahji, near Akka in Israel, which is the burial place of Baha'u'llah. This is the holiest shrine of the Baha'i world and a focal point for its global unity.

Regular Worship

The Baha'i religion has no set worship services and no ordained priesthood. Devotional programmes are simple and consist of prayers, meditations, and the reading of sections from the sacred scriptures of the Faith and of other world religions. Music is encouraged and in the *Houses of Worship* (see below) this is provided by an unaccompanied choir.

Firesides

Most Baha'i gatherings take place in people's homes. Small regular meetings in homes for discussion are known as *Firesides* at which outsiders who have expressed an interest in the Faith may be present. These meetings usually begin and end with prayers and include information and discussion. Other meetings, for example *Nineteen-Day Feasts* (see below), may be held in local Baha'i Centres.

Houses of Worship

Across the world there are seven purpose-built *Houses of Worship* (Sydney in Australia; Chicago in the USA; Frankfurt in Germany; Panama City in Central America; New Delhi in India; Apia in Western Samoa and Kampala in Uganda). *Houses of Worship* are at present of continental rather than national or local significance.

They were built at the request of *Baha'u'llah*, who gave them the name *Mashriqu'l-Adhkar* (Dawning Place of God's Praise), and they are built to his specifications. Each is nine sided and surmounted by a dome, standing in large gardens with fountains, trees and flowers. Together with the place of worship itself there are also additional buildings for educational, charitable and social purposes, for example old people's homes and orphanages. *Baha'u'llah* believed that this would ensure that Baha'i worship would always be closely associated with the beauty of nature and art together with practical work for the amelioration of poor social conditions, general education and administration.

There are regular services at the *Houses of Worship* which are open to all. The oldest surviving House of Worship is at Wilmette (Illinois, USA) otherwise known as the Mother Temple of the West and was dedicated in 1953. Sites for the development of a further one hundred *Houses of Worship* have been purchased.

BAHA'I CALENDAR AND FESTIVALS

Calendar

Baha'is follow a solar calendar which was inaugurated by the *Bab* and consists of nineteen months each containing nineteen days. Each day begins at sunset. *Nineteen-Day Feasts* are thus held on the first day of each Baha'i month. The year is fixed and begins at the March equinox.

The Baha'i era (denoted by the letters "BE") dates from the declaration of the *Bab* in 1844. As such, according to the Baha'i calendar in 1993-94 CE it is 150 BE. The *Bab* named the months after what he considered to be God's attributes. For example, the first two months of the Baha'i year as translated to English are called Splendour and Glory.

Festivals

The following are notable occasions in the Baha'i calendar (dates are given according to their location in the Gregorian calendar):

Feast of Naw-Ruz
(March 20th or 21st depending on the Spring Equinox)

This is the Baha'i New Year and the first of the nine Baha'i holy days. On this day the nineteen day fast of the month of Ala (see below) finishes. This is a particularly joyful time of celebration.

Feast of Ridvan
(April 21st–May 2nd)

This is the most important day in the Baha'i calendar, described by *Baha'u'llah* as "the Lord of Feasts". It commemorates *Baha'u'llah*'s Declaration of his mission. Celebrations take place and the feast commemorates the twelve days *Baha'u'llah* spent in Ridvan garden before leaving Baghdad and during which his Declaration took place. On the first day of *Ridvan* the local Spiritual Assemblies are elected.

Ninth Day of Ridvan (see above).

Twelfth Day of Ridvan (see above).

Anniversary of the Declaration of the Bab
(May 23rd)

This date also coincides with the birthday of *Abdu'l-Baha*. Celebrations take place relating to the *Bab's* revelation of his mission to his first disciple, Mulla Hussayn, in 1844.

Anniversary of the Ascension of Baha'u'llah
(May 29th)

A solemn day of prayer and discussion commemorating the passing away, in 1892 in Akka, of *Baha'u'llah* after being released from prison there.

Martyrdom of the Bab
(July 9th)

A solemn day of prayer and discussion.

Anniversary of the Birth of the Bab
(October 20th)

The *Bab* was born in Shiraz, Persia, in 1819.

Anniversary of the Birth of Baha'u'llah
(November 12th)

Baha'u'llah was born in Tehran, Persia, in 1817.

Day of the Covenant
(November 26th)

This day is dedicated to *Abdu'l-Baha*.

Ascension of Abdu'l-Baha
(November 28th)

A solemn day of prayer and discussion.

Period of the Fast
(March 2nd–21st)

This is the Baha'i month of *Ala* in which Baha'is abstain from food and drink from sunrise to sunset. The fast is not binding for children under fifteen years or adults over seventy, nor for travellers or those who are to old or too weak (for example because of illness or giving birth). It is considered a time for reflection on spiritual progress and for detachment from material desires.

On the *Feast of Ridvan* Baha'is are only forbidden to work during its first, ninth and twelfth days. On the other festival days, Bahai's should not work at all, except on the *Day of the Covenant* and on the *Ascension of Abdu'l-Baha*.

Consultation on community affairs takes place in the forum of the *Local Assembly* every nineteen days at a gathering called a *Nineteen-Day Feast*. Only Baha'is may attend the business part of this gathering which has three purposes: devotional (corporate prayers and readings), business (consultation on the affairs of the community other than personal matters) and social. *Local Spiritual Assemblies* also do work to spread knowledge of the Faith in their locality by regularly holding events such as open meetings and lectures.

BAHA'I ORGANISATIONS

The Consultative Principle

Baha'i organisations work on the basis of the principle of *consultation*. This entails gathering information from a wide range of sources and perspectives; being frank but courteous about one's views; owning as the idea of the group an idea put forward by an individual; and striving for unanimity. However, if unanimity cannot be achieved then a majority vote may be taken although in this case all must be united behind the final decision of the majority.

Local Spiritual Assemblies

The key Baha'i organisations are administrative bodies called *Spiritual Assemblies* which are to be found at local and national levels. They are run by elected officers. The basis for the development of this administrative order was laid down by *Abdu'l-Baha* based on what could be established from *Baha'u'llah's* writings. Baha'is in the UK live in over four hundred communities with about two hundred of these constituting *Local Spiritual Assemblies*.

To form a *Local Spiritual Assembly* a community must have a minimum of nine members over twenty-one years of age. *Local Spiritual Assemblies* are given responsibility for making decisions on all matters of common action on the part of the community. They serve a social function by arranging meetings and holding Baha'i property in trust.

Each year, on the first day of *Ridvan*, nine people are elected to serve on the *Local Assembly*. All Baha'is of twenty-one years or more who reside in the *Assembly's* area of jurisdiction have the right to vote and to serve on the *Assembly* if elected. There are no prior candidatures or nominations and canvassing is forbidden.

Local Groups

A Baha'i *Local Group* is formed where there are not sufficient numbers to meet the criteria for forming a *Local Spiritual Assembly*.

National Level

There are national centres for administration which may also serve as teaching centres and publishing houses. In 1992, there were one hundred and sixty-five of these *National Spiritual Assemblies* worldwide. The first Baha'i National Assembly for the UK was elected in 1923, and was one of the first to be established anywhere in the world. Most have their own headquarters buildings known as *Haziratu'l-Quds* (the Sacred Fold). In 1937 the National Assembly of the Baha'is of the UK set up the Baha'i Publishing Trust to publish and sell Baha'i literature. In 1939 it was incorporated as an Unlimited Company without Share Capital.

International Level

At an international level, the *Universal House of Justice* is the supreme governing body of the Baha'is and is based in Haifa, Israel. Since 1972, it has had a formal constitution and it maintains authority over all other Baha'i institutions. The nine members of the house are elected every five years by all the *National Spiritual Assemblies*. One of the main functions of the *House of Justice* is to legislate on matters not expressly revealed in the teachings.

In 1948 *Baha'i International Community* was established, and under the supervision of the *Universal House of Justice* it is linked to the United Nations as a non-governmental organisation. Through this organisation the Baha'i comm-unity participates in conferences on social issues such as human rights and supports organisations like UNICEF and WHO. The *Baha'i Comm-unity International* was accredited with Class II consultative status with the United Nations ECOSOC in 1970 and with UNICEF in 1976.

Personnel

Bahai's have no priesthood or professional clergy and contact with Baha'i organisations can be made with the secretaries of *Local Assemblies* or, on a national basis, with the administrative staff of Baha'i Community of the United Kingdom.

BIBLIOGRAPHY

Ashfarian, P, *Directory of Baha'i Book Collectors, Bibliophiles and Researchers*, Ashfarian, Los Angeles, 1984.

Baha'i International Community, *The Baha'is: A Profile of the Baha'i Faith and its Worldwide Community*, Baha'i International Community, New York, 1992.

Baha'i Publishing Trust, *Baha'i Prayers*, Baha'i Publishing Trust, London, 1975.

Baha'i Publishing Trust, *Principles of Baha'i Administration*, Baha'i Publishing Trust, London, (4th edition), 1976.

Balyuzi, H M, *Baha'u'llah: The King of Glory*, George Ronald, Oxford, 1963.

Balyuzi, H M, *Abdu'l-Baha*, George Ronald, Oxford, 1971.

Balyuzi, H M, *The Bab*, George Ronald, Oxford, 1973.

Braun, E, *A Reader's Guide: The Development of Baha'i Literature in English*, George Ronald, Oxford, 1986.

Collins, W, *Bibliography of English-Language Works on the Babi and Baha'i Faiths, 1844-1985*, George Ronald, London, 1990.

Esslemont, J E, *Baha'u'llah and the New Era*, Baha'i Publishing Trust, London, 1974.

Ferraby, J, *All Things Made New - An Introduction to the Baha'i Faith*, Baha'i Publishing Trust, London, 1987.

Hainsworth, P, *Baha'i Focus on Human Rights*, Baha'i Publishing Trust, London, 1985.

Hainsworth, P, *Baha'i Focus on Peace*, Baha'i Publishing Trust, London, 1986.

Hatcher, W S and Martin, J D, *The Baha'i Faith: The Emerging Global Religion*, Harper and Row, San Francisco, 1984.

MacEoin, D, *Early Babi Doctrine and History*, Kalimat Press, Los Angeles, forthcoming.

Momen, M, *The Babi and Baha'i Religions, 1844-1944: Some Contemporary Western Accounts*, George Ronald, Oxford, 1981.

Smith, P, *The Babi and Baha'i Religions From Messianic Shi'ism to a World Religion*, Cambridge University Press, Cambridge, 1987.

BAHA'I UK ORGANISATIONS

Baha'i *Local Groups* are listed under the entry for the Baha'i Community of the United Kingdom as well as one or two *Local Spiritual Assemblies* which did not wish full details to appear in the directory.

A *Local Group* can be formed where there are a number of Baha'is in a locality but the criteria for forming a *Local Spiritual Assembly* are not met. These criteria are that there should be at least nine Baha'is over the age of twenty-one.

Baha'i Community of the United Kingdom
27 Rutland Gate
London SW7 1PD
Tel: 071-584-2566
Contact: Baha'i Information Office
National headquarters. The community aims to promote the principles of the Baha'i Faith and the teachings of Baha'u'llah. It works for the reconciliation of races and religions and fosters a public awareness of the Earth as one country and all people as its citizens. It represents local membership groups and local Spiritual Assemblies which are mainly concerned with worship and community activities involving adults, youth and children. Contact details on most Baha'i Local Spiritual Assemblies are given in the listings of Baha'i local organisations. Baha'i Local Groups are not, however, included in that section but are, instead, listed below together with a number of Local Spiritual Assemblies which have preferred not to give local contact details. Contact with all these groups can be made through the national office of the Baha'i community of the United Kingdom. The Baha'i Community of the United Kingdom is affiliated to The Inter Faith Network for the UK.

Scotland
Angus Baha'i Local Group
Annandale and Eskdale Baha'i Local Group
Argyle and Bute Baha'i Local Group
Clackmanan Baha'i Local Group
Clydesdale Baha'i Local Group
Cuningham Baha'i Local Group
Dunfermline Baha'i Local Group
East Lothian Baha'i Local Group
Eastwood Baha'i Local Group
Gordon Baha'i Local Group
Hamilton Baha'i Local Group
Kyle and Carrick Baha'i Local Group
Kilmarnock Baha'i Local Group
Kincardine and Deeside Baha'i Local Group
Lochaber Baha'i Local Group
Midlothian Baha'i Local Group
Monklands Baha'i Local Group
Motherwell Baha'i Local Group
Mull Baha'i Local Group
Renfrew Baha'i Local Group
Ross and Cromarty Baha'i Local Group
Roxburgh Baha'i Local Group
Strathkelvin Baha'i Local Group

Wales
Blaenau Gwent Baha'i Local Group
Cynon Valley Baha'i Local Group
Delyn Baha'i Local Group

Dinefwr Baha'i Local Group
Dwfor Baha'i Local Group
Islwyn Baha'i Local Group
Llanelli Baha'i Local Group
Meirionnydd Baha'i Local Group
Presli Baha'i Local Group
Radnor Baha'i Local Group
Rhondda Baha'i Local Group
Rhuddlan Baha'i Local Group
Rhymney Valley Baha'i Local Group
Torfaen Baha'i Local Group
Wrexham Maelor Baha'i Local Group
Ynys Mon Baha'i Local Group

Northern Ireland

Cookstown Baha'i Local Group
Craigavan Local Group
Down Baha'i Local Group
Dungannon Baha'i Local Group
Larne Baha'i Local Group
Magherafelt Baha'i Local Group
Moyle Baha'i Local Group
Newry and Mourne Baha'i Local Group

North East England

Alnwick Baha'i Local Group
Blyth Valley Baha'i Local Group
Chester-Le-Street Baha'i Local Group
Langbaurgh Baha'i Local Group
Middlesborough Baha'i Local Group
Stockton-on-Tees Baha'i Local Group
Sunderland Baha'i Local Group
Wear Valley Baha'i Local Group

Yorkshire and Humberside

Barnsley Baha'i Local Group
Calderdale Baha'i Local Group
Craven Baha'i Local Group
East Yorkshire Baha'i Local Group
Great Grimsby Baha'i Local Group
Harrogate Baha'i Local Group
Selby Baha'i Local Group
Scarborough Baha'i Local Group

North West England

Barrow-in-Furness Baha'i Local Group
Blackburn Baha'i Local Group
Blackpool Baha'i Local Group
Bolton Baha'i Local Group
Bury Baha'i Local Group
Congleton Baha'i Local Group
Fylde Baha'i Local Group
Oldham Baha'i Local Group
Ribble Valley Baha'i Local Group

Tameside Baha'i Local Group
Warrington Baha'i Local Group
West Lancashire Baha'i Local Group
Wigan Baha'i Local Group
Wyre Baha'i Local Group
Vale Royal Baha'i Local Group

English East Midlands

Amber Valley Baha'i Local Group
Ashfield Baha'i Local Group
Broxtowe Baha'i Local Group
East Northamptonshire Baha'i Local Group
Hinckley and Bosworth Baha'i Local Group
Kettering Baha'i Local Group
Newark and Sherwood Baha'i Local Group
North West Leicestershire Bahai Local Group
Rushcliffe Baha'i Local Group
South Northamptonshire Baha'i Local Group
Wellingborough Baha'i Local Group

English West Midlands

Banbridge Baha'i Local Group
Bridgenorth Baha'i Local Group
Bromsgrove Baha'i Local Group
Cannock Chase Baha'i Local Group
Dudley Baha'i Local Group
East Staffordshire Baha'i Local Group
Lichfield Baha'i Local Group
Montgomery Baha'i Local Group
Newcastle-under-Lyme Baha'i Local Group
North Shropshire Baha'i Local Group
Redditch Baha'i Local Group
Rugby Baha'i Local Group
Stafford Baha'i Local Group
Stoke-on-Trent Baha'i Local Group
Stratford-upon-Avon Baha'i Local Group
Tamworth Baha'i Local Group
Tewkesbury Baha'i Local Group
Walsall Baha'i Local Group
Wolverhampton Baha'i Local Group

East Anglia

Babergh Baha'i Local Group
Breckland Baha'i Local Group
Broadland Baha'i Local Group
East Cambridgeshire Baha'i Local Group
Great Yarmouth Baha'i Local Group
Ipswich Baha'i Local Group
Lincoln Baha'i Local Group
North Kesteven Baha'i Local Group
North Norfolk Baha'i Local Group
South Norfolk Baha'i Local Group
West Lindsey Baha'i Local Group

South East England (North)

Barking and Dagenham Baha'i Local Group
Basildon Baha'i Local Group
Braintree Baha'i Local Group
Brentwood Baha'i Local Group
Bridgnorth Baha'i Local Group
Broxbourne Baha'i Local Group
Chichester Baha'i Local Group
Colchester Baha'i Local Group
East Hertfordshire Baha'i Local Group
Harlow Baha'i Local Group
Newbury Baha'i Local Group
North Hertfordshire Baha'i Local Group
St Alban's Baha'i Local Group
South Buckinghamshire Baha'i Local Group
Southend-on-Sea Baha'i Local Group
Thurrock Baha'i Local Group
West Oxfordshire Baha'i Local Group

London

Camden Baha'i Local Group
Greenwich Baha'i Local Group
Hackney Baha'i Local Group
Lewisham Baha'i Local Spiritual Assembly

South East England (South)

Arun Baha'i Local Group
Basingstoke and Deane Baha'i Local Group
Chichester Baha'i Local Spiritual Assembly
Crawley Bahai Local Group
Croydon Baha'i Local Group
Dover Baha'i Local Group
Eastbourne Baha'i Local Spiritual Assembly
Eastleigh Baha'i Local Group
Gravesham Baha'i Local Spiritual Assembly
Hart Baha'i Local Group
Havant Baha'i Local Group
Horsham Baha'i Local Group
Jersey Baha'i Local Group
Medway Baha'i Local Group
New Forest Baha'i Local Group
Rushmoor Baha'i Local Group
South Wight Baha'i Local Group
Surrey Heath Baha'i Local Group
Swale Baha'i Local Group
Test Valley Baha'i Local Group
Wimbourne Baha'i Local Group

South West England

Gloucester Baha'i Local Group
Isles of Scilly Baha'i Local Group
Kennet Baha'i Local Group
Kerrier Baha'i Local Group
Leominster Baha'i Local Group

Mid Devon Baha'i Local Group
North Cornwall Baha'i Local Group
North Devon Baha'i Local Group
North Dorset Baha'i Local Group
Purbeck Baha'i Local Group
Restormel Baha'i Local Group
Salisbury Baha'i Local Group
Sedgemoor Baha'i Local Group
South Hams Baha'i Local Group
South Somerset Baha'i Local Group
Teingbridge Baha'i Local Group
Tewkesbury Baha'i Local Group
Wansdyke Baha'i Local Group
West Dorset Baha'i Local Group
Wychavon Baha'i Local Group
Wyre Forest Baha'i Local Group

Baha'i Publishing Trust

6 Mount Pleasant
Oakham
Leicestershire LE15 6HU
Tel: 0572-722780
Fax: 0572-724280
The official agency of the UK Baha'i community selling books and audio-visual materials on the Baha'i Faith in over fifty languages. An expanding list presents a distinctive Baha'i approach to religious and racial unity, personal and social transformation, peace, justice and world order. Definitive editions of the writings of Baha'u'llah and works on his life and teachings are also available.

Baha'i Service for the Blind

14 Chishill Road
Heydon
Royston
Hertfordshire SG8 8PW
Tel: 0763-838309 (home)
Contact: Virginia Barnes
Exists to maintain a library of Baha'i teachings in braille and on tapes for blind people.

BAHA'I LOCAL SPIRITUAL ASSEMBLIES

SCOTLAND

WALES

NORTHERN IRELAND

NORTH EAST ENGLAND

YORKSHIRE AND HUMBERSIDE

NORTH WEST ENGLAND

ENGLISH EAST MIDLANDS

ENGLISH WEST MIDLANDS

EAST ANGLIA

SOUTH EAST ENGLAND (NORTH)

LONDON (E)

LONDON (N)

LONDON (NW)

LONDON (SE)

LONDON (SW)

LONDON (W)

SOUTH EAST ENGLAND (SOUTH)

SOUTH WEST ENGLAND

All Baha'i *Local Spiritual Assemblies* engage in basically the same kind of activities as outlined in the section on "Introducing the Baha'i Community". Therefore in this section, no self-descriptions are attached to Baha'i local contact details.

Baha'i *Local Spiritual Assemblies* can be formed when there are at least nine Baha'is over the age of twenty-one in a locality

SCOTLAND

Aberdeen Baha'i Local Spiritual Assembly
147 North Deeside Road
Bieldside
Aberdeen AB1 9EA (home)
Tel: 0224–861217 (home)
Contact: Mr Samy Helmy
Office: Secretary

Skye and Lochalsh Baha'i Local Spiritual Assembly
Corry Cottage
Broadford
Isle of Skye IV49 9AA (home)
Tel: 0471–822284 (home)
Contact: Mrs Patricia McNicol
Office: Secretary

Moray Baha'i Local Spiritual Assembly
Hillfolds
Drybridge
Buckie
Grampian AB56 2JY (home)
Tel: 0542–32110 (home)
Contact: Mrs Jean Hunter
Office: Secretary

North East Fife Baha'i Local Spiritual Assembly
The Old Mill
Dura Den
Cupar
Fife KY15 5TJ (home)
Tel: 0334–53319 (home)
Contact: Mrs Pamela Sabet
Office: Secretary

Nithsdale Baha'i Local Spiritual Assembly
95 Georgetown Road
Dumfries
Dumfries and Galloway DG1 4DG (home)
Tel: 0387–62730 (home)
Contact: Mrs Jacqueline Mehrabi
Office: Secretary

Dundee Baha'i Local Spiritual Assembly
51 Park Road
Dundee DD3 8LB (home)
Tel: 0382–827418 (home)
Contact: Mr Farhad Varjavandi
Office: Secretary

Banff and Buchan Baha'i Local Spiritual Assembly
11 Clinton Crescent
New Pitsligo
Frazerburgh
Grampian AB43 4AB (home)
Tel: 07717-478 (home)
Contact: Mr Stephen Miller
Office: Secretary

East Kilbride Baha'i Local Spiritual Assembly
110 Eider Place
Greenhills
East Kilbride
Glasgow G75 8UD (home)
Tel: 03552-63109 (home)
Contact: Mrs Nahid Varghai
Office: Secretary

Glasgow Baha'i Local Spiritual Assembly
12 Glencairn Drive
Pollockshaws
Glasgow G41 4QN (home)
Tel: 041-424-1131 (home)
Contact: Mr Allan Forsyth
Office: Secretary

Edinbugh Baha'i Local Spiritual Assembly
26 North Fort Street
Edinburgh EH6 4ND
Tel: 031-554-2446
Contact: Ms Fleur Hemmati

Inverness Baha'i Local Spiritual Assembly
15 Moray Park Terrace
Culloden
Inverness IV1 2RQ (home)
Tel: 0463-792230 (home)
Contact: Mrs F Khavari
Office: Secretary

Stewartry Baha'i Local Spiritual Assembly
27 High Street
Kirkcudbright
Dumfries and Galloway DG6 4JZ (home)
Contact: Mrs Susan Parsons
Office: Secretary

Orkney Baha'i Local Spiritual Assembly
The Baha'i Centre
"Inchvannie"
3 Old Scapa Road
Kirkwall
Orkney KW15 1BB

Tel: 085687-3853
Contact: Mrs Marjorie Giorgi
Office: Centre Manager

Shetland Baha'i Local Spiritual Assembly
10 Burnside
Lerwick
Shetland ZE1 0QH (home)
Tel: 0595-6257 (home)
Contact: Mr Leslie Sinclair
Office: Secretary

Uist Baha'i Local Spiritual Assembly
16 Dunrossil Place
Lochmaddy
North Uist
Western Isles PA82 5AB (home)
Tel: 08763-285 (home)
Contact: Mrs Jean Payne
Office: Secretary

Perth and Kinross Baha'i Local Spiritual Assembly
Flat 2 Denside
Methven
Perth
Tayside (home)
Tel: 0738-84700 (home)
Contact: Mrs Sandra Matthews
Office: Secretary

Stirling Baha'i Local Spiritual Assembly
The Lodge
Braendam
Thornhill
Stirling FK8 3QH (home)
Tel: 0786-85679 (home)
Contact: Mr Graham Barnes
Office: Secretary

Lewis and Harris Baha'i Local Spiritual Assembly
Stornoway
Isle of Lewis (home)
Tel: 0851-706105 (home)
Contact: Mr and Mrs Emerson
Office: Secretary

WALES

Arfon Baha'i Local Spiritual Assembly
Pwllau Dwr
Waterfall
Llanberis

Caernarfon
Gwynedd LL55 4TH (home)
Tel: 0286-871034 (home)
Contact: Mrs Christine Wagg
Office: Secretary

Cardiff Baha'i Local Spiritual Assembly
14 Alfreda Road
Whitchurch
Cardiff CF4 2EH (home)
Tel: 0222-625316 (home)
Contact: Mrs Tish Roskams
Office: Secretary

Aberconwy Baha'i Local Spiritual Assembly
15 Drws-y-Nant
Glan Conwy
Gwynedd LL28 5EQ (home)
Tel: 0492-573268 (home)
Contact: Mrs Joan Birch
Office: Secretary

Brecknock Baha'i Local Spiritual Assembly
Tan-y-Coed
Llanwrtyd Wells
Powys LD5 4TB (home)
Tel: 05913-363 (home)
Contact: Mrs Robina Nicholson
Office: Secretary

Newport Baha'i Local Spiritual Assembly
12 Alt-yr-yn Wan
Newport NP9 5GB (home)
Tel: 0633-250171 (home)
Contact: Mrs Mahnaz Firooxmand
Office: Secretary

Colwyn Baha'i Local Spiritual Assembly
4 Fairmount Street
Old Colwyn
Clwyd LL29 9NF (home)
Contact: Mrs Nassera Mustari
Office: Secretary

Vale of Glamorgan Baha'i Local Spiritual Assembly
90 High View Road
Penarth
South Glamorgan CF6 1HX
Tel: 0222-709386 (home)
Contact: Miss Shirin Foroughi (home)
Office: Secretary

Swansea Baha'i Local Spiritual Assembly
63 Lloyd Road
Treboeth
Swansea SA5 9EU (home)
Tel: 0792-702423 (home)
Contact: Mrs Josie Akhurst
Office: Secretary

Taff-Ely Baha'i Local Spiritual Assembly
38 Parkland Road
Tonyrefail
Mid Glamorgan CF39 8PE (home)
Tel: 0443-670114 (home)
Contact: Mrs Seema Melville
Office: Secretary

NORTHERN IRELAND

Ballymena Baha'i Local Spiritual Assembly
37 Deramore Crescent
Ballymena BT43 7EG (home)
Tel: 0266-40287 (home)
Contact: Mr James Holmlund
Office: Secretary

North Down Baha'i Local Spiritual Assembly
25 Windsor Gardens
Bangor BT20 3DD (home)
Contact: Mrs Greta Galbraith
Office: Secretary

Belfast Baha'i Local Spiritual Assembly
442 Springfield Road
Belfast BT12 7DW (home)
Tel: 0232-321752
Contact: Mrs Pippa Cookson
Office: Secretary

Coleraine Baha'i Local Spiritual Assembly
17 Corbally Road
Knockertotan
Coleraine BT52 2LZ (home)
Contact: Dr Joan Clay
Office: Secretary

Lisburn Baha'i Local Spiritual Assembly
5 Cairnmore Crescent
Lisburn BT28 2QE (home)
Contact: Mrs Susan Agahi-Esfahani
Office: Secretary

Londonderry Baha'i Local Spiritual Assembly
13 Limavady Road
Londonderry BT47 1JU (home)
Tel: 0504-311072 (home)
Contact: Dr Keith Munro
Office: Secretary

Newtownabbey Baha'i Local Spiritual Assembly
11d Ardmillan Drive
Rathcoole
Newtownabbey BT37 9AZ (home)
Tel: 0232-852439 (home)
Contact: Mr Peter Black
Office: Secretary

Ards Baha'i Local Spiritual Assembly
7 Chapel Island Park
Newtownards BT23 3BG (home)
Tel: 0247-814551 (home)
Contact: Miss Shahla Gushtasbi
Office: Secretary

Antrim Baha'i Local Spiritual Assembly
34 The Gables
Randalstown BT41 3JY (home)
Tel: 0849-479522 (home)
Contact: Mr Amal Ma'ani
Office: Secretary

Omagh Baha'i Local Spiritual Assembly
57 Tattysallagh Road
Tattysallagh
Omagh BT78 5BR (home)
Tel: 0662-898912 (home)
Contact: Mrs Bernadette Cahill
Office: Secretary

NORTH EAST ENGLAND

Durham Baha'i Local Spiritual Assembly
14 Mayorswell Field
Durham DH1 1JW (home)
Tel: 091-386-1698 (home)
Contact: Mrs Margaret Gosden
Office: Secretary

Gateshead Baha'i Local Spiritual Assembly
185 Whitehall Road
Gateshead
Tyne and Wear (home)
Tel: 091-477-3338 (home)
Contact: Mr Ian Holland
Office: Secretary

Tynedale Baha'i Local Spiritual Assembly
Whamlands
Ninebanks
Hexham
Northumberland NE47 8HJ (home)
Contact: Mrs Rowena Winfield
Office: Secretary

Newcastle-Upon-Tyne Baha'i Local Spiritual Assembly
44 Queens Road
Jesmond
Newcastle-upon-Tyne NE2 2PQ (home)
Tel: 091-281-8597 (home)
Contact: Mrs Gillian Lambden
Office: Secretary

North Tyneside Baha'i Local Spiritual Assembly
6 Belsay Avenue
Whitley Bay
Tyne and Wear NE25 8PZ (home)
Tel: 091-251-9775 (home)
Contact: Mr Farzad Froughi
Office: Secretary

YORKSHIRE AND HUMBERSIDE

Bradford Baha'i Local Spiritual Assembly
Moor House
Moor Farm
607 Allerton Road
Bradford BD15 8AB (home)
Tel: 0274-544758 (home)
Contact: Mrs Shirley Hallam

Doncaster Baha'i Local Spiritual Assembly
309 Beckett Road
Wheatley
Doncaster DN2 4LD (home)
Tel: 0302-321904 (home)
Contact: Mrs Eunice Self
Office: Secretary

Kirklees Baha'i Local Spiritual Assembly
65 Grosvenor Road
Dalton
Huddersfield HD5 9JB (home)
Tel: 0484-429490 (home)
Contact: Mr Khosro Deihim
Office: Secretary

Kingston-upon-Hull Baha'i Local Spiritual Assembly

17 Cadeleigh Close
Bransholme
Hull HU7 4DA (home)
Tel: 0482-837617 (home)
Contact: Mrs Charin Rotella
Office: Secretary

Leeds Baha'i Local Spiritual Assembly

12 William Street
Churwell Morley
Leeds L27 (home)
Contact: Mrs Bahereh Saadat-Yazdi
Office: Secretary

Scunthorpe Baha'i Local Spiritual Assembly

38 Cliff Closes Road
Scunthorpe DN15 7HU (home)
Tel: 0742-843299 (home)
Contact: Mrs Carole Dehghani
Office: Secretary

Sheffield Baha'i Local Spiritual Assembly

49 Albany Road
Netheridge
Sheffield S7 1DN (home)
Tel: 0742-588906 (home)
Contact: Mrs Elizabeth Albrow
Office: Secretary

Wakefield Baha'i Local Spiritual Assembly

Virginia Cottage
164 Shay Lane
Walton
Wakefield WF2 6NP (home)
Contact: Mrs Elisabet Mitchell
Office: Secretary

York Baha'i Local Spiritual Assembly

West View
112 Clifton
York Y03 6BA (home)
Tel: 0904-641657 (home)
Contact: Mrs Patricia Castle
Office: Secretary

NORTH WEST ENGLAND

Burnley Baha'i Local Spiritual Assembly

Baha'i Centre
9 Colne Road
Burnley BB10 1LD (home)

Tel: 0282-832973 (home)
Contact: The Secretary

Isle of Man Baha'i Local Spiritual Assembly

12 Selborne Road
Douglas
Isle of Man (home)
Tel: 0624-77326 (home)
Contact: Mr John Maher
Office: Secretary

South Lakeland Baha'i Local Spiritual Assembly

15 Mint Street
Kendal
Cumbria LA9 6DS (home)
Tel: 0539-727770
Contact: Mr and Mrs Foster
Office: Secretary

Liverpool Baha'i Local Spiritual Assembly

Baha'i Centre
3 Langdale Road
Wavertree
Liverpool L15 3LA
Tel: 051-733-8614 (home)
Contact: Secretary

Manchester Baha'i Local Spiritual Assembly

Baha'i Centre
360 Wilmslow Road
Fallowfield
Manchester M14 6AJ
Contact: Secretary

Salford Baha'i Local Spiritual Assembly

10 Pendlecroft Avenue
Pendlebury
Swinton
Manchester M27 2TH (home)
Tel: 061-737-2956 (home)
Contact: Miss Joyce Yap
Office: Secretary

Pendle Baha'i Local Spiritual Assembly

99 Carr Road
Nelson
Lancashire BB9 7SS
Tel: 0282-691364 (home)
Contact: Mrs Dorothy Mac Innes
Office: Secretary

St Helens Baha'i Local Spiritual Assembly
18 Park Road North
Newton Le Willows
Merseyside WA12 9TE (home)
Tel: 0925-222372 (home)
Contact: Mrs Pauline Samson
Office: Secretary

Preston Baha'i Local Spiritual Assembly
19 Dunbar Road
Preston PR2 3YE (home)
Tel: 0772-733294 (home)
Contact: Mrs Joyce Sabour
Office: Secretary

Trafford Baha'i Local Spiritual Assembly
41 Bankfield Road
Sale
Cheshire M33 5QD (home)
Tel: 061-962-0817 (home)
Contact: Mrs Shohreh Ashraf-Cooper
Office: Secretary

Sefton Baha'i Local Spiritual Assembly
1 Crescent Road
Birkdale
Southport
Merseyside PR8 4SR (home)
Tel: 0704-550359 (home)
Contact: Mrs Susan Pierlejewski
Office: Secretary

Macclesfield Baha'i Local Spiritual Assembly
Little Beeches
Bollin Way
Prestbury
Stockport
Cheshire SK10 4BX (home)
Tel: 0625-829511 (home)
Contact: Mrs Ruth Habibi
Office: Secretary

Stockport Baha'i Local Spiritual Assembly
23 Mountfield Road
Bramhall
Stockport SK7 1LZ (home)
Tel: 061-439-1239 (home)
Contact: Mrs Catherine Eckersley
Office: Secretary

Allerdale Baha'i Local Spiritual Assembly
14 Longthwaite Road
Wigton
Cumbria CA7 9PN (home)

Tel: 09673-42869 (home)
Contact: Mrs Lorna Silverstein
Office: Secretary

Wirral Baha'i Local Spiritual Assembly
57 Hillfield Drive
Heswall
Wirral
Merseyside L61 6UJ (home)
Tel: 051-342-2800 (home)
Contact: Mrs Caroline Mazloom
Office: Secretary

ENGLISH EAST MIDLANDS

Chesterfield Baha'i Local Spiritual Assembly
12 Boythorpe Crescent
Boythorpe
Chesterfield
Derbyshire S40 2NX (home)
Tel: 0246-211753 (home)
Contact: Mr Jonathan Atkinson
Office: Secretary

Derby Baha'i Local Spiritual Assembly
27 Ferrers way
Darley Abbey
Derby DE22 2BA (home)
Tel: 0332-557463 (home)
Contact: Dr Farshid Taleb
Office: Secretary

Leicester Baha'i Local Spiritual Assembly
18 Severn Street
Leicester LE2 0NN (home)
Tel: 0533-415323 (home)
Contact: Mr Ramin Badii-Azandahi
Office: Secretary

Daventry Baha'i Local Spiritual Assembly
75 Froxhill Crescent
Brixworth
Northampton NN6 9LN (home)
Tel: 0604-881547 (home)
Contact: Mrs Mina Beint
Office: Secretary

Northampton Baha'i Local Spiritual Assembly
22 Lister Drive
Northampton NN4 9XE (home)
Tel: 0604-769825 (home)
Contact: Mrs Susan Phillips
Office: Secretary

Gedling Baha'i Local Spiritual Assembly
7 St Austins Drive
Carlton
Nottingham NG4 3EY (home)
Tel: 0602-618139 (home)
Contact: Mr Dallas Simpson
Office: Secretary

Nottingham Baha'i Local Spiritual Assembly
67 Russell Avenue
Wollaton
Nottingham NG8 2BP (home)
Tel: 0602-283724 (home)
Contact: Miss Margaret Earnshaw
Office: Secretary

Rutland Baha'i Local Spiritual Assembly
67 Kings Road
Oakham
Leicestershire LE15 6PB (home)
Tel: 0572-724179 (home)
Contact: Mr George Ballentyne
Office: Secretary

Peterborough Baha'i Local Group
31 Danish Court
Werrington
Peterborough
Cambridgeshire (home)
Tel: 0733-324630 (home)
Contact: Mr Shahram Firoozmand
Office: Secretary

ENGLISH WEST MIDLANDS

Birmingham Baha'i Local Spiritual Assembly
42 Paton Grove
Moseley
Birmingham B13 9TG (home)
Contact: Mrs Violette Zamiadi-Owen
Office: Secretary

Coventry Baha'i Local Spiritual Assembly
6 Stonehaven Drive
Finham
Coventry CV3 6EX
Tel: 0203-412695 (home)
Contact: Mrs Rosemary Prichard
Office: Secretary

**Nuneaton and Bedworth Baha'i Local
Spiritual Assembly**
Exhall Grange School
Wheelwright Lane

Coventry CV7 9HQ
Tel: 0203-366926
Contact: Mrs Patricia King
Office: Secretary

Solihull Baha'i Local Spiritual Assembly
11 Bracebridge Close
Balsall Common
Coventry CV7 7QJ (home)
Tel: 0676-534137 (home)
Contact: Mrs Christine Eyton
Office: Secretary

**Shrewsbury and Atcham Baha'i Local
Spiritual Assembly**
15 Burton Street
Castlefields
Shrewsbury
Shropshire SY1 2LW (home)
Tel: 0743-3834 (home)
Contact: Mrs Denise Samari
Office: Secretary

Warwick Baha'i Local Spiritual Assembly
151 Station Lane
Lapworth
Solihull
West Midlands B94 6JH (home)
Tel: 0564-782335 (home)
Contact: Mrs Nassrin Afnan-Granfar
Office: Secretary

Wrekin Baha'i Local Spiritual Assembly
54 Castlecroft
Stirchley
Telford
Shropshire TF3 1UE (home)
Contact: Mrs Kerry Day
Office: Secretary

EAST ANGLIA

Cambridge Baha'i Local Spiritual Assembly
P O Box 277
Cambridge CB1 1AA
Contact: Secretary

Huntingdon Baha'i Local Group
7 Lawrence Road
Ramsey
Huntingdon
Cambridge PE17 1UY (home)
Tel: 0487-814724 (home)

Contact: Mrs Donya Stokes
Office: Secretary

Waveney Baha'i Local Spiritual Assembly
14 Eastern Way
Lowestoft
Suffolk NR32 2HE (home)
Tel: 0502-515887 (home)
Contact: Mrs Maureen Bell
Office: Secretary

Norwich Baha'i Local Spiritual Assembly
502 Hall Road
South Tuckswood
Norwich NR4 6NQ (home)
Contact: Miss Melanie Attfield
Office: Secretary

Suffolk Coastal Baha'i Local Spiritual Assembly
Roseholme
Curlew Green
Saxmundham
Suffolk IP17 2RA (home)
Tel: 0728-602874 (home)
Contact: Mr Hugh McKinley
Office: Secretary

SOUTH EAST ENGLAND (NORTH)

Vale of White Horse Baha'i Local Spiritual Assembly
24 Gardiner Close
Abingdon
Oxfordshire OX14 3XA (home)
Tel: 0865-841515 (home)
Contact: Mrs Erica Leith
Office: Secretary

Chiltern Baha'i Local Spiritual Assembly
4 Oaktree Place
New Road
Amersham
Buckinghamshire HP6 6LH (home)
Tel: 0494-433189 (home)
Contact: Mrs Naghmeh Majidi-Maguire
Office: Secretary

Aylesbury Vale Baha'i Local Spiritual Assembly
27 Queen Street
Aylesbury
Buckinghamshire HP20 1LU (home)
Tel: 0296-28273 (home)

Contact: Mr David Powell
Office: Secretary

North Bedfordshire Baha'i Local Spiritual Assembly
12 Langdale
Bedford MK41 9EG (home)
Tel: 0234-357186 (home)
Contact: Miss Farnoush Fadaei-Zanjani
Contact: Secretary

Mid Bedfordshire Baha'i Local Spiritual Assembly
30 Lincoln Crescent
Biggleswade
Bedfordshire SG18 8HW (home)
Tel: 0767-601008 (home)
Contact: Mr Steven Beutelspacher
Office: Secretary

Hertsmere Baha'i Local Spiritual Assembly
Carmel
11b King George Avenue
Bushey
Hertfordshire WD2 3NT (home)
Tel: 081-950-2561 (home)
Contact: Miss Nahid Moshtael
Office: Secretary

Colchester Baha'i Local Spiritual Assembly
40 Fingringhoe Road
Langenhoe
Colchester
Essex C05 7LB (home)
Tel: 0206-735386 (home)
Contact: Mrs B Begent
Office: Secretary

Dacorum Baha'i Local Spiritual Assembly
11 Lapwing Close
Grovehill
Hemel Hempstead
Hertfordshire HP2 6DS (home)
Tel: 0442-230863 (home)
Contact: Mr Ian Hay
Office: Secretary

Wycombe Baha'i Local Spiritual Assembly
11 Wellfield
Hazlemere
High Wycombe
Buckinghamshire HP15 7TJ (home)
Tel: 0494-814551 (home)

Contact: Mr Shahram Alaee
Office: Secretary

Hounslow Baha'i Local Spiritual Assembly
P O Box 189
Hounslow
Middlesex TW5 9YA
Contact: Secretary

Redbridge Baha'i Local Spiritual Assembly
1 Clinton Crescent
Hainault
Ilford
Essex IG6 3AH (home)
Tel: 081–500–0620 (home)
Contact: Mrs Carol Khorsandyon
Office: Secretary

Luton Baha'i Local Spiritual Assembly
19 Fairoak Drive
Luton LU2 7TD (home)
Contact: Mrs Feryal Cook
Office: Secretary

Windsor and Maidenhead Baha'i Local Spiritual Assembly
56 Whurley Way
Maidenhead
Berkshire SL6 7ST (home)
Tel: 0628–35125 (home)
Contact: Mrs Taranah Majidi–Sheppherd
Office: Secretary

Milton Keynes Baha'i Local Spiritual Assembly
38A Bradwell Road
Loughton
Milton Keynes
Buckinghamshire MK5 8AJ (home)
Tel: 0908–671734 (home)
Contact: Mrs Malihe Sanatian
Office: Secretary

Hillingdon Baha'i Local Spiritual Assembly
312 Long Lane
North Hillingdon
Middlesex UB10 9PF
Tel: 0895–74479
Contact: Mrs Shahrokh Zabihi
Office: Secretary

Oxford Baha'i Local Spiritual Assembly
36 Binswood Avenue
Headington
Oxford OX3 8NZ (home)
Tel: 0865–64677 (home)
Contact: Dr Roger Kingdon
Office: Secretary

Harrow Baha'i Local Spiritual Assembly
8 Limedene Close
Uxbridge Road
Pinner
Middlesex HA5 3PX (home)
Tel: 081–868–0130 (home)
Contact: Mrs Homa Saadat
Office: Secretary

Reading Baha'i Local Spiritual Assembly
2 Blenheim Road
Reading RG1 5NQ (home)
Tel: 0734–62851 (home)
Contact: Mrs Mitra Sabet-Parry
Office: Secretary

Wokingham Baha'i Local Spiritual Assembly
14 Bodmin Road
Woodley
Reading RG5 3RZ (home)
Tel: 0734–666809 (home)
Contact: Mrs Tharereh Zoghi Javady
Office: Secretary

Havering Baha'i Local Spiritual Assembly
12 Lytton Road
Romford
Essex RM2 5SL
Tel: 0424–46297
Contact: Dr John Lester
Office: Secretary

Slough Baha'i Local Spiritual Assembly
130 Franham Road
Slough
Berkshire SL1 4XA (home)
Tel: 0753–527162 (home)
Contact: Mrs Ellie Rahimi
Office: Secretary

Stevenage Baha'i Local Spiritual Assembly
60 Buckthorn Avenue
Stevenage
Hertfordshire SG1 1TU (home)
Tel: 0438–355983 (home)

Contact: Mr Oliver Christopherson
Office: Secretary

Three Rivers Baha'i Local Spiritual Assembly
P 0 Box 489
Watford WD1 5LA
Tel: 0923-282237 (home)
Contact: Mrs Southall
Office: Secretary

Watford Baha'i Local Spiritual Assembly
55 Hare Crescent
Leavesden
Watford WD2 7EE (home)
Tel: 0923-671135 (home)
Contact: Mrs Iran Ghobad
Office: The Secretary

South Oxfordshire Baha'i Local Spiritual Assembly
17 Sherburn Street
Watlington
Oxfordshire OX9 5BT (home)
Tel: 049161-3200 (home)
Contact: Mr Hugh Fixsen
Office: Secretary

Welwyn Hatfield Baha'i Local Spiritual Assembly
4 Lodge Field
Welwyn Garden City
Hertfordshire AL7 1SD
Tel: 0707-334859 (home)
Contact: Mrs Azita Saberian
Office: Secretary

LONDON (E POSTCODES)

Newham Baha'i Local Spiritual Assembly
9 Jasper Road
Parkquay
Becton
London E16 3TR (home)
Contact: Mrs Arman Thaker
Office: Secretary

LONDON (N POSTCODES)

Barnet Baha'i Local Spiritual Assembly
99 Marshall Close
New Southgate
London N11 1TG

Tel: 081-361-8102
Contact: Mr Alaee

Haringey Baha'i Local Spiritual Assembly
21 Alfloxton Avenue
Tottenham
London N15 3DD (home)
Tel: 081-888-7436 (home)
Contact: Miss Teresa Parsons
Office: Secretary

Islington Baha'i Local Spiritual Assembly
49 Tytherton Road
London N19 (home)
Tel: 071-281-8650 (home)
Contact: Anne King-Hall
Office: Secretary

LONDON (NW POSTCODES)

Brent Baha'i Local Spiritual Assembly
14 Sheldon Road
Mapesbury
London NW2 3AJ (home)
Tel: 081-450-4481 (home)
Contact: Mrs Lucille Rochester
Office: Secretary

City of Westminster Baha'i Local Spiritual Assembly
Penthouse Flat 7
60 Dewalden House
Allitsen Road
Westminster
London NW8 7BA (home)
Contact: Miss Shabnam Rahnema
Office: Secretary

LONDON (SE POSTCODES)

Southwark Baha'i Local Spiritual Assembly
38 Kirwyn Way
Bethwin Road
London SE5 0YA (home)
Tel: 071-703-2515 (home)
Contact: Mr Danesh Sarooshi
Office: Secretary

LONDON (SW POSTCODES)

Hammersmith and Fulham Baha'i Local Spiritual Assembly
Flat 6
123 New Kings Road
Fulham
London SW6 4SL (home)
Tel: 071-731-0964 (home)
Contact: Mr Victor Folhas
Office: Secretary

Lambeth Baha'i Local Spiritual Assembly
8 Eythorne Road
London SW9 7RH (home)
Tel: 071-582-6674 (home)
Contact: Ms Jean Reynard
Office: Secretary

Wandsworth Baha'i Local Spiritual Assembly
87 Exeter House
Putney Heath
London SW15 3TQ (home)
Tel: 081-788-2106 (home)
Contact: Mrs Christine Nicholas
Office: Secretary

Merton Baha'i Local Spiritual Assembly
P 0 Box 899
London SW19 4XN
Contact: Secretary

LONDON (W POSTCODES)

Ealing Baha'i Community
P O Box 1392
London W5 2QX
Tel: 081-994-3631
Contact: Ms J O'Brien
Office: Secretary

Kensington and Chelsea Baha'i Local Spiritual Assembly
56 Cottesmore Court
Stanford Road
London W8 5QW (home)
Tel: 071-937-4442 (home)
Contact: Miss Roxana Djalili
Office: Secretary

SOUTH EAST ENGLAND (SOUTH)

Runnymede Baha'i Local Spiritual Assembly
c/o Imperial College
Silwood Park
Ascot
Berkshire SL5 7PY
Contact: Mrs Samantha Rohani-Najafabadi
Office: Secretary

Ashford Baha'i Local Spiritual Assembly
4 Bunkley Terrace
Hamstreet
Ashford
Kent TN26 2HF
Tel: 023-373-3604
Contact: Mrs Lesley Brisley
Office: Secretary

Brighton Baha'i Local Spiritual Assembly
Baha'i Centre
19 Stanford Avenue
Brighton BN1 6GA
Tel: 0273-505895
Contact: Secretary

Bromley Baha'i Local Spiritual Assembly
13 Cecil Way
Hayes
Bromley
Kent BR2 7JU (home)
Tel: 081-462-5177 (home)
Contact: Mrs Susan Brice
Office: Secretary

Bracknell Baha'i Local Spiritual Assembly
10 Reynolds Green
College Town
Camberley
Surrey GU15 4FL (home)
Tel: 0276-600735 (home)
Contact: Mr Shameen Khorassani
Office: Secretary

Canterbury Baha'i Local Spiritual Assembly
5 Rhodaus Close
Canterbury
Kent CT1 2RE (home)
Tel: 0227-768458 (home)
Contact: Mr Arthur Weinberg

Shepway Baha'i Local Spiritual Assembly

Flat 4
61 Bouverie Road West
Folkstone
Kent CT20 2RN (home)
Tel: 0303-57020 (home)
Contact: Mrs Bela Saminaden
Office: Secretary

Waverley Baha'i Local Spiritual Assembly

11 Nursery Road
Godalming
Surrey GU7 3JU (home)
Tel: 0438-415773 (home)
Contact: Mrs Carolyn Neogi
Office: Secretary

Guildford Baha'i Local Spiritual Assembly

12 Lapwing Grove
Merrow Park
Guildford
Surrey GU4 7DZ (home)
Tel: 0483-68926 (home)
Contact: Mr Edgar Boyett
Office: Secretary

Hastings Baha'i Local Spiritual Assembly

153 Linley Drive
Hastings
East Sussex TN34 2BX (home)
Tel: 0424-446363 (home)
Contact: Mrs Linda Bailey
Office: Secretary

Mid Sussex Baha'i Local Spiritual Assembly

48 Lucastes Avenue
Haywards Heath
West Sussex RN16 1JY (home)
Tel: 0444-451783 (home)
Contact: Mrs Hannah Mehrnoosh Rezwan
Office: Secretary

Tonbridge Wells Baha'i Local Spiritual Assembly

12 Hardwick Road
Hildenborough
Kent TN11 9LA (home)
Tel: 0732-833511 (home)
Contact: Mrs Jean Gash
Office: Secretary

Hove and Portslade Baha'i Local Spiritual Assembly

Flat 10
2 Fourth Avenue
Hove
BN3 2PH (home)
Tel: 071-955-5000 (bleep 356)
Tel: 0273-725028 (home)
Contact: Miss Mojgan Hajatdoost-Sani
Office: Secretary

Mole Valley Baha'i Local Spiritual Assembly

7 Yarm Close
Leatherhead
Surrey KT22 8NZ (home)
Tel: 0372-375782 (home)
Contact: Mrs Thelma Batchelor
Office: Secretary

Lewes Baha'i Local Spiritual Assembly

4 Council Cottages
Swanborough
Lewes
East Sussex BN7 3PQ (home)
Tel: 0273-480660 (home)
Contact: Mr Russell Hill
Office: Secretary

Maidstone Baha'i Local Spiritual Assembly

1 Waldron Drive
Lorse
Maidstone
Kent ME15 9TJ (home)
Tel: 0622-741296 (home)
Contact: David and Jackie Grant

Thanet Baha'i Local Spiritual Assembly

30 Sandhurst Road
Northdown Park
Cliftonville
Margate
Kent CT9 3JQ (home)
Tel: 0843-223894 (home)
Contact: Mrs Gail Kasiri
Office: Secretary

Gillingham Baha'i Local Spiritual Assembly

39 Moor Park Close
Rainham
Kent ME8 8QS (home)
Tel: 0634-389364 (home)
Contact: Mrs Sharon Forghani Ashrafi
Office: Secretary

Reigate and Banstead Baha'i Local Spiritual Assembly
6 Woodlands Road
Redhill
Surrey RH1 6HA (home)
Tel: 0737-765325 (home)
Contact: Mr Martin Kay
Office: Secretary

Richmond-upon-Thames Baha'i Local Spiritual Assembly
7 Willow Bank
Ham
Richmond
Surrey TW10 7Q4
Tel: 081-940-3896
Contact: Mr David Town
Office: Secretary

Medina Baha'i Local Spiritual Assembly
91 Broadway Crescent
Binstead
Ryde
Isle of Wight PO33 3QT (home)
Tel: 0983-63888 (home)
Contact: Mrs Francis Philbrow
Office: Secretary

Guernsey Baha'i Local Spiritual Assembly
Landour Cottage
Cordier Hill
St Peter Port
Guernsey GY1 1JJ (home)
Tel: 0481-728824 (home)
Contact: Mrs Sandra Jenkins
Office: Secretary

Sevenoaks Baha'i Local Spiritual Assembly
15 Shendon Close
Solefields Road
Sevenoaks
Kent TN13 1PQ (home)
Tel: 0732-461778 (home)
Contact: Mrs Marian Rallings
Office: Secretary

Southampton Baha'i Local Spiritual Assembly
22 Hampton Close
Blackfield
Southampton SO4 1WQ (home)
Tel: 0703-894109 (home)
Contact: Mr and Mrs Tully

Adur Baha'i Local Spiritual Assembly
56 Meadway Court
Southwick
West Sussex BN42 4SL (home)
Tel: 0273-594725 (home)
Contact: Mrs Sylvia Reeve
Office: Secretary

Sutton Baha'i Local Spiritual Assembly
86 Albion Road
Sutton
Surrey SM2 5TE
Tel: 081-661-6697
Contact: Mrs Shiva Hobson
Office: Secretary

Tunbrige and Malling Baha'i Local Spiritual Assembly
32 The Chase
Tunbridge
Kent TN10 3HP (home)
Tel: 0732-362037 (home)
Contact: Dr Clare Whitehead
Office: Secretary

Wealden Baha'i Local Spiritual Assembly
8 Campbell Close
Uckfield
East Sussex TN22 1DR (home)
Tel: 0825-761443 (home)
Contact: Mr Paul Booth
Office: Secretary

Portsmouth Baha'i Local Spiritual Assembly
9 Oakhurst Gardens
Widley
Waterlooville
Hampshire PO7 5AX (home)
Tel: 0705-378405 (home)
Contact: Mr H Javid
Office: Secretary

Bexley Baha'i Local Spiritual Assembly
53 Balliol Road
Welling
Kent DA16 1PQ (home)
Tel: 081-303-3641 (home)
Contact: Mr Jeremy Lockyer
Office: Secretary

Winchester Baha'i Local Spiritual Assembly
Ty Croeso
21 Hyde Close
Winchester SO23 7DT (home)

Tel: 0962-865924 (home)
Contact: Mrs Barbara Lewis
Office: Secretary

Woking Baha'i Local Spiritual Assembly
8 Thorsden Close
Woking GU22 7QX
Tel: 0483-740607
Contact: Miss Ladan Lamakan
Office: Secretary

Tandridge Baha'i Local Spiritual Assembly
Overdale
Park View Road
Woldingham
Surrey CR3 7DJ (home)
Tel: 0833-652288 (home)
Fax: 0833-652244 (home)
Contact: Shadram Braunstein
Office: Secretary

Worthing Baha'i Local Spiritual Assembly
24 Sheldon Court
Bath Road
Worthing BN11 4QD (home)
Tel: 0903-502046 (home)
Contact: Miss Helen Barzideh
Office: Secretary

SOUTH WEST ENGLAND

Bath Baha'i Local Spiritual Assembly
27 Grosvenor Place
London Road
Bath BA1 6BA (home)
Tel: 0225-339485
Tel: 0225-334242 (home)
Contact: Mr Martin Burroughs
Office: Secretary

Bournemouth Baha'i Local Spiritual Assembly
81M Jewell Road
Bournemouth BH8 0JM (home)
Tel: 0202-302062 (home)
Contact: Mrs Marjorie Smith
Office: Secretary

Bristol Baha'i Local Spiritual Assembly
49 Sea Mills Lane
Stoke Bishop
Bristol BS9 1DR (home)
Tel: 0272-681470 (home)

Contact: Mrs Lynne Randall
Office: Secretary

Northavon Baha'i Local Spiritual Assembly
26 Grange Avenue
Little Stoke
Bristol BS12 6JY (home)
Tel: 0272-793949 (home)
Contact: Mrs Shahin Missaghi
Office: Secretary

Woodspring Baha'i Local Spiritual Assembly
26 St Marys Park Road
Portishead
Bristol
Avon (home)
Tel: 0272-842734 (home)
Contact: Mrs Janet Hammond
Office: Secretary

Christchurch Baha'i Local Spiritual Assembly
10 Saulfland House
Saulfland Drive
Christchurch
Dorset BH23 4QW (home)
Tel: 0425-277830 (home)
Contact: Mrs Kathleen Hyett
Office: Secretary

Mendip Baha'i Local Spiritual Assembly
Cranmore Tower
Cranmore
Somerset BA4 4LF (home)
Tel: 0749-880742 (home)
Contact: Mrs Jill Shahbahrami
Office: Secretary

Penwith Baha'i Local Spiritual Assembly
39 Mellanear Road
Hayle
Cornwall TR27 4QT (home)
Tel: 0736-754241 (home)
Contact: Mrs Sharon Edwards
Office: Secretary

Hereford Baha'i Local Spiritual Assembly
4 Windermere Road
Hereford HR4 9PR
Tel: 0432-277903 (home)
Contact: Mrs Zarin Hulme
Office: Secretary

North Wiltshire Baha'i Local Spiritual Assembly

14 Michael Pyms Road
Malmesbury
Wiltshire SN16 9TY
Contact: Mr Shamim Mirzai
Office: Secretary

Torbay Baha'i Local Spiritual Assembly

6 Tarraway Road
Preston
Paignton
Devon TQ3 2DU (home)
Tel: 0803-522428 (home)
Contact: Mrs Carole Huxtable
Office: Secretary

Plymouth Baha'i Local Spiritual Assembly

Ellenvale
Beechwood Avenue
Mutley
Plymouth PL4 4QW (home)
Tel: 0752-267569 (home)
Contact: Mrs Jaleh Sanjari-Monshizadeh
Office: Secretary

Poole Baha'i Local Spiritual Assembly

Sandbourne House Rest Home
1 Sandecotes Road
Parkstone
Poole BH14 8NT (home)
Tel: 0202-747704 (home)
Fax: 0202-747704 (home)
Contact: Mr Terence Shephard
Office: Chair

Thamesdown Baha'i Local Spiritual Assembly

13 Radcot Close
Nine Elms
Shaw
Swindon SN5 9UY (home)
Tel: 0793-879230 (home)
Contact: Miss Mojdeh Pourshafi
Office: Secretary

Taunton Deane Baha'i Local Spiritual Assembly

1 Sawyers Hill
West Buckland
Wellington
Somerset TA2 9LA
Contact: Mrs Kena Bunton
Office: Secretary

THE BUDDHIST
COMMUNITY

INTRODUCING THE BUDDHIST COMMUNITY

BUDDHISM IN THE UNITED KINGDOM

Today, throughout the UK, a wide variety of Buddhist organisations, *viharas*, monasteries, centres and more informal groups are to be found, reflecting both the variety of ethnic groups and also the different schools of thought and practice to be found amongst Buddhists. It is now estimated that, including a high percentage of the ethnically Chinese people of the UK as Buddhists, there are around 130,000 Buddhists in the UK out of an estimated world Buddhist population of 327,000,000.

Although Buddhist activity is not as focused upon religious buildings as some other religious traditions the directory records approximately 130 *viharas*, monasteries and other Buddhist centres, whilst many other groups meet in private houses or in hired halls.

Beginnings

In the course of the nineteenth century, a significant academic interest developed in relation to the study of Buddhism and, as an increasing number of English translations of Buddhist texts began to be made available, more and more individuals developed an interest in Buddhism as a philosophy and a way of life.

In 1881 the Pali Text Society was founded, which further fostered this development, and in 1899 the first English person to be ordained as a Buddhist monk took his vows in Colombo, Sri Lanka. This monk's original name was Gordon Douglas, but on his ordination he took the name of Bhikkhu Asoka. However, he did not return to Britain, and so the first Buddhist missionary to visit the country was Anagarika Dharmapala, who visited in 1893, 1896 and again in 1904. In 1898 another Englishman, Alan Bennett, went to study Buddhism in Sri Lanka. In 1901, whilst in Burma, he was ordained as a monk, taking the name Venerable Ananda Metteyya.

In 1907, the Buddhist Society of Great Britain and Ireland was formed to receive a Buddhist mission which was led by Ananda Metteyya in 1908. In 1924 the original Buddhist Society merged with the Buddhist Centre of the

UPDATE SHEET

If any information in the listings sections of the directory requires updating or correcting, please complete this form according to each field of information set out below and the description of these in pages 18-19 of the directory.

Name: ....

Address: ....

....

....

.... Post Code ....

Telephone: ....

Telephone (home): ....

Fax: ....

Fax (home): ....

Contact: ....

Office: ....

Self-description:

....

....

....

....

....

....

.... (if necessary, continue overleaf)

Return completed form to: Religious Resource and Research Centre
University of Derby
Mickleover
Derby DE3 5GX

Theosophical Society. In 1926, the merged body became the Buddhist Lodge of the Theosophical Society. In 1943 a new Buddhist Society emerged from the Lodge as a separate organisation. Also in 1926, as a consequence of a Sri Lankan Buddhist mission to Britain by Anagarika Dharmapala, a branch of the Maha Bodhi Society was founded, and in 1928 a monastery was established for Sinhalese monks.

Migration

During the 1950s and 1960s increased immigration from New Commonwealth countries strengthened Buddhism in the UK with the arrival of various minority ethnic communities of Chinese and other Asian origins who followed Buddhist religious practice. The Buddhist community grew still further with the arrival of Buddhist refugees from the Tibetan diaspora of Buddhist teachers following the 1959 flight of the Dalai Lama from Chinese-occupied Tibet and later with refugees from Vietnam and Sri Lanka.

The languages spoken by Buddhists reflect the ethnic diversity of Buddhism in this country. With respect to the scriptures and Buddhist teaching, both Pali and Sanskrit are used together with English, Pali being used predominantly by *Theravada* Buddhist groups and *Sanskrit* by *Mahayana* group.

ORIGINS AND DEVELOPMENT OF BUDDHISM

Gotama Buddha

Buddhism does not present itself as a "revealed" religion and it does not believe in a personal deity. It makes no claims to possess a divinely revealed book and it has no central organisational authority. The teachings of Buddhism are the inheritance of one man's search for truth. That man was the Indian Prince Siddhattha Gotama (Pali), also known as Siddhartha Gautama (Sanskrit), or in the *Mahayana* Buddhist tradition as Sakyamuni (literally the muni or sage of the *sakya* people.) He is acknowledged to be a *Buddha*.

The term *Buddha* is derived from the word *budh* (meaning to understand or to be awakened) and is therefore not a personal name but a title given to an "Enlightened" or "Awakened" Being. Gotama *Buddha* lived in North India, but Buddhist tradition has also postulated other *Buddhas* in other places and epochs of time.

Siddhattha Gotama was born in Lumbini, in what is today Nepal, in the fifth century BCE and grew up nearby in Kapilavatthu. As a prince, his early life was rich, comfortable, and shielded from the vicissitudes of life. Eventually, however, he asked his charioteer to take him to see life in the city. Here he saw for himself the suffering of an old man, a sick man, and a corpse that were sights which he had never seen before. He also saw the serenity of a mendicant.

This experience awakened in him a feeling of great compassion and a desire to find a way to alleviate the sufferings of humankind. So, at the age of twenty-nine, he began a spiritual search which lasted for six years until it reached its culmination in his *Enlightenment* under the Bo Tree (now known as the Bodhi Tree), the place also known as Bodh Gaya in North India.

As a prince he had experienced a life of luxury and had found it unsatisfactory. During this period of searching, he experienced the other extremes of self-denial and self-mortification. This, too, he found unsatisfactory, so he decided to take a more balanced approach. He ate some food and regained the strength that his austerities had cost him. He then sat down under the Bo Tree in one last attempt to break through to that which he was seeking and it is said that on the night of the full moon in May he finally attained the state of Nibbana (Pali) or Nirvana (Sanskrit). After this he preached to five ascetics in the Deer Park near Benares, and when they responded as his disciples, the sangha (Buddhist community) was born. At the age of eighty he died at Kushinagara and entered into what Buddhists describe as his parinirvana (passing away).

Transmission

As Buddhism spread it moved northwards to Tibet and eastwards into what is now China,

Korea and Japan. The form of Buddhism traditionally associated with these countries therefore is now known as the *Northern Transmission*. This *Northern Transmission* is related to the tradition of Buddhism known as the *Mahayana*. The so-called *Southern Transmission* took *Theravada* Buddhism to the countries which are now known as Sri Lanka, Thailand, Cambodia, Laos, Burma and Vietnam. In the present millenium Buddhism died out in India until its revival in 1956 through the *Ambedkarite* movement .

SOURCES OF BUDDHIST BELIEF AND PRACTICES

The Three Refuges

Buddhists speak of "Going for Refuge" in the *triratna* (three Jewels) which is an affirmation that summarises the nature of their commitment as Buddhists and the sources of Buddhist life: "I take refuge in the *Buddha*; I take refuge in the *dhamma*; I take refuge in the *sangha*."

The historical Buddha is revered as the bringer of the Buddhist teachings although the emphasis of Buddhism is not so much on the person of Gotama as on the *Dhamma* (Pali) or *Dhama* (Sanskrit) - the Teaching. Strictly speaking, Gotama is not viewed as the founder of the *Dhamma*. Rather, it exists independently of him and he is viewed as its exponent for the present age.

Buddhists are those who claim to have found these teachings to be valid for themselves. In the early stages of Buddhist training one can learn the details of the teachings, but in the end every individual must discover them in their own experience and not simply as what they have been taught. However, whilst Buddhists must find truth for themselves, Buddhism is not a purely individualistic religion. The *sangha* or community of monks and nuns plays a key role in Buddhist life in terms of offering guidance to others along the Path.

Buddha

In the *Theravada* tradition the reference to the *Buddha* is to the historical figure of Gotama, who is venerated as the one who began the

transmission of the current Teaching. Many Buddhist homes and temples therefore contain images of him as aids to meditation. Among *Mahayana* Buddhists, there is not only the historical guide and exemplar of the historical *Buddha*, but also a belief in the existence of a transcendent or archetypal reality of which the historical *Buddha* is seen as one manifestation. Going to the *Buddha* for refuge therefore means accepting the *Buddha* as the ultimate spiritual guide and example for one's life.

Dhamma

The *dhamma* or teaching of the *Buddha* is quintessentially expressed in the so-called *Four Noble Truths* and the *Noble Eightfold Path* of Buddhist teaching. These are otherwise known as the *Middle Way* after the *Buddha's* experience of rejecting both the excesses of self-indulgence and self-denial. Going for refuge to the *dhamma* means focusing one's energies in understanding, practising and realising the Teaching of the *Buddha* in one's own life and the life of others.

Sangha

Among the majority of Buddhists the *sangha* (see below) is traditionally understood to be the community of monks and nuns who have devoted their entire lives to following the *Buddha's* teaching in all respects and to sharing that teaching with others. Among other Buddhists, and particularly in some parts of western Buddhism, the *sangha* is understood to include all followers of the *Buddha*.

Pali Canon

There are several canons of scripture which have a place in explaining the *dhamma*. The *Pali Canon* contains some of the oldest material and its teachings which include those of the *Buddha* and his disciples are generally recognised by all Buddhist schools. Most of these texts have been translated into English. This canon is also known as the *Tipitaka*, meaning the Three Baskets, since its manuscripts were originally kept in three different baskets - the *Vinaya-pitaka* (Basket of

[Monastic] Discipline); the *Sutta-pitaka* (the Basket of Discourses); and the *Abhidhamma-pitaka* (the Basket of Further Teachings).

Sutras

The *Mahayana* tradition also uses a range of texts from the *Sutta-pitaka* known as *sutras* in Sanskrit and *suttas* in Pali. The name *sutra* refers to the idea of a single thread running through the discourse. In the *Mahayana* tradition these include some six hundred Chinese and Tibetan language texts. Among the more widely known are the *Saddharma-pundarika* (the Lotus of the True Dharma), and the collection of sutras known as *Prajna-paramita* (the Perfection of Wisdom).

These *sutras* were gathered into canonical collections of writings. The Chinese canon is known as the *Ta-ts'ang-ching* (Great Scripture Store) and its standard modern edition consists of fifty-five volumes with forty-five supplementary volumes. The Tibetan Canon consists of the *bKa'gyur* (pronounced "Kangyur" and meaning "the Translation of the Word of the Buddha") which is ninety-eight volumes long, and the *bStan'gyur* ("Translation of Treatises") which, in its Peking edition, is in two hundred and twenty-four volumes.

Jataka Stories

In addition to the canonical texts, both *Theravada* and *Mahayana* Buddhists refer to the five hundred *Jataka* stories said to have been told by the *Buddha* to his followers about his former lives. They form the basis of much popular teaching and reflection in Buddhist countries.

KEY BUDDHIST BELIEFS

Four Noble Truths

The *Cattari Ariyasaccani* (Four Noble Truths) are at the heart of the *dhamma*. They are the truths of: *dukkha, samudaya, nirodha* and *magga*.

Dukkha (Unsatisfactoriness)

Dukkha can often be found translated into English as "suffering". However, this translation is misleading and perhaps it is best understood as "unsatisfactoriness". Suffering is only one of the meanings of *dukkha*, which is a word that also implies imperfection and impermanence. In his first sermon, the Buddha said: "Birth is *dukkha*, ageing is *dukkha*, sickness is *dukkha*, death is *dukkha*; sorrow, lamentation, grief and despair are *dukkha*; association with what one dislikes is *dukkha*; separation from what one likes is *dukkha*; not to get what one wants is *dukkha*."

Samudaya (Origin of Unsatisfactoriness)

Samudaya (the origin of *dukkha*), is perceived by Buddhists to lie in *tanha*, that is the thirsting or craving which is a powerful mental force characteristic of human and animal life and is seen as the principal force behind dukkha. Of its very nature, this thirst can never be satisfied but reproduces itself.

Such craving is a desire for, and an attachment to, not just material things but also mental objects. Craving can also manifest itself in a thirst for continued existence. But its opposite (the desire for non-existence) can also be a manifestation of the same craving. Both result in *dukkha*. *Samudaya* is related to the concepts of *kamma* (cause and effect), *rebirth* (not trans-migration of a soul, because Buddhism affirms no continuing soul) and *dependent origination* (that all phenomena have their causes). Craving leads to rebirth(s) in the sense that *kammic* effects accumulate and attach themselves to new lives.

Nirodha (Cessation of Dukkha)

Nirodha is the transcendence of *tanha* (thirsting) and the cessation of *dukkha* and is known as *Nibbana* (Pali) or *Nirvana* (Sanskrit). The full meaning of *Nibbana* cannot be adequately described in human language. In literal terms it means "quenching" or "extinction" but this does not, as has often been misunderstood, mean that *Nibbana* is a state of self-annihilation. The "quenching" and "extinction" is rather of *dukkha* and its causes which Buddhists affirm can be realised during this life, as in the case of Gotama *Buddha* himself.

Majjhima Patipada (The Middle Way)

The first three *Noble Truths* analyse the human condition and affirm the possibility of transcending *dukkha*. The fourth *Noble Truth* teaches the way in which this can be approached. This is by means of the *Majjhima Patipada* (Middle Way) of life between austerity and comfort. The fourth *Noble Truth* therefore emphasises the importance of the practice of truth alongside the study of truth necessitated by the first three *Noble Truths*. All four *Noble Truths* are understood to be a unity and the fourth *Noble Truth* leads one into a way of life based upon the *Noble Eightfold Path* (see section on Buddhist Life below).

The Three Signs of Being

The *Four Noble Truths* and the *Eightfold Noble Path* are connected with the basic Buddhist concepts of k*arma* and *samsara*, and also with the other two characteristics of existence which go together with *dukkha*, namely, *anicca* (impermanence) and *anatta* (not-self). Together, *dukkha*, *anicca* and *anatta* constitute what Buddhism speaks of as "the three signs of being".

Kamma is seen as a natural law of life, inherent in the nature of things. Actions have their consequences and whether a particular action has good or bad *kammic* effects depends upon the intention behind each action.

Anicca underlines that all phenomena in life are impermanent. Nothing can therefore be relied upon or built upon in any ultimate sense.

Anatta is the teaching that there is no permanent metaphysical self. An "everyday self" is recognised but rather than being something fixed it is seen as an ever-changing composite of five *khandhas* (aggregates): *rupa* (the material form), sankharas (mental configurations), *sanna* (perceptions), *vedana* (feeling), *and vinnana* (discriminatory consciousness).

Samsara

Samsara (the wheel of birth, death and rebirth) is not the reincarnation or transmigration of a soul because, as we have seen, Buddhism does not posit the continuing existence of a substantial or permanent soul. This is because the individual is understood to be a cluster of various elements held together by desire.

Buddhists prefer to speak of "rebirth" or "rebecoming" rather than of transmigration. This rebirth is possible on a number of levels of life (not just the human) and throughout aeons of time. Depending on the *karma* accumulated in one's lifetime the rebirth or rebecoming will be of different kinds. The goal of Buddhism is ultimately not to gain a better future rebirth, but to escape altogether from this wheel of rebirth and death and attain *Nibbana*. Being born as a human being is viewed as a precious opportunity to achieve this.

Shunyata

Shunyata (Emptiness) is of great importance in the *Mahayana* tradition where the idea of *anatta* (Pali) or *anatman* (Sanskrit) underwent further development. It came to be seen that all existence is devoid of any abiding essence. In other words, it is "empty" of any ultimate characteristics. To see this is to recognise the ultimately fluid and interconnected nature of all phenomena. The deep realisation of *Shunnyata* is said to be the ground for the *Boddhisattva's* activity.

Bodhi

Bodhi literally means "awakening" and refers to *Enlightenment*. This is the state of spiritual perfection or Buddhahood which is the goal of the Buddhist spiritual life. It comprises the perfection of *Pama* (Pali) or *Prajna* (Sanskrit), meaning wisdom, together with *karuna* (Pali) meaning compassion. This entails a complete seeing into the ultimate nature of existence and a totally self-less and empathetic response to all forms of life.

TRADITIONS IN BUDDHISM

The principal traditions in Buddhism are generally described as the *Theravada* (Way of the Elders) and the *Mahayana* (often translated as the Great Vehicle - *maha* meaning "great" and *yana* meaning "vehicle").

The particular form of Buddhism which came to predominate in Tibet is often seen as a part of the *Mahayana* but it is also sometimes described as the *Triyana* because it embraces three *yanas* (vehicles), known as the *Vajrayana* (thunderbolt or diamond path), the *Tantrayana* and the *Mahayana*.

Within each of the major traditions there are also different schools of thought and practice which emphasise particular practices and/or aspects of Buddhism. In the West there are, in addition, newer developments which do not fully identify with any one traditional branch of Buddhism and some of which aspire to contribute to the evolution of a new Western and distinctive transmission of Buddhism.

Theravada

The ideal of the *Theravada* tradition is to become an *arahat*, an individual who has found his or her own release from the cycle of birth and death. Its hallmarks are renunciation, self-reliance and a focus upon the historical *Buddha*. The *Theravada* tradition (Way of the Elders) is based upon the *Pali Canon* of the Buddhist scriptures and is today mainly represented in the Buddhism of Sri Lanka, Burma, Laos, Cambodia, Thailand and Viet Nam. It is therefore sometimes known as the *Southern Transmission*. Variations within the *Theravada* tradition also reflect the different cultural contexts in which the tradition has taken shape.

In older books on Buddhism it is also sometimes referred to as the *Hinayana* (Little Vehicle) although the origins of this term are to be found in a disparaging contrast with *Mahayana* (Great Vehicle) Buddhism. Historically, the term more properly refers to the pre-*Mahayana* tradition of Buddhism which existed in India rather than to the forms of Buddhism found in Sri Lanka and the Southern Transmission. Variations within the *Theravada* tradition reflect geographical differences in practice rather than ther existence of different schools.

Mahayana

The particular characteristics of the *Mahayana* tradition include an emphasis on the ideal of the *Bodhisattva*, the Enlightened Being who, out of compassion, delays his or her own entry into *Nirvana* in order to help others. The true *Nirvana* is seen as being attained with the achievement of Buddhahood to which the path of the *Bodhisattva* is believed to lead. The *Mahayana* is sometimes referred to as the *Bodhisattvayana* (the way of the *Bodhisattva)*.

Mahayana Buddhism believes in a series of archetypal *Buddhas* which are manifested in different ways and at different times throughout the aeons of time and of which Siddhartha Gautama is believed to be one. There is also a belief in various levels of truth adapted to the temperament and understanding of the listeners by what is called "skilful means".

The *Mahayana* tradition (Great Vehicle) is not the name of a single tradition but is a generic name for the wide number of schools of Buddhism which have been represented primarily in China, Japan, Korea and Tibet. It is therefore sometimes known as the *Northern Transmission*. Each grouping within the tradition is associated with one or more *Sutras* (Sanskrit) or *suttas* (Pali) accepted as authoritative teachings of the *Buddha*.

Tibetan Buddhism

There are four main lineage traditions in *Tibetan Buddhism*.

The oldest of the Tibetan schools is the *Nyingmapa*, in which the focus is upon meditation and visualisation. It is the school from which the well-known *Tibetan Book of the Dead* comes and it traces its tradition back to the Indian Buddhist Padmasambhava.

The *Sakyapa* school traces its tradition back to the Indian saint Ratnakarasanti. The *Kagyupa* school traces its origins to Marpa, who is believed to have brought it into Tibet having been a disciple of the Indian *tantric* master Naropa. This school especially reveres Milarepa, after whom the school divided into four further sub-schools. The

Gelugpa school emerged out of the earlier *Kadampa* lineage and the *Dalai Lama* is the Head of this lineage.

Zen Buddhism

Much of the *Mahayana* tradition developed an elaborate philosophical corpus but *Zen* Buddhism also stresses meditation and other more direct means to *Enlightenment*. All forms of *Zen* Buddhism focus on the practice of *zazen* (sitting meditation) and aim for the student to achieve a directness of knowledge and insight signified by the word *satori*, sometimes translated into English as "seeing one's true nature".

In the *Soto Zen* tradition the emphasis is on *shikan taza* ("just sitting"), which is also known as *Serene Reflection Meditation*, whereas in the *Rinzai* tradition, *koan* (enigmatic questions designed to engender and test genuine insight) are also employed in what are known as *sanzen* (interviews) with a *Zen Master*.

Pure Land

Pure Land Buddhism is a devotional tendency within *Mahayana* Buddhism based on a development of the cult of Amitabha, who is seen as one of the heavenly *Buddhas* of the *Mahayana*. In Japan (where Amitabha is known as Amida) the school is found in two main branches - the *Jodo Shu* (Pure Land School) and the *Jodo Shinshu* (True Pure Land School).

Both schools believe that we live in such a degenerate age that we cannot save ourselves and must therefore depend upon the infinite mercy of Amitabha (or Amida) Buddha and his *tariki* ("other power"). Both recite the *Nembutsu*, which is the *mantra Namu-Amida-butsu* (hail to Amida Buddha), as a central part of their practice. The difference between *Jodo shu* and *Jodo Shinshu* is mainly one of emphasis, with *Jodo Shinshu* (often simply called *Shin*) emphasising the complete abandonment of *jiriki* (self-effort).

BUDDHIST LIFE

Noble Eightfold Path

In Buddhist teaching the *Arya Astangika (Noble Eightfold Path)* is the way to approach the overcoming of *dukkha*. The eight aspects of the Path are traditionally grouped into three. The first two aspects of the Path are concerned with wisdom; the next three with morality; and the final three with meditation. All aspects of the eightfold path are, however, interdependent.

Correct Vision

Samma ditthi (correct vision) heads the *Noble Eightfold Path* leading to the Buddhist goal of *Nibbana*. More precisely, it is corrected vision, acquired through familiarity with the Buddhist philosophy of life, learning to view life as being impermanent and unsatisfactory and therefore as not-self, in other words as *anicca*, *dukkha* and *anatta* (see below).

Right Thought

Learning to think correctly about life through corrected vision generates the second aspect of the way, *samma sankappa* (right thought).

Right Speech

With the basic corrections of vision and thought, the follower of the Way makes no mistakes in speech or conduct. Corrected speech is *samma vaca* which causes no injury to oneself or others.

Right Action

Samma kammanta (right action) consists of abstinence from actions which would result in the destruction of life, theft and misconduct in sexual behaviour and replaces these with ethical living. For the Buddhist layperson, ethical living is summarised in the *Panca Silani* (the Five Precepts - see below).

Right Livelihood

Samma ajiva (right livelihood) is concerned with

the fundamental principle of *ahimsa* (harmlessness). This means not earning one's living in ways which are inconsistent with the *Noble Eightfold Path*.

Right Effort

Samma vayama (right effort) demonstrates that Buddhism is not a religion of passivity. Rather, it requires an effort of attentiveness to the way in which life is lived and an effort to sustain and generate good as well as to refrain from what is harmful.

Right Mindfulness

Samma sati (right mindfulness) is traditionally said to have four foundations: the body and its activity; feelings; states of mind; and mental contents. Whatever enters the mind, if observed with mindfulness, will be found to be subject to three characteristics: *dukkha* (unsatisfactoriness); *anicca* (impermanence); and *anatta* (not-self).

Right Concentration

Samma samadhi (right concentration) can be nurtured through the practice of meditation. Among the variety of techniques used in the course of Buddhist meditation, two key elements are usually identified: *samatha* (tranquillity) and *vipassana* (insight).

The Five Precepts

The *Panca Silani* or *Five Precepts* are the basic rules for living of lay Buddhists. They enjoin refraining from killing living beings; from taking what is not given; from misusing sexual pleasure; from telling lies and using abusive or cruel speech; and from self-intoxication through drink or drugs. For the lay Buddhist this is the basis of *Samma Kammanta* (Right Action), which is one aspect of the *Arya Astangika Magga* (the Noble Eightfold Path).

Meditation

Meditation plays a central role for people seeking to live according to the *Four Noble Truths* with the *Eightfold Path*. The *Four Noble Truths* with the *Eightfold Path* are concerned with the development of Faith, Patience, Mindfulness, Energy and Wisdom as the five foundations of the developing spiritual life of Buddhists. Wisdom and compassion are especially emphasised and for the Buddhist to grow in these two key virtues, meditation must be linked with teaching.

There are numerous methods of meditation within the various branches of Buddhism and they all require training, but there are two basic forms which underlie the variety of methods. These are *samatha* (calm meditation) and *vipassana* (insight meditation)

Samatha meditation is concerned with promoting states of mind characterised by calm, concentration and mindfulness in order to integrate the emotions and develop positive energies. Common forms of *samatha* meditation are engaging in mindfulness of breathing and in the practice of radiating loving-kindness.

Vipassana meditation is concerned with the clarity of seeing things as they really are and in realising the three signs of being. It is unique to Buddhism and is seen as being crucial to *Enlightenment*.

Aids to Meditation

In the *Mahayana* tradition there are variations on, and developments of, these basic forms. The Tibetan tradition teaches visualisation of *Buddhas* and *Bodhisattvas* in what is known as *sadhana*.

Various additional techniques may also be used. *Mantras* are archetypal sound symbols which, when chanted, are believed to resonate in ways that have a deep spiritual efficacy. *Mandalas* are sacred circles depicting the teachings of Buddhism and in Tibetan Buddhism they are either permanently painted on *thang-ka* (scrolls) or are temporarily made from different coloured sands or other such materials. *Mudras* are hand gestures which, like *mantras*, have an effect beyond themselves.

In *Zen* Buddhism great attention is paid to *zazen* (sitting meditation) as well as to daily observances and work periods. In *Rinzai Zen* this is supplemented by wrestling with the enigmatic sayings known as *koan*. Transcending the limitations of thought and entering the state of *munen* (no thought) is important in *Zen*. This state is not one of thoughtlessness, but of an "at-one-ness" which has passed beyond the distinction of subject and object and prevails not just when meditating but also when one is engaged in the activities of daily life, including during physical work, which is seen as an important part of the practice.

Vegetarianism

The emphasis in Buddhism is on the avoidance of intentional killing. In *Theravada* Buddhism monks and nuns are allowed to eat meat if they have not seen, heard or suspected that the animal had been specifically killed for them, especially if it is offered to them as alms, which is the only way in which they are able to obtain food.

The precept of right livelihood certainly excludes "trade in flesh". Therefore being a butcher, hunter or fisher are jobs that committed Buddhists would avoid. In general, even where Buddhists are not fully vegetarian, what are perceived as the higher forms of life would be avoided and eggs or fish would be eaten instead. In Chinese forms of Buddhism garlic and onions are also avoided since they are thought to heat the blood and so make meditation more difficult.

BUDDHIST WORSHIP

Buildings for Worship

Buddhist buildings of various types can be found in Britain, each reflecting the different traditions, schools and ethnic groupings of the Buddhists who use them.

Styles range from the stark simplicity of *Zen* Buddhist meditation halls through to the elaborate ornateness of *Tibetan Buddhist* temples. Some may be in residential houses with a room acting as the central shrine room. Others are extensive buildings such as the Samye Ling Tibetan Centre in Scotland and still others are relatively small, purpose-built structures such as the Peace Pagodas in Milton Keynes and

Battersea Park in London.

Despite this variety there are a number of common features. A Buddhist building contains a *Buddharupa* (statue of the *Buddha*); it is a place where teaching and meditation take place; and it has accommodation associated with it for the resident monks or nuns. It thus physically focuses the three refuges of Buddhism - the *Buddha*, the *Dhamma* and the *Sangha*.

Shrines and Buddharupas

Most Buddhists also have a small shrine in their homes. The *Buddharupa* is usually found in a central position within the shrine area. In front of the *Buddharupa* will usually be an incense holder and by its side and flowers and candles. *Puja* is devotion which is carried out alongside meditation, although in Buddhism it is not directed to a god. Rather, it expresses *shraddha* (faith), which is central in Buddhism. This is not blind faith, but confidence based on knowledge.

The offering of incense is symbolic of devotion and also induces a pleasant atmosphere. Lighted candles symbolise the light which the *Buddha's* teaching brings to the world. There are vases of flowers and sometimes other small offerings such as small pieces of Buddhist texts wrapped in silk cloth. *Tibetan Buddhists* place bowls of water in the shrine. In the *Zen* tradition, offerings of food and tea are also made.

BUDDHIST CALENDAR AND FESTIVALS

Calendar

Buddhist religious festivals are based on the lunar calendar and many of the major festivals are celebrated on full moon days. However the actual festivals and their dates and meanings vary according to Buddhist tradition and the national/ethnic origins of the group concerned.

Because of these national/ethnic variations and the lunar cycle, individuals cannot easily predict the exact dates of particular festivals. Many Buddhists therefore rely upon printed calendars such as the one produced at the Tibetan Medical Centre in Dharamsala, India, which is consulted by Tibetan Buddhists all over the world.

Festivals

Uposatha Days

Are observed at full moon and new moon and also on the days half way through the lunar fortnight. The full moon and the new moon observances are the most important. On these days monks and devout lay Buddhists engage in more intense religious activities. The way in which these days are observed varies considerably among Buddhists, but it usually includes a visit to a monastery to make offerings of food to the monks and to pay one's respect to *Buddha* images and shrines.

Parinirvana
(February)

Mahayana Buddhists mark the final passing away of Gautama *Buddha* at Kushinagara, India, at the age of eighty.

The Rains Retreat
(June/July – September/October)

Is an annual feature of the *Theravada* monastic calendar which monks and nuns observe for three months and in Thai Buddhism is known as *Vassa*. During this period monks and nuns should remain in one place except for emergencies.

Kathina Day
(October/November)

Is celebrated by *Theravadins* and follows the *Rains Retreat* either on its final day or within one month. On this day, the laity present monks with a cloth which the monks make into a robe on the same day. The precise date of observance varies according to when the rainy seasons are in the various countries.

Wesak or Buddha Day
(May)

Wesak is the Sri Lankan name for this festival (known as *Vaisakha Puja* among Thai Buddhists), which occurs on the full moon day of the second month. It commemorates the Birth, *Enlightenment* and *Parinibbana* (Pali) or *Parinirvana* (Sanskrit), meaning the "passing away" of the *Buddha*, all of which are believed by *Theravadins* to have occurred on the same day of the year. *Mahayana* Buddhists celebrate these on different days of the year. In the West, it is generally known as *Buddha Day* and it is usually observed in common by Buddhists of all varieties.

Poya

Are five full moon days of special importance in Sri Lankan Buddhism and are named after the lunar months in which they occur. *Wesak* is one of these months/festivals.

Poson
(June)

Is the Sri Lankan name for the month and the festival which marks the conversion of Sri Lanka to Buddhism through the Venerable Mahinda, son of the Emperor Asoka, who brought the *dhamma* to what is now Sri Lanka in 250BCE.

Asalha (Dhammachakra Day)
(July/August)

Is the anniversary of the *Buddha's* first sermon to the five ascetics in the Deer Park near Benares in India. It is celebrated by *Theravadins* and the Friends of the Western Buddhist Order. The sermon was called the *Turning of the Wheel of the Law*, which is the meaning of *Dhammachakra*. The day also marks the beginning of the *Rains Retreat*. In Thai Buddhism it is known by the name of *Asalha Puja*.

Sangha Day
(November)

Is celebrated by the Friends of the Western Buddhist Order and sometimes by other western Buddhists as an expression of the spiritual community of all Buddhists.

Bodhi Day
(December)

Mahayana Buddhists celebrate Gautama's attainment of *Enlightenment* under the Bodhi tree in Bodh Gaya, India.

New Year

Is not a specifically religious festival for Buddhists, apart from the incorporation of some elements of Buddhist practice into its observance, but it is generally celebrated by Buddhists as a major festival. The Sri Lankan and Thai New Year fall in mid–April and in Thai tradition, New Year also involves a water festival.

Padmasambhava Day

Is celebrated among *Tibetan Buddhists* in honour of Padmasambhava as the founder of Buddhism in Tibet.

Some *Mahayana* Buddhists also have festival days for various *Bodhisattvas* and for the founders of particular temples and monasteries. In Japanese schools of Buddhism, the Spring and Autumn equinoxes are celebrated as times of change and for remembrance of the dead.

BUDDHIST ORGANISATIONS

In Britain today, the numerically strongest traditions are the *Theravada* tradition, followed by *Tibetan Buddhism* and *Zen* Buddhism of the *Mahayana* tradition and the Western-founded Friends of the Western Buddhist Order (FWBO).

Theravada Organisations

Theravada in the UK includes ethnically European followers. There are also substantial groups of people with personal or ancestral roots in the traditional *Theravada* countries such as Sri Lanka, Burma and Thailand. Another group are the *Ambedkarites*, followers of Dr Ambedkar who led a social movement in India among low and "scheduled caste" Indians, many of whom eventually converted to Buddhism from

Hinduism.

The British Mahabodhi Society was founded by Anagarika Dharmapala as long ago as 1926, in London, and a *vihara* was soon founded, which operated until 1940. After the war, in 1954, the London Buddhist Vihara was established with Sri Lankan teachers. A Thai Buddhist *vihara* of the traditional Thai style, known as the Buddhapadipa Temple, was opened in South West London in 1966 by the King and Queen of Thailand. The Burmese community opened a *vihara* – the West Midlands Buddhist Centre/ Birmingham Buddhist Vihara in 1978.

Western *Theravada* Buddhists have also established a Western Sangha. In 1956 the English Sangha Trust was set up to further this goal, and in 1962 it founded the Hampstead Buddhist Vihara. The efforts to establish a Western *sangha* eventually bore fruit in 1977 with the work of Venerable Sumedho, an American-born monk, who formed a group of western monks and nuns trained in the Thai forest tradition which, in 1979, founded the Chithurst Forest Monastery. This *sangha* has formed branches in Northumberland (1981) and in Devon (1984). In 1985 the Amaravati Buddhist Monastery was established near Hemel Hempstead. The Western Sangha should be distinguished from the Friends of the Western Buddhist Order (see below).

Mahayana Buddhist Organisations

The *Mahayana* tradition in Britain is represented by diverse religious and ethnic groups.

Tibetan Buddhist Organisations

In 1959 there was a great diaspora of Tibetan *Lamas* following the Lhasa uprising against Chinese rule and the flight into exile of the Dalai Lama. European Buddhists offered help to Tibetan refugees such as Chogyam Trungpa, a onetime Abbot of the Surmang group of monasteries in Tibet. He came, in 1963, to study in Oxford. In 1967 he and Akong Rinpoche, the former Abbot of Drolma Lhakhang Monastery, founded the first Tibetan Buddhist Centre in the

West at Johnstone House in Dumfriesshire. It was named Samye Ling, after the first Buddhist monastery in Tibet. There are now many other Tibetan centres.

In *Tibetan Buddhism* there are several similar but distinct Buddhist schools with their own monastic orders. The *Kagyupa* and *Gelugpa* schools are numerically the strongest Tibetan traditions in Britain. The former tends towards the attainment of direct mystical experience and is represented by the Samye Ling monastery in Scotland, whilst the latter has a more graduated approach and is represented by the Manjushri Institute, begun in 1976 at Conishead Priory by pupils of Lama Thubten Yeshe.

The *New Kadampa* tradition is a development from the Manjushri Institute and has many centres throughout the UK. Growing out of the Tibetan traditions is also an esoteric and *Tantric* strand of Buddhism.

Zen Buddhist Organisations

The Japanese Buddhist Dr D T Suzuki attended the 1936 World Congress of Faiths in London and although some of his work was concerned with *Pure Land* and other forms of *Mahayana* Buddhism he is considered as having introduced *Zen* to the West and specifically the *Rinzai* school.

The *Soto* and the *Rinzai* schools represent Japanese forms of *Zen* which are the strongest forms in Britain, although there is also *Ch'an*, (Chinese *Zen*). *Rinzai Zen* is practised in the Buddhist Society and is led, since 1972, by Venerable Myokyo-ni, founder of Shobo-an, a training temple in North London. The Throssel Hole Priory, founded in Northumberland in 1972, practises *Soto Zen*.

Pure Land Buddhist Organisations

Shin Buddhism has been the most influential *Pure Land* school in Britain. The Shin Buddhist Association of Great Britain was founded in 1976 and the Pure Land Buddhist Fellowship in 1977.

Some Other Japanese Buddhist Groups

Soka Gakkai International of the UK and a range of other similar Japanese groups tend to have a lay orientation and non-ascetic approach to Buddhist practice.

Among the *Nichiren* societies the Lotus Sutra plays a central role. Nichiren Shoshu is the Western wing of the Japanese Soka Gakkai organisation and came to Britain during the 1980s. It is based on faith in the power of the mantra *Namu-myoho-renge-kyo*; on study of Buddhist teaching as presented by Nichiren and his successors; and the twice daily practice of reciting the *mantra* in front of the *Gohonzon* (a scroll on which the *mantra* is written).

Other Japanese groups include Rissho Kosei-Kai, founded by Revd Nikkyo Niwano and Mrs M Nagakuma, and the Nipponzan Myohoji Order, founded by Nichidatsu Fuji. This latter Order is well-known for its pacifism and the Peace Pagodas it built in Milton Keynes (1980) and London (1985). It, too, is based on the recitation of the *mantra, Namu-myoho-renge-kyo*.

Friends of the Western Buddhist Order

In 1967, Sangharakshita, an Englishman who was ordained into the three major traditions of Buddhism while living in India, returned to the UK and established the Friends of the Western Buddhist Order (FWBO).

The FWBO is a new Buddhist movement which seeks to avoid divisions between monks and laity and between the national and religious traditions of Eastern forms of Buddhism. It seeks to find new ways of living out the basic principles of Buddhism through the commitment of its members to the *Three Jewels* shared by all Buddhists, but by working them out in terms of the cultural context of the modern West. In doing this, it draws upon all the traditions of Eastern Buddhism whilst maintaining a strong involvement with Western culture.

Many people involved in the FWBO live in single-sex residential communities and work in co-operative businesses, but there are also those who live monastic lives in retreat centres and others who have ordinary jobs. The FWBO has twenty-seven urban and rural retreat centres in the UK, especially in London and East Anglia.

Personnel

The *sangha* of monks and nuns is central in Theravada Buddhism. Its monks are known as *bhikkhus* and nuns as *bhikkhunis*, which literally means "almsmen" and "almswomen", reflecting the originally mendicant lifestyle of the *sangha*. They can be recognised by their shaved heads and orange or ochre robes. They do not personally possess money and do not eat after mid-day. They differ from Christian monks and nuns in that they do not take vows of obedience and their vows are not necessarily binding upon them for life. Indeed, among Thai and Burmese Buddhists young men temporarily take the lower samanera (ordination) as a kind of rite of passage into adulthood.

Those who take the lower ordination are called upon to live by the *Ten Precepts*. These include the *Five Precepts* taken by strongly committed laity, with the exception that instead of refraining from sexual misconduct, there is to be abstinence from all misuse of the senses. In addition, one is to avoid the following: eating at unseasonable times; dancing, singing and visiting musical shows; wearing garlands, perfumes and unguents, finery and adornments; high or luxurious beds; and the handling of gold or silver.

After the higher ordination monks and nuns live according to the extensive monastic code known as the *vinaya*. In the *Northern Transmission*, this also includes nuns, who live on a similar basis to monks, but according to a more flexible interpretation of the *vinaya*.

Whilst the original role of the *Sangha* was to work for their own spiritual development and to share the *dhamma* with others, the Buddhist laity have often called upon them to officiate in priest-like ways at rites of passage and they have also often become involved in tasks relating to education and health care. In the Tibetan tradition a *Lama* is often a monk or a nun, but does not need to be so, and there are lay people who are accomplished in skilful means and are revered as *Lamas*.

In *Soto Zen*, the teachers are generally monks and nuns or priests, although in Britain there are also a number of lay ministers who have a limited role in teaching. In the Japanese tradition a married priesthood was introduced after the Meiji Restoration of 1868 when the Japanese Government compelled monks to marry (although nuns remained celibate) in order to reduce the numbers of the *sangha*. In general, in all of Japanese Buddhism, the monastic-lay distinction became less pronounced and home shrines rather than temples are the main focus for devotion.

The ordination of women as nuns was, in the *Buddha's* day, a relative innovation and the *Buddha* only instituted the *bhikkhuni* order after the pleading of his widowed foster mother and the request of the monk Ananda. The order was founded on the basis that the nuns followed eight special rules, intended for their protection. Buddhism argues for the equality of men and women in their spiritual potential and on several occasions Gotama defended the equality of the sexes in this regard. In the higher realms of rebirth a person or entity is not conceived of as having any gender.

The *bhikkhuni* order survived only in Northern Buddhism. In *Tibetan Buddhism* there was controversy over the validity of their ordination, which did not come from the Indian line but was introduced in the twelfth century. In other *Mahayana* schools, the spiritual equality of women and men is recognised and women receive full ordination and follow the same precepts as men. The number of nuns worldwide has been increasing throughout this century.

In the Western Buddhist Order members are ordained either as *Dharmacharis* (males) or as *Dharmacharinis* (females). Some members of the Order live monastic lifestyles whilst others have families. Within the Order these differences in lifestyle are not seen as being differences in status. All members of the Order follow *Ten Precepts* (a different list from the ten *shramanera* precepts) which lay down basic ethical principles governing actions of body, speech and mind.

BIBLIOGRAPHY

Almond, P C, *The British Discovery of Buddhism*, Cambridge University Press, Cambridge, 1988.

Bechert, H and Gombrich, R, *The World of Buddhism*, Thames and Hudson, London, 1984.

Buddhist Society, *The Buddhist Directory*, The Buddhist Society, London, 1991.

Connolly, P and Erricker, C, *The Presence and Practice of Buddhism*, West Sussex Institute of Higher Education, 1985.

Conze, E, *A Short History of Buddhism*, Allen and Unwin, 1980.

Conze, E, *Buddhist Scriptures*, Penguin, Harmondworth, 1959.

Dumoulin, H, *Buddhism in the Modern World*, Collier Macmillan, London, 1976.

Gombrich, R, *Theravada Buddhism: A Social History from Ancient Benares to Modern Colombo*, Routledge and Kegan Paul, London, 1988.

Goonewardene, A, *The Fundamental Buddhist Philosophy of the Four Noble Truths and the Noble Eightfold Path*, Buddhism for Schools and Colleges Series, Paper 1; *Introducing Buddhism*, Paper 2; *Life of the Buddha*, Paper 4; *Life of the Buddha*, Paper 5; *Geographical Development of Buddhism In Outline, Part I*, Paper 6, *Geographical Development of Buddhism in Outline, Part II*, Paper 7; *The Buddhist Councils*, Paper 8; *The Schools and Traditions of Buddhism (in outline) and Their Common Features*, Paper 9; The Buddhist Society, London, undated.

Harvey, P, *An Introduction to Buddhism: Teachings, History, and Practices*, Cambridge University Press, Cambridge, 1990.

Humphries, C, *Buddhism*, Penguin, Harmondsworth, 1951.

Humphries, C, *Sixty Years of Buddhism in England 1907-1967: A History and a Survey*, The Buddhist Society, London, 1968.

Oliver, I, *Buddhism in Britain*, Rider and Company, London, 1979.

Pauling, C, *Introducing Buddhism*, Windhorse Publications, Glasgow, 1993.

Rahula, W, *What the Buddha Taught*, Gordon Fraser, Bedford, 1959.

Saddhatissa, H, *The Buddha's Way*, Allen and Unwin, London, 1971.

Sangharakshita, *New Currents in Western Buddhism*, Windhorse Publications, Glasgow, 1990.

Sangharakshita, *A Guide to the Buddhist Path*, Windhorse Publications, Glasgow, 1991.

Sangharakshita, *The Three Jewels*, Windhorse Publications, Glasgow, 1992.

Snelling, J, *The Buddhist Handbook: A Complete Guide to Buddhist Teaching and Practice*, Rider, London, 1987.

Snelling, J, *The Elements of Buddhism*, Element Books, Dorset, 1990.

Subhuti, *Buddhism for Today*, Element Books, London, 1983

Subhuti, *The Buddhist Vision*, Element Books, London, 1983.

Williams, P, *Mahayana Buddhism: The Doctrinal Foundations*, Routledge and Kegan Paul, London, 1989.

Wisdom Publications, *The International Buddhist Directory*, Wisdom Publications, London, 1984.

BUDDHIST UK ORGANISATIONS

Together with a number of Buddhist bodies set up to operate beyond local and regional boundaries, this list of Buddhist UK organisations also includes a number of specific monasteries or centres. Whilst these are based in particular locations they are also points of reference for a wider network of Buddhist groups which look to them for support and guidance. Such monasteries and centres are therefore included in the listings of Buddhist UK organisations.

Amaravati Buddhist Centre and Associated Monasteries

Great Gaddesden
Hemel Hempstead
Hertfordshire HP1 3BZ
Tel: 044284-2455
Contact: The Abbot

A monastery established in 1984 primarily to provide a way to support those in training following the Buddhist monastic conventions and related to Wat Pah Pong and Wat Pah Nanachat in Thailand. It has a resident community of monks, nuns and postulants under the guidance of Venerable Ajahn Sumedho. Facilities include ample but simple accommodation for visitors; the Christmas Humphreys Memorial Library; a children's room and large grounds. There is a separate group of retreat buildings used for organised group retreats led by members of the resident community. Members of the community also visit outlying groups and schools on invitation. There is puja at 5.00am and 7.30pm; a beginners' meditation class every Friday from 8.00pm-9.30pm and a meditation workshop on Saturdays from 1.00pm-5.00pm. Visitors are welcome but should first contact the guestmaster. Public activities and accomodation are suspended during January and February when the community is in silent retreat. Amaravati is associated with Chithurst Buddhist Monastery in Sussex, Harnham Buddhist Monastery in Northumberland, and the Devon Vihara in Devon.

Angulimala the Buddhist Prison Chaplaincy Organisation

The Forest Hermitage
Lower Fulbrook
Nr Sherbourne
Warwick CV35 8AS
Tel: 0926-624385
Fax: 0926-624385
Contact: Spiritual Director

Involving some forty chaplains in the field, supported by a wider membership of friends and well-wishers, the organisation aims to: make available facilities for the teaching and practice of Buddhism in prisons; to recruit and advise a team of Buddhist visiting chaplains to be available as soon as there is a call for their services; act in an advisory capacity and to liase with the Home Office chaplaincy officials and with individual chaplains in prisons and provide an aftercare and advisory service for prisoners after release. It also attempts to provide pen-friends for prisoners, reading material and tapes, and appropriate Buddhist artefacts like rosary beads and Buddha-rupas. All Buddhist traditions are accepted. It is recognised by the Home Office as the official representative of Buddhism in all matters concerning the prison service.

British Buddhist Association

11 Biddulph Road
Maida Vale
London W9 1JA
Tel: 071–286–5575
Contact: A Haviland-Nye
Office: Director
Association of British practitioners and teachers. It promotes the educational, religious and meditation aspects of the Buddha's teaching in a structured way for those who have a professional interest and others who are able to give systematic attention and radical reflection to it. It is non-sectarian and seeks to express religious devotion in ways suitable to Western practitioners.

British Kempo Yoga Association

40 Deansway
East Finchley
London NW3

British Shingon Buddhist Association

58 Mansfield Road
London NW8
Tel: 071–486–7313 (home)
The Association follows the Chinese Shingon tradition.

Buddhism Psychology and Psychiatry Group

Springfield
Cliftonville
Northampton
Tel: 0604–30082
Contact: Dr Kedar Dwivedi
Office: Chairman
A membership group and forum for sharing of experience, interests and ideas regarding links and parallels between Buddhism and modern psychology, psychiatry and allied professions.

Buddhism Publishing Group

Sharpham Coachyard
Ashpringham
Totnes
Devon TQ9 7UT
Tel: 0803–732082
Contact: Richard St Ruth
Office: Publisher

A publishing house which publishes Buddhist books and the magazine "Buddhism Now". It also holds an annual residential summer school in Leicester.

Buddhist Hospice Trust

P O Box 123
Ashford TN24 9TF
Tel: 081–789–6170
Contact: Ray Wills
A charity established to explore Buddhist approaches to dying, death and bereavement. It is non-sectarian and welcomes both Buddhists and non-Buddhists. Through Buddhism, the Buddhist Hospice Trust hopes to help people transcend much of the fear and spiritual distress that so often surrounds death. Its current projects are "The Ananda Network" which arranges local meetings and companionship for the dying; an information and a resource centre which provides advice and help; a house of refuge; education seminars; study days and workshops on aspects of death.

Buddhist Society

58 Eccleston Square
London SW1V 1PH
Tel: 071–834–5858
Contact: Mr Ronald Maddox
Office: General Secretary
Open to all who feel able to subscribe to the aims of the Society. Individual membership (metropolitan) is £16.00 p.a. and joint membership £24.00 p.a. The rates for the Provinces at £11.50 p.a. for individuals and £16.50 p.a. joint subscription. The Society was founded in 1924 by Christmas Humphreys and is multi-traditional. It aims to publish and make known the principles of Buddhism and to encourage the study and practice of these principles. Activities include beginners' and study classes; publications; special lectures; seminars; meditation training; cassette recordings; correspondence courses; and annual summer school. Affiliated to The Inter Faith Network for the UK.

Dharma Therapy Trust

12 Victoria Place
Bedminster
Bristol BS3 3BP
Tel: 0272–639089
Contact: John Allman
Office: Chairperson
A charitable trust under the spiritual direction of Venerable Geshe Damcho Yonten from Drepung Loseling Monastery. Through voluntary contributions the trust is able to sponsor regular visits

from Tibetan doctors, make donations to the Tibetan Monastic community and subsidise the teaching of Mahayana Buddhism.

Federation of Ambedkarite and Buddhist Organisations

2/4 Ffordd Ffynnon
Prestatyn
Clwyd LL19 8BA
Tel: 0745-562587
Contact: Mr C Chahal
Office: Chairperson

Friends of the Western Buddhist Order (FWBO)

FWBO Liaison Office
St. Mark's Studio
Chillingworth Road
London N7 8QJ
Tel: 071-700-3077
Contact: Dharmachari Kulananda
Office: Secretary
Central Office. The FWBO aims to teach Buddhism and meditation and to support practising Buddhists. It holds classes in Buddhism, meditation and related subjects at centres and retreat centres throughout Britain. Associated with these are a number of residential spiritual communities and right livelihood businesses. The FWBO is non-sectarian, regarding the whole of the Buddhist tradition as relevant to Western Buddhists. The Western Buddhist Order itself is a spiritual community of men and women which is neither lay nor monastic. It publishes its own magazine, "Golden Drum", as well as books for study. Affiliated to The Inter Faith Network for the UK.

International Ambedkar Institute UK

8 Kingsland Road
London E2 8DA
Tel: 071-729-6341
Fax: 071-729-6341
Contact: Mr C Gautam
Office: Member of Steering Committee
A membership group which meets from time to time to discuss and promote the welfare of the downtrodden people of India.

Jodo Shu Foundation of Great Britain

48 Laburnum Crescent
Kettering
Northamptonshire NN16 9PJ
Tel: 0536-517782 (home)
The Foundation is the British representative of the Japanese Jodo Shu Pure Land tradition, centred upon

the invocation of Amida Buddha. Jodo was brought to Japan from China by Honen (1133-1212) in the twelfth century.

Maha Bodhi Society of Sri Lanka (UK)

London Buddhist Vihara
5 Heathfield Gardens
Chiswick
London W4 4JU
Tel: 081-995-9493
Fax: 081-742-3107
Contact: Venerable Pandith M Vajiragnana
Office: Abbot
A membership group which aims to: assist enquiring individuals and groups in a better understanding of Buddhism; be of service to Buddhists in their devotional needs; encourage Buddhists in further study of the Dhamma and to encourage all to live the righteous way of life as prescribed by the Buddha. The society is open to all and there are no membership charges, other than for courses linked to other bodies. Numerous courses are offered at all levels on the Dhamma and there are regular meditation instruction and retreats; discussion groups; an excellent reference library and bookstall; and open hospitality to all who seriously wish for knowledge on Buddhism, particularly the Theravada School. Affiliated to The Inter Faith Network for the UK.

Manjushri Institute

Conishead Priory
Ulverston
Cumbria LA12 9QQ
Tel: 0229-54029
Contact: Secretary
A Mahayana Buddhist Centre and residential community and a member of the New Kadampa tradition. It is one of the largest Dharma centres in the West and the home of Geshe Kelsang Gyatso, the highly respected meditation master and scholar. There is a residential community of seventy-five including lay and ordained members who help with the running of the centre and participate in the education programme.

Network of Engaged Buddhists

Plas Plwca
Cwmrheidol
Aberystwyth
Dyfed SY23 3NB (home)
Tel: 097-084-603 (home)
Contact: Ken Jones
Office: Secretary
A membership network which is a fellowship of

people who are trying to combine inner peace seeking and outward social concern in ways which support and enrich both endeavours. The Network offers a means of sharing problems, feelings and experiences (good or bad) with others of the same heart and mind. It is an attempt to be both an affinity group and a pressure group, giving the chance for personal and social transfromation. It publishes a journal called "Indra's Net". Together with this, retreats and workshops are organised. Speakers attend to speak on issues requested by the members.

Soka Gakkai International of the United Kingdom

Taplow Court
Taplow
Maidenhead SL6 0ER
Tel: 0628-773-163
Fax: 0628-773-055
Contact: Mr J Delnevo
Office: Executive Assistant
SGI-UK is the United Kingdom affiliate of Soka Gakkai International, a lay society whose members practice the Buddhism of Nichiren Daishonin. The SGI is a non-Governmental Organisation (NGO) affiliated to the United nations. SGI-UK, which has its headquarters at Taplow Court in Buckinghamshire, works on a national level to strengthen links between members, encourage their faith and fulfill the aims of SGI. It is a religious charity registered with the Charity Commissioners of England and Wales. Local discussion meetings are held throughout the UK. All enquiries to the central headquarters will be referred to members in the locality of the enquirer.

Office of Tibet

Linburn House
342 Kilburn High Road
London NW6 2QJ
Tel: 071-328-8422
Fax: 071-372-5449
The office administers the temporal and spiritual affairs of His Holiness the Dalai Lama, the leader of the Tibetan people. His international headquarters is in Dharamsala, HP, North India.

Order of Buddhist Contemplatives

Throssel Hole Priory
Carrshield
Hexham
Northumberland NE47 8AL
Tel: 0434-345-204
Fax: 0434-345216

Contact: Guestmaster
A training monastery for both male and female monks and a lay retreat centre, it is a Serene Reflection (Soto Zen) monastery founded in 1972 by Revd Master Jiyu-Kennett after her return from many years study in Japan. The teaching emphasises that all beings have the Buddha nature and can realise their full spiritual potential through the practice of meditation. Men and women train together in a tradition that has kept true to its Buddhist roots while finding appropriate forms within a western context.

Pali Text Society

73 Lime Walk
Headington
Oxford OX3 7AD
Tel: 0865-742125
The Pali Text Society is a charity publishing texts, translations, dictionaries and primers. It aims to increase public awareness of Buddhist (mainly Theravadin) literature and to make the Pali language accessible to as many as possible. In this spirit, the Society also funds a few fellowships in Pali Scholarship.

Pure Land Buddhist Foundation of Great Britain

48 Laburnham Crescent
Kettering
Northamptonshire
Tel: 0536-517782 (home)
The Foundation follows the Japanese Pure Land School and is led by Michael Carr.

RIGPA Fellowship

330 Caledonian Road
London N1 1BB
Tel: 071-700-0185
Contact: Heidi Lindstedt
The RIGPA Fellowship is an international network of Tibetan Buddhist centres founded and led by Sogyal Rinpoche. Sogyal Rinpoche is a Lama born and raised in Tibet and recognised as an incarnation of the nineteenth century mystic yogi Terton Sogyal. RIGPA's aim is to encourage a true understanding of Buddhism and to link the Buddhist approach to that of western disciplines such as psychotherapy and counselling, medicine, healing and care for the dying, and the London centre serves as both the national and international centre for this work. It offers a complete introduction to, and grounding in, the Buddha Dharma through courses, weekend workshops and retreats. The centre aims to provide inspiration and support in the heart of the city, integrating spiritual practice with everyday life and work. Tapes of Sogyal

Rinpoche's teachings, a wide variety of books on Buddhism, Tibetan handicrafts, artefacts and related items are available from the RIGPA shop during course times.

Sakyadhita

27 Ford Street
Nuneaton
Warwickshire CV10 8AR
Tel: 0203-351123
Contact: Wendy Barzetovic
Sakyadhita (meaning "daughters of the Buddha") is the name of the International Association of Buddhist Women which was founded in Bodhgaya, India, in 1987. Its objectives are to: promote world peace through the practice of the Buddha's teachings; create a network of communications for Buddhist women throughout the world; promote harmony and understanding among the various Buddhist traditions; encourage and help educate women as teachers of Buddhadharma; provide improved facilities for women to study and practice the teachings; conduct research on monastic discipline and the role of women in Buddhism. It is committed to pursuing the Buddhist ideal of positive human development and especially the advancement of the spiritual welfare of the world's women.

Samatha Trust

The Samatha Centre
Greenstreete
Llangunllo
Powys LD7 1SP
Tel: 0223-249732 (home)
Contact: Dave Hall
Office: Secretary
An organisation which exists to foster the practice and teaching of meditation in the Theravada Buddhist tradition. Established by the pupils of a Thai monk, it seeks to develop this tradition in the context of lay life in the west. The group teaches Samantha-Vipassana meditation in the Theravada Buddhist tradition.

Shin Buddhist Association of Great Britain

7 Cissbury Avenue
Findon Valley
Worthing
West Sussex BN14 0DN
Contact: Revd Jack Austin
Office: Secretary
The association is a membership group following the Jodo Shin Shu (the True Teaching of the Pure Land) school founded by Shinran Shonin in Japan during the thirteenth century CE. The Shin Buddhist

Association was founded in London in 1976, under the patronage of the then Chief Abbot of Nishi Hongwanji, His Eminence Kosho Otanhi. The group is affiliated with Nishi Hongwanji, Kyoto, Japan. It encourages the study of Buddha-Dharma generally and of Shinran Shonin's insights in particular, and it urges the application of this teaching in the daily lives of followers.

Society for the Advancement of Buddhist Understanding

c/o Mitutoyo UK Ltd.
Joule Road
West Point Business Park
Andover
Hampshire SP10 3UT
Tel: 0264-353123
Contact: Mitsuo Tajima
Office: Director
A representative body of the Bukkyo Dendo Kyokai in Japan (established in 1965). It has the objective of promoting the Buddhist faith in the UK. The society does not promote any particular denominational or sectarian doctrine, but seeks to promote and propagate a modern understanding of the Buddhist spirit. It has sponsored a wide range of activities and programs to reach out to "even one more person" and to sell and donate a book "The Teachings of Buddha" to hotels, libraries, schools and individuals who are interested in knowing what Buddhism is. It also aims to establish a Buddhist chair called The Numata Chair in some universities in the UK for research and education in Buddhism.

Vipassana Trust

Dhamma Dipa
The Marches
Harewood End
Hereford HR2 8NG
Tel: 098-987-234
Contact: Manager
A non-sectarian educational charity. Vipassana, one of the meditation techniques taught by the Buddha, is a practical method of self-knowledge and self-awareness leading to freedom from mental tensions and greater balance of the mind. People of all faiths or of no particular faith will benefit greatly from this meditation. The trust runs ten day courses in Vipassana meditation at the retreat centre.

BUDDHIST CENTRES AND LOCAL ORGANISATIONS

SCOTLAND

WALES

NORTHERN IRELAND

NORTH EAST ENGLAND

YORKSHIRE AND HUMBERSIDE

NORTH WEST ENGLAND

ENGLISH EAST MIDLANDS

ENGLISH WEST MIDLANDS

EAST ANGLIA

SOUTH EAST ENGLAND (NORTH)

LONDON (E)

LONDON (N)

LONDON (NW)

LONDON (SE)

LONDON (SW)

LONDON (W)

LONDON (WC)

SOUTH EAST ENGLAND (SOUTH)

SOUTH WEST ENGLAND

There are a variety of forms of Buddhist local organisations in the UK that are listed in this directory. These include *viharas* where monks live; centres with residential Buddhist communities, lay and/or monastic; as well as groups which meet in the homes of members or in hired premises.

SCOTLAND

Aberdeen Serene Reflection Meditation Group
33 Bredero Drive
Banchory
Aberdeen AR3 32B
Tel: 03302-4339 (home)
Contact: Bob McGraw
Office: External contact
A group of people who meet together to meditate. It follows the Serene Reflection Meditation Tradition (Soto Zen), which stems from Japan, in the Mahayana tradition. The practice, which is firmly rooted in the Buddhist tradition, consists of formal meditation, keeping the moral precepts of Buddhism, teaching that all beings have the Buddha nature and that it is important to awaken the heart of compassion.

Dhanakosa Retreat Centre
Ledcreich
Balquidder
Perthshire FK19 8PQ
Tel: 08774-213
Contact: Dharmachari Varaghosa
The retreat centre is a former hotel situated on the shores of Loch Voil in the Scottish Highlands. It is associated with the Glasgow Buddhist Centre and is a part of the Friends of the Western Buddhist Order (FWBO). It houses a small resident community. Regular weekend and week-long retreats are held including introductions to meditation and Buddhism, as well as yoga and hill walking. To book and for more details, contact the Glasgow Buddhist Centre, Tel: 041-333-0524.

Buddhist Organisations in Edinburgh
12 Saxe Coburg Street
Edinburgh EH3 5BN (home)
Contact: Ms Jody Higgs
A contact organisation. As there are a number of practising Buddhist groups in Edinburgh – one Soto Zen group, one Theravada group and two or three Tibetan groups (although these change) this organisation hopefully serves as a contact group giving up to date information about meeting times and places of all the Edinburgh Buddhist groups.

Edinburgh Dharma Study Group
34 Corstorphine Road
Edinburgh EH12 6HP
Tel: 031-337-6349 (home)
Contact: Rod Burstall (home)
Office: Secretary

A meditation and study centre for practice and study in the Tibetan Kagyu tradition of Buddhism, meeting for silent meditation, classes and discussions. It is affiliated to Vajradhatu, a group of Buddhist centres founded by the late Chogyam Trungpa Rinpoche, whose books such as "The Myth of Freedom" are widely available. Activities include Buddhist meditation and study.

Edinburgh Friends of the Western Buddhist Order

23 Temple Park Crescent
Edinburgh EH11 1JF
Tel: 031-299-6344
Contact: Dharmachari Tejamitra
Regular meetings are held as well as Dharma courses, regular classes, day and weekend events, and stress management courses, all of which are run by members of the Western Buddhist Order.

Edinburgh Mahayana Buddhist Centre

161 1F2 Rose Street
Edinburgh EH2 4LS
Tel: 031-225-1181
Contact: Rebekah Rooley
Office: Co-ordinator
A branch of the Madhyamaka Centre in the New Kadampa tradition of Buddhism. The centre is a place for the study of the pure Buddhist view, meditation and action, and offers weekly teachings and meditation classes together with the occasional one day and weekend course. Longer courses and retreats are also run from time to time. Contact the above address or phone for the latest brochure of events.

Edinburgh Serene Reflection Meditation Group

The Salisbury Centre
2 Salisbury Road
Edinburgh EH16 5AB
Tel: 031-667-5438
Tel: 031-667-5870 (home)
Contact: Rawdon Goodier
A meditation group affiliated to Throssel Hole Priory which follows the Serene Reflection Meditation tradition (Soto Zen). Its emphasis, firmly within the main line of Mahayana Buddhism, is on meditation, keeping the moral precepts and the development of compassion for oneself and all beings. The core of the group's practice is formal sitting meditation at meetings which are held on Monday, Wednesday and Friday. In addition, one day or weekend retreats are periodically held, usually led by a priest from the Throssel Hole Priory.

Edinburgh Theravada Buddhist Group

Edinburgh
Lothian
Tel: 031-332-3711 (home)
The group follows the Theravada tradition and has links with the Harnham Vihara.

Kagyu Samye Ling

Eskdalmuir
Dumfriesshire DG13 0QL
Tel: 03873 73232
Fax: 03873-73223
Contact: Dr S Akong Tarap
Office: Abbot and Director
A community of approximately one hundred and twenty people concerned with fostering compassion and understanding which, in particular, strives to help people to help themselves. Samye Ling is a charitable trust which has been established for twenty-five years and is now called Rokpa UK. It helps people in need of food and clothing and in dealing with emotional problems. The centre is open to the public and there are courses in Buddhist studies at all levels and workshops in self-development including T'ai Ch'i, Yoga, therapy, art therapy, acupuncture and massage. There is a daily programme of meditation and prayer with individual instruction available upon request from highly qualified teachers. The centre is also involved in the purchase and development of Holy Island as an inter-faith project.

Glasgow Buddhist Centre

329 Sauchihall Street
Glasgow G2 3HW
Tel: 041-333-0524
Contact: The Secretary
Public centre open to anyone who is interested in Western Buddhism and/or learning to meditate. It aims to make both meditation and Buddhism accessible to twentieth century Glaswegians. It runs weekly classes, day and evening, and has a well stocked Buddhist bookshop.

Glasgow Mahayana Buddhist Centre

38 Cleveland Street
Glasgow G3 7AE
Tel: 041-248-6261/0387-64171
Contact: Anne Mackinnon
Office: Co-ordinator
A branch of the Manjushri Centre in the New Kadampa tradition of Buddhism. The centre is a place for the study of the pure Buddhist view, meditation and action, and offers weekly teachings and meditation classes together with the occasional one day and

weekend course. Longer courses and retreats are also run from time to time. Contact the above address or phone for the latest brochure of events.

Glasgow Theravada Buddhist Group

3 Corrie Grove
Glasgow G44 3PP
Tel: 041-637-9731 (home)
Contact: James Scott
Office: Treasurer
A membership group which meets regularly to meditate together, usually under the guidance of a visiting monk. Visits are also made to the nearest monastery (Belsay in Northumberland). Activities include meditation meetings and support of the monastic sangha.

Samye Dzong - Glasgow

23 Bruce Road
Glasgow G41 5EE
Tel: 041-429-1875
Owned by the ROKPA trust, its activities are carried out under the guidance of Dr Akong Tulku Rinpoche, Abbot and Director of Samye Ling Tibetan Centre in Eskdaelmuir. Its objectives are to: provide free food to the homeless of Glasgow; be a *Dharma* centre where wisdom can be offered to all; and offering lovingkindness to the homeless people of Glasgow.

Soto Zen Buddhist Group

c/o Fraser
Flat 3/1
4 Vinicombe Street
Glasgow G12 8BG
Tel: 041-339-3888 (home)
Contact: Mr John Fraser
A membership group affiliated to the International Zen Association in Paris and established by the late Taisen Deshimaru. The group exists to promote the practice of Zazen (sitting meditation) and is part of the Soto Zen tradition established by Dogen. The group devotes itself to wholehearted practice, with no particular goal or profit.

Stranraer Mahayana Buddhist Centre

East Burland House
Glenluce
Dumfries and Galloway DG8 0NW
Tel: 058-13491
Contact: Pattie Christie
Office: Co-ordinator
A branch of the Manjushri Centre in the New Kadampa tradition of Buddhism. The centre is a place

for the study of the pure Buddhist view, meditation and action, and offers weekly teachings and meditation classes together with the occasional one day and weekend course. Longer courses and retreats are also run from time to time. Contact the above address or phone for the latest brochure of events.

Isle of Islay Buddhist Group

Damaoidh
Port Charlotte
Isle of Islay
Argyll PA48 7UD
Tel: 049-685-357 (home)
Contact: Liz Sykes
Office: Founder Member
A small group which meets once a month, usually in the local high school. Anyone interested in Buddhism is welcome to join the group, but no one is ever under pressure to commit themselves. Meetings start with a short meditation followed by study and discussion of Buddhist teachings.

St Andrews Buddhist Group

5 Park Street
St Andrews
Fife
Tel: 0334-75944 (home)
Contact: Mrs Cecilia Dyckhoff
The group follows the Theravada tradition.

FWBO in St Andrews

28 George Terrace
St Monans
Fife KY10 2AY
Tel: 0333-730447
Contact: Peter Challoner
A group of the Friends of the Western Buddhist Order.

Kongokita

26 Caledonian Road
Saltcoats
Ayrshire
The group follows the Kenpo Yoga tradition.

Vajrasattva Centre

Baron's Court
Sanquar
Dumfries and Galloway DG4 6EB
Tel: 0659-506278
Contact: Gerry Haddock
Office: Co-ordinator
A branch of the Manjushri Centre in the New Kadampa tradition of Buddhism. The centre is a place

for the study of the pure Buddhist view, meditation and action, and offers weekly teachings and meditation classes together with the occasional one day and weekend course. Longer courses and retreats are also run from time to time. Contact the above address or phone for the latest brochure of events.

WALES

Aberystwyth Buddhist Group
Gelli Pardarn
Pen-y-Craig Hill
Llanbadarn
Aberystwyth
Dyfed
Tel: 097084-603 (home)
The Group is multi-traditional.

Bangor Buddhist Fellowship
62 Carneddi Road
Bethesda
Bangor
Gwynedd
Tel: 0248-601109 (home)
The fellowship is multi-traditional.

Dharma Study Group
9 North Road
Builth Wells
Powys LD2 3BU
Tel: 0982-552502
Contact: Richard Bramhall
Dharma Study Group under the direction of Vajradhatu – the lay organisation founded by the late Vidyadhara, Chogyam Trungpa, Rinpoche to protect and disseminate the Kagyu teachings. Practices are: Shamatha/vipashana; oryoki. There are no regular meetings but informal interviews, meditation instruction, group practice, and classes in the basic view can be arranged to suit anyone interested.

Cardiff Buddhist Community
97a Albany Road
Roath
Cardiff CF2 3LP

Cardiff Mahayana Buddhist Centre
Cardiff
Tel: 0273-732917
Contact: Carla Collenette
Office: Co-ordinator
A branch of the Amitabha Centre in the New Kadampa tradition of Buddhism. The centre is a place for the study of the pure Buddhist view, meditation

and action, and offers weekly teachings and meditation classes together with the occasional one day and weekend course. Longer courses and retreats are also run from time to time. Contact the above address or phone for the latest brochure of events. Contact can additionally be made through Alison Riach, Tel: 0222-486228.

Cardiff Serene Reflection Soto Zen Buddhist Meditation Group
114 Parc-y-fro
Creigiau
Cardiff CF4 8SB (home)
Tel: 0222-890034 (home)
Contact: George Norwell
Office: Group organisers
A meditation group which follows the teaching of the thirteenth century Japanese Zen Master Dogen, as taught by Reverend Master (Roshi) Jiyu-Kennett, founder of the Throssel Hole Priory. The Prior of Reading Buddhist Priory, a senior disciple of Reverend Master Jiyu-Kennett, visits to give talks, spiritual counselling and to lead retreats. Activities include meditation practice.

Dorje Dzong
100 Mardy Street
Grangetown
Cardiff CF1 7QU
Tel: 0222-374196 (home)
Contact: Leighton Cooke
Office: Director
Follows the Tibetan tradition.

Lam Rim Buddhist Group
Milarepa House
51 Ferry Road
Grangetown
Cardiff CF1 7DW
Tel: 0222-373927
Contact: Judith Harte
The Group follows the Tibetan tradition and is led by Geshe Damcho Yonten.

Sang-ngak-cho-dzong Tibetan Tantric Periphery
5 Court Close
Whitchurch
Cardiff CF4 1JR
Tel: 0222-620332 (home)
Contact: Revd Ngakchungma Nordzin Pamo
Office: Honorary Secretary
Fortress of Awareness-spell in the White tradition of the Nyingma School, following the Khordong and

Chang Ter Lineages under the patronage of H H Khordong Terchen Tulku Chhimed Rigdzin Rinpoche and the spiritual direction of Ngakpa Chogyam Ogyen Togen. Sang-Ngak-Cho-Dzong was founded in 1980. In Tibetan Nyingma Buddhism the emphasis is on practice rather than philosophy. The White School represents the non-monastic Tantric practitioners who live in the community and use ordinary life as the life blood of their practice, which is well suited to Westerners. There are regular groups meeting in Britain, Europe and the USA. There are also retreats and courses in different locations throughout the year.

North Wales Buddhist Centre

89 Llanerch Road West
Colwyn Bay
Clwyd LL28 4AS
Tel: 0492-540414
Contact: Nigel Spaull
Office: Co-ordinator
A branch of the Manjushri Centre in the New Kadampa tradition of Buddhism. The centre is a place for the study of the pure Buddhist view, meditation and action, and offers weekly teachings and meditation classes together with the occasional one day and weekend course. Longer courses and retreats are also run from time to time. Contact the above address or phone for the latest brochure of events.

Llangollen Buddhist Group

c/o Vajraloka Buddhist Meditation Centre
Tyn-y-Ddol
Treddol
nr Corwen
Clwyd LL21 OEN
Tel: 0978-755521
Contact: Secretary
A group associated with the Friends of the Western Buddhist Order (FWBO) devoted to the practice of meditation and Buddhism. Regular classes and courses on meditation and Buddhism led by teachers from Vajraloka and Taraloka Retreat Centres.

Vajrakuta Dharma Study Centre for Men

Blaenddol House
Treddol
nr Corwen
Clwyd LL21 OEN
Tel: 0490-81406
Contact: Dharmachari Kamalshila
A retreat centre devoted to study and part of the Friends of the Western Buddhist Order (FWBO). Vajrakuta houses a community of men dedicated to

studying, teaching and writing about Buddhism. The community runs regular retreats and seminars aimed primarily at men who are involved in the FWBO.

Vajraloka Buddhist Meditation Centre

Tyn-y-Ddol
Treddol
nr Corwen
Clwyd LL21 OEN
Tel: 0490-81-406
Office: Secretary
Vajraloka is the Meditation Retreat Centre of the Friends of the Western Buddhist Order set amid the rugged beauty of North Wales. Meditation has been practiced here since the centre's opening in 1980. The centre provides a programme of retreats ranging from those with no previous experience to those with many years experience of the teaching and practice of Buddhist meditation.

Gwent Zazen Group

6 Ruskin Close
Silver Birches
Fairwater
Cwmbran
Gwent NP44 4QX
Tel: 0633-874-882 (home)
Contact: Mr Kevin Davies
Place of practice. The group practices Zen meditation. Zen is not a philosophy, a system of ethics or a religion, but it enables practitioners to reach the source of all philosophies, ethics and religions. Zen is learning about oneself, in order to go beyond the contradictions within which our "I" ordinarily imprisons us and move on to a more harmonious and natural way of being. Zen transforms everyday lives here and now.

Machynlleth Buddhist Group

Melangell
Maenguryn Street
Machynlleth
Powys SY20
Tel: 0654-703054
Contact: Emily Tomalin
The group meets every Monday at 8.30pm for meditation, discussion and fellowship. It welcomes enquirers, beginners and practitioners in all the Buddhist traditions.

Buddhist Retreat

Croesfryn
Bryncroes

Nr Sarn
Pwellheli LL53 8EY
Tel: 071-359-1394

Lam Rim Buddhist Group
Pentwyn Manor
Penrhos
Nr Raglan
Gwent NP5 2LE
Tel: 060-085383
The group follows the Tibetan tradition and is led by Geshe Damcho Yonten.

Kandro Gar Buddhist Society
13 Oakland Road
Mumbles
Swansea
Gwynedd SA3 4AQ
Contact: Tony Court
The society follows the Tibetan Nyingma tradition and is led by Venerable Ngakpa Chogyam.

Swansea Buddhist Group
42 Eaton Crescent
Uplands
Swansea SA1 4QL
Tel: 0792-466539 (home)
Contact: Mr Duncan Spowart
A membership group associated with the Friends of the Western Buddhist Order. It aims to teach meditation and Buddhism and to organise retreats. The FWBO uses a Triyana approach to teach Buddhism and includes aspects from Theravadin, Mahayana and Vajrayana schools. Newcomers to Buddhism or meditation are welcome to attend. Group activities centre around education and worship.

Swansea Mahayana Buddhist Centre
13 Bayview Crescent
Brynmill
Swansea
West Glamorgan
Tel: 0792-650593
Fax: 0792-302719
Contact: Jon Mortin
Office: Co-ordinator
A branch of the Amitabha Centre in the New Kadampa tradition of Buddhism. The centre is a place for the study of the pure Buddhist view, meditation and action, and offers weekly teachings and meditation classes together with the occasional one day and weekend course. Longer courses and retreats are also run from time to time. Contact the above address or phone for the latest brochure of events

NORTHERN IRELAND

Tashi Khyil Tibetan Buddhist Centre
54 Derryboye Road
Crossgar
County Down BT30 9LJ
Tel: 0238-541 581
Contact: Lynn McDaid
Tibetan Mahayana Buddhism.

Asanga Institute Centre
23 Woodcroft Park
Holywood
County Down BT1 80PS
Tel: 0232-427720
Contact: Paddy Boyle
A Buddhist meditation group which practices the teachings of the Buddha. Through these teachings and training comes understanding of ourselves and the nature of our own minds and through this comes peace with ourselves. Anyone is welcome to come and take from the group what they need. There is no desire on the part of the group to pressure people into joining and becoming Buddhists. People are responsible for themselves and their own activities. There are no fees or charges. The group holds meetings once a week for meditation and listening to Buddhist teachings. Weekend meditation retreats are also held together with an intensive five to ten day meditation retreat.

NORTH EAST ENGLAND

Ratanagiri: Harnham Buddhist Monastery
Belsay
Northumberland NE20 0HF
Tel: 0661-881-612
Fax: 0661-881-612
The monastery is a branch of the Amaravati Buddhist Centre, following the Theravada tradition under the spiritual direction of Ajahn Sumedho Bhikkhu. It has guest accomodation for those who would like to stay and keep the eight precepts and weekend and ten day retreats are held. The senior monks teach regularly in cities in the north of England and Scotland and, on invitation, talks are given at schools and groups. School groups are welcome to visit. Visits are made from the monastery to local prisons.

Atisha Mahayana Buddhist Centre

9 Milton Street
Darlington
County Durham DL1 4ET
Tel: 0325-365265
Contact: Denis Calderon
Office: Director

Durham Buddhist Meditation Group

Woodlea
13 North Crescent
North End
Durham City DH1 4NE
Tel: 091-384-3913 (home)
Contact: Dr Peter Harvey
Office: Organiser and Meditation Teacher
A meditation group which aims to enable people to develop greater calm, awareness and inner strength through the practice of "mindfulness of breathing" and related practices such as the cultivation of lovingkindness. The group is affiliated to the Samatha Trust, a national organisation. Its activities include Theravada Buddhist meditation classes once a week for thirty weeks for beginners and once a month for non-beginners.

Durham University Buddhist Society

St. Cuthbert's Society
12 Saddle Street
Durham City DH1 3JU
Contact: Judy Tice
Office: Secretary

Newcastle Buddhist Group

Newcastle-Upon-Tyne
Tel: 0532-405880
A centre of the Friends of the Western Buddhist Order. For details contact the Leeds Buddhist Centre, Tel: 0532-405880.

Newcastle Mahayana Buddhist Centre

Newcastle-upon-Tyne
Tel: 0325-365265
Contact: Adrianne Astbury
A branch of the Atisha Centre (9 Milton Street, Darlington, County Durham) in the New Kadampa tradition of Buddhism. The centre is a place for the study of the pure Buddhist view, meditation and action, and offers weekly teachings and meditation classes together with the occasional one day and weekend course. Longer courses and retreats are also run from time to time. Contact the above address or phone for the latest brochure of events.

Newcastle Serene Reflection Meditation Group

18 First Avenue
Heaton
Newcastle-upon-Tyne NE6 5YE
Tel: 091-2651404 (home)
Contact: Dave Hurcombe
Office: Lay Minister
A meditation group which meets every Thursday evening in Newcastle. Meetings include Zazen (sitting meditation); walking meditation; scripture recitation and ceremonial. Monks from Throssel Hole Priory visit regularly and visits to the Priory are organised regularly. Newcomers are very welcome and basic meditation instruction is available. The group practices Serene Reflection meditation.

Newcastle University Buddhist Society

Dept of Plant Biology
The University
Newcastle-upon-Tyne
Tyne and Wear
Tel: 091-232-8511 Ext 3899
Contact: Gilliam Craig
A meditation group that emphasises that all beings have the Buddha nature and can realise their full spiritual potential through the practice of meditation. Men and women train together in a tradition that has kept true to its Buddhist roots whilst finding appropriate forms within a Western context. The order of Buddhist contemplatives follows the Serene Reflection Meditation tradition (Soto Zen) and has its headquarters at Shasta Abbey in the USA where Revd Master Jiyu-Kennett is the Abbess and spiritual director. The group is affiliated to Throssel Hole Priory, a monastery of the Order of Buddhist Contemplatives. Its main activities are instruction and Buddhist training under guidance from Throssel Hole Priory.

Quannon House (Eigenwelt)

53 Grosvenor Place
Jesmond
Newcastle-upon-Tyne NE2 2RD
Tel: 091-281-5592
Contact: David Brazier
The centre offers short and long term courses and events on the relationship between Eastern, primarily Buddhist, practice and western psychotherapies, as well as a venue for study and meditation. Activities include meditation meetings, courses and psychotherapy. A range of occasional publications is available. The centre also has a house in France which

can be used for courses, retreats and peaceful holidays. Contact can also be made through Caroline Beech at the address and telephone number above.

Sunderland University Buddhist Meditation Group

Room 208
Forster Building
University of Sunderland
Chester Road
Sunderland
Tyne and Wear
Tel: 091-5152174
Tel: 091-3843913 (home)
Contact: Dr Peter Harvey
Office: Organiser
A meditation group which aims to enable people (students, staff and those in the region) to develop greater calm, awareness and inner strength through the practice of "mindfulness of breathing" and related practices such as lovingkindness practice. The group is affiliated to the Samatha Trust, a national organisation. Theravada Buddhist meditation classes are held once a week in term time.

YORKSHIRE AND HUMBERSIDE

Bradford Buddhist Group
15 Silverhill Drive
Bradford BD3 7LF
Tel: 0274-667265 (home)
Contact: George Abramson

Bradford Dhammapala
7 Eastcroft
Wyke
Bradford BD12 9AS
Tel: 0274-670865
Contact: Ann Voist
Theravada Buddhist meditation group

Bradford Mahayana Buddhist Centre
20 Midgeley Road
Baildon
Bradford
Tel: 0274-582456
Contact: George Squires
Office: Co-ordinator
A branch of the Losang Dragpa Centre in the New Kadampa tradition of Buddhism. The centre is a place for the study of the pure Buddhist view, meditation and action, and offers weekly teachings and meditation classes together with the occasional one day and

weekend course. Longer courses and retreats are also run from time to time.Contact the above address or phone for the latest brochure of events.

Doncaster Buddhist Group
7 Oak Tree Road
Bawtry
Doncaster DN10 6LD
Tel: 0302-711058 (home)
Contact: Mr Martin Smith
The group provides facilities for all Buddhists but emphasises the Theravada tradition. It uses guidance from the nearby Harnham Vihara.

Doncaster Mahayana Buddhist Centre
Doncaster
South Yorkshire
Tel: 0742-723212
Contact: Kelsang Rinchen
A branch of the Gyaltsabje Centre (85 Brunswick Street, Sheffield, S10 2FL) in the New Kadampa tradition of Buddhism. The centre is a place for the study of the pure Buddhist view, meditation and action, and offers weekly teachings and meditation classes together with the occasional one day and weekend course. Longer courses and retreats are also run from time to time. Contact the above address or phone for the latest brochure of events.

Halifax Mahayana Buddhist Centre
Halifax
West Yorkshire
Tel: 0535-661817
Contact: Sarah Firieron
Office: Co-ordinator
A branch of the Losang Dragpa Centre (312 Skipton Road, Beechcliffe, Keighley, West Yorkshire, BD20 6AT) in the New Kadampa tradition of Buddhism. The centre is a place for the study of the pure Buddhist view, meditation and action, and offers weekly teachings and meditation classes together with the occasional one day and weekend course. Longer courses and retreats are also run from time to time. Contact the above address or phone for the latest brochure of events.

Harrogate Buddhist Group
137 Bramham Drive
Oakdale Court
Harrogate HG3 3TZ
Tel: 0423-500174 (home)
The group is multi-traditional.

Harrogate Serene Reflection Meditation Group

Harrogate
North Yorkshire
Tel: 0423-888528
Tel: 0423-885490 (home)

Jampa Ling Centre

Banks House
Dacre Banks
Harrogate
North Yorkshire HG3 4EL
Tel: 0423-781514/0423-780389
Fax: 0423-781516
Contact: Cliff Barton
Office: Co-ordinator
A branch of the Madhyamaka Centre in the New Kadampa tradition of Buddhism. The centre is a place for the study of the pure Buddhist view, meditation and action, and offers weekly teachings and meditation classes together with the occasional one day and weekend course. Longer courses and retreats are also run from time to time. Contact the above address or phone for the latest brochure of events.

Vajrapani Buddhist Centre

Brian Jackson Centre
New North Parade
Huddersfield
West Yorkshire
Tel: 0535-661817
Tel: 0484-865007 (home)
Contact: Jim Sheridan

Hull Mahayana Buddhist Centre

Centre 88
Saner Street
Hull HU3 2TR
Tel: 0482-631744
Contact: Brian Pope
Follows the Mahayana Gelugpa (Tibetan) tradition, in particular the teachings of Geshe Kelsang Gyatso.

Khedrubje Centre

43 Hutt Street
Hull HU3 1QL
Tel: 0482-229899
Contact: Malcolme Ward
Office: Acting Director
A centre in the New Kadampa Tradition.

Losang Dragpa Centre

312 Skipton Road
Beechcliffe

Keighley BD20 6AT
Tel: 0535-661817 (12.00noon – 3.00pm)
Contact: Rosie Wallwork
Office: Administrative Director
A place of worship and residential community. The centre is a charity and registered company which owns a five bedroomed house where regular classes are held and in which a group of people live as a small but increasing Buddhist community which also has branches in Huddersfield and Bradford. The main aim of the organisation is to promote the doctrine of Jetsong Khapa through the programmes which the centre offers and through the practice of pure moral discipline. Its activities include the offering of a general programme and a foundation programme for everyone and a teachers' training programme for those who have done the foundation programme.

Leeds Buddhist Centre

148 Harehills Avenue
Leeds LS8 4EU
Tel: 0532-405880
Contact: Secretary
A public centre which exists to help bring about Western Buddhism. Buddhism is a universal religion/way of life, applicable to all, not the property of any one culture. Now that Buddhism has come West it needs to be communicated in a way that is understandable to the Western mind. The centre is open to all, offers to teach meditation and provides a facility where people can meditate together. Study classes are held on all aspects of Buddhist teaching.

Leeds Buddhist Group

c/o Dept of Theology and Religious Studies
University of Leeds
173 Woodhouse Lane
Leeds LS2 9JT
Tel: 0532-564330 (home)
Contact: Ken Brown
A Buddhist group embracing all traditions of Buddhism. It provides a meeting place for practicing Buddhists and helps newcomers to learn more about Buddhism and meditation. Activities include discussions, talks, meditation, and a lending library. Information and instruction are available to newcomers.

Leeds Mahayana Buddhist Centre

12 Granby Terrace
Leeds LS6 3BB
Tel: 0532-784085
Contact: C/o Mandy Coutier

Office: Co-ordinator
A centre in the New Kadampa Tradition

Leeds University Buddhist Society
c/o Students Union
Leeds University
Leeds
West Yorkshire
Contact: Secretary
The society was founded by students associated with the Friends of the Western Buddhist Order. It aims to introduce students and other to the benefits of meditation and Buddhism as effective means of self-transformation, rather than as objects of academic study alone. Activities include introductory talks and courses by members of the Western Buddhist Order and weekly meetings in term time at the students union on Wednesdays at 2.00pm.

Ratnasambhava Centre
3 St Michael's Terrace
Headingley
Leeds LS6 3BQ
Tel: 0532-784764
Contact: Polly Belchetz
Office: Co-ordinator
A branch of Madhyamaka Centre in the New Kadampa tradition of Buddhism. The centre is a place for the study of the pure Buddhist view, meditation and action, and offers weekly teachings and meditation classes together with the occasional one day and weekend course. Longer courses and retreats are also run from time to time. Contact the above address or phone for the latest brochure of events.

Friends of the Western Buddhist Order (Sheffield)
354 Crookesmoor Road
Sheffield S10 1BH
Tel: 0742-687435 (home)
Contact: Secretary
A small Buddhist centre and membership group with regular courses in both meditation and Buddhism. There are study and discussion groups for those who wish to deepen their involvement. Teaching is normally by members of the Western Buddhist Order.

Gyaltsabje Buddhist Centre
8 Sandbeck Place
Sheffield
South Yorkshire
Tel: 0742-682359 (home)
Contact: Liz Williams
Office: Director

Place of worship and study. It aims to promote the Buddhist faith through the activities of teaching, studying and practice, all within the Buddhist tradition of Jetsongkhapa, through the three education programmes: the general programme, the foundation programme and the teacher training programme. Its activities include worship and teaching.

Sheffield Buddhist Group
197 Edmund Road
Sheffield S2
The group follows the Theravada and Zen traditions.

Wakefield Mahayana Buddhist Centre
Wakefield
West Yorkshire
Tel: 0535-661817
Contact: Ani Kelsang Chodzom
A branch of the Losang Dragpa Centre (312 Skipton Road, Kieghley, West Yorkshire) in the New Kadampa tradition of Buddhism. The centre is a place for the study of the pure Buddhist view, meditation and action, and offers weekly teachings and meditation classes together with the occasional one day and weekend course. Longer courses and retreats are also run from time to time. Contact the above address or phone for the latest brochure of events.

Madhyamaka Buddhist Centre
Kilnwick Percy Hall
Pocklington
York Y04 2UF
Tel: 0759-304832
Fax: 0759-305962
Contact: Trevor Towle
Office: Course Secretary
A study and meditation centre which offers evening classes, day courses, retreats and longer study programmes in Mahayana Buddhism. There are courses to suit everyone from non-Buddhists to serious practioners. The centre is based at Kilnwick Percy Hall, a beautiful Georgian mansion situated at the foot of the Yorkshire Wolds. There are both lay and ordained members and visitors are very welcome in the afternoons or to stay overnight.

York Mahayana Buddhist Centre
Osbourne House
School Lane
Fulford
York
North Yorkshire
Tel: 0904-621508

Contact: c/o Alan Curtis
Office: Co-ordinator
A centre in the New Kadampa Tradition

NORTH WEST ENGLAND

Lancashire Buddhist Centre (FWBO)

301–303 Union Road
Oswaldtwistle
Accrington BB5 3HS
Tel: 0254-392605
Contact: Secretary
The Lancashire Buddhist Centre is run under the auspices of the Friends of the Western Buddhist Order and holds meditation classes, courses and retreats for people of any experience level as well as indirect activities such as Yoga and massage.

Barrow-in-Furness Mahayana Buddhist Centre

Thyme Cottage
58-60 Northscale
Barrow-in-Furness
Cumbria
Tel: 0229-472563
Tel: c/o Jack Roskell
New Kadampa tradition.

Blackburn Mahayana Buddhist Centre

39 New Bank Road
Blackburn BB2 6JL
Tel: 0253-695272
Contact: Santu Chatterjee
Office: Co-ordinator
A branch of the Vajravarahi Centre in the New Kadampa tradition of Buddhism. The centre is a place for the study of the pure Buddhist view, meditation and action, and offers weekly teachings and meditation classes together with the occasional one day and weekend course. Longer courses and retreats are also run from time to time. Contact the above address or phone for the latest brochure of events.

Kearjra Centre

8 Brecon Close
Blackpool FY1 5AY
Tel: 0253-695272
Fax: 0253-407525
Contact: Neil Carman
Office: Co-ordinator
A branch of the Manjushri Centre in the New Kadampa tradition of Buddhism. The centre is a place for the study of the pure Buddhist view, meditation and action, and offers weekly teachings and meditation

classes together with the occasional one day and weekend course. Longer courses and retreats are also run from time to time. Contact the above address or phone for the latest brochure of events.

Bolton Mahayana Buddhist Centre

357 Darwen Road
Bromley Cross
Bolton BL7 9BY (home)
Tel: 0204-308001 (home)
Contact: Gerry Van Breemen
Office: Co-ordinator
The Bolton Centre has been established to provide a facility where people can study the teaching of the Buddha and practice meditation in the New Kadampa Tradition. Classes are held for prayers, talks, meditation and discussion.

Carlisle Mahayana Buddhist Centre

Carlisle
Cumbria
Tel: 0222-486228
Contact: Les Robson
Office: Co-ordinator
A branch of Manjushri Centre (Conishead Priory, Ulverston, LA12 9QQ) in the New Kadampa tradition of Buddhism. The centre is a place for the study of the pure Buddhist view, meditation and action, and offers weekly teachings and meditation classes together with the occasional one day and weekend course. Longer courses and retreats are also run from time to time. Contact the above address or phone for the latest brochure of events.

Chester Mahayana Buddhist Centre

Chester
Cheshire
Tel: 0270-664050
Contact: Peter Willetts
A branch of the Amitayus Centre (c/o Amitayus Centre, 173 Ruskin Road, Crewe, Cheshire, CW2 7JX) in the New Kadampa tradition of Buddhism. The centre is a place for the study of the pure Buddhist view, meditation and action, and offers weekly teachings and meditation classes together with the occasional one day and weekend course. Longer courses and retreats are also run from time to time. Contact the above address or phone for the latest brochure of events.

Chester Zen Group

23 Hamilton Street
Hoole
Chester CH2 3JG

Tel: 0224–351012 (home)
Contact: Ms. Sylvia Young
The group follows the Soto Zen tradition under the spiritual guidance of Zen Master Hogen Daido (Yamahata), but all traditions and beginners are welcome. Activities include weekly meetings on Sunday mornings and an annual sesshin led by Master Hogan.

Burnley Mahayana Buddhist Centre
3 School Lane
Laneshawbridge
Colne
Lancashire
Tel: 0282–864389
Contact: Freda Simms
Office: Co-ordinator
A branch of the Losang Dragpa Centre in the New Kadampa tradition of Buddhism. The centre is a place for the study of the pure Buddhist view, meditation and action, and offers weekly teachings and meditation classes together with the occasional one day and weekend course. Longer courses and retreats are also run from time to time.Contact the above address or phone for the latest brochure of events.

Kagyu Dzong
15 Bath Street
Colne
Lancashire BB8 9JQ
Tel: 0282–870154
Contact: Mr R Scholes
Office: Secretary
A meditation and membership group. Kagyu Dzong has been established both to serve as a focus for the community of students of Karma Rinpoche and Ngakpa Jampa Thaye in this area, and to make the teaching of the Buddha available in a contemporary setting for a wider audience. Meditation practice and the provision of facilities for teachings are given by Lama Karma Thinley Rinpoche and his regent as well as other invited dharma masters.

Amitayus Centre
173 Ruskin Road
Crewe
Cheshire CW2 7JX
Tel: 0270–664050
Fax: 0270–250160
Contact: Peter Willets
Office: Education Programme Co-ordinator
A centre in the New Kadampa tradition of Buddhism. The centre is a place for the study of the pure Buddhist view, meditation and action, and offers weekly

teachings and meditation classes together with the occasional one day and weekend course. Longer courses and retreats are also run from time to time. Contact the above address or phone for the latest brochure of events.

Isle of Man Buddhist Group
38 Oakhill Close
Glen Park
Douglas
Isle of Man
Tel: 0624–28999
Contact: Mike Kewley
The group aims to practice and make known the principles of Buddhism on the island. The spiritual director is Dr Rewata Dhamma of the West Midlands Buddhist Vihara who visits to teach and lead meditation retreats in the Theravada tradition.

Hanley Mahayana Buddhist Centre
Hanley
Staffordshire
Tel: 0270–664050
Contact: Peter Willets
Office: Co-ordinator
A branch of the Amitayus Centre (173 Ruskin Road, Crewe, CW2 7JX) in the New Kadampa tradition of Buddhism. The centre is a place for the study of the pure Buddhist view, meditation and action, and offers weekly teachings and meditation classes together with the occasional one day and weekend course. Longer courses and retreats are also run from time to time. Contact the above address or phone for the latest brochure of events.

Kendal Mahayana Buddhist Centre
26 Lound Road
Kendal
Cumbria LA9 7EA
Tel: 0539–731984
Contact: Lynne Irish
Office: Co-ordinator
New Kadampa tradition.

Ch'an Association
41 Rutland Avenue
Lancaster LA1 4EX
Tel: 0524–388778
Contact: Richard Hunn
The Association follows the teachings of Hsu-Yun (1840-1959). There is also a small Chinese/English translation society and Chinese Buddhist Archives consisting mainly of Mahayana/Ch'an texts and records and documents relating to the late Hsu-Yun.

Chenrezig Centre

21 Portland Street
Lancaster LA1 1SZ
Tel: 0524–68437
Contact: c/o Richard Lupsom
Founded in 1984 by Geshe Kelsang Gyatso Rinpoche, Chenrezig's Spiritual Director. It follows the "General Programme" which provides an introduction to the basic Buddhist view, meditation and action, following texts by Geshe Kelsang Gyatso. Meetings are held weekly and include talks, meditation and discussion. It is a centre in the New Kadampa Tradition.

Lancaster Buddhist Meditation Group

51 South Road
Lancaster
Tel: 0524–62484
Contact: c/o Hilary Schofield
The group follows a Tibetan Mahayana tradition and is led by Geshe Kelsang.

Lancaster FWBO Group

c/o Lancaster University
Lancaster LA1 4YG
Tel: 0524–592690
Fax: 0524–63806
Contact: Isobel Derricourt
A group of Buddhists from Friends of the Western Buddhist Order who meet every Friday evening to meditate together, worship and study. An order member from the Lancashire Friends of the Western Buddhist Order Centre visits alternate weeks to guide study. The group meets in Lancaster.

Lancaster Serene Reflection Meditation Group

Friends Meeting House
Meeting House Lane
Lancaster LA1 1TX
Tel: 0524–34031 (home)
Contact: Paul Taylor
A meditation group which provides a setting for the mutual encouragement and support of people following the practice of the Serene Reflection Meditation tradition of Buddhism (Soto Zen). It regularly invites Monks from Throssel Hole Priory in Northumberland to give talks and lead retreats. Newcomers are welcome and meditation instruction is available. Weekly meetings are held for meditation practice.

Lancaster University Buddhist Society

c/o The Chaplaincy Centre
Lancaster University
Lancaster LA1 4TX

Tibetan Buddhist Centre

Ashfield
35 Westbourne Road
Lancaster LA1 5DX
Tel: 0524–63503
Contact: Malcolm Songest

Duldzin Buddhist Centre

Bluecoats Arts Centre
School Lane
Liverpool L1 3BX
Tel: 051-727-5506 (home)
Contact: Brian Jones
Office: Co-ordinator
A place of study and a member of the New Kadampa tradition, under the spiritual guidance of Geshe Kelsang Gyatso Rinpoche. The purpose of the centre is to provide a facility for systematic study and meditation for people living in the Liverpool area. The General Programme, which provides a general introduction to the Buddhist view, meditation and action is offered on Mondays at 7.30pm.

Friends of the Western Buddhist Order (Liverpool)

Mangala
Flat 6
31 Greenheys Road
Liverpool L8 0SX
Tel: 051-726-9050
Contact: Dharmachari Mangala
A group associated with the Friends of the Western Buddhist Order devoted to the practice of meditation and Buddhism. Regular classes and courses are held on meditation and Buddhism.

Kampo Gangra Shedrup Ling

30a Brompton Avenue
Liverpool L17 3BU
Tel: 051-733-2336 (home)
Contact: c/o Geoff Ashmore
Shedrup Ling is headed by Venerable Ngakpa Jampa.

Macclesfield Mahayana Buddhist Centre

Macclesfield
Cheshire
Tel: 0298–72026
Fax: 0298–27620
Contact: Ani Kelsang Gama

A branch of the Tara Centre (36 St Johns Road, Buxton, Derbyshire, SK17 6XG) in the New Kadampa tradition of Buddhism. The centre is a place for the study of the pure Buddhist view, meditation and action, and offers weekly teachings and meditation classes together with the occasional one day and weekend course. Longer courses and retreats are also run from time to time. Contact the above address or phone for the latest brochure of events.

Kagyu Ling Buddhist Centre

1 Totnes Road
Chorlton
Manchester M21 2XF
Tel: 061-860-7347
Contact: Angela Brady
A meditation centre and member of the Dechen community of Buddhist centres under the guidance of the Western dharma master Ngakpa Jampa Thaye. The foundation of the centre was inspired by Karma Thinley Rinpoche. The centre has a shrine room. Members come from the Greater Manchester area and meet regularly to practice meditation and receive teachings.

Manchester Buddhist Centre

538 Wilbraham Road
Chorlton-cum-Hardy
Manchester M21 1LD
Tel: 061-860-4267
Contact: Secretary
A meditation and teaching centre of the Friends of the Western Buddhist Order which aims to make available the teachings of Buddhism to people in and around Manchester and to make these teachings relevant and practicable to such people living in the modern West.

Manchester Centre for Buddhist Meditation

21 High Lane
Chorlton-Cum-Hardy
Manchester M21 1DJ
Tel: 061-881-0038 (home)
Contact: Charles Shaw
A meditation centre which was founded in 1977 by a group of people who had been practising Samatha for a number of years. The centre is also used on an occasional basis for religious and cultural purposes by groups of Sri Lankan and Thai people. Activities include meditation classes, groups exploring various aspects of the teaching of the Buddha, talks, days of meditation practice and practical work involving the practice.

Manchester Mahayana Buddhist Centre

37 Whitelaw Road
Chorlton-cum-Hardy
Manchester M21 1HG
Tel: 061-881-0663
Contact: Jeff Simm
Office: Co- ordinator
An education and meditation group which is a branch of the New Kadampa Tradition of Buddhism. Founded by the fourteenth century Tibetan scholar and meditator Je Tsonghapa, this pure tradition was brought to the west fifteen years ago by Geshe Kelsang Syavso. It offers a structured programme of teaching on the Buddhadharma New Kadampa Tradition

Manchester University Buddhist Society

c/o Students' Union
Oxford Road
Manchester M13 9PL
Tel: 061-275-3149
Contact: Secretary
A society affiliated to Manchester Students Union, using its facilities and aiming to introduce Buddhism to the University community (although not exclusively). It is comprised of a meditation teacher, chairperson, secretary, treasurer and publicity secretary. It is linked to the Manchester Samartha Association and the National Samatha Trust. The society holds weekly meditation sessions and holds lectures by invited guest speakers.

Tibetan Buddhist Centre

Top Flat
3 Hague Road
Didsbury
Manchester M20
Tel: 061-434-1972 (home)
Contact: David Stoh

Vairochana Centre

4 Wibbersley Park
Flixton
Manchester M31 3JQ
Tel: 061-747-5416
Contact: John Richardson
Office: Co-ordinator
A branch of the Tara Centre in the New Kadampa tradition of Buddhism. The centre is a place for the study of the pure Buddhist view, meditation and action, and offers weekly teachings and meditation classes together with the occasional one day and weekend course. Longer courses and retreats are also run from time to time. Contact the above address or phone for the latest brochure of events.

Vajra Varahi Buddhist Centre

38 Deepdale Road
Preston
Lancashire PR1 5AQ
Tel: 0772-59094
Contact: Mrs E Maher
A centre in the New Kadampa Tradition

Zen Buddhist Meditation Centre

36 Victoria Parade
Ashton
Preston
Lancashire
Tel: 0772-726031
Contact: Mr and Mrs Brandon

Rossendale Samatha Group

c/o Weavers' Cottage
Fall Barn Fold
Rawtenstall
Lancashire
Tel: 0282-416770
Contact: Stephen Hartley
A group in the tradition of Theravada and breathing mindfulness.

West Cumbria Mahayana Buddhist Centre

80 John Street
Workington
Cumbria CA14 3BT
Tel: 0900-68156 (home)
Contact: Margaret Porter
Office: Co-ordinator
The centre is a small branch of the Manjushri Institute in Ulverstone and comes under the spiritual guidance of Venerable Geshe Kelsang Gyatso Rinpoche, the resident teacher at Manjushri. A Buddhist monk travels each week from Ulverston to give teachings and meditation. Meetings are held every Wednesday at the Workington Sixth Form Centre. Activities include the study of the teachings of Buddha and the practice of meditation.

ENGLISH EAST MIDLANDS

Tara Buddhist Centre

36 St Johns Road
Buxton
Derbyshire SK17 6XG
Tel: 0298-27620
Contact: Steve Booth
The centre aims to provide for all people interested in the Buddha's teachings and meditation and follows the Tibetan tradition of Je Tsong Khapa under the spiritual guidance of Venerable Geshe Kelsang Gyatso. Its resident teacher is Ani Valerie Bruce, a nun from the Manjushri Institute. Activities include a full teaching programme on all aspects of Buddhism within the tradition of the Centre; a library of books and a selection of audio and video tapes; and meetings on most evenings and at weekends.

Chekhawa Centre

c/o 53 Leytonstone Drive
Derby DE22 4GV
Tel: 0332-369594
Contact: Kevin Grantham
A branch of the Tara Centre. The centre is a place for the study of the pure Buddhist view, meditation and action, and offers weekly teachings and meditation classes together with the occasional one day and weekend course. Longer courses and retreats are also run from time to time. Contact the above address or phone for the latest brochure of events which are held at St Helens House, Derby.

East Midlands Buddhist Association

9 Una Avenue
Narborough Road South
Leicester LE3 2GS
Tel: 0533-825003
Contact: Venerable D Ratanajothi
Office: A resident monk
The aim of the association is to practise and make known the principles of Buddhism. It was founded in 1992. Regular meetings are held every Sunday at 6.00pm and include puja, meditation and discussion. A library is available for the use of members. A newsletter which is called "The Wisdom" is published quarterly. Newcomers are welcome. The Vihara is open 9.00am–9.00pm.

Leicester Buddhist Group

Leicester
Tel: 021-449-5279
A group associated with the Friends of the Western Buddhist Order devoted to the practice of meditation and Buddhism. Contact is through the Birmingham Buddhist Centre.

Leicester Buddhist Society

6 Half Moon Crescent
Oadby
Leicester LE2 4HD
Tel: 0533-712339
Contact: Mr D Russell

Office: Chairperson

The society is multi-traditional and multi-cultural. Activities include meditation and Dharma study.

Leicester Mahayana Buddhist Centre

142 Victoria Park Road
Leicester LE2 1XD
Tel: 0532-784764
Contact: Maz Kent

A branch of the Tara Centre in the New Kadampa tradition of Buddhism. The centre is a place for the study of the pure Buddhist view, meditation and action, and offers weekly teachings and meditation classes together with the occasional one day and weekend course. Longer courses and retreats are also run from time to time. Contact the above address or phone for the latest brochure of events.

Pure Land Relaxation and Meditation Centre with Japanese Garden

North Clifton
Nr Newark
Nottinghamshire NG23 7AT
Tel: 0777-228-567

A meditation centre. In a moment of "enlightenment", Maitreya saw the absolute perfection and beauty intrinsic in all things, the essence of life. The clarity and joy of that experience and its profundity, gave rise to the strong wish to share this with everyone by helping them to experience it too by means of simple meditation. Maitreya has created a Japanese garden at his Pureland Centre, and in it is reflected the meditation experience that he teaches. The centre offers facilities for relaxation and meditation practice. The garden is open to the public from Easter to the end of October.

Telford Serene Reflection Meditation Group

Thirlwall
62 Shrewsbury Road
Edgmond
Newport
Shropshire TF10 8HX
Tel: 0952-825780
Contact: Mr and Mrs Richards
Office: Lay Ministers

A meditation group affiliated to Throssel Hole Priory, a Monastery of the Order of Buddhist Contemplatives. The teaching emphasises that all beings have the Buddha nature and can realise their full spiritual potential through the practice of meditation. Men and women train together in a tradition that has kept true to its Buddhist roots while finding appropriate forms within a Western context. The

Order of Buddhist Contemplatives follows the Serene Reflection Meditation tradition (Soto Zen) and has its headquarters at Shasta Abbey in the USA, where Revd Master Jiyu-Kennet is the Abbess and Spiritual Director. Activities include meditation instruction and Buddhist training under guidance from Throssel Hole Priory.

Mahayana Buddhist Centre

64 Russell Street
Nottingham NG7 6GZ
Tel: 0602-484848 Ext 3813

Nottingham and District Buddhist Society

26 Millicent Road
West Bridgford
Nottingham NG2 7PZ
Contact: Alan MacCormick
Office: Secretary

The society welcomes anyone interested in practising Buddhism. Most members follow the Soto Zen tradition and this is reflected in the emphasis on sitting meditation as the basic practice. It has a small library and encourages contacts with other Buddhist organisations. Meetings are at the Secretary's house at 8.00pm on Mondays.

Nottingham Buddhist Group

Nottingham
Tel: 021-449-5279

A group associated with the Friends of the Western Buddhist Order devoted to the practice of meditation and Buddhism. Contact through the Birmingham Buddhist Centre.

Nottingham Mahayana Buddhist Centre (Akshobya Centre)

3 Fern Avenue
Carrington
Nottingham NG5 1BG
Tel: 0602-625158
Contact: Eldi De Persis

A subsidiary branch of the larger centre "Madhyamaka". The group has a very mixed attendance, from people that are slightly interested in Tibetan Buddhism to people who have been practising for many years. It follows the teachings of Mahayana Buddhism under the spiritual direction of Geshe Kelsang Gyatso Rinpoche, a highly acclaimed Tibetan meditation master and teacher. It meets for two hours a week during which a western Tibetan monk gives teachings and guided meditation, discussion is held and tea and biscuits are served.

Blythe Bridge Mahayana Buddhist Centre

The Old Nick
Seven Chimneys
Warslow
Derbyshire SK17 0JR
Tel: 0298-84635 (evenings)
Contact: Ros Prince
Office: Co-ordinator

A branch of the Tara Centre in the New Kadampa tradition of Buddhism. The centre is a place for the study of the pure Buddhist view, meditation and action, and offers weekly teachings and meditation classes together with the occasional one day and weekend course. Longer courses and retreats are also run from time to time. Contact the above address or phone for the latest brochure of events.

ENGLISH WEST MIDLANDS

Baba Saheb Ambedkar Buddhist Association

13 Booth Street
Handsworth
Birmingham B21 0NG
Tel: 021-523-8254
Tel: 021-358-5766 (home)
Contact: Mr Devinder Kumar Chander
Office: General Secretary

A place of worship which is open for anyone to come for meditation as a quick relief for peace of mind and self-confidence. The monk is very experienced and can give advice on personal development to men and women from all walks of life without obligation. Activities include worship and community welfare.

Birmingham Buddhist Centre

135 Salisbury Road
Moseley
Birmingham B13 8LA
Tel: 021-449-5279
Contact: Secretary

A centre of Friends of the Western Buddhist Order which is a worldwide movement with activities in over seventeen countries. The aim is to make Buddhism available in a way which is appropriate for the West, drawing on all the major Buddhist traditions. Activities include the practice and teaching of Buddhism and meditation, Buddhist communities and "right livelihood" businesses, school visits and talks.

Birmingham Buddhist Vihara

47 Carlyle Road
Edgbaston
Birmingham B16 9BH
Tel: 021-454-6591
Contact: Dr Rewata Dhamma
Office: Spiritual Director

A place of worship and an independent charitable trust established to provide facilities for local people to study Buddhism and Buddhist meditation, devotional practice, cultural celebration and for spiritual advice and help.

Birmingham Karma Ling Tibetan Buddhist Centre

41 Carlyle Road
Edgbaston
Birmingham B16 9BH
Tel: 021-454-2782
Contact: Simon Romer
Office: Secretary

A place of worship. The centre has a shrine room in the Tibetan tradition and houses a small community of Sangha and lay people. Courses are organised on occasion and limited accomodation can be provided. The centre practices the Karma Kagyu Tibetan tradition.

Dr Ambedkar Buddhist Society

Buddha Vihara
5 Hampton Road
Aston
Birmingham B6 6AN
Contact: F C Chauhan
Office: General Secretary

There are books on Buddhist festivals and the birth anniversary of Dr B R Ambedkar.

Indian Buddhist Society UK

Nanda House
9 Carlisle Road
Edgbaston
Birmingham B16 9BH
Tel: 021-455-7285
Contact: Hind Rattan Sansari Lal
Office: Secretary

The society is mainly devoted to the study of Buddhism and practice of meditation. It welcomes any Buddhist or non-Buddhist to meetings without discrimination.

Samantabhadra Buddhist Centre

The Friends Meeting House
930 Bristol Road
Selly Oak
Birmingham
Tel: 021-355-6456 (home)
Contact: Chris Baker

Office: Co-ordinator

The centre was founded in February 1992 by the Tara Centre, a residential Buddhist College in Buxton, Derbyshire. It is a member of the New Kadampa tradition under the spiritual guidance of Venerable Geshe Kelsang Gyatso. The centre meets every Tuesday night at 7.30pm for teachings, meditation and discussion with an experienced teacher. The centre can also be contacted through Steve Palmer, Tel: 021-523-8309 (home).

Soto Zen Zazen Group
Buddhist Vihara
13 Booth Street
Handsworth
Birmingham
Tel: 021-429-4080
Contact: Venerable Kassapa

Stourbridge Zen Meditation Group
Birmingham
Tel: 0384-373301
Contact: David Richards
Affiliated to Throssel Hole Priory (Northumberland, Hexham), the group meets weekly. Under the guidance of the Priory (a Buddhist training monastery and retreat centre) the group follows the Soto Zen tradition. It is hoped that, in the future, lectures will be given by monks from the Priory and retreats will be arranged. Full meditation instruction is available and everyone is welcome.

Coventry Mahayana Buddhist Centre
70 Torrington Avenue
Tile Hill
Coventry CV4 9AR
Tel: 0203-442714
Contact: Paul and Sally Clement
A branch of the Tara Centre in the New Kadampa tradition of Buddhism. The centre is a place for the study of the pure Buddhist view, meditation and action, and offers weekly teachings and meditation classes together with the occasional one day and weekend course. Longer courses and retreats are also run from time to time. Contact the above address or phone for the latest brochure of events.

Shrewsbury Mahayana Buddhist Centre
Shrewsbury
Shropshire
Tel: 0270-664050
Contact: Richard Scotford
Office: Co-ordinator
A branch of the Amitayus Centre (173 Ruskin Road,

Crewe, Cheshire, CW2 7JX) in the New Kadampa tradition of Buddhism. The centre is a place for the study of the pure Buddhist view, meditation and action, and offers weekly teachings and meditation classes together with the occasional one day and weekend course. Longer courses and retreats are also run from time to time. Contact the above address or phone for the latest brochure of events.

Sakya Ling Buddhist Centre
146 Neville Road
Shirley
Solihull
West Midlands B90 2QX
Tel: 021-745-2550
Contact: Secretary
A Sakya Buddhist meeting place. One of a number of Buddhist groups and centres in the UK guided by Ngakpa Jampa Thaye and known as the Deehen community. The centre enables people to learn Buddhist mediation and practice to Buddha's teachings. Pujas are practiced on special days.

Stafford Buddhist Society
47 Burton Manor Road
Stafford ST17 9QQ
Tel: 0785-41450
Contact: Peter Morrell
A membership group which no longer meets, but has a large library of Buddhist literature and videos which are available for use. The group responds to enquiries and provides a Buddhist chaplaincy to Drake Hall Prison, near Eccleshall in Staffordshire.

North Staffordshire Zazen Group
21 Longton Road
Trentham
Stoke-on-Trent ST4 8ND
Tel: 0782-657851
Contact: John Forse
The group follows the Soto Zen tradition. It aims to enable people within the area or vicinity to practice Soto Zen Meditation together, at group meetings. Activities include Serene Reflection meditation.

Telford Buddhist Group
c/o Hadley Information Office
21 Gladstone House
Hadley
Telford
Shropshire TF1 4NF
Tel: 0952-222334
Tel: 0952-240283 (home)
Contact: Mr D D Ahir

Office: Community Development Worker
There is only a small Buddhist community in Telford and their main place of worship is the Buddha Vihara in Upper Zoar Street, Pennfields, Wolverhampton, Tel: 0902-715094.

Forest Hermitage (Wat Pah Santidhamma)

Lower Fulbrook
Near Sherbourne
Warwick CV35 8AS
Tel: 0926-624385
Fax: 0926-624385
Contact: Abbot
A Buddhist monastery following closely the practices and traditions of the forest wats of North East Thailand.

Taraloka Buddhist Retreat Centre for Women

Taraloka
Cornhill Farm
Bettisfield
Nr Whitchurch
Shropshire SY13 2LD
Tel: 094-875-646
Contact: Secretary
A Friends of the Western Buddhist Order retreat centre. The community consists of Buddhist women involved with the FWBO. Retreats are run especially for women of any range of experience. It was established in 1985 and caters for women from all over the world who want to find out more about Buddhism and meditation.

Buddha Vihara

Upper Zoar Street
Pennfields
Wolverhampton WV3 0JH
Tel: 0902-341186
Contact: Mr Mohan Lal Mehmi
Office: Secretary
A purpose-built Theravada and Ambedkarite Vihara, opened in 1991, and with residence for five monks. A community hall is also planned in memory of Dr Ambedkar, the distinguished modern leader of a Buddhist revival movement in India. Meditation is practiced and classes are held to learn about meditation and Buddha dharma. There are women's classes for Asian women with learning difficulties and youth activities are held throughout the holidays. Buddhist monks are available for advice and personal discussion with the general public.

Ti Sarana Centre

81 Jeffcock Road
Pennfield
Wolverhampton WV3 7AG
Tel: 0902-343860

Wolverhampton Centre for Mahayana Buddhism

60 Elmdon Road
Oxley
Wolverhampton WV10 6XJ
Tel: 0902-788741 (home)
Contact: William Giddings
Office: Organiser
A centre which aims to provide further information regarding the Kagyu school of Buddhism and its main UK activities. Buddhism is quite vast in the sense of its diversity. Many newcomers are attracted but often need clarification, especially if their encounter is via a difficult translation of highly specialised literature. The centre offers a contact point through which further contacts can be made.

Wolverhampton Mahayana Buddhist Centre

Wolverhampton
West Midlands
Tel: 0298-72026
Fax: 0298-27620
Contact: Ani Kelsang Gama
A branch of the Tara Centre (36 St Johns Road, Buxton, Derbyshire, SK17 6XG) in the New Kadampa tradition of Buddhism. The centre is a place for the study of the pure Buddhist view, meditation and action, and offers weekly teachings and meditation classes together with the occasional one day and weekend course. Longer courses and retreats are also run from time to time. Contact the above address or phone for the latest brochure of events.

EAST ANGLIA

Wangford Zen Group

34 Elm Farm Cottages
Wangford
Beccles
Suffolk NR34 8BA
Tel: 050-278-437 (home)
Contact: Dick Feakins
A membership group to encourage the practice of Buddhism and promote awareness of its principles under the spiritual direction of Nen Myohyo-ni, Zen centre. Activities include meditation and discussion.

Water Hall Retreat Centre

Water Hall Retreat Centre
Great Ashfield
Bury St Edmonds
Suffolk IP31 3HP
Tel: 0359-42130
Contact: Secretary
A centre of the Friends of the Western Buddhist Order. Set in the countryside within easy reach from London, Water Hall is associated with the London Buddhist Centre and is used by them to complement their programme. The centre is also available as a study and conference centre. It is a venue for a range of retreats - from Yoga and massage to performing arts retreats.

Ashvagosha Centre

Cambridge Mahayana Buddhist Centre
Cambridge
Tel: 0223-242313
Contact: Carl Lewis
Office: Co-ordinator
A branch of the Manjushri Centre in the New Kadampa tradition of Buddhism. The centre is a place for the study of the pure Buddhist view, meditation and action, and offers weekly teachings and meditation classes together with the occasional one day and weekend course. Longer courses and retreats are also run from time to time. Contact the above address or phone for the latest brochure of events.

Cambridge Buddhist Society

32 Greens Road
Cambridge CB4 5EF
Tel: 0223-66079
Contact: Simon Baugh
The society is an umbrella organisation which holds public meetings with speakers from a wide range of Buddhist traditions. It provides information on local activities such as meditation classes and about groups in Cambridge following particular traditions. It meets on the last Friday of every month at 7.15pm at the Friends Meeting House, Jesus Lane, Cambridge (except August and December).

Cambridge Samatha Association

322 Mill Road
Cambridge CB1 3NN
Tel: 0223-240293
Contact: Alan Hines
The Association aims to follow the tradition of Samatha-vipassana meditation, mainly anapanasati (mindfulness of breathing) in the Theravadin tradition. Activities include beginners' meditation courses, and meditation and study groups for the more experienced. Practice days and weekends are also arranged, together with mindful working and meditation retreats at National Samatha Centre in Wales.

Cambridge University Buddhism and Meditation Society

Cambridge Buddhist Centre
25 Newmarket Road
Cambridge CB5 8EG
Tel: 0223-460252
Contact: Dharmachari Ratnaprabha
University society associated with the Friends of the Western Buddhist Order meeting in college rooms during term-time. It caters for anyone wishing to learn basic meditation practices and also for people wishing to investigate non-sectarian Buddhism, discuss its personal relevance to them and how to practice it. Activities include meditation classes, retreats and discussion groups and lectures on Buddhism. Meetings at 4 Glisson Road, Cambridge.

Cambridge University Buddhist Society

c/o The Oriental Studies Faculty
The University
Cambridge
Tel: 0223-840196
Contact: Ms Carmen Blacker
Office: Treasurer
The group is multi-traditional.

Friends of the Western Buddhist Order Cambridge Buddhist Centre

25 Newmarket Road
Cambridge CB5 8EG
Tel: 0223-460252
Contact: Dharmachari Amaraketu
Office: Centre director
A centre of the Friends of the Western Buddhist Order where meditation and Buddhism are taught and practiced based on the "Western" translation of Buddhism by the English monk and teacher Sangharakshita who founded the Friends of the Western Buddhist Order and the Western Buddhist Order in 1967. The Centre is open to all.

Nezang Buddhist Meditation Group

5 Sedley Taylor Road
Cambridge CB2 2PW
Tel: 0223-240090 (home)
Contact: Lama Ato Rinpoche
Office: Buddhist Teacher
A meditation group established by Lama Ato

Rinpoche in 1986 at the request of his students. Meetings are open to all and there is no formal membership. There is no charge for admission but donations are welcome. Meetings are held monthly (except in August and September) on a Saturday afternoon and usually comprise of a Dharma talk, Buddhist chanting and a period of meditation.

Kongoryuji Temple
London Road
East Dereham
Norfolk NR19 1AJ
Tel: 0362-693962 (home)
Fax: 0362-693962 (home)
Contact: Ms Bell
Office: Secretary
The Temple and its associated buildings has meditation, retreats and rituals for the practice of Chinese/Japanese esoteric Buddhism and is a representative member of the European Union of Buddhists. Regular activities consist of study, research and retreats, details of which can be obtained. The Temple produces its own secular and religious literature upon a wide range of relevant oriental arts and organises seminars here and in Eastern Europe. There is an extensive research library of texts in English, Sanskrit, Chinese and Japanese (including a section on Gnostic Christianity) and many other languages.

Lincoln Mahayana Buddhist Centre
Tudor Rose
Walkreith
Nr Gainsborough
Lincolnshire DN21 3DF
Tel: 0427-611535
Contact: Fred Cronshaw
Office: Co-ordinator
A branch of the Gyaltsabje Centre in the New Kadampa tradition of Buddhism. The centre is a place for the study of the pure Buddhist view, meditation and action, and offers weekly teachings and meditation classes together with the occasional one day and weekend course. Longer courses and retreats are also run from time to time. Contact the above address or phone for the latest brochure of events.

Diss Buddhist Group
13 Heather Way
Great Moulton
Norfolk NR15 2HP
Tel: 0379-77669
Contact: Sthirabuddhi
Office: Secretary

A membership group which is part of the international Friends of the Western Buddhist Order and tries to practice the Buddhist principles of individual spiritual development. Activities include meditation and teaching of Buddhism.

Ipswich Buddhist Group
Ipswich
Suffolk
Tel: 0473-211516
Contact: Saddharaja
A group of the Friends of the Western Buddhist Order which has a full time centre and community and runs regular courses and classes including an introductory meditation class on Thursday nights at 7.30pm

Norwich Buddhist Centre
41a All Saints Green
Norwich NR1 3LY
Tel: 0603-627034
Contact: Secretary
A place of worship and education run by members of the Western Buddhist Order. As well as running classes and courses, the centre acts as a focus for a broader Buddhist community that includes residential communities for men and women and two businesses. Activities include meditation classes, courses in Buddhism for newcomers and study groups. Pujas and festival activities are organised for practising Buddhists, regular retreats are run and there is a bookshop and tape library.

Norwich Mahayana Buddhist Centre
36 Thorpe Park
Glendinning Road
Norwich NR1 11YS
Tel: 0603-622198
Contact: Patrick Dye
Office: Co-ordinator
A centre in the New Kadampa Tradition

Norwich Serene Reflection Meditation Group
194 Earlham Road
Norwich NR2 3RW
Tel: 0603-53160 (home)
Contact: Sally Robertshaw
A membership group which is affiliated to Throssel Hole Priory and follows the Serene Reflection Meditation tradition (Soto Zen). This tradition stems from Japan, where it was introduced from China by Great Master Dogen in the thirteenth century. Its emphasis, firmly within the tradition of Mahayana Buddhism, is upon meditation, keeping the moral

precepts, and the development of compassion for oneself and all beings. There are weekly group meetings which include meditation and scripture recitation. The group welcomes newcomers and basic instruction in Serene Reflection Meditation is available.

Padmaloka Buddhist Retreat Centre for Men

"Padmaloka"
Lesingham House
Surlingham
Norwich NR14 7AL
Tel: 050-88-8112
Contact: Retreat Organiser
A retreat centre for men only which forms part of the Friends of the Western Buddhist order (FWBO). It is not open for casual visits and bookings are essential. Facilities are available for Buddhist study, worship and meditation.

Relyukai

196 Unthank Road
Norwich NR2 2AH
Tel: 0603-501151 (home)
Relyukai was founded in 1924 in Japan by Kakutaro Kubo (1892-1944). The international headquarters is in Tokyo. The British group is led by Tsugunari Kubo.

Tashi Ling Tibetan Buddhist Group

Pear Tree Cottages
Poringland Road
Stoke Holy Cross
Norwich NR14 8NW
Tel: 0603-616872 (home)
Contact: c/o Campbell Purton
Office: Chairperson
Tashi Ling is a Tibetan Buddist group under the guidance of Lama Ato Rinpoche. It is non secular in its approach and welcomes all who are interested in Buddhism. The regular meetings include a short puja, silent meditation and the opportunity for discussion and study of Buddhist texts.

University of East Anglia Buddhist Society

c/o Students Union
University of East Anglia
Norwich NR4 7TJ
Contact: The Secretary
A membership group founded by students associated with the Friends of the Western Buddhist Order. The society aims to introduce students and others to the benefits of meditation and Buddhism as effective

means of self-transformation, rather than as objects of academic study alone. It engages in learning about and practising Buddhism.

Cromer Buddhist Group

Hacienda
Tower Lane
Sidestrand
Norfolk
Tel: 026-378-359
Contact: Sonny Mann
A small meditation and study group which is part of the Friends of the Western Buddhist Order in Norwich and a place of worship to the Buddha where worship is defined as worthiness, honour or respect which is due. The group meets for meditation and study of the Dharma and believes in encouraging people to open up and be honest with each other and to stop being judgemental in dealing with others.

SOUTH EAST ENGLAND (NORTH)

Essex Buddhist Society

c/o 134 Long Riding
Basildon
Essex
Tel: 0268-26346 (home)

Pure Land Buddhist Fellowship

Hawthorn
Hillcrest Avenue
Basildon
Essex SS16 6EQ
Tel: 0268-419095 (home)
Contact: Nick Cook
The fellowship is a network of friends following the Japanese Pure Land tradition. It aims to help those cut off from Buddhist centres and anyone else interested in the Pure Land Path. It does this by keeping in touch by telephone and letter, by providing information and encouragement, by bi-monthly meetings and festival celebrations in and around London.

Bedfordshire Buddhist Society

3 Pear Tree View
Elstow
Bedford MK42 9YN
Tel: 0234-357381
Contact: Tony Cook
Office: Chairperson
A membership group which provides, in the Bedfordshire area, an opportunity to study and practice Buddhism. Meetings are open to all faiths (or those with no faith) who might be interested in finding

out more about Buddhism. There is no membership fee and the society is run by voluntary donation. Meditation instruction is available. Monthly meetings are held for teaching, discussion and meditation. A weekly meditation group meets.

Buckingham Zen Group

6 Chandos Road
Buckingham MK18 1AH
Tel: 0280-813962 (home)
Contact: Mr H MacCarthy
The group's study and practice is within the Soto Zen tradition and it is affiliated to the Throssle Hole Priory. Activities include weekly meditation meetings with sitting and walking meditation; an annual retreat led by a priest from the Priory; occasional visits to Buddhist meetings and events; and meditation instruction.

Colchester Buddhist Group

c/o Octagon Architects and Designers
143 Hythe Hill
Colchester
Essex C01 2NF
Tel: 0206-798889 (work)
Contact: Dharmachari Harshaprabha
Office: Chairman
A meditation and Buddhism teaching centre which is a part of the the Friends of the Western Buddhist Order (FWBO). Meditation and Buddhism are taught and practised through classes, courses and festivals which are open to all. Meetings are held weekly at the Trinity Centre, 21 Trinity Street, Colchester. Contact by correspondence can be made through Kelvin Youngs, 2 Ships Cottages, Wheatsheaf Lane, Colchester.

Harlow Buddhist Group

192 The Hornbeans
Harlow
Essex CM20 1PL
Tel: 0279-427768
Contact: Dharmachari Shantinayaka
Office: Secretary
A group of the Friends of the Western Buddhist Order. Classes are held every Tuesday evening at the Latton Bush Centre in Harlow. Members of the Western Buddhist Order teach meditation and offer study and discussion of the dharma.

Harlow Buddhist Society

Dana House
385 Longbanks
Harlow

Essex CM18 7PF
Tel: 0297-434768 (home, pm only)
Contact: Dennis Wood
Office: Secretary
The Society is affiliated to Chithurst Monastery and Amaravati. It is taught by Pamutto. The society has been in existence for twenty-five years and broadly follows the Theravada tradition. It has regular visits from the monks and nuns of the Amaravati Buddhist Centre. It offers a self-help therapy group for those who suffer with stress and anxiety. Non-religious meditation classes and beginners' meditation classes are also offered.

Dr Ambedkar Mission Society Bedford

19 Henderson Way
Kempston
Bedfordshire
Tel: 0234-854336 (home)
Contact: Mr Arun Kumar
Office: General Secretary
A membership group which mainly provides welfare services.

Leigh Buddhist Group

c/o Twycross Villa
5 North Street
Leigh-on-Sea
Essex
Contact: Ms. Barbara Walters
The group is a branch of the South East Essex Buddhist Group and is a Theravadin Group in close connection with the monks and nuns at Amaravati Buddhist Centre. Buddhists of all traditions are welcome to the meetings. Activities include sitting meetings followed by a Buddhist reading or taped lecture of Venerable Ajahn Sumedho, with discussions and tea, every Friday at 7.45pm.

South East Essex Buddhist Group

21 Woodlands Park
Leigh-on-Sea
Essex SS9 3TX
Tel: 0702-559241
Contact: Rob Howell

Institute of Oriental Philosophy

Taplow Court
Taplow
Maidenhead
Berkshire SL6 0ER
Tel: 0628-776719
Fax: 0628-773055
Contact: James Cresswell

Office: Manager

A research and study centre associated with SGI-UK, a lay Buddhist organisation. The centre is based around a library (open to scholars). Lectures are held regularly, delivered by Professors of philosophy and religion. Research is undertaken into various aspects of religion, including its relationship to the environment, science and society.

Nipponzan Myohoji

Peace Pagoda
Willen
Milton Keynes
Buckinghamshire MK15 0BA
Tel: 0908-663-652
Contact: Handa Shonin
Office: Senior Monk

A monastery and outdoor shrine. Nipponzan Myohoji is the name of a Buddhist order founded by the most Venerable Nichidatsu Fujii (1885-1985). It is totally dedicated to prayer and action for world peace by beating a hand-drum and chanting "na-mu myo ho ren ge kyo"; by building Peace Pagodas (the first started after the Hiroshima massacre); and by organising gatherings of people of every political, religious and cultural backgrounds. The Peace Pagoda is an outdoor shrine dedicated to world peace. Activities include daily prayer for peace, walking peacemarches and organising inter-faith peace vigils.

Dhamma School

Trinity College
Oxford 0X1 3BH
Tel: 0865-279900
Fax: 0865-279911
Contact: Dr Peter Carey

Founded in 1992 as a registered UK Charity, The Dhamma School works for the development of a Buddhist-based education in the UK and is in the prcess of establishing an infant/primary school in East Sussex, which will be open to the children of Buddhist and non-Buddhist families.

Longchen Foundation

30 Beechey Avenue
Old Marston
Oxford OX3 0JU
Tel: 0865-725569 (home)
Contact: Dr Shenpen Hookham
Office: Assistant Director

The foundation follows the Nyingma Kagyu tradition of Tibetan Buddhism, principally following the teaching and inspiration of His Holiness Dilgo Khyentse Rinpoche, Vidyadhara Chogyam Trungpa

Rinpoche and Khentso Tsultrim Gyamtso Rinpoche. The Director of the Foundation is Rigdzin Shipko, a British pupil of those teachers and himself a recognised teacher of the tradition. The Foundation runs retreats and training in all aspects of the Buddhist path.

Oxford Friends of the Western Buddhist Order

186 Crowley Road
Oxford OX4 1UE
Tel: 0865-728794
Fax: 0865-792941
Contact: Amritavajra
Office: Chairperson

A spiritual community which is part of the Friends of the Western Buddhist Order network. Group members attempt to live their lives in a Western context taking the essential principles of Buddhism as a guide. They do not follow any particular school of Buddhism but instead adopt a non-sectarian approach to Budhhism. At all centres meditation is taught as well as more general introductions to the theory and practice of Buddhism.

Oxford Mahayana Buddhist Centre

Oxford
Tel: 0225-840500
Contact: June Judge

A branch of the Manjushri Centre in the New Kadampa tradition of Buddhism. The centre is a place for the study of the pure Buddhist view, meditation and action, and offers weekly teachings and meditation classes together with the occasional one day and weekend course. Longer courses and retreats are also run from time to time. Contact the above address or phone for the latest brochure of events. Meetings at West Oxford Community Centre, Binsey Lane, Oxford (please ring to confirm).

Oxford Theravadin Group

Trinity College
Oxford OX1 3BH
Tel: 0865-57876 (home)
Fax: 0865-279911
Contact: Dr Peter Carey

A meditation group with activities including meditation meetings and the practice and study of Buddhist scriptures. Meetings are held twice weekly in full term, with morning and evening Pujas.

Oxford University Buddhist Society

8 Earl Street
Oxford OX2 9JA

Tel: 0865-726312
Contact: Jane George
The society is multi-traditional.

Oxford Zen Buddhism
95 Fairacres
Oxford
Tel: 0865-61234
Tel: 0865-721227 (home)
Contact: Clive Sherlock
The group follows the Zen tradition.

Samatha Association
8 Earl Street
Oxford OX2 9JA
Tel: 0865-726312
Contact: Jane George
The association offers practical instruction in a form of Samatha - vipassana (calm-concentration and insight) meditation based on mindfulness of breathing and derived from the Thai tradition.

Theravdin Buddhist Group
197a Cumnor Hill
Oxford
Tel: 0865-863147
Contact: Bernard Pottle

Berkshire Buddhist Group
Tilehurst
Reading
Berkshire
Tel: 0734-680023 (home)
Contact: Andy Taylor
An informal group whose spiritual head is Ajahn Sumedho. Monks and nuns from Chithurst and Amaravati regularly visit. Activities include talks and discussion on Buddhism and daily life practice and weekly meetings in Reading on Thursdays, which begin with puja and meditation. Special nights are set aside for beginners and newcomers.

Reading Buddhist Priory
Reading
Berkshire
Tel: 0734-860750
Contact: The Prior
A sub-priory of Throssel Hole priory in Northumberland. The existence of the priory in an urban setting and the daily life of the priest in residence provides an example and a source of inspiration for lay Buddhists who live and work in a similar setting. People may visit and join in meditation periods,

ceremonies and classes at any time. Its main activities are the teaching and practice of the Serene Reflection Meditation tradition.

Meditation and Retreat Centre
12 Meadow Close
Ruislip
Middlesex HA4 8AP
Tel: 0895-635738
Contact: Jasmine Koller
A meditation centre where people interested in learning and sharing meditation practice can meet, discuss and participate in a living practice. It is mainly for followers of the Buddhist path, but other schools of thought are welcome. Evening sessions on a Monday are for "seasoned" practitioners and Thursdays for beginners. There may be as few as three people or as many as twenty. There is no charge.

Marpa House
Rectory Lane
Ashdon
Saffron Walden
Essex CB10 2HN
Tel: 0799584-415
Contact: Secretary
The spiritual director, the Venerable Lama Chime Rinpoche established the house in 1973 with its residential and retreat facilities. The centre encourages a deeper understanding of the nature of the mind, developing unshakeable confidence through the study and practice of the Mahamudra and Dzogchen traditions of Tibet and conducting daily pujas and meditation. Guest or day visitors are always welcome. For bookings, information and course details, contact the Secretary.

Dr Ambedkar Buddhist Association
12 Featherstone Road
Southall
Middlesex
Tel: 081-571-5412
Contact: Mr H L Virdee
Office: General Secretary
A Theravada Buddhist lay association dedicated to the practical application of Dr Ambedkar's teachings with the ultimate aim of the attainment of Nirvana and also the uplift of Dalits or Untouchables, the abolition of the caste system as well as of dowries. The material wellbeing of persons is considered an essential prerequisite to Nirvana.

Samatha Association

34 Royal Road
Teddington
Middlesex TW11 0SB
Tel: 081-977-2476
Contact: Paul Beck
This school derives from a Thai tradition and develops calm, concentration and insight. Classes are held in mindfulness of breathing meditation and there are meetings in various London locations.

Shantideva Centre (Windsor)

4 The Drive
Langley
Windsor
Berkshire SL3 7DB
Tel: 0753-586703
Contact: Diedre Lofters
Office: Co-ordinator
A branch of the Madhayamaka Centre in the New Kadampa tradition of Buddhism. The centre is a place for the study of the pure Buddhist view, meditation and action, and offers weekly teachings and meditation classes together with the occasional one day and weekend course. Longer courses and retreats are also run from time to time. Contact the above address or phone for the latest brochure of events.

Surrey Buddhist Centre Meditation Group

Wold Cottage
Goose Lane
Mayford
Woking
Surrey GU22 0NW
Tel: 0483-727170
Tel: 0483-768759 (home)
Contact: Chris Hidred
The group follows no specific tradition and anyone with an interest in Buddhism or meditation is welcome to attend. There are meetings on Wednesdays for meditation and reflection on the Buddhist way of generosity, kindness, virtue and serenity. Visits are made by monks and nuns from the Zen and Theravada tradition for guidance and instruction.

Nichiren Shoshu Buddhist Group

14 Queens Avenue
Woodford Green
Essex IG8 0JE
Tel: 081-504-6372
Contact: c/o Ms P De Witt

LONDON (E POSTCODES)

Amrita Dzong

Unit 21F
Perseverance Works
38 Kingsland Road
London E2
Contact: David F Mayor
Office: Acting Secretary
The address above is the place of worship. The Acting Secretary can be contacted at 88 Handside Lane, Welwyn Garden City, Hertfordshire, AL8 6SJ.

London Buddhist Centre

51 Roman Road
Bethnal Green
London E2 0HU
Tel: 081-981-1225
Contact: The Secretary
Office: Secretary
Teaching and meditation centre. At the centre meditation is taught to anyone who wishes to learn. There are also courses in meditation as well as Buddhism. For those familiar with the practices and interested in Buddhism there are practice evenings, retreats and festivals.

Buddhist Cultural Institute

88 Ruskin Avenue
East Ham
London E12 6PW
Tel: 081-472-4701

Ambedkar International Mission

Buddha Vihara
84 Dacre Road
Plaistow
London E13 0PR
Tel: 081-470-1879
Contact: Saptal Muman
Office: General Secretary
The vihara is run by an Indian Buddhist group in the Theravada tradition. It is led by Venerable Dr Siri Sumana, a Sri Lankan Buddhist monk.

Buddha Vihara

84 Dacre Road
Plaistow
London E13 0PR
Contact: Secretary
The Vihara is in the Theravada tradition and is led by Venerable Nagasena Thera.

LONDON (N POSTCODES)

Jamyang Meditation Centre
10 Finsbury Park Road
London N4 2JZ
Tel: 071-359-1394
Fax: 071-405-3814
A place of worship. Jamyang exists to enable people to benefit from Buddha's teaching in their daily lives through Buddhist meditation practices, teachings and initiations from the Gelug tradition of Tibetan Buddhism. Principally, this involves subduing one's own mind, not harming others, developing compassion and spiritual growth through meditation and study. There are meditation classes and teachings at all levels and a comprehensively stocked bookshop. Lamas visit the centre.

Hampstead Buddhist Group
278 Holly Lodge Mansions
Oakeshott Avenue
Highgate
London N6 6EB
Tel: 081-348-0537
Office: Secretary
A Theravadan Buddhist group associated with the Forest Sangha at Chithurst and Amaravati Monastaries, the spiritual head of which is Venerable Ajahn Sumedho. Meetings are held every Wednesday at 7.15pm for 7.30pm in the Constable Room at Burgh House, New End Square, London NW3.

North London Buddhist Centre
St Mark's Studios
Chillingworth Road
London N7 8QJ
Tel: 071-700-3075
Contact: Secretary
A meditation and Buddhism teaching centre which is part of the Friends of the Western Buddhist Order. Meditation and Buddhism are taught and practised through classes, courses and festivals which are open to all.

LONDON (NW POSTCODES)

Dzogchen Community
29 Jeffrey's Street
Camden Town
London NW1
Tel: 071-485-3108 (home)
The community follows the Tibetan Buddhist tradition under the spiritual guidance of Nambkhai Norbu Rinpoche. Activities include meetings on Sundays and Tuesdays at various locations for meditation and tantra yoga; publishing; mail order book supply; yantra yoga workshops; and translation of Tibetan works.

London Zen Society
10 Belmont Street
London NW1 8HH
Tel: 071-485-9576
Contact: Junando
Office: Resident Monk

London Soto Zen Group
23 Westbere Road
London NW2 3SP
Tel: 071-794-3109 (home)
Contact: Mr Duncan Sellers
The Soto Zen tradition is followed under the direction of the Throssel Hole Priory in Northumberland. Activities include weekly meditations on Tuesdays at 7.30pm, which includes periods of sitting (Zazen) and walking (Kinhin) meditation; monthly day-long meetings with Zazen, scriptures, lectures and working meditation.

Kongoruji London
58 Mansfield Road
London NW3
Contact: Shifu T Dukes
Kongoruji follows the Chinese Singon tradition and is led in London by Shifu T Dukes and Acarya Ryushu.

London Dhamma Group
32 King Henry's Road
London NW3
Tel: 071-586-5416 (home)
The group follows the Theravada tradition.

Vajradhatu Dharma Study Group
1 Compayne Gardens
London NW6
Tel: 081-968-3813

Britain Burma Buddhist Trust
1 Old Church Lane
London NW9 8TG
Tel: 081-200-6898
Contact: Resident Monks
Followers of the Theravada Buddhist tradition with meditation instruction in the Mahasi Sayadaw Tradition, under the spiritual direction of Venerable Dr Rewata Dhamma. Activities include daily puja and meditation from 8.00am-9.00am; 5.30am-6.00am;

children's Dhamma classes on Saturdays at 9.00am. Personal instruction in meditation and retreats can be arranged at any mutually convenient time.

Sri Saddhatissa International Buddhist Centre
311 Kingsbury Road
London NW9 9PE
Tel: 081-204-3301
Fax: 081-206-1179
Contact: Venerable Galayaye Piyadassi
Office: Head of Centre
A place of worship and meditation, with affiliated organisations, for the promotion of educational and cultural activities. It is administered by Buddhist monks and a committee of lay members of the International Buddhist Association. It perceives Buddhism as primarily concerned with man and the human situation. Through the teachings of the Buddha, the centre aims to show the individual how to liberate himself from his existential predicament through a practical way of life based on principles of moral conduct, and the cultivation of the mind and wisdom through meditation practices.

Heruka Buddhist Centre
13 Woodstock Road
Golders Green
London NW11 8ES
Tel: 081-455-7563
Fax: 081-905-5280
Contact: Hugh Clift
Office: Administrative Director
Spiritual group. By participating in the programmes taught at the centre one can gradually overcome negativities such as anger, jealousy and cultivate in their place positive qualities such as wisdom, patience and loving kindness. In this way more meaningful and constructive lives can be led bringing increased peace and happiness to oneself and others. The centre offers structured study and meditation programmes, specially designed to fulfil the wishes of those who would like to study Buddhism systematically and thereby deepen their experience of the essential practices.

LONDON (SE POSTCODES)

Linh-Son Buddhist Association in the UK
89 Bromley Road
Catford
London SE6 2UF
Tel: 081-461-1887
Contact: Secretary

This Vietnamese Buddhist Temple is under the guidance of the Venerable Thich Huyen Vi and, in England, of the Venerable Thich Tri Canh (resident). It serves the Chinese as well as the Vietnamese community. Activities include classes at the communal centre and youth activities for Chinese and Vietnamese young people. Teaching is at present given in Vietnamese.

Lewisham Nichiren Shoshu Buddhists
The Cedars
Belmont Hill
London SE13

Padma Cho Ling
68 Blenheim Grove
Peckham
London SE15 4QL
Tel: 071-732-0183
Contact: Mr Stephen Hodge
Non-residential teaching centre, with visitors welcome by appointment. It follows a broad Mahayana tradition (Tibetan, Sanskrit, Chinese and Japanese). It aims to teach the main scriptural languages of Mahayana Buddhism (Tibetan, Sanskrit, Chinese and Japanese) and to study and translate important texts. It works by personal tuition courses and commissioning of translations.

Viet Nam Buddhists
52 Bellenden Road
Peckham
London SE15 5BB
Tel: 071-701-2930 (home)
Contact: Chua Linh Son
Vietnamese Buddhism came to Britain with Vietnamese immigrants and refugees following the Vietnam War and is distinctive in its merger of Theravada and Zen traditions.

Kongo Raiden Zen Order
c/o 16 Moreton House
Otto Street
London SE17
The order follows the Chinese Zen tradition.

Mushindokai
c/o 16 Moreton House
Otto Street
London SE17
Mushindokai follows the Zen tradition.

LONDON (SW POSTCODES)

Rissho Kosei-Kai

Flat 6
83 Sudbourne Road
Brixton
London SW2 5AF
Tel: 071-326-1363 (home)
Contact: Ms Jill Sullivan
Affiliated to the Japanese school. Rissho Kosei-Kai stands for the Society for the Establishment of Righteousness and Friendly Intercourse. It is a Nichiren group. It holds meetings and other activities including Hoza.

Dharmadhatu

27 Belmont Close
London SW4
Tel: 071-720-3207
Contact: Susan Rhodes
Office: Co-ordinator
A study and meditation centre founded by students of Chogyam Trungpa Rinpoche (author of many books). It is part of a larger organisation - Vajradhatu - which has centres in Europe, North America and Canada. Meditation is in the Karma Kagyu style. The centre holds regular short courses on different aspects of Buddhism and meditation, regular meditation sessions with trained instructors available on Monday (7.30-9.30pm), Wednesday (7.00pm-9.30pm) and Sunday (10.30am-1.30pm). There is also Shambhala training - a series of weekends teaching meditation in a non-secular setting.

South London Buddhist Centre

8 Trouville Road
Clapham
London SW4 8QL
Tel: 081-673-5570
Contact: Dharmachari Vimalaraja
A meditation and Buddhism teaching centre which is part of the Friends of the Western Buddhist Order (FWBO). Meditation and Buddhism are taught and practised through classes, courses and festivals which are open to all.

Nipponzan Myohoji

Peace Pagoda
Battersea Park
London SW11 4NJ
Tel: 071-228-9620
Contact: Venerable S Nagase
Religious order and temple. Nipponzan Myohoji was founded by the Most Venerable Nichidatsu Fujii

(1885-1985) who was closely associated with Mahatma Ghandi. The London Peace Pagoda was built by monks and nuns of Nipponzan Myohoji and many volunteers in association with the Greater London Council. It was inaugurated in May 1985 and its main concern and activity is prayer for world peace. There is an annual celebration of the London Peace Pagoda in the first Saturday of July. Daily prayers are held at the temple where all are welcome to attend. Events are organised such as an inter-faith walk to remember Nagasaki, culminating in placing paper lanterns with candles in them to remember the victims.

South London Buddhist Group

Northcote Library
Northcote Road
London SW11
Contact: c/o P M Warren

Vajradhatu-Dharma Study Group

74 Tantallion Road
London SW12
Tel: 081-673-6115
Vajradhatu is an association of Buddhist and meditation and study centres under the direction and guidance of Vidyadhara Chogyam Trungpa Rinpoche, of which there are five in Britain, twenty in Europe, and others throughout the world. They are run by experienced students of the Vidyadhara who have attended his intensive three-month Seminar programme and have been appointed by him as meditation instructors and teachers. The tradition followed is the Tibetan Kagyu/Nyingma school founded by Lama Marpa of Lhagypa in eleventh century Tibet. The International headquarters is in Halifax, Nova Scotia, Canada. It aims to provide instruction and guidance in meditation and the facilities necessary for study and practice. Its activities include study sessions on Mondays between 7.30pm-9.00pm; meditation practice on Thursdays between 7.30pm-9.30pm; tapes of the Vidyadhara and his unpublished teachings; step-by-step instruction through the three Yana approach from beginning instruction in meditation and the basics of Hinayana understanding, to full involvement with the Vajrayana of Tibetan Buddhism and the personal teaching of Chogyam Trungpa Rinpoche.

Buddhapadipa Temple

14 Calonne Road
Wimbledon Parkside
London SW19 5HJ
Tel: 081-946-1357

Fax: 081-944-5788
Contact: Secretary
Five Dhammaduta Bhikkus and five Dhammaduta assistants (belonging to the Buddhist Mission to the UK) are resident at the temple. They have been selected by the Sangha Supreme Council of Thailand to travel abroad and propagate the teaching of the Buddha. Lay groups at the Temple include the Sub-Committee for the Buddhist Mission in the UK; the Young Buddhist Group of the UK and the Lay Buddhist Association. The Temple is a religious centre and the Theravada Buddhist Research Centre. The ten monks spread the teachings of the Buddha. Religious ceremonies and festivals are held including the teaching of Theravada Buddhism and the practice of daily meditation and retreats. The theory of Buddhism is taught together with Insight meditation (vipassana) and a forested garden is provided for meditation practice.

Santosa Buddhist Group

c/o The Quaker Meeting House
40 Spencer Hill Road
Wimbledon
London SW19
Tel: 081-549-6375 (home)
Contact: Mike Pearce
The group meets weekly for meditation and study in the Theravadan tradition. There is a fortnightly meeting with a monk or a nun from Chithurst Forest Monastery (Hampshire).

Sub-Committee for the Buddhist Mission in the UK

The Buddhapadipa Temple
14 Calonne Road
Wimbledon
London SW19 5HJ
Tel: 081-946-1357

Young Buddhist Association

The Buddhapadipa Temple
14 Calonne Road
Wimbledon
London SW19 5HJ
Tel: 081-946-1357
Contact: Secretary
A place of worship and membership group which provides for the study of Buddhism, the teaching of the Thai language (in association with the Buddhist monks at the Temple) and the organisation of religious festivals.

LONDON (W POSTCODES)

West London Buddhist Centre

112 Westbourne Park Road
London W2 5PL
Tel: 071-727-9382
Contact: Dharmachari Moksharaja
Office: Chair
A meditation and teaching centre of the Friends of the Western Buddhist Order. Activities include teaching meditation, discussion and Puja. Classes and courses in meditation, Buddhism and related topics are organised most evenings during the week and at weekends for people with different degrees of experience and involvement in Buddhism. It is also possible to visit the centre during the day by prior arrangement.

London Buddhist Vihara

5 Heathfield Gardens
Chiswick
London W4 4JU
Tel: 081-995-9493
Fax: 081-742-3107
Contact: Secretary
A leading centre for Theravada Buddhism. Formed in 1926 by Anagarika Dharmapala, the Vihara was the first Buddhist monastery to be established outside the continent of Asia. It has continued its missionary activities with resident bhikkhus (monks) from Sri Lanka throughout this period, with the exception of the 1940s due to the Second World War. The Vihara moved to Chiswick during 1964 when the Anagarika Dharmapala Trust of Sri Lanka purchased the freehold property at Heathfield Gardens. The Vihara is managed by the Anagarika Dharmapala Trust and administered in conjunction with the Maha Bodhi Society of Sri Lanka which also appoints the resident Dhammaduta Bhikkhus. The Vihara is open daily to all devotees and visitors from 9.00am-9.00pm. The Vihara's library is also housed here. The bookstall is open daily from 9.00am-9.00pm. and stocks over two hundred paperbacks covering all aspects of Theravada Buddhism. A Buddhist service is held every Sunday (except during August) from 5.00pm-5.45pm. The Vihara conducts a full programme of courses at varying levels. Subjects covered include: Bhavana (meditation) instruction and practice; beginners' Buddhism; Dhamma study (advanced); Abhidhamma (Buddhist psychology); Pali language (the language of the Buddhist Canon) and Sinhala language. Children's Sunday school is held each Sunday afternoon (excluding school holidays) and children aged four to sixteen years old are encouraged to attend. The Vihara holds a retreat on the last Saturday of each month (except August and December) from 1.30pm-8.00pm.

Liu Academy

13 Gunnersbury Avenue
Ealing Common
London W5
Tel: 081-993-2549
The Academy follows the Taoist and Ch'an traditions.

LONDON (WC POSTCODES)

Covent Garden Meditation Centre

48 Shelton Street
London WC2
Tel: 081-981-1225
A meditation and Buddhism teaching centre which is a part of the Friends of the Western Buddhist Order (FWBO). The centre holds several classes and courses each weekday as well as regular weekend events, mainly aimed at beginners or people relatively new to meditation and Buddhism. All bookings should be made via the London Buddhist Centre.

SOUTH EAST ENGLAND (SOUTH)

Chichester Serene Reflection (Soto Zen) Meditation Group

Highfield
Dairy Lane
Walberton
Arundel
West Sussex BN18 0PT
Tel: 0243-551315 (home)
Contact: Mr C A Barker
Office: Secretary
A meditation group which believes that the essence of Soto Zen (Serene Reflection Meditation) is to discover one's true nature. It is to sit still with an open, alert and bright mind, neither suppressing nor indulging the thoughts and feelings that arise. In meditation one learns how to accept oneself and the world as it is. The group is affiliated to Throssel Hole Priory (Soto Zen Buddhist Monastery). Activities include weekly meetings (Thursdays 8.00pm) for meditation (Soto Zen) and listening to taped talks by senior monks from Throssel Hole Priory. Occasionally a monk visits the group.

Bodhisattva Centre and Brighton Mahayana Buddhist Centre

Bodhisattva Centre
11 Vernon Terrace
Brighton BN1
Tel: 0273-732917
Contact: Jane Kaye
Office: Administrative Director

A residential centre which aims to provide a community where people in the locality may live and study systematically the teachings of Buddha. There are six residents and a teacher who is a monk and lives there part time. The centre offers a variety of meditation courses; weekend, week and more extensive term time courses which will be open for all to attend. There will be a foundation programme based upon the main texts in the centre's New Kadampa tradition of Buddhism and systematic study of the Buddhist Scriptures will be undertaken. The Centre offers accomodation for both residents and visitors and will be open for the general public to visit. In the longer term, following requests from residents in those areas, it is hoped to open smaller centres along the South East coast, in Hastings, Chichester and Southampton.

Brighton Buddhist Centre

15 Park Crescent Place
Brighton BN2 3HF
Tel: 0273-698420 (home)
Contact: Dharmachari Yashodeva
Office: Chairperson
Friends of the Western Buddhist Order. Of the many elements of the FWBO, its activities include meditation, physical training, physical disciplines, study groups retreats and social welfare projects. It is for people who may seek meditation practice to take the stress out of life, or for those who base their entire lifestyle on the ideal of human perfection.

Brighton Buddhist Meditation Group

Brighton Natural Health Centre
Regent Street
Brighton BN1 1UL
Tel: 0273-696955 ext 5163 (daytime only)
Contact: Tony Pannett
The group follows the Theravada tradition and offers simple procedures for self-awareness meditation as taught by the Buddhist monks and nuns from the Chithurst Buddhist Monastery. Meetings are held weekly and are open to all. A monk or nun visits the group to lead meditation or give talks. Meditation is undertaken in a natural atmosphere.

Maitrikara

24 Freshfield street
Brighton BN2 2ZG
Tel: 0273-675803 (home)
Contact: Larry Gethin
Maitrikara: Source of loving kindness. Maitrikara is a Tibetan Buddhist meditation and study group. The aim of the group is to explore practical methods of

generating loving kindness and compassion as a path to enlightenment. We follow as guidance for our meditation the profound texts of the great sage Atisha, "The Seven Point Mind Training" and its commentary "Enlightened Courage" by the great spiritual master HH Dilgo Khyentse Rinpoche.

Sussex University Buddhist Studies Association
c/o Students Union
University of Sussex
Brighton
East Sussex
Contact: Secretary
An association of the Friends of the Western Buddhist Order. It meets during term time only on Friday afternoons between 4.00pm and 6.00pm and holds meditation on Tuesdays between 12.30pm and 1.30pm. Talks and courses are provided by members of the FWBO.

East Kent Mahayana Buddhist Centre (Canterbury)
Canterbury
Kent
Tel: 0293-7232917
Contact: Dave Everard
Office: Co-ordinator
A branch of the Bodhisatva Centre (11, Vernon Terrace, Brighton, BN1 3JG) in the New Kadampa tradition of Buddhism. The centre is a place for the study of the pure Buddhist view, meditation and action, and offers weekly teachings and meditation classes together with the occasional one day and weekend course. Longer courses and retreats are also run from time to time. Contact the above address or phone for the latest brochure of events.

Chichester Mahayana Buddhist Centre
Chichester
West Sussex
Tel: 0293-7232917
Contact: Dave Everard
A branch of the Bodhisatva Centre (11 Vernon Terrace, Brighton, BN1 3JG) in the New Kadampa tradition of Buddhism. The centre is a place for the study of the pure Buddhist view, meditation and action, and offers weekly teachings and meditation classes together with the occasional one day and weekend course. Longer courses and retreats are also run from time to time. Contact the above address or phone for the latest brochure of events.

Isle of Wight Buddhist Group
182 Park Road
Cowes
Isle of Wight
Tel: 0983-299695
Contact: S Wintle

Croydon Buddhist Centre
96–98 High Street
Croydon
Surrey CRO 1ND
Tel: 081-688-8624
Contact: Centre Manager
A meditation and teaching centre which exists to help and encourage people to develop spiritually within the framework of Buddhism. It is part of Friends of the Western Buddhist Order and thus presents Buddhism in a way which is not dependent on Eastern cultural forms.

Hastings Buddhist Society
Cincla Cottage
Pett Level
Hastings
Kent TN35 4EE
Tel: 0424-813176
Contact: Mr Alan Dipper
The Group follows the Japanese Soto Zen tradition. Activities include Zen meditation, general instruction on Buddhism, discussion.

Kingston Buddhist Group
Kingston-upon-Thames
Surrey
Tel: 081-541-0617
Contact: Penny Kuner

Kingston Meditation Group
Kingston-upon-Thames
Kingston-upon-Thames
Surrey
A group associated with the Friends of the Western Buddhist Order devoted to the practice of meditation and Buddhism. Contact is through the Croydon Buddhist Centre, Tel: 081-688-8624.

Yon-Hwa-Sa (Lotus House)
18 Rosebery Road
Kingston-upon-Thames
Surrey KT1 3LN
Tel: 081-549-6092
Contact: Venerable Jisu Sunim
A newly-built (1989) Korean Buddhist temple, under

the guidance of Venerable Jisu Sunim (resident). The core practice is formal, rather than unique, Korean style Bobhoe mainly for Korean residents.

Mid Kent and Medway Buddhist Group

60 Marion Crescent
Maidstone
Kent ME16 0HJ
Tel: 0622-751202
Contact: Joan Hamze
The group follows the Theravada tradition.

Cittaviveka - Chithurst Buddhist Monastery

nr Petersfield
Hampshire GU31 5EU
Tel: 0730-814986
Fax: 0730-817334
Contact: Ajahn Sucitto
Office: Abbot
The purpose of the monastery is to provide facilities for the support and guidance of Theravada monks and nuns following the forest tradition of North East Thailand. Aspirants live for one or two years as postulants (anagarikas) who keep the Eight Precepts. They may then receive full acceptance as monks (bhikkhus) and nuns (siladhara) undertaking five years of initial guidance in the monastic rule and the Buddha's teaching. The monastery is under the spiritual direction of Venerable Sumedho Mahathera. Life involves a rhythm of meditation and caring for the monastery and grounds following the example of Venerable Ajahn Chah of Wat Nong Pah Pong in Thailand. There are 5.00am and 7.30pm pujas every day and longer vigils on the quarter moons. There is shared accommodation for guests who are asked to live according to the monastic lifestyle. Enquiries should be made to the guest monk or nun before arrival. A community newsletter is published.

Petersfield Buddhist Group

8 St. Peter's Road
Petersfield
Hampshire GU32 3HX
Tel: 0730-63040 (home)
Contact: A S Brettell
The spiritual director is A S Brettell, and the tradition followed is Soto Zen. The group's aim is to aid people to come to Enlightenment through the practice of Zazen, and to give opportunities through group meetings to discuss, learn and correct the errors arising in the practice of zazen and thus to stimulate the awareness of Buddha Mind among the group

members. Meetings are held at 7.30pm on the last Sunday of each month (except August) at the Petersfield Community Centre.

Gaden Thubten Ling

71 Duncan Road
Southsea
Portsmouth PO5 2QU
Tel: 0705-815519
In the Tibetan Gelugpa tradition, it was founded in September 1988 by Geshe Tsultrim Gyeltsen, who is resident director of Thubten Dhargye Ling in Los Angeles, and travels regularly to England to give teachings at this and other centres.

Portsmouth Buddhist Group

71 Duncan Road
Southsea
Portsmouth
Hampshire
Tel: 0705-815519

Southsea Zen Group

c/o 36 Castle Road
Southsea
Portsmouth PO5 3DE
Tel: 0705-754490 (home)
Contact: Mr Peter Lavin
Members of this group are lay trainees practising together within the Soto Zen tradition, using the Serene Reflection (Shikan Taza) form of meditation and the ceremonial forms and rules of training of Throssel Hole Priory. Activities include weekly meditation meetings; bi-annual retreats led by a monk from the Throssel Hole Priory; and instruction in meditation.

Royal Tunbridge Wells Mahayana Buddhist Centre

Royal Tunbridge Wells
Kent
Tel: 0273-732917
Contact: Dave Everard
A branch of the Bodhisatva Centre (11 Vernon Terrace, Brighton, BN1 3JG) in the New Kadampa tradition of Buddhism. The centre is a place for the study of the pure Buddhist view, meditation and action, and offers weekly teachings and meditation classes together with the occasional one day and weekend course. Longer courses and retreats are also run from time to time. Contact the above address or phone for the latest brochure of events.

Isle of Wight Buddhist Society

49 Argylle Street
Ryde
Isle of Wight
Tel: 754–755 (home)
Contact: Eric Gould
The society follows the Theravada tradition.

Salisbury Serene Reflection Meditation Group

19 Kelsay Road
Salisbury
Wiltshire
Tel: 0722-29854
Contact: Derek Evens
The group follows the Serene Reflection Meditation tradition (Soto Zen), which stems from Japan, within the tradition of Mahayana Buddhism

Thames Meditation Society

Thames Buddhist Vihara
Dulverton Road
Selsdon
Surrey CR2 8PJ
Tel: 081-657-7120
Contact: Venerable P Somaratana Thera
Office: Head of Vihara
The Vihara is open to all, although since the resident monks are Sinhalese, services are mostly attended by Sri Lankan Buddhists. The Vihara follows the Theravada-Vipassana tradition and is under the spiritual direction of Venerable Pahalagama Somaratana and Pandit Horana Pannasekera. It was established in 1981 with the aim of providing a place of worship, meditation, discussion and meeting for Buddhists in England. Its activities include the provision of a shrine room for puja, meditation, sermons and pirith chanting; daily puja and Chanting Paritta at 6.00pm-7.30pm; Sunday evening special meditation from 6.00pm-7.30pm; Sunday School for the Sinhalese language and Dhamma for children from 4.00pm-6.00pm; regular classes in Abhidamma on Wednesdays and Pali studies are available by appointment. There are also occasional Vipassana meditation courses, and a Buddhist bookshop and lending library is maintained.

Hampshire Buddhist Society

21 Langton Road
Bishop's Waltham
Southampton S03 1GF (home)
Tel: 0489-895301 (home)
Contact: Jill Chapman
Office: Honorary Secretary

The society is non–sectarian and has close links with both the Chithurst Monastery near Petersfield and the Zen Centre in London. Its object is to make available the principles of Buddhism and the application of these principles. Membership is open to all who support these objectives.

Rivendell Retreat Centre

Chillies Lane
High Hurstwood
Uckfield
Sussex TN22 4AA
Tel: 0825-732594
Contact: Dharmachari Viryabodhi
The centre is associated with the Croydon Buddhist Centre and is a part of the Friends of the Western Buddhist Order. It houses a resident community and holds regular weekend and week-long retreats for people, including a programme of retreats introducing meditation and Buddhism. Booking is through the Croydon Buddhist Centre, Tel: 081-688-8624. There is also a weekly meditation class.

Whitchurch Serene Reflection Meditation Group

97 Micheldever Road
Whitchurch
Hampshire RG28 7JH
Tel: 0256-892567
Contact: Tony and Virginia Lee
Office: Lay Ministers
A meditation group affiliated to Throssel Hole Priory, Northumberland. It aims to teach Buddhist meditation in the Soto Zen, Serene Reflection Meditation tradition which stems from Japan, where it was introduced from China by the Great Master Dogen in the thirteenth century. Its emphasis, firmly within the tradition of Mahayana Buddhism, is upon meditation, keeping the Precepts, and the development of compassion for oneself and all beings. The group meets every Thursday evening in a private house. Newcomers are welcome and meditation instruction is given.

University of Kent Buddhist Society

19 Manor Road
Tankerton
Whitstable
Kent
Contact: c/o Zamantha Walker

Surrey Buddhist Centre Meditation Group

Wold Cottage
Goose Lane

Mayford
Woking
Surrey GU22 0NW
Tel: 0483-727170
Tel: 0483-768759 (home)
Contact: Chris Hidred
The group follows no specific tradition and anyone with an interest in Buddhism or meditation is welcome to attend. There are meetings on Wednesdays for meditation and reflection on the Buddhist way of generosity, kindness, virtue and serenity. Visits are made by monks and nuns from the Zen and Theravada tradition for guidance and instruction.

SOUTH WEST ENGLAND

Bath Buddhist Group
12 Station Road
Lower Weston
Bath BA1 3DY
Tel: 0225-337918 (home)
Contact: Rosie Ray
The group is run by lay people but regular contacts are maintained with teaching, including visits, from the Chithurst Bhikkus. It is, however, open across all traditions, especially the Theravadin, Tibetan and Zen traditions. It aims to promote an interest in Buddhism and to encourage its study and application in all traditions. Its activities include meditation, visiting speakers, talks and discussions.

Bath Mahayana Buddhist Centre
14 Malborough Buildings
Bath BA1 2LX (home)
Tel: 0225-481609
Contact: c/o Edward Dinsdale
Office: Co-ordinator
The centre studies the pure Buddhist view - that of meditation and action and offers weekly teachings with one day and weekend courses.

Bristol Buddhist Centre
9 Cromwell Road
St. Andrews
Bristol BS6 5HD
Tel: 0272-249991
Contact: Dharmachari Achalavajra
Office: Chairman
The centre aims to establish a thriving community of practicing Buddhists thus enabling the teaching of Buddhism to be communicated as widely as possible. To this end it teaches meditation, communication and Buddhism. Retreats are held to encourage

communities in a working relationship. The centre also contains a bookshop, library, tape library and meditation rooms. Activities include meditation, communication skills, Buddhist practice and worship.

Bristol Mahayana Buddhist Centre
Basement Flat
6 Bathwell Road
Totterdown
Bristol BS4 3AN
Tel: 0272-720856
Contact: Katerina Laurino
A branch of the Amitabha Centre in the New Kadampa tradition of Buddhism. The centre is a place for the study of the pure Buddhist view, meditation and action, and offers weekly teachings and meditation classes together with the occasional one day and weekend course. Longer courses and retreats are also run from time to time. Contact the above address or phone for the latest brochure of events.

Bristol Samatha Meditation Group
26 Morgan Street
St Agnes
Bristol BS2 9LQ
Tel: 0272-411902
Contact: Rupert Gethim
A group in the Theravada Tradition. Activities include instruction in Samatha meditation.

Bristol Theravada Meditation Group.
Bristol
Avon
Tel: 0272-684089 (home)
Contact: Nirodha
Office: Meditation Teacher
The Group follows the Theravada tradition and is led by Ajahn Sumedho. It takes a gentle and kindly approach to the development of mindfulness, clarity and equanimity, letting go gradually of those habits and desires which obsure realisation of our true nature. Personal guidance is offered on meditation practice and Buddhist teaching, authorised by Ajahn Sumedho, Head of the English Theravada Sangha. Activities include meditation and teaching.

Bristol University Buddhist Society
c/o Department of Theology
Bristol University
Tyndalls Park Road
Bristol
Avon
Tel: 0272-303030
Contact: Rupert Gethin

Bristol University Meditation and Buddhist Group

University of Bristol
Queen's Road
Clifton
Bristol
Avon
Office: Secretary
The group is associated with the Friends of the Western Buddhist Order and all events are open to both students and non-students. It aims to introduce students and others to the benefits of meditation and Buddhism as effective means of self-transformation, rather than as objects of academic study alone. Activities include introductory meditation classes and courses, talks and courses by members of the Western Buddhist Order; weekly meetings during term-time, held at the Student's Union; and two introductory retreats held each term by members of the Western Buddhist Order.

Lam Rim Bristol Buddhist Centre

12 Victoria Place
Bedminster
Bristol BS3 3BP
Tel: 0272-639089
Lam Rim Bristol follows the Dharma teachings as presented in the Lam Rim (graduated path) tradition of Atisha and Tsong Kha Pa (Tibetan Geluk). The Spiritual Director is Geshe Damcho Yonten. The centre has been developed for the study of Mahayana Buddhism, following the Gelugpa tradition of Tibetan Buddhists. A health section provides training in complementary treatments and advice on health to all sections of the community. Evening teaching, weeks or weekends are held for meditation, prayer and for a greater knowledge of Tibetan Buddhist teaching.

Sakya Thinley Richen Ling

Sakya Centre
27 Lilymead Avenue
Knowle
Bristol BS4 2BY
Tel: 0272-712961
Contact: David Armstrong
A study and practice centre which exists to make available all aspects of Buddha's teachings according to the Sakya tradition of Tibetan Buddhism. This is done under the guidance of Lama Jampa Thaye who teaches regularly at the centre and gives personal guidance to committed students and newcomers. The collective name given to all of Nyakpa Jampa's students in the

UK is the Dechen Community. Introductory talks on Buddhism are given and the study and practice of Buddhism is carried out.

Zen Dojo Bristol

91 Gloucester Road
Bristol BS7 8AT
Tel: 0272-253301 (home)
Contact: John Daley
Office: Secretary
A Zen Buddhist group which follows the teaching and practice of Soto Zen Buddhism as transmitted by Taisen Deshimaru Roshi and believes that the essence of Zen is the practice of correct meditation or Zazen. Sitting cross-legged on a cushion, back straight, nape of the neck stretched, chin drawn in, breathing calmly, minds freed of all fetters, concentrate on breathing out powerfully and profoundly and on the different points of posture.

South Devon Ch'an Buddhism Study and Meditation Group

7 Upton Manor Park
Brixham
Devon TQ5 9QP (home)
Tel: 0803-855219 (home)
Contact: Ken Robinson
Office: Organiser
A membership group with weekly meetings for local people who are interested in Buddhism and meditation in general and in the teachings and practices of Ch'an (Zen) in particular. Periods of meditation are followed by talks and discussions which are adapted as necessary to meet the needs of beginners as well as those with some prior knowledge and experience. Activities include study and meditation.

International Meditation Centre

Splatts House
Heddington
Calne
Wiltshire SN11 0PE
Tel: 0380-850-238
Fax: 0380-850-833
Contact: Miss Virginia Judkins
Office: Trust Secretary
Residential meditation centre founded in 1979 by the Sayagyi U Ba Khin Memorial Trust. The trust owns and runs the centre. The centre holds ten-day courses in Theravada Buddhist meditation as taught by Sayagyi U Ba Khin of Burma. The meditation consists of the trainings in Anapana and Vipassana meditation. In Anapana meditation, the student concentrates the attention on the breath in order to achieve

one-pointedness of mind. In Vipassana meditation, the meditator focuses the concentrated mind inside him/herself and experiences the realities of mind and body. This purifies the mind and leads to the shedding of worries and anxieties and ultimately to the experience of the unconditioned Nibbana. Courses are attended by people from many different denominations, ages and backgrounds as no religious conversion is required for the practice of this meditation. The Centre can also be contacted through Mrs Virgina Newton, also a Trust Secretary, at the address, telephone and Fax numbers above.

Cheltenham Mahayana Buddhist Centre

Cheltenham
Gloucestershire
Tel: 0225-840500
Contact: Carla Collenette
A branch of the Amitabha Centre in the New Kadampa tradition of Buddhism. The centre is a place for the study of the pure Buddhist view, meditation and action, and offers weekly teachings and meditation classes together with the occasional one day and weekend course. Longer courses and retreats are also run from time to time. Contact the above address or phone for the latest brochure of events.

Exeter Theravadin Buddhist Group

66 Pennsylvania Road
Exeter EX4 6DF
Tel: 0392-75534 (home)
Contact: Mr Donald Cross
Senior Bhikkhus from Chithurst monastery are resident at the Devon Vihara and visit the group to give Dhamma talks and guidance on meditation. Those visiting for the first time should first telephone to ensure that a teacher is present when they come. Activities include weekly meetings on Wednesdays at 7.30pm.

Exeter Zazenkai

14 Monkswell Road
Exeter EX4 7AX
Tel: 0392-221147
Contact: Tony Doubleday
Regular Zazen schedule with students of Genpo Merzel Sensei.

Exeter Zen Meditation Group

c/o Parklands
Clyst Honiton
Exeter
Devon
Tel: 0392-64903

Contact: Mike and Lyn Sheldon
The Group is affiliated to the Throssel Hole Priory. Activities include weekly meditation meetings including periods of sitting meditation (Zazen) and walking meditation (Kinhin) followed by tea, local retreats held at least once a year and meditation instruction.

Kanzeon Sangha

14 Monkswell Road
Exeter EX4 7AX (home)
Tel: 0392-221147 (home)
Contact: c/o Tony Doubleday
Office: Co-ordinator
Kanzeon Sangha is the collective name for the international community of students of Genpo Mezel Sensei, a fully qualified teacher in Zen and heir to the lineage of Taizan Maezumi Roshi of the Zen Centre of Los Angeles. Genpo Sensei's students include both monks, nuns and lay people. His teaching lineage derives from both the Soto and Rinzai systems of Japanese Zen, and the practice of these are therefore offered to students depending on their individual needs. Zen meditation retreats are held by Genpo Mezel Sensei and his senior students.

"Karma Naro" Tibetan Buddhist Centre

Middle Wenallt
Llanigon
Hay-on-Wye
Hereford HR3 5QD
Tel: 0497-847377
Contact: Kurt Schaffhauser
The centre follows the "Karma Kagyu" Tibetan tradition and is non-residential. Group meetings for practice are held four to six times per month in a private shrine room. Retreat facilities and visiting teachers are occasionally available. Day visits by appointment only. Ring or write for details..

Devon Buddhist Vihara

Odle Cottage
Upottery
nr Honiton
Devon EX14 9QE
Tel: 0404-891251
The Vihara is a branch of Amaravati Buddhist Centre, a Theravadin Order which is under the spiritual direction of Venerable Sumedho Mahathera. It houses a small Sangha community and provides a centre for the study and practice of Buddhism. Its lifestyle includes daily puja and meditation as well as other work. On Thursday and Sunday evenings, the regular meditation is followed by a talk. The senior Bhikkhu

is always willing to meet visitors and those seeking spiritual guidance. There is accomodation for guests who are asked to live in harmony with the monastic lifestyle. Enquiries should be made with the guestmaster before arriving. The senior Bhikkhu also makes regular visits to local Buddhist groups and to colleges, schools, prisons, public meetings etc. and is always willing to consider suitable rquests for dhamma teachings. A quarterly newsletter of the Vihara is available on request.

Golden Rosary Heritage

9-11 Crenville Road
Lostwithiel
Cornwall
The Golden Rosary Heritage was founded by Orgyen Jampa Gendum and focuses on the Tibetan traditon.

Gaia House Trust

Woodlands Road
Denbury
Nr Newton Abbot
Devon TQ12 6DY
Tel: 0803-813188
Contact: The Manager
Gaia House, set in the quiet Devon countryside, provides a full programme of retreats in Insight Meditation as well as offering facilities for individual retreats. The teaching of the simple act of awareness, rooted in the Buddhist tradition, frees the mind of confusion and negativity and encourages the emergence of wisdom and compassion.

Yeovil Buddhist Meditation Group

Meadowcroft
2 Hamdon View
Norton-Sub-Hamdon
Somerset
Tel: 0935-88-316
Contact: David Greenhorne

Sakya Thinley Namgyal Ling

9 Fairfield Close
Overy Tracey
Devon TQ13 9BH
Tel: 0626-833015

Mousehole Buddhist Group

Penaluna
Clodgy Moor
Penzance
Cornwall TR19 6UR
Tel: 0736-731449 (home)
Contact: Bill Picard

Office: Contact Secretary
A meditation group composed of people living in the area who wish to practice Zazen. Advice and help is given to those who are starting. The group owns a Zendo at Gilly Lane, Whitecross, Penzence where weekly meditation and retreats are held from 7.00pm-9.00pm. There are no residential facilities. Anyone interested in Zen meditation who wishes to attend is welcome. The Zendo is open for private meditation if requested.

Whitecross Buddhist Centre

Gilly Lane
Whitecross
Penzance
Cornwall TR20 8BZ
Tel: 0736-740759/0736-50057
Contact: Secretary
A meditation centre situated in the small hamlet of Whitecross. The Centre is based on the Soto Zen meditation tradition. Newcomers including non-Buddhists are always welcome. It is recommended that newcomers attend on Monday evenings commencing at 7.00pm with meditation, tea and discussion. All ages, male and female are welcome. For further information please write or telephone beforehand.

Wells Buddhist Group

Mulbery Cottage
Bread Street
Pilton
Somerset BA4 4BQ (home)
Tel: 074-890357 (home)
Contact: Joe King
Office: Programme co-ordinator
A small group of lay Buddhists which meets twice a month for meditation, taped talks and discussion. Meetings include meditation and occasionally speakers from a range of Buddhist traditions. Monks from the Devon Vihara regularly come to the group to lead the meditation and teach.

Plymouth Buddhist Group

By The Down
Sampford Spiney
Yelverton
Plymouth PL20 6LE
Tel: 0822-616803
Contact: Mr C Louden
The group has weekly meetings for meditation and chanting, regular visits by a monk or other speaker and a small library of books and cassettes.

Plymouth Theravada Buddhists

34 Torridge Road
Plympton
Devon PL7 3DQ
Tel: 0752343-710 (home)
Contact: Dave Pengelly
A small group which follows the Theravada tradition, but which is open to all who wish to follow the Dhamma, whatever school they may be interested in. The spiritual director of the group is Ajahn Sumedho. Meetings are held on Monday evenings at 7.45pm with an emphasis on meditation and following the instruction offered by the visiting Bhikku. Retreats and the celebration of Wesak and other festivals are also organised.

Salisbury Serene Reflection Meditation Group

19 Kelsay Road
Salisbury
Wiltshire
Tel: 0722-29854
Contact: Derek Evens
Follows the Serene Reflection Meditation tradition (Soto Zen), which stems from Japan, within the tradition of Mahayana Buddhism

Saltash Buddhist Group

7 Tavy Road
Saltash
Cornwall PL12 6DE
Tel: 0752-846096 (home)
Contact: Dharmachari Jayaratna
A group which meets to learn and practice Buddhist meditation; also to study the Buddha's teachings and their relevance to life in the West today. This group is part of the Friends of the Western Buddhist Order.

Taunton Buddhist Group

96 Eastgate Gardens
Tancred Street
Taunton TA1 3RD
Tel: 0823-321059
Contact: Martin Sinclair

Cornwall Buddhist Group

Resugga
St Erme
Truro TR4 9BL
Tel: 0872-79519
Contact: Jane Browne
A very small group of Buddhists who meet occasionally for study and devotional activities. The main concern is to study Buddhist practice based on the Thai Forest tradition of wisdom and meditation. A monk from the Devon Vihara visits the group once a quarter. Retreats lasting ten days are held once a year. New members are always welcome.

Umberleigh Meditation Group

Manormead
Umberleigh
North Devon EX37 9DX
Tel: 0769-60699 (home)
Contacts: John and Maxine Saban
An informal membership group with weekly meetings where all are welcome to join in with their own practice of meditation or contemplation. Beginners can be instructed in basic techniques. The group meditates for one hour followed by informal discussion and tea.

South Dorset Buddhist Group

3 New Close Gardens
Rodwell
Weymouth DT4 8RG
Tel: 0305-786821 (home)
Contact: Mrs B Walters
Office: leader
A Buddhist group which meets every week to meditate together and study Buddhist teachings, under the guidance of Venerable Ajahn Sumedho and the monks and nuns of the Theravadin Buddhist tradition. Mutual support is offered in practicing the skilful path of the Buddha and living in a way that is kind, compassionate and aware. The group has strong links with the Theravada Buddhist monks at the Devon Vihara, near Honiton.

Western Zen Retreats

Winterhead Hill Farm
Shipham
Winscombe
Avon BS25 1RS
Tel: 093484-2231 (home)
Contact: Dr John Crook
Office: Authorised Ch'an Teacher
Zen meditation groups recruited by contact and advertisement. It aims to teach Buddhist practice through Zen and Ch'an (Chinese Zen) meditation utilising a range of methods, ancient and modern. It runs retreats in Zen Buddhism for participants who apply for the periodic events held in a mid-Wales centre. In addition, orthodox Ch'an retreats are run as authorised by Master Sheng Yen of Taiwan.

Worcester Buddhist Centre Karma Young Due

110 Lansdowne Road
Worcester WR3 8JL
Tel: 0905-20104 (home)

Worcester Buddhist Group Nitartha School

33 Broughton Avenue
St John's
Worcester
Tel: 0905-420555 (home)
Contact: Dave Rowley
The group is led by Michale Hookham and follows the Nitartha School of Buddhism.

KEY TO TERMS USED IN BUDDHIST ORGANISATIONAL TITLES

Note: This is not a complete glossary of significant Buddhist terms. It is a guide to the meaning and/or background of some of the words used in the titles of Buddhist organisations listed in this directory. More information on the italicised words can be tracked down elsewhere in the key and/or in the section on Introducing the Buddhist Community by using the directory's Keyword Index.

Akshobhya

Sanskrit literally meaning "immovable". As a monk Akshobyhya is said to have taken a vow never to harbour anger towards a living being. He suceeded in this and became a *Buddha* thus symbolising the defeat of passions. Iconographically he is often seen riding a blue elephant.

Amaravati

The name of a South Indian city which was an important centre for Buddhist art and learning in the third century CE and had a *stupa* containing some relics of the *Buddha*. Its Pali meaning is "the deathless realm."

Ambedkar

Bhimrao Raniji Ambedkar (1891-1956) was a jurist who converted from Hinduism to Buddhism in 1956 together with five hundred thousand of the so-called "untouchables", members of the "scheduled castes" of Indian society who felt discriminated against by virtue of their caste position. He founded the Buddhist Society of India and developed a movement which emphasised the social implications of Buddhism as a religion rejecting caste and other similar distinctions.

Ambedkarite

That which pertains to the movement founded by Dr Ambedkar.

Amitayus

Sanskrit word meaning "infinite life". *Amitayus* is the name in the *Mahayana* tradition for a manifestation of the *Buddha* who is depicted as holding a container in which is the nectar of immortality.

Amrita

Sanskrit for "immortal", relating to water of life.

Angulimala

The name of a murderer who became a disciple of the *Buddha* and eventually became an *Arahant*.

Asanga

The name of the founder of the *Yogachara* School (or *Yogacara*) which began in the fourth century CE. *Yogachara* is Sanskrit and literally means "application of yoga". According to this school, everything that exists is "mind only".

Atisha

A Buddhist scholar (980/90-1055) who founded the *Kadampa* school of *Tibetan* Buddhism.

Baba

Hindi term meaning "father" or "daddy" (in the familiar form) and used in modern Indian languages as a title of respect.

Bodhi

Sanskrit and Pali for "awakening", a synonym for Enlightenment.

Buddhapadipa

Pali for "Buddha's lamp".

Ch'an

A shortened form of *Ch'an-na,* which is a Chinese school of *Mahayana* Buddhism that developed in the sixth and seventh centuries CE and stresses the possibility of sudden and direct enlightenment (see also entry for *Zen* below).

Chenrezig

Tibetan literally meaning "looking with clear eyes". It is a Tibetan word for Avalokiteshvara, the *Bodhisattva* of Compassion who is viewed as the founder of the Tibetan people. The Tibetan leader, the *Dalai Lama,* is viewed as an incarnation of Chenrezig.

Cittaviveka

Pali and Sanskrit for "mental discrimination". It also carries the sense of "silent mind", an attitude of great equanimity.

Dhamma

Pali version of the Sanskrit *dharma* (see below) for "cosmic law", "righteousness", "ethics" (see Introducing the Buddhist Community). It also is used for "truth" or the "teaching" of the Buddha.

Dhammapala

Pali literally meaning "guarding of the teaching". In *Mahayana* Buddhism, the *dharmapalas* protect one from dangers and bad influences for one's spiritual development. Dharmapala is also the name of a Sinhalese Buddhist (1865-1933) who founded the Mahabodhi Society in 1891, the objective of which was the restoration of the Mahabodhi monastery in Bodh-gaya. In 1925, he founded the Maha Bodhi Society of Great Britain.

Dharma

Sanskrit form of Pali *dhamma* (see above).

Dharmadhatu

Sanskrit meaning "realm of dharma". In *Mahayana* Buddhism this is believed to be the true nature of all things. In the East, Buddhism is simply known as the *Dharma.*

Dorje

Tibetan for "diamond" or "thunderbolt", literally meaning "lord of stones". In *Tibetan Buddhism* diamonds are symbolic of clarity of insight on the path to *Enlightenment.* It is the equivalent to the Sanskrit *Vajra* (see below).

Dragpa

Tibetan meaning "wrathful".

Dzogchen

Tibetan for "great perfection". This is the description of the central teaching which the *Nyingmapa* school of *Tibetan Buddhism* consider to be the most definitive and secret teaching of the Buddha. In this, purity of mind is understood to always be present and only to need realising.

Dzong

Tibetan meaning "bastion".

Gyaltsabje

Tibetan meaning "Lord Regent".

Heruka

A wrathful *Buddha* form in *Tibetan Buddhism.*

Jodo

From *Jodo-shin-shu* which is Japanese literally meaning "The School of the Pure Land". The school was of Indian origin and was prevalent in China, but in this form it is extant as a school of Japanese Buddhism founded by Shinran. It is a lay school which emphasises the help of tariki, meaning "other power", in attaining the goal of the *Pure Land.* This is believed to be achieved through trusting in Amidha Buddha for help.

Kagyu

Tibetan meaning "transmission of expertise", it is the name of one of the four principal schools of *Tibetan Buddhism.* It places an emphasis on the direct transmission of teaching from teacher to disciple. *Karma Kagyu* is a grouping within the wider school.

Kandro

Tibetan literally meaning "those who fly through space". It refers to female spiritual beings (in Sanskrit called *dakhini*) some of which are quite worldly and others of which are enlightened.

Kanzeon

The Japanese for Avalokiteshvara, the *Bodhisattva* of Compassion within *Mahayana* Buddhism.

Karma

Sanskrit for "deed", but encompassing a wide range of meanings including mental, verbal and physical actions, their consequences, the totality of the actions and consequences connected with an individual, and also cause and effect in terms of morality.

Kempo

The title for Tibetan Masters of Philosophy using entailing nine years of intensive study.

Khyil

Tibetan meaning "centre". It combines with *khor* (see above) to make a *khyil khor*, otherwise known as a *mandala* .

Lam

Tibetan meaning "path".

Ling

Tibetan meaning "place".

Liu

Chinese meaning "six" and also a name.

Madhyamika

Sanskrit meaning "teaching of the Middle Way". In the context of Buddhist organisational names, the middle way relates to the Buddhist school known as the *Madhyamika* which comes from the Sanskrit *madhyma* meaning "the middle", and which was founded by the teachers Nagajuna and Aryadeva. In this context, rather than being a term for describing Buddhism as a whole (see introduction to the Buddhist community), the term "middle way" refers to a philosophical position in the debate between the existence or non-existence of things. In this debate the middle way focuses instead on *shunyata* (emptiness) and hence is also known by the alternative name of the *Shunyatavada* (meaning "Teaching of Emptiness").

Maha

Sanskrit meaning "great".

Mahayana

Sanskrit literally meaning "great vehicle" and describing the form of Buddhism which developed stressing the ideal of the *Bodhisattva*.

Maitreya

Sanskrit meaning "loving one". In *Tibetan Buddhism*, devotion to Maitreya is particularly strong and he is viewed as the embodiment of universal compassion, who is expected to come as the next and also the fifth and last of the line of earthly *Buddhas*.

Manjushri

Sanskrit for "he who is noble and gentle". In all *Mahayana* Buddhist schools it is the name of the *Bodhisattva* of Wisdom. In *Tibetan Buddhism*, and especially with the *Gelugpa* school, Manjushri is a particularly important figure. Great scholars are believed to be his *tulku* (incarnations). In wrathful aspect, Manjushri is depicted in *Tibetan Buddhism* as Yamantaka (meaning "Subduer of the Lord of Death") and appears as a fearsome looking bull-headed deity.

Marpa

The name of the "man from Mar" (1012-1097 CE), a *yogi* from Southern Tibet and the Master of Milarepa who is the principal founder in the *Kagyupa* school's transmission. Marpa represents the ideal of the married householder who committed himself to the *dharma*. He was the translator into Tibetan of many Sanskrit texts.

Mushindokai

Mushin is Japanese for "empty heart" and is a *Zen* Buddhist expression for freedom from any notions and opinions.

Naro

Tibetan for Naropa, the name of a Buddhist teacher.

Nichiren

Japanese from *Nichiren-shu* meaning "the School of the Lotus of the Sun", named after its founder Nichiren (1222-1282 CE). Based upon the Lotus Sutra, the title of which is believed to summarise Buddhism and is recited in the formula *namu myoho renge-kyo*, meaning "veneration to the sutra of the lotus of the good law". It is believed that through recitation of this formula, Buddhahood can be attained. The school and organisations based within it have an emphasis on the earthly *Buddha* realm and Buddhist sociopolitical action. *Nichiren sho-shu* ("True School of Nichiren") venerates Nichiren as a *Buddha*. The Soka Gakkai, Rissho Koseikai and Nipponzan Myohoji (see below) organisations are based on the idea of this *Nichiren* school.

Nipponzan Myohoji

The name of a Japanese Buddhist revival movement which takes its name from its main Temple. It is also known as the Movement of the Wondrous Law of the Lotus Sutra. It was founded in 1917 by Fuji Nichidatsu and sought to base itself on the teachings of Nichiren. Nichidatsu became a radical pacifist and the movement advocates world peace and builds peace *pagodas* throughout the world and its servants beat drums for peace.

Nitartha

Sanskrit meaning "of which the meaning is expounded". Refers to the explicit teaching which is to be taken literally, as distinct from teaching expressed obliquely or metaphorically.

Padma

Sanskrit for "lotus".

Padmaloka

From the Sanskrit *padma* (see above) meaning "lotus" and the Sanskrit *loka*, meaning "universe". The lotus is a water lily and in Buddhism it is a symbol of the true nature of things unstained by the mud of *samsara* and ignorance. In Buddhist art, the lotus appears as a throne for the *Buddha* and in the *Pure Land* school of *Mahayana* Buddhism it is the major symbol for Buddhist doctrine.

Pali

A language derived from Sanskrit in which the *Theravada* scriptures and commentaries are written and which is considered to be the language closest to that spoken by the *Buddha* himself.

Pure Land

The pure lands are seen as transcendent paradises ruled over by *Buddhas*. In folk belief they are geographical locations, but fundamentally they stand for states of mind on the way to *Nirvana*.

Ratnasambhava

Sanskrit literally meaning "Jewel-Born One". He is one of the transcendent *Buddhas* and is usually seen iconographically as riding a lion or horse or making the gesture of granting a wish.

Rigpa

Tibetan meaning "enlightened intelligence."

Rim

Tibetan for "unbiased". It comes from a nineteenth century movement in *Tibetan Buddhism* which sought to overcome sectarianism. Today it especially influences the *Karma Kagyu* and *Nyingmapa* schools of *Tibetan Buddhism*.

Rissho Kosei Kai

Japanese meaning "Society for the Establishment of Justice and Community for the Rise (of the Buddha)". It is a movement which seeks to base itself upon the teachings of Nichiren. It was founded in 1938 by Niwano Nikkyo and Naganuma Myoko. It emphasises the salvific power of the Lotus Sutra and the socio-political dimensions of Buddhism.

Saddhatissa

The name of a Sinhalese Buddhist monk of the Maha Bodhi Society and author of many books on Buddhism.

Sakya

Sanskrit name of the noble clan from which Siddhartha Gotama, the historical *Buddha*, came. At that time, the clan ruled one of India's sixteen states which covered part of present-day Nepal.

Samatha

Sanskrit for "living in tranquillity", a meditation tradition found in all Buddhist schools. In the *Gelugpa* school of *Tibetan Buddhism samatha* meditation is seen as a precondition for *vipashyana* (insight).

Samye

Tibetan meaning "beyond concept". It was the name of the first major Buddhist monastery of Tibet and is now used in the title of the Samye Ling Buddhist Monastery in Scotland.

Sangha

Sanskrit and Pali meaning "group". In Buddhism it refers to the Buddhist community as a whole and to the community of Buddhist monks, nuns and novices.

Sarana

Pali for "refuge" (Sanskrit is *shrana*). Appears in the

trisarana (*tri* means "three") or threefold refuge of Buddhism - to take refuge in the *Buddha*, the *Dharma* and the *Sangha*.

Shantideva

A monk of the seventh to eigth centuries associated with the *Madhyamika* school of *Mahayana* Buddhism.

Shin

The short form of *Shin-shu*, the Japanese Buddhist school founded by Shinran (1173-1262 CE) which focuses on venerating Amidha Buddha with the formula of the *nembutsu*. It believes in the necessity for complete trust in the *tariki* ("other power") of Amidha Buddha which it is believed can even overcome an accumulation of negative *karma*. It is a lay group and has no monks, unlike the *Jodo Shu* school.

Shingon

Japanese for "School of the True Word", founded by Kukai (774-835 CE) which places great importance on the so-called "three secrets" of body, thought and speech.

Shu

Japanese for "school" as *Jodo Shu*, "the School of the Pure Land" in which reciting the name of Amidha Buddha (the *nembutsu*) is seen as a method of strengthening trust in him. The school was brought to Japan by Enin (793-864 CE). The present Japanese school was founded by Honen (1133-1212 CE) and uses the formula of recitation "namu amidha butsu", meaning "veneration to Buddha Amidha". The *Jodo Shu*, unlike the *Jodo-Shinshu*, has a monastic life.

Soka Gakkai

Literally meaning "Scientific Society for the Creation of Values", it is a modern Buddhist movement founded by Makiguchi Tsunesabwo in Japan in 1930. It is in the *Nichiren* tradition of Buddhism.

Soto

The name of one of the largest Japanese *Zen* Buddhist schools, brought to Japan from China in the thirteenth century by the Japanese Master Dogen. It has a focus on the practice of *zazen* (see below), meaning "sitting meditation".

Tantric

That which pertains to *Tantra*, which is a Sanskrit word referring to a type of scriptures. In *Tibetan Buddhism* it is a term which refers to the *Vajrayana* as a major tradition of Buddhism and also to various texts and their associated systems of meditation. There are various *Tantras* according to the spiritual capabilities of the practioners.

Tara

Sanskrit for "saviour". Tara is said to be an emanation from the *Bodhisattva* Avolokiteshvara. She embodies the feminine aspect of compassion, although she is seen in both peaceful and wrathful depictions as well as in various colours, the Green Tara and the White Tara forms being the most frequently seen.

Taraloka

The name of a women's retreat centre, meaning literally "the place of Tara".

Tashi

Chinese for "great master" - the equivalent of *daishi* in Japanese. It is an honorific title.

Theravada

Pali meaning "teaching of the elders of the order". *Theravada* Buddhism sees itself as the closest to original Buddhism.

Theravadin

That which pertains to the *Theravada* tradition.

Thinley

Tibetan for "enlightened activity".

Vairochana

sanskrit literally meaning "he who is like the sun". One of the transcendent *Buddhas* iconographically depicted making the *mudra* of wisdom. In the development of *Mahayana* Buddhism. He came to be seen as the *Adi-Buddha* or original *Buddha*.

Vajra

Sanskrit meaning "diamond" and, in the Hindu tradition, Sanskrit for "thunderbolt", as used of the Hindu god Indra. In Buddhism it relates to indestructibility and is found as part of the name of the *Vajrayana* tradition of Buddhism (see below entry on *Dorje*).

Vajradhatu

From the Tibetan *vajra* (see above), meaning "diamond", and the Sanskrit and Pali *dhatu*, meaning "realm" or "region". It is the name of a famous *mandala* meaning "the Diamond Realm".

Vajraloka

From the Tibetan *vajra* (see above), meaning "diamond" and the Sanskrit *loka* meaning "universe". It is the name of a Friends of the Western Buddhist Order meditation centre in Wales.

Vajrasattva

Sanskrit meaning "Diamond Being". He is depicted in white and is associated with purification. The *mantra* associated with him is used in all schools of *Tibetan Buddhism*.

Vihara

Sanskrit/Pali for "resting place". It is used of the residence of monks. The first *viharas* were simply houses placed at the disposal of the *Buddha* for his growing *sangha* (see above).

Vipassana

Pali (Sanskrit is *vipasyana* or *vipashyana*) for "insight" or "clear sight" which is related to the "three signs of being" (see introductory materials on Buddhism). It is a meditation discipline which, together with *samatha* (calming of the mind), is necessary for *Enlightenment*.

Wat

The name describing Thai Buddhist temples.

Yoga

Sanskrit for "joining". In a religious context, it refers to a particular religious practice or discipline usually involving bodily postures, breathing and meditation. The *Tantric* practices of *Tibetan Buddhism* are known as *yoga* and its saints, such as Milarepa, are called *yogis*.

Zazen

Japanese *za* means "sitting" and when put together with the word *zen*, meaning "meditation", refers to a basic practice of *Zen*. *Zazen* is free of any object of meditation but consists of a state of alert attention in which *Enlightenment* can be achieved.

Zazenkai

Japanese for "*zazen* meeting", an occasion where followers of *Zen* meet to practise and hear teaching in the tradition.

Zen

A Japanese abbreviation of the word *zenna*, which represents the Japanese way of reading the Chinese *ch'an-na* (or, in its short form, *ch'an*). In turn, the Chinese version relates to the Sanskrit *dhyana*, which refers to the state in which dualism of mind is overcome. In the *Theravada* tradition, this is known by the Pali word *jhana*, meaning the highest form of concentration. *Ch'an* was developed in China in the 6th and 7th centuries CE out of the meeting between *Mahayana* Buddhism and Taoism. It focuses on the possibility of a direct and immediate breakthrough to *Enlightenment*.

THE CHRISTIAN COMMUNITY

INTRODUCING THE CHRISTIAN COMMUNITY

CHRISTIANS IN THE UNITED KINGDOM

Christianity is a worldwide religion with around 1,800,000,000 followers organised in many different traditions, organisational forms and structures. It is also the principal religious tradition of the UK in terms of the numbers of its adherents and the length of its historical presence. In its various forms, it has significantly shaped the history as well as the contemporary life of these islands and their four nations, including their legal structures, public institutions and cultural inheritance.

There are approximately 37,600,000 people in the UK who regard themselves as Christians. Figures for the number of places of worship are not available for the UK, but for England and Wales there are 29,539 certified places of Christian worship other than those of the Church of England and Church in Wales which together have 16,562 recorded places of worship. 15,097 of these are buildings of the Church of England.

Origins in the UK

Christianity was introduced into Britain by itinerant missionaries from Ireland and from continental Europe during the first century CE. Over the next four hundred years it survived and developed in parts of Wales, Ireland, Scotland and northern England. It did so in a form known as *Celtic Christianity*. This had its own distinctive ethos and was independent of the organisational structures of *Western Christendom* which had began to develop around the *Bishop* of Rome (the *Pope*).

In 597 CE, Augustine, an emissary of Pope Gregory the Great of Rome, arrived in Kent. He was made the first *Archbishop* of Canterbury, which was the base for his missionary work, and was given authority by the *Pope* (see below) over the *bishops* in the rest of Britain. In Wales and Ireland Celtic forms Christianity continued an independent life for some centuries and in Scotland conformity with Rome was concluded only in the eleventh century during the rule of King Malcolm III and Queen Margaret.

Protestant Reformation

With the consolidation of Western Christianity under the jurisdiction of the *Pope*, until the *Reformation*, (see below) Christians in the different parts of these islands which make up the UK of today remained part of *Western Christendom*. This form of Christianity was known as "Roman" or "Western Catholic" (meaning universal).

During the sixteenth and seventeenth centuries *Western Christendom* underwent major religious and political upheavals. This period is referred to as the *Reformation* when attempts were made in a number of European countries by *Protestants* (those who protested against the existing order of things) to remodel the Christian Church in a way which was believed by them to reflect more truly the earliest forms of Christianity.

In England and Wales, the Church changed to reflect these movements (see below) and after King Henry VIII's political break with the *Papacy*, the Church of England was brought into being as the established form of religion.

At this time, many new *Protestant denominations* (organisational streams) began in England, Wales and Scotland. In the following centuries, new forms of *Protestant* Christianity continued to emerge. After a period in which *Roman Catholics* were persecuted, the Roman Catholic Church also emerged again into public religious life in the UK.

Denominational and Ethnic Diversity

The Christian scene in Britain has been renewed and diversified by such events as the rise of Methodism and the *Evangelical* (see below) revival in England and Wales in the eighteenth century when people experienced Christian conviction in a very strong and personal form; the Oxford Movement, bringing a renewed stress on *liturgy* (from the Greek *leitourgia*, meaning worship); and the creation of the Salvation Army in the nineteenth century.

Today, Christianity in the UK is found in various organisational forms and is ethnically diverse. Through a variety of migratory movements, groups of Christians have arrived bringing their own distinctive forms of Christianity with them, such as the French Reformed Huguenots or the Irish Roman Catholics (who soon outnumbered indigenous Catholics in many parts of England, Wales and Scotland).

In the twentieth century these were joined by Greek, Russian and other *Eastern Orthodox* (see below) Christians as well as members of the *Pentecostal* and *Holiness* Churches of mainly Afro-Caribbean membership, who now form a small but growing and increasingly significant proportion of the practising Christian community, especially in England. There are also groupings of Chinese Christians from Hong Kong, and of Asian Christians with ethnic origins in the Indian sub-continent.

Numbers and Geography

Together with the total community numbers of 37,600,000 the total active membership of the various Christian Churches stands at 7,023,000.

The proportions of active members, however, vary considerably between the four nations of these islands, with England at eleven per cent, Wales at seventeen per cent, Scotland at thirty per cent, and Northern Ireland at seventy per cent. Denominational proportions also vary between the four nations.

In England, the Church of England is the numerically strongest Church, but in Wales it is the *Free Churches* (see below), in Scotland the Presbyterian Church, and in Northern Ireland, the Roman Catholic Church.

This pattern is, however, the subject of considerable change in terms of numerical growth and decline, with the *Independents* and *Orthodox* Churches growing steadily, as well as the *Baptist* and *Pentecostal* Churches in some parts of the UK. Parallel to this, there has been a significant decline in the active membership of the *Roman Catholic*, *Anglican* and *Presbyterian* Churches contributing to an overall decline of active Church membership in recent decades.

ORIGINS AND DEVELOPMENT OF CHRISTIANITY

Early Years

Christianity began in Judea, Samaria and Galilee with the life and teaching of Jesus of Nazareth whom his followers believed to be the promised *Messiah* of Jewish tradition. For this reason, the history of the Jewish people is understood by Christians to be a part of the origins of the Christian faith.

After beginning as a group of disciples within Judaism, the Christian Church became distinct from Judaism and spread throughout the Roman Empire to include non-Jewish members. For a long period its followers were persecuted, but eventually, beginning with the conversion of the Roman Emperor Constantine, Christianity ceased to be a persecuted religion and gradually became the official religion of the Roman Empire.

As time went on, the Roman Empire became divided into Eastern and Western parts, in each of which different forms of Christianity became predominant. Although the Churches in the Eastern and Western parts of the Empire had much in common, they grew apart and differences of doctrine and practice began to emerge. By the twelfth century these had resulted in the specific forms of *Eastern* and *Western Christendom* which are the historical roots of the various forms of *Eastern Orthodox* and *Roman Catholic* Christianity of the contemporary world.

Eastern and Western Christendom

After the rise of Islam, the Churches of *Eastern Christendom* in the Middle East and in North Africa found themselves in the situation of religious minorities. By contrast, in *Western Christendom*, Christianity became the major religious tradition, almost entirely supplanting indigenous pagan traditions. In the Middle Ages, Western Christendom was seen as a socio-political unity under two poles of authority. On the one hand, there was the secular power of the Holy Roman Emperor, and on the other, the ecclesiastical and spiritual authority of the *Pope* (the Bishop of Rome, the senior *bishop* of the Church). There was a considerable struggle between these secular and spiritual authorities until the *Reformation* in the sixteenth century signalled the fragmentation of *Western Christendom*.

The Protestant Reformation and the Missionary Movement

Following the *Reformation*, many *Protestant* Churches developed as national Churches having a close relationship with the states in which they were set.

With growing European awareness of the world beyond Europe, both *Protestant* and *Roman Catholic* Christians increasingly became convinced of the need to spread the message of Christianity and to found communities of Christian believers in the countries where European colonies were being established. This development, known as the *missionary movement*, began with the *Roman Catholic* missions of the sixteenth and seventeenth centuries to China, Goa, Japan and the New World and reached its peak during the latter part of the nineteenth century and the first half of the twentieth, with Christian Churches of many denominations being established on every continent.

This process, in turn, contributed to the development of the *ecumenical* (see below for more details) movement towards unity of study and action among the Christian Churches of the world.

Whilst individual Christian missionaries were undoubtedly motivated by genuine Christian convictions about their responsibility for spreading the Christian message, the relationship of this movement to European colonialism and imperialism has, with hindsight, been criticised by many of the European Churches and by the newly established Churches in other continents.

Nevertheless, the missionaries made a significant impact and today, the global focus of Christianity has shifted significantly from Europe and North America, to Africa and Latin America. This shift is reflected in the membership of global Christian organisations such as the World Council of

Churches and is, in the coming millenium, likely to continue.

SOURCES OF CHRISTIAN BELIEFS AND PRACTICES

Scriptures

The Christian scriptures are composed of what Christians have traditionally called the "Old" and "New" *Testaments*, together forming the *Bible*.

The early Christian community affirmed the books of the Jewish Bible as also being scriptures of the Christian Church. They believed that one God speaks through both the Jewish law and prophets as recorded in the Hebrew Scriptures (commonly known among Christians as the *Old Testament*) as well as through Jesus as testified to in the *Gospels*, *Epistles* and other writings (which collectively came to be known among Christians as the *New Testament.*).

The Christian *Old Testament* is similar in content to the Jewish *Tanakh* (see introduction to the Jewish Community), though different in its internal order after the first five books. The *New Testament* is a collection of texts dating from the first and second centuries which describe the impact of Jesus upon the Christian community and beliefs about him, as well as the formation of the early Christian community and the ethical implications of Christian belief.

The four *Gospels* (from the Saxon word *Godspell*, meaning Good News) tell the story and describe the significance of Jesus. They are given the names of four of the first *disciples* (see below) of Jesus - Matthew, Mark, Luke and John.

Then there is the *Book of Acts* which describes the spread of early Christianity; the *Epistles,* in which the leaders of the early Church address problems and issues which arose in the Christian communities; and other writings (such as the *Book of Revelation* which records a series of visions).

The *canon* (or normative contents) of the *New Testament* emerged out of a process of debate and discussion concerning the authenticity and authority of writings which were in circulation among the early Christian communities. The present contents of these scriptures were finalised by a Church Council held in Carthage in 397 CE.

There is still some difference of opinion among Christians today concerning the place within the Scriptures of the books which are collectively known as the *Apocrypha* (literally, the "hidden things") and which cover the so-called *Inter-testamental* period of history between the Greek and Roman occupations of Palestine. *Roman Catholics,* for example, and some other Christians, understand these books to be fully a part of the Scriptures, whilst others see their religious value as less authoritative.

The Scriptures are central to Christian life. However some Christians understand them as being the literal words of God whilst others see them as human testimony, guided by the Spirit of God in all central matters of belief and practice, which bear witness to Jesus as the revelation of God in human flesh.

The Church

The body of those who follow Jesus is known as the *Church*. On the basis of the books which are believed to be sacred scripture the *Church* provides guidance both for the individual Christian believer as well as for Christian communities.

Whilst the Greek word (*ecclesia*) which is translated as *Church* originally referred to the community of believers, the English word *Church* has also come to be used in a variety of other ways. Sometimes (and usually when it begins with a capital letter) it can refer to particular national bodies or world communions such as the Methodist Church or the Roman Catholic Church; sometimes it refers to the buildings in which Christian worship takes place (as when people refer to "the church on the corner of the street") or the local Christian group which is found there (and in these cases the word usually begins with a small "c").

The Creeds

In the early centuries of Christianity *creeds* or summary statements of orthodox beliefs were

143

composed, the most commonly used of which are the Apostles' Creed and the Nicene Creed.

These continue to play a significant role in the worship and doctrinal understandings of the majority of Christians. There are, however, branches of Christianity which have historically been suspicious of the adequacy of credal formulae. Despite this lack of unanimity on the role of creeds the majority of Christians of most branches of Christianity would hold in common a number of key beliefs and concepts.

Tradition

For *Orthodox, Roman Catholic* and *Anglican* Christians, tradition is also a key source of belief and practice. The writers of the texts of the so-called *Patristic* period (the period of the early Church *Fathers*) are of great importance for many Christians. This is particularly the case among *Orthodox* Christians. Also important for sustaining belief and practice, although less authoritative, are the writings of the great Christian *saints* (see below) throughout history.

KEY CHRISTIAN BELIEFS

Jesus

Christianity can today be found in a wide variety of forms, many of which are mirrored in the diversity of Churches and Christian traditions found in the UK. The common focus of Christianity is upon the life and teachings of Jesus of Nazareth. Although Christian groups differ to some extent in their interpretations of the exact significance of his teaching, life and death and *resurrection* (rising from death), all Christian groups have these matters at the heart of their teaching and way of life.

The earliest Christian confession of faith appears to have been the expression "Jesus is Lord" - in other words, he was seen as the criterion by which all of life was to be judged and evaluated.

The name *Christian* was originally a nickname given to the followers of Jesus who was confessed by these early followers to be the *Christ*. The English word *Christ* comes from the Greek *Christos* which is, in turn, a translation of the

Hebrew *Mashiah*. Although this word often appears together with Jesus as if Jesus Christ is a personal name, Jesus is in fact the personal name and *Christ* is a title because the early Christians believed that Jesus fulfilled the expectations of the Jewish people for the *Messiah* (the Anointed One - a coming deliverer).

Christians turn to the four *Gospels* and the Book of the Acts of the Apostles for an account and explanation of the origins of Christianity and the story of Jesus and its significance.

These indicate that Jesus was born in Bethlehem, approximately two thousand years ago; that he grew up in the town of Nazareth in the region known as the Galilee; that when he was about thirty years old he began to teach, heal and travel through Judea, Samaria and Galilee with a group of *disciples* (learners) from among whom he chose twelve *apostles* (messengers - from the Greek *apostolos*); that he associated with the disreputable and social and religious outcasts.

They also indicate that he taught that the self-righteous were less likely to be accepted by God than these outcasts; that he came into conflict with the Jewish authorities; that he was arrested by the Roman occupiers of the country and put to death by *crucifixion*; that within three days his tomb was empty and his disciples reported meeting with him, talking with him and eating with him; and that the disciples believed that he had been raised from the dead and had ascended to be with God the Father.

The *Acts of the Apostles* describes the early Christian community's experience of the coming of the Holy Spirit and the spread of the new faith. These texts and the *Epistles* (from the Greek *epistole*, meaning "letter") reveal the significance of Jesus for the earliest Christians and show something of Christianity's development in a variety of different locations throughout the Mediterranean area. The *Epistles*, in particular, portray Jesus as the key to God's eternal activity in the world, and they attempt to apply his teaching to the daily lives of the early Christian communities.

God, Incarnation and Revelation

Christians are monotheists. They believe that there is one God who has been revealed as *Creator* and *Sustainer* of all that is. They also believe that whilst this one God has manifested himself in many different places and times, and in particular through the history and faith of the Jewish people, he has shown his nature most clearly in the life, teaching, death and *resurrection* of Jesus of Nazareth.

Indeed, it is traditionally believed that God himself was present in Jesus, born as a Jew, and that in and through Jesus, God took humanity upon himself and was most fully revealed. This is called the *incarnation* (from the Latin word for body). In the classical definition of the Council of Chalcedon this is expressed by the paradoxical statement that Jesus was both fully human and fully divine. By this the belief was expressed that Jesus was fully human in all respects except for *sin* (falling short of the will of God) and yet also that God was fully present in his human vulnerability.

It is because of belief in the *incarnation* that, in Christian understanding, Jesus' teachings, such as the well-known Sermon on the Mount, cannot ultimately be separated from his life, death and *resurrection* as the embodiment of the nature of God. Through Jesus, understood as the revelation of God made flesh, the nature of God is pre-eminently seen as being that of self-giving love (signified by the use of the Greek word *agape*, one of three Greek words translated into English by the word love, the others approximating more to love as friendship and love as sexual love).

The epitome of this self-giving love is seen in the death of Jesus, by *crucifixion* (a Roman method of execution for political rebels) on a *cross* (the implement of execution). In the death of Jesus, Christians believe that God plumbed the depths of human experience in death as the last enemy. The belief in the *resurrection* affirms that this last enemy has been conquered and, because of this conquest of death by Jesus, no other powers can bind and enslave any who put their trust in him.

Atonement

Jesus is therefore seen as the pivotal historical focus of God's activity. This activity is first of all seen as *creative* and God is understood as the origin of all things, both seen and unseen. It is also seen as *redemptive* (putting right that which has gone wrong), because the world and human beings within it are seen as fundamentally flawed.

This has classically been expressed in Christian doctrine by the ideas of *the Fall* and of *Original Sin* - that there is something about the human condition which, although it is seen as being in the *image of God* and thus reflecting his nature to some extent, is also fundamentally wrong prior to any individual ethical choices being made. Therefore in the Christian vision, human nature is not perfectable by human effort alone, but only with the assistance of divine help (often expressed by the word *grace*).

This divine intervention is seen as objectively taking place in the death and *resurrection* of Jesus. Convictions about it are therefore often expressed using the language of sacrifice. By overcoming the final enemy of death, Christians believe that in Jesus God has brought about an *atonement* (at-one-ment or reconciliation) between humanity and God.

This objective *atonement* is believed to open up the way for those who believe in Jesus to participate in his *resurrection* victory over the powers of death and sin. Acting as *Redeemer*, God therefore brings the world back to its purpose as originally intended by God acting as *Creator*. Christianity affirms that this will be finally achieved at the end of all things when God will become "all in all", and that the life, death and *resurrection* of Jesus is an *eschatological* (from the Greek word *eschaton*, meaning the "last things") foretaste and signalling of this.

The Holy Trinity

Jesus is seen as the most complete expression and revelation of God, but the Christian vision of God is wider than that which is seen in the person of Jesus alone and this conviction about the finally unfathomable nature of God is expressed in the Christian doctrine, which is also referred to as a *Mystery* of the *Holy Trinity*.

In this doctrine, God is said to be three persons (not to be understood in the modern English language sense of three independent individuals) in one God. In this belief all things are affirmed to be created by the Father, through *Christ*, (spoken of as the *Son*, although this does not imply physical sonship) and in the Spirit.

It is important to realise that this doctrine is not intended to be understood as tritheism (belief in three individual Gods). It is, rather, intended to express belief in one God in a way which signifies the dynamic interrelationship of community, interdependence and unity. Christian people's experience of God is of God as Father, of God revealed in and through Jesus, and also of being inspired and empowered by God's Holy Spirit.

Historically, the doctrine developed as a formulation of the Christian people's threefold experience of the presence and activity of God rather than in abstract philosophical speculation.

By this doctrine Christians give expression to their experience and faith that it is by the Spirit of God, in and through God revealed and active in Jesus, that Christians worship God as the Father, the *Creator* and *Redeemer* of all things, seeking to do his will, and believing that they are enabled to participate in the eternal communion of God, the Father, Son and Holy Spirit.

The Virgin Mary

The Virgin Mary is a focus of devotion for millions of Christians. Hundreds of Church buildings in the UK that are within the *Roman Catholic*, *Anglican* and *Orthodox* traditions are named after her.

However, Christians have varying views about the precise place which Mary has within Christian doctrine and life. In general they have traditionally believed that Jesus had no human father but was conceived by the Virgin Mary through the Holy Spirit and that she is to be honoured for her role of being the Mother of Jesus. The *Roman Catholic* and *Orthodox*

traditions, however, emphasise this unique role more than the *Protestant* Churches do.

Orthodox tradition calls Mary *Theotokos* (Greek for God-bearer) since it is through her that the incarnation is believed to have taken place. She is therefore held to have a special role as a link between the spiritual and material worlds. Among *Roman Catholics* Mary is known as the *Queen of Heaven*. In both the *Orthodox* and *Roman Catholic* traditions, Christian believers regularly address prayers to Mary, asking her to intercede with Jesus on behalf of those who pray to her. Some in the *Anglican* tradition also share in the veneration of Mary.

The official teaching of the *Roman Catholic* Church goes beyond the veneration of Mary as the most honoured of human beings to proclaim its belief that Mary, by the singular *grace* of God, was born without *original sin*. This is known as the doctrine of the *Immaculate Conception*. The vast majority of *Protestant* Christians do not accept this doctrine and also would not normally pray to Mary, even though she is held in honour by them as the Mother of Jesus.

The Saints

In some branches of Christianity, individual Christian men and women, who are recognised to have led particularly holy and exemplary lives manifesting the grace and power of God, are venerated within Christian corporate worship. They are called *saints* and are looked to for help and support in the individual Christian's prayers. This is particularly true of both *Orthodox* and *Roman Catholic* Christianity where veneration of the *saints* underlines the sense of the Church as being composed of all Christian people, both present and past.

Many Church buildings are named after individual *saints* and *saints* are often associated with places of Christian pilgrimage. In the early Christian Church, the scriptures referred to all Christians believers as "the saints" (meaning the "set apart ones") as distinct from the more specialised and restrictive use of the term which developed in the course of Church history.

TRADITIONS IN CHRISTIANITY

The principal Christian traditions are the *Roman Catholic, Orthodox, Protestant* and *Pentecostal* traditions. The *Anglican* tradition, of which the Church of England is a part, sees itself as both *Reformed* and *Catholic* in tradition. These traditions share many of the key beliefs described above, but they also have their own distinctive teachings, ethos and emphases, some of which are indicated below:

Roman Catholic

The Roman Catholic Church is a global Church which has around a half of the world's Christians. It understands itself as having a number of characteristics supporting its claim to be in an authentic line of transmission of the Christian faith from the earliest apostles until today.

First of all, this sense of continuity is expressed as its *Apostolicity*. The line of succession from the first leaders of the Church who were appointed by Jesus, and particularly from the Apostle Peter (whose successor is understood by *Roman Catholic* Christians to be the *Pope,* by virtue of his office as the Bishop of Rome) is believed to be safeguarded by the order of the *bishops* who are in communion with the *Pope*. The *bishops* are responsible for the teaching and discipline of the Church and for ordaining *priests* to serve local Christian communities.

It is on the basis of this belief in the *Apostolic Succession* that the *Roman Catholic* Church believes it has preserved the authentic Tradition of the Christian Church. In *Roman Catholic* teaching, tradition is also seen as a source of authority, together with the Scriptures, as both are interpreted by the teaching authority of the Church. This teaching authority is seen as being expressed in Church Councils, such as the most recent one, the Second Vatican Council, as well as in the collective role of the *bishops* of the Church and especially that of the *Pope* making authoritative pronouncements.

Combined with this *Apostolicity* and Tradition, however, is the Roman Catholic Church's commitment to *Catholicity*. This refers to the universality and unity-in-diversity of the Church in all geographical contexts and also throughout space and time.

There is therefore a great sense of belonging to a living tradition reflecting the diversity of humanity and yet kept in unity particularly by celebration of the *Mass* (see below) as the focus of unity. Participation in the *Roman Catholic Mass* generally requires a belonging to the structures of the Church in the sense of being in communion with the *bishops* and the *Pope* who are seen as maintaining the Church's *Apostolicity*.

Orthodox

The Churches of the *Orthodox* tradition of Christianity understand themselves to represent the tradition and practice of the undivided Church before the separation of Eastern and Western Christendom. *Orthodoxy* thus claims to represent a more original form of Christianity whose doctrine has not been distorted by alien philosophical speculations nor its style of Church government by inappropriate political traditions of secular power and authority.

The *Orthodox* give central importance to the doctrine of the *Holy Trinity*. It is this, in fact, which lies behind the important controversy between Orthodoxy and Western Christendom known as the *filioque* controversy. This is the debate over whether, within the creeds of the Church it should be said that, with reference to Trinitarian doctrine, the Spirit "proceeds from the Father", the source of all Godhead (the *Orthodox* position) or "from the Father and the Son" (the Western position). In the Western understanding its formulation expresses that the Spirit of God is always manifested in terms of the character and person of Jesus. The *Orthodox* are concerned that such a formulation subordinates the role of Spirit to that of Jesus.

The *Orthodox* tradition has a great emphasis on prayer, on spirituality and on celebration of the *Liturgy*. In Church government, it has so-called *autocephalous* (Greek meaning independently governed) Churches with their own *patriarchs* (senior bishops), although all *Orthodox* Churches recognise the Patriarch of Constantinople as the so-called *Ecumenical Patriarch* or senior *Patriarch*.

Protestant

Protestant is the name given to the Christian groupings whose particular character derives from the sixteenth and seventeenth century division in the Church in Europe which is generally referred to as the *Reformation*.

Among *Protestant* Churches there is a great variety in terms of belief and practice, particularly with respect to how the Church should be internally governed and organised (see section on Christian Organisations and Personnel).

There are also significant differences between those *Protestant* Christian traditions which have seen a close relationship with the State and/or the nation in a positive light (for example, the *Anglican* Church of England in England and the *Presbyterian* Church of Scotland in Scotland) and those traditions, generally known as the *Free Churches*, which have advocated the complete separation of the Church and the State (such as the *Baptists*).

In general, the *Protestant* tradition emphasises the supremacy of the scriptures in all matters of belief and Church government, although it also emphasises the role of the individual believer, under the guidance of the Holy Spirit, in reading and interpreting the text of the Bible. It places emphasis upon the centrality of personal faith in Jesus and in some *Protestant* traditions, such as *Methodism,* this has also been supplemented by a focus on the need for an individual personal experience of *conversion* (from the Greek word *metanoia* meaning "change of mind").

Most *Protestant* Churches also place particular emphasis upon preaching as the proclamation of the Word of God in scripture, through which God is believed to offer eternal life in Christ, through the Holy Spirit, and which is believed to promote the authority and foundation for Christian life.

Anglican

The *Anglican* tradition is a worldwide Christian tradition composed of autonomous Churches which owe their historical origins to the emergence of the Church of England in its

attempt to be comprehensive and which therefore understand themselves as being both *Reformed* and *Catholic* in tradition. This special self-understanding results from the distinctive course of events of the *Reformation* in England and Wales.

Anglicanism strives for balance in all things. In doctrine, this is expressed by affirming scripture, tradition and human reason as God–given instruments for interpreting revelation. In matters of authority reason is seen as a necessary interpreter of scripture and tradition, and in matters of church order individual and *parochial* (the level of the local *parish*) freedom is combined with an *episcopal* (the order of *bishops*) Church structure.

There is also an attempt to balance a developed liturgical life and private devotion with a focus on scripture and social responsibility. This ideal is described as one of *comprehensiveness* in terms of embracing a breadth of Christian belief and practice and contains several identifiable theological and *liturgical* (from the Greek *leiturgia* and referring to styles of worship) streams of life – *Evangelical* (sometimes called *Low Church*), *Anglo-Catholic* (sometimes called *High Church*), *Broad Church* (or *Liberal)* and *Charismatic* (see below for an expanation of these terms).

Pentecostal

The *Pentecostal* tradition is historically rooted in *Protestantism* but there are good doctrinal and numerical reasons for regarding it as a new tradition of Christianity which has come to global prominence in the course of the twentieth century. The *Pentecostal* tradition shares with the *Protestant* tradition generally a commitment to the primacy of the scriptures for individual and Church life, as well as the necessity of personal faith in, and commitment to, Jesus.

However, *Pentecostalism* goes further to assert that there is no gap in terms of the power and love of God between what was available to the first Christian believers as recorded in the scriptural book *The Acts of the Apostles* and that which is available to Christians today.

Pentecostals believe in the necessity of experiencing this power and love as well as believing in it, and see an event which they describe as the experience of *baptism in the Spirit* as being the occasion in and through which individuals can gain access to the spiritual gifts of God.

In classical *Pentecostal* practice, the outward sign of this *baptism in the Spirit* has often been seen as the ability to engage in what is described as *speaking in tongues*. More technically this phenomenon is known as *glossolalia* (from the Greek). This involves the individual engaging in the production of sounds, directed in praise and worship to God, which do not make up words of the person's day-to-day language. However, although this has become particularly identified with *Pentecostalism*, the tradition's own emphasis is not solely upon this gift but upon all the spiritual gifts of God, including the gifts of prophecy and healing and their availability to Christian believers today.

Restorationist and House Church Movements

During the 1970s and 1980s, European Christianity has seen the growth of the so-called *Restorationist* and *House Church* movements. These represent a sector of Christian life in the UK which has organised itself separately from the traditional Christian denominations.

Christians in these movements often feel that the older Churches have stifled the real spirit of Christianity in outmoded structures. They therefore seek to develop forms of organisation and networking which they believe to be more consistent with those that were found among the earliest Christian communities. Some of these groups meet in private houses and are thus known as *House Churches*, whilst others meet in their own, larger, buildings or in secular buildings such as schools and cinemas.

Quakers and Unitarians

As well as the traditions outlined above, there are also groups which do not fit neatly into any of these categories but which have a historical and, in many cases, a contemporary connection with the *Protestant* tradition.

Among these are the *Quakers* (officially known as the Religious Society of Friends) and the *Unitarians*. Both of these traditions have historical roots in *Protestant* Christianity. At the same time, both contain people who would not wish to be restricted, as they would understand it, by the orthodoxies of belief or forms of Church order of the *Protestant* or other Churches. Indeed, some of the members of these traditions would not wish to be identified specifically as Christian in any way which they believed separated them from people of other religions or, sometimes, also from humanists.

Churchmanship

Within many of the Church organisations of these major traditions of Christianity there are streams or tendencies of what is often called *churchmanship*. In other words, there are groups of Christians in all the major traditions who have particular emphases within their Christian understanding and life. Among the principal tendencies are the following.

Anglo-Catholic

Anglo-Catholics are *Anglican* Christians who emphasise the *Catholic* inheritance of the *Anglican* tradition and use many externals of *Catholic* practice, especially in their worship including, for example, devotion to Mary.

Charismatic

Charismatic Christianity is the name given to a movement which is historically related to the *Pentecostal* branch of Christianity, but which is now present in all other major branches of Christianity. It is characterised by an emphasis on the direct experience of the Holy Spirit being available to Christian believers today, including the possibility that the Holy Spirit can produce miraculous works in the contemporary world. *Charismatic* Christians do not necessarily adopt particular items of *Pentecostal* theology or practice such as the emphasis on speaking with tongues as a necessary evidence of *baptism in the Spirit* or, indeed, even the idea of a specific identifiable event described by this name.

Evangelical

Evangelicals are Christians who draw upon the inheritance of the *Reformation* particularly as it developed in the eighteenth and nineteenth centuries, and try to practise a form of Christianity which they believe is true to the Christian scriptures, viewed as being the supreme authority for Christian life which must be based upon a personal decision of faith in Jesus. This also entails efforts to bring others into the Christian Church by means of *evangelism* (meaning Good News - from the Greek word *euangelion*). *Evangelism* means the sharing of good news of what Christians believe God has done in and offers through Jesus.

Whilst *Evangelical* Christians are centrally concerned with this, other Christians who would not use this word to describe their own form of Christianity, also engage in *evangelism* since bearing witness to Jesus is understood to be obligatory upon all Christians.

Liberal

Liberal Christians are those Christians who place emphasis on a contextualised understanding and practice of Christianity in the modern world and believe that rationality and contemporary relevance are crucially important for the meaning and communication of the Christian message.

The Ecumenical Movement

Particularly during the twentieth century, the *Ecumenical Movement* (from the Greek *oikumene*, meaning the whole inhabited earth) has developed in Christianity and represents a desire among Christians of all traditions to find a universal Christian fellowship which transcends all divisions and boundaries.

This global movement has sometimes found expression in the search for common Church structures and organisations and attempts to form united Churches out of two or more formerly separate Churches. The United Reformed Church is one example of a new Church structure formed in the UK from *Presbyterian*, *Congregationalist* and *Churches of Christ* traditions. It has also sought to achieve closer co-operation and working relationships in common projects between Christians who remain in distinct organisational structures, which is the current model being followed by the Council of Churches for Britain and Ireland and also by the various so-called *"ecumenical instruments"* (see Christian listings) operating at the national levels within the British Isles.

CHRISTIAN LIFE

Christian believers are called upon to live according to the pattern of Jesus' life which is seen as being characterised by sacrificial, reciprocal and self-giving love or *agape* (the Greek word for this form of love, as in Jesus' command to his disciples to "love one another as I have loved you"). It is believed that Christians are given the Holy Spirit of God to enable them to live in this way.

Sin and Grace

Without the assistance of the power of God, Christianity sees human beings as being gripped by self-centredness and powers beyond their control. This condition is described as an enslavement to *sin*. The release which believers experience when they put their trust in God through Jesus is spoken of as *salvation*. This means liberation from all that enslaves human beings in terms of self-centredness. In Christian life there is a dynamic tension between the belief that one is already freed from *sin* and yet one is not yet fully free.

The activity by which God is believed to draw people into his purposes is referred to as *grace*, which is a word that expresses dependence upon the gift of God's power in contrast to reliance upon human goodness or self-sufficiency. It is believed that although Jesus was crucified God raised him from death and that his death and *resurrection* are now the means for opening up a new quality of life (known as *eternal life*) to all who put their trust in him.

This trust is described by the word *faith*, which is understood to be evoked and sustained through the power of God known as the Holy Spirit who is God at work in and among believers. Christians believe that they can draw upon this power of God through their practice of prayer and that they are supported in their practice of the Christian life by participation in fellowship with other Christian believers within the Church.

Baptism

The rite of *baptism* in water accompanied by prayer is understood as marking a person's entry into the Christian Church. For this reason, in many older church buildings the baptismal *font* (in most Churches a small, standing receptacle which holds the water used in *baptism*) is often found near the door of the Church underlining the symbolism of the rite of *baptism*.

In the *Anglican, Roman Catholic, Reformed,* and *Orthodox* Churches the baptismal rite is generally administered to babies or infants presented for *baptism* by their parents who, together with friends or relatives designated as *Godparents*, make promises on behalf of the infant. In all of these Churches except the *Orthodox* Churches infant *baptism* is usually conducted by use of a small token amount of water being poured on the child's head. In the *Orthodox* Churches, the baby is immersed three times in the baptismal waters. In some traditions infant *baptism* is often popularly known as *Christening*, from the ancient practice of giving candidates for *baptism* a Christian name to indicate their new identity as believers and members of the *Church*.

Some Christian traditions, such as the *Baptist* and *Pentecostal* movements, believe that *baptism* should only be administered to those who are capable of a conscious and personal confession of Christian faith. In these traditions *baptism* is therefore normally administered only to teenagers and adults professing Christian belief, generally by complete immersion in the baptismal waters. Such Churches generally have specially constructed sunken *baptistries* (or tanks) designed for this purpose.

There are a few Christian traditions, such as that of the Society of Friends and the Salvation Army which do not practise *baptism* since their emphasis is on a spiritual and inner *baptism* rather than on outward signs such as washing in water.

Confirmation

In the *Anglican* tradition, *confirmation* is available to those wishing to confirm their faith and baptism. In the *Roman Catholic* tradition, *confirmation* is a completion of *baptism*, making possible the fuller life given at *baptism* and is necessary for complete initiation into the Church and is associated with the Christian believer receiving the Holy Spirit of God in a special way. Among those who have grown up within the Church *confirmation* often takes place in the early teenage years, although it may be later.

Ethics and Discipleship

Christians understand themselves as *disciples* (learners) of Jesus who are called to follow his example. However, ethical decision-making in particular cases is conducted differently by Christians in different traditions. For all Christians, the example of Jesus and the teachings of the Bible are key sources for decision and practice. For Christians in the *Protestant* tradition, however, the role of individual conscience is also quite important in deciding how to apply the teachings of the Bible.

This is also true in the *Roman Catholic* tradition, although in forming conscience, there is a strong emphasis on the corporate teaching of the Church expressed in particular through its *bishops* and, supremely, through the Councils of the Church and the official pronouncements of the *Pope* (known as *Encyclicals*). These are often very specific in the guidance they give to individual believers and some aspects are reinforced through the application of measures of Church discipline.

Christians do not generally have any dietary regulations although some Christians observe the discipline of abstaining from certain foods during the season of *Lent* (see the section on Calendar and Festivals). There are also some, especially those within the *Protestant* tradition, who refrain from drinking alcohol.

Monks, Nuns and Religious

The majority of Christians lead ordinary lives at work in the world and in families, but from the earliest years of Christianity some have felt called to form special groups in which they could aim to share a more complete devotion to Jesus and to the pattern of his life and work. This has involved taking lifetime vows of poverty, chastity and obedience.

Those who are part of *Orders* and are known as *monks* (men) and *nuns* (women) make what are known as "solemn vows". There are also members of *Congregations* (and these are the majority) who are called *Religious* and who make what are known as "simple vows". Both kinds of vow are, however, generally binding. There are also *Religious Brothers* who are not necessarily *monks*, but who chose not to be ordained *priests* whilst making vows to live in community.

Monks and *nuns* and *Religious* can be found in the contemporary *Roman Catholic, Orthodox* and *Anglican* Churches. The particular pattern of life of a group of *monks* and *nuns* or *Religious* varies according to the self-understanding of the group of which they are a part which is, in turn, based upon the life and teachings of its founder. Some are more concerned with prayer and meditation and retreat from the world whilst others are more concerned with practical service in the world.

Among the more well-known *Orders* that have grown up in Western Christianity are the Jesuits (founded by St. Ignatius of Loyola and known for teaching and missionary work); the *Benedictines* (founded by St. Benedict and with an emphasis on prayer, work and the reading of holy books), the *Dominicans* (known for intellectual study and rigour), and the *Carmelites* (known for silent prayer and meditation).

Many other organisations and groups exist within and with the blessing of the Churches, having developed as responses to particular contemporary needs or in order to strengthen and renew Christian life, including some *ecumenical* communities such as Iona in Scotland and Lee Abbey in Devon, England.

CHRISTIAN WORSHIP

Some Christian buildings are referred to as "*churches*", but in some *Protestant* branches of Christianity, especially among the so-called *Free Churches*, this word is generally reserved for describing the people who make up the community of the Church.

In these cases, in England and Wales (though not generally in Scotland or Ireland) the word *chapel* is used to describe the building, instead of *church*. However, the word *chapel* is also used among *Roman Catholics* and *Anglicans* to denote a small *church* building or a small part of a larger building.

Some Christians do not meet in recognisably religious buildings at all but in one another's homes or in public meeting places such as schools or cinemas, as with the so-called *House Church movement* which is a growing form of Christian life in the UK.

Church Buildings

From the outside, Christian places of worship are very varied in appearance, although buildings which are many centuries old have a range of recognisable external features. One of the most famous is the church tower or spire which can make church buildings geographical landmarks in both town and countryside. Very old buildings of this kind are generally now in the *Anglican* Christian tradition, although in origin many of them pre-date the *Reformation*. At the other end of the spectrum, some Christian places of worship have the external appearance of a simple rectangular hall.

Once inside a building there is again a very wide variety in terms of what might be found. At one end of this spectrum, if visiting a *Baptist* Chapel one will often find an interior which is generally bare of religious symbols except perhaps for a wooden cross on the wall, but is focused at one end on the *pulpit* (the raised platform from which the preacher addresses the congregation) and perhaps has a simple table from which the service of *Holy Communion* (see below) is led.

In most *Protestant* and *Catholic* churches there will be seats for the congregation, but in *Orthodox* Churches the congregation will, in general, stand during the service. A place of worship in the *Orthodox* tradition may be brightly coloured and have many religious pictures called *icons* which are believed to make available to the worshipper the spiritual realities they depict in iconographic form. Rather than an elevated *pulpit* there may be a modest *lectern* (reading desk). Instead of a simple table for *Communion*, the *Orthodox* Church will have an *altar* which is hidden from general view behind a screen known as an *iconostasis*. This is a screen which is covered in *icons* and has doors in the middle through which the *priest* passes to bring the bread and wine out from the altar to the congregation.

In *Roman Catholic* and *Anglo-Catholic Anglican* Churches the main focal point is the *altar*. There will also be statues of the Virgin Mary and perhaps also of saints. These statues are held in reverence by the worshippers although they are understood to be no more than images which help to focus devotion. In *Orthodox*, *Roman Catholic* and *Anglo-Catholic Anglican* churches, services of worship may be accompanied by the use of incense.

Holy Communion

For the majority of Christians the service of *Holy Communion* is the most characteristic and central act of Christian worship, although some Christians such as the Society of Friends (popularly known as the Quakers) and the Salvation Army do not observe it. *Communion* means sharing (from the Latin *communio*).

It is believed that the act was instituted by Jesus himself at what is known as the *Last Supper* when Jesus blessed bread and wine which he shared with his disciples before his crucifixion. The *Holy Communion* is also known as the *Eucharist* (from

the Greek word *eucharistea*, meaning thanksgiving); among *Roman Catholics* as the *Mass* (probably originating from Latin words spoken at the end of the service "*ita missa est*" meaning "go, you are dismissed"); among the *Orthodox* Churches as the *Divine Liturgy* (originating from the Greek word *leitourgia*, meaning service); and among some *Protestant* Churches as the *Lord's Supper* or the *Breaking of Bread*.

The content, interpretation and frequency of this event varies considerably among Christians of different traditions. *Roman Catholic* churches celebrate the *Mass* daily as well as some *Anglican* churches (especially those in the *Anglo-Catholic* tradition). Other Churches do so weekly on Sundays. *Baptist* and *United Reformed* churches might do so only once or twice a month. In most of these Churches, preaching is integral to the celebration of *Holy Communion*.

The form of the *eucharist* differs between different Churches. Most *Roman Catholics* only sometimes receive wine and generally receive a flat wafer of unleavened bread. *Orthodox* Christians receive a small piece of bread dipped in wine from a long spoon. In some *Protestant* Churches bread is taken from a single loaf and each individual receives an individual cup of wine (which may be non-alcoholic). In most churches, the wine is drunk from a common cup.

In *Roman Catholic*, *Orthodox* and *Anglican* Churches the congregation usually go up to the front of the church to receive the communion either from the *priest* or from *eucharistic ministers* who are lay people authorised to assist the priest in the distribution of the *Mass*. In many *Protestant* Churches the bread and wine is taken out to the congregation by lay officers of the church or is passed from member to member.

The *Protestant* traditions generally see *Holy Communion* as a remembrance of the death and resurrection with God's act of *atonement* in Jesus being symbolised by the bread and wine representing his body and blood. Some see this more in terms of memory and memorial whilst others emphasise the spiritual nourishment of the believer with a sense of reliance upon the indwelling Spirit of God.

Among the *Roman Catholics* and the *Orthodox* the elements of the bread and wine are seen as, in a real sense, re-presenting the body and blood so that in the sharing of the bread and wine the faithful can actually have communion with the risen Jesus. Among *Roman Catholics, First Communion*, often undertaken by children at around the age of seven or eight, is of great personal and family significance and marks a personal acceptance of the *baptismal* vows made by godparents on behalf of the child.

Preaching

All the denominations in the UK give an important place to *preaching* within worship. This is particularly the case within the Churches of the *Reformation* and among Churches established following the *Evangelical Revival* of the seventeenth and eighteenth centuries. These denominations give equal prominence to preaching of the Word and to the celebration of the sacrament of Holy *Communion*. Preaching is normally a particular responsibility of *ordained ministers*, but most Churches also recognise appropriately trained lay preachers who share in the ministry of preaching based upon the scriptures.

Prayer

In addition to *eucharistic* worship, all Churches also have other corporate forms of public prayer. In both public and private prayer the *Lord's Prayer* is important. It is the prayer which Jesus is recorded in the *Gospels* as having taught his first disciples and is therefore a pattern for all Christian prayer. In addition to participating in corporate prayer and worship many individual Christians have private and personal disciplines of prayer, scriptural study and meditation.

CHRISTIAN CALENDAR AND FESTIVALS

The Christian Calendar

The Christian calendar dates world history in relation to what was originally believed to have been the year of the birth of Jesus. Because of the

Christian belief in the *incarnation*, this is seen as being the pivotal point of world history. It is in this context that the letters "AD" (from the first letters of the Latin words *Anno Domini*, meaning "In the Year of our Lord") and "BC" for "Before Christ" came to be used for dating world history.

Sunday

Christianity inherited its seven day week from Judaism. Sunday is generally observed as the day of assembly for Christian worship because it is the day of the week on which Jesus is believed to have been raised from death and is therefore a weekly celebration of this *resurrection* and new beginning.

The exception to this is in the so-called *Sabbatarian* or *Seventh Day* Churches which believe that the commandment to the Jews to keep the seventh day (Saturday) holy is still binding after the coming of Jesus.

The form of Sunday observance varies widely among Christians with many *Roman Catholics* attending *Mass* on Sunday or perhaps Saturday evening since, following the Biblical tradition, the day (in this case, Sunday) is seen as commencing in the evening. Some *Protestants* refrain from employment or secular recreation for the whole day together with their participation in morning and evening worship.

The Church Year and Festivals

The liturgical year marking key events and commemorating special events is particularly important for *Roman Catholics, Orthodox* and *Anglicans*. Most *Protestant* Churches of the *Reformed* and *Congregational* traditions formally and corporately observe only those days which they feel are central to the Christian story – that is, Sundays, *Holy Week, Easter, Pentecost* and *Christmas* (see below). In some small Christian groupings these are seen as, at best, of marginal importance, and at worst as a corruption of pure Christianity.

The cycle of festivals in the Christian year is threefold. There is an *Easter* cycle, the dates of which vary in relation to the Gregorian calendar in common social use in the UK. The *Christmas* cycle of festivals has dates which are fixed within the Gregorian calendar. There is then a third cycle of festivals and commemorations of saints and martyrs of the Church which are observed on fixed dates within the Gregorian calendar. A number of *Orthodox* Churches follow the so-called Julian calendar which, in the present century, is thirteen days behind the date of the Gregorian calendar.

The *Roman Catholic Church* has prescribed certain days as holy days of obligation when believers are expected to attend Mass. In England, Scotland and Wales, this includes all Sundays together with *Christmas Day, Ascension Day*, the *Assumption of the Blessed Virgin Mary, All Saints' Day, Saints Peter and Paul*, and in England and Wales only, *Corpus Christi* and *Epiphany*.

Advent
(November-December)

For Western Churches, *Advent* marks the beginning of the liturgical cycle. *Advent* means "coming" and it refers to the coming of Jesus into the world. The season is observed by Western Christians as a solemn preparatory season for Christmas, beginning from the fourth Sunday before *Christmas*.

Christmas
(December 25th)

Celebrates the birth of Jesus, the precise date of which is unknown, but the Roman Church fixed it on 25th December to coincide with the winter solstice. Some *Orthodox* Churches keep to the pre-Gregorian calendar date for the celebration of the birth of Jesus, which is on 7th January. The twelfth night of Christmas closes the Christmas season since it marks the story of the coming of the Magi or Wise Men to visit the infant Jesus.

Feast of the Holy Innocents
(28th December)

Commemorates the killing of innocent children in Bethlehem by King Herod out of his fear of the message of the wise men concerning the birth of a new king.

Epiphany
(January)

The word is Greek meaning "manifestation". In the *Orthodox* Churches, this refers to the manifestation of Jesus at his baptism as the son of God. In the Western Churches *Epiphany* celebrates Jesus' adoration by the Magi or Wise Men and his being revealed to the *Gentiles* (non-Jews).

Shrove Tuesday
(February)

Is the day before the start of *Lent* and has a number of traditional and popular cultural customs attached to it. The name comes from the Middle English word *shriven* which referred to the practice of making confession before the beginning of *Lent*. The popular custom of making pancakes arose from the need to get rid of eggs before *Lent* when fasting begins.

Lent
(February-March/April)

Is a period of forty days, excluding Sundays, between *Ash Wednesday* and the Saturday before *Easter*. It is a preparation for *Easter*. Its roots can be found in the *Gospel* stories of Jesus being tempted for forty days in the wilderness prior to the commencement of his public ministry. In the *Orthodox* tradition it is known as the *Great Fast* and starts on the Monday before the first Sunday of *Lent* rather than on the Wednesday as in the Western Churches. It is a season of penitence and preparation in which Christians often abstain from some foods and/or luxuries.

Ash Wednesday
(February)

Is the first day of *Lent* and is called this because in some Churches the *priest* marks the forehead of believers with a little ash as a sign of penitence before God. In the *Roman Catholic* tradition it is a day of fasting and abstinence.

The Annunciation of the Blessed Virgin Mary
(March)

Celebrates the announcement of the Angel Gabriel to Mary that she is to give birth to a son to be called Jesus and her assent to this.

Passion Sunday
(March)

On the fifth Sunday in *Lent*, Christians begin to concentrate their thoughts on the *Passion* (or suffering) of Jesus.

Holy Week
(March/April)

The last week of *Lent* which is dedicated to remembering the suffering and death of Jesus.

Palm Sunday
(March/April)

This is the first day of *Holy Week*. On this day Christians are often given pieces of palm leaf in the form of a cross which recall the *Gospel* accounts of how Jesus was greeted by crowds waving palm leaves as he entered into Jerusalem in the last week of his life.

Maundy Thursday
(March/April)

This Thursday in *Holy Week* commemorates the day on which, at his *Last Supper* with his disciples, Jesus instituted the *Holy Communion*. It was also the occasion of Jesus' command to his disciples to wash one another's feet as a sign of mutual humility and service. A feet washing ceremony is held on this day in some Churches. It is also the day on which Jesus gave his disciples the commandment to love one another and when he prayed in a special way for the their unity. In churches in the *Catholic* tradition the altars are generally stripped bare at the end of this day.

Good Friday
(March/April)

The Friday of *Holy Week* which commemorates the crucifixion of Jesus is generally an austere and solemn day, but is called "Good" because Christians believe salvation to be effected through the *crucifixion*. The symbolism of the cross of Jesus lies behind the traditional practice of eating buns marked with a cross on this day. In the Roman Catholic Church, it is a day of fasting and abstinence from meals.

Holy Saturday
(March/April)

In some Christian traditions, special services take place in preparation for *Easter,* and involve the lighting of a *Paschal candle* and the renewal of *baptismal* vows.

Easter
(March/April)

The name derives from the old English *eastre* which was the name for the Spring festival. *Easter* commemorates the resurrection of Jesus and is therefore the central Christian festival and full of joy. It is celebrated on the first Sunday following the first full moon after the vernal equinox. This is also the first Sunday after *Passover* (the Jewish festival of Unleavened Bread).

Its date therefore varies within the solar calendar adopted by western countries. The giving of *Easter* eggs appears to be a survival of an ancient fertility custom. The celebration of *Easter* continues fifty days to *Pentecost* and includes *Ascension*.

Ascension Day
(May)

Is celebrated on the fortieth day after *Easter* and commemorates the last earthly appearance of the Risen Christ. His *ascension* marks his transcending of all earthly limitations. It is always celebrated on a Thursday.

Pentecost
(May/June)

The name derives from the Greek *pentecoste*, meaning fiftieth day and is celebrated on the seventh Sunday after Easter. *Pentecost* (or the Feast of Weeks) is a Jewish harvest festival which has been given a different meaning by the Church. For Christians, it marks the outpouring of the Holy Spirit upon the followers of Jesus and the commencement of the Church's mission to spread the message about Jesus throughout the world. It is sometimes known as *Whitsuntide* which comes from the custom of converts presenting themselves on this day for *baptism* dressed in white clothes.

Trinity Sunday
(June)

Is celebrated in the West on the Sunday following *Pentecost*. The *Orthodox* Churches celebrate *All Saints* on this day. *Trinity Sunday* is devoted to contemplation of the mystery of God which Christians see as an indivisible unity and yet revealed in the inter-related communion of God the Father, Son and Holy Spirit.

Corpus Christi
(June)

Is particularly a *Roman Catholic* festival and celebrates belief in the presence of Jesus in the eucharist in a more joyful way than is the case on *Maundy Thursday* which is a more solemn occasion prior to the observance of *Good Friday*.

Transfiguration
(August)

Recalls the shining of Jesus' face and clothes on the so-called Mount of Transfiguration, when his heavenly glory is believed to have been revealed to his disciples.

Assumption of the Blessed Virgin Mary
(August)

Roman Catholics and *Orthodox* (who call it the *Dormition* - the falling asleep of the Mother of God) celebrates the taking up of Mary, body and soul, into heaven.

Birth of the Blessed Virgin Mary
(September)

Is a feast commemorating the birth of the Mother of Jesus.

St. Michael and All Angels
(September)

Sometimes known as *Michaelmas* is a season of the Western Church's year in which the ordination of *priests* and *deacons* very often takes place.

Harvest Festival
(September/October)

Although it is not an official part of any Church year the observance of a *Harvest Festival* has become a regular event in many Churches. It celebrates the creativity of God in creation. Such festivals became common from the Middle Ages onwards and in modern times displays of foodstuffs are often made in church and these are then distributed to the needy after the festival is over.

All Saints Day
(1st November)

Since the names of all saints cannot be known this festival commemorates all who are saints. It is popularly associated with *Hallowe'en* (from *all hallows e'en,* the night before *All Saints Day*). *Hallowe'en* really originates in the ancient Celtic and Pagan festival of *Samhain*, which marks the turning of the year and a time when the veil between different realities is seen to be at its thinnest - hence its popular associations.

Immaculate Conception of the Blessed Virgin Mary
(December)

Roman Catholics celebrate the belief that Mary the Mother of Jesus was herself born free of *Original Sin* in order to leave her sinless for the bearing of Jesus.

CHRISTIAN ORGANISATIONS

There are a numerous Christian organisations working within the principal Christian traditions in the UK. In what follows, attention is focused on the Church bodies as such (often described as *ecclesiastical* bodies – from the Latin word *ecclesia* meaning Church).

There are in addition very many Christian organisations with particular foci for their work, some of which are Church-sponsored, others of which are voluntary associations of Christians, such as the Christian Ecology Group and the Christian Disabled Fellowship. The current directory does not attempt to give details of this large sector of organisations. Details can, however, be found by consulting *The UK Christian Handbook*.

The principal characteristics of the ecclesiastical organisations which might be encountered in the UK reflect the wider, global Christian traditions of which they are a part. By reason of history and contemporary circumstances they are, however, to be found in different proportions within the UK and its various nations than is the case internationally.

These variations are closely related to the diverse but connected national histories and societies of these islands. In particular, the contemporary patterns of Christian organisation reflect the various national outworkings of the events of the *Reformation*.

As a religious movement which had political dimensions, the *Reformation* affected different parts of these islands in different ways. In England and Wales it led to the formation of what is now called the Church of England through the 1534 Act of Supremacy of King Henry VIII which made the monarch Supreme Governor of the Church in England and therefore made the Church in England and Wales independent of the jurisdiction of Rome.

The English Church preserved many of the characteristics of *Catholic* Christianity, but it also embraced certain *Protestant* features such as a renewed stress on the role of the Christian scriptures to be read and studied in the English language of ordinary believers rather than in Latin which was accessible only to *priests,* scholars and others who had received a formal education.

During the sixteenth and early seventeenth centuries the Bible and the *Book of Common Prayer* (containing prescribed orders of worship) were translated into Welsh and were quickly accepted into common use in the Churches of Wales.

In the period which followed in England, Christians who continued allegiance to the Bishop of Rome (*Roman Catholics*) were persecuted under King Edward VI (1549-63). Then, under the Catholic Queen Mary (1553-58), *Protestants* (the collective name for the various branches of *Reformation* Christians – including *Lutherans, Zwinglians* and *Calvinists*) were persecuted. Under Queen Elizabeth I, the position was again reversed. By the end of the sixteenth century, *Congregationalists* (those who believe that spiritual authority resides in the local congregation rather than in supra-local Church structures)were emerging, followed during the seventeenth century by *Baptists* and *Quakers* (the popular name for members of the Religious Society of Friends).

In Wales, the substantial majority of the Churches which were formed as a result of these developments worshipped and conducted their congregational and individual Christian life in the Welsh language. Today in Wales, the Union of Welsh Independents, the majority of congregations in the Baptist Union of Wales and the Presbyterian Church of Wales, and churches within the Cymru District of the Methodist Church, continue to conduct their worship and congregational life in Welsh.

After the period of political and religious upheaval which followed the English civil war and the restoration of the monarchy, the 1662 Act of Uniformity led to over one thousand clergy being ejected from their parishes in England due to their refusal to be bound by its provisions which included compulsory use of the *Book of Common Prayer* .

In Scotland, the *Reformation* movement of *Calvinism* (after John Calvin, the French reformer) had the greatest impact. In 1560 the Church of Scotland was reformed along *Calvinist* principles and with a *Presbyterian* form of Church government (based upon a collective of local church leadership of both clergy and non-clerical *elders*, known as *the presbytery*, from the Greek *presbuteros* meaning elder).

Following the union of the crowns of England and Scotland, attempts were made to impose an *Episcopalian* (from the Greek *episcope*, meaning oversight) model centred upon *bishops* operating at the regional level. Those who supported the *Episcopalian* model formed the minority Scottish Episcopal Church which after years of repression eventually became free to play its part in Scottish Christianity. The *Presbyterian* form became the Church of Scotland which is the Established Church in Scotland.

Anglican Churches

There are four distinct *Anglican* Churches in these islands which correspond to its main nations. The Church of England, the Episcopal Church in Scotland, the Church in Wales, and the Church of Ireland (which operates in both Northern Ireland and the Republic of Ireland.) According to the *Christian Handbook 1994/95* there are 26,800,000 Anglicans in the UK. In England and Wales there are 16,562 Anglican places of worship recorded with the General Register Office.

At the regional level, the Churches of the *Anglican* tradition are organised into *Provinces* and *dioceses*. At the local level, they are organised into *parishes* (the neighbourhood area) and *deaneries* (larger groupings of *parishes*). In England, Church of England *parishes* are legal entities and taken together cover the whole country.

The Church of England is the mother Church of the *Anglican* Churches worldwide and the Archbishop of Canterbury is looked to for international leadership within the *Anglican* tradition. It is also the Established Church in England and has a special position in the State which is indicated by a number of its senior *Bishops* having places in the House of Lords.

The Church of England has two *Provinces* (of Canterbury and York) and forty-three dioceses. Although an *Episcopal Church* (led by Bishops),

the legal Government of the Church of England is its *General Synod* which includes three categories of *diocesan* representatives: laity, *priests* and *bishops*, with similar synods operating at *diocesan* and *deanery* levels.

The Episcopal Church of Scotland has seven *dioceses*. It is the smallest of the *Anglican* Churches in these islands and its numerical strength is concentrated in Perthshire and in the north and east of Scotland. The Church of Ireland has two *Provinces* (Dublin and Armagh). The Province of Dublin is almost entirely in the Republic whilst Armagh is mostly in Northern Ireland. The Church in Wales has six *dioceses* and is a bi-lingual Church.

These Anglican Churches in Scotland, Ireland and Wales are not established Churches, the disestablishment of the Church of England in Wales having led, in 1920, to the formation of the Church in Wales.

Roman Catholic Church

Although there is a continuity in English *Roman Catholic* tradition which goes back beyond Henry VIII's repudiation of *Papal* authority, the *Roman Catholic* Church's contemporary strength in England and Wales is mainly due to the nineteenth and early twentieth century immigration of *Roman Catholics* from Ireland.

According to the *UK Christian Handbook 1994/95* there are 5,600,000 *Roman Catholics* in England and Wales, and in England and Wales there are 3,692 places of Roman Catholic worship, certified as such with the Registrar General.

In Scotland, *Roman Catholic* Christianity and *Papal* authority were abolished in 1560, but the *Catholic* tradition survived in the south west and also in the highlands and islands of north-west Scotland. Immigration from Ireland also increased the Scottish *Catholic* population, with a concentration around Glasgow.

In Ireland as a whole the Roman Catholic Church is by far the largest Christian tradition. It is also numerically the largest single Church in Northern Ireland even though *Catholics* are only approximately forty per cent of Northern Ireland's total population. In these islands the Roman Catholic Church has three national *Bishops' Conferences*. There is the Bishops' Conference for England and Wales, another for Scotland, and another for Ireland. However, *Roman Catholic* life is more focused upon the *diocesan* rather than the national level.

Orthodox Churches

The *Orthodox* Churches can be found in numerical strength in the Middle East, and around the Mediterranean and also throughout Eastern Europe. In the UK they are a relatively recent presence, with the arrival of significant migrant groups of Greeks, Russians, Serbs and other ethnic groups with a traditional relationship to *Orthodox* Christianity. The *Orthodox* Churches in the UK are, in fact, still related to these national and ethnic *Orthodox* Churches. The Greek Orthodox Church is numerically the largest, principally due to immigration from Cyprus.

The *UK Christian Handbook 1994/95* gives a figure of 500,000 *Orthodox* in the UK. The Registrar General's lists of places of worship for England and Wales does not keep a running total for a separate category of *Orthodox* churches.

There are now also a growing number of Churches of the *Oriental Orthodox* tradition including Armenians, Copts and Ethiopians. Because the *Orthodox* are not numerically strong, their members are geographically scattered and there is usually only one *Diocese* for each Church. There is, however, a Council of Oriental and Orthodox Churches which seeks to group these Churches together co-operatively.

Protestant Churches

Presbyterianism

The numerically largest *Protestant* tradition in the British Isles is *Presbyterianism*. The *UK Christian Handbook 1994/95* gives a figure of 1,500,000 *Presbyterians* in the UK, and the Registrar General's list of places of worship gives 1,780 registered places of worship for the United Reformed Church in England and Wales.

Its main bodies are the Church of Scotland, the Presbyterian Church in Ireland, the Presbyterian Church of Wales and the United Reformed Church (which also includes the Churches of Christ and Congregationalist traditions, having been formed initially in 1972 through the uniting of the Presbyterian Church of England and the Congregational Union). Also active in Scotland are a number of smaller Presbyterian bodies – the Free Church of Scotland, the Free Presbyterian Church of Scotland, the Reformed Presbyterian Church of Scotland and the United Free Church of Scotland.

The word *Presbyterian* comes from the Greek word *presbuteros*, meaning *elder* or *minister* and refers to the local leadership of a Christian community. *Presbyterianism* is so called because of its emphasis on the collective and local leadership of such elders which are known as *presbyteries* (to be distinguished from the name of the houses in which *Roman Catholic* parish *priests* generally live which are also known as *presbyteries*).

Methodism

Methodism is the second most numerous *Protestant* tradition in the UK. Its origins go back to the eighteenth century religious movement connected with the work of the brothers, John and Charles Wesley. The Methodist Church of Great Britain is the largest Methodist body. Smaller *Methodist* bodies are the Free Methodist Church, the Wesleyan Reform Union, the Independent Methodist Connexion and the Methodist Church in Ireland. *Methodist* numerical strength is concentrated in England, especially in the South West, the Isle of Wight, and the northern counties.

The *UK Christian Handbook 1994/95* gives a figure of 1,300,00 *Methodists* in the UK. There are 7,781 *Methodist* places of worship recorded in the Registrar General's list of certified places of worship.

The word *Methodist* emerged because it was used to described the systematic and methodical approaches to the training of Christian people which were adopted by the Wesleys. *Methodism* is organised on the basis of local *congregations* grouped together into what are known as *circuits*. These circuits are then part of wider regional bodies known as *Districts* and all are governed by a national *Conference*.

Baptist movement

The *Baptist* movement emerged at the beginning of the sixteenth century. Today *Baptists* are organised into four main Unions with some overlap of membership. There is the Baptist Union of Great Britain, the Baptist Union of Scotland, the Baptist Union of Wales, and the Baptist Union of Ireland.

The Baptist Union of Great Britain is the largest of these. There are, however, also smaller groups of *Seventh Day* and *Strict Baptists*. *Baptists* are strongest in the counties to the north of London and around the Bristol Channel, as well as to some extent in the south east of England.

The *UK Christian Handbook 1994/95* gives a figure of 600,000 Baptists in the UK and in England and Wales the Registrar General lists 3,351 certified *Baptists places of worship*. The word *Baptist* is used because of this tradition's practice of reserving *baptism*, as a rite of Christian initiation, to those who have confessed personal Christian faith rather than administering it to babies.

The individual *congregation* is the basic unit of *Baptist* Church life, but *congregations* are grouped together into *Districts* which often operate at the level of large towns, small cities or counties. At the more regional level there are *Associations*, which often cover a number of counties and there is an annual *Assembly*. Regional level leadership is provided by *Area Superintendents* who operate in what are called *Areas*, which generally incorporate a number of *Associations*.

Congregationalism

Congregationalists accounted for seventy per cent of the membership of the United Reformed Church at its formation in 1972. Continuing *Congregational* groups which did not join the United Reformed Church include the Union of Welsh Independents and the Congregational Union of Scotland, as well as the Congregational Union of Ireland and the Congregational Federation. *Congregational* structures are similar to *Baptist* ones.

The *UK Christian Handbook 1994/95* does not give a separate figure for *Congregationalists* in the UK, but the Registrar General's list for England and Wales gives 1,385 certified *Congregationalist* places of worship.

Salvation Army

The Salvation Army originated with the work of William Booth who tried to respond to both the social and the spiritual needs of the industrial working class. Its members can be recognised by their distinctive military style uniforms and it is well known for its social service projects among the poor and homeless. The Salvation Army is organised into local *corps*, which are then grouped into regional level *Divisions*. It does not administer the sacraments of *baptism* or the *eucharist* .

The *UK Christian Handbook 1994/95* does not give a separate figure for *Salvationists* in the UK, but the Registrar General's list for England and Wales gives 942 certified Salvation Army places of worship.

Brethren

The *Brethren* movement was formed in the nineteenth century with Plymouth as an important centre. From this the popular name of "Plymouth Brethren" is derived, although its members have never accepted this designation. The Exclusive Brethren and the Churches of God in the British Isles and Overseas are also a part of the *Brethren* movement understand more generally. Churches of the *Brethren* tradition are local, independent *congregations* believing in what they understood to be a more truly original pattern of New Testament Christianity.

The *UK Christian Handbook 1994/95* does not give a separate figure for *Brethran* in the UK, but the Registrar General's list for England and Wales gives 953 certified *Brethren* places of worship.

Pentecostalist Churches

Pentecostalists include the Assemblies of God, the Elim Pentecostal Church, the Apostolic Church and a significant number of black-majority Churches, many of which have roots in Caribbean, North American and indigenous African forms of Christianity. In reality, the Churches which are often referred to as black-led Churches are very diverse in terms of their doctrines, practices and forms of Church organisation, ranging from *Pentecostal* and *Holiness* Churches, through to *Sabbatarian* and other traditions.

Some of these Churches (for example, the New Testament Church of God) are becoming numerically quite significant. Others are quite local and consist only of one or two congregations although they quite often co-operate with other larger groups within the framework of co-ordinating organisations such as the International Ministerial Council of Great Britain and the Council of African and Afro-Caribbean Churches. Together with the *House Church* movement, this branch of Christianity represents a fast-growing and increasingly significant section of Christianity in the UK.

The *UK Christian Handbook 1994/95* gives a figure of 300,000 *Pentecostalists* in the UK. The Registrar General's list of certified places of worship in England and Wales does not keep a separate running total of churches under the category of *Pentecostalist*.

Ecumenical Structures

The Council of Churches for Britain and Ireland (see Christian organisational listings), founded in 1990 as a result of the *Inter-Church Process*, links some thirty of the numerically largest Churches and a number of other bodies in Britain and Ireland. Together with other smaller bodies operating at the levels of the four nations it is

known as an *ecumenical instrument*. The national *ecumenical instruments* are Churches Together in England (CTE), Action of Churches Together in Scotland (ACTS), Churches Together in Wales (CYTUN), the Irish Council of Churches (ICC) and Irish Inter-Church Meeting.

At the European level many *Protestant* and *Orthodox* Churches belong to the Conference of European Churches (CEC) and at an international level to the World Council of Churches (WCC). At a local level, many individual congregations and parishes co-operate in what are known as local Councils of Churches or Churches Together (of which there are approximately 1,100 in England) or in Local Ecumenical Projects (LEPs), of which there are approximately 800 in England.

Personnel

Local Leadership

In most of the Christian Churches, the generality of members of the Church are collectively known as the *laity* (from the Greek word *laos*, meaning people). In some *Protestant* Churches the *laity* can, in principle at least, conduct all the ceremonies, rites and functions of the Church even if in practice these are actually carried out by designated leaders.

Ordained leadership

The names and functions of the designated religious leadership of various Christian Churches varies according to their tradition, although broad categories of personnel can be discerned among *ordained* (set apart and recognised) leaders of the *Roman Catholic*, *Orthodox* and *Protestant* Churches.

Among some of the Churches which have a shorter history in the UK and have geographical origins in Africa and the Caribbean an even wider variety of titles and functions can be found. For example, among a number of the African churches there is a specific office of *prophet* or *prophetess*. Other Christian groups within the *House Church* and *Restorationist* movements recognise leaders who have wider than local ministries and special gifts of ministry as *apostles*, a word which other Christians generally reserve for the first disciples of Jesus who are believed to have had a uniquely special role within the Christian community.

In the *Roman Catholic, Anglican* and *Orthodox* traditions, ordained leadership at the local level is provided by religious leaders and functionaries who are known as *priests*. In the Western *Roman Catholic* tradition *priests* are not allowed to marry, although in the *Anglican* and *Orthodox* tradition they may be married. *Priests* are authorised to preside at the communion service, to baptise and to preach. In these traditions, *priests* are seen both as representing the people to God and also as representing Christ to the congregation as the focal agents through which God responds to the Christian community. This is especially believed to be the case in the *Holy Communion* and other means through which Christians are believed to receive divine grace.

In these traditions, presiding at the *Communion* is reserved for *priests*. In the *Anglican* tradition authorised lay people can preach, and there is also an ordained order of ministry known as *diaconate* (from the Greek word - *diakonos*, meaning servant). This is technically an order in its own right, although *priests*-to-be are first of all ordained *deacon* as a stage on the way to full ordination to the priesthood. The *diaconate* exists in other Christian traditions, too, sometimes as a permanent order of ministry.

Protestant Churches generally have a more functional view of their local ordained leadership in which preaching from the scriptures is of central or even greater importance than the leading of the *Holy Communion*. In the *Protestant* Churches ordained local leaders are known as *ministers* (Baptist, Methodist, United Reformed Church of Scotland as well as other *Reformed* Churches); *pastors* (Christian Brethren, many branches of the *Pentecostal* movement, and some *Baptist* congregations).

In the *Roman Catholic* and *Orthodox* traditions the priesthood is not open to women. Within the Anglican tradition, the Church of England has recently decided to proceed with the ordination of women to the *priesthood*. In the Church of

Ireland there are already women priests and decisions on the issue are to be taken in 1994 in the Episcopal Church of Scotland and the Church in Wales. For many years there have been divided convictions on this issue even though there have been been women *priests* in other parts of the worldwide *Anglican* tradition.

In the *Protestant* Churches women are generally able to serve as local ministers and some have also assumed responsibilities in regional and national leadership. In all Churches, local clergy have a role in pastoral care of the congregation as well as in preaching and administering the *sacraments*.

In the understanding of the established Church of England, the *priest's* duty of pastoral care extends to anyone in the parish area, regardless of whether or not they are *Anglican* or even Christian.

Regional, National and International Leadership

In the *Orthodox, Roman Catholic* and *Anglican* traditions the focus of unity of the Church's leadership is vested in the *bishops*. *Bishops* are senior clergy who are responsible for the geographical and ecclesiastical areas known as *dioceses*. Since *Roman Catholic priests* cannot marry, *Roman Catholic bishops* are unmarried. *Anglican bishops* may be married, but whilst *Orthodox priests* may marry before ordination as *priests*, the office of *bishop* in the *Orthodox* Churches is only open to *monks* and therefore married *priests* cannot become *bishops*.

In the *Protestant* Churches regional leaders are known by a wide variety of titles such as *Area Superintendent* (Baptist), *Moderator* (United Reformed Church) and *Chairman* (Methodist).

The Church of England has two *Archbishops*, namely, the Archbishop of Canterbury and the Archbishop of York. The Archbishop of Canterbury is the Church of England's senior bishop and, indeed, is recognised as having a special seniority in the worldwide *Anglican* communion. In the *Protestant* Churches national leaders usually have very functional titles such as *General Secretary* (Baptist Union of Great Britain), *Moderator* of the General Assembly (Church of

Scotland) or *President* of the Methodist Conference (Methodist Church).

In the *Orthodox* Churches, senior *Archbishops* are known by the title of *Patriarch* (which means great father), and *Patriarchs* may have responsibilities which extend across national boundaries.

In the Roman Catholic Church, a group of senior bishops and *Archbishops* from all over the world are recognised as *cardinals*. These *cardinals* elect the *Pope* (meaning Father) who is installed as Bishop of Rome and is recognised as supreme head (*Pontiff*) of the *Roman Catholic* Church throughout the world and is often referred to by *Roman Catholics* as the *Holy Father*.

Among *Protestant* Churches, the international leadership, like the national leadership, has a variety of more functional titles such as *General Secretary* of the World Alliance of Reformed Churches or *General Secretary* of the Lutheran World Federation, which are co-ordinating rather than authoritative bodies.

BIBLIOGRAPHY

Attwater, D, *A Dictionary of Mary*, P J Kennedy, Longmans, 1957.

Ballard, P and Jones, D (eds), *This Land and People: Y Wlad a'r Bobl Hyn: A Symposium on Christian and Welsh National Identity*, Collegiate Centre of Theology, University College, Cardiff (revised edition) 1980.

Barraclough, G (ed), *The Christian World*, Abrams, London, 1981

Barrett, D, *The World Christian Encyclopaedia: A Comparative Study of Churches and Religions in the Modern World, AD1900-2000*, Oxford University Press, Oxford, 1982.

Bisset, P, *The Kirk and Her Scotland*, Handsel Press, Edinburgh, 1986.

Bettenson, H, *Documents of the Christian Church*, Oxford University Press, London, 1975.

Bowden, J, *Dictionary of Christian Theology*, SCM Press, London, 1983.

Brierley, P, *Irish Christian Handbook*, MARC Europe, London, 1992.

Brierley, P, *UK Christian Handbook 1994/95*, Christian Research Association, London, 1994/5.

Childress, J F, and Macquarrie, J (eds), *A New Dictionary of Christian Ethics*, SCM, London, (2nd edition) 1987.

Coggins, RJ, and Houlden, J L, *A Directory of Biblical Interpretation*, SCM, London, 1990.

Cross, F L, and Livingstone, E A (eds), *Oxford Dictionary of the Christian Church*, Oxford University Press, London, (2nd revised edition) 1974.

Davies, J G, *A New Dictionary of Liturgy and Worship*, SCM, London, 1986.

Dickens, A G, *The English Reformation*, Collins, London, 1967.

Dupre, L and Saliers, D E (eds), *Christian Spirituality: Reformation and Modern*, SCM, London, 1989.

Edwards, D L, *Christian England*, Collins, London, 1985.

Gerloff, R, *A Plea for British Black Theologies: The Black Church Movement in Britain in its Transatlantic Cultural and Theological Interaction, Parts I and II*, Peter Lang, Frankfurt am Main, Germany, 1992.

Hastings, A, *A History of English Christianity, 1920-1985*, Collins, London, 1986.

Inter-Church Process, *Reflections: How Churches View Their Life and Mission*, British Council of Churches, London, 1986.

Keeley, R, *The Lion Handbook of Christian Belief*, Lion Publishing, Tring, 1982.

Latourette, K, *A History of Christianity*, (2 volumes), Harper and Row, London, 1975.

Lossky, V; Bonino, M; Pobee, J; Stransky, T; Wainwright G; and Webb, P, *Dictionary of the Ecumenical Movement*, World Council of Churches, Geneva, 1991.

Macquarrie, J and Childs, J, *A New Dictionary of Christian Ethics*, SCM, London, 1986.

McGinn, B and Meyendorff, J (eds), *Christian Spirituality: Origins to the Twelfth Century*, SCM, London, 1986.

McKenzie, P, *The Christians: Their Practices and Beliefs*, SPCK, London, 1988.

McManners, J (ed), *The Oxford Illustrated History of Christianity*, Oxford University Press, Oxford, 1990.

Raitt, J (ed), *Christian Spirituality: High Middle Ages and Reformation*, SCM, London, 1987.

Smart, N, *The Phenomenon of Christianity*, Collins, London, 1979.

Wakefield, G, *A Dictionary of Christian Spirituality,* SCM, London, 1983.

Walker, A, *Restoring the Kingdom: The Radical Christianity of the House Church Movement*, Hodder and Stoughton, London, 1988.

CHRISTIAN UNITED KINGDOM ORGANISATIONS

UK ECUMENICAL INSTRUMENTS

UK CHURCHES AND COUNCILS OF CHURCHES AFFILIATED TO ECUMENICAL INSTRUMENTS

GROUPS CONNECTED WITH UK ECUMENICAL INSTRUMENTS

SOME OTHER CHURCHES AND BODIES

This section includes ecumenical instruments operating at a UK level or in one of the four nations of these islands; Churches or Councils of Churches affiliated to one or more of these *ecumenical instruments*; groups connected with these *ecumenical instruments* as either agencies, commissions or observers; and details of some other Churches and Christian bodies operating at a UK level.

Churches which do not have a widespread presence in the UK are affiliated to Councils of Churches listed here are simply listed under the relevant entry for the Council to which they belong but without further details being given. For further details, directory users are referred to the relevant Councils of Churches which maintain lists of contact information and other details on their affiliated bodies.

There are a very large number of Christian voluntary organisations, the details of which are not included here. For further details of these, directory users are referred to the *UK Christian Handbook 1994/5*.

ECUMENICAL INSTRUMENT (UK)

Council of Churches for Britain and Ireland
Inter-Church House
35 Lower Marsh
London SE1 7RL
Tel: 071-620-4444
Fax: 071-928-0010
Contact: Revd Canon John Reardon
Office: General Secretary
The Council's main concern is to co-ordinate the work of its thirty member Churches and twenty member bodies in Britain and Ireland to enable them to co-operate and work together for the unity of the Churches in the service of the world. It has specialist staff for public affairs (social responsibility), international affairs, church life, women and men and youth, and commissions on mission, racial justice and inter-faith relations. The Churches' Commission for Inter-Faith Relations is co-ordinated by Revd Canon Dr Christopher Lamb and is affiliated to The Inter Faith Network for the UK.

The full members of the Council include:
Baptist Union of Great Britain
Cherubim and Seraphim Council of Churches
Church in Wales
Church of England
Church of Ireland
Church of Scotland
Congregational Federation
Congregational Union of Scotland
Council of African and Afro-Caribbean Churches (UK)
Council of Oriental Orthodox Christian Churches
Greek Orthodox Church
Independent Methodist Churches
International Ministerial Council of Great Britain
Joint Council for Anglo-Caribbean Churches
Lutheran Council of Great Britain
Methodist Church
Methodist Church in Ireland
Moravian Church
New Testament Assembly
Presbyterian Church of Wales
Religious Society of Friends
Roman Catholic Church in England and Wales
Roman Catholic Church in Scotland
Russian Orthodox Church
Salvation Army (British Territory)
Scottish Episcopal Church
Undeb Yr Annibynwyr Cymraeg
   (Union of Welsh Independents)
United Free Church of Scotland
United Reformed Church
Wesleyan Holiness Church

Bodies in association with the Council include:

Action by Christians Against Torture
Afro-West Indian United Council of Churches
Association of Centres of Adult Theological
    Education
Association of Interchurch Families
Centre for Black and White Christian Partnership
Ecumenical Committee for Corporate
    Responsibility
Ecumenical Forum for European Christian Women
Feed the Minds
Fellowship of Prayer for Unity
Fellowship of St Alban and St Sergius
Free Church Federal Council
National Association of Christian Communities
    and Networks
New Assembly of Churches
Student Christian Movement
Women's Interchurch Council
Young Men's Christian Association
Young Women's Christian Association

Observers of the Council include:

Roman Catholic Church in Ireland
Seventh Day Adventist Church

Commissions include:

Churches Commission for Inter-Faith Relations
Churches Commission for Racial Justice
Churches Commission on Mission

Agencies include:

Catholic Fund for Overseas Development
Christian Aid
SCIAF (Scottish Catholic International Aid Fund)

Formal Networks include:

Christian Concern for Southern Africa
Churches' Advisory Council for Local
    Broadcasting
Churches' Consortium on Industrial Mission
Churches' East-West European Relations
    Network
Churches' Stewardship Network
Environmental Issues Network
Justice, Peace and Integrity of Creation Group
Standing Committee on Theological Education

ECUMENICAL INSTRUMENT (ENGLAND)

Churches Together in England

Inter-Church House
35 Lower Marsh
London SE1 7RL
Tel: 071-620-4444
Fax: 071-928-5771
Contact: Revd Canon Martin Reardon
Office: General Secretary

National representative body. It exists as a formal and visible sign of the Churches' commitment as they seek a deepening of their communion with Christ and with one another. It also provides a means by which the Churches proclaim the Gospel together by common witness and service. It encourages its twenty one member Churches to work together. It also works through fifty county, new town or metropolitan area ecumenical bodies which try to help the Churches to witness and work together at district/diocesan level. There are two Field Officers who service these bodies. There is a Forum meeting of about three hundred representatives every other year and an Enabling Group of fifty representatives meets four times a year. There are a number of co-ordinating groups through which the Churches work together nationally, for example, in community work, evangelisation, education, theology, youth work and in support of local ecumenism. There are several Agencies which work ecumenically in aid and development, local broadcasting, promoting volunteers in England and in answering enquiries about the faith. A news bulletin called "Pilgrim Post" is published six times a year and costs £10 a year including postage.

Member Churches include:

Baptist Union of Great Britain
Cherubim and Seraphim Council of Churches
Church of England
Church of Scotland
Congregational Federation
Council of African and Afro-Caribbean Churches (UK)
Council of Oriental Orthodox Churches
Greek Orthodox Church
Independent Methodist Churches
International Ministerial Council of Great Britain
Joint Council for Anglo-Caribbean Churches
Lutheran Council of Great Britain
Methodist Church
Moravian Church
New Testament Assembly
Religious Society of Friends
Roman Catholic Church in England and Wales
Russian Orthodox Church

Salvation Army
United Reformed Church
Wesleyan Holiness Church

Bodies in Association include:
Afro-West Indian United Council of Churches
Association of Inter-Church Families
Bible Society
Fellowship of Prayer for Unity
Focolare Movement
Free Church Federal Council
National Association of Christian Communities
  and Networks
National Retreat Association
New Assembly of Churches
Student Christian Movement
Young Men's Christian Association
Young Women's Christian Association

ECUMENICAL INSTRUMENT (SCOTLAND)

Action of Churches Together in Scotland
Scottish Churches House
Dunblane
Perthshire FK15 0AJ
Tel: 0786-823588
Fax: 0786-825844
Contact: Revd Maxwell Craig
Office: General Secretary

Member Churches include:
Church of Scotland
Congregational Union of Scotland
Methodist Church
Religious Society of Friends
Roman Catholic Church in Scotland
Salvation Army
Scottish Episcopal Church
United Free Church
United Reformed Church

Agencies:
Churches Agency for Inter-Faith Relations in
Scotland

ECUMENICAL INSTRUMENT (WALES)

CYTUN: Churches Together in Wales (Eglwysi Ynghyd Yng Nghymru)
First Floor
21 St Helen's Road
Swansea SA1 4AP
Tel: 0792-460876
Contact: Revd Noel A Davies

Office: General Secretary
CYTUN is an ecumenical instrument which enables deeper partnership between the denominations in Wales in ecumenical affairs, evangelism and issues relating to Wales and the world. It is also in regular contact, through a mailing list, with about one hundred and thirty local ecumenical groups. It unites in pilgrimage Churches which confess Jesus Christ as God and Saviour according to the Scriptures, and seeks to deepen their communion with God and one another and to fulfil their mission through shared witness and service. It aims to enable the Churches to deepen their partnership, to share their resources, and to grow to a fuller unity. It conducts its activites through representatives of its eleven member denominations with Commissions for Ecumenical Affairs, Evangelism, and Wales & the World as well as through specialist networks on issues such as Aids, industry and economic affairs. There are also groups in existence on women and youth whose relations with CYTUN are currently being explored.

Full Members of CYTUN include:
Churches and Denominations with Headquarters in Wales:
Eglwys Bresbyteraidd Cymru (Presbyterian
  Church of Wales)
Eglwys Yng Nghymru (Church in Wales)
Undeb Bedyddwyr Cymru (Baptist Union of
  Wales)
Undeb Yr Annibynwyr Cymraeg (Union of Welsh
  Independents)

Churches and Denominations with Headquarters in England:
Byddin Yr Iachawdwriaeth (Salvation Army)
Cymdeithas Grefyddol Y Cyfeillion (Religious
  Society of Friends)
Eglwys Ddiwygiedig Unedig (United Reformed
  Church)
Eglwys Fethodistaidd (Methodist Church)
Eglwys Gatholig Rufeinig (Roman Catholic
  Church)
Gynghrair Gynulleidfaol (Congregational
  Federation)
Undeb Bedyddwyr Prydain Eglwys Cffamadd
(Baptist Union of Great Britain Covenanted
  Churches)

Observers:
Eglwys Adfentaidd Y Seithfed Dydd (Seventh Day
  Adventist Church)
Eglwys Liwtheraidd (Lutheran Church)
Yr Eglwys Uniongred (Orthodox Church)

ECUMENICAL INSTRUMENT (IRELAND)

Irish Council of Churches

Inter-Church Centre
48 Elmwood Avenue
Belfast BT9 6AZ
Tel: 0232-663145
Fax: 0232-381737
Contact: Dr David Stevens
Office: General Secretary
Constituted by Christian communions in Ireland willing to join in united efforts to promote the spiritual, physical, moral and social welfare of the people and the extension of the rule of Christ among all nations and over every region of life. The Council consists of sixty-five members appointed by member Churches. There are three Boards: Community Affairs; Inter-Church Affairs; and Overseas Affairs. The Council puts considerable emphasis on peace and reconciliation work. A peace programme has been developed since July 1978 in conjunction with the Irish Commission for Justice and Peace and materials for schools and adult Bible study guides have been produced.

The member Churches of the Council include:
Church of Ireland
Irish District of the Moravian Church
Lutheran Church in Ireland
Methodist Church in Ireland
Non-Subscribing Presbyterian Church of Ireland
Presbyterian Church in Ireland
Religious Society of Friends
Salvation Army

GROUPINGS OF CHURCHES (UK)

Afro-West Indian United Council of Churches

New Testament Church of God
Arcadian Gardens
High Road
Wood Green
London N22
Tel: 081-888-9427
Contact: Revd Eric Brown
Office: General Secretary
Membership of the Council is open to Christian Churches in the United Kingdom with predominantly Afro-Caribbean membership. Its aims are to: advance the Christian religion; advance the education of the public and, in particular but without prejudice to the foregoing, such members of the public who are of the Afro-Caribbean communities; relieve, either generally or individually, persons who are members of the Afro-Caribbean communities who are in conditions of need, hardship and distress; enhance the spiritual welfare of the community; advance the educational, cultural and social wellbeing of the members of the Afro-Caribbean communities and to promote and develop such programmes as would achieve the above-mentioned objectives. Its activities include bi-annual regional meetings in London and Birmingham, and an Annual General Meeting. Affiliated to The Inter Faith Network for the UK.

Member bodies include:
Bibleway Church of our Lord Jesus Christ
   Worldwide
Community Church of God
Melchisedec Spiritual Baptist Church
New Testament Assembly
New Testament Church of God
Pentecostal Revival Fellowship
Redemption Church of God
Shiloh United Church of Christ Apostolic
   Worldwide
United Church of God
Wesleyan Holiness Church

Cherubim and Seraphim Council of Churches

175 Earlham Grove
Forest Gate
London E7 9AP
Tel: 081-534-5101
Contact: Mr O A Sofolawe
Office: Secretary

Council of African and Afro-Caribbean Churches (UK)

31 Norton House
Sidney Road
London SW9 OUJ
Tel: 071-274-5589
Contact: The Most Revd Father Olu Abiola
Office: Chairman
A medium through which all African and Afro-Caribbean Churches and those Churches which are in sympathy with African ways of worship may work with joint efforts to bring recognition to the member Churches and perform those services which Churches cannot conveniently provide for themselves. The Council aims to work for the unity, dignity, and brother/sisterhood of humankind. Activities are by correspondence and monthly meetings and the Council is mainly concerned for the inadequate provision for spiritual, social and economic needs, especially lack of premises for worship and

organisation. Affiliated to the Inter Faith Network for the UK.

Member bodies include:

Aladura International Church
All Saints Born Again Christ Healing Church
Atunbi Church of Christ
Celestial Church of Christ
Cherubim and Seraphim Church (Imole)
Cherubim and Seraphim Church Movement
Cherubim and Seraphim Society St Stephen's
   Church
Christ Apostolic Church
Christ the King Pentecostal Church
Christ the Resurrection Church
Chrystal El-Shaddai Church of Christ
Church of Salvation
Church of the Lord Brotherhood
Divine Prayer Society
ESO New Temple Cherubim and Seraphim
   Church
Eternal Glory Church
Eternal Order of the Morning Star
Holy Mount Zion Revival Church
Holy Order of Cherubim and Seraphim Church
Iraw Ogo Jesu
Jesus Christ of Nazareth Healing Church
Kimbanguist Church
Melchisedec Spiritual Baptist Church
Musama Disco Christo Church
Pentecostal Revival Church of Christ
United Prayerist of Christ Church
St James Cherubim and Seraphim Redemption
   Church
St John the Divine Spiritual Baptist Church
St Francis Spiritual Baptist Church

Council of Oriental Orthodox Christian Churches

Armenian Vicarage
Iverna Gardens
London W8 6BR
Tel: 071-937-0152
Contact: Rt Revd Archbishop Yegishe Gizirian

Member bodies include:

Armenian Apostolic Church
Coptic Orthodox Church
Ethopian Orthodox Church
Mar Thoma Syrian Church
Syian Orthodox Church

ENFYS - Covenanted Churches in Wales (Eglwysi Cyfamodol Yng Nghymru)

Church in Wales Centre
Woodland Place
Penarth
South Glamorgan CF6 2EX
Tel: 0222-705278
Fax: 0222-712413
Contact: Revd Gethin Abraham-Williams
Office: General Secretary
Functions to enable partner churches to move towards visible unity. At the local level, ENFYS promotes the creation of ecumenical projects, including shared use of new or existing church plant. The goal of all its work is to facilitate the task of Christian mission in Wales. The national organisation relates to its regional bodies by up to six representatives chosen by each covenanting partner, and by means of a bi-lingual news letter twice a year. Use is also made of area planning committees where these exist. Main activities are to promote unity between the episcopal and non-episcopal Protestant Churches of Wales. A specialist panel drafts liturgies (baptismal, eucharistic) and reports on membership, confirmation and ministerial recognition. Area planning committees are active in Gwynedd, South Glamorgan and North Dyfed. They exist to promote the implementation of the 1975 covenant and to disseminate information about the work of ENFYS and can be contacted through the main office.

Bodies covenanted together in ENFYS are:

Church in Wales (Eglwys Yng Nghymru)
Covenanted Baptist Churches (Yr Eglwysi
   Bedyddiedig Cyfamodol yng Nghymru)
Methodist Church (Eglwys Fethodistaidd)
Presbyterian Church of Wales (Eglwys
   Bresbyberraidd Cymru)
United Reformed Church (Eglwys Ddiwygiedig
   Unedig)

Free Church Federal Council

27 Tavistock Square
London WC1H 9HH
Tel: 071-387-8413
Fax: 071-383-0150
Contact: Revd David Staple
Office: General Secretary
Co-ordinates and represents eighteen constituent denominations and includes a Women's Council, an education committee and a Hospital Chaplaincy Board. There are no regional bodies but correspondence can be made with Secretaries of Local Councils.

Member bodies of the Council include:
Afro-West Indian United Council of Churches
Baptist Union of Great Britain
Baptist Union of Wales
Congregational Federation
Council of African and Afro-Caribbean Churches
Countess of Huntingdon's Connexion
Fellowship of Churches of Christ
Free Church of England
Independent Methodist Churches
Methodist Church
Moravian Church
New Testament Church of God
Old Baptist Union
Presbyterian Church of Wales
Salvation Army
Union of Welsh Independents
United Reformed Church in the United Kingdom
Wesleyan Reform Union

Free Church Council for Wales
(Cyngor Eglwysi Rhyddion Cymru)
Ty Ilston
94 Mansel Street
Swansea SA15 5TZ
Tel: 0792-655546
Contact: Revd Peter Richards
Office: General Secretary
The Council co-ordinates the work of Welsh and English language non-conformist denominations in Wales. There are regional bodies for Welsh churches in North Wales and South Wales, and there is a regional Council for English Churches. There are also approximately two hundred and twenty local level Free Church Councils.

Menber bodies of the Council include:
Baptist Union of Wales (Udeb Bedyddwyr Cymru)
Union of Welsh Independents
   (Undeb Yr Annibynwyr Cymraeg)
Presbyterian Church of Wales
   (Eglwys Bresbyterraidd Cymru)
Methodist Church (Eglwys Fethodistaidd)

International Ministerial Council of Great Britain
55 Tudor Walk
Watford WD2 4NY
Tel: 0923-239266
Contact: Rt Revd David A Douglas
Office: Moderator
It is an ecumenical Council of Churches which is a member of the Council of Churches in Britain and Ireland and Churches Together in England. It relates to local member bodies by constant dialogue in meetings, assemblies and training seminars. It is a uniting body and a licensing body. It plays a major role in bringing together understanding and working relationships as widely as possible between all faiths. It also takes into account the effects of poverty and deprivation and the fight against discrimination of any kind in all places. It supports refugees seeking asylum and others seeking refugee status because of persecution or hunger. Its main activities are liaising with Government on overseas missionary activities, ecumenical education, theological education, publications, racial justice, social welfare, ministerial training and ecumenical representation.

Member bodies include:
Beneficial Christ's Church
Bethel Apostolic Church
Born Again Evangelistic Ministry
Calvary Healing Temple
Christ Believers' Fellowship
Christian Care Fellowship
Church of the Lord Jesus Christ Apostolic
Divine Healing Pentecostal Church of Christ
Evangelical Mission of Europe
Pentecostal Association of Ghana
Shiloh United Church of Christ Apostolic
   Worldwide

Joint Council for Anglo-Caribbean Churches
141 Railton Road
Brixton
London SE24 0LT
Tel: 071-737-6542/081-539-3828
Contact: Revd Esme Beswick
Office: General Secretary

Member bodies include:
Bible Truth Church of God
Church of God Assembly
Church of God Independent
Church of God Pentecostal
Firstborn Church of the Living God
Humble Heart Church
Mount Hermon Church of God Assembly
Mount Refuge Firstborn Church
New Testament Assembly
Union Reformed Church
Universal Group of Apostles
Zion Pentecostal Church of God

New Assembly of Churches
15 Oldridge Road
London SW12 8PL
Tel: 081-673-0595
Contact: Revd C Jones

Office: General Secretary

Founded in 1985, the Assembly brings together twenty of the largest black-led churches and a large number of black people. It aims to fight racism, discrimination, prejudice and intolerance between different religions, races and colours in order to work for the betterment of human relations. It co-ordinates clergy in the main towns and cities of Britain engaged in activities like welfare work, community support, and developing ecumenical social links with other religious bodies.

Member bodies include:

African Methodist Zion Church
All Nations Christian Fellowship
Assemblies of the First Born
Calvary Church of God in Christ
Church of God Worldwide Mission
  Faith Chapel
International Fellowship for Christ
New Life Assembly
New Testament Assembly
New Testament Church of God
Pilgrim Union Church of God
Seventh Day Adventists
Shiloh United Church of Christ Apostolic
  Worldwide

CHURCHES IN THE UK

Armenian Apostolic Oriental Orthodox Church

St Peter's Church
Cranley Gardens
London SW7 3BB
Tel: 071-9370152
Contact: Rt Revd Archbishop Yegishe Gizirian
Office: Primate of the Armenian Church UK

Baptist Union of Great Britain

Baptist House
P O Box 44
Didcot
Oxfordshire OX11 8RT
Tel: 0235-512077
Fax: 0235-811537
Contact: Revd David Coffey
Office: General Secretary

The Baptist Union consists of over two thousand member churches which also belong to twenty-nine geographical Associations that, in turn, are member bodies of the Union. The Union is a Protestant denomination arising out of the Reformation. It belongs to the independent congregational type of Church practising believers' baptism and believing a local congregation gathered in prayer can discern and apply the mind of Christ without recourse to hierarchical authorities or priests. It affirms strongly the priesthood of all believers though it does set aside women and men as trained and ordained ministers of the word and sacrament. The national office provides representational functions to Baptist organisations at European and world levels, also ecumenically to Churches Together in England, the Council of Churches for Britain and Ireland, the Conference of European Churches and the World Council of Churches. It has specialist staff in the areas of finance, administration, evangelism, social action, education and training, youth, publications, promotion, ministry, ecumenism and legal matters.

Baptist Union of Ireland

117 Lisburn Road
Belfast BT9 7AF
Tel: 0232-663108
Contact: Revd J R Grant
Office: Secretary

Baptist Union of Scotland

14 Aytoun Road
Glasgow G41 5RT
Tel: 041-423-6169
Fax: 041-424-1422
Contact: Revd Peter Barber
Office: General Secretary

The Union understands itself as a fellowship of autonomous Baptist churches which choose to affiliate together to strengthen their relations with each other, to extend Christ's mission in Scotland, to be unified on matters of mutual concern and to promote a Baptist understanding of the Christian faith. Each local church voluntarily associates with the national Baptist Union whose headquarters are primarily administrative. The main concerns are fellowship between the churches, mission, support of the churches' needs, co-ordination of decision makers. There are a variety of committees – for youth, women and social action. The Union has thirteen regional associations comprised of local churches of which there are one hundred and sixty-nine.

Baptist Union of Wales (Undeb Bedyddwyr Cymru)

Ty Ilston
94 Mansel Street
Swansea SA1 5TU
Tel: 0792-655468
Contact: Revd Peter D Richards
Office: General Secretary

Church in Wales (Eglwys Yng Nghymru)

39 Cathedral Road
Cardiff CF1 9XL
Tel: 0222-231638
Contact: Mr J W D McIntyre
Office: Secretary

Church of England General Synod

General Synod
Church House
Great Smith Street
London SW1P 3NZ
Tel: 071-222 9011
Fax: 071-233-2660
Contact: Mr Philip J C Mawer
Office: Secretary General

The Church's General Synod functions to consider matters concerning the Church of England, to make provision in respect thereof and to consider and express opinion on any other matters of religious or public interest. There are twenty-one Advisory Committees and permanent Commissions of the General Synod. The Synod works through regional bodies known as Dioceses. The Diocese is the basic territorial unit of administration in the Church of England. Each Diocese is sub-divided into two or more Archdeaconries which are in turn divided into Parishes. Each Diocese is presided over by a Bishop who is head of his Diocese pastorally as well as administratively.

Church of Ireland

Church of Ireland House
Church Avenue
Rathmines
Dublin 6
Republic of Ireland
Tel: 0001-978422
Fax: 001-978821
Contact: Mr R H Sherwood
Office: Chief Officer and Secretary

The Church is a Province of the Anglican communion and includes both Northern Ireland and the Republic of Ireland. Most decisions are made at national level on a "recommendation" from the Dioceses. Its main activity is the promotion of the Anglican faith and it works through a Board of Education, a Youth Council, a Council for the Church Overseas, a Church Unity Committee, a Council for Mission, Ministry of Healing, and a Board for Social Responsibility.

Church of Scotland

121 George Street
Edinburgh EH2 4YN
Tel: 031-2255722
Contact: Revd James L Weatherhead
Office: Principal Clerk

Congregational Federation

4 Castle Gate
Nottingham NG1 7AS
Tel: 0602-413801
Contact: Pastor Graham M Adams
Office: General Secretary

The Federation believes that Congregational Churches while independent, should not be isolationist. It therefore provides the opportunity for mutual sharing and caring, mission and evangelism. The Federation is made up of some three hundred local churches of the Congregational Way, who are themselves organised into one of eleven geographical areas. The local churches in a region elect people to the various committees of the national body. The Federation gives support to local churches by providing training for ministers, pastors and lay people, providing material and opportunities to engage in mission at home and overseas and representing various national bodies connected with social responsibility, youth work and women's work.

Congregational Federation Wales (Gynghrair Gynulleidfaol)

Crosslyn
Spittal
Haverfordwest
Dyfed SA62 5QT (home)
Tel: 0437-87260 (home)
Contact: Revd C L Gillham
Office: Secretary

Twenty-nine congregations and one Local Ecumenical Project.

Congregational Union of Ireland

38 Edgecumbe Gardens
Belfast BT4 2EH
Tel: 0232-653140
Contact: Revd Malcolm Coles
Office: Secretary

Congregational Union of Scotland

P O Box 189
Glasgow G1 2BX
Tel: 041-332-7667
Fax: 041-332-8463
Contact: Revd Robert Waters

Office: General Secretary

The Union has inherited both the classical pattern of Congregationalism with its high ideals of autonomy and freedom and the Presbyterian rigidity and pragmatism of the Evangelical Union. It lives with the tension of these two styles, the financial difficulties of all small denominations and the endeavour to become relevant to contemporary society. The Church is involved in ecumenical interaction and has been involved at a world level through the Council for World Mission. There are ninety-six local congregations from the Shetlands to Dumfriesshire but mainly in the Midland belt and on the East Coast. They are divided for administration purposes into ten districts and have District Councils which have no authority or responsibility but exist for fellowship and sharing or information. The major area of work is mission with a World Mission and Service Department. There is also lesser activity with youth, women, social work etc.

Coptic Orthodox Church
Allen Street
Kensington
London W8 6UX
Tel: 071-603-6701
Contact: Revd Fr Bishoy Baousha
Office: Head of the Church

Ethiopian Orthodox Church
253b Ladbroke Grove
London W10 6HF
Tel: 081-960-3848
Contact: Very Revd Aragawi Wolde Gabriel
Office: Head Priest and Administrator

Covenanted Baptist Churches in Wales (Yr Eglwysi Bedyddiedig Cyfamodol yng Nghymru)
11 Edward VII Avenue
Newport
South Glamorgan NP9 4NG (home)
Tel: 0633-262277
Contact: Revd Rodney Matthews
Office: Secretary
Has fourteen member congregations.

Countess of Huntingdon's Connexion
69 Jubilee Road
Middleton
Manchester M24 2LT
Tel: 061-643-4108
Contact: Mrs Marjorie J Crossley
Office: Secretary

Fellowship of Churches of Christ
1 Wheatley Drive
Carlton
Nottingham NG4 1FE
Tel: 0602-874676
Contact: Mr Clarence Dover
Office: Secretary

Free Church of England
28 Sedgebrook
Liden
Swindon SN3 6EY
Tel: 0793-695838
Contact: Rt Revd Dr Arthur Ward
Office: General Secretary

Greek Orthodox Church
Thyateira House
5 Craven Hill
London W2 3EN
Tel: 071-723-4787
Fax: 071-224-9301
Contact: His Eminence Archbishop Gregorios of Thyateira and Great Britain
Office: Head of the Greek Orthodox Church in Great Britain

The Greek Orthodox Church in Great Britain is under the pastoral guidance of Archbishop Gregorios who in turn is answerable to the Ecumenical Patriarchate in Constantinople. It is directly in the line of succession from the Apostles, adhering faithfully to the traditions that it inherited from the beginning of Christianity. It relates to its local parishes by direct rule. Its activities are liturgical, pastoral, spiritual. Each Parish has a ladies auxiliary society, a Greek school, youth organisations and clergy.

Independent Methodist Churches
Resource Centre
Fleet Street
Pemberton
Wigan WN5 0DS
Tel: 0942-223526
Fax: 0942-227768
Contact: Mr John Day
Office: General Secretary

Irish District Conference of the Moravian Church
158 Finaghy Road South
Belfast BT10 0DH
Tel: 0232-619755
Contact: Revd L Broadbent
Office: Chair

The Moravian Church Irish District Conference is not an autonomous "national" body but rather a sub-district of the Moravian Church (British Province) in Britain/Ireland and reference should be made to that entry for further information which may be required.

Irish Episcopal Conference

Iona
65 Newry Road
Dundalk
County Louth
Republic of Ireland
Tel: 042-38087
Contact: Rev Hugh Connolly

Lutheran Church in Ireland
(Evangelisch-Lutherische Kirche in Irland)

St Finian's Lutheran Church and Lutherhaus
24 Adelaide Road
Dublin 2
Republic of Ireland
Tel: 6766548
Contact: Pastor Paul G Fritz
The Church includes Northern Ireland. Outside Dublin, where the Church was established in 1697, there are smaller congregations in Belfast, Sligo, Galway, Limerick, Killarney, Wexford and Castlepollard. The membership of one thousand is mostly of German background, but American, Scandinavian and African Lutherans attend English services. In Belfast, the congregation meets on the last Sunday in the month in the Moravian Church at 2.00pm.

Lutheran Council of Great Britain

8 Collingham Gardens
London SW5 0HU
Tel: 071-373-1141
Contact: Very Revd Robert J Patkai
Office: Chairman

Mar Thoma Syrian Church

Mar Thoma Centre
22 Altmore Avenue
London E6 2BY
Tel: 081-471-2446
Contact: Revd Abey T Mammen
Office: Vicar
Main activities are worship, witness, charitable work and social work. Services are held at St Catherine Cree Church, 86 Leadenhall Street, EC3.

Methodist Church

1 Central Buildings
Westminster
London SW1H 9NH
Tel: 071-222 8010
Fax: 071-233-1295
Contact: Revd Brian E Beck
Office: Secretary

Methodist Church in Ireland

1 Fountainville Avenue
Belfast BT9 6AN
Tel: 0232-324554
Fax: 0232-239467
Contact: Revd Edmund T I Mawhinney
Office: Secretary
The Methodist Church in Ireland has its origins in the eighteenth century revival. Today, there are sixty thousand Methodists organised in eight districts with two hundred and thirty-four churches. It has developed a wide ranging social work, mainly through the activities of five City Missions. In the nineteenth century it established Methodist College, Belfast and Wesley College, Dublin, for general education, and in the 1940s, Gurteern Agricultural College in County Tipperary. At national level it has an Irish Methodist Youth Department, a Methodist Women's Association, a Council on Social Responsibility and other Connexional Committees. At more regional and local levels it carries out its activities through District Synods and Boards.

Moravian Church in Great Britain and Ireland

Moravian Church House
5 Muswell Hill
London N10 3TJ
Tel: 081-883-3409
Fax: 081-442-0012
Contact: Rev F Linyard
The Church originated in the fifteenth century in central Europe and came to Britain in the eighteenth century. The Synod, with the Provincial Board and various elected Committees, is responsible for the different departments of Church life. "In essentials, unity; in non-essentials, liberty; in all things, charity" sums up the Church's spirit.

New Testament Assembly

70 Vicarage Road
Leyton
London E10 5EF
Tel: 081-539-2755
Contact: Revd I O Smith

New Testament Assembly (Pentecostal)

7 Beechcroft Road
Tooting
London SW17 7BU
Tel: 081-672-9416
Contact: Bishop Melvin L Powell
Office: Bishop

New Testament Church of God

Main House
Overstone Park
Overstone
Northampton NN6 0AD
Tel: 0604-643311
Fax: 0604-790254
Contact: Revd Dr Selwyn E Arnold
Office: National Overseer
The Church is firmly committed to a Conservative Pentecostal Evangelical theology, dedicated to see every member fully motivated in Christ and actively involved in Evangelism as a lifestyle, in order to reach all people with the Gospel of Christ and provide meaningful fellowship and training for Evangelism of the Kingdom of God. There are regional Districts which act in a supervisory, promotional and business capacity. They are responsible for ensuring that national programmes are implemented in all local churches comprising the district and are supervised by an Overseer. As a centralised body, the national level serves as an administrative head. Its main activities include the propagation of the Gospel through its local fellowships. It provides information, representation and administration for all churches as well as promotion, legislation, public relations and doctrinal interpretation. The Church has departments for women, youth, evangelism, social responsibility, laymen and a theological college.

Non-Subscribing Presbyterian Church of Ireland

102 Carrickfergus road
Larne
County Antrim BT40 3JX
Contact: Revd Dr J W Nelson
Office: Clerk of the Synod

Old Baptist Union

32 Wessex Gardens
Totley Brook
Sheffield S17 3PQ
Tel: 0742-352739
Contact: Revd Arthur Sommers
Office: Administrator

Orthodox Church in Wales (Yr Eglwys Uniongred)

11 Heol Manod
Blaenau Festiniog
Gwynned LL41 4DE
Tel: 0766-831272
Contact: Venerable Abbot Father Deniol
Two parishes and one monastery.

Presbyterian Church in Ireland

Church House
Fisherwick Place
Belfast BT1 6DW
Tel: 0232-322284
Fax: 0232-236609
Contact: Revd S Hutchinson
Office: Clerk of Assembly
A Presbyterian Church established by Scottish settlers in the seventeenth century. Most of its three hundred and twenty thousand members are in Northern Ireland, but four per cent live in the Irish Republic. The Church is a member of the World Alliance of Reformed Churches who trace their origins to the Protestant Reformation in Geneva in the sixteenth century. Activities include mission work at home and overseas, social responsibility, women's work, education (including Sunday schools), youth work and world development. Each area of twenty-five to thirty congregations comprises a presbytery which exercises supervision over them. Presbyteries are grouped into five regional synods, which meet only once a year. The Church's supreme court, the General Assembly, meets for a week at the beginning of June.

Presbyterian Church of Wales (Eglwys Bresbyteraidd Cymru)

53 Richmond Road
Cardiff CF2 3UP
Tel: 0222-494913
Contact: Revd D H Owen
Office: General Secretary

Religious Society of Friends in Ireland

Swanbrooke House
Bloomfield Avenue
Dublin 4
Ireland
Tel: 01-6683684
Fax: 01-6677693
Contact: Valerie O'Brien
Office: Recording Clerk

Religious Society of Friends (Quakers)

Friends House
Euston Road
London NW1 2BJ
Tel: 071-387-3601
Fax: 071-388-1977
Contact: Donald Southall
Office: Recording Clerk
Quaker meetings for worship are based on silent waiting upon God, rather than liturgy or creeds. There is no separate ministry or priesthood. The experience of meeting for worship leads to our testimonies for social action and peace. There are over four hundred meeting houses in the UK, and meetings are open to all. Information is available from Quaker Home Service. There are three main departments: Quaker Home Service; Quaker Peace and Service (includes overseas work) and Quaker Social Responsibility and Education. The Society is a member of the Council of Churches for Britain and Ireland.

Roman Catholic Church in England and Wales

39 Eccleston Square
London SW1V 1PD
Tel: 071-630 8220
Fax: 071-630-5166
Contact: Rt Revd Mgr P Carroll
Office: General Secretary
At a regional level the Church has Dioceses throughout England and Wales. The Catholic Bishops' Conference for England and Wales has a Committee for Other Faiths which is chaired by Bishop Charles Henderson, 6a Cresswell Park, London, SE3 9RD, Tel: 081-318-1094. The Committee is affiliated to The Inter Faith Network for the UK. Bishop Henderson also chairs the Committee for Catholic- Jewish Relations, 97 Cole Park Road, Twickenham, Middlesex, TW1 1HX, Tel: 081-892-1186.

Roman Catholic Church in Scotland

Bishops' Conference of Scotland
General Secretariat
64 Aitken Street
Airdrie ML6 6LT
Tel: 0236-764061
Fax: 0236-762489
Contact: Rt Revd Mgr Henry Docherty
Office: General Secretary
The Roman Catholic Church in Scotland is consituted in two ecclesiastical Provinces: St Andrews and Edinburgh, and Glasgow. The former consists of the Archdiocese of St Andrews and Edinburgh and the Dioceses of Aberdeen, Argyll and Isles, Dunkeld and Galloway and the latter of the Archdiocese of Glasgow and the Dioceses of Motherwell and Paisley - totalling eight Dioceses in all. The estimated Catholic population is over seven hundred and forty thousand, making it by far the second largest Church after the Church of Scotland, with which it has developed close ecumenical co-operation, not least through ACTS (Action of Churches Together in Scotland) and the CCBI (Council of Churches for Britain and Ireland). Education, social care, justice and peace, public and international/European affairs, inter-faith and race relations are among the many areas where the Church's various Commissions and other agencies are actively and ecumenically involved.

Russian Orthodox Church

All Saints
Ennismore Gardens
London SW7 1NH
Tel: 071-584-0096
Contact: Metropolitan Anthony Bloom
Office: Metropolitan

Salvation Army

101 Queen Victoria Street
London EC4P 4EP
Tel: 071-236-5222
Office: Chief Secretary
Founded by William Booth in 1865, the Salvation Army's evangelical and social work has spread to more than ninety countries. It remains a "permanent mission to the unconverted", ministering to the total man with heart to God and hand to man. For evangelical work it relates nationally through a network of twenty-four Divisions of varying size which act as intermediaries between the London headquarters and the local groups. The headquarters also acts as a resource centre for the local "corps", providing inspirational support and supervision for officers "in the field". There are also fourteen provincial officers for social service. The objects of the Salvation Army are, "The advancement of the Christian religion... of education, the relief of poverty, and other charitable objects beneficial to society as a whole." Its activities include centres for the homeless, the alcoholic, and deprived children which cater annually for thousands of people. Hospitals and clinics provide healing and hope. Schools and institutions provide education. No Salvationist believes that people can be made whole by the ministry to the body and mind alone.

Scottish Episcopal Church

21 Grosvenor Crescent
Edinburgh EH12 5EE
Tel: 031-225-6357
Contact: Mr John G Davies
Office: Secretary General
At a regional level the Church has Dioceses throughout Scotland.

Seventh Day Adventist Church (Scottish Mission)

"Maylea"
5 Ochilview Gardens
Crieff
Perthshire PH7 3EJ
Tel: 0764-653090
Contact: A R Rodd
Office: President
It has ten congregations in membership.

Seventh Day Adventist Church (Irish Mission)

Newry Road
Banbridge
County Down BT32 3HF
Tel: 08206-26361
Fax: 08206-26361
Contact: A D Hodges
Office: President
It has twelve congregations in membership.

Seventh Day Adventist Church (UK & Eire Headquarters)

Stanborough Park
Watford WD2 6JP
Tel: 0923-672251
Fax: 0923-893212
Contact: C R Perry
Office: President
The headquarters co-ordinates the work of a number of regional bodies. The Church's main activities are the communication of the Gospel through active personal and public evangelism. It does this through departments for youth, education, communications, radio, community services, personal ministries, stewardship, Sabbath school, family life, religious liberty, health and temperance, Asian affairs, ministerial, Bible correspondence, and a relief and development agency. Seventh Day Adventists are mainline Christians who, in their teachings, believe in the Bible as their rule of faith and Jesus Christ as Saviour. They advocate a lifestyle based on obedience to Christ and his commandments; seeking in their global ministry to address humanitarian needs amongst peoples of all ethnic and cultural backgrounds.

Seventh Day Adventists Church (Welsh Mission)

Glan Yr Afon
10 Heol Y Wen
Caerphilly
Mid Glamorgan CF8 3EY
Tel: 0222-882097
Contact: PR Clee
Office: President

Syrian Orthodox Church

20 Great Peter Street
Westminster
London SW1 2BU
Tel: 081-222-5279
Contact: Metropolitan Timothius Aphfen Abodi

Union of Welsh Independents (Undeb yr Annibynwyr Cymraeg)

Y John Penry
11 St Helen's Rd.
Swansea SA1 4AL
Tel: 0792-467040
Contact: Revd Derwyn Morris Jones
Office: General Secretary

United Free Church of Scotland

11 Newton Close
Glasgow G3 7PR
Tel: 041-332-3435
Contact: Mrs Isabel Baird
Office: General Secretary

United Reformed Church in the United Kingdom

86 Tavistock Place
London WC1H 9RT
Tel: 071-916-2020
Fax: 071-916-2021
Contact: Revd Anthony Burnham
Office: General Secretary
A member of the Reformed family in the mainstream of the Christian church. Formed by a union of Congregational and Presbyterian churches (1972) and Churches of Christ (1981). As a united church it is committed to take further steps towards the unity of all God's people. Its structure has four levels: local church, District Council, Provincial Synod and General Assembly. The main functions of the General Assembly are to be the central organ of the Church and to oversee its total work. Areas of specialist work are mission and ecumenical work - home and abroad; church and society; the church's ministry; youth and children's work and lay training.

Wesleyan Holiness Church
Holyhead Road
Handsworth
Birmingham B21 0LA
Tel: 021-523-7849
Contact: Revd Kecios Gray
Office: Superintendent

GROUPS CONNECTED WITH UK ECUMENICAL INSTRUMENTS

Action by Christians Against Torture
Quex Road Methodist Church
Kilburn
London NW6 4PR
Tel: 071-372-7347
Contact: Graham Sparkes
Office: Secretary
The organisation is a national and ecumenical one with around three hundred individual members and fifty group members spread across Britain, mostly in England and Scotland although Ireland also falls within its remit. All members are mailed from its central office. It is affiliated to FIACAT, the International Federation of Christians Against Torture. Its members campaign against torture through awareness-raising, prayer, letter writing and other similar actions as focused through the regular mailings. It proclaims torture to be a crime against God and humanity and it offers an opportunity to campaign ecumenically against this and to support its victims. Remembering Christ's torture - the crucifixion - it strives to make the resurrection promise a reality in people's lives and to affirm life in its fullness as given by God.

Action by Christians Against Torture (Wales)
16 Melbourne Road
Llanishen
Cardiff CF4 5NH
Tel: 0222-757339
Contact: Karen Wontner
Office: Secretary
A campaign of the Churches in Wales which encourages and supports individuals, groups and congregations to pray and campaign on behalf of prisoners of conscience who have suffered torture. It contacts a mailing list of approximately five hundred, three or four times a year.

ACATE (Association of Centres of Adult Theological Education)
41 Holywell Hill
St Albans
AL1 1HE
Tel: 0727-830802
Fax: 0727-844469
Contact: Revd L Oglesby
Office: Honorary Secretary
A voluntary association covering Britain and Ireland, it has a committee which is elected triennially to provide local, regional and national organisational links with centres of adult theological education that are in membership.

Association of Interchurch Families
Inter-Church House
35-41 Lower Marsh
London SE1 7RL
Tel: 071-620-4444
Fax: 071-928-0010
Contact: Ruth Reardon
Office: Secretary
A national organisation which has area groups in different parts of the country. Representatives meet in committee and for conferences. It offers information and support for interchurch families (usually where one partner is a practising Roman Catholic and the other a committed member of another communion) and for mixed marriages where one or both may have ceased to practice but denominational differences play a part. It is also a voice for interchurch families who wish to share their concerns with their churches. Its main activities are information, publications, counselling and networking.

Bible Society
Stonehill Green
Westlea
Swindon SN5 7DG
Tel: 0793-513713
Fax: 0793-512539

CAFOD (Catholic Fund for Overseas Development)
2 Romero Close
Stockwell Road
London SW9 9TY
Tel: 071-733-7900

Centre for Black and White Christian Partnership
Selly Oak Colleges
Birmingham B29 6LQ
Tel: 021-472-7952
Fax: 021-472-8852
Contact: Rt Revd Patrick Kalilombe
Office: Executive Director

Churches today are being drawn into contact and relationships with other communities with whom there has traditionally been very little effective interaction. The Centre works to build relationships not only between different denominations but between different cultural understandings and racial traditions. For it to succeed, proper training and experience is required. The Centre's main activities are in: Education (a two year part-time University course); Inter-Church Relations (facilitating fora and seminars); Library (collecting a comprehensive library on the histories and theologies of black–majority Churches); and International Links (linking with overseas Churches who seek to address questions of inter-racial and inter-cultural relationships).

CEWERN (Churches' East-West European Relations Network)

1b Friend Street
London EC1V 7NS
Tel: 071-833-1001
Contact: Mrs Sheila Brain
Office: Executive Secretary
CEWERN is a network of approximately seventy individual members from the UK and Ireland (some representing wider bodies or organisations, and including some overseas members) and twelve corporate bodies (mainly Churches in England, Scotland and Wales). It is an official Network of the Council of Churches for Britain and Ireland. It aims to support and inform Church officers concerned with links with Eastern Europe by offering the expertise of specialists in the field. It also acts as a network for individuals to share information and contact one another. The quarterly newsletter "East-West" is the most important means of communication, but regular briefing meetings are also held. Members value their links with the Christian Churches in Eastern Europe and offer them support and solidarity. It is fully ecumenical and has links with all the major Churches (including the Orthodox). It main activities include promoting contacts with Eastern European Churches; encouragement of visits to exchange information; briefing and debriefing of official delegations.

Christian Aid

P O Box 100
London SE1 7RT
Tel: 071-620-4444
Fax: 071-620-0719
Contact: Revd Michael H Taylor
Office: Director
Central office of the official relief and development agency of forty British and Irish Churches. Christian

Aid works where the need is greatest, in more than seventy countries. It is supported by many individuals of different faiths who care about the dignity and worth of every person. This belief leads Christian Aid to search for creative ways to address the root causes of poverty, injustice and the denial of the most basic rights to life. As a result, it spends up to ten per cent of its income on education and related campaigning. Overseas it has no permanent staff or offices, preferring to link directly with the poor through local church or other organisations whose programmes aim to strengthen people towards self-reliance.

Christian Concern for Southern Africa

54 Camberwell Road
London SE5
Tel: 071-701-1831

Churches' Advisory Council for Local Broadcasting (CACLB)

P O Box 124
Westcliff-on-Sea
Essex S10 0QU
Tel: 0702-348369
Fax: 0702-348369
Contact: Mr Jeff Bonser
Office: General Secretary
The Council is an ecumenical Christian body for the advancement of the Christian faith on radio and television. It is the formal network of the Council of Churches for Britain and Ireland and consists of representatives of the main Christian denominations, national inter-Church bodies, Christian broadcast training organisations and the broadcasting authorities. The Council acts on behalf of the Churches in the field of local broadcasting, monitors local media developments and advises the Churches on appropriate responses. Through its Association of Christians in Local Broadcasting, which has individual membership, it helps and advises local broadcasters and provides a continuing fellowship for them.

Churches' Agency for Inter-Faith Relations in Scotland

36 Queen's Drive
Glasgow G42
Tel: 041-423-2971
Contact: Father Gordian Marshall
Office: Convenor

Churches' Commission for Inter-Faith Relations

Church House
Great Smith Street

Westminster
London SW1P 3NZ
Tel: 071-222-9011
Fax: 071-799-2714
Contact: Revd Canon Dr Christopher Lamb
Office: Secretary
The Churches' Commission for Inter-Faith Relations represents the concern of fifteen major British denominations and Councils of Churches for strong and creative, inter-faith relationships in Britain. It monitors current developments in our religiously plural society, and promotes responses from the Churches which are true to Christian integrity and religious freedom.

Churches' Commission on Mission
Inter-Church House
35-41 Lower Marsh
London SE1 7RL
Tel: 071-620-4444
Fax: 071-928-0010
Contact: Revd Donald W Elliott
Office: Commission Secretary
The Commission brings together representatives of Churches, mission organisations and Christian development agencies to pool experience and insight on particular mission challenges arising in Britain and Ireland or overseas, and to guide Churches and other organisations in their response together and individually. The Commission relates to similar ecumenical Commissions for England, Ireland, Scotland and Wales. Its main activities are information, strategy, representation and international visitor exchange.

Churches' Consortium on Industrial Mission
Church House
Great Smith Street
London SW1P 3NZ
Tel: 071-222-9011
Contact: Chris Beales

Churches' Joint Education Policy Committee
Church House
Great Smith Street
London SW1P 3NZ
Tel: 071-222-9011
Contact: Joint Secretaries
The Committee is a consultative body which co-ordinates the views and interests of the Churches within and beyond the ecumenical bodies of the Churches in England and Wales. Its membership consists of representatives of the major Churches/denominations in England and Wales. Its

main activity is representing the concerns of the Churches regarding public education (primary, secondary and tertiary) to Her Majesty's Government and to others.

Churches' Stewardship Network
The Diocesan Office
Auckland Castle
Bishop Auckland
County Durham DL14 7QJ
Tel: 9388-604823

CYTUN Commission for Evangelism
St Joseph's Covent
Llantaman Abbey
Cwmbran
Gwent NP44 3YJ
Tel: 06333-3232

Ecumenical Committee for Corporate Responsibility
11 Burnham Wood
Fareham
Hampshire PO16 7UD
Tel: 0329-239390
Fax: 0329-238711
Contact: Revd Crispin White
Office: Co-ordinator
ECCR seeks to be a British focus for the study of corporate responsibility in both the Churches and Transnational Corporations (TNCS). It concentrates on British-based TNCs and on the responsibilities of the Churches which invest in them, as well as in producing educational material to facilitate representation or campaigning by the Churches.

Ecumenical Forum for European Christian Women
10a Osbourne Terrace
Edinburgh EH12 2HE
Tel: 031-337-7107
Contact: Mrs Joyce Gray

Environmental Issues Network
National Agricultural Centre
Stoneleigh Park
Warwickshire CV8 2LZ
Tel: 0203-696969
Fax: 0203-696900
Contact: Eve Dennis
Office: Secretary
The Environmental Issues Network is a "clearing house" for environmental concerns and projects arising nationally, internationally or

denominationally. It meets twice yearly and has representatives from all the main Christian Churches and Christian Aid, Catholic Fund for Overseas Development, and Christian Ecology Link. It is in correspondence linking with Covenanting Churches of the Council of Churches for Britain and Ireland in Scotland, Wales and Northern Ireland.

Feed the Minds
Robertson House
Leas Road
Guildford GU1 4QW
Tel: 0483-577877
Fax: 0483-301387
Contact: Dr Alwyn Marriage
Office: Director
Feed the Minds is a Christian charity which funds literary, literature and communications projects in developing countries and Eastern Europe.

Fellowship of Prayer for Unity
6 Broad Avenue
Queen's Park
Bournemouth BH8 9HG
Tel: 0202-393438
Contact: Revd Paul Renyard
Office: Chaplain

Fellowship of St Alban and St Sergius
52 Ladbroke Grove
London W11 2PB
Tel: 071-727-7713
Contact: Dr Gordon Kendal

Focolare Movement
3 Abbeville Road
London SW4 9LA
Tel: 081-673-32222
Contact: Mari Ponticaccia
An international movement started by Chiara Lubich in 1943 in Trento, Italy. Its principal aim is to contribute to the fulfilment of the prayer of Jesus "May they all be one". Contact can also be made through Dimitri Breyant, 34 Earls Court Square, London, SW5 9DQ, Tel: 071-373-9808.

Joint Committee for Hospital Chaplaincy
Church House
Great Smith Street
London SW1P 3NZ
Tel: 071-222-9011
The Committee consists of four representatives each of the Church of England, Roman Catholic Church and the Free Churches and is responsible for advising

and co-ordinating policy on chaplaincy in hospitals in England and Wales.

Justice, Peace and Integrity of Creation Group
39 Eccleston Square
London SW1V 1PD
Tel: 071-834-5138
Fax: 071-630-5166
Contact: Revd Bob Beresford
Office: Secretary
The group promotes and maintains the concepts of peace, justice and creation as one whole and not three separate concerns. It corresponds with bodies and individuals in Ireland, Wales and Scotland which have similar concerns. Its main activities include exchange of information among member bodies of the Council of Churches for Britain and Ireland on justice, peace and the integrity of creation topics; publicity concerning these themes; and organisation of meetings for facilitating exchange of information.

National Association of Christian Communities and Networks (NACCAN)
Woodbrooke
1046 Bristol Road
Birmingham B29 6LJ
Tel: 021-472-8079 (24 hour answering machine)
Registered charity No: 283972.

SCIAF (Scottish Catholic International Aid Fund)
5 Oswald Street
Glasgow G1 4SR
Tel: 041-221-4447

Standing Committee on Theological Education
Baptist Church House
129 Broadway
Didcot
Oxfordshire OX11 8RT
Tel: 0235-512077
Fax: 0235-811537
Contact: Revd M Goodspeed
Office: Secretary
The Standing Committee on Theological Education (probably soon to become the Churches Consultative Group on Theological Education) is a committee of the Council of Churches for Britain and Ireland and aims to help denominational representatives to understand and take action in the field of theological education. This includes adult lay and ordained education. It does not itself take these actions but

fosters inter-Church co-operation that will initiate further consultation and activity. Its main activities are the co-ordination and encouragement of British national Church bodies and associated bodies in the world of theological education.

Student Christian Movement
186 St Paul's Road
Balsall Heath
Birmingham B12 8LZ
Tel: 021-440-3000
Fax: 021-446-4060
Contact: Mrs Helen Lidgett
Office: General Secretary
The Student Christian Movement exists to promote "an understanding of the Christian faith which is ecumenical, enquiring and socially aware" amongst students in Higher Education. The movement has a branch structure with contacts in about sixty Universities and Colleges. It is affiliated to the Council of Churches for Britain and Ireland, the World Student Christian Federation and the British Youth Council.

Women's Inter-Church Council
c/o 27 Tavistock Square
London WC1H 9HH
Tel: 071-387-8413
Tel: 071-383-0150
Contact: Ms Pauline Butcher
Office: Co-Moderator

Young Men's Christian Association
640 Forest Road
London E17 3DZ
Tel: 081-520-5599
Contact: Mr N Valley
Office: National Secretary

Young Women's Christian Association
YWCA Headquarters
Clarendon House
52 Cornmarket Street
Oxford OX1 3EJ
Tel: 0865-726110
Fax: 0865-204805
Contact: Mrs Carol Saker
Office: Director of Youth, Community and Education

SOME OTHER CHURCHES AND BODIES

EVANGELICAL CHRISTIANITY

Evangelical Alliance
Whitefield House
186 Kennington Park Road
London SE11 4BT
Tel: 081-582-0228
Fax: 071-582-0221
Contact: Revd Clive Calver
Office: General Director
A national alliance of Evangelical churches, societies and individuals representing one million people from a dozen denominations. It promotes unity and co-operation among Evangelical churches and organisations and provides services to them across the UK through national alliances in Scotland, Wales, Northern Ireland and England. It encourages joint action in areas such as drug abuse, employment projects, evangelism, prayer, issues of religious liberty and education. It has more than thirty local Evangelical Fellowships (LEFs) which are alliances of local churches that give regional expression to the national aims and objectives of the Evangelical Alliance.

ORTHODOX CHURCHES

Assyrian Church of the East
89 Leighton Road
Ealing
London W13 9DR
Tel: 081-579-7259
Contact: Revd Yonan Yowel Yonan
Office: Archdeacon

Byelorussian Autocephalic Orthodox Church
Holy Mother of God of Zyrovicy Church
Chapel Road
Rainsborough
Prestwich
Manchester M22 4JW
Tel: 061-740-8230
Contact: Very Revd Father John Ababurko
Office: Administrator

Ukrainian Autocephalous Orthodox Church
1a Norton Avenue
Acton
London W3 8AJ
Tel: 081-992-4689
Contact: Very Revd Protopresbyter Sylvester

Bochateretz
Office: Chairman of Diocese in Great Britain

PENTECOSTAL CHURCHES

Apostolic Union of Great Britain

Brynwr Road
Penygoes
Llanelli
Dyfed SA14 7PA
Tel: 0269-842349
Contact: Revd Ernest Hammond
Office: General Secretary

Assemblies of God in Great Britain and Ireland

106 Tabot Street
Nottingham NG1 5GH
Tel: 0602-474525
Fax: 0602-474639
Contact: Mr Basil Varnan
Office: General Administrator

RELIGIOUS

Conference of Religious in England and Wales (CMRS)

114 Mount Street
London W1Y 6AH
Tel: 071-493-1817
Fax: 071-409-2321
Contact: Sister Gabriel Robin
Office: General Secretary
It exists for the benefit of all Roman Catholic religions in England and Wales. Its formal membership is limited to the major superior of each institute or an officially appointed delegate. Since 1992, superiors of Anglican Communities can enjoy associate membership. It aims to help religions make their contribution to the life of the Church and society and to promote the welfare of individual institutes and their members through their respective leaders.

RESTORATIONIST/HOUSE CHURCH MOVEMENT

Pioneer Team

P0 Box 97c
Esher
Surrey KT10 9LP
Tel: 0932-789681
Fax: 0932-789691
Contact: Mr Gerald Coates
Office: Team Leader

The Team understands itself to be orthodox in faith and informal in approach to evangelise Britain through personal contact and a wide range of meetings through the local church and inter-church projects. It understands itself as a tool to train leaders in the Evangelical faith and to create different models of evangelism. It also understands itself as an initiator of social action initiatives encouraging people to be good news as well as to talk good news. It works through a core group who meet regularly to plan, pray and discuss and through a much wider national Team who oversee the doctrinal, moral and relational qualities of the network. Regional groupings are developing. The Team is active in evangelism; church planting; caring for existing churches; leadership development; and evangelism training courses. It has special emphases on youth and social action (including Aids Care Education and Training) and Romania Aid.

UNITARIAN AND FREE CHRISTIAN

General Assembly of Unitarian and Free Christian Churches

Essex Hall
1-6 Essex Street
Strand
London
WC2R 3HY
Tel: 071-240-2384
Fax: 071-240-3089
Contact: Dr Roy W Smith
Office: General Secretary
Seeks to unite in fellowship bodies which uphold religious freedom for their members unconstrained by creeds. It promotes enquiring and inclusive religion, upholding the liberal Christian tradition, but also seeking to learn from the spiritual, cultural and intellectual insights of all humanity. Local autonomous congregations are linked for mutual support in District Associations, which in turn are affiliated to the national body. District Associations exist to unite together Unitarian and Free Christian congregations, providing financial and other assistance to local congregations and promoting Unitarianism in the area. The General Assembly establishes and develops contacts with many liberal religious movements around the world. It also represents the denomination on ecumenical and other national bodies. It has departments or committees working in the following fields: youth, social responsibility, religious education, information, congregational development, ministry, lay training etc.

CHRISTIAN REGIONAL ORGANISATIONS

SCOTLAND

WALES

IRELAND

NORTH EAST ENGLAND

YORKSHIRE AND HUMBERSIDE

NORTH WEST ENGLAND

ENGLISH EAST MIDLANDS

ENGLISH WEST MIDLANDS

EAST ANGLIA

SOUTH EAST ENGLAND (NORTH)

LONDON

SOUTH EAST ENGLAND (SOUTH)

SOUTH WEST ENGLAND

Details of regional bodies are only given for some of the larger and most widespread Churches listed in the UK Christian listings. Where details are not included here, in the case of England these can be obtained from the UK ecumenical body to which they belong or from the regional ecumenical instruments. In Scotland, Wales and Ireland, they can be obtained from the relevant national ecumenical instruments.

Regional organisations within each specific denomination engage in similiar activities and their roles are outlined in the section on "Introducing the Christian Community". Therefore, no self-descriptions are generally attached to regional contact details, except in some cases for the number of congregations or parishes.

Within each region, Christian regional bodies are grouped firstly according to the denominational tradition to which they belong and then by alphabetical order of the town or city in which they are located. Some regional bodies appear in more than one region because they operate across the regional boundaries used in the directory.

SCOTLAND

Details of the following regional bodies are found in this section:
Baptist Union of Scotland Areas
Church of Scotland Presbyteries
Congregational Union of Scotland Areas
Free Church of Scotland Synods
Methodist Church Districts
Roman Catholic Dioceses
Salvation Army Divisions
Scottish Episcopal Church Dioceses

BAPTIST UNION OF SCOTLAND AREAS

Baptist Union of Scotland Tayside Area
46 Monifieth Road
Broughty Ferry
Dundee DD5 2RY
Tel: 0382-78408
Contact: Mrs Aileen Small
Eighteen congregations.

Baptist Union of Scotland South West Area
Crosbie Hall
Southwood Road
Monkton
Ayrshire KA9 1UR
Tel: 0292-311470
Fax: 0292-317147
Contact: Mr J W McInnes
Office: Secretary
Sixteen churches.

CHURCH OF SCOTLAND PRESBYTERIES

Church of Scotland Aberdeen Presbytery
24 Rosehill Drive
Aberdeen AB2 2JJ
Tel: 0224-484155
Contact: Revd Andrew Douglas
Office: Presbytery Clerk
Forty-six congregations.

Church of Scotland Kincardine and Deeside Presbytery
The Manse
Aboyne
Aberdeenshire AB34 4YN
Tel: 03398-81233
Office: Presbytery Clerk

Church of Scotland Lorn and Mull Presbytery
Appin
Argyll PA38 4DD
Tel: 063173-206
Contact: Revd Walter M Ritchie
Office: Presbytery Clerk

Church of Scotland West Lothian Presbytery
St John's Manse
Mid Street
Bathgate
Lothian EH48 1QD
Tel: 0506-53146
Contact: Revd Duncan Shaw
Office: Presbytery Clerk

Church of Scotland Lanark Presbytery
Monreith
2 Springdale Drive
Biggar
Strathclyde ML12 6AZ
Tel: 0899-20536
Contact: Revd Jospeh Hardie
Office: Presbytery Clerk

Church of Scotland South Argyll Presbytery
The Manse
Southend
Campbeltown
Strathclyde PA28 6RQ
Tel: 058683-274
Contact: Revd Roderick McNidder
Office: Presbytery Clerk

Church of Scotland Annandale and Eskdale Presbytery
The Manse
Gretna Green
Carlisle
Cumbria CA6 5DU
Tel: 0461-38313
Contact: Revd Bryan Haston
Office: Presbytery Clerk

Church of Scotland Ayr Presbytery
30 Garden Street
Dalyrymple
Strathclyde KA6 6DG
Tel: 0292-289220
Contact: Revd C L Johnston
Office: Presbytery Clerk

Church of Scotland Stirling Presbytery
13 Harvieston Road
Dollar
Central FK14 7HG
Tel: 02594-42609
Contact: Revd George McCutcheon
Office: Presbytery Clerk

Church of Scotland Dumfries and Kirkcudbright Presbytery
11 Laurieknowe
Dumfries
Dumfries and Galloway DG2 7AH
Tel: 0387-52929
Contact: Revd Gordon M A Savage
Office: Presbytery Clerk

Church of Scotland Dundee Presbytery
3 Coupar Angus Road
Dundee DD2 3HG
Tel: 0382-611415
Contact: Revd James Roy
Office: Presbytery Clerk

Church of Scotland Dunfermline Presbytery
Townhill Manse
Dunfermline KY12 0EZ
Tel: 0383-723835
Contact: Revd William Farquhar
Office: Presbytery Clerk

Church of Scotland Edinburgh Presbytery
10 Palmerston Place
Edinburgh EH12 5AA
Tel: 031-225-9137
Contact: Revd W Peter Graham
Office: Presbytery Clerk

Church of Scotland Moray Presbytery
1 Seaview Farm Paddock
Cummingston
Burghead
Elgin
Grampian IV30 2XY
Tel: 0384-830890 (home)
Contact: Revd John T Stuart
Office: Presbytery Clerk

Church of Scotland Falkirk Presbytery
30 Russell Street
Falkirk
Central FK2 7HS
Tel: 0324-24461

Contact: Revd D E McClements
Office: Presbytery Clerk

Church of Scotland Orkney Presbytery
Gowanhill
5 Hill of Heddle
Finstown
Orkney KW17 2LH
Tel: 085676-213
Contact: Revd David Williams
Office: Presbytery Clerk

Church of Scotland Lochaber Presbytery
McIntosh Manse
Auchintore Road
Fort William
Highlands PH33 6RQ
Tel: 0397-702054
Contact: Revd Alan Ramsay
Office: Presbytery Clerk

Church of Scotland Melrose and Peebles Presbytery
10 Elm Grove
Galashiels
Borders TD1 3JA
Tel: 0896-3261
Contact: Revd Charles A Duncan
Office: Presbytery Clerk

Church of Scotland Irvine and Kilmarnock Presbytery
Galston
Ayrshire KA4
Contact: Revd T J Loudon Blair
Office: Presbytery Clerk

Church of Scotland Dumbarton Presbytery
8 Collylinn Road
Bearsden
Glasgow G61 4PN
Tel: 041-942-0366
Contact: Revd David P Munro
Office: Presbytery Clerk

Church of Scotland Glasgow Presbytery
260 Bath Street
Glasgow G2 4JP
Tel: 041-332-6006
Fax: 041-332-6606
Contact: Revd Alexander Cunningham
Office: Presbytery Clerk

Church of Scotland Paisley Presbytery
Uplawmoor
Glasgow G78 4AF
Tel: 0505-850215
Contact: Revd John Cubie
Office: Presbytery Clerk
Forty congregations.

Church of Scotland Duns Presbytery
The Manse
Edinburgh Road
Greenlaw
Berwickshire TD10 6XF
Tel: 03616-218
Contact: Revd Ian G Witherspoon
Office: Presbytery Clerk

Church of Scotland Greenock Presbytery
105 Newark Street
Greenock PA16 7TW
Tel: 0475-39602
Contact: Revd David Mill
Office: Presbytery Clerk

Church of Scotland Uist Presbytery
Griminish
Isle of Benbecula PA88 5QA
Tel: 0870-2180
Contact: Revd Adrian Varwell
Office: Presbytery Clerk

Church of Scotland Hamilton Presbytery
Presbytery Office
18 Haddow Street
Hamilton ML3 7HX
Tel: 0698-28637
Tel: 0698-860260 (home)
Contact: Revd James H Wilson
Office: Presbytery Clerk

Church of Scotland Sedbury Presbytery
Teviot Manse
Buccleuch Road
Hawick
Borders TD9 0EL (home)
Tel: 0450-72150 (home)
Contact: Revd Neil R Combe
Office: Presbytery Clerk

Church of Scotland Ross Presbytery
Kilmuir and Logie Easter Manse
Delny
Invergordon
Highlands IV18 0NW

Tel: 0862-842280
Contact: Revd Roderick Maclean Mackinnon
Office: Presbytery Clerk

Church of Scotland Sutherland Presbytery
The Manse
Lairg
Sutherland IV27 4EH
Tel: 0549-2373
Contact: Revd J L Goskirk
Office: Presbytery Clerk

Church of Scotland Shetland Presbytery
30 Commercial Road
Lerwick
Shetland Islands
Tel: 0595-3240
Contact: Revd Magnus Cheyne
Office: Presbytery Clerk

Church of Scotland Locharron Presbytery
The Manse
Locharron
Isle of Skye IV54 8YD
Tel: 05202-278
Contact: Revd Allan MacArthur
Office: Presbytery Clerk

Church of Scotland Dunkeld and Meigle
Manse of Meigle
Meigle
Perthshire PH12 8SB
Tel: 08284-278
Contact: Revd Fraser M C Stewart
Office: Presbytery Clerk

Church of Scotland Ardrossan Presbytery
Manse of St Columba's
Kilbirnie
Ayrshire KA25 7JU
Tel: 0505-683342
Fax: 0505-683342
Contact: Revd David Broster
Office: Presbytery Clerk

Church of Scotland Angus Presbytery
The Manse
Hillside
Montrose
Tayside DD10 9HT
Tel: 067483-288
Contact: Revd A F M Downie
Office: Presbytery Clerk

Church of Scotland Abernethy Presbytery
The Manse
Nethy Bridge
Ivernes-shire PH25 3DG (home)
Tel: 047982-280 (home)
Contact: Revd James MacEwan
Office: Presbytery Clerk

Church of Scotland Lothian Presbytery
46 St James Gardens
Penicuik
Lothian EH26 9DU
Tel: 0698-676123
Contact: Revd J McL Ritchie
Office: Presbytery Clerk

Church of Scotland Perth Presbytery
5 Strathearn Terrace
Perth PH2 0LS
Tel: 0738-21709
Contact: Revd G G Stewart
Office: Presbytery Clerk

Church of Scotland Buchan Presbytery
Hatton
Peterhead
Grampian AB42 7QQ
Tel: 077984-229
Contact: Revd R Neilsen
Office: Presbytery Clerk
Forty congregations in twenty-nine charges.

Church of Scotland Dunoon Presbytery
12 Crichton Road
Rothesay
Isle of Bute PA20 9JR
Tel: 0700-502797
Contact: Revd Ronald Samuel
Office: Presbytery Clerk

Church of Scotland St Andrews Presbytery
34 Claybraes
St Andrews KY16 8RS
Tel: 0334-73606
Contact: Revd John Patterson
Office: Presbytery Clerk

Church of Scotland Gordon Presbytery
The Manse
Skene
Grampian AB32 6XX
Tel: 0224-743277
Contact: Revd Ian U Thomson
Office: Presbytery Clerk

Church of Scotland Lewis Presbytery

Martin's Memorial Manse
Matheson Road
Stornoway PA87 2LR
Tel: 0851-702206
Contact: Revd T S Sinclair
Office: Presbytery Clerk

Church of Scotland Wigtown and Stranraer Presbytery

High Kirk Manse
Leswalt High Road
Stranraer DG9 0AA
Tel: 0776-3268
Contact: Revd D W Dutton
Office: Presbytery Clerk

Church of Scotland Caithness Presbytery

The Manse
Watten
Highlands
Tel: 095582-220
Contact: Revd Michael Mappin
Office: Presbytery Clerk

CONGREGATIONAL UNION OF SCOTLAND AREAS

Congregational Union of Scotland Mid-Lanark Association

146 Campbell Street
Wishaw ML2 8HU
Contact: Miss E I King
Office: Secretary
Tel: 0698-373419
Fifteen churches.

FREE CHURCH OF SCOTLAND SYNODS

Free Church of Scotland Western Synod

Free Church Manse
Isle of Lewis PA86 9AG
Tel: 0851-73208
Contact: Revd Donald MacDonald
Office: Clerk

Free Church of Scotland Southern Synod

24 Markethill Road
East Kilbride
Glasgow G74 4AD
Tel: 0355-227353
Contact: Rev J MacIver
Office: Clerk

Free Church of Scotland Northern Synod

Free Church Manse
Scotsburn Road
Tain
Ross-shire IV19 1PR
Tel: 0862-2156
Contact: Revd Innes M MacRae
Office: Clerk

METHODIST CHURCH DISTRICTS

Methodist Church Shetland District

Burnside
Houl Road
Scalloway
Shetland ZE1 0UA
Tel: 0595-88204
Contact: Revd Leslie Hann
Office: Secretary of Synod
Twenty congregations.

Methodist Church in Scotland

21 Queen Street
Stirling FK8 1HL
Tel: 0786-74601
Contact: Revd Walter Attwood
Office: Secretary
Fifteen circuits and forty-eight congregations/parishes.

ROMAN CATHOLIC DIOCESES

Roman Catholic Diocese of Aberdeen

Bishop's House
156 King's Gate
Aberdeen AB2 6BR
Tel: 0224-319154
Fax: 0224-645401
Contact: Rt Revd Mario Joseph Conti
Office: Bishop
Seventy churches and other mass centres which are contained in thirty-eight parishes.

Roman Catholic Diocese of Galloway

Candida Casa
8 Corsehill Road
Ayr KA7 2ST
Tel: 0292-266750
Contact: Rt Revd Maurice Taylor
Office: Bishop
Forty-seven parishes.

Roman Catholic Diocese of Dunkeld

Diocesan Centre
26 Roseangle
Dundee DD1 4LY
Tel: 0382-25453
Contact: Revd Michael Milton
Office: Diocesan Secretary
Thirty-nine parishes.

Roman Catholic Archdiocese of St Andrews and Edinburgh

Diocesan Centre
106 Whitehouse Loan
Edinburgh EH9 1BD
Tel: 031-452 8244
Fax: 031-452 9153
Contact: Revd Desmond Lynagh
Office: Assistant to the Moderator of the Diocesan Curia
One hundred parishes.

Roman Catholic Archdiocese of Glasgow

Curial Offices
196 Clyde Street
Glasgow G1 4JY
Tel: 041-226-5898
Fax: 041-221-1962
Contact: The Chancellor
One hundred and six parishes.

Roman Catholic Diocese of Motherwell

Diocesan Centre
Coursington Road
Motherwell ML1 1PW
Tel: 0698-269114/0698-275655
Fax: 0698-275630
Contact: Rev Thomas M Gault
Office: Chancellor
The Roman Catholic Diocese of Motherwell comprises seventy-three parishes in Lanarkshire and part of the City of Glasgow. The central administration and the Bishop's office is contained within the Diocesan Centre in Motherwell. The pastoral office and renewal programme of the Diocese is administered from the Diocesan Pastoral Centre, 50 Bonkle Road, Newmains.

Roman Catholic Diocese of Argyll and the Isles

Bishop's House
Esplanade
Oban PA34 5AB
Tel: 0631-62010
Contact: Rt Revd Roderick Wright
Office: Bishop

Roman Catholic Diocese of Paisley

Cathedral House
8 East Buchanan Street
Paisley PA1 1HS
Tel: 041-889-2404
Contact: Rt Revd Mgr Neil C McGory
Thirty-five local parishes.

SALVATION ARMY DIVISIONS

Salvation Army North Scotland Division

Citadel Chambers
26 Castle Street
Aberdeen AB1 1AD
Tel: 0224-574166
Contact: Major Ronald Smith
Office: Divisional Commander

Salvation Army East Scotland Division

5 East Adam Street
Edinburgh EH8 9TF
Tel: 031-662-4441
Fax: 031-662-4085
Contact: Major Robin Forsyth
Office: Divisional Commander

Salvation Army West Scotland Division

Houldsworth Street
Glasgow G3 8DU
Tel: 041-221-3378
Fax: 041-221-8846
Contact: Lt Col Lincoln Parkhouse
Office: Divisional Commander
Fifty-three Corps.

SCOTTISH EPISCOPAL CHURCH DIOCESES

Scottish Episcopal Church Diocese of Aberdeen and Orkney

Diocesan Centre
39 King's Crescent
Aberdeen AB2 3HP
Tel: 0224-636653
Fax: 0224-636186
Contact: Rt Revd Bruce Cameron
Office: Bishop

Scottish Episcopal Church: Diocese of Brechin

35 Carlogie Road
Carnoustie
Tayside DD7 6HA
Tel: 0241-55781

Contact: Revd K R A Dall
Office: Diocesan Secretary

Scottish Episcopal Church Diocese of Edinburgh
Diocesan Centre
Walpole Hall
Chester Street
Edinburgh EH3 7EN
Tel: 031-226-3358
Fax: 031-225-3181
Contact: Miss E A Brady
Office: Diocesan Secretary
Fifty-nine congregations/parishes.

Scottish Episcopal Church Diocese of Glasgow and Galloway
Diocesan Office
5 St Vincent Place
Glasgow G1 2DH
Tel: 041-221-5720
Contact: Mr Andrew Chirnside
Office: Diocesan Secretary

Scottish Episcopal Church Diocese of Moray, Ross and Caithness
1 Seaview Farm Paddock
Cummingston
Burghead
Elgin
Grampian IV30 2XY
Tel: 0343-830890 (home)
Contact: Mr Alan W Campbell
Office: Diocesan Secretary

Scottish Episcopal Church Diocese of St Andrews, Dunkeld and Dunblane
Bishop's House
Fairmount Road
Perth PH2 7AP
Tel: 0738-21580
Fax: 0738-441326
Contact: Mrs D Bruce-Gardyne
Office: Diocesan Secretary
Forty-eight congregations/parishes.

Scottish Episcopal Church Diocese of Argyll and the Isles
Bishop's Office
The Pines
Ardconnel Road
Oban
Strathclyde PH34 5DR
Tel: 0631-66912

Fax: 0631-66912
Contact: Mr Christopher Hall
Office: Secretary

WALES
Details of the following regional bodies are found in this section:
Regional Ecumenical Instruments
Baptist Union of Great Britain Areas
Baptist Union of Wales Associations
Church in Wales Dioceses
Congregational Federation
Lutheran Church in Wales
Methodist Church Districts
Orthodox Church
Religious Society of Friends
Roman Catholic Dioceses
Salvation Army Districts
Seventh Day Adventist Church
Unitarian and Free Christian Regional Bodies
United Reformed Church Provinces

REGIONAL ECUMENICAL INSTRUMENTS

Churches Together in Clwyd (Cytun Clwyd)
55 Fordd Pentre
Mold
Clwyd CH7 1UY (home)
Tel: 0352-700104 (home)
Contact: Freda Hynes
Office: Secretary

BAPTIST UNION OF GREAT BRITAIN AREAS

Baptist Union of Great Britain South Wales Area
19 Melrose Close
St Mellons
Cardiff CF3 9SW
Tel: 0222-795919
Contact: Revd Peter D Manson
Office: General Superintendent
Covers East Glamorgan English Baptist; Gwent English Baptist; and West Wales English Baptist Associations. One hundred and sixty local congregations.

BAPTIST UNION OF WALES ASSOCIATIONS

Baptist Union of Wales Anglesey Association
Dolydd
Anglesey

Gwynedd
Contact: Rev Emlyn John

Baptist Union of Wales East Glamorgan Association
17 Ivor Terrace
Dowlais
Mid Glamorgan
Contact: Revd Wynne Leifion

Baptist Union of Wales Pembrokeshire Baptist Association
Morawel
78 Stryd Fawr
Abergwaun
Fishguard
Dyfed SA65 9AU (home)
Tel: 0348-872190 (home)
Contact: Revd D Carl Williams
Office: Secretary
Seventy-two churches (thirty-seven with Welsh language services and thirty-five with English language services).

Baptist Union of Wales DFM
Rhydlfar
Glynceiriog
Llangollen
Clwyd
Contact: Miss Jones

Baptist Union of Wales Radnor and Montgomery Association
Arosfa
Hillfield
Llanidloes
Powys
Contact: Meredith Powell

Baptist Union of Wales Arfon Association
Brynmore
Penygroes
Gwynedd
Contact: John Treharne

Baptist Union of Wales West Glamorgan Association
Hafan
10 Wern View
Pontrhydyfen
Port Talbot
West Glamorgan
Contact: Eric Williams

Baptist Union of Wales Gwent Association
12 Park Place
Risca
Gwent NP1 6AS (home)
Tel: 0633-601764 (home)
Contact: Revd I Murdoch Smith
Office: Secretary
Fifty-eight congregations.

Baptist Union of Wales Brecon Association
Llynfi Cottage
Pontithel
Talgarth
Powys
Contact: Gaynor Davies

CHURCH IN WALES DIOCESES

Church in Wales Diocese of St Davids
Diocesan Office
Abergwili
Carmarthen SA31 2JG
Tel: 0267-236145
Contact: Mr D Vincent Lloyd
Office: Diocesan Secretary
Represents three hundred and forty-five churches within one hundred and twenty-eight parishes.

Church in Wales Diocese of Bangor
Diocesan Office
Cathedral Close
Bangor LL57 1RL
Tel: 0248-354999
Fax: 0248-353882
Contact: Mr Philip Davies
Office: Diocesan Secretary
Eighty-eight parishes.

Church in Wales Diocese of Llandaff
Board for Social Responsibility
Heol Fair
Llandaff
Cardiff CF5 2EE
Tel: 0222-578899
Fax: 0222-576198
Contact: Gareth Foster
Office: Social Responsibility Officer
One hundred and thirty parishes. Community-based, Deanery Social Responsibility Groups, partnership projects and involvements such as Cardiff Interfaith and Welsh Refugee Council.

Church in Wales Diocese of Monmouth

64 Caerau Road
Newport NP9 4HJ
Tel: 0633-267490
Contact: Mr M W Brothers
Office: Diocesan Secretary
Approximately one hundred and ninety congregations.

Church in Wales Diocese of St Asaph

Diocesan Office
High Street
St Asaph
Clwyd LL17 0RD
Tel: 0745-582245
Fax: 0745-584301
Contact: Mr Christopher Seaton
Office: Diocesan Secretary

Church in Wales Diocese of Swansea and Brecon

The Church and House of the Good Shepherd
Eastmoor
Clyne Common
Swansea SA3 3JA
Tel: 0792-402616
Contact: Major D Hugh Thomas
Office: Diocesan Secretary
Eighty-four incumbencies covering two hundred and fifteen churches.

CONGREGATIONAL FEDERATION

Congregational Federation

Croslyn
Spittal
Haverfordwest
Dyfed SA62 5QT
Contact: Revd C L Gillham

LUTHERAN CHURCH IN WALES

Lutheran Church Wales (Yr Eglwys Liwtheraidd)

32 Heol-y-Fein
Rhiwbina
Cardiff CF4 6NT
Contact: Revd H Volker

METHODIST CHURCH DISTRICTS

Methodist Church Cymru District

Llys Myfyr
Yr Ala
Pwllheli
Gwynedd LL20 8DU
Tel: 0758-612608
Contact: Revd R Glyn Williams
Office: Secretary

Methodist Church North Wales District

12 Kenelm Road
Rhos-on-Sea
Clywd LL28 4EE
Tel: 0492-544737
Contact: Revd Bert Morris
Office: Secretary

Methodist Church North Wales District

Ingleside
98 Chester Road
Gresford
Wrexham
Clwyd
Tel: 0978-852883
Contact: Revd D H Ryan
Seventy congregations.

Methodist Church South Wales District

47 Sketty Park Road
Sketty
Swansea SA2 9AS
Tel: 0792-203938
Contact: Revd John Atkinson
Office: Synod Secretary
Two hundred and six local congregations.

ROMAN CATHOLIC DIOCESES

Roman Catholic Archdiocese of Cardiff

Archbishop's House
43 Cathedral Road
Cardiff CF1 9HD
Tel: 0222-220411
Fax: 0222-345950
Contact: Archbishop's Secretary
One hundred and six local congregations.

Roman Catholic Diocese of Menevia

Curial Office
115 Walter Road
Swansea SA1 5RE

Tel: 0792-644017
Contact: Sister Mary Carr
Office: Secretary

Roman Catholic Diocese of Wrexham

Bishops House
Sontley Road
Wrexham LL13 7EN
Tel: 0978-262726
Contact: Rt Revd Mgr Philip Webb

ORTHODOX CHURCH

Orthodox Church in Wales

11 Heol Manod
Blaenau Ffestiniog
Gwynedd LL41 4DE
Tel: 0766-831272
Contact: Venerable Abbot Father Deiniol
There is also a monastery in Newtown, Powys.

SALVATION ARMY DIVISIONS

Salvation Army South Wales Division

38 Cathedral Road
Cardiff CF1 9SU
Tel: 0222-341399
Contact: Major Dorothy Graham
Office: Divisional Secretary
Around forty Corps.

Salvation Army North Wales Division

Divisional Headquarters
401 Prescot road
Liverpool L13
Contact: Major A Bennett

UNITARIAN AND FREE CHRISTIAN BODIES

General Assembly of Unitarian and Free Christian Churches South East Wales Society

10 Tan y Lan Terrace
Morriston
Swansea SA6 7DU
Tel: 0792-794542
Contact: Revd E W Phillips
Office: Secretary
Seven congregations.

UNITED REFORMED CHURCH PROVINCES

United Reformed Church Wales Province

Provincial Office
URC
Minster Road
Cardiff CF2 5AS
Tel: 0222-499938
Contact: Mr John Rhys
Office: Synod Clerk
One hundred and fifty-three local churches in six districts.

IRELAND

Details of the following regional bodies are found in this section:
Baptist Union of Ireland Areas
Church of Ireland Dioceses
Roman Catholic Dioceses
Salvation Army Divisions
Presbyterian Church in Ireland Synods

BAPTIST UNION OF IRELAND AREAS

Baptist Union of Ireland Northern Area

The Manse
55 Taylor's Town Road
Toomebridge BT41 3RW
Contact: Pastor Rogers

CHURCH OF IRELAND DIOCESES

Church of Ireland Diocese of Armagh

Church House
Armagh BT61 7DZ
Tel: 0861-522858
Contact: J R McConnell
Office: Diocesan Secretary

Church of Ireland Diocese of Clogher

The Rectory
Rossfad
Ballinamallard
County Fermanagh BT94 2LS
Tel: 08036581-477
Contact: Revd Canon T R Moore
Office: Diocesan Secretary

Church of Ireland Diocese of Down and Dromore and Diocese of Connor

Diocesan Office
Church of Ireland House

12 Talbot Street
Belfast BT1 2QH
Tel: 0232-322268
Contact: T N Wilson
Office: Diocesan Secretary
The Diocese of Down and Dromore has seventy-nine parishes and the Diocese of Connor has eighty-one parishes.

Church of Ireland Diocese of Derry and Raphoe
Diocesan Office
London Street
Londonderry BT48 6RQ
Tel: 080504-262440
Contact: A McConnell
Office: Diocesan Secretary

ROMAN CATHOLIC DIOCESES

Roman Catholic Archdiocese of Armagh
Ara Coeli
Armagh BT61 7QY
Tel: 0861-522045
Fax: 0861-526182
Contact: Cardinal Daly
Office: Archbishop & Primate

Roman Catholic Archdiocese of Dublin
Archbishop's House
Dublin 9
Republic of Ireland
Tel: 010-3531-373732
Contact: Most Revd Desmond Connell
Office: Archbishop & Primate

Roman Catholic Archdiocese of Tuam
Archbishop's House
Tuam
County Galway
Republic of Ireland
Tel: 010353-09324166
Contact: Most Revd Jospeh Cassidy

Roman Catholic Archdiocese of Cashell and Emly
Archbishop's House
Thurles
County Tipperary
Republic of Ireland
0504-21512
Contact: Most Revd Dermot Clifford
Office: Archbishop

SALVATION ARMY DIVISIONS

Salvation Army Northern Ireland Division
4 Curtis Street
Belfast BT1 2ND
Tel: 0232-324730
Contact: Lt Col Joan Wilson
Office: Divisional Commander

PRESBYTERIAN CHURCH IN IRELAND SYNODS

Presbyterian Church in Ireland Synod of Derry and Omagh
Contact: Vacant
Office: Clerk
The Synod consists of the four Presbyteries of Derry/Straban, Foyle, Omagh, and Tyrone which collectively have one hundred and sixteen congregations. The General Assembly is the next court above ours.

NORTH EAST ENGLAND
Details of the following regional bodies are found in this section:
Regional Ecumenical Instruments
Baptist Union Areas
Church of England Dioceses
Methodist Church Districts
Roman Catholic Church Dioceses
Salvation Army Divisions
Seventh Day Adventist Conferences
United Reformed Church Provinces

REGIONAL ECUMENICAL INSTRUMENTS

Durham Ecumenical Relations Group
20 Dickens Wynd
Elvets Moor
Durham DH1 3QY
Tel: 091-386-0473
Contact: Revd Jean Mayland
Office: Local Unity Adviser

North East Churches Association
Hillcroft House
Sour Milk Hill Lane
Low Fell
Gateshead NE9 5RU
Tel: 091-482-3158
Contact: Revd Brian Howell
Office: Chairperson

Newcastle Church Relations Group
Bishop's House
29 Moor Road South
Newcastle-upon-Tyne NE3 1PA
Tel: 091-285-2220
Fax: 091-213-0728
Contact: Rt Rev Kenneth Gill
Office: Secretary

BAPTIST UNION AREAS

**Baptist Union of Great Britain North
Eastern Area**
26 Weetwood Road
Leeds LS16 5LP
Tel: 0532-785946 (home)
Contact: Revd John Nicholson
Office: General Superintendent
One hundred and sixty local congregations.

CHURCH OF ENGLAND DIOCESES

Church of England Diocese of Durham
Diocesan Office
Auckland Castle
Bishop Auckland DL14 7QJ
Tel: 0388-604515
Fax: 0388-603695
Contact: Mr William Hurworth
Office: Diocesan Secretary

Church of England Diocese of Newcastle
Church House
Grainger Park Road
Newcastle-upon-Tyne NE4 8SX
Tel: 091-226-0622
Fax: 091-226-0780
Contact: Mr David Hide
Office: Diocesan Secretary
One hundred and seventy-six local parishes and two
hundred and fifty-two congregations.

METHODIST DISTRICTS

Methodist Church Darlington District
57 Thames Avenue
Guisborough
Cleveland TS14 8AR
Tel: 0287-632770
Contact: Revd Graham S Smith
Office: Secretary
Two hundred and forty local congregations.

**Methodist Church Newcastle-upon-Tyne
District**
2 Pilton Road
Westerhope
Newcastle-upon-Tyne NE5 4PP
Tel: 091-286-9655
Contact: J W Wesley Blakey
Approximately twenty-two circuits and two hundred
and forty congregations.

ROMAN CATHOLIC DIOCESES

Roman Catholic Diocese of Middlesbrough
Bishops House
16 Cambridge Road
Middlesbrough TS5 5NN
Tel: 0642-818253
Contact: Rt Revd John Crowley

**Roman Catholic Diocese of Hexham and
Newcastle**
Bishops House
East Denton Hall
800 West Road
Newcastle-upon-Tyne NE5 2BJ
Tel: 091-228-0003
Fax: 091-274-0432
Contact: Rt Revd Ambrose Griffiths
Office: Bishop of Hexham and Newcastle

SALVATION ARMY DIVISIONS

Salvation Army Durham and Tees Division
82 Trimdon Avenue
Acklam
Middlesbrough TS5 8SB
Tel: 0642 819673
Fax: 0332-514323
Contact: Major Shaw Clifton
Office: Divisional Commander
Thirty Corps.

Salvation Army Northern Division
2 Hutton Terrace
Newcastle-upon-Tyne NE2 1QT
Tel: 091-281-4202
Contact: Major John Pearce-Haydon
Office: Divisional Commander
Thirty-six congregations.

SEVENTH DAY ADVENTIST CONFERENCE

Seventh day Adventist Church North England Conference
22 Zulla Road
Mapperley Park
Nottingham NG3 5DB
Tel: 0602–606312
Fax: 0602–691476
Contact: Pastor Mike J Stickland
Office: President
Ninety congregations

UNITED REFORMED CHURCH PROVINCES

United Reformed Church Northern Province
St James Church
Northumberland Road
Newcastle-Upon-Tyne NE1 8SG
Tel: 0748–86349
Contact: Revd Peter Poulter
Office: Synod Clerk

YORKSHIRE AND HUMBERSIDE
Details of the following regional bodies are found in this section:
Regional Ecumenical Instruments
Baptist Union Areas
Church of England Dioceses
Congregational Federation Areas
Methodist Church Districts
New Testament Church of God Districts
Roman Catholic Dioceses
Salvation Army Divisions
Seventh Day Adventist Conferences
Unitarian and Free Christian Regional Bodies
United Reformed Church Provinces

REGIONAL ECUMENICAL INSTRUMENTS

West Yorkshire Ecumenical Council and Sponsoring Body
32 Merton Road
Bradford BD7 1RE
Tel: 0274–732567
Contact: Revd W T Snelson
Office: Ecumenical Officer

Humberside Churches Council
The Vicarage
Skirlaugh
Hull HU11 5HE
Tel: 0964–562259
Contact: Revd David W Perry
Office: Ecumenical Officer

North Humberside Sponsoring Body
The Vicarage
Skirlaugh
Hull HU11 5HE
Tel: 0964–562259
Contact: Revd David W Perry
Office: Ecumenical Officer

Churches Together in South Yorkshire
109 Devonshire Street
Sheffield S3 7SB
Tel: 0742–766194
Fax: 0742–724154
Approximately four hundred and fifty congregations/parishes.

Churches Together in Lincolnshire and South Humberside
11 Rowan Drive
Silk Willoughby
Sleaford
Linconshire NG34 8PQ
Tel: 0529–303207
Contact: Revd Brian Levick
Office: County Ecumenical Officer

Churches Together in Wakefield
11 Woodthorpe Drive
Sandal
Wakefield WF2 6HT
Contact: Mrs S F Cooombes
Office: Lay Secretary

South Cleveland and North Yorkshire Ecumenical Council
St Bede's Pastoral Centre
21 Blossom Street
York YO2 2AQ
Tel: 0904–611597
Contact: Revd Chris Ellis
Office: Ecumenical Officer

BAPTIST UNION AREAS

Baptist Union of Great Britain North Eastern Area
26 Weetwood Road
Leeds LS16 5LP
Tel: 0532–785946 (home)

Contact: Revd John Nicholson
Office: General Superintendent
One hundred and sixty local congregations.

CHURCH OF ENGLAND DIOCESES

Church of England Diocese of Bradford
9 Garden Lane
Heaton
Bradford BD9 5QJ
Tel: 0274-543891
Contact: Mr Philip Lewis
Office: Adviser in Inter-Faith Matters
One hundred and thirty-three local parishes.

Church of England Diocese of Ripon
St Martin's Vicarage
2a St Martin's View
Leeds LS7 3LB
Tel: 0532-624271 (home)
Contact: Revd R W Shaw
Office: Diocesan Race Relations Officer
One hundred and sixty-one parishes.

Church of England Diocese of Sheffield
Diocesan Church House
95-99 Effingham Street
Rotherham S65 1BL
Tel: 0709-837457
Fax: 0709-837556
Contact: Mr C A Beck
Office: Diocesan Secretary
One hundred and seventy-one local parishes and two hundred and twenty-two local congregations.

Church of England Diocese of Wakefield
Church House
1 South Parade
Wakefield WF1 1LP
Tel: 0924-371802
Fax: 0924-364834
Contact: Mr A Wells
Office: Acting Diocesan Secretary
One hundred and ninety-one parishes and two hundred and fifty-four congregtions.

Church of England Diocese of York
Church House
Ogleforth
York YO1 2JE
Tel: 0904-611696
Fax: 0904-620375
Contact: Mr Keith W Dodgson

Office: Diocesan Secretary
Four hundred and seventy-four local parishes.

CONGREGATIONAL FEDERATION AREAS

Congregational Federation North East Area
5 Hallgate Road
Crosspool
Sheffield S10 5GL (home)
Tel: 0742-680377 (home)
Contact: Mrs J P Bradley
Office: Secretary
Twenty local congregations.

METHODIST CHURCH DISTRICTS

Methodist Church Leeds District
54 Whitecote Hill
Leeds LS13 2HU
Tel: 0532-570563
Contact: Revd Colin Vere
Office: Secretary

Methodist Church West Yorkshire District
10 Knowler Hill
Liversedge
West Yorkshire WF15 6PH
Tel: 0924-402219
Contact: Revd J Harry Scott
Office: Secretary

Methodist Church Lincoln and Grimsby District
193 Ashby Road
Old Brumby
Scunthorpe DN16 2AQ
Tel: 0724-843053
Contact: Revd John D Robinson
Office: Secretary

Methodist Church Sheffield District
65 Stafford Road
Sheffield S11 2SF
Tel: 0742-797596
Fax: 0742-781412
Contact: Revd Bryan Rippin
Office: Chairman
Two hundred and ninety local congregations.

Methodist Church York and Hull District
36 Orchard Paddock
Haxby

York YO3 3DP (home)
Tel: 0904–768326
Contact: Revd Keith A Reed
Office: Secretary
Three hundred and thirty local congregations.

NEW TESTAMENT CHURCH OF GOD DISTRICTS

New Testament Church of God
Jonson Street
Sheffield S3
Tel: 0742–739565
Fax: 0742–728722
Contact: Revd B Grey

ROMAN CATHOLIC DIOCESES

Roman Catholic Diocese of Leeds
Bishops House
13 North Grange Road
Headingley
Leeds LS6 2BR
Tel: 0532–304533
Fax: 0532–789890
Contact: Revd Andrew Summersgill
Contact: Bishop's Secretary

Roman Catholic Diocese of Hallam
"Quarters"
Carsick Hill Way
Sheffield S10 3LT
Tel: 0742–309101
Fax: 0742–305722
Contact: Rt Revd Gerald Moverley
Office: Bishop of Hallam
Sixty-five Parishes and twenty Convents.

SALVATION ARMY DIVISIONS

Salvation Army Central and West Yorkshire District
Whitfield Avenue
Leeds LS10 2QE
Tel: 0532–771700
Contact: Lieut Colonel Douglas Rayner
Office: Divisional Commander
Forty-seven corps.

Salvation Army South Yorkshire Division
Citadel Chambers
44 Pinstone Street
Sheffield S1 2HN
Tel: 0742–760672

Contact: Major Roy Smith
Office: Divisional Commander

SEVENTH DAY ADVENTIST CONFERENCE

Seventh day Adventist Church North England Conference
22 Zulla Road
Mapperley Park
Nottingham NG3 5DB
Tel: 0602–606312
Fax: 0602–691476
Contact: Pastor Mike J Stickland
Office: President
Ninety congregations.

UNITARIAN AND FREE CHRISTIAN REGIONAL BODIES

Yorkshire Union of Unitarian and Free Christian Churches
Mill Hill Chapel
City Square
Leeds LS1 5EB
Tel: 0532–433845
Tel: 0532–589228 (home)
Contact: Revd A C Fitzpatrick
Office: Honorary Secretary
Eleven local congregations.

UNITED REFORMED CHURCH PROVINCES

United Reformed Church Yorkshire Province
43 Hunslet Lane
Leeds LS10 1JW
Tel: 0532–451267
Fax: 0532–341145
Contact: Mr Douglas Thacker
Office: Synod Clerk
One hundred and thirty-seven local churches.

NORTH WEST ENGLAND
Details of the following regional bodies are found in this section:
Regional Ecumenical Instruments
Baptist Union Areas
Church of England Dioceses
Congregational Federation Areas
Methodist Church Districts
Roman Catholic Dioceses
Salvation Army Divisions

Seventh Day Adventist Conference
United Reformed Church Provinces

REGIONAL ECUMENICAL INSTRUMENTS

Churches Together in Cumbria
Church House
West Walls
Carlisle CA3 8UE
Tel: 0228-22573
Contact: Lady Anne Kerr
Office: Ecumenical Officer

Churches Together in Cheshire
5 Abbey Green
Chester CH1 2JH
Tel: 0244-347500
Contact: Canon Michael Rees
Office: Ecumenical Officer

Merseyside and Region Churches Ecumenical Assembly
Friends Meeting House
65 Paradise Street
Liverpool L1 3BP
Tel: 051-709-0125
Contact: Rev Bob Andrews
Office: Ecumenical Officer
About nine hundred and fifty local congregations and parishes including Church of England, Roman Catholic, Methodist, United Reformed Church, Baptist and others.

Greater Manchester County Ecumenical Council
St Peter's House
Oxford Road
Manchester M13 9GH
Tel: 061-273-5508
Contact: Revd Simon Oxley
Office: Ecumenical Officer

Lancashire Church Leaders' Council
c/o Bishop of Salford
Wardley Hall
Worsley
Manchester M28 5ND
Contact: Revd Donald A Parsons

Churches Together in Man
Glenfaba Lodge
Patrick
Peel

Isle of Man
Tel: 0624-842388
Contact: Dr David Moore
Office: Secretary

BAPTIST UNION AREAS

Baptist Union of Great Britain North West Area
14 Cedar Road
Great Sankey
Warrington WA5 3BU
Tel: 0925-722155
Contact: Revd Keith Hobbs
Office: Area Superintendent

CHURCH OF ENGLAND DIOCESES

Church of England Diocese of Blackburn
c/o Bishop's House
Ribchester Road
Blackburn BB1 9EF
Tel: 0254-248234
Office: Diocesan Inter-Faith Adviser
Two hundred and sixty-five parishes in the Diocese.

Church of England Diocese of Carlisle
Church House
West Walls
Carlisle CA3 8UE
Tel: 0228-22573
Fax: 0228-48769
Contact: Revd Canon David T I Jenkins
Office: Diocesan Secretary
Two hundred and seventy parishes and one hundred and seventy-eight pastoral units.

Church of England Diocese of Chester
Diocesan House
Raymond Street
Chester
Cheshire
Tel: 0244-379222
Fax: 0244-383835
Contact: Peter J Mills
Office: Diocesan Secretary

Church of England Diocese of Sodor and Man
24 Athol Street
Douglas
Isle of Man
Tel: 0624-675367

Contact: Worshipful P W S Farrant
Office: Vicar General

Church of England Diocese of Liverpool

Church House
Hanover Street
Liverpool L1 3DW
Tel: 051-709-9722
Fax: 051-709-2885
Contact: Mr K W Cawdron
Office: Diocesan Secretary
Two hundred and six local parishes totalling two hundred and fifty-seven local congregations.

Church of England Diocese of Manchester

Diocesan Church House
Diocesan Secretary
90 Deansgate
Manchester M3 2GH
Tel: 061-833-9521
Fax: 061-833-2751
Contact: Mrs J A Park
Office: Diocesan Secrtary

CONGREGATIONAL FEDERATION AREAS

Congregational Federation North West Area

13 Springhead Avenue
Springhead
Oldham OL4 5SP
Tel: 061-624-8778
Contact: Revd Donald G Openshaw
Office: Secretary
Forty-three congregations.

METHODIST CHURCH DISTRICTS

Methodist Church Cumbria District

Glenmillars
Ambleside
Cumbria LA22 9AG
Tel: 05394-33232
Office: Secretary

Methodist Church Bolton and Rochdale District

5 Hill Side
Heaton
Bolton BL1 5DT
Tel: 0204-843302
Contact: Revd David B Reddish
Office: Chairperson

One hundred and fifteen churches within fourteen circuits.

Methodist Church Isle of Man District

12 Ballamillaghyn
Mount Rule
Braddan
Douglas
Isle of Man
Tel: 0624-851975
Contact: Rev Maurice B Johnson
Office: Secretary
Thirty-nine local churches (grouped in 3 circuits) are represented.

Methodist Church Liverpool District

10 Hayles Green
Liverpool L25 4SG (home)
Tel: 051-525-2484
Tel: 051-722-3536 (home)
Contact: Rev Donald A Bullen
Office: Secretary of the Synod
Nineteen circuits and approximately one hundred and fifty churches.

Methodist Church Manchester and Stockport District

10 Dene Brow
Denton
Manchester M34 1PX
Tel: 061-320-6224
Contact: Revd Alec M Roberts
Office: Secretary

Methodist Church North Lancashire District

28 Lower Greenfield
Ingol
Preston PR2 3ZT
Tel: 0772-733496
Fax: 0772-733496
Contact: Revd G Michael Wearing
Office: Chairman of the District
One hundred and fifty local churches.

ROMAN CATHOLIC DIOCESES

Roman Catholic Diocese of Shrewsbury

Curial Offices
2 Park Road South
Birkenhead
Merseyside L43 4UX
Tel: 051-652-9855
Fax: 051-653-5172

Contact: Bishop's Secretary
One hundred and twenty parishes.

Roman Catholic Diocese of Lancaster
Bishops House
Cannon Hill
Lancaster LA1 5NG
Tel: 0524–32231
Fax: 0524–849296
Contact: Rt Revd John Brewer
Office: Bishop
One hundred and ten local parishes in North Lancashire and Cumbria.

Roman Catholic Archdiocese of Liverpool
Curial Offices
Brownlow Hill
Liverpool L3 5RG
Tel: 051–709-3666
Fax: 051–709-6531

Roman Catholic Diocese of Salford
Wardley Hall
Worsley
Manchester M28 5ND
Tel: 061-794-2825
Contact: Rt Revd Patrick Kelly

SALVATION ARMY DIVISIONS

Salvation Army Liverpool and North Wales Division
401 Prescot Road
Liverpool L13 3BT
Tel: 051–220-4210
Contact: Major Alan Bennett
Office: Divisional Commander
Thirty-one local congregations are represented.

Salvation Army North-West Division
38 Broadgate
Preston PR1 8DU
Tel: 0772-254373
Contact: Major Margaret Primrose
Office: Divisional Commander
Represents twenty-three corps.

Salvation Army Manchester Division
80 Eccles New Road
Salford M5 2RU
Tel: 061 737 4294
Contact: Major John Hassard
Office: Divisional Commander

UNITARIAN AND FREE CHRISTIAN REGIONAL BODIES

Manchester District Association of Unitarian and Free Christian Churches (Incoporated)
Cross Street Chapel
Cross Street
Manchester M2 1NL
Tel: 061–928-1687
Contact: Mr Geoffrey Head
Office: Honorary General Secretary
Fifteen local congregations.

SEVENTH DAY ADVENTIST CONFERENCE

Seventh Day Adventist North England Conference
22 Zulla Road
Mapperley Park
Nottingham NG3 5DB
Tel: 0602-606312
Fax: 0602-691476
Contact: Pastor Mike Stickland
Office: President
Ninety congregations.

UNITED REFORMED CHURCH PROVINCES

United Reformed Church Mersey Province
The Annexe
Trinity with Palm Grove Church
63 Alton Road
Birkenhead
Merseyside L43 1UZ
Tel: 051-653-7096
Contact: Revd Angus W Duncan
Office: Synod Clerk

United Reformed Church North Western Province
Provincial Office
Franklin Street
Patricroft
Eccles
Manchester M30 0QZ
Tel: 061-789-5583
Fax: 061-707-9117
Contact: Revd R A Wollaston
Office: Synod Clerk
One hundred and sixty-three congregations.

ENGLISH EAST MIDLANDS

Details of the following regional bodies are found in this section:

Regional Ecumenical Instruments
Baptist Union Areas
Church of England Dioceses
Congregational Federation Areas
Methodist Church Districts
Roman Catholic Dioceses
Salvation Army Divisions
Seventh Day Adventist Conferences
United Reformed Church Provinces

REGIONAL ECUMENICAL INSTRUMENTS

Churches Together in Nottinghamshire

The Earth
Blessingfield
Nottinghamshire NG12 2LG
Tel: 0602-817981
Contact: Mr John Fox
Office: Secretary

Churches Together in Leicestershire

Church House
3/5 St Martins East
Leicester LE1 5FX
Tel: 0533-627445
Fax: 0533-532889
Contact: Mr Jonathan Cryer
Office: Secretary
Ecumenical County Sponsoring body for Christian denominations in Leicestershire. Membership is open to Churches which are members of Churches Together in England. Copy of the constituion available on request from the Secretary.

Staffordshire Plus Ecumenical Council

56 Uttoxeter Road
Hill Ridware
Rugeley
Staffordshire WS15 3QU
Tel: 0543-492023
Contact: Revd Sheila Finn
Office: Ecumenical Officer

Churches Together in Derbyshire

4 Solway Rise
Dronfield
Woodhouse
Sheffield S18 5ZR (home)
Tel: 0246-413528

Contact: Mr Dennis Collins
Office: Secretary

Northamptonshire Ecumenical Council

The Rectory
Stanwick
Wellingborough NN9 6PP
Tel: 0933-622317
Contact: Revd Canon A Russell Twyford
Office: Secretary

BAPTIST UNION AREAS

Baptist Union of Great Britain Central Area

6 Sunridge Close
Newport Pagnell
MK16 0LT
Tel: 0908-616093
Contact: Revd Roy Freestone
Office: General Superintendent
Covers Bedfordshire; Buckinghamshire; Hertfordshire and Northamptonshire Associations. One hundred and sixty-two constituted churches and several additional congregations.

Baptist Union of Great Britain East Midlands Area

26 Frances Grove
Hucknall
Nottingham NG15 8DD
Tel: 0602-640804
Contact: Revd Edmund Pilling
Office: General Superintendent
One hundred and seventy-four churches.

CHURCH OF ENGLAND DIOCESES

Church of England Diocese of Derby

Derby Church House
Full Street
Derby DE1 3DR
Tel: 0332-382233
Fax: 0332-292969
Contact: Mr Robert J Carey
Office: Diocesan Secretary

Church of England Diocese of Leicester

Church House
3/5 St Martins East
Leicester LE1 5FX
Tel: 0533-627445
Fax: 0533-532889
Contact: Mr Jonathan P Cryer
Office: Diocesan Secretary

One hundred and forty-three Benefices and two hundred and fifty parishes.

Church of England Diocese of Lincoln
The Old Palace
Lincoln LN2 1PU
Tel: 0522-529241
Fax: 0522-512717
Contact: Capt David Williamson
Office: Diocesan Secretary
Five hundred and forty-nine parishes.

Church of England Diocese of Southwell
Dunham House
8 Westgate
Southwell
Nottinghamshire NG25 0JL
Tel: 0636-814331
Fax: 0636-815084
Contact: Mr B R E Noake
Office: Diocesan Secretary
Three hundred and fourteen local congregations and two hundred and sixty local parishes.

METHODIST CHURCH DISTRICTS

Methodist Church Oxford and Leicester District
48 Station Road
Wigston Magna
Leicester LE8 2DJ
Tel: 0533-571069 (home)
Contact: Revd Martin T Smithson
Office: Secretary
Twenty-one circuits and two hundred and eighty-eight churches.

Methodist Church Nottingham and Derby District
20 Rufford Avenue
New Ollerton
Newark
Nottinghamshire NG22 9PN
Tel: 0623-860354
Contact: Revd David C Gibson
Office: Secretary

Methodist Church Lincoln and Grimsby District
193 Ashby Road
Scunthorpe DN16 2AQ
Tel: 0274-843053
Contact: Revd John Robinson
Office: Secretary

ROMAN CATHOLIC CHURCH DIOCESES

Roman Catholic Diocese of Northampton
Bishops House
Marriott Street
Northampton NN2 6AW
Tel: 0604-715635
Fax: 0604-792186
Contact: Rt Revd Leo McCartie

Roman Catholic Diocese of Nottingham
27 Cavendish Road East
The Park
Nottingham NG7 1BB
Tel: 0602-474786
Fax: 0602-475325
Contact: Rt Revd James J McGuinness
Office: Bishop

SALVATION ARMY DIVISIONS

Salvation Army East Midlands Division
8 Tower Street
Northampton NN1 2SN
Tel: 0604- 20792
Contact: Major William Main
Office: Divisional Commander

Salvation Army Nottingham Division
397 Aspley Lane
Nottingham NG8 5RQ
Tel: 0602-295365
Contact: Major David Phillips
Office: Divisonal Commander
Forty-five corps.

SEVENTH DAY ADVENTIST CONFERENCES

Seventh Day Adventist Church North England Conference
22 Zulla Road
Mapperley Park
Nottingham NG3 5DB
Tel: 0602-606312
Fax: 0602-691476
Contact: Pastor Mike J Stickland
Office: President
Ninety congregations.

UNITED REFORMED CHURCH PROVINCES

United Reformed Church East Midlands Province

Sherwood United Reformed Church
1 Edwards Lane
Sherwood
Nottingham NG5 3AA
Tel: 0602-609241
Contact: Revd A Christopher White
Office: Synod Clerk
One hundred and sixty-one churches in six different Districts.

ENGLISH WEST MIDLANDS

Details of the following regional bodies are found in this section:
Regional Ecumenical Instruments
Baptist Union Areas
Church of England Dioceses
Congregational Federation Areas
Methodist Church Districts
New Testament Church of God Districts
Roman Catholic Dioceses
Salvation Army Divisions
Seventh Day Adventist Conferences
Unitarian and Free Christian Regional Bodies
United Reformed Church Provinces

REGIONAL ECUMENICAL INSTRUMENTS

Birmingham Council of Christian Churches

Carrs Lane Church Centre
Birmingham B4 7SX
Tel: 021-643-6603
Contact: Revd Christine Craven
Office: General Secretary
Acts as a resource for some thirty local councils of churches. All the denominations that belong to Churches Together in England are affiliated to Birmingham Council of Christian Churches.

West Midlands Churches Committee

Carrs Lane Church Centre
Birmingham B4 7SX
Tel: 021-643-6603
Contact: Revd Christine Craven
Office: General Secretary
Provides a point of contact between different denominations in the West Midlands area.

Churches Together in Shropshire (except Telford)

Hunter's Moon
Sheet Road
Ludlow
Shropshire SY8 1LH
Tel: 0584-872522
Fax: 0584-876675
Contact: Mrs Averil Norton
Office: Ecumenical Secretary

Coventry and Warwickshire Ecumenical Council

Horeston Grange Church Centre
off Camborne Drive
Nuneaton CV11 6GU
Tel: 0203-642406
Tel: 0203-352551 (home)
Contact: Revd Neil Bishop
Office: Ecumenical Officer
The five main Christian denominations: Anglican, Baptist, Methodist, Roman Catholic and United Reformed Church plus representatives of the Councils of Churches in Coventry and Warwickshire (two district councils and twelve town or area councils).

Churches Together in Herefordshire

9 Kent Avenue
Ross-on-Wye
Herefordshire HR9 5AH
Tel: 0989-64770
Contact: Miss Pansy James
Office: Ecumenical Officer

Staffordshire Plus Ecumenical Council

56 Uttoxeter Road
Hill Ridware
Rugeley
Staffordshire WS15 3QU
Tel: 0543-492023
Contact: Revd Sheila Finn
Office: Ecumenical Officer

Telford Christian Council

Parkfield
Park Avenue
Madeley
Telford
Shropshire TF7 5AB
Tel: 0952-585731
Contact: Revd Prebendary Dr Colin Hill
Office: Development Officer for Mission and Ministry

A network of seventy-three churches from twelve denominations. Its main activities are encouraging ecumenical co-operation; managing a range of community projects; overseeing specialist ministries in industry, youth, town centre and communications; and running Revelations, a large Christian bookshop.

Worcester County Ecumenical Council
The Rectory
Clifton-on-Teme
Worcester WR6 6DJ
Tel: 088-65-483
Contact: Revd Clifford Owen
Office: Secretary

BAPTIST UNION AREAS

Baptist Union of Great Britain West Midland Area
137 Newhall Street
Birmingham B3 1SF
Tel: 021-212-4842
Fax: 021-212-4512
Contact: Revd Neil Hall
Office: General Superintendent
Two Baptist Associations: West Midlands with one hundred and thirty-five affiliated churches and Worcestershire with twenty-seven affiliated churches.

CHURCH OF ENGLAND DIOCESES

Church of England Diocese of Birmingham
175 Harborne Park Road
Harborne
Birmingham B17 0BH
Tel: 021-428-1114
Fax: 021-427-5141
Contact: Revd Canon James G Pendorf
Office: Diocesan Secretary
One hundred and sixty-eight parishes.

Church of England Diocese of Coventry
Church House
Palmerston Road
Coventry CV5 6FJ
Tel: 0203-674328
Fax: 0203-674328
Contact: Mr John H Allen
Office: Diocesan Secretary

Church of England Diocese of Hereford
Diocesan Office
The Palace
Hereford HR4 9BL

Tel: 0432-353863
Contact: Diocesan Secretary

Church of England Diocese of Lichfield
St Mary's House
The Close
Lichfield
Staffordshire WS13 7LD
Tel: 0543-414551
Fax: 0543 205935
Contact: D R Taylor
Office: Diocesan Secretary
Four hundred and fifty-three local parishes and six hundred and twenty-four local congregations.

Church of England Diocese of Worcester
The Old Palace
Deansway
Worcester WR1 2JE
Tel: 0905-20537
Fax: 0905-612302
Contact: Mr John G Stanbury
Office: Diocesan Secretary
One hundred and eighty-eight parishes and two hundred and sixty-nine churches.

CONGREGATIONAL FEDERATION AREAS

Congregational Federation North West Midlands and North Wales Area
4 The Village
Kingswinford
DY6 8AY
Tel: 0384-273397
Contact: Revd Deborah J Martin
Office: Secretary
Fifteen local congregations.

Congregational Federation South West Midlands Area
2 Claremont Villas
All Saints Road
Uplands
Stroud
Gloucestershire GL5 1TS
Tel: 0453-766274
Contact: Mrs Emily Upjohn
Office: Secretary

METHODIST CHURCH DISTRICTS

Methodist Church Birmingham District

36 Amesbury Road
Moseley
Birmingham
Tel: 021-449-0131
Fax: 021-449-0131
Contact: Revd Donald M Eadie
Office: Chairman of District
The District has a Multi-Faith Committee, whose Secretary is Revd Ian Summerscales, Tel: 021-449-0804.

Methodist Church Chester and Stoke District

9 Fairview Avenue
Alsager
Stoke-on-Trent ST7 2NW
Tel: 0270-882243 (home)
Contact: Andrew L Gunstone
Office: Secretary of the District Synod. Twenty-four circuits including two hundred and sixty chapels.

Methodist Church Wolverhampton and Shrewsbury District

Trinity Manse
Hustons Hill
Codsall
Wolverhampton WV8 2ER
Tel: 0902-842256
Contact: Revd Derrick R Lander
Office: Secretary
Twenty-six circuits and four hundred churches approximately.

NEW TESTAMENT CHURCH OF GOD DISTRICTS

New Testament Church of God Coventry District

8 The Rowans
off Silverbirch Avenue
Bedworth
Warwickshire CV12 0ND
Tel: 0203-313970 (home)
Tel: 0203-687502
Three congregations.

New Testament Church of God Birmingham District

143 Sandwell Road
Handsworth
Birmingham B21 8PD
Tel: 021-554-1358
Tel: 021-554-7752 (home)
Contact: Revd S U Thompson
Office: District Overseer

New Testament Church of God Derby District

59 Harrow Drive
Burton-on-Trent DE14 3AY (home)
Tel: 0283-41395 (home)
Contact: Revd K Channer
Office: District Overseer and Chairman
Four congregations.

ROMAN CATHOLIC DIOCESES

Roman Catholic Diocese of Shrewsbury

Curial Offices
2 Park Road South
Birkenhead
Merseyside L43 4UX
Tel: 051-652-9855
Fax: 051-653-5172
Contact: Bishop's Secretary
One hundred and twenty parishes.

Roman Catholic Archdiocese of Birmingham

Cathedral House
St Chad's Queensway
Birmingham B4 6EU
Tel: 021-236-2251
Fax: 021-226-9266
Contact: Very Revd Kieran Conry
Office: Administrator
Two hundred and twenty-seven parishes.

SALVATION ARMY DIVISIONS

Salvation Army Birmingham Division

24 St Chad's Queensway
Birmingham B4 6HH
Tel: 021-236-7226
Fax: 021-236-1263
Contact: Lt Col Cyril Halstead
Office: Divisional Commander
Headquarters for the West Midlands Divison covering forty-eight places of worship and Christian care community centres.

SEVENTH DAY ADVENTIST CONFERENCES

Seventh Day Adventist North England Conference

22 Zulla Road
Mapperley Park
Nottingham NG3 5DB
Tel: 0602-606312
Fax: 0602-691476
Contact: Pastor Mike Stickland
Office: President
Ninety congregations.

UNITARIAN AND FREE CHRISTIAN REGIONAL BODIES

General Assembly of Unitarian and Free Christian Churches Midland Union

7 Greenhill Road
Moseley
Birmingham B13 9SR
Tel: 021-449-1298
Contact: Revd V Marshall
Office: Secretary
Twenty congregations.

UNITED REFORMED CHURCH PROVINCES

United Reformed Church: West Midlands Province

479 Lode Lane
Solihull
West Midlands B92 8NT
Tel: 021-783-1177
Contact: Mr Ronald N Webb
Office: Provincial Officer

EAST ANGLIA

Details of the following regional bodies are found in this section:
Regional Ecumenical Instruments
Baptist Union Areas
Church of England Dioceses
Congregational Federation Areas
Methodist Church Districts
Roman Catholic Dioceses
Salvation Army Divisions
Seventh Day Adventist Conferences
Unitarian and Free Christian Regional Bodies
United Reformed Church Provinces

REGIONAL ECUMENICAL INSTRUMENTS

Cambridgeshire Ecumenical Council

The Vicarage
Stapleford
Cambridge CB2 5BG
Tel: 0223-842150
Contact: Revd Frank Fisher
Office: Secretary
Five hundred and forty-six local congregations.

Suffolk Churches Together

Diocesan House
13 Tower Street
Ipswich IP1 3BG
Tel: 0473-211028
Fax: 0473-232407
Contact: Revd Colin Bevington
Office: Ecumenical Officer

Norfolk Churches Together

Marsham Rectory
Norwich NR10 5PP
Tel: 0263-733249
Contact: Revd Robin Hewetson
Office: Secretary

Churches Together in Lincolnshire and South Humberside

11 Rowan Drive
Silk Willoughby
Sleaford
Linconshire NG34 8PQ
Tel: 0529-303207
Contact: Revd Brian Levick
Office: County Ecumenical Officer

BAPTIST UNION AREAS

Baptist Union of Great Britain Eastern Area

35 Chaucer Way
Lexden
Colchester
Essex CO3 4HE
Tel: 0206-570673 (home)
Contact: Revd D Harper
Office: General Superintendent
One hundred and eighty local congregations.

CHURCH OF ENGLAND DIOCESES

Church of England Diocese of Ely
Diocesan Office
Bishop Woodford House
Barton Road
Ely
Cambridgesghire CB7 4DX
Tel: 0353-663579
Fax: 0353-666148
Contact: Mr David R Phillips
Office: Diocesan Secretary

Church of England Diocese of St Edmundsbury and Ipswich
Diocesan House
13 Tower Street
Ipswich IP1 3BG
Tel: 0473-211028
Fax: 0473-232407
Contact: Mr Ian Dodd
Office: Diocesan Secretary

Church of England Diocese of Lincoln
The Old Palace
Lincoln LN2 1PU
Tel: 0522-529241
Fax: 0522-512717
Contact: Capt David Williamson
Office: Diocesan Secretary
Five hundred and forty-nine parishes.

Church of England Diocese of Norwich
Diocesan Office
Dereham Road
Easton
Norwich NR9 5ES
Tel: 0603-880853
Fax: 0603-881083
Contact: Dr Brain W Martin
Office: Diocesan Secretary
Five hundred and ninety-nine parishes including six hundred and fifty-one church buildings.

Church of England Diocese of Peterborough
The Palace
Peterborough PE1 1YB
Tel: 0733-64448
Fax: 0733-555271
Contact: Mr Philip M Haines
Office: Diocesan Secretary
Three hundred and fifty-six parishes, three hundred and eighty-nine churches and one hundred and seventy-three benefices.

CONGREGATIONAL FEDERATION AREAS

Congregational Federation Eastern Area
79 Ranelagh Road
Felixstowe
Suffolk IP11 7HY
Tel: 0394-274345
Contact: Mrs Margaret Morris
Office: Secretary
Twenty-six congregations.

METHODIST CHURCH DISTRICTS

Methodist Church East Anglia District
24 Townsend Road
Norwich NR4 6RG
Tel: 0603-52257
Contact: Malcolm L Bradely
Office: Chairman
Three hundred and fifty-one local congregations.

Methodist Church Lincoln and Grimsby District
193 Ashby Road
Old Brumby
Scunthorpe DN16 2AQ
Tel: 0724-843053
Contact: Revd John D Robinson
Office: Secretary

ROMAN CATHOLIC DIOCESES

Roman Catholic Diocese of East Anglia
The White House
21 Upgate
Poringland
Norwich NR14 7SH
Tel: 05086-492202
Fax: 05086-495358
Contact: Rt Revd Alan Clark
Office: Bishop
Sixty local parishes.

SALVATION ARMY DIVISIONS

Salvation Army Eastern Counties Division
7 College Road
Norwich NR2 3JW
Tel: 0603 53525
Fax: 0603-506385
Contact: Major Robert Street
Office: Divisional Commander
Forty corps.

UNITARIAN AND FREE CHRISTIAN REGIONAL BODIES

General Assembly of Unitarian and Free Christian Churches Eastern Union
34 New Cut
Hadleigh
Ipswich IP7 5DA (home)
Tel: 0473-823720
Contact: Mrs M Crabtree
Office: Secretary
Seven congregations and one fellowship.

UNITED REFORMED CHURCH PROVINCES

United Reformed Church Eastern Province
The United Reformed church
Stowmarket
Suffolk IP14 1AD
Tel: 0449-615130
Contact: Mr William McVey
Office: Synod Clerk

SOUTH EAST ENGLAND (NORTH)
Details of the following regional bodies are found in this section:
Regional Ecumenical Instruments
Baptist Union Areas
Church of England Dioceses
Methodist Church Districts
Roman Catholic Dioceses
Salvation Army Divisions
Seventh Day Adventist Conferences
United Reformed Church Provinces

REGIONAL ECUMENICAL INSTRUMENTS

Buckinghamshire Ecumenical Council
Flinstone House
Dunsmore
Aylesbury
Buckinghsmahire HP22 6QH
Tel: 0296-624480
Fax: 0296-624480
Contact: Dr John Kilburn
Office: County Ecumenical Officer
Approximately eighty-five congregations.

West/North West London Church Leaders Group
Whitchurch Rectory
St Lawrence Close
Edgware
Middlesex HA8 6RB
Tel: 081-952-0019
Contact: Revd David Knight
Office: Secretary

Churches Together in Bedfordshire
Flat 1
43 Benslow Lane
Hitchin
Hertfordshire SG4 9RE
Tel: 0462-452784 (home)
Contact: Mrs Jenny Nicholson
Office: Secretary

Churches Together in Hertfordshire
Flat 1
43 Benslow Lane
Hitchin
Hertfordshire SG4 9RE
Tel: 0462-452784 (home)
Contact: Mrs Jenny Nicholson
Office: Secretary

Churches Together in West London
Our Lady and St Christopher
32 High Street
Cranford
Hounslow
Middlesex TW5 9RG
Contact: Revd Peter Sharp

Barking Area Church Leaders' Group
118 Henly Road
Ipswich IP1 4NN
Tel: 0473-253661
Contact: Revd John H Clarke
Office: Secretary

Essex Churches Consultative Council
118 Henley Road
Ipswich IP1 4NN
Tel: 0473-253661
Contact: Revd John H Clarke
Office: Ecumenical Officer

Milton Keynes Christian Council
c/o Church of Christ the Cornerstone
300 Saxon Gate West
Milton Keynes
Buckinghamshire MK9 2ES
Tel: 0908-230655
Contact: Revd Hugh G Cross

Office: Ecumenical Moderator
Sixty-six local congregations and parishes.

Churches Together in Berkshire
Greccio
St Cassian's Centre
Kintbury
Newbury
Berkshire RG15 0SR
Tel: 0488-58152
Contact: Sister Janet Wilcox

Oxfordshire Ecumenical Council
3 Berens Road
Shrivenham
Oxfordshire SN6 8EG
Tel: 0793-783118
Contact: Mr Norman Le Fort
Office: Executive Secretary

BAPTIST UNION AREAS

Baptist Union of Great Britain Eastern Area
35 Chaucer Way
Lexden
Colchester
Essex CO3 4HE
Tel: 0206-570673 (home)
Contact: Revd D Harper
Office: General Superintendent
One hundred and eighty local congregations.

Baptist Union of Great Britain Southern Area
70 Westwood Road
Newbury
Berkshire RG14 7TL
Tel: 0635-31464
Contact: Revd Geoffrey Reynolds
Office: General Superintendent
Covers Berkshire; Oxfordshire & East Gloucestershire; and Southern Associations with one hundred and seventy-six congregations.

Baptist Union of Great Britain Central Area
6 Sunridge Close
Newport Pagnell
MK16 0LT
Tel: 0908-616093
Contact: Revd Roy Freestone
Office: General Superintendent
Covers Bedfordshire; Buckinghamshire; Hertfordshire and Northamptonshire Associations.

One hundred and sixty-two constituted churches and several additional congregations.

CHURCH OF ENGLAND DIOCESES

Church of England Diocese of Chelmsford
53 New Street
Chelmsford
Essex CM1 1AT
Tel: 0245-266731
Fax: 0245-492786
Contact: Mr John C Reddington
Office: Diocesan Secretary
Four hundred and ninety-two parishes and six hundred and fifteen congregations.

Church of England Diocese of Oxford
Diocesan Church House
North Hinksey
Oxford OX2 0NB
Tel: 0865-244566
Fax: 0865-790470
Contact: Mr T C Landsbert
Office: Diocesan Secretary
Six hundred and twenty-three local congregations.

Church of England Diocese of St Albans
41 Holywell Hill
St Albans AL1 1HE
Tel: 0727-854532
Fax: 0727-844469
Contact: Mr L M Nicholls
Office: Diocesan Secretary

METHODIST CHURCH DISTRICTS

Methodist Church London North East District
2 South Road
Bishop's Stortford CM23 3JH
Tel: 0279-654475
Contact: Revd Michael Hayman
Office: Secretary of the Synod

Methodist Church London South West District
76 Coombe Lane West
Kingston-upon-Thames KT2 7DA
Tel: 081-949-3340
Fax: 081-949-3340
Contact: Revd Martin Broadbent
Office: Chairman
Two hundred and ten local congregations.

Methodist Church Oxford and Leicester District

48 Station Road
Wigston Magna
Leicester LE8 2DJ
Tel: 0533-571069 (home)
Contact: Revd Martin T Smithson
Office: Secretary
Twenty-one circuits and two hundred and eighty-eight churches.

Methodist Church London North West District

54 Hardinge Road
London NW10 3PJ
Tel: 081-459-2522
Contact: Revd R Stephen J Penrose
Office: Secretary
Twenty-nine circuits with a total membership of approximately seventeen thousand.

ROMAN CATHOLIC DIOCESES

Roman Catholic Diocese of Brentwood

Cathedral House
Ingrave Road
Brentwood
Essex CM15 8AT
Tel: 0277-214821
Fax: 0277-214060
Contact: Very Revd Gordon Read
Office: Chancellor
Ninety-four local parishes.

Roman Catholic Archdiocese of Westminster

Archbishops House
Ambrosden Avenue
London SW1P 1QJ
Tel: 071-834-7452
Contact: Vicar General

SALVATION ARMY DIVISONS

Salvation Army North London Division

9 Salisbury Road
Barnet
Hertfordshire EN5 4JW
Tel: 081-447-1422
Contact: Major Keith Banks
Office: Divisional Commander
Thirty-five local congregations.

SEVENTH DAY ADVENTIST CONFERENCES

Seventh Day Adventist Church South England Conference

25 St John's Road
Watford WD1 1PY
Tel: 0923-232728
Contact: Pastor D W McFarlane
Office: President
One hundred and twenty-two local congregations.

UNITED REFORMED CHURCH PROVINCES

United Reformed Church Eastern Province

The United Reformed Church
Stowmarket
Suffolk IP14 1AD
Tel: 0449-615130
Contact: Mr William McVey
Office: Synod Clerk

United Reformed Church Thames North Province

4 Duncan Court
Green Lanes
Wichmore
N21 3RL
Tel: 081-360-1773
Contact: Revd G W Satchell
Office: Synod Clerk

LONDON

Details of the following regional bodies are found in this section:
Regional Ecumenical Instruments
Baptist Union Areas
Church of England Dioceses
Church of Scotland Presbyteries
Methodist Church Districts
Roman Catholic Dioceses
Salvation Army Divisions
Seventh Day Adventist Conferences
Unitarian and Free Christian Regional Bodies
United Reformed Church Provinces

REGIONAL ECUMENICAL INSTRUMENTS

Barking Area Church Leaders' Group

118 Henley Road
Ipswich IP1 4NN
Tel: 0473-253661

Contact: Revd John H Clarke
Office: Secretary

Essex Churches Consultative Council

118 Henley Road
Ipswich IP1 4NN
Tel: 0473-253661
Contact: Revd John H Clarke
Office: Ecumenical Officer

Churches Together in North London

33 Crediton Hill
West End Lane
London NW6 1HS
Contact: Revd Greta Morgan

Churches Together in North West London

St Matthew's Vicarage
St Mary's Road
London NW10 4AU
Contact: Revd Keith Robus

East London Church Leaders Group

The Rectory Flat
St Mary's Church
Stoke Newington Church Street
London N16 9ES
Tel: 071-249-6138
Contact: Revd David Woodside
Office: Secretary

South London Church Leaders Group

8b Hilly Fields Crescent
Brockley
London SE4 1QA
Tel: 081-469-0013
Contact: Rt Revd A Peter Hall
Office: Member

South London Churches Sponsoring Body

All Saints' Vicarage
12 Beulah Hill
Upper Norwood
London SE19 3LS
Tel: 081-653-2820
Contact: Sister Jane Middleton
Office: Secretary

BAPTIST UNION AREAS

Baptist Union of Great Britain Metropolitan Area

25 Springwell Road
Streatham
London SW16 2QU
Tel: 081-769-6519
Fax: 081-769-6519
Contact: Revd Douglas McBain
Office: General Superintendent
Covers Baptist congregations in the whole of Greater London.

CHURCH OF ENGLAND DIOCESES

Church of England Diocese of London

London Diocesan House
30 Causton Street
London SW1P 4AU
Tel: 071-821-9351
Fax: 071-821-0424
Contact: Revd Bob Marshall
Office: Communications Officer
Covers Church of England parishes in London north of the Thames.

Church of England Diocese of Southwark

Trinity House
4 Chapel Court
Borough High Street
London SE1 1HW
Tel: 071-403-8686
Fax: 071-403-4770
Contact: Mr Martin C Cawte
Office: Diocesan Secretary
Three hundred and twelve local parishes and three hundred and ninety local congregations.

CHURCH OF SCOTLAND PRESBYTERIES

Church of Scotland England Presbytery

St Columba's Presbytery
Pont Street
London SW1X 0BD
Tel: 071-584-2321
Contact: Revd W A Cairns
Office: Presbytery Clerk

METHODIST CHURCH DISTRICTS

Methodist Church London South West District

76 Coombe Lane West
Kingston-upon-Thames KT2 7DA
Tel: 081-949-3340
Fax: 081-949-3340
Contact: Revd Martin Broadbent
Office: Chairman
Two hundred and ten local congregations.

Methodist Church London South East District

8 Elgin Road
Croydon
Surrey CR0 6XA
Tel: 081-654-2845
Contact: Revd Roger Cresswell
Office: Secretary

Methodist Church London North West District

54 Hardinge Road
London NW10 3PJ
Tel: 081-459-2522
Contact: Revd R Stephen J Penrose
Office: Secretary
Twenty-nine circuits with a total membership of approximately seventeen thousand.

ROMAN CATHOLIC DIOCESES

Roman Catholic Archdiocese of Southwark

Archbishops House
St Georges Road
Southwark
London SE1 6HX
Tel: 071-928-2495
Fax: 071-928-7833
Contact: Revd Richard Moth
Office: Vice-Chancellor
One hundred and eighty-six local parishes. Covers South London and Kent.

Roman Catholic Archdiocese of Westminster

Archbishops House
Ambrosden Avenue
London SW1P 1QJ
Tel: 071-834-7452
Contact: The Vicar General

SALVATION ARMY DIVISIONS

Salvation Army East London Division

432 Forest Road
Walthamstow
London E1 4PY
Tel: 081-520-2244
Fax: 081-520-3755
Contact: Major Stanley Cleaves
Office: Divisional Secretary

Salvation Army South London Division

25 Brownhill Road
Catford
London SE6 2HE
Tel: 081-698-1041
Contact: Major Keith Burridge
Office: Divisional Commander
Thirty-three local congregations.

Salvation Army West London Division

10 Crown Street
Acton
London W3 8SB
Tel: 081-992-2268
Contact: Lt Col Michael Pressland
Office: Divisional Commander
Forty-eight local congregations.

SEVENTH DAY ADVENTIST CONFERENCE

Seventh Day Adventist Church South England Conference

25 St John's Road
Watford WD1 1PY
Tel: 0923-232728
Contact: Pastor D W McFarlane
Office: President
One hundred and twenty-two local congregations.

UNITARIAN AND FREE CHRISTIAN REGIONAL BODIES

General Assembly of Unitarian and Free Christian Churches and South East Provincial Assembly

Essex Hall
1-6 Essex Street
Strand
London WC2R 3HY
Tel: 071-240-2384
Contact: Mrs W Adams

Office: Secretary
Thirty-two local congregations.

UNITED REFORMED CHURCH PROVINCES

United Reformed Church Southern Province
Synod Office
East Croydon United Reformed Church
Addiscombe Grove
Croydon
Surrey CR0 5LP
Tel: 081-688-3730
Contact: Revd Harold Grief
Office: Synod Clerk

United Reformed Church Thames North Province
The City Temple
Holborn Viaduct
London EC1A 2DE
Tel: 071-583-8701
Fax: 071-353-1558
Contact: Revd Janet Sowerbutts
Office: Provincial Moderator
One hundred and sixty-five local congregations.

SOUTH EAST ENGLAND (SOUTH)

Details of the following regional bodies are found in this section:
Regional Ecumenical Instruments
Baptist Union Areas
Church of England Dioceses
Congregational Federation Areas
Methodist Church Districts
Roman Catholic Dioceses
Salvation Army Divisions
Seventh Day Adventist Conferences
Unitarian and Free Christian Regional Bodies
United Reformed Church Provinces

REGIONAL ECUMENICAL INSTRUMENTS

Churches Together in Kent
5 Randolph Close
Canterbury CT1 3AZ
Tel: 0227-452009
Contact: Revd Canon Alan Dawkins
Office: Ecumenical Officer

Sussex Churches
68 The Mount
Court Farm Road

Hove BN3 7QR
Tel: 0273-771493
Contact: Mr D R Curry
Office: Ecumenical Officer
Associated with it are sixty-five local ecumenical groups covering five hundred and fifty churches.

Churches Together in Hampshire and the Islands
6 West Road
Woolston
Southampton S02 9AJ
Tel: 0703-446948
Contact: Ms Carol Cunio
Office: Ecumenical Officer

Churches Together in Surrey
Woodbrow
Woodham Lane
Woking
Surrey GU21 5SR
Tel: 0932-343874
Contact: Mrs Barbara Brash

BAPTIST UNION AREAS

Baptist Union of Great Britain South Eastern Area
41 Newlands Road
Tunbridge Wells
Kent TN4 9AS
Tel: 0892-530033
Contact: Revd Peter Tongeman
Office: General Superintendent
Covers Kent; Sussex; Surrey & North East Hampshire Associations. One hundred and forty congregations.

CHURCH OF ENGLAND DIOCESES

Church of England Diocese of Canterbury
Diocesan House
Lady Wootton's Green
Canterbury CT1 1NQ
Tel: 0227-459401
Fax: 0227-450964
Contact: Mr David S Kemp
Office: Diocesan Secretary
Two hundred and eighty-two parishes.

Church of England Diocese of Guildford
Diocesan House
Quarry Street
Guildford
Surrey GU1 3XG

Tel: 0483-571826
Fax: 0483-67896
Contact: Mrs S Hastings
Office: Diocesan Communications Officer
One hundred and sixty-four local parishes.

Church of England Diocese of Chichester

Diocesan Church House
9 Brunswick Square
Hove
East Sussex BN3 1EN
Tel: 0273-329023
Fax: 0273-821810
Five hundred and thirty congregations and three hundred and ninety-three parishes.

Church of England Diocese of Portsmouth

Cathedral House
St Thomas Street
Portsmouth P01 2HA
Tel: 0705-825731
Fax: 0705-752967
Contact: Mr M F Jordan
Office: Diocesan Secretary
One hundred and fifty congregations/parishes.

Church of England Diocese of Rochester

Diocesan Office
St Nicholas Church
Boley Hill
Rochester
Kent ME1 1SL
Tel: 0634-830333
Fax: 0634-829463
Contact: Mr Peter G H Law
Office: Diocesan Secretary

Church of England Diocese of Winchester

Church House
9 The Close
Winchester SO23 9LS
Tel: 0962-844644
Fax: 0962-842376
Contact: Mr Raymond Anderton
Office: Diocesan Secretary

CONGREGATIONAL FEDERATION AREAS

Congregational Federation South East Area

17 Overbrook
West Horsley
Leatherhead
Surrey KT24 6BH (home)

Tel: 0483-282541
Thirty-two local congregations.

METHODIST CHURCH DISTRICTS

Methodist Church London South East District

8 Elgin Road
Croydon
Surrey CR0 6XA
Tel: 081-654-2845
Contact: Revd Roger Cresswell
Office: Secretary

Methodist Church Southampton District

29 Weysprings
Haslemere
Surrey GU27 1DF
Tel: 0428-642921
Contact: Revd Stephen J Marr
Office: Secretary

Methodist Church Channel Islands District

West Lea
Route des Quennevais
St Brelade
Jersey
Tel: 0534-43933
Contact: Revd Colin Hough
Office: Chairman
Thirty-three congregations.

ROMAN CATHOLIC CHURCH DIOCESES

Roman Catholic Diocese of Arundel and Brighton

Bishop's House
Upper Drive
Hove BN3 6NE
Tel: 0273-506387
Contact: Right Revd Mgr Canon John Hull
Office: Vicar General

Roman Catholic Diocese of Portsmouth

Bishop's House
Edinburgh Road
Portsmouth P01 3HG
Tel: 0705-820894
Fax: 0705-863086
Contact: Right Revd Crispian Hollis
Office: Bishop
One hundred and twenty local parishes.

SALVATION ARMY DIVISIONS

Salvation Army Canterbury Division
24 Old Dover Road
Canterbury CT1 3JB
Tel: 0227-463069
Contact: Lt Col Jessie Dawson
Office: Divisional Commander

Salvation Army Southampton and Channel Islands Division
111a Lodge Road
Southampton S02 ORE
Tel: 0703-333348
Fax: 0703-330027
Contact: Lt Col Nigel Mason
Office: Divisional Commander

SEVENTH DAY ADVENTIST CONFERENCE

Seventh Day Adventist Church South England Conference
25 St John's Road
Watford WD1 1PY
Tel: 0923-232728
Contact: Pastor D W McFarlane
Office: President
One hundred and twenty-two local congregations.

UNITARIAN AND FREE CHRISTIAN REGIONAL BODIES

General Assembly of Unitarian and Free Christian Churches Southern Unitarian Association
70 Hunnyhill
Newport
Isle of Wight P030 5HN (home)
Tel: 0983-524419 (home)
Contact: Mrs S J Jackson
Office: Honorary Secretary
Four member churches.

UNITED REFORMED CHURCH PROVINCES

United Reformed Church Southern Province
Synod Office
East Croydon United Reformed Church
Addiscombe Grove
Croydon
Surrey CR0 5LP
Tel: 081-688-3730

Contact: Mrs Christine Meekison
Office: Synod Clerk

United Reformed Church Wessex Province
King's Road
Chandler's Ford
Eastleigh
Southampton SO5 2EY
Tel: 0703-266548
Contact: Revd Nelson W Bainbridge
Office: Provincial Moderator
One hundred and sixty-nine congregations.

SOUTH WEST ENGLAND
Details of the following regional bodies are found in this section:
Regional Ecumenical Instruments
Baptist Union Areas
Church of England Dioceses
Congregational Federation Areas
Methodist Church Districts
Roman Catholic Dioceses
Salvation Army Divisions
Seventh Day Adventist Conferences
United Reformed Church Provinces

REGIONAL ECUMENICAL INSTRUMENTS

Greater Bristol Ecumenical Council
St Nicholas House
Lawford's Gate
Bristol BS5 ORE
Tel: 0272-542133
Contact: Mr Brian J H Blancharde
Office: Executive Secretary
Thirteen denominations (and two associated groups), committed to each other through consultation and co-operation in shared Christian life and witness.

Churches Together in Gloucestershire
Warden Hill United Reformed Church
Salisbury Road
Warden Hill
Cheltenham GL51 5BY
Contact: Revd Flora Winfield
Office: Ecumenical Officer

Wiltshire Churches Together
16 Sherwood Avenue
Melksham
Wiltshire SN12 7HJ
Tel: 0225-704748

Contact: Miss Anne Doyle
Office: Ecumenical Secretary

Christians Together in Devon
174 Beacon Park Road
Beacon Park
Plymouth PL2 2QS
Tel: 0752-605503
Contact: Clare Giarchi
Office: Ecumenical Officer

Churches Together in Cornwall
5 David Penhaligon Way
Barrack Lane
Truro TR21 2XT
Tel: 0872-42241
Contact: Dorothy Jamal
Office: County Ecumenical Officer

Somerset and South Avon Ecumenical Council
7 Kidder Bank
Wells
Somerset BA5 3JT
Tel: 0749-677773
Contact: Mr Ian Mills
Office: Ecumenical Officer
Approximately one thousand congregations/parishes.

Churches Together in Dorset
15 Avenue Road
Wimborne
Dorset BH21 1BS (home)
Tel: 0202-841807 (home)
Contact: Mr Steve Potts
Office: Ecumenical Officer

BAPTIST UNION AREAS

Baptist Union of Great Britain Western Area
15 Fenshurst Gardens
Long Ashton
Bristol BS18 9AU
Tel: 0275-394101
Contact: Revd Roger Hayden
Office: General Superintendent
One hundred and twenty-seven local congregations.

Baptist Union of Great Britain South Western Area
10 Lymeborne Avenue
Exeter EX1 3AU
Tel: 0392-221736
Contact: Revd Gwynne Edwards

Office: General Superintendent
Covers Devon & Cornwall and Western Association.

CHURCH OF ENGLAND DIOCESES

Church of England Diocese of Bristol
Diocesan Church House
23 Great George Street
Bristol BS1 5QZ
Tel: 0272-214411
Fax: 0272-250460
Contact: Mrs L E Farrall
Office: Diocesan Secretary
Two hundred and four congregations and one hundred and sixty-nine parishes.

Church of England Diocese of Exeter
Diocesan House
Palace Gate
Exeter EX1 1HX
Tel: 0392-72686
Contact: Revd R R Huddleson
Office: Diocesan Secretary
Five hundred and eight local congregations/ parishes.

Church of England Diocese of Gloucester
Church House
College Green
Gloucester GL1 2LY
Tel: 0452-410022
Fax: 0452-308324
Contact: Mr R Anderton
Office: Diocesan Secretary
Three hundred and twenty-four parishes and four hundred and twenty-one churches.

Church of England Diocese of Salisbury
Church House
Crane Street
Salisbury SP1 2QE
Tel: 0722-411922
Fax: 0722-411990
Contact: Lt Col C Christopher G Ross
Office: Diocesan Secretary
Four hundred and fifty-two Parishes.

Church of England Diocese of Truro
Diocesan House
Kenryn
Truro
Cornwall TR1 3DU
Tel: 0872-74351
Fax: 0872-222510
Contact: Mr C B Gorton

Office: Diocesan Secretary
Two hundred and twenty-seven local congregations.

Church of England Diocese of Bath and Wells
Diocesan Office
The Old Deanery
Wells
Somerset BA5 2UG
Tel: 0749-670777
Fax: 0749-674240
Contact: Mr Nicholas Denison
Office: Diocesan Secretary
Four hundred and ninety-three parishes.

CONGREGATIONAL FEDERATION AREAS

Congregational Federation South West Area
31 Dunning Court
Dowell Street
Honiton
Devon EX14 8FQ
Tel: 0404-44300
Thirty-one congregations.

Congregational Federation South West Midlands Area
2 Claremont Villas
All Saints Road
Uplands
Gloucestershire GL5 1TS
Tel: 0453-766274
Contact: Mrs Emily Upjohn
Office: Secretary

METHODIST CHURCH DISTRICTS

Methodist Church Plymouth and Exeter District
6 Gatefield Road
Londonderry Farm
Bideford
Devon EX39 3QX
Tel: 0237-423568
Contact: Revd Peter Nock
Office: Secretary

Methodist Church Bristol District
80 Leckhampton Road
Cheltenham GL53 0BN
Tel: 4242-524889
Contact: Revd Ian Suttie
Office: Secretary

Methodist Church Cornwall District
The Manse
Coads Green
Launceston
Cornwall PL15 7LU
Tel: 0566-82240
Contact: Revd W Keith Roberts
Office: Secretary
Twenty-one circuits with three hundred and forty-three churches.

ROMAN CATHOLIC DIOCESES

Roman Catholic Diocese of Clifton
St. Anthony's Presbytery
Satchfield Crescent
Henbury
Bristol BS10 7BE
Tel: 0272-502509
Contact: Rt Revd Mgr Canon William Mitchell
Office: Vicar General
One hundred and seven parishes.

Roman Catholic Diocese of Plymouth
Vescourt
Hartley Road
Plymouth PL3 5LR
Tel: 0752-772950
Fax: 0752-772950 (phone first)
Contact: Rt Revd C Budd
Office: Bishop of Plymouth

SALVATION ARMY DIVISIONS

Salvation Army Bristol Division
468 Filton Avenue
Horfield
Bristol BS7 0LX
Tel: 0272-696172
Contact: Major Clifford Hurcum
Office: Divisional Commander
Thirty-four local corps and centres.

Salvation Army South West Division
47a North Road East
Plymouth PL4 6AY
Tel: 0752-665844
Contact: Major Alan Atherton
Office: Divisional Commander
Thirty-two Corps.

SEVENTH DAY ADVENTIST CONFERENCE

Seventh Day Adventist Church South England Conference

25 St John's Road
Watford WD1 1PY
Tel: 0923-232728
Contact: Pastor D W McFarlane
Office: President
One hundred and twenty-two local congregations.

UNITED REFORMED CHURCH PROVINCES

United Reformed Church: South Western Province

26 Stapleton Close
Highworth
Wiltshire SN6 7DR
Tel: 0793-762641
Tel: 051-722-3536 (home)

KEY TO TERMS IN CHRISTIAN ORGANISATIONAL LISTINGS

Note: This is not a complete glossary of significant Christian terms. It is a guide to the meaning and/or background of some of the words used in the titles of Christian organisations listed in this directory. More information on the italicised words can be tracked down either elsewhere in the key and/or in the section on "Introducing the Christian Community" by using the directory's Keyword Index.

Adventist

From the Latin for "coming" and related to both the first coming of Jesus in Palestine and also to the traditional Christian hope of his *Second Coming* in glory at the end of all things. The *Adventist* Churches have a strong belief in this hope. Many are also *Seventh Day* Churches which means that they continue to observe Saturday as their day of rest and worship in continuity with the *Shabbat* of the Jewish people.

Agency

One of the possible categories under which a body or organisations may be affiliated to a UK or national *ecumenical instrument*. It is applicable to bodies such as Christian Aid which are not *ecclesiastical* organisations in the sense of being Churches themselves, but which are agencies of the Churches working together on specific issues.

Alliance

The word *alliance* appears in the title of the Evangelical Alliance and expresses the nature of the organisation as a coming together of a variety of different Churches, organisations and individuals.

Apostolic

From the Greek word *apostolos* meaning "one who is sent", the word was first applied to the first twelve disciples of Jesus and then to a wider group of leaders in the early Christian Church. The word *apostolic* is often used to emphasise the continuity of Christian tradition which is consistent with the teaching of the leaders of the early Church. In this sense, the word applies to the self-understanding of Churches such as the Roman Catholic Church. However, many groups or Churches which use the word in their title are signalling a self-understanding which is concerned with an attempt to to get back to what they perceive as the original pattern of early Church life prior to what they believe are alien doctrinal and organisational accretions arising from Greek philosophy and Roman social structures. Many of these groups or Churches baptise in the name of Jesus only and are not *Trinitarian*.

Archdiocese

In the *Roman Catholic Church* a *diocese* (see below) of which the senior bishop is an *Archbishop* .

Area

The Baptist Union of Great Britain uses the word to describe the geographical region for which there is an *Area Superintendent* who has pastoral care of the Churches and *ministers* within this area. An *Area* is usually composed of a number of *Associations* which cover one or more counties. Associations are made up of *Districts* which are, in turn, composed of individual local *congregations*. Baptist *Areas* are not decision-making bodies.

Assembly

The name for a national gathering of representatives which is used by a number of Churches such as the Baptist Union of Great Britain and the United Reformed Church. It is also part of the title of some Churches and, as such, indicates that these Churches have a strong local Church polity in which the national level of representation is seen as an expression of the primarily local character of the Church.

Association

The name of a regional level grouping of *congregations* in both the *Baptist* and *Congregational* traditions, often covering a number of counties and composed of local *Districts*. Also used of voluntary groupings of individual Christians as, for example, in the Association of Inter Church families.

Autocephalic

From the Greek *autokephalos* literally meaning "himself the head". Many Churches in the *Orthodox* tradition have their own national *synods* whilst remaining in communion with the *Patriarch* of Constantinople.

Baptist

The name of a Christian movement which is present in the UK in a number of organisational forms, the largest of which is the Baptist Union of Great Britain. The name derives from the the word *baptism* which describes the act of Christian initiation which Baptists believe is appropriate for those who can exercise faith and commitment in their own right rather than it being exercised on their behalf by parents and godparents. *Baptists* characteristically have a local level of Church government focused on individual *congregations*.

Catholic

From the Greek *katholicos* and meaning "universal" or "general". It is often used to signify membership of the Church in all places and times and some individual Churches use it to underline their self-understanding of being in continuity with this universal Christian community. It is used in this sense, for example, by the Roman Catholic Church.

Chaplaincy

Is the name given to a form of authorised and recognised Christian presence in a variety of social institutions such as universities, hospitals and the armed forces.

Cherubim

The name of the highest order of angels in Christian angelology often grouped together with *seraphim* (see below). It is part of the name of the *Cherubim and Seraphim* Christian movement which originated in West Africa.

Christ

From the Greek *Christos* meaning "anointed one" which, in turn, comes from the Hebrew *Mashiah*. When used of Jesus this title underlines that he is believed by Christians to be the promised one of Jewish expectation and therefore in the line of the Jewish king David, but exercising a spiritual Kingship in inaugurating *the Kingdom of God*.

Christian

Originally a nickname applied in Antioch to the early followers of Jesus confessed as the *Christ* . The earliest Christian self-description appears to have been "followers of the Way". However, as often occurs, names given by outsiders are appropriated by those to whom they are applied.

Church

From the Greek *kuriakos* meaning "belonging to the Lord (*kurios*)" and related to the Scots *kirk*. It is now used for the collective body of Christian believers. Sometimes it refers to these believers in the universal sense of the Church in all times and places. In other instances, it refers only to Christians in one local geographical place and time. Often it refers to a particular ecclesiastical and organisational form of Christianity as in, for example, the Methodist Church. It is also often used with a small "c" to describe the building in which Christians worship.

Churches Together

Part of the title adopted by a number of what are known as *ecumenical instruments* operating at national, regional and local levels of Church life. It is followed by a particular geographical referent such as Churches Together in England or Churches Together in Derbyshire. The title expresses a vision or stage of Christian unity in which the integrity of each individual Christian tradition and denomination is recognised whilst also affirming their oneness in fundamental Christian belief and common action.

Commission

The collective name of a formal body of people appointed by their Churches to serve the *ecumenical instruments* of the Council of Churches for Britain and Ireland in relation to a particular aspect of Christian life or work which the Churches have prioritised as an area for co-operative work, such as the Churches' Commission for Inter-Faith Relations.

Conference

The name given to the national governing body of the Methodist Church and also the regional bodies of the Seventh Day Adventist Church.

Congregational

The name of a Christian tradition which emphasises the independence of the local church or *congregation*. Most *congregations* within this tradition in England joined the United Reformed Church although some continue as part of the Congregational Federation.

Connexion

The name given to the national form of organisation in a number of Christian traditions including the Countess of Huntingdon Churches and some *Methodist* traditions.

Council

A *Council of Churches* is usually the name of a formal gathering of Church representatives. Historically, the word is used of the Councils of the early undivided Church which defined orthodox doctrine and practice. It is now used to describe organisations formed in order to assist different Churches to work together at various geographical levels. For example, the Council of African and Afro-Caribbean Churches and many local Councils of Churches in towns and cities throughout the UK.

Countess of Huntingdon

Selina, Countess of Huntingdon (1707-1791) was the founder, in 1790, of this grouping of local churches in the tradition of *Calvinistic Methodism* known as the Countess of Huntingdon's *Connexion* (see above).

Covenanted

The idea of a *covenant* comes from the Jewish concept of a *brith* which is a legal term expresssing the mutual obligations of the parties involved. The Covenanted Churches in Wales have therefore covenanted together in the sense of moving beyond loose co-operation into a more formalised mutual responsibility and recognition with the aim of visible unity.

Diocese

From the Greek *diokesis*, it is the name of the regional level of Church organisation in Churches with *episcopalian* traditions such as the *Anglican* Churches and the Roman Catholic Church. A *diocese* is presided over by a *bishop*.

District

The name of the regional level of organisation in the Methodist Church and the New Testament Church of God and of more localised groupings of congregations within the various Baptist Unions in the UK and in the United Reformed Church.

Division

The name of a regional level of organisation in the Salvation Army .

Ecumenical

From the Greek *oikoumene* meaning "the whole inhabited earth". More often it has come to describe the relations between the various Christian Churches, traditions and denominations in their attempts to give expression to Christian unity.

Episcopal

From the Greek *episcope* meaning "oversight". It is a word which describes the form of Church government adopted by Churches with *bishops* .

Evangelical

From the Greek *euangelion* meaning "good news ". It is a word of eighteenth century origin and is usually used of Christians in many different Churches and traditions to emphasise continuity with what is understood to be historic Christianity, a central place for the Bible as the inspired and authoritative Word of God, and the necessity of a personal experience of faith and conversion to Jesus.

Federation

The name of the national form of organisation of the continuing *Congregational* tradition in England and Wales (in Scotland it is called a *Union*, see below). It expresses the particular vision of the *Congregational* tradition where the emphasis is on the local *congregation*.

Free Church

The *Free Churches* are those Churches in England and Wales which historically sought to separate religion from the State which include traditions such as Baptist, Methodist and Congregational. The Free Church of Scotland indicates by its name that it is not a part of the Established Church of Scotland.

Friends

The Religious Society of Friends is the preferred name of those who are often more popularly known as the *Quakers* (see below).

Holiness

The *Holiness* tradition of Christianity is historically rooted in a belief in the possibility of a "second blessing" following conversion understood as a *baptism* in the Holy Spirit leading to holiness of life rather than to an emphasis on spiritual gifts as in the *Pentecostal* tradition.

Inter-Church

Was the name given to the process of seeking new expressions of Christian unity which was begun in the 1980s under the title of the *Inter-Church Process*. A number of bodies which had their origins in this vision of Christian unity still have the word within their titles.

Lutheran

The name of the Christian tradition originating in the work of the German *Protestant* reformer Martin Luther.

Methodist

The name of the tradition which finds its origin in the work of the brothers John and Charles Wesley. It began within the Church of England with groups of believers sharing a common discipline, but eventually became a distinctive Christian tradition with its own forms of Church organisation.

Ministry

Originates with the Greek word *diakonia* meaning "service". It can apply to particular forms of Christian work undertaken by any Christians, lay or *ordained*, but in a number of Churches it specifically applies in a special sense to those who have become *ordained ministers* of those Churches.

Ministerial

That which pertains to *ministry* (see above), particularly in the sense of *ordained* service.

Orthodox

Describes the tradition of Christianity found in what was originally the Eastern Roman Empire rather than that which grew up in Western Europe focused on the primacy of the Bishop of Rome.

Pentecostal

From the Greek *pentecoste* meaning "fiftieth day". It is the name of the Christian festival commemorating the descent of the Holy Spirit upon the first disciples fifty days after the *resurrection* of Jesus. It is used of those Churches which have sought to recover the role of the Holy Spirit in the life and experience of the Christian believer, including the exercise of gifts of prophecy, healing, and speaking in tongues.

Presbyterian

From the Greek word *presbuteros* meaning "elder", it is indicative of a form of Church government in which ordained *ministers* and *elders* from local *congregations* form Church structures at the level of the *presbytery* (local), the *synod* (regional) and the *General Assembly* (national).

Protestant

From the *Protestatio* (Latin for "protest") made by a minority of reformers against the Catholic majority in the Diet of Spyer in 1529CE. It now applies as a general description of those Churches which appeal to the Christian scriptures rather than to Church *Tradition* as the primary source of authority in the Church.

Province

In *Episcopal* (see above) Churches it is a geographical unit made up of a number of *dioceses* and originally arose because such areas were coincidental with the Provinces of the Roman Empire. It is also used by the United Reformed Church for its regional level of Church organisation.

Reformed

The name of the Christian tradition which takes its inspiration from the theological work of Swiss *Protestant* (see above) leader John Calvin. It appears in the title of the United Reformed Church.

Roman Catholic

The name of the numerically largest Christian Church of which the head is the Bishop of Rome, known as the *Pope* .

Salvation Army

The name of the movement founded by William

Booth in order to bring the Christian message to the industrial working class in the late nineteenth century. Its members have military-style uniforms and its structures and titles reflect military terminology. *Salvation* is the word used by Christians to describe liberation from sin and self-centredness and the establishment of wholeness.

Seraphim

The name of an order of angels in Christian angelology often grouped together with *cherubim* (see below). It is part of the name of the Cherubim and Seraphim Christian movement which originated in West Africa.

Seventh Day

Appears in the title of those Christians who observe Saturday as the day of worship and rest believing that the beginning of the Christian era did not abrogate the commandment given to the Jewish people to observe the Sabbath Day and keep it holy. *Seventh Day* Christians also generally do not celebrate Christmas as a Christian festival.

Synod

The name of a regional form of church government in a number of Churches, including those within the *Presbyterian* traditions of Christianity, for example, the Church of Scotland. It is also used at the regional level with respect to the Methodist Synods and in the Anglican tradition at the local (*Deanery Synod*), regional (*Diocesan Synod*) and national (*General Synod*) levels.

Theology

The name given to what was traditionally viewed as the science of the knowledge of God, from the Greek words *theos* meaning God and *logos* meaning word and used, in a number of fields, with reference to rational thought.

Theological

That which pertains to *theology* (see above).

Union

Part of the organisational title of the Congregational Union in Scotland and the Baptist Union of Great Britain. In both cases, it emphasises the local nature of the tradition.

Unitarian

The name of the Christian tradition which does not accept the traditional doctrinal formulations of *Trinitarian* theology. The Church has a strong belief in religious tolerance and in the religious role of human reason.

Wesleyan

The brothers John and Charles Wesley were founders of what was originally a movement within the Church of England but which eventually became a separate Christian tradition.

THE HINDU
COMMUNITY

INTRODUCING THE HINDU COMMUNITY

HINDUISM IN THE UNITED KINGDOM

Migration

Small numbers of Hindus have visited and worked in the UK for centuries. However, it was not until the 1950s and 1960s that significant numbers of Hindus settled here.

Some migrants came to Britain directly from India. With the development of Africanisation policies in the newly independent African states, others came from the countries to which their foreparents had previously migrated, such as Kenya, Tanzania, Uganda, Zambia, and Malawi. Between 1965 and 1972 some of these came as economic migrants and others, especially those from Uganda, came seeking refuge from persecution. Other Hindu migrants came later from Fiji and Guyana.

Estimates of the size of the Hindu community in the UK vary considerably. A widely used estimate is around 400,000 although some work being done within the community suggests the possibility of a significantly higher figure. Hindus are now settled in most large towns and cities in the UK with the largest Hindu communities being in Greater London (especially in Wembley and Harrow), Birmingham, Coventry, Leicester and Manchester. The directory records around 130 Hindu places of worship in the UK.

Ethnic Composition

Of the Hindu migrants as a whole, in ethnic terms seventy per cent are Gujarati (including its Northern Kutch region); fifteen per cent are Panjabi; and the remainder have their ancestral origins in Uttar Pradesh, West Bengal, and the Southern states as well as in other countries such as Sri Lanka. Hindus in the UK may speak one or more of several languages, the most common ones being English, Gujarati, Hindi (the national language of India), and Panjabi.

The International Society for Krishna Consciousness (ISKCON), popularly known as the Hare Krishna Movement, has people from a wide range of ethnic origins amongst its membership. Some other groups which relate to

228

Hindu philosophy and practice also have a wider membership of this kind.

ORIGINS AND DEVELOPMENT OF HINDUISM

Origins

The term "Hindu" is related to the Sanskrit word Sindhu which is the name of a river. It was specifically used of the river which is today called the Indus but, as a result of the native pronunciation of the term by the peoples who came from Afghanistan and Persia, the word became "Hindu". Hinduism is an ancient tradition with no single founder or teacher although some teachers are given prominence by most Hindus and these include the following: Shankara (788–820CE), Ramanuja (1017–1137CE), Madhva (1239-1319CE), Chaitanya (1486-1534CE) and Vallabha (1479-1531CE). The terms "Hindu" and "Hinduism" are not found in any Indian scriptural writings. Followers of the tradition prefer the phrase *Sanatana Dharma* (eternal teachings or truths).

Variety

Because of its ancient origins and its vision of truth, Hinduism embraces a very wide range of belief and practices, with ethnic, linguistic, and doctrinal variations. Within Hinduism's various schools of thought a whole range of philosophical positions, religious practices and devotional foci are accepted. Hinduism is therefore often described more as a way of life.

However, within its diversity there are a number of beliefs and practices which are generally accepted and its diverse systems of thought have been tested, codified and accepted throughout the centuries. The greatest degree of commonality is in the Hindu adherence to the *Vedas* (see below).

SOURCES OF HINDU BELIEFS AND PRACTICES

Hinduism has a number of sacred texts which lie at the roots of its tradition and practice. A distinction has sometimes been made within Hinduism between the *sruti* (that which is revealed) and *smrti* (that which has been remembered) texts. Some Hindus believe that *smrti* such as the *Puranas* and the *Ramayana* are less authoritative than the *sruti*. However, many *Vaishnavas* (see below) see the *sruti* and the *smrti* as being on the same level and the *Mahabharata* is considered by some to be the "fifth *Veda*."

The *Laws of Manu* are ancient texts which are sources for Hindu social, ethical and ritual practice.

Vedas

The *Vedas* (literally meaning "knowledge") include materials dating back to 3000 BCE or even earlier. They are believed to be *sruti*. The three original *Vedas,* the *Rigveda, Samaveda*, and *Yajurveda*, are hymns for use in sacrificial ritual. The *Atharveda* contains incantations and other ritual material. There are also three other constituents of the *Vedas*: the *Brahmanas* and *Aranyakas* and the *Upanishads*. The *Brahmanas* and *Aranyakas* are specifically concerned with Hindu ritual whereas the one hundred and eight *Upanishads* contain more philosophical material which discusses the nature and purpose of existence.

Epics

The *smrti* include the *Ramayana* and the *Mahabharata*, long epic poems which contain stories about the incarnations of Vishnu or, according to some, incarnations of Krishna. These stories illustrate Hindu conceptions of divinity, of human nature and of *dharma* (see below). They deal with the morality which can guide personal life and protect the social order.

The *Ramayana* tells the story of how Rama rescued his wife Sita from the forces of evil headed by Ravana. The *Mahabarata* tells a story centred around the battle of Kurukshetra at the beginning of which prince Arjuna is taught the significance of *dharma* (see below) by Krishna, who acts as the fabled bowman's charioteer. The story illustrates the result of following one's own interpretation of *dharma* rather than that laid down by Krishna, which is to dedicate all actions to him without attachment to their results. It illustrates and inspires heroism in dealing with adverse circumstances.

Most of the characters in the *Mahabharata*, with the specific exception of the Pandavas, failed to follow Krishna's teaching and thus met with misery and defeat. In this way the shortcomings of self-serving conventional moral duties are revealed and the supreme morality of service to the Lord is emphasised.

The *Bhagavad-Gita* (the Song of the Blessed Lord) is an excerpt from the *Mahabharata*. Copies are often wrapped in cotton or silk cloth for protection and it is one of the most important and frequently cited of the scriptures for many Hindus in the UK today. It is believed to encapsulate and illustrate the importance of *dharma* and the intrinsic link between *dharma* and *karma*.

The *Puranas* contain stories concerning the exploits of the incarnations of the deities, the demigods and the great sages of Hindu tradition (which some Hindus interpret as mythological truth and others as historical), together with an exposition of Hindu theology and religious practice.

KEY HINDU BELIEFS

One and Many

Within the Hindu *dharma* there are monotheists (believers in one God) as well as those who argue that it is not contradictory to believe that the divine is simultaneously both one and many.

It is the existence within the Hindu tradition of a multiplicity of forms and representations of the divine together with belief in a multiplicity of *devas* and *devis* (demi-gods and demi-goddesses) which the *Vedas* number at three hundred and thirty million that has led many people outside of Hinduism to describe it as polytheistic.

More often, though, at least in its more theologically developed forms, it adheres to a philosophy of *advaita* (see section on "Traditions in Hinduism"), a form of monism, or *dvaita* (see also section below, "Traditions in Hinduism") which is monotheistic. Both schools accept the existence of One Supreme. This is understood

either impersonally as the all-pervading Brahman (the *advaita* position) or as a Supreme Person (the *dvaita* position), usually represented by Vishnu, or Krishna or, sometimes, by Shiva.

Simultaneously with accepting One Supreme in either understanding outlined above, Hindus also accept the existence of many higher beings. Among the best known of these gods and goddesses of Hinduism are: Indra (god of rain), Surya (sun god), Chandra (moon god), Ganesha (remover of obstacles), Yama (god of death), Sarasvati (goddess of learning), Lakshmi (goddess of wealth) and Hanuman (monkey servant of Rama).

Hinduism also recognises a female principle in its view of the Divine. The female form of the universal energy of existence is referred to as *shakti*. The female consort of Shiva is also known by the personal name of Shakti or Durga, seen as personified material energy symbolising universal power. The consort of Vishnu is Lakshmi, known as the Goddess of Fortune. Sarasvati, is the consort of Brahma and is known as the Goddess of Education and the Arts.

Atman and Karma

Although there is a variety of beliefs about the Divine found within the Hindu community, Hindus in general share a belief in *karma* and the transmigration of *atman*.

Atman is the spirit as distinct from the material body made from *prakriti* (inert matter) which is understood to be composed of three *gunas* (qualities) namely: *sattva* (goodness), *rajas* (passion) and *tamas* (ignorance). These affect the make-up of each individual human being according to the proportions in which they are found.

It is the energy of the *atman* which activates the body and fills it with consciousness. At death the *atman* is believed to leave the body and its present actions are believed to determine the nature and circumstances of its next life. This is in keeping with the law of *karma*, a universal principle which states that all activities reap certain reactions – good, bad or mixed, depending upon the quality of the person performing the actions.

Maya

Maya is the state of illusion which comes about through ignorance of the *Sanatana Dharma* (the eternal truth). Hinduism speaks more of "ignorance" and "knowledge" than of "evil" and "good". The illusion of *maya* and our dependence upon the world of appearances decreases as our knowledge increases.

Hindus believe that there has been a gradual degradation of civilisation in the current age, which is itself part of a cycle of ages. This present age is known as the *Kali Yuga* and it is believed to have begun about five thousand years ago with the departure of Krishna and the compilation of the *Vedas*.

Moksha

Hindus understand the ultimate goal of all living beings to be the transcendence of *samsara* (the cycle of birth and death). This is known as *moksha* (liberation).

In the *advaita* view of Hinduism (see below) the goal of Hindu practice is to realise union between *atman* and *Brahman* understood as *atman* becoming one with *Brahman*, by merging into the Supreme Spirit.

In the *dvaita* view (also see below), union is understood as serving the Supreme Personality of the Godhead eternally. In this view, there is a qualitative rather than a quantitative union.

Dharma

The concept of *dharma* is central to Hinduism. It has no exact English language equivalent although it is often loosely translated as "religion" or "duty". Its linguistic root is the Sanskrit *dhr* meaning "to sustain". Its meaning is therefore approximately "the intrinsic property of something" or "that which sustains". Thus, the *dharma* of water is its wetness and the *dharma* of human beings (and indeed of all living beings) is seen as service to the Divine.

TRADITIONS IN HINDUISM

The Six Darshanas

Classically, there are six *Darshanas* (orthodox systems of Hindu philosophy). These are the *Mimamsa, Nyaya, Vaisesika, Samkhya, Yoga* and *Vedanta*. They are each concerned with different aspects of knowledge: *Mimamsa* is concerned with action and responsibility; *Nyaya* with logic; *Vaisesika* with the analysis of matter in terms of its atomic structure; *Samkhya* with the analysis of matter in terms of its functioning; *Yoga* with mystical knowledge; and *Vedanta* with philosophical knowledge.

The different systems developed at different points in time and exist side by side in the Hindu tradition resulting in a variety of philosophies, ranging from atheistic to theistic and monist to dualist.

Despite their diffferences, in all these systems the common theme is that of the goal of human existence being liberation of the *atman* from the cycle of birth and death. There is also a common commitment to the idea that the spiritual life consists of three principal paths: *karma yoga* (way of action), *jnana yoga* (way of knowledge) and *bhakti yoga* (way of devotion).

Vedanta: Dvaita and Advaita

Today, a majority of Hindus subscribe to the *Vedanta* system. *Vedanta* literally means "the essence or quintessence of the *Vedas*" or "the conclusion of all knowledge". Within this system there are, however, two main traditions of understanding - the *dvaita* and the *advaita*. These traditions differ in their conception of the nature of the Divine and of the relationship between the self and the Divine.

Dvaita

The *dvaitins* are Personalist monotheists, believing that the nature of the Divine is that of an Unlimited Supreme Personality. In this tradition, the atman is seen as eternally distinct from the Godhead and as dependent upon the Divine for its liberation. *Dvaitins* believe some Deities to be *avatara* (manifestations and incarnations) of the Godhead. Besides these manifestations of God, it is also believed that there are numerous *devas* and *devis*, each of whom has specific administrative functions within the material sphere.

Advaita

The *advaita* tradition places all *avataras*, *devas* and *devis* in the same category since it regards each as being a manifestation of the supra-personal Supreme Spirit which is often called Brahman, but has no personal name or gender and is seen more in terms of permeative energy than of personality.

Brahman is believed to have been manifested in a variety of different times and places and personified in many different forms. Because of this, *advaitins* believe that union with Brahman can be attained through the worship of any deity which one chooses for oneself.

In the *advaita* view, Brahman is seen as the underlying principle behind the universe from which is manifested the trinity of creative force (personified as Brahma), preservative force (personified as Vishnu) and dissolving force (personified as Shiva). Everything in the universe is part of an eternal cycle in which it is created, maintained for some time, and is finally destroyed and annihilated. Ultimately, in *advaita* philosophy, only the divine is the Real, and everything else is an illusion, except in a relative and limited sense.

Although *dvaita* and *advaita* represent the two basic traditions within the *Vedanta*, these can be found in subtly variant schools of thought associated with famous Hindu teachers and philosophers. These include the following:

Advaita-Vedanta

Non-dualist Vedanta, a philosophy propounded by Shankara (788-820CE), in which it is believed that the *jiva* (living entity) is identical with God and this has simply to be realised.

Vishishta-Advaita

A qualified non-dualism propounded by Ramanuja (1017-1137CE) which holds that there is a difference between God and the living entities and so the oneness between them is seen to be qualitative and not quantitative

Shuddha-Dvaita

A pure dualism propounded by Madhva (1239-1319CE) in which all of reality is seen as being composed of three separate elements – the Supreme Lord, the living entities and the material world. Madhva maintained even more strongly than Ramanuja the distinctiveness of these three, and particularly that between the soul and God.

Dvaitadvaita

A philosophy of oneness and difference propounded by Nimbarka.

Shuddha-advaita

A purified monism taught by Vishnuswami (a predecessor of Vallabha).

Achintya-bedha-abheda Tattva

A school propounding an inconceivable simultaneous oneness and difference associated with Chaitanya (1486-1534CE), the teacher who considered that the living entities and the Supreme Spirit are inconceivably both one and different at the same time.

The *dvaita* and *advaita* traditions with their variant schools outlined above, are associated with groupings which can be encountered within the Hindu community in the UK under the names of *Vaishnavites*, *Shaivites* and *Shaktas*.

Vaishnavites

Shaivites worshippers of Vishnu and stand in the dvaita tradition of understanding the Divine and its relationship with humanity, seeing Vishnu as the Divine Personal Reality of the *dvaita* tradition.

Shaivites and Shaktas

Shaivites are worshippers of Shiva and *Shaktas* are worshippers of Shakti or Durga, the consort of Shiva. These groupings are generally in the *advaita* tradition of understanding the Divine, in which Shiva, Shakti or Durga are seen as alternative manifestations of the supra- personal energy of Brahman.

HINDU LIFE

The Four Aims

The traditional Hindu view of human life is characterised by the *catur varga* (four aims) for human existence: *dharma* (religious life) as a foundation for everything else; *artha* (economic development) as a necessity for life; *kama* (sense gratification) as necessary to keep a healthy body and mind, but the desire for which should also be minimised, either through regulation or renunciation; and *moksha* (liberation) from the cycle of birth and death. Among *Vaishnavas* some would say that *bhakti* (devotion to the divine) is a fifth and final goal and that *prema* (love of God) and selfless devotion is higher than the desire for liberation.

Values

There are a number of core ideal values which are shared by most Hindus, although in practice they are subject to interpretations which result in varying degrees of observance: a general adoption of vegetarianism; tolerance of all races and religions; controlled relations between the sexes in which marriage is considered sacred and divorce, pre-marital or extra-marital sexual relationships are firmly discouraged; sacredness of the cow whose milk sustains human life; and an appreciation of the equality of all living beings and the sanctity of life.

Generally Hindus do not engage in activity aimed at converting non-Hindus to Hinduism, but they do seek to promote the *Sanatana Dharma* among all people.

Dharma

An understanding of one's personal and social role within the cosmic order of things is at the centre of Hindu life. Understanding *sva-dharma* (literally, "one's own dharma") in its relationship to *varna* (social position, class or caste) and *ashrama* (meaning "stage in life" or "spiritual order") is crucial. *Dharma* collectively understood is the morality by which a given social order is protected. Particular *dharmas* are connected with particular *varnas* and *ashramas* (see below) of which, in each case, there are believed to be four.

Varna

In the Hindu ideal, everyone has a *varna* and *varnas* are understood to be co-operative rather than competitive. Each *varna* regulates itself among its own membership and at the same time is answerable to the other *varnas* for the wellbeing of the whole society.

A person's *varna* traditionally indicates his or her status and responsibility, and thus the kind of duty which he or she must execute to transmigrate into a higher existence. According to the *Bhagavad Gita* an individual's *varna* is ascertained according to the qualities they develop and their tendency towards a particular kind of work.

Some Hindus say that it was only later that the system became rigidly hereditary, whereas others maintain that it was always so. Traditionally, members of the four *varnas* are seen as being interdependent although each have separate and distinct social roles:

Brahmins

Intelligentsia and priests characterised by austerity, knowledge and self-control.

Kshatriyas

Administrators and military characterised by power, courage and leadership.

Vaishyas

Merchants and agriculturalists whose work is in producing and trading.

Sudras

Working class who labour and serve.

In addition, there are those who fall outside this traditional system and who have been called "outcastes" or "untouchables", often suffering social discrimination as a result, but whom the Hindu leader *Mahatma* (Great Soul) Gandhi called *Harijans* (children of God).

Jati

Within each *varna* a person belongs to a *jati* (specific group). These *jati* are often popularly referred to as "sub-*castes*". The significance of *varna* and *jati* varies according, for example, to Gujarati or Panjabi ethnic background, but is of particularly strong significance among Gujaratis.

Many Hindu organisations in the UK are based on these groupings, although some are specifically organised to involve people from a variety of different backgrounds. Examples of Gujarati *jatis* include the *Patidars* (traders), *Mochis* (shoemakers), *Lohanas* (traders), and *Anavil Brahmins* (agriculturalists).

Although these groups may indicate the traditional occupational backgrounds of a person's ancestral group, in the UK they do not usually define one's social or economic position in the wider society. *Caste* groups do, however, remain a significant social and economic factor for many aspects of Hindu life in the UK.

Gender Roles

Hinduism advocates equality between women and men but with differentiation of roles as laid down in *Manusmrti* (the *Law of Manu*), in most of which a woman's role is seen as being primarily that of an educator of children and housekeeper, with a man's role being perceived as having overall authority with responsible for the financial provision for the family. In the UK,

specific gender roles vary from family to family.

Ashramas

The *Ashramas* are the four "stages of life" which have traditionally applied, in differing degrees, to males in the first three *varnas*.

In this ideal pattern a man first becomes a *brahmacharya* (student) living an ascetic life studying under a *Guru*. Next, one becomes a *grihastha* (householder) for whom marriage, children and family are the main focus of responsibility. The third stage is that of a *vanaprastha* (retirement) which can only be entered into after the completion of social obligations through the marriage of all one's daughters and preferably also of one's sons.

Some Hindus also believe that it is first necessary to secure a line of descent by one's son begetting a grandson before it is possible to enter into the *vanaprastha* stage. This *ashrama* is traditionally a time when there are increasing periods of withdrawal from society in order to enable more concentration on the spiritual dimension of life. The fourth and final stage is that of the *sannyas*, who has renounced all earthly ties and is considered socially dead.

Traditionally, *brahmins* go through all four *ashramas, kshatriyas* never directly take *sannyasa*, and *vaishyas* do not not take *vanaprastha* or *sannyasa*, with *sudras* only accepting the householder *ashrama*. Some early texts allow for the possibility of becoming a *sannyasi* without going through all the stages. Whilst the *ashrama* system has not been fully operative since medieval times, the pattern of study followed by familial responsibilities and finally withdrawal from the world is a powerful ideal for many Hindus, including those in the UK.

Vegetarianism

Most Hindus are vegetarians and even those who are not are required to abstain from beef. Hindu vegetarianism arises from a belief in the principle of *ahimsa* (non-harming) and thus generally precludes the eating of meat, fish or eggs. Sometimes onions and garlic are also not eaten because they are considered to be foods which have a negative effect on human development.

Milk, yoghurt, butter and ghee are usually acceptable because no killing has taken place and they are considered to be foods which promote *sattva* (harmony). However, products which have either been cooked in or contain by-products from slaughtered animals would not be acceptable to strict Hindu vegetarians. For example, neither ice cream or cheese which contains rennet (extracted from the pancreas of the cow) or other animal fats, nor chips which have been cooked in animal fats would be accepted. Hindus may also refrain from intoxicating drinks such as alcohol, and in some cases from tea and coffee too.

Within Hinduism there are a variety of views on the permissability of a range of foods and drinks. When preparing their own food, many Hindus would offer their food to a deity before eating it.

HINDU WORSHIP

The practice of domestic worship is widespread. In their own homes, Hindus have small areas of worship containing *murtis* (see below) of favourite deities. In addition to private worship some fairly large gatherings for worship may also take place in private homes.

However, Hindus also attend a place of worship to associate with saintly persons from whom they can enquire about spiritual topics. In a land in which Hindus are in a minority, worship at the *mandir* (see below) fulfils a vital social function, providing an opportunity to meet, discuss social issues and consolidate faith together.

Mandirs

At present in Britain *mandirs* are generally converted public buildings and private houses, with only a few purpose-built buildings. Differences in terms of the *murtis* (figures that represent deities) and pictures of holy people found in *mandirs* may reflect the variations of caste, devotional group and ethnicity within the Hindu tradition. However, *mandirs* in the UK are far more likely to be multi-sect, multi-caste and multi-ethnic than *mandirs* in India would be.

This is because of the minority position of Hindus and the financial constraints within which they must operate.

As well as the hall for worship, *mandirs* may also have other facilities on their premises, such as social, educational, and administrative rooms.

Murtis

Inside the *mandir*, there is usually a main hall with a shrine where the *murtis* of the Temple stand. There may also be other side altars.

Murtis are sometimes difficult to understand among those who are outsiders to the Hindu tradition. They are more than purely symbolic representations of deities and yet Hindus also do not believe that the reality of the deities is limited to a particular *murti* in a particular place. They are specifically dedicated and are venerated as deities, being dressed in the finest fabrics and decorated with ornaments, jewellery and garlands of flowers. This is in order to foster a mood of *seva* (sacrifice and selfless service) by centring people's devotion on the deity.

The *murtis* are usually made of marble, but can also be made of wood, stone or metal. For the believer, the presence of a particular deity is manifested by *murtis* with specific characteristics. For example, Ganesha is represented by an elephant headed *murti* with four arms; Krishna is represented as a cowherder seen cross-legged, playing flute, and accompanied by his favourite *gopi* (spiritual consort) Radha.

These deities are often accompanied by *murtis* of their *vahana*, the animal or bird on which they ride. For example, the god Shiva rides on the bull, Nandi. Brightly coloured sweet smelling flowers are laid before the figures or hung over them as garlands. Only the priest is permitted to enter the *Garbha-griha* (inner sanctum).

Other Features and Activities

In the main hall there may also be one or more *Vyasasanas*. These are decorated thrones for *swamis* (religious teachers) to sit on when teaching. Other items which are likely to be encountered in a *mandir* include: incense to purify the air and create a spiritual atmosphere; the *OM* symbol to symbolise the primaeval sound representing God in the simplest form; the *swastika* (not to be confused with the Nazi reversed swastika) which, in Hinduism, is a sign of auspiciousness.

One might also find a conch shell, the sound of which assists concentration on worship; a *trishul* which is the Trident weapon of Shiva and represents God, soul and the ignorance through which the soul is held in bondage; a coconut which is believed to represent three eyed Shiva and is symbolic of life by being firm on the outside but sweet on the inside; images of the *lotus* which is an ancient symbol of the cosmos and of humanity; a *kalasha* which is a pot representing the human body: its mouth is Vishnu, its base is Brahma and the middle Shiva; the water in it stands for the purity and love of the divine.

Corporate devotional activities include prayer; meditation on sacred words, *mantras* (syllables or sentences); *bhajans* and *kirtan* (singing songs and *mantras*); *pravachan* (religious lectures) and *havan* (the sacred fire ceremony); as well as study of sacred texts. When visiting the *mandir*, it is customary for Hindus to take some kind of offering, for example, foods, gifts for the deity or donations of money. Before entering the *mandir* the worshipper removes shoes, and on entering offers respect to the deities either by folding their hands or bowing down and laying prostrate.

In the *arti* ceremony performed several times a day, the priest offers articles of worship to the deity including lighted ghee lamps, incense, water for bathing, small napkins for drying, flowers and peacock and yak-tail fans, whilst worshippers sing a special hymn, clap their hands and say *mantras*. Many Hindu temples welcome non-Hindu visitors to *arti*. Before *arti* food is offered to the deity and is blessed for later distribution.

HINDU CALENDAR AND FESTIVALS

Calendar

The Hindu year is based on the waxing and waning of the moon and there are five and a quarter days difference between this and the Gregorian year. There are both lunar and solar festivals. Hence, the English months do not always coincide with the Hindu seasons, and so festival dates do not remain the same each year within the framework of the Gregorian calendar. The Hindu calendar year is therefore shorter than the Gregorian calendar year and the difference is made up by inserting an additional or leap month.

Festivals

There are many Hindu festivals, but the following are some of the principal ones. The rough time of their occurrence indicated below refers to the Gregorian calendar in common use in the UK:

Shivaratri
(February/March).

Worship dedicated to Lord Shiva. Devotees spend the night at the temple chanting and singing. Water is poured continuously, as an offering, onto the *Linga*, the symbolic form of Lord Shiva.

Holi
(March)

Is associated with Prahlad Maharaja, a great devotee of Lord Krishna. In India, traditionally, coloured dyes and water are sprinkled on the participants to welcome Spring, although in the UK the climate can curtail this traditional practice.

Rama Navami

Occurs in Spring and celebrates the birth of Lord Rama. Fasting occurs.

Janamashtami
(August/September)

Celebrates the birth of Krishna who is believed to have appeared five thousand years ago in the district of Mathura, India to deliver the pious, destroy miscreants and establish the principles of true religion.

Navaratri
(September/October)

A ten day long festival of dancing held in honour of the Goddesses known as Lakshmi, Durga and Sarasvati.

Divali or Deepavali
(October/November)

Marks the end of the Hindu year. The festival celebrates the victory of good over evil forces as recounted in the story of Rama's victory over the evil demon king Ravana as told in the *Ramayana*. The festival is also a time when Hindus worship the Goddess Lakshmi (Goddess of prosperity) and is known as the "festival of lights" because of the *divas* (small oil lamps). These are lit for a variety of reasons including the guiding of Lakshmi to the home and in order to guide Ram and Sita back to Ram's kingdom of Ayodhya, from which they had been exiled for fourteen years.

Annakuta/Bestvarash

Is the day after *Divali*. It is the Hindu new year. Large quantities of sweets and other food stuffs are brought to the temple to be offered to the deities in celebration of a story from Krishna's childhood concerned with Mount Govardhan.

Pilgrimages

Pilgrimages also form an important part of Hindu religious observance. Visits to holy sites in India may be undertaken with special intentions in mind, such as cure of disease or blessing on a family.

In the *advaita* tradition of Hinduism the most holy of all places of pilgrimage is Varanasi (also known as Benares). This is situated on the sacred River Ganga (Ganges) and is especially sacred to those Hindus who venerate Shiva and Rama. Pilgrims who have visited the River Ganga often bring home bottles of water from the river to place in their family shrines. Dying people may request that their ashes will be spread in the river.

In the *dvaita* tradition of Hinduism, Vrindavana is of special importance because of its connection with Krishna.

HINDU ORGANISATIONS

The Hindu community in the UK is organised in a range of different ways. The first Hindu organisations were set up in the late 1950s. Since then a variety of different kinds of groupings have developed, many of which serve multiple functions, including discussion of political issues, youth activities, language classes, womens' groups, trust funds, education and propagation of Indian culture, in addition to what are often understood to be more specifically religious activities. Some of the local and national groupings are part of international organisations based on the sub-continent.

Caste Associations

Caste groups are organised on both a national and local level. They have functions ranging from social networking through to voluntary welfare support and provision. Local organisations may be affiliated to a national organisation. For example, the Gujarati Federation of Anavil Samaj is an organisation representing members of the Anavil caste and has local branches in Birmingham, Coventry, Leicester, East London, and North London.

The national *caste* organisations are set up to co-ordinate joint events between local groups and to provide a networking function across the country. National caste organisations often produce annual directories of members of the local *caste* groups affiliated to them although these are not readily available to the general public. *Caste* Associations are sometimes recognisable from the caste name in their title, for example, the National Association of Patidar Samaj (Patidar) or Brahma Samaj Manchester (Brahmin).

A particular organisation may be composed of Hindus from a specific caste group who also share a common linguistic and ethnic background, such as the Sri Kutch Leva Patel Samaj, which is open to members of the Patel caste from the Kutch region in India. Most of these groups are represented at both national and local levels.

However, different patterns of settlement have influenced patterns of organisational development and therefore not all groups are found in significant numbers in all localities in the UK. For example, there has been a natural tendency for particular caste groups to gather in specific areas, such as Mochis in Leeds, Lohanas in Leicester and North London and this is reflected in the type of organisations which are set up in these areas.

Spiritual Movements

Sampradaya (spiritual movements) are groupings follow the teachings and practices of various *gurus*. Gurus are spiritual leaders who are seen by their followers as providing great insight and guidance regarding spiritual matters. A number of relatively modern Hindu groupings have a strong presence in the UK.

Swaminarayan Hindus in the UK are pre-dominantly of Gujarati origin and follow teachings in the line of Sahajananda Swami (1781-1830) who is believed to be an incarnation of the Supreme Lord. The group combines traditional Hindu practices with specific customs of its own, including the strict separation of men and women in the Hindu temple. There are various *Swaminarayan* groupings in the UK, reflecting different views concerning the proper line of succession to Sahajananda Swami. The largest in the UK is the Akshar Purushottam Sanstha (the Swaminarayan Hindu Mission) which looks to the leadership of Pramukh Swami and whose main UK Centre is in Neasden, London; another is the group which looks for leadership to Acharya Tejendrapasa Pande and whose main UK centre is in Willesden Lane, London..

Other devotional groups include the *Pushtimarag Sampradaya* (founded in the sixteenth century) whose members follow Vallabha.

International Society for Krishna Consciousness (ISKCON) devotees follow A C Bhaktivedanta

Swami Prabhupada's (1895-1977) teachings in the Chaitanya Vaishnava tradition. The first ISKCON temple in the UK was opened in 1969. The society owns Bhaktivedanta Manor in Hertfordshire where every summer a festival involving thousands of Hindus from all over the UK is held to celebrate *Krishna-Janmastami*.

Members of Arya Samaj follow the teachings of Saiva Svami Dayananda Sarasvati who rejected the concept of untouchability and worked to overcome what he believed was the low status accorded to women. Hindus in the Arya Samaj stress the purity of the Vedas and reject post-Vedic Hindu teachings.

There are also a whole variety of Hindu related movements and groups which practice the disciplines of *yoga*. Some of these focus purely on the more physical exercises of *Hatha Yoga* whilst others seek to present a complete religious approach through *Raja Yoga*. Some groups are connected with the wider Hindu community, others are more or less independent.

Representative Groups

There is no single national representative organisation of Hindus in the United Kingdom, although there are plans, in which the National Council of Hindu Temples is playing a significant role, to try and launch such an umbrella organisation in the course of 1994.

For the moment, there are various groupings aspiring to operate nationally. Some have temples affiliated to them, such as the National Council of Hindu Temples, whilst others have affiliated groups and individuals, such as Vishwa Hindu Parishad (UK). A number of local and regional areas have seen the development of representative groups such as the Hindu Council (Brent), the Hindu Council of Birmingham, the Leicester Gujarat Hindu Association and the Hindu Council of the North.

Ethnic Groups

Some groups are organised on the basis of a specific shared ethnic or linguistic background. Punjabis or Gujaratis or Bengalis have often joined together to form associations. Such groups can sometimes be recognised by the inclusion of regional or ethnic names in their titles, for example, the Gujarat Hindu Society in Preston.

Personnel

A Hindu priest is a *Brahmin* and is also often referred to as *Pandit*, *Maharaj* or *Pujari*. Priests are usually male, women may also be priests, as for example, in the ISKCON movements. Priests may be resident in the *mandir*, being appointed and paid for by the congregation. Their role is to conduct religious ceremonies in Sanskrit (the very ancient language of India) and to tend the holy shrines.

The *mandir* is usually governed by a managing committee with a president and a secretary. Many *pandits* are from India, staying only for a temporary period before returning home. As such, they will not necessarily speak English. Therefore when wishing to visit a *mandir* it may be preferable to contact the secretary or president of the *mandir*.

Swamis or *gurus* are religious teachers, and they are venerated by Hindus because they are learned in the scriptures and know the methods of worship. Their service to the divine sometimes also aids their devotees. If they are well known on a national or international scale they may be invited to come and talk to a group on a particular subject.

BIBLIOGRAPHY

Bowen, D G (ed), *Hinduism in England*, Faculty of Contemporary Studies, Bradford College, Bradford, 1986.

Brockington, J L, *Sacred Thread: Hinduism in Its Continuity and Diversity*, Edinburgh University Press, Edinburgh, 1981.

Burghart, R *Hinduism in Great Britain: The Perpetuation of Religion in an Alien Cultural Milieu*, Tavistock, London, 1987.

Chauduri, N C, *Hinduism: A Religion to Live By*, Chatto and Windus, London, 1979.

Henley, A, *Caring for Hindus and Their Families: Religious Aspects of Care*, National Extension College, Cambridge, 1983.

Jackson, R and Nesbitt, E, *Listening to Hindus*, Unwin Hyman, London, 1990.

Jackson, R and Nesbitt, E, *Hindu Children in Britain*, Trentham Books, Stoke-on-Trent, 1993.

Jackson R and Killingley, D, *Moral Issues in the Hindu Tradition*, Trentham Books, Stoke-on-Trent, 1991.

Kanitkar, H and Jackson, R, *Hindus in Britain*, School of Oriental and African Studies, London, 1982.

Kanitkar, V P (Hemant), *What We Believe, We are Hindus*, The Saint Andrew Press, Edinburgh, 1987.

King, U, *A Report on Hinduism in Britain* Community Religions Project Research Papers, No 2, University of Leeds Department of Theology and Religious Studies, Leeds, 1984

Knott, K, "Other Religious Traditions" in Thomas, T, (ed), *The British, Their Religious Beliefs and Practices*, Routledge, London, 1988.

Knott, K and Toon, R, *Hindus, Muslims and Sikhs in Britain: Problems in the Estimation of Religious Statisics, Religious Research Papers, No 6*, Department of Sociology, University of Leeds, Leeds, 1982.

Knott, K, "Hindu Communities in Britain", in Badham, P (ed), *Religion, State and Society in Modern Britain*, Edwin Mellen Press, Lampeter, 1989.

Law, J, *The Religious Beliefs and Practices of Hindus in Derby*, Community Religions Project Papers (new series), University of Leeds, Leeds, 1991.

National Council of Hindu Temples, *Hinduism*, National Council of Hindu Temples, 1983.

Nesbitt, E, *My Dad's Hindu, My Mum's Side Are Sikhs: Studies in Religious Identity*, Arts, Culture and Education Research Papers, National Foundation for Arts Education, University of Warwick, Coventry, 1991.

Stutley, M, *Hinduism The Eternal Law*, Crucible, Wellingborough, 1985.

Stutley, M & J, *A Dictionary of Hinduism*, Routledge and Kegan Paul, London, 1987.

Swami Praphupada, A C, *Bhagavad Gita As It Is*, Bhaktivedanta Book Trust, Hertfordshire, 1986.

Zaehner, R C (ed), *Hindu Scriptures*, J M Dent and Sons, London, 1986.

HINDU UK ORGANISATIONS

The organisations listed in this section include both head offices of organisations with branches throughout the country and organisations which aspire to serve the Hindu community on a UK-wide level.

Arya Pratinidhi Sabha (UK)

Flat B
3 Chapel Road
Hounslow
Middlesex TW3 1XT
Tel: 081-569-6403
Contact: Professor S N Bharadwaj
Office: President
Membership is open to any Arya Samaj in the United Kingdom. At present there are six Arya Samajes in the UK which are affiliated to Arya Pratinidhi Sabha (UK) - Arya Samaj London; Arya Samaj West Midland, Birmingham; Arya Samaj, Birmingham; Arya Samaj, Coventry; Arya Samaj, Milton Keynes; and Arya Samaj, Middlesex. It aims to: propagate the Vedic religion in the UK; devise means and take measures for its propagation; and establish and maintain libraries and centres of learning of the Vedic Dharma (religion). Its activities include printing and publishing tracts, magazines and books for the purpose of propagating the teaching of the Vedas, our revealed books, and accepting and administering gifts and donations in conformity with the aims and objects of the Sabha. There is a regular monthly newsletter and circulars are issued to members on special occasions. An annual brochure is produced containing articles and advertisements on the occasion of Diwali, our Festival of Lights, in October/November. Affiliated to The Inter Faith Network for the UK.

Bharatiya Vidya Bhavan

4a Castletown Road
London W14 9HQ
Tel: 071-381-3086
Fax: 071-381-8728
Contact: Mathoor Krishnamurti
Office: Executive Director
The Bhavan is a cultural centre trying to propagate to all who are interested the best of Indian culture through its classes on music, dance, yoga, languages and philosophy. It has an all-Faiths prayer hall and teaches Indian music, dance, Yoga, drama, languages. Religious festivals from different faith traditions are celebrated and lectures, talks and seminars are arranged on multi-faith topics. Affiliated to The Inter Faith Network for the United Kingdom.

Chouis Gam Patidar Samaj (UK)

9 Liley Gardens
Alperton
Middlesex HA9 9UE
Contact: A M Patel

Federation of Anavil Samajes

Hollybank Post Office
306 Haunch Lane
King's Heath
Birmingham B13 0QS
Tel: 021-444-2045 (Home)
Contact: Mr Baldev Naik
Office: President

Federation of Brahmin Associations of Europe

125 Warwick Road
London N11
Tel: 081-368-4881
Contact: Mr Dakshesh Gor
Office: Secretary

Federation of Hindu Organisations

56 Gead Corn Road
Thornton Heath
Surrey

Federation of Patidar Associations

Patidar House
22 London Road
Wembley
Middlesex
Tel: 081-795-1648

Hindu Swayamsevek Sangh (UK)

4 Cross Street
Leicester LE4 5BA
Tel: 0533-611303
Fax: 0533-611931
Contact: Mr Pravin V Ruparelia
Office: National Secretary
Organisational headquarters. The organisation's objective is to provide and propagate Hindu thoughts, ideals and values of life, and to promote unity among Hindus and harmonious relations with other faiths. It works chiefly among Hindu youth and has branches all over the country. Activities include games, physical training, yoga, youth leadership training courses, outdoor camps, celebration of festivals and lectures.

ISKCON Communications

2 St. James' Road
Watford WD1 8EA
Tel: 0923-249144
Fax: 0923-238677
Contact: Bhagavat Dharma das
Office: Communication Officer
Liaison office of ISKCON (International Society for Krishna Consciousness). The office aims to facilitate communications between the movement and various interested groups such as the media, educationalists, national and local government and other religious faiths. The office also aims to enhance communication between the Hare Krishna movement's UK branches.

ISKCON Educational Services

Bhaktivedanta manor
Letchmore Heath
Watford WD2 8EP
Tel: 0923-859578
Fax: 0923-852896
Contact: Rasamandala Das
Office: Director
ISKCON Educational Services is a department of ISKCON (International Society for Krishna Consciousness) and oversees and promotes the Society's interaction with the educational system. ISKCON Educational Services aims to assist students, teachers, scholars and educationalists in general with their study of the Hindu tradition. Their headquarters, Bhaktivedanta Manor, set in seventeen acres of parkland, lakes and gardens provides excellent facilities for these purposes. Staff can also put interested parties in touch with other temples throughout the UK. Services include: arranging trips to temples; providing guest speakers; organising cultural presentations; answering enquiries from students, teachers and others and providing resources on Hinduism, Vedanta and Vaishnavism; providing free accomodation to students, teachers and academics where it assists in their research.

Jan Kshatriya Sevak Mandal UK

32 Mount Pleasant Road
Chigwell
Essex
Tel: 081-500-4639 (home)
Representative body of the Jansari community of Gujarat in India. The organisation aims to promote Hindu religion, Indian culture and the Gujarati language for the benefit of the Jansari community in the UK. Its activities include cultural and Hindu religious programmes.

Lohana Community of the UK

580 North Circular Road
London NW2 7PY
Tel: 081-450-1967
Fax: 081-208-1266
Contact: Dhiraj Kataria

National Association of Patidar Samaj

102 Junction Road
Archway
London N19 5QY
Tel: 071-263-6269
Contact: R G Amin
Office: Co-ordinator
Membership group and representative organisation. A charitable organisation which plays a supportive role that aims to make close links with voluntary and statutory bodies irrespective of gender, age or disability. It organises events and activities that provide cultural exchange and create understanding and relations between different communities. It aims to establish itself more efficiently and therefore prevent social isolation and alienation. It provides arts, recreational and educational activities; social and cultural events; advice and help to develop services for the Asian elderly; and liaison with different departments such as the social services, health and other welfare rights. There is also a women's group.

National Council of Hindu Temples

c/o Shree Sanatan Mandir
Weymouth Street
off Catherine Street
Leicester LE4 6FP
Tel: 0533-661402
Membership is open to Hindu Temples and similar religious organisations and public bodies. The Council aims to: promote Hindu religion; maintain uniformity among Hindu Temples; provide advice and information for local and public authorities and government departments. It works by: organising meetings and youth festivals; providing necessary information on request; giving lectures in schools and colleges; inviting learned saints, preachers or philosophers to deliver lectures and by participating in inter-faith activities. An annual calendar and a regular newsletter are produced, together with booklets on "Hindu Funeral Rites" and "Hinduism". It is on the Board of the Department of the Environment's Inner Cities Religion Council. Affiliated to The Inter Faith Network for the United Kingdom.

National Council of Vanik Associations

37 Baron's Court
Church Lane
Kingsbury NW9 8AD
Tel: 081-205-6673 (home)
Contact: Mr R D Shah
Office: General Secretary

Sri Aurobindo Society of GB

82 Bell Street
London NW1

Swaminarayan Hindu Mission

54-56 Meadow Garth
Neasden
London NW10 8HD
Tel: 081-965-2651
Tel: 081-445-6903 (home)
Fax: 081-503-7773
Contact: Dr R B Shah
Office: Interfaith Committee
A national organisation with a place of worship in Neasden. The organisation tries to enhance the physical, mental, and social qualities of the members, and to develop the spirit of service to other human beings during natural calamities here and abroad, irrespective of caste, colour and creed. Its members are encouraged from childhood to abstain from vices and refrain from alcohol, tobacco and drug misuse. They are trained how to be good law abiding citizens and how to provide an excellent example of team work. The organisation is in the process of building a new marble temple. Activities include: regular daily prayers and religious discourses; activities for children, youth and women; Gujarati classes; medical screening and advice. Affiliated to The Inter Faith Network for the UK.

Vanik Association of the United Kingdom

44 St. Oswald Road
London SW16
Tel: 081-764-8843
Contact: Mrs Naybaben Harish Savadia
Office: General Secretary

Vishwa Hindu Parishad (UK)

45 Kidderminster Road
West Croydon
Surrey CRO 2UF
Contact: Mr Thakorbai Patel
Any person eighteen years or older who agrees with the objectives of the Parishad is eligible to be a member. It is part of an international organisation founded to assist in the establishment of networks of Hindus, especially those who have migrated from India in the recent past. It has centres in many countries of the world. It aims to unite Hindus with a view to instill in them devotion to the principles and practices of Hindu ways of life; cultivate in them a spirit of self-respect for themselves and their ways of life and respect for the people of all colours, creeds, races and religions; establish and reinforce contacts with Hindus

all over the world; provide medical aid to the poor and needy people; provide help to people in grief caused by natural calamities like flood, fire and famine and to award scholarships, and provide books and other educational needs for deserving students. Its activities include weekly, fortnightly or monthly meetings of the centres of the Parishad, by recitation of scriptures; devotional songs; celebrations of all Hindu festivals; seminars and symposia on cultural and religious aspects of Hindu ways of life; conferences and workshops. Children's programmes are organised to impart cultural heritage and camps for youngsters and adults are aimed at providing experience of collective life. It publishes "Hindu Vishwa" - a quarterly periodical for members. Affiliated to The Inter Faith Network for the UK.

HINDU TEMPLES AND LOCAL ORGANISATIONS

SCOTLAND

WALES

NORTHERN IRELAND

NORTH EAST ENGLAND

YORKSHIRE AND HUMBERSIDE

NORTH WEST ENGLAND

ENGLISH EAST MIDLANDS

ENGLISH WEST MIDLANDS

EAST ANGLIA

SOUTH EAST ENGLAND (NORTH)

LONDON (E)

LONDON (N)

LONDON (NW)

LONDON (SE)

LONDON (SW)

LONDON (W)

LONDON (WC)

SOUTH EAST ENGLAND (SOUTH)

SOUTH WEST ENGLAND

A variety of forms of Hindu local organisations are listed in this directory. These include *mandirs*, many of which are in buildings adapted from other original uses. Only a few being pupose-built; *caste* groups and other organisations meeting either in hired premises or in the homes of their members.

SCOTLAND

Tayside Hindu Centre and Temple

10 Taylers Lane
Dundee
Tayside
Tel: 0382-69652
Contact: Mr N Gopal
Office: Chairman

Hindu Temple and Community Centre

St Andrew Place
Edinburgh EH6 7ED
Tel: 031-663-4689 (home)
Contact: Dinesh Joshi
Office: Secretary
Place of worship. Activities include worship and social activities.

Greenhills Hindu Mandir Sabha

40 Alder Place
Greenhills
Glasgow G7

Hindu Mandir Sabha

10 Great George Street
Glasgow G12 8PD
Tel: 041-334-1274
Contact: Mr M L N Murthy
Office: General Secretary
Place of worship. A Hindu centre, serving the community in and around Glasgow. At present, there is a priest looking after the temple and the religious needs of the community. The temple is open on Sundays from 11.00am and weekdays (Monday–Saturday) from 7.00am to 10.00am and 7.00pm to 9.00pm. Some of the Hindu festivals are celebrated. Activities are organised for youth and women as well as worship.

ISKCON (Scotland)

"Karuna Bhavan"
Bankhouse Road
Lesmahagow
Lanarkshire ML11 0ES
Tel: 0555-894790
Contact: Balabhadra
Office: President
A well organised and immaculately clean temple with a beautiful shrine. Visiting parties are most welcome (by prior arrangement). The centre organises cultural presentations for schools and colleges, and variety programmes for the elderly, the infirm, and all types of social and community organisations.

WALES

ISKCON Cardiff

18 Greenfield Place
Caerphilly
Mid Glamorgan
Tel: 0222-831579
Contact: Tarakanath
Office: President
A small centre with weekly meetings and
Bhagavad-Gita study groups. Enquiries welcome.

Shree Kutchi Leva Patel Samaj

Mardy Street
Grangetown
Cardiff
South Glamorgan
Tel: 0222-372032
Contact: Mr Vishram Varsani
Office: Trustee
Provides social and religious activities.

Swaminarayan Temple

Merches Place
Grangetown
Cardiff CF1 7QU
South Glamorgan
Tel: 0222-371128
Contact: Mr Naran Patel

Gwent Hindu Community

6 Gaudi Walk
Rogerstone
Newport
Gwent (home)
Tel: 0633-893141 (home)
Contact: Mr D O Trevedi

NORTHERN IRELAND

Hindu Mandir

Clifton Street
Carlisle Circus
Belfast

International Society for Krishna Consciousness (ISKCON)

Brooklands
140 Upper Dunmurray Lane
Belfast
Tel: 0232-620530
Fax: 0247-852796
Contact: Kesava devi dasi
Office: Secretary

Place of worship and residential theological college. A
large Edwardian building with spacious gardens,
situated some six miles from the centre of Belfast. It is
open daily and activities include theological training
for men and women; worship; propagation of
non-sectarian God-consciousness through the
distribution of literature; the sanctification of food and
the congregational chanting of the Lord's holy names.
A special programme is held every Sunday at 4.00pm
with a lift service available to and from the city centre.

NORTH EAST ENGLAND

Hindu Cultural Society Cleveland

143 Hall Drive
Acklam
Middlesbrough TS5 7HU
Tel: 0642-825965
Contact: Dr V M Dave
Office: President
Place of worship and cultural centre. A registered
charity still in need of financial support as the centre is
not fully properly furnished and equipped to carry out
many of the activities the society wishes to organise.
Socio-religious activities for all Hindus including
elderly, young, and women.

Hindu Temple

Corner of Baxter Avenue
172 West Road
Fenham
Newcastle-upon-Tyne NE4 9QB
Tel: 091-273-3364
Contact: Mr Krishan Kant Attri
Office: Priest

ISKCON Newcastle

21 Leazes Park Road
Newcastle-upon-Tyne NE1 4PF
Tel: 091-222-0150
Tel: 091-378-0749
Contact: Divya Simha
Office: Temple President
Place of worship. ISKCON (International Society for
Krishna Consciousness) is a cultural organisation
dedicated to the re-spiritualisation of humanity,
known popularly as the Hare Krishna Movement. It
is a missionary branch of the Vedic tradition whose
members are technically known as Gaudiya
Vaishnavas and are worshippers of Lord Vishnu or
Krishna following an ancient tradition in which Sri
Caitanya Mahaprabhu appeared five hundred years
ago in Bengal. Sri Caitanya Mahaprabhu is accepted
by ISKCON members as the incarnation of Krishna

(Sanskrit name for God) in this present age. He stressed the chanting of the Hare Krishna Maha Mantra as most effective for spiritual purification. Chanting the names of God is the main activity of ISKCON. Other activities include distribution of literature; public worship; teaching Eastern philosophy; a wide range of cultural activities; food distribution to the homeless through "food for life". Guest speakers are available. Group visits can be made by prior arrangement.

Istree Samaj

10 Eastlands
High Heaton
Newcastle-upon-Tyne NE7 7YE
Tel: 091-2811509
Contact: Mrs Ravi Chowdhry
A membership group of twenty-five to thirty women who meet on a regular basis at least once a month in each others' homes. Basically a self-help group which gives emotional support and advice and refers members to the relevant agencies for welfare advice and help. The group socialises over tea provided by the host and in this way the older women have contact with professional people who can discuss their problems and seek help from others where and when it is needed. It was established in 1975 and continues to function to date, with younger members joining to keep the cultural tradition alive. Activities include collective worship in the form of Bhajan and Kirtan.

YORKSHIRE AND HUMBERSIDE

Bharata Mandal

14 Sawrey Place
Bradford BD7

Bhartiya Mandal (Gujarati Samaj)

150 Listerhills Road
Bradford BD7

Bradford Hindu Temple and Cultural Society

321 Leeds Road
Bradford BD3 9LS
Tel: 0274-725923
Contact: Mr Dayal Shaima
Office: General Secretary
Place of worship. Activities include worship, cultural activities, and welfare.

Hindu Swayamsevak Sangh Cultural Arts Centre

52 Rugby Place
Bradford BD7 2DF
Tel: 0274-577395

Fax: 0274-521211
Contact: Paresh Rathod
A voluntary group whose main objects are to promote the Hindu religion (dharma) and to educate the public in Hindu ideals and way of life. The Sangh lays an emphasis on building up character and self-discipline, and keeping the ideals and values most cherished by Hindus. Youth and cultural activities and religious events are undertaken. There is also a women's section known as Hindu Sevaki Samiti.

Leuva Patidar Samaj

Legrams Hill Lane
off Legrams Lane
Bradford BD7 2BA
West Yorkshire
Tel: 0274-575718
Affiliated to the Hindu Council of the North.

Shree Hindu Temple and Community Centre

Thornton Lane
Off Little Horton
Bradford BD5 9DN
Tel: 0274-578115
Contact: Mr Balu Lad
Office: Secretary
Place of worship and community centre run by the Shree Prajapati Association, Bradford. The work of the centre is all on a voluntary basis. The following deities are installed in the temple: Ganesh, Goddess Amba, Lord Krishna and Radha, Ram, Sita, Laxman, Lord Vishwa Karma, Shiva and Hanuman. Religious and cultural activities are carried out as well as welfare for the community at large. The temple is open from 10.00am-11.00am and 6.45pm-8.00pm during which Arti (prayers) is conducted. This centre provides facilities for the study of Hinduism for schools, colleges, teacher training centres and voluntary organisations around Bradford and throughout the North of England.

Shree Prajapati Association Bradford

Shree Hindu Temple
Thornton Lane
Off Little Horton lane
Bradford BD5 9DN
Tel: 0274-578115
Contact: Mr Balu Lad
Office: Secretary
Religious organisation which runs the temple and community centre at the same address. Affiliated to the Hindu Council of the North.

Hindu Community
4 Holyrood Road
Town Moor
Doncaster DN2 5HR

Punjabi Hindu Society
50 Bawtry Road
Bessacarr
Doncaster DN4 7BQ
Tel: 0302-535126 (home)
Contact: Mr B Ram

Sanatan Dharam Society
2 Holyrood Road
Town Moor
Doncaster DN2 5HB
Tel: 0302-363732
Contact: Mr R A Gugg

Shree Sita Ram Temple
20 Zetland Street
Huddersfield HD1 2RA
Tel: 0484-431515 (home)
Contact: Raizada Sanjeev Bali
Office: Vice-President

Hindu Samaj
68 Manor Drive
Leeds LS6

Sanatan Temple and Community Centre
281 Chapeltown Road
Leeds LS7 3JT
Tel: 0532-622358
Contact: Mr Om Prakash Sharma
Place of worship. The Temple has a non-restrictive and universal outlook. It has statues of various deities and also the Holy Vedas. People interested in understanding Hinduism are invited to visit the Temple by arrangement. All the major Hindu festivals are celebrated. Other activities include Hindi classes, Indian classical dancing classes for young girls. There are sessions of karate instruction and training from time to time.

Shree Hindu Mandir
36 Alexandra Road
Leeds LS6 1RF
Tel: 0532-612342
Contact: Mr Shah
Office: President
Affiliated to the Hindu Council of the North.

Shree Ram Krishna Bhajan Mandal
26 Warmsley Road
Leeds LS6
Tel: 0532-753327

Swaminarayan Hindu Mission
23 Eddison Walk
Adel
Leeds LS16 8DA (home)
Contact: Dr Vijay R Pancholi
Office: Chair
A group which meets for prayer at least once a week.

Hindu Temple and Community Centre
1-10 Richmond Street
Sheffield S3

Sheffield and District Hindu Samaj
11 Denbank Avenue
Crosspool
Sheffield S10
Contact: D R Naik

Tantra Yoga Group
36 Redcar Road
Sheffield S10
Contact: Dr I S Johnson

Sheffield Durga Puja Committee
19 Kirkdale
Worksop
Nottinghamshire S81 0HA
Contact: Dr B N Patel

NORTH WEST ENGLAND

Shree Bhartiya Mandal
103 Union Road
Ashton-under-Lyne OL6 8JN
Tel: 061-330-2085
Contact: Mr Mistry
Office: Honorary Secretary
The organisation is a community centre which caters for the elderly and other cross-sections of the Indian community in Tameside. The centre also offers a place of worship and religious education by inviting prominant saints from India. Activities include mother tongue teaching offered to Indian youth by running an evening school; an unemployment training project is run from the centre funded by Manchester TEC; worship; services to the elderly; youth sports and social

activities; mother tongue teaching; women; cultural and social activities. Affiliated to the Hindu Council of the North.

Shree Jalaram Bhajan Mandal
58 Kenyon Street
Ashton-under-Lyne
Lancashire
Contact: Mr V Kara

Shree Prajapati Association UK
5 Holden Street
Ashton-under-Lyne
Lancashire
Contact: Mr Kanti Mistry

Swaminarayan Hindu Mission
29 Russell Street
Ashton-under-Lyne
Lancashire
Tel: 061-330-5196
Contact: Vinubhai D Patel
Office: President
Place of worship. The Mission aims to preserve the Hindu culture and religion in society. It promotes youth activities, language classes and religious programmes.

Swaminarayan Hindu Mission
230 Stamford Street
Ashton-under-Lyne
Lancashire

Blackburn Hindu Centre
11 The Dene
Beardwood
Blackburn BB2 7QS
Tel: 0254-678183
Contact: Mr A Chudasama
Office: General Secretary
A voluntary membership organisation established in 1973 to uphold Hinduism. The centre celebrates religious and cultural events and festivals; teaches Gujarati to children (seven to fifteen years old); and offers advice on social and welfare matters. Tours are held to Hindu temples in the UK. The group participates in fund raising events (local or national), promotes cultural activities, and gives talks on Hinduism to any religious, educational establishments and voluntary groups in Blackburn and Lancashire. Affiliated to the Hindu Council of the North.

Blackburn Lohana Union
4 Durham Close
Blackburn
Lancashire
Contact: Mr N Lakhani

Hindu Elderly Persons Association
23 Columbia Way
Blackburn
Lancashire
Tel: 0254-64130
Contact: Mr A Dayal

Shree Jansari Gnati Mandal
33 Maple Street
Blackburn
Lancashire
Tel: 0254-677988
Contact: Shanti Dayal
Office: Mr Dayal
Voluntary body. This organisation believes in upholding the community spirit and cultural participation to keep the community alive and active. It celebrates cultural festivals.

Vishwa Hindu Parishad
168 St Aidanes Avenue
Blackburn BB2 4AY
Contact: Thakorbhai B Patel

Krishna Temple
24 Chiltern Drive
Tongue Fold
Bolton BL2 6AP
Contact: V Patel

Mandhata Hitradak Mandal (Bolton)
Krishna Temple
10 Beverley Road
Bolton BL1 4DT
Tel: 0204-386893
Contact: Mr G R Patel
Office: President
Affiliated to the Hindu Council of the North.

Shree Krishna Mandir
10 Beverley Road
BoltonBL1 4DT
Tel: 0204-386893

Shree Kutchhi Leva Patel Society

13 Jauncey Street
Bolton
Lancashire

Shree Kutch Leva Patel Society

50 Church Street
Bolton
Lancashire

Shree Kutch Satsang Swaminarayan Temple

11 Adelaide Street
Bolton BL3 3NT
Tel: 0204–652604
Contact: Secretary
A place of worship and religious organisation established in the UK now for over twenty years. Activities include Gujarati classes, youth club and comprhensive library containing literature on Hindu/Indian culture. It is the first purpose-built Hindu temple in the North-West and welcomes visits from both individuals and organisations.

Shree Sorathia Prajapati Community UK

39 Hawthorne Road
Bolton BL3 5RF
Tel: 0204–655111
Contact: Mr M M Singadia
Branch organisation. The Bolton branch is dedicated to meet the cultural and religious needs of our community. The SSPC is also committed to work with other communities in Bolton irrespective of their cultural and religious backgrounds. The group aims to maintain their cultural heritage. Social, welfare, educational and religious activities are organised for everyone in the community. There is a women's group and a youth group.

Swaminarayan Sidhat Mandal

c/o 164 Deane Road
Bolton BL3 5DL
Contact: Secretary

Vishwa Hindu Parishad Bolton

Community Centre
Chorley Old Road
Bolton BL1 3AA
Tel: 0204–391367
Contact: Mr I S Patel
Celebrates Hindu festivals and also has prayers each day. In addition, it has youth activities and an Asian elderly day centre.

Hindu Religious Gandhi Hall

21 Troutebeck Road
Gatley
Cheshire SK8 4RP

Lohana Association Manchester

48-50 Market Street
Hyde
Cheshire SK14 1AH
Contact: Mr S Robheru
Office: Secretary
Affiliated to the Hindu Council of the North.

Shree Hindu Society

10 Langton Close
Scullers Point
Halton Road
Lancaster LA1 2TJ (Home)
Tel: 0524–849705 (home)
Contact: Praful Upadhyay
Office: President

Hare Krishna Centre (ISKCON)

114 Bold Street
Liverpool L1 4HY
Tel: 051-708-9400
Contact: Titikshu
Office: President
This temple is situated in the heart of the City Centre, three minutes walk from Central Station and five minutes from Lime Street. A programme is held each Sunday at 2.30pm with meditation, discussion and a vegetarian feast. Guest speakers are available and group visits can be arranged. Enquiries welcome.

Hindu Cultural Organisation

Edge Lane
Liverpool L7
Tel: 051-263-7965
Contact: Kiran Dawar
Office: Youth worker
Place of worship and community centre. The centre aims to provide a focus for the Hindu community in Merseyside and to assist in creating understanding between the Hindu community and the local community by providing facilities and organising events which cross religious and cultural boundaries. Activities include: badminton and table tennis in the sports hall; Hindi and Bengali classes every week on Sunday; worship; and a children's day once a month.

Sangam Youth Group
Flat 3
68 Huskisson Street
Liverpool L8

Brahma Sanaj Manchester
26 Prestbury Road
Wilmslow
Cheshire SK9 2LL
Contact: Mr Kantibhai Joshi

Hindu Swayamsevak Sangh
Karam House
79 Lever Street
Manchester M1 1FL
Tel: 061-236-8621
Fax: 061-228-0056
Contact: Mr T L Gupta
Office: Public Relations Officer
Youth group.

ISKCON Manchester
20 Mayfield Road
Whalley Range
Manchester M16 8FT
Tel: 061-226-4416
Contact: Krishna Dharma
Office: Director
A Hare Krishna Temple. Open house is every Sunday at 2.00pm where there is an introductory talk, a worship ceremony and, of course, a free vegetarian meal. "Food For Life" operates daily distribution of free meals in the City Centre. The Society also runs a subsidised restaurant for the needy in Moss Side. Guest speakers are available upon request. Group visits welcome by prior arrangement.

North West Gujerati Samaj
60 Grenham Avenue
Hulme
Manchester M15 4HD

Sri Aurobindo Yoga and Information Society
35 Circular Road
Withington
Manchester M20 9ZZ
Tel: 061-434-1919
Contact: Mr Mahendra Bhatt
Office: President
Affiliated to the Hindu Council of the North.

Shree Radha Krishna Mandir
Gandhi Hall
4 Brunswick Road

Withington
Manchester M20 4RS
Tel: 061-445-1134
Contact: Mr J K Sharma
Office: Secretary
Place of worship. The object of the society is the advancement of Hinduism by: offering facilities for religious functions; providing a central place of worship with a resident Hindu priest; arranging lectures and discourses on Hinduism; encouraging service to the community and generally taking on roles which will further the active and corporate life of the society. Affiliated to the Hindu Council of the North.

Vishwa Hindu Parishad
Karam House
79 Lever Street
Manchester M1 1FL
Tel: 061-236-8621
Contact: Mr T L Gupta

Bharat Bhavan Temple and Community Centre
57-59 Fern Street
Oldham OL8 1SH
Tel: 061-633-0043
Contact: Ms Suraj Agravat
Office: Community Advice Worker
Affiliated to the Hindu Council of the North.

India Culture and Social Centre
Couldhurst Community Centre
Rochdale Road
Oldham
Lancashire
Tel: 061-682-5189
Contact: Mr Kanu Patel
Office: President
Affiliated to the Hindu Council of the North.

Shree Swaminarayan Temple
Lee Street
Oldham OL8 1BG
Tel: 061-652-0993

Andhra Social and Community Organisation
28 St Mary's Street
Preston PR1 5LN
Tel: 0772-793924
Contact: Mr K V Babu
Place of worship and community centre. There is a prayer hall of Lord Venkateswara (Lord of the Seven Hills) and also a social and community centre used by Hindus of the Andhra and Telugu traditions of

Hinduism. Prayer of Suprabhata Seva is held every month. There is a social and cultural programme including celebration of festivals and a library of Telugu books, videos, and magazines.

Hindu Council of the North

c/o Gujarat Hindu Society
South Meadow Lane
Preston PR1 8JN
Tel: 0772-53901
Contact: Mr C M Limbachia
Office: President
Thirteen Hindu Associations are affiliated to the Council.

Preston Gujerat Hindu Society

South Meadow Lane
Preston PR1 8JN
Tel: 0772-53901
Contact: Mr D H Nayee
Office: Secretary
Place of worship, cultural and recreational centre. The society preaches Hinduism to its members and furthers the promotion and preservation of Hindu culture, maintaining harmony with the host community and establishing understanding among organisations, institutions and authorities about Hindus and their needs. Activities involve youth, women and the elderly, worship and mother tongue teaching. Affiliated to the Hindu Council of the North.

Swaminarayan Hindu Mission

8a Avenham Place
Preston PR1 3SX
Tel: 0772-562252
Contact: Mr Gandhi

Lord Rama Krishna Temple

7 Haydock Street
Warrington WA2 7OM
Tel: 0925-572042
Tel: 0925-724672 (home)
Contact: Mr R Kumar
Office: Chairperson
Place of worship and cultural centre. It aims to provide cultural, social physical and religious activities for members of the Indian community and to be engaged in the task of educating people to understand and appreciate the culture of fellow beings. It tries to cement relations with all people through physical, social, religious, cultural, educational and character building activities.

ENGLISH EAST MIDLANDS

Geeta Bhawan Hindu Temple

312 Normanton Road
Derby DE3 6WE
Tel: 0332-380407
Contact: Mr R A Shastri
Office: President
A place of worship for all Hindus irrespective of caste, creed or linguistic origin. The temple aims to explain the Hindu faith to the followers of other faiths in order to bring harmony. It believes that inter-faith relations are very essential since we live in a multi-faith society. The temple preaches the Vedic (Hindu) faith and manages various groups: Hindu Women's Association, Hindu Youth Club and Hindu Welfare Association.

Hindu Welfare Association

c/o Geeta Bhawan Temple
312 Normanton Road
Derby DE3 6WE
Tel: 0332-380407
Contact: Swayam Parkash Joshi
Advisory service for welfare, social and cultural issues. It aims to give help and support to the elderly and disabled people and for various welfare needs of the community as well as to give counselling to young people facing problems in their marriages. The resources available are translations, technical aids, tape, administrative support and transport. Meetings are held once a month at Geeta Bhawan Hindu Temple.

Hindu Womens Association

143 Clarence Road
Derby DE3 6LS
Tel: 0332-49114
Contact: Mrs Sudesh Chabba
The Association provides a counselling service for Hindu women who are members of the Geeta Bhawan Hindu Temple. Any matter can be discussed with members who are from a similar background.

Lohana Community

28 Mostyn Avenue
Littleover
Derby DE3 6HW
Tel: 0332-77128
Contact: Mr M Modi
Office: Secretary
Members of this organisation are all Hindus who worship at the Geeta Bhavan Temple. Outings to various temples in the country are arranged. A Guru is invited to give lectures on Hinduism. There are

nearly eighty families which belong to this organisation. Activities include regular worship and celebration of Hindu festivals.

Asian Sports Club and Cultural Centre
25 Windermere Drive
Leicester LE7 7GG
Tel: 0533-555876
Contact: Mr Jitendrabhai Patel
Office: Honorary Secretary
Affiliated to the Leicester Gujarat Hindu Association.

Audich Gadhia Brahmasamaj
62 Lockerbie Avenue
Leicester LE4 7NJ
Tel: 0533-660612
Contact: Mr Indubhai Vyas
Office: Honorary Secretary
Affiliated to the Leicester Gujarat Hindu Association

Bajarang Bali Bhajan Mandal
16 Brambling Road
Leicester
Tel: 0533-519041

Charotaria Leuva Patidar Samaj
29 Shipley Road
Leicester
Tel: 0533-681821
Contact: Mr Nagarbhai Patel
Office: Honorary Secretary
Affiliated to the Leicester Gujarat Hindu Association.

Charotar Patidar Samaj (Leicester)
41 Melton Road
Leicester LE4 6PN
Tel: 0533-680101
Contact: Honorary Secretary
Affiliated to the Leicester Gujarat Hindu Association.

Fiji Sanatan Dharam Ramayan Mandli
77 Strathmore Avenue
Rushey Mead
Leicester LE4 7HE
Tel: 0533-666649 (home)
Contact: Mr James Sankar
Office: Secretary
It aims to serve the Fijian community in Leicester, preserving their religious and cultural heritage, and promoting the community to other communities in Leicester. Activities include community action, ethnic minorities, fund raising, information, religious, self-help and social.

Geeta Bhavan
70 Clarendon Park Road
Leicester LE2 3AD
Tel: 0553-707756
Tel: 0553-350667 (home)
Contact: Mr M C Prasher
Office: Secretary
Place of worship and Community Centre run by the Hindu Religious and Cultural Society. The society (for Hindi and Punjabi speaking Hindus) was established in 1981 with a few members. Most of the membership was of Punjabi speaking Hindus in Leicester. The building was acquired in 1988. It has a big hall, kitchen, meeting rooms, play group and a Satsang hall upstairs. All the religious and cultural festivals of the Hindu calendar are celebrated, and information is provided. Activities include worship for all, sports activities for youths, language teaching, trips, drop-in centre and club.

Gujarat Hindu Association
51 Loughborough Road
Leicester
Tel: 0533-668266
Contact: Mr Ramanbhai Barber
Office: General secretary
An umbrella group with over fifty organisations representing nearly sixty thousand people (a quarter of the population of Leicester). The organisation aims to create unity and to promote educational, cultural, religious and social activities. Activities include annual celebrations of India Independence day; Gandhi's birthday; Navratri festival (nine nights of dancing festively), Raas and Garba (competitions); and various cultural events and sports festivals for youth. It also co-ordinates activities with Leicester city and Leicestershire county councils for the benefit of members.

Gujarati Arya Association
10 Burnaby Avenue
Leicester LE5 3QX
Contact: Mr Chimanbhai Champanaria
Office: Honorary Secretary
Affiliated to the Leicester Gujarat Hindu Association.

Gujarati Valand Gnati Mandal
30 Kensington Street
Leicester LE4 5GL
Tel: 0533-530422
Contact: Arun Nayer
Office: Honorary Secretary
Affiliated to the Leicester Gujarat Hindu Association.

Gurjar Kshtriya Gnati Mandal
3 Agar Street
Leicester LE4 6NE
Tel: 0533-682401
Contact: Mr P J Manani
Office: Honorary Secretary
Affiliated to the Leicester Gujarat Hindu Association.

Haveli Shreeji Dwar
58 Loughborough Road
Leicester LE4 5LD
Tel: 0533-682425
Contact: Mr G P Goswami
Office: Priest
Place of worship.

Hindu Association
40 Highfield Street
Leicester

Hindu Religious and Cultural Society
6 Brancaster Close
Leicester LE4 0LA
Tel: 0533-350667
Contact: Mr M C Prasher
Office: Secretary
Religious society. A registered charity set up in 1981 with the aims of celebrating Hindu festivals and spreading the doctrines of the Sanatan Dharma. Most members are Punjabi Hindus. The society encourages people to learn Hindi. The society also wishes to help attain the social, educational and cultural needs of Hindus in this country. In 1988 the society bought the Geeta Bhavan and Hindu Community Centre. Activities include Hindi teaching, involvement with race and educational issues concerning Hindus, a drop-in centre and games provision for youth and women.

Hindu Sevika Samiti
60 Homeway Road
Leicester

Hindu Temple and Community Association
75 Prospect Hill
Leicester
Tel: 0533-622221
Contact: Mr Rashmikant Joshi
Office: Honorary Secretary
Affiliated to the Leicester Gujarat Hindu Association.

Hindu Temple (Sanatan Mandir)
7 Shakerdale Road
Wipston
Leicester

Indian Cultural Society
47 Tavistock Drive
Leicester
Tel: 0533-730357
Contact: Dr H D Vyas
Office: Honorary Secretary
Affiliated to the Leicester Gujarat Hindu Association.

Indian Education Society
10 Woodbridge Road
Leicester
Tel: 0533-681071
Contact: Mr Jayantilal Mistry
Office: Honorary Secretary
Affiliated to the Leicester Gujarat Hindu Association.

ISKCON Leicester
21 Thoresby Street
Evington
Leicester LE5 4GU
Tel: 0533-413118
Contact: Paul
Office: Vice-President
This centre features a gorgeous temple room for worship and meditation. Programmes are held every Sunday from 3.00pm until 6.00pm. "Food For Life" operates from here, feeding the homeless in the City Centre. Guest speakers are available for schools, colleges, and other communities.

Jalaram Prathna Mandal
85 Narborough Road
Leicester LE3 0LF
Tel: 0533-540117
Tel: 0533-899711 (home)
Contact: T V Morjaria
Office: President
A place of worship dedicated to Saint Jalaram who hails from Gujarat and a little town called "Virpur". Shree Jalaram Bapa, as he is popularly known, is famous for his miracles. When anyone, irrespective of caste, creed or colour is in trouble and prays to him he is known to have solved their problem. They usually set aside money or come personally to the Temple to pray. People travel from France, Canada, America and Kenya to fulfill the promise given to him. Activities include worship and religious education for children. Affiliated to the Leicester Gujarat Hindu Association.

Jalaram Satsang Mandal

254 Hinckley Road
Leicester
Tel: 0533-858560
Contact: Mrs Indiraben Thobhani
Office: Honorary Secretary
Affiliated to the Leicester Gujarat Hindu Association.

Leicester Sangit Kala Kendra

c/o Mr. Patel
27 Bradbourne Street
Leicester

Leicester Shree Brahma Samaj

15 Belgrave Road
Leicester LE4 6AR
Tel: 0533-624339
Tel: 0533-889069 (home)
Contact: Mohanlal M Bhogaita
Office: President
Place of worship. The organisation is building a new Lord Shiva Temple and extension to the building and Temple for daily worship and weddings. This will be the largest Temple of its kind in Europe. The organisation, established in 1972, has four hundred members. The existing Temple building was bought by the Brahmin community of Leicester in 1977. All Hindu ceremonies are celebrated throughout the year and all are welcome to join in the activities. Other activities include daily worship, social, welfare and educational activities. The President's home address for making contact is 23 Burleigh Avenue, Wigston, Leicestershire, LE18 1FJ. Affiliated to the Leicester Gujarat Hindu Association.

Leicestershire Brahma Samaj

15 Belgrave Road
Leicester LE4 6AR
Tel: 0533-624359
Contact: R Joshi
Office: Secretary
Place of worship and membership group. Worship, cultural, youth and women's activities are undertaken.

Leuva Patidar Samaj (SD)

3 Saltcoates Avenue
Leicester LE4 7NP
Tel: 0533-682625
Contact: Mr Ratilal Patel
Office: Honorary Secretary
Affiliated to the Leicester Gujarat Hindu Association.

Lohana Mahila Mandal

3 Dorset Street
Leicester LE4 6BG

Mahatma Gandhi Foundation

152 Belgrave Road
Leicester LE4 5AJ

Maher Community Association

19 The Oval
Oadby
Leicester LE2 5JB
Contact: Mr Jaimal Odedra
Office: Honorary Secretary
Affiliated to the Leicester Gujarat Hindu Association.

Maisuria Gnati Mandal

Sawday Street
Leicester

Navnat Vanik Social Service Group

2/21 Taurus Close
Leicester
Tel: 0533-621769
Contact: Mr Z Chhatrisha
Office: Chairman
Affiliated to the Leicester Gujarat Hindu Association.

Pancholi Samaj

38 Gipsy Road
Leicester LE4 **Tel:** 0533-764864

Parajiya Pattni Association

46 Patton Street
Leicester

Rajput Bhoi Gnati Samaj Association

51 Woodgreen Walk
Leicester

Rajput Gnati Mandal

87 Buller Road
Leicester

Rajput Sangathan Samaj

61 Lancashire Street
Leicester LE4 7PF
Tel: 0533-610793
Contact: Mr Jayantilal Rajput
Office: Honorary Secretary
Affiliated to the Leicester Gujarat Hindu Association.

Rana Samaj

85 Coral Street
Leicester LE4 5BG
Tel: 0533-661165
Contact: Mr Bharatbhai Rana
Office: Honorary Secretary
Affiliated to the Leicester Gujarat Hindu Association.

R K Yuvak Mandal

61 Osbourne Road
Leicester

Sarvodaya Arya Samaj

13 Rowsley Avenue
Leicester

Sarvodaya Mahila Mandal

c/o Janta Store
Belgrave Road
Leicester

Sewa Samaj

7 Parkville Street
Leicester

Shakti Forum

1 Dashwood Road
Leicester LE2 1PH
Tel: 0533-733962
Contact: Ranju Parmar
Office: Secretary
Educates children in Gujarati. Other activities include
sports, education, leisure, women's and religious
activities.

Shree Anavil Samaj

59 Acorn Street
Leicester
Tel: 0533-664890
Contact: Honorary Secretary
Affiliated to the Leicester Gujarat Hindu Association

Shree Bardai Brahman Samaj UK

38 Stanley Drive
Humberstone
Leicester LE5 1EA
Tel: 0533-716545
Contact: Mr Harishbhai Joshi
Office: Honorary Secretary
Affiliated to the Leicester Gujarat Hindu Association.

Shree Bodali Sewa Mandal

38 Windermere Street
Leicester

Shree Darji Gnati Mandal

21 Sawley Street
Leicester LE5 5JR

Shree Gurjar Kshatriya Gnati Mandal

3 Agar Street
Leicester LE4 6NE
Tel: 0533-682401
Contact: Mr P J Manani
Office: Honorary Secretary

Shree Hindu Temple

47 Cromford Street
Leicester LE2 0FW
Tel: 0533-625455
Tel: 0533-513787 (home)
Contact: Mr G R Patel
Office: Secretary
The temple provides Hindu religious, cultural and
social activities plus education and a library. Activities
include advisory work, work with children, elderly
people, ethnic minorities, social, education, and
religious activities.

Shree Hindu Temple and Community Centre

36 Chatsworth Street
Leicester LE2 0FP
Tel: 0533-625455

Shree Jansari Gnati Mandal

42 Silverstone Drive
Leicester
Tel: 0533-682257
Contact: Mr Dipakhai Vadher
Office: Honorary Secretary
Affiliated to the Leicester Gujarat Hindu Association.

Shree Jansari Gnati Mandal Gayatri Nivas

21 Brixham Drive
Wigston
Leicester

Shree Ji Dwar

152 Belgrave Road
Leicester
Tel: 0533-661805
Contact: Mr Chandubhai Mattani
Office: Honorary Secretary

Shree Jignashu Satsang Mandal
Mahatma Gandhi House
Block 10
First Floor
61 Dorset Street
Leicester LE4 6BH
Contact: Mr Bhimjibhai Kotecha
Affiliated to the Leicester Gujarat Hindu Association.

Shree Limbachia Gnati Mandal
14 Buller Road
Leicester
Tel: 0533-680189
Contact: Mr M M Nai
Office: Honorary Secretary
Affiliated to the Leicester Gujarat Hindu Association.

Shree Lohana Mahajan Hindu Community Organisation
Hildyard Road
Leicester
Tel: 0533-664643
Contact: Mr Prafulbhai Thakrar
Office: Honorary Secretary
Place of worship and organisation. The aim of the organisation is to promote religion and culture and to run the Shree Ram Mandir. Affiliated to the Leicester Gujarat Hindu Association.

Shree Lohana Youth League
c/o Shree Lohana Mahan Hindu Community Organisation
Hildyard Road
Leicester

Shree Mandata Samaj Sahayak Mandal
Melbourne Rd/Hartington Rd
Leicester
Tel: 0533-623648
Contact: Mr M R Patel
Office: Honorary Secretary
Affiliated to the Leicester Gujarat Hindu Association.

Shree Matiyiya Patidar Samaj
3 Colebrooke Close
Leicester LE5 5NG
Contact: Mr Ramanlal Patel
Office: Honorary Secretary
Affiliated to the Leicester Gujarat Hindu Association.

Shree Navrang Society
15 Rushford Drive
Leicester LE4 7UF
Tel: 0533-767816

Contact: Mr Girishbhai Maher
Office: Honorary Secretary
Affiliated to the Leicester Gujarat Hindu Association.

Shree Osthrathia Prajapati Community
75 Moores Road
Leicester

Shree Pancholi Samaj
38-40 Gipsy Lane
Leicester LE4 6QH
Tel: 0533-665738
Contact: Mr Mahendrabhai Pancholi
Office: Honorary Secretary
Affiliated to the Leicester Gujarat Hindu Association.

Shree Prajapati Association
25 Gelert Avenue
Leicester LE5 2NS
Tel: 0533-431059
Contact: Mr U K Mistry
Office: Honorary Secretary
Affiliated to the Leicester Gujarat Hindu Association.

Shree Prajapati Sports Club
55 Percival Road
North Evington
Leicester LE5 3NS
Tel: 0533-5120269

Shree Radhakrupa Satsang Mandal
36 Abney Street
Leicester LE5 5AA
Tel: 0533-547343
Contact: Mrs Kamuben N Joshi
Affiliated to the Leicester Gujarat Hindu Association.

Shree Rajput Bhoiraj Gnati
2 Jubilee Drive
Leicester LE3 9LJ
Tel: 0533-877827
Contact: Mr Kantilal Daudia
Affiliated to the Leicester Gujarat Hindu Association.

Shree Sanatan Mandir
Weymouth Street
off Catherine Street
Leicester LE4 6FP
Tel: 0533-661402
Contact: Mr Ramanbhai Barber
Office: President
A place for Hindu worship, Hindu culture and social aspects for all the people who have faith and believe in

Hinduism. The temple remains open for seven days a week between 8.00am and 1.00pm and 4.00pm and 9.30pm. During religious holidays and festivals the temple remains open the whole day. The temple also has an annexe on Belper Street which runs as a sports centre and recreation centre for the ethnic minorities irrespective of colour or creed of all ages. Affiliated to the Leicester Gujarat Hindu Association.

Shree Sanatan Mandir Community Centre
Belper Street
Leicester LE4 6ED
Tel: 0533-666156

Shree Sarvodaya Samaj
20 Ingersby Drive
Leicester LE5 6HA
Tel: 0533-413639
Contact: Mr Kantilal Solanki
Office: Honorary Secretary
Affiliated to the Leicester Gujarat Hindu Association.

Shree Satsang Mandal
53 Moira Street
Leicester LE4 6LB
Tel: 0533-666668
Contact: Mrs P J Patel
Office: Honorary Secretary
Affiliated to the Leicester Gujarat Hindu Association.

Shree Shakti Mandir
Moira Street
Leicester LE4 6NH
Tel: 0533-664138
Contact: K V Purohit
Office: Chairperson
The organisation aims to meet the social and religious needs of the immediate community. Activities include advisory work, counselling, education, information, religious activities, social activities and work with families. Affiliated to the Leicester Gujarat Hindu Association.

Shree Sitaram Seva Trust (UK)
27 Melton Road
Leicester LE4 6PN
Tel: 0533-667393
Contact: Mr Himatbhai Ghelani
Office: Honorary Secretary
Affiliated to the Leicester Gujarat Hindu Association.

Shree Sorathia Prajapati Community (UK)
2 Arran Road
Leicester LE4 7NA

Tel: 0533-660482
Contact: Mr Gordhanbhai Gohel
Office: Honorary Secretary

Shree Swaminarayan Satsang Mandal
32 Rendell Road
Leicester LE4 5LE
Tel: 0533-667021

Shree UK Luhar Gnati Mandal
32 Evington Drive
Leicester LE5 5PB
Tel: 0533-524288
Contact: Mr Rameshbhai Sidpara
Office: Honorary Secretary
Affiliated to the Leicester Gujarat Hindu Association.

Shree UK R K Seva Samaj
9 Osmaston Road
Leicester

Shree Wanza Community
c/o 64 Harrow Road
Leicester
Tel: 0533-543562

Shree Yamuna Mandal
56 Burfield Street
Leicester LE4 6AN
Tel: 0533-680282
Contact: Miss C S Parmar
Office: Committee member
Voluntary religious organisation which helps elderly and young with social and moral difficulties and with language problems. Activities include work with elderly people, ethnic minorities, families, youth, religious activities, social work, volunteer support and social activities.

Shri Ji Dwar
152 Belgrave Road
Leicester
Tel: 0533-661805
Contact: Mr Chandhubhai Mattani
Office: Honorary Secretary
Affiliated to the Leicester Gujarat Hindu Association.

Sorathia Prajapati Community (UK)
2 Arran Road
Leicester LE4 7NA
Tel: 0533-660482

Contact: Mr Gordhanbhai Gohel
Office: Honorary Secretary
Affiliated to the Leicester Gujarat Hindu Association.

Swaminarayan Hindu Mission

3 St James Street
Off Humberstone Gate
Leicester LE1 3SU
Tel: 0533-623791
Office: President
Place of worship and branch of the Bochasanwasi Shri Akshar Purushottam Sanstha based in India. The UK organisation has its headquarters in London and temples all over the UK. Founded on the peaceful teachings of Lord Swaminarayan, the mission symbolises Hinduism in its purest form. Activities are educational, social, cultural, moral and spiritual. The main emphasis is on child and youth development. Affiliated to the Leicester Gujarat Hindu Association.

Vanik Samaj (Leicester)

60 Belgrave Road
Leicester LE4
Tel: 0533-622662
Contact: Vanmali Gordhandas
Office: President
Religious and social activities.

Vasenev Satsang Mandal

44 Paton Street
Leicester

Vishwa Hindu Parishad

4 Cross Street
Leicester LE2 1HH
Tel: 0533-611303

Geeta Bhawan

Leamington Street
Loughborough LE11 1UH
Tel: 0509-231257
Contact: Dr S R Chhabra
Office: Secretary
A place of worship which aims to cater for the religious, social, educational, spiritual and cultural needs of the Punjabi Hindu community in particular and the public at large. Membership limited to the borough of Charnwood. Activities include the celebration of religious and national festivals, worship, indoor sports (evenings), and other community activities.

Limbachia Hittechu Mandal

4a Boyer Street
Loughborough
Leicestershire
Tel: 0509-239897
Contact: Mr Nareshbhai Valand
Office: Honorary Secretary
Affiliated to the Leicester Gujarat Hindu Association.

Shree Ram Krishna Centre

Alfred Street
Loughborough LE11 1NG
Tel: 0509-237396
Contact: Secretary
Place of worship and community centre. Activities include community action, work with elderly people, ethnic minorities, families, women, youth, religious activities, play groups and language classes in Hindi, Gujurati, Bengali and Punjabi.

Melton Asian Community

4 Field Close
Melton Mowbray
Leicestershire LE13 1DS
Tel: 0664-63746
Contact: Mr Chetan Bharti
Office: Honorary Secretary
Affiliated to the Leicester Gujarat Hindu Association.

Brahma Samaj Nottingham

4 Haynes Close
Clifton Estate
Nottingham NG11 8SN

Gujarat Samaj Nottingham

16 Derby Grove
Nottingham

Hindu Temple and Cultural Centre

215 Carlton Road
Nottingham NG3 2FX
Tel: 0602-598284
Contact: Mrs Mohindra
Office: Secretary
A place of worship and social and cultural group which is managed by an elected body. There is a resident priest who takes the morning and evening worship. On Sunday there is the main service and all the Hindu families gather together. After worshipping everyone meets together socially. Activities include worship, Hindi classes, youth groups, yoga classes, and a luncheon club for senior citizens.

ISKCON Nottingham

313 Wollaton Road
Nottingham NG8 1FS
Tel: 0602-281371 (home)
Contact: Paul Oliver
Office: President
Weekly meetings and discussion groups. Guest speakers on Hinduism, Vaishnavism and related topics. All enquiries welcome.

Swaminarayan Hindu Mission

8 Howseman Gardens
Meadows
Nottingham NG2 2HX
Tel: 0602-865848
Contact: Diyeshbhai Rughani

Pravasi Mandal Asian Men's Group

c/o Victoria Centre
Palk Road
Wellingborough NN8 1HR
Contact: Mr Kataria
Office: President

Swaminarayan Hindu Mission

16–20 Mill Road
Wellingborough NN8 1PE
Tel: 0933-315961 (home)
Contact: Mukeshbhai Pabari

Wellingborough District Hindu Association

133 Highfield Road
Wellingborough NN8 1PL
Tel: 0933-222250
Contact: Dinesh Kopecha
Office: Chair
A religious organisation that has a purpose built Temple which caters for the needs of the Hindu community. It is an institution used widely by the host community and many schools visit it for Religious Education studies. The Hindu Association has a wide representation in various statutory and voluntary bodies. Its activities cater for the needs of the Hindu community by activities for youth, women and the elderly and it provides cultural activities and sports and recreation.

ENGLISH WEST MIDLANDS

Shree Ramakrishna International Temple

88a Wellington Road
Bilston
West Midlands

Arjuna Yoga Society

Ladywood Community Centre
Ledbury Close
Ladywood
Birmingham

Arya Samaj Birmingham

167 Holly Road
Handsworth
Birmingham B20 2BZ

Birmingham Pragmati Mandal

107 Dearman Road
Birmingham B11

Bochasanwasi Shree Akshar Purshottami Sanstha

23-43 Ivor Road
Sparkhill
Birmingham

Hindu Council of Birmingham

c/o Shree Geeta Bhavan Mandir
107–115 Heathfield Road
Birminmgham B19 1YL
The Council represents the Hindu Community in Birmingham, both in the wider community and with the local authority, as a body recognised by the City Council. It has a paid officer and around fifty affiliated organisations. It consult with the community and represent it on both religious and community matters.

Hindu Mission (UK)

13 Leyton Road
Birmingham

Hindu Swayamsevak Sangh

22 Pipson Road
Sparkhill
Birmingham B11
Tel: 021-773-2214
Contact: Mr Ramesh Shah

Indian Cultural Centre

360 Soho Road
Birmingham B21

ISKCON Birmingham

84 Stanmore Road
Edgbaston
Birmingham B16 9BT
Tel: 021-420-4999
Contact: Govinda Bhasya

Office: Temple President

A place of worship and meditation where one can discover the timeless wisdom of the Vedas. These ancient scriptures provide flawless knowledge on all subject matters so that mankind may live simply, think highly and progress steadily towards the goal of life - pure love of God. Programmes are held every Sunday 3.00pm-6.00pm with meditation, a Bhagavad-Gita discussion group and a vegetarian feast. Books and religious artefacts are available and the centre can also provide lectures for colleges, schools and other institutions. Groups are welcome by prior arrangement. The centre also serves as a base for "Food For Life" which distributes free meals to the homeless in the inner-city.

Kalyan Ashram Trust Aid Committee

17 Victoria Road
Birmingham B23

Kalyan Ashram Trust Aid Committee

32 Fernley Road
Birmingham B11

Lohana Association

65 Yardley Wood Road
Birmingham B13

Mabarun Hindu Cultural Association

132 Alexander Road
Acocks Green
Birmingham B27 6HB
Contact: P K Deb

Shree Gita Bhavan and Charitable Trust

107-115 Heathfield Road
Handsworth
Birmingham B19 1HE
Tel: 021-554-4120
Contact: Mr Gupta
Office: General Secretary

Place of worship and community centre. A temple with two learned priests who have a thorough knowledge of Hinduism. Daily preaching and acts of worship are performed. A magazine on Hinduism is published annually. Hindu weddings are often held. There is a youth club; cultural and religious library; mother tongue teaching in school and a women's group. Cultural activities take place. The temple welcomes parties of visitors.

Shree Hindu Community Centre and Temple

541a Warwick Road
Tysley
Birmingham B11 2JP
Tel: 021-707-3154
Tel: 021-772-4277 (home)
Contact: P A Amin
Office: President

Place of worship and community centre. The organisation aims to promote Hindu culture and to improve the quality of life of the members and the local community by facilitating activities and promoting harmony amongst the multi-cultural and multi-racial society. The premises consist of a temple, priest's residence, multi-purpose hall, community kitchen, auditorium, employment resource centre and play group room. Activities are religious, cultural, social, recreational, educational, and welfare for all including youth, women, elderly and toddlers.

Shree Krishna Mandir

Henley Street
Sparkbrook
Birmingham
Tel: 021-230-5610
Contact: Mr Dinesh Chauhan

Shree Ram Mandir

8 Walford Road
Sparkhill
Birmingham B12
Tel: 021-773-5735
Contact: N V Gohil
Office: Secretary

Place of worship. Activities include sports for young people and religious services every morning and evening.

Shree Sorathia Prajapati (UK)

105 Brockhurst Rpad
Hodge Hill
Birmingham B36 8JE

Shree UK Luhar Gnati Mandal

1 Grogg Grove
Northfield
Birmingham B35 5HR

Shri Venkateswara (Bahaji Temple of the United Kingdom)

c/o 10 Slater street
Great Bridge

Tipton
West Midlands
Contact: Dr V P Narajan Rao

Swaminarayan Hindu Mission

Satsang Bhavan
23–43 Ivor Road
Sparkhill
Birmingham B11 4NR
Tel: 021-474-6811
Contact: Rameshbhai Joshi

Vedic Mission (Arya Samaj)

127 Frederick Road
Aston
Birmingham B6 6BP
Tel: 021-553-0236 (home)
Contact: Mr G Chandra
Office: President
Religious organisation. The Mission aims to enhance the Vedic dharma by achieving the following objectives, namely to: open and establish Vedic religious centres; offer facilities for religious functions and performance of all religious sacraments and rites; provide books and other literature on Arya Samaj, the Vedas and the Hindu religion; open Sunday schools for the younger children and to provide religious worship facilities. Religious worship is organised in a hired school hall. The "Aryan Voice" is published as a forum for introducing young people of marriageable age to each other.

Vishwa Hindu Parishad (Birmingham Branch)

208 Mansel Road
Small Heath
Birmingham B10 9NL (home)
Tel: 021-773-1985 (home)
Contact: Mr M T Parmar
Office: Chairperson
Local branch organisation. Activities include celebration of Holi, Navratri, Diwali, New Year, Play-scheme, Gujarati and Hindi classes, and teaching the Ramayana and Mahabharat.

Young Hindu Association

c/o Hindu Temple
Heathfield Road
Birmingham B20
Tel: 021-554-4120
Contact: K K Gupta
Office: General Secretary

Young Hindu Progressive Mandal

3 Parkside Road
Handsworth Wood
Birmingham B20

Bawa Balak Nath Ji Mandir

Proffitt Avenue
Coventry
West Midlands
Tel: 0203-686590

Hindu Temple Society

274 Stoney Stanton Road
Foleshill
Coventry CV6 5DJ
Tel: 0203-685898
Contact: S C Anand
Office: General Secretary
Place of worship. The temple has statues of Lord Rama, Sita, Laxman, Lord Krishna, Radha, Hanuman Ji, Shiv Ji Ling and Jagdhambe Mata Ji installed according to Vedic rituals. Activities include Hindi and music classes on Fridays and Arti and Bhajans every day. During the week lectures on Hinduism are delivered by the priest.

Institute of Indian Culture and Studies

16 Knoll Drive
Styvechale
Coventry
West Midlands
Tel: 0203-314266

Sanatan Dharam Hindu Temple

56 Mason Road
Foleshill
Coventry CV6 7FJ
Tel: 0203-685125
Tel: 0203-455984 (home)
Contact: Mr Ramesh Bhardwaj
Office: Secretary

Shree Kadwa Patidar Samaj (UK)

10 Cannon Close
Coventry
West Midlands

Shree Krishna Mandir

Harnel Lane West
Nr Halfords
Coventry CV1 4FB
Tel: 0203-256981
Contact: B G Garala
Office: Secretary

Shree Radha Krishna Cultural Centre (ISKCON)

Kingfield Road
Radford
Coventry
West Midlands
Tel: Haridas
Contact: 0203-555420 (home)
The temple offers a programme of worship, discussion and vegetarian refreshments each evening from 7.00pm-9.00pm (4.00pm-9.00pm on Sundays, including a Sunday School). The centre has a comprehensive library for the public and is open all day over the weekend. Guest speakers and cultural presentations are available for schools and community social organisations. Group visits can be arranged.

Shree Sorathia Prajaptisam

20 Brinklow Road
Coventry CV3 2HY
Contact: Mr H K Pakhamia

Shree Hindu Samaj Mandir

18 Salisbury Street
Off Walsall Road
Darlaston WS10 8BQ
Tel: 021-526-2344
Contact: Mr D Patel
Office: Co-ordinator
An organisation for worship and welfare activities.

Shree Krishna Temple and Gujarati Hindu Centre

Hope Street
Off Churchfield Street
Dudley DY2
Tel: 0384-253253
Contact: Mr R D Patel
Office: Secretary

Hindu Religious Association and Temple

10b High Street
Leamington Spa CV31 1LW
Tel: 0926-452247
Contact: Mr Tara
Office: Chairman
Place of worship. The organisation, run by volunteers, is about ten years old, and the temple situated in the town centre has existed for three years. The organisation welcomes school children and teachers who wish to learn about Hinduism (Krishna Consciousness). It celebrates festivals and holds regular Satsangs.

Shree Hindu Gujarati Samaj

366 Higham Lane
Weddington
Nuneaton
Warwickshire
Contact: Secretary
Place of worship and religious organisation which follows and worships Lord Swaminarayan. The majority of our worshippers come from the state of Gujarat in India. It is a charitable body and was established in 1977. Activities include the celebration of all Hindu festivals, sports club for youth and mother tongue teaching (Gujerati) generally for children under sixteen years (Sunday school).

Shree Kalyan Mandal

4 Kimbereley Road
Rugby CV21 2SU
Tel: 0788-573515
Contact: Mr Ambaram Mistry
Office: Chair
A place of worship and centre for Hindus where all religious festivals are celebrated and regular prayers are held daily.

Mahan Sabha

10 Church Way
Stirchley
Telford
Shropshire
Contact: Mr B Marjaria

Shree Hindu Mandir

139 Darlaston Road
Walsall WS1 4JL
Tel 0922-647428
Contact: Mr Patel

Shree Ram Mandir

Ford Street
Pleck
Walsall W52 9BU
Tel: 0922-724024

Hindu Samaj Mandas Temple

18 Salisbury Street
Wednesbury
West Midlands
Tel: 021-526-2344

Shree Krishna Mandir

25 Dilliars Walk
West Bromwich

West Midlands
Tel: 021-553-1163
Contact: Mr C O Patel

Shree Krishna Mandir
81 Old Meeting Street
West Bromwich B70 9SZ
Tel: 021-553-1144
Tel: 021-553-3860 (home)
Contact: President

Gujarati Centre
Mander Street
Wolverhampton
West Midlands

Hindu Association
54 Villiers Avenue
Bilston
Wolverhampton WV14 6QY
Tel: 0902-45277
Contact: Ms M Patel

Shri Krishan Mandir
123 Penn Road
Wolverhampton WV3 0DU
Tel: 0902-772416
Contact: Mr T R Bhardwaj
Office: Secretary
A purpose-built place of worship open every day
(except 1.00-4.00pm). It caters for five hundred
people for weddings or parties. Activities include
worship, marriage ceremonies, welfare of young and
old, counselling of the bereaved. Kitchen facilities are
available every Tuesday evening (7.00-9.00pm). The
temple opens for Bhandhar (food) specially prepared
by a particular family. Bhajans are sung for two hours
by the Devotees or special parties invited by the host.

Sri Ram Krishna Temple
39 Wellington Road
Bilston
Wolverhampton
West Midlands

EAST ANGLIA

Bharat Hindu Samaj
Rock Road
Peterborough
Cambridgeshire
Contact: Mr Joshi
Office: Treasurer

SOUTH EAST ENGLAND (NORTH)

Basildon Hindu Association
69 Wickham Place
Basildon
Essex
Contact: Mr Amalani
Office: President

Hindu Society of Bedford
105 Wentworth Drive
Bedford
Contact: Dr Khiani

Jan Kshatriya Sevak Mandal (UK)
32 Mount Pleasant Road
Chigwell
Essex IG7 5ER
Contact: B N D Vadher
Office: Secretary
Affiliated to the Hindu Council (Brent).

Shree Matyia Patidar Samaj (UK)
6 Berkely Court
Mayfare
Croxley Green
Hertfordshire

Luton Bhartiya Association
10 Backwood Avenue
Dunstable
Bedfordshire

Vishwakarma Association
50a Brookhill Road
East Barnet
Hertfordshire EN4 8SL
Tel: 081-447-0049
Contact: Mr Rajni Bakrania
Office: Secretary
Affiliated to the Hindu Council (Brent).

Brahmin Society - North London
17 Argyll Road
Edgware
Middlesex HA8 5HB
Tel: 081-951-3840 (home)
Contact: Mr Kamlesh Rajyaguru
Office: Secretary
Affiliated to the Hindu Council (Brent).

United Sports Club

77 Bilton Road
Perivale
Greenford
Middlesex UB6 7BB
Tel: 081-998-4609 (home)
Contact: Mrs Taraben Patel
Office: Secretary
Affiliated to the Hindu Council (Brent).

Middlesex Eckankar Satsang Society

124 Elthorne Avenue
Hanwell
Middlesex W7
Contact: Mr and Mrs Grewal

Cutch Social and Cultural Society

26 St. Paul's Avenue
Kenton
Harrow
Middlesex HA3 9PS
Tel: 081-204-6488 (home)
Contact: Mr Jethalal Savani
Office: Secretary
Affiliated to the Hindu Council (Brent).

Harrow Lohana Education Group

287a Kenton Lane
Harrow
Middlesex HA3 8RR (home)
A voluntary membership group concerned with
Gujarati language, Hindu religion and Indian music
and dance. It aims to preserve its linguistic, religious,
cultural, social and educational heritage and is
concerned about the implications of practising its faith
in western society. Its activities are therefore aimed at
preserving these riches and roots whilst remaining
within the mainstream of British society. It runs
Sunday morning classes at the Canons High School,
Shaldon Road, Edgware for about two hundred and
fifty children in the Hindu religion, Gujarati language
and Indian dance and music. It also helps to prepare
students for GCSE and other examinations and holds
seminars, book displays, debates, discussions and
fund-raising activities for charities.

Hindu Swayamsewak Sangh

31 Devonshire Road
Harrow
Middlesex HA1 4LS
Tel: 081-863-1042
Contact: Mr Jayantibhai Patel
Office: Secretary
Affiliated to the Hindu Council (Brent).

Kadwa Patidar Samaj UK

41 The Ridgeway
Kenton
Harrow
Middlesex HA3 0LN
Tel: 081-907-0832 (home)
Contact: Miss Hansaben Kansagra
Office: Secretary
Affiliated to the Hindu Council (Brent).

Kingsbury Asian Elders Group

305 Byron Road
Wealdstone
Harrow
Middlesex HA3 7TE
Tel: 081-427-2594 (work)
Tel: 081-863-3847 (home)
Contact: Mr Dhirubhai Lavingia
Office: Secretary
Affiliated to the Hindu Council (Brent) and the Brent
Indian Association. The group meets at the Chalkhill
Youth and Community Centre, Poplar Grove, off
Barnhill Road, Wembley, Middlesex

Kutch Madhapar Karyalaya UK

31 Ruskin Gardens
Kenton
Harrow
Middlesex HA3 9PX
Contact: Mr Harilal Murji Halai
Office: Chairman
Affiliated to the Hindu Council (Brent).

Maharashtra Mandal (London)

59 Preston Hill
Harrow
Middlesex

Milip Mandal

21 Kynaston Wood
Harrow
Middlesex

Navnat Vanik Mandal

10 Radley Gardens
Kenton
Harrow
Middlesex

Pushtimargiya Vaishnav - Mahila Samaj

Charnwood
147 Uxbridge Road
Harrow
Middlesex HA3 6DG

Tel: 081-954-2142 (home)
Contact: Madhuben Somani
Office: Secretary
Affiliated to the Hindu Council (Brent).

Rajput Seva Samaj

3 Darcy Gardens
Kenton
Harrow
Middlesex
Contact: Rasik Vaghel
Office: President
Affiliated to the Hindu Council (Brent).

Ram Nivas - Gujrat Vaishnav Mandal

26 Greenhill Way
Harrow
Middlesex

Samanvaya Parivar

69 Marlborough Hill
Harrow
Middlesex HA1 1TZ
Tel: 081-427-4494 (home)
Contact: Mr Lalitbhai Thakkar
Office: Secretary
Affiliated to the Hindu Council (Brent).

Shree Madhavashram

1 Chapman Crescent
off Kenton Road
Kenton
Harrow
Middlesex HA3 0TU
Tel: 081-459-0275 (work)
Tel: 081-204-9233 (home)
Contact: J M Patel

Swaminarayan Temple

3 Vaughan Road
Harrow
Middlesex
Tel: 081-422-3337

Vanza Society of North London

95 Northumberland Avenue
Harrow
Middlesex HA2 7RA
Tel: 081-866-7264
Contact: Mr Kishor Davdra
Office: Secretary
Affiliated to the Hindu Council (Brent).

Young Lohana Association

106 Emsleigh Avenue
Kenton
Harrow
Middlesex HA3 8JA
Contact: Mr Sunil Radia
Office: Secretary
Affiliated to the Hindu Council (Brent).

Kshatriya Sabha (London)

90 North Hyde Road
Hayes
Middlesex

Sarvajanik Pragati Mandal

22 Commonwealth Avenue
Hayes
Middlesex
Tel: 081-561-7395
Contact: Mr Suresh Patel
Office: Secretary
Affiliated to the Hindu Council (Brent).

Shree Gurjar Kshatriya Ganati Mandal (London)

50 Spencer Avenue
Hayes
Middlesex UB4 0QY

Shree Limbachia Gnati Mandal

3 Strone Way
Yeading
Hayes
Middlesex UB4 9RU
Contact: Mr Mahendra Solankee
Office: Secretary
Affiliated to the Hindu Council (Brent).

Hindu Cultural Society

170 Chairborough Road
High Wycombe
Buckinghamshire

Hindu Swayamsevak Sangh, Vikram Shakha

5 Rosemary Avenue
Hounslow
Middlesex TW4 7DE
Contact: Mr H Makwana
Boys club and youth activities

Sarvodaya Sangh

213 Wellington Road South
Hounslow

Middlesex TW4 5HA
Tel: 081-572-6084 (home)
Contact: Mr Damjibhai Limbachia
Office: Secretary
Affiliated to the Hindu Council (Brent).

Shree Lohana Youth Mandal (Southall)

116 St. Stephen's Road
Hounslow
Middlesex

Shree Sorathia Prajapati Community

80 Berkeley Avenue
Cranford
Hounslow
Middlesex TW4 6LA
Contact: Mr N G Pankhania
Office: Honarary Secretary
Membership Group. Aims to advance the Gujarati language and culture and Hindu religion. Activities include youth and family groups for welfare, sports and cultural activities.

Shree Sorathia Prajapati Youth Community

12 Laburnam Road
Hounslow
Middlesex
Tel: 081-577-0986

Vedic Mission

15 Spring Grove Crescent
Hounslow
Middlesex

Vedic Mission (Arya Samaj) London

14 Penderel Road
Hounslow
Middlesex

Visva Adhyatmik Sanathan

48 Sutton Lane
Hounslow
Middlesex TW3 3BD
Tel: 081-572-9227
Contact: Mr B K Sidher
Office: Joint Secretary
Community centre. Provides facilities for a range of activities for youth, women, the needy, the disabled and for education.

Vishwa Hindu Parishad/Sanatana International (UK)

53 Manor Avenue
Hounslow
Middlesex TW4 7JN
Tel: 081-572-2784 (home)
Contact: Mr Gian Gaur
Office: Secretary
The organisation aims to: maintain cultural heritage and thereby enhance it and to worship and celebrate many religious and social occasions; advance the Hindu religion and provide a central place of worship; offer facilities for religious functions; arrange lectures and discussions on Hindu religion and to provide facilities for teaching of mother tongue languages and library. It also aims to provide educational recreation, yoga, classical music facilities, and offer advice and information of various kinds.

West London Hindu Temple Trust

15 Waye Avenue
Cranford
Hounslow
Middlesex

Hindu Cultural Society

30 Heathdale Avenue
Hounslow West
Middlesex TW4 7HD
Tel: 081-570-1552 (home)
Contact: S R Rattan
Provides religious, cultural and social facilities to the Hindu Community.

Ilford Hindu Centre (Vishwa Hindu Parishad)

43 Cleveland Road
Ilford
Essex IG7 7EE
Tel: 081-553-5471
Contact: Mrs L K Gautam
Office: Secretary
Place of worship. The main aim of the organisation, Vishwa Hindu Parishad, is to unite all Hindus under one umbrella. It seeks to expand and propagate the Hindu Dharma (way of life) to youth, widening their awareness to the spiritual side of the "oneness" of the whole universe. It also aims to solve socio–religious problems of the Hindu community in the UK. Religious gatherings are organised to celebrate various Hindu festivals and other milestones in the long and glorious history of the Hindus. Mother tongue teaching classes are held regularly for youths. Facilities are provided for learning Indian classical music. There

is a matrimonial service. The organisation is involved with welfare work amongst orphans from time to time.

London Hindu Sanghan
398 Thorold Road
Ilford
Essex IG1 4HF

National Association of Patidar Samaj (E London)
53 Green Lane
Ilford
Essex

Bardai Brahmin Samaj London
79 Buttermere Place
Linden Lea
Leavesden
Hertfordshire WD2 7DW
Tel: 0923-670911 (home)
Contact: Mr Bipin Thanki
Office: Secretary
Affiliated to the Hindu Council (Brent).

Southend and District Hindu Association
10 Stonehill Close
Leigh-on-Sea
Essex SS9 4AZ
Tel: 0702-348944 Ext 6408 (work)
Tel: 0702-524851 (home)
Contact: Mr M D Solanki

Athia Samaj
120 Benson Close
Luton LU3 3QR
Contact: Mr Dhirajlal Makan
Office: Secretary
Affiliated to the Hindu Council (Brent).

Hindu Mandir/Centre
Hereford Road
Luton LU4 0PS

Hindu Temple
Cardigan Road
Luton
Bedfordshire

Luton Bharatiya Association
10 Clifton Road
Luton
Bedfordshire

Luton Bharatiya Association
78 Stanton Road
Luton LU4 0BJ

Satsang Mandal
56 Leyhill Drive
Luton
Bedfordshire

Shree Sanatan Seva Samaj Hindu Mandir/Centre
Hereford Road
Lewsey Farm
Luton LU4 0PS
Tel: 0582-663414
Contact: Mr M M Gandhi
Office: President
A place of worship and community centre for religious, cultural, educational, social and recreational activities including the celebration of Hindu festivals, religious discourses, music, dance and performing arts and Gujarati, music and dance classes. The centre is used for weddings and engagements. Two services (morning and evening) are held.

Sanatan Dharma Vedanta Mandir
35 Crosslands
Stantonbury
Milton Keynes
Buckinghamshire MK14 6AY
Tel: 0908-318711
Contact: Mrs Pushpa Pandit
Office: President
A Hindu organisation and registered charity whose main activities are arranging Hindu religious, cultural and social functions for the benefit of Hindus in Milton Keynes and the surrounding areas. Steps are being taken to build a traditional Hindu Temple. The functions are open to all communities. Activities include arranging religious festivals and Hindu cultural programmes and running language, music and dancing classes.

Chovis Gam Patidar Samaj UK
69 Lancaster Road
Northolt
Middlesex UB5 4TD
Tel: 081-423-1986 (home)
Contact: Mr Indravadan Patel
Office: Secretary
Affiliated to the Hindu Council (Brent).

Panch Gam Union (POSON UK)

17 Manor Avenue
Northolt
Middlesex UB5 5BZ
Contact: Mr C C Patel
Office: President
Affiliated to the Hindu Council (Brent).

Malawi Hindu Association

8 Woodgate Crescent
Northwood
Middlesex HA6 3RB
Tel: 09238-26842 (home)
Contact: Mr N H Thakrar
Office: Secretary
Affiliated to the Hindu Council (Brent).

Lohana Community North London

50 Argyle Road
North Harrow
Middlesex HA2 7AJ
Contact: Mr Jamnadas Raithatha
Office: Secretary
Affiliated to the Hindu Council (Brent).

Matiya Patidar Samaj

122 East Lane
North Wembley
Middlesex HA0 3NL
Tel: 081-904-2380 (home)
Contact: Mr Bipik Uka
Office: Secretary
Affiliated to the Hindu Council (Brent).

SEVAK

Clifton Lodge
12 Pasture Road
North Wembley
Middlesex NA0 3JD
Tel: 081-908-0402 (home)
Contact: Mrs Kundan Gill
Office: Secretary
Affiliated to the Hindu Council (Brent).

Berkshire Mandir

c/o St Bartholomew Church
72 London Road
Reading RG1 5AS
Tel: 0734-751291
Contact: Mr R Mall

Gujrat Samaj

8 Willowside
Woodley

Reading
Berkshire
Tel: 0734-697722
Contact: Mr T Desai
A well established membership group of fifteen years which sponsors lots of youth, women, worship, welfare, family and socialising activities. These includes sports clubs, prayers, outings and language classes. Main events and functions held about four times a year.

Reading Hare Krishna Society

56 George Street
Caversham
Reading RG4 8DH
Tel: 0734-471154
Contact: Steve Shiner
Office: Vice President
A branch of ISKCON which aims to bring spiritual knowledge to society and achieve unity and peace throughout the world, propagate a consciousness of Krishna, and bring members together for teaching a simpler, natural way of life. Everyone is welcome to the group and admission is free. Activities include Mantra meditation, bhakti yoga, music, philosophy, lectures, questions and answers and a vegetarian meal.

Reading Hindu Temple

343 Wokingham Road
Earley
Reading RG6 2EB
Tel: 0734-750356
Contact: Secretary

Essex Hindu Society UK

72 Billet Road
Romford
Essex RM6 5PP
Tel: 081-599-7106
Contact: Shri V Chuttoo
Office: President
A membership group which aims to promote Hinduism. Its activities include organising religious and cultural events.

Bharata Samaj

37 Stowe Crescent
Ruislip
Middlesex HA4 7SR
Tel: 0895-676939
Contact: Dr B Bhargava
A religious organisation involved in educational,

community, cultural and religious activities and campaigns. It produces a newspaper and works for educational campaigns and community cohesion.

Hindu Cultural Society of Slough
Keele Drive
Slough
Berkshire
Tel: 0753-530686
Contact: Resident Priest
A religious organisation which runs the Hindu Temple which is open seven days a week for people wishing to pray, join in Satsang, religious lectures and devotional songs. A resident priest is there at all times.

Sarvodaya Bhajan Mandal
34 Wellesley Road
Slough
Berkshire

Saurashtra Leva Patel Samaj
87 Kendal Drive
Slough
Berkshire

Serena Memorial Hall
Burlington Road
Slough
Berkshire

Bhatia Association UK
60/62 Endsleigh Road
Southall
Middlesex UB2 5QN
Contact: President
Affiliated to the Hindu Council (Brent).

Brahmarishi Mission (International)
114 Hammond Road
Southall
Middlesex UB2
Tel: 081-571-3879
Fax: 0895-233633 ring first (home)
Contact: S C Sang
Office: General Secretary and Trustee
An organisation well established in India, the UK, Holland, Canada and the USA. The head of the organisation is H H Brahmarishi Shri Vishvatma and its teachings are based on the universal brotherhood of mankind derived from the Vedanta and Sankhya philosophy, with authentic references from the Vedas, Uphanishads, Geeta and Ramayana. Training is provided in Bhakti Yoga, Gnan Yoga, Karma Yoga and Hatha Yoga. Karamkand and cultural awareness

service is provided by a qualified acharya and astrologer. Meetings and lectures are held weekly on Fridays.

Durga Ma Vidyalya
17 Elmfield Road
Southall
Middlesex
Tel: 081-574-0016

Hindu Cultural Society
17 St Crispin Close
Southall
Middlesex

Shree Baba Balaknathji Temple
51 Orchard Road
Southall
Middlesex

Shree Ram Mandir
22 King Street
Southall
Middlesex UB2
Tel: 081-574-5376
Contact: Mrs S Whig
Office: Trustee/co-ordinator

Shree Sanatan Dharma Mandal
125 Cranleigh Gardens
Southall
Middlesex

Shree Sorathia Prajapati Youth Mandal (Southall)
162 Hambrough Road
Southall
Middlesex

Shree Sorthia Prajapati Community (Southall)
14 Hartington Road
Southall
Middlesex UB2 5AU

Shree Vishwa Hindu Mandir
2 Lady Margaret Road
Southall
Middlesex UB1 2RA
Tel: 081-574-3870
Contact: Mr R P Verma
Office: General Secretary
A place of worship and registered charity providing for

the community social and welfare services to further the scope of its constitution. Activities include free mother tongue teaching, training and practice of music and dance, advice on immigration and welfare problems and celebration of Hindu religious festivals.

Shri Krishan Sewa Ashram

15 Elmfield Road
Southall
Middlesex
Tel: 081-571-6931

Southall Hindu Cultural Society

82 Saxon Road
Southall
Middlesex UB1 1QJ
Tel: 081-574-6079
Contact: B D Mohan
Office: Hon General Secretary
The society runs Hindi and Sanskrit classes, organises lectures, debates and talks on Hinduism; trains people to work as Purohits; organises Havans at the premises and elsewhere and provides a priest for Hindu ceremonies.

Hare Krishna Centre (ISKCON Romford)

24 Alexandra Road
South Hornchurch
Essex RM13 7AA
Tel: 0708-553147
Contact: Jayadeva Das
A place of worship where visitors can experience the tranquil yet vibrant atmosphere generated through meditation on the Maha Mantra: (Hare Krishna, Hare Krishna, Krishna Krishna Hare Hare/Hare Rama Hare Rama, Rama Rama, Hare Hare). This prayer is sung congregationally and chanted privately on beads. Activities include weekly worship, study groups and food distribution. Guest speakers and group visits can also be arranged.

Gujarati Arya Association

24 Formby Avenue
Stanmore
Middlesex HA7 2JZ
Tel: 081-907-1014
Contact: Mr Narottamdas Champaneri
Office: Secretary
Affiliated to the Hindu Council (Brent).

Kutch Leva Patel Community

58 Lamorna Grove
Stanmore
Middlesex

Tel: 081-951-3405 (home)
Contact: Mr Virjibhai Varsani
Office: Secretary
Affiliated to the Hindu Council (Brent).

Prajapati Association

30 Morley Crescent West
Stanmore
Middlesex HA7 2LW
Tel: 081-907-5086
Contact: Mr Jayantilal Mistry
Office: Secretary
Affiliated to the Hindu Council (Brent).

Bavis Gam Patidar Samaj UK

950 Harrow Road
Sudbury
Middlesex HA0 2PY
Tel: 081-904-4936 (home)
Contact: Ms Shobhaben Patel
Office: Secretary
Affiliated to the Hindu Council (Brent).

Bhaktivedanta Manor (ISKCON)

Letchmore Heath
Watford WD2 8EP
Tel: 0923-857244
Contact: Receptionist
Set in the Hertfordshire countryside just beyond the bustle of London. Built at the turn of the century, its distinctive mock-Tudor style has made it a setting for several successful feature films. In 1973 it was purchased for the Society by former-Beatle George Harrison, and is now a residential theological college for more than fifty trainee priests. It has become the most important Hindu establishment in Britain, and on festival occasions such as Janmashtami attracts more than twenty thousand visitors. The magnificent shrine is acclaimed for its highest standards of cleanliness and devotion. There are seventeen acres of parkland, lake and gardens and a dozen cows graze peacefully on the pasture. The centre also includes a fully equipped theatre room, a colourful shop and the first Hindu school within the UK. Bhaktivedanta manor is open every day of the year from 7.00am-9.30pm, and everyone is welcome. Priests are available to perform weddings and other rites of passage. Organisations, school groups and parties are regularly catered for. With prior notice we can arrange conducted tours, cultural presentations, full traditional lunch and a range of academic programmes.

Vedic Centre of Understanding
63 Jubilee Road
Watford
Hertfordshire

Bavis Gam Samaj
24 St John's Road
Wembley
Middlesex HA9 7JQ
Tel: 081-903-8621 (home)
Contact: Mr Ravidnra Patel
Office: Secretary
Affiliated to the Hindu Council (Brent).

Chovis Gam Patidar Samaj
36 Mayfields
Wembley
Middlesex

Hindu Council (Brent)
7 The Leadings
Wembley Park
Middlesex HA9 9DT
Tel: 081-961-5444
Tel: 081-908-0192 (home)
Fax: 081-961-6811
Contact: Mr Venilal Vaghela
Office: Secretary General
An umbrella organisation with over fifty-three affiliated organisations. It aims to promote, advance, aid and support the propagation of Hindu philosophy of life and Hindu Dharma. Activities include printing, publishing, selling and gratuitously distributing Hindu religious and cultural literature and editing and publishing newsletters and journals. It also makes representations to the local or government authorities on all matters of common interest to Hindus.

Kalaniketan
31 Horsenden Crescent
Greenford
Middlesex UB6
Tel: 081-422-7647 (home)
Contact: Mr Mansukh Unadkat
Office: Secretary
Affiliated to the Hindu Council (Brent).

Lohana Community North London
130 Harrowdene Road
Wembley
Middlesex HA20 2JF

London Sevashram Sangha
19 Bassingham Road
Wembley
Middlesex

Mandhata Youth and Community Association
84 Swinderby Road
Wembley
Middlesex HA0 4SG
Tel: 081-903-4312
Contact: Mr Bharat Patel
Office: Secretary
Affiliated to the Hindu Council (Brent).

Palana Europe Society
47 Glendale Gardens
Wembley
Middlesex HA9 8PR
Tel: 081-904-5760 (home)
Contact: Mr Amritlal Patel
Office: Secretary
Affiliated to the Hindu Council (Brent).

Sanatan Seva Mandal
21 Dean Court
Wembley
Middlesex HA0 3PU
Tel: 081-904-1759
Fax: 071-603-0858
Contact: C D Pattni
Office: Chairperson
A registered charity with free membership. The organisation seeks to provide shelter, welfare and education to orphan and destitute children; relief of poverty in rural areas and relief work in the event of natural disasters. To carry out these activities the organisation, in association with its counterpart in India, runs a Boarding School and an Old Age home at Dwarka; a secondary school at Toopani and an eye clinic in Rajgir, Bihar, India. Every year it organises over thirty medical/eye camps giving medical relief and eyesight to thousands. It has provided relief supplies to flood and earthquake victims in India and given medical and educational aid to children in East Africa.

Sarvajanik Pragati Mandal
50 Clayton Avenue
Wembley
Middlesex HA0 4TL
Affiliated to the Hindu Council (Brent).

Saurashtra Leva Patel
20 Christhcurch Green
Wembley
Middlesex
Tel: 081–903–7968 (home)
Contact: Mr Kantilal Patel
Office: President
Affiliated to the Hindu Council (Brent).

Shakti Mandir
28 Talbot Road
Wembley
Middlesex

Shavika Satsang Mandal
12 Audrey Gardens
Wembley
Middlesex
Contact: Mrs V Dharani

Shree Satavis Gam Patidar Samaj (Europe)
11 Woodford Place
Wembley
Middlesex HA9 8TE

Vallabhnidhi UK
80 Ealing Road
Wembley
Middlesex HA0 4TH
Tel: 081–903–9195
Contact: Mr Nalinikant Pandya
Office: Secretary
Affiliated to the Hindu Council (Brent).

Vishwa Hindu Parishad Wembley
93 Swinderly Road
Wembley
Middlesex
Tel: 081–903–2466 (home)
Contact: Vinod Wadher
Office: Secretary
A membership group which aims to: consolidate and strengthen the Hindu society; protect, develop and spread the Hindu ethical and spiritual values of life; establish and reinforce contacts with and help the Hindu brethren living abroad; undertake missionary activities; found and maintain orphanages, rescue homes, homes for widows and old and infirm persons and arrange festivals, lectures promoting Hindu ideology. No age limit. Affiliated to the Hindu Council (Brent).

Wanza Samaj UK
7 The Leadings
Wembley Park
Middlesex HA9 9DT
Tel: 081–908–0192 (home)
Contact: Mr Venilal Vaghela
Office: Secretary
Affiliated to the Hindu Council (Brent).

Swaminarayan Hindu Mission
CIPRICE
Fanton Chase
Wickford
Essex SS11 8QX
Tel: 0268–765188
Contact: Bipinbhai Desai

LONDON (E POSTCODES)

Tower Hamlets Sanatan Association
37 Noble Court
Cable Street
London E1 8HS
Tel: 071–481–9707
Tel: 081–550–2846 (home)
Contact: Mr P K R Chowdhury
Office: General Secretary
Membership group. A voluntary organisation and registered charity. It was founded in 1983 for the promotion of cultural, social and general welfare of Hindu people living in Tower Hamlets and neighbouring London boroughs. The Association celebrates Durga Puja and Dusserah, Kali Puja and Diwali and other Hindu festivals every year. Other activities include the celebration of Hindu religious and cultural festivals as well as supplementary education and welfare advice.

Hackney Hindu Council
498 Kingsland Road
Hackney
London E4

Shree Kutch Leva Patel Community UK (Newham)
35 Heigham Road
East Ham
London E6 2JL
Tel: 081–471–4760
Contact: Mrs V Patel
Office: Secretary

Shree Narayana Guru Mission of the UK
6 St Olaves Road
East Ham
London E6 2PM
Tel: 081-552-5289 (home)
Contact: Mr K C Ashok Kumar
Office: General Secretary
Membership group. The group aims to propagate the principles and teachings of Sri Narayana Guru, to impart all kinds of social welfare services including child welfare. It aims to keep a good morality among the new generations, considering the whole of humanity as a single community. It meets at the Trinity Centre, East Avenue, London E12.

Aarti Society
37 Dunbar Road
Forest Gate
London E7 9HH
Tel: 081-472-2718
Contact: Mrs R J Patel

Balak Mahan Vidhyala
102 Osborne Road
Forest Gate
London E7 0PL
Tel: 081-519-0619
Contact: Mr B S Gahir

Hindu Swayamsevak Sangh (Newham)
20 Sprowston Road
Forest Gate
London E7 8HZ
Tel: 081-471-4647 (home)
Contact: Mr H Bhudia
Meets at the Upton Centre, Claude Road, Plaistow, London E13.

Shree Kutch Swaminarayan Temple
22-24 Shaftsbury Road
Forest Gate
London E7 8PD
Tel: 081-470-9375
Contact: Mr Shamjavay

Bavis Gam Patidar Samaj UK
76 Leslie Road
Leytonstone
London E11 4HG

Lakshmi Narayana Trust
202 Browning Road
Manor Park
London E12 6NX

Tel: 081-471-3430
Contact: Dr P Alagrajah
Office: Chairperson

London Sri Murugan Temple
78 Church Road
Manor Park
London E12 6AF
Tel: 081-478-8433
Contact: Mr Sampathkumer

Mahalakshmi Temple
272 High Street North
Manor Park
London E12 6SA
Tel: 081-552-5082
Contact: Dr P A Alagrajah

East London and Essex Brahma Samaj
Upton Centre
Off Bishops Avenue
Claude Road
Plaistow
London E13 0PU

Lohana Community East London
110 Howards Road
Plaistow
London E13 8AY
Contact: Mr Swesh Tejwah

Shree Swaminarayan Hindu Mission UK (Newham)
1a Lucas Avenue
Plaistow
London E13 0QP
Tel: 081-472-3795 (home)
Contact: Mr S C Amin
Office: Secretary

Upton Community Centre
Upton Park
London E13 0PU
Tel: 081-552-8647
Contact: Mr Hamant
Used by many Hindu groups.

Vishwa Hindu Parishad (Newham Branch)
518 Green Street
Plaistow
London E13 9DA
Contact: Mr D P Sharma

Radha Krishna Temple and Hindu Centre (E. London)

5 Cedars Road
Stratford
London E15 4NE
Tel: 081-534-8879
Contact: Mr B Goyal
Office: Secretary
Place of worship also offering a welfare service and cultural activities.

London Brahma Samaj

3 Glenovern Lodge
Landsdowne Road
South Woodford
London E18

LONDON (N POSTCODES)

Shree Aden Depala Mitra Mandal (UK)

67a Church Lane
London N2 8DR
Tel: 081-442-1552

Shree Aden Mandal

Church Lane
London N2
Tel: 081-444-2054

Highgate Temple

Basement Annexe
200a Archway Road
Highgate
London N6

Tamil Hindu Association

200 Archway Road
Archway
London N6

Krishna Yoga Mandir

57 Balham Road
Edmonton
London N9 7AH
Tel: 081-363-9187
Contact: Pandit K C Krishnatreya
Office: Founder
Sanatan Vedic Hindu scriptural research institute. The main emphasis is on scriptural learning – learning Vedas, Puranas, Smriti-Shastras, Itihasas (Ramayana and Mahabharata) as a means of realising Sachchidanand Swaroop Parameshwara (Supreme Lord attributed as Absolute Truth, Infinate Consciousness, and Everlasting Bliss) through Yoga of Surrender, learning, and service to the Lord and his creation. Activities include teaching Hinduism, conducting rituals and distributing literature on Hinduism.

Hindu Cultural Society

321 Coney Hatch Lane
Friern Barnet
London N11

Hackney Gujarati Samaj

22 Lynmouth Road
London N12 6XL

Bhadran Bandhu Samaj (UK)

2 Connaught Gardens
London N13

Sanatan Hindu Mandir

102 Junction Road
Archway
London N19 5GY
Tel: 071-263-6269
Contact: RG Amin
Office: Co-ordinator
This is a Sanatan (Eternal Truth) Hindu Mandir (Temple), a place of worship for anyone who likes to follow. All the religious days are observed and celebrated and there is daily puja and Aarti – Morning Aarti is at 9.30am; noon Aarti is at 11.30am; and evening Aarti is at 6.30pm. The temple is open, Monday to Sunday 9.00am-7.00pm.

LONDON (NW POSTCODES)

Sojitra Samaj

21 Gainsborough Gardens
London NW1 9BJ

Kshatriya Association UK

2a Villiers Road
London NW2 5PH
Contact: Mr Anil Mohanlal
Office: Secretary
Affiliated to the Hindu Council (Brent).

Maharashtra Mandal (London)

306 Dollis Hill Lane
London NW2 6HH
Tel 081-450-5009

Sattavis Gam Patidar Samaj
52 Dersingham Road
Cricklewood
London NW2 1SL
Tel: 081–452–3561 (home)
Contact: Mr Ashokumar Patel
Office: Secretary
Affiliated to the Hindu Council (Brent).

Shishukunj
98 Chaplin Road
London NW2 5PR
Tel: 081–459–1545
Contact: Mr Ashokbhai Shah
Office: President
Affiliated to the Hindu Council (Brent).

Shree Cutch Leva Patel Community (UK)
43 Chaplin Road
London NW2

Shree Sanatan Dharma Trust
12 Sidmouth Road
London NW2

Shri Swaminarayan Temple
220–222 Willesden Lane
London NW2
Tel: 081–459–4506
Tel: 081–451–1763

Krishna Centre
4 Carlingford Road
London NW3
Contact: Secretary

Brahmin Centre North London
10 Holders Hill Drive
London NW4 1NL
Tel: 081–203–3053
Contact: Mr T H Vyas

Karamsad Samaj
70 Great North Way
Hendon
London NW4 1HS

Swaminarayan Sidhant Sajeevan Mandal
3 Neeld Crescent
Hendon
London NW4

Hindu Centre London
39 Grafton Terrace
London NW5 4JA
Tel: 071–485–8200
Contact: President
A social, cultural and religious organisation. The centre aims to bring mutual understanding, unity and harmony between Eastern and Western thought. It provides facilities for Hindu religious ceremonies and arranges lectures and discussions on Hinduism.

North London Brahma Samaj
18 Hall Drive
London NW7

Shree Kadwa Patidar Samaj UK
117 Devonshire Road
London NW7 1EA

Anand Overseas Brotherhood
4 Winchester Avenue
Kingsbury
London NW9 9SY
Contact: Mr Ramesh Patel
Office: Secretary
Affiliated to the Hindu Council (Brent).

Bhakti Mandal
28 Silkfield Road
London NW9 6QU

Hindu Cultural Society (Youth Wing)
277 Salmon Street
London NW9 8YA
Tel: 081–205–5188 (home)
Contact: c/o Mrs P Bhargava
Office: Secretary

Maharashtra Mandal (London)
9 Talbot Court
Blackbird Hill
London NW9

Navnat Vanik Association of the United Kingdom
43 Burgess Avenue
London NW9 8TX
Tel: 081–205–0856 (home)
Contact: Mr Bhupendra J Shah
Office: General Secretary
Affiliated to the Hindu Council (Brent).

Parajiya Pattni Association
3 Adamas Close
Kingsbury
London NW9
Tel: 081-205-2675 (home)
Contact: Mr Kishore Pattni
Office: Secretary
Affiliated to the Hindu Council (Brent).

Sojitra Samaj
36 Byron Avenue
London NW9

Brahmbhatt Samaj
12 Bath Hurst Gardens
London NW10

Dharmaj Samaj
35 Landsdown Grove
London NW10 4RG

Mirzapur Association
37 Prout Grove
London NW10 1PU
Contact: Mr Veljibhai Hirani
Office: Secretary
Affiliated to the Hindu Council (Brent).

Shree Swaminarayan Temple
220 Willesden Lane
London NW10
Tel: 081-452-0388 (home)
Contact: Mr Hirani
Office: Secretary

Swaminarayan Hindu Mission
54/62 Meadow Garth
Off Brentfield Road
Neasden
London NW10 8HD
Tel: 081-965-2651
Tel: 081-445-6903 (home)
Contact: Dr R B Shah
Affiliated to the Hindu Council (Brent).

Willesden Asian Centre
9 Victoria Mansion
Grange Road
London NW10 2RG
Contact: Mr Girish Mehta
Office: President
Affiliated to the Hindu Council (Brent).

Asian Indian Society
23 Woodstock Road
Golders Green
London NW11

Shree Swaminarayan Hindu Temple
874 Finchley Road
Golders Green
London NW11

Shree Vishwakarma Association of UK
56 Ridge Hill
Golders Green
London NW11 8PS

Shri Sanatan Dharma Sabha (London)
36 Elmcroft Crescent
London NW11

LONDON (SE POSTCODES)

Hindu Mandir
51 Crescent Road
Plumstead
London SE18
Tel: 081-855-1148

Hindu Swayasevak Sangh
Woolwich Branch
27 Vicarage Park
Plumstead
London SE18
Tel: 081-854-4143

Shri-Kutch Swaminarayan Temple
7 Conway Road
Woolwich
London SE18
Tel: 081-854-3254

Shree Radha Krishna Cultural Centre (ISKCON)
42 Enmore Road
South Norwood
London SE25 5NG
Tel: 081-656-4296
Contact: Mr Nipan Malde
Office: Secretary
A temple with facilities for worship and welfare activities. A weekly programme, open to the public, is held every Sunday from 5.00-8.00pm. The Centre also features a shop selling books and religious artefacts

and can arrange guest speakers. Group visits from schools, colleges and other community groups are welcome by prior arrangement.

Swaminarayan Temple
St Margaret's Grove
Plumstead
London SE18 7RL
Tel: 081-854-0823

LONDON (SW POSTCODES)

Caribbean Hindu Society
16 Ostade Road
Brixton Hill
Lambeth
London SW2 2BB
Tel: 081-674-0755
Contact: Mr Ganesh Lall
Office: Co-ordinator
Place of worship and community centre. The society promotes Hindu religion and culture. It provides a place of worship which is open to the local community regardless of race or religion. In addition, there is also a community centre on the ground floor with cooking and games facilities for the young as well as the elderly. Classes in mother tongue languages, Indian music and dance and supplementary education are held during the weekend. Activities include youth, worship and education.

Radha-Krishna Temple
33 Balham High Road
London SW12
Tel: 081-673-6437
Contact: The Secretary
Has a woman's shelter/refuge.

Hindu Mission
1 Hepworth Road
London SW16

Hindu Sevika Samiti UK
10 De Mont Fort Road
London SW16 1L2
Contact: Mrs S Dave

Gujarat Samaj
35 Manville Road
London SW17

Gujarati Brahma Samaj
294 Franciscan Road
Tooting
London SW17
Tel: 081-672-1918
Contact: Mr J Thaker

Hindu Association
60 Brithwale Crescent
London SW17

Hindu Mission
60 Brithwale Crescent
London SW17

Hindu Society
673 Garrett Lane
London SW17 0PB
Tel: 081-944-0251
Contact: Mr Y K Buchar
Office: President
There is a Senior Citizens' Club every Thursday and Friday, for which the contact person is O P Phakey at the above telephone number and address. There are yoga classes every Tuesday evening, and every Sunday from 11.00am-1.00pm there are Hindi classes. Once or twice a month Havan is held from 6.00pm-9.00pm and festivals are celebrated.

Millan Asian Centre
57 Trinity Road
Tooting Bec
London SW17 7SD

Rajput Dhobi Youth
127 Hebdon Road
London SW17 7NL
Contact: Mr Umesh Solanki
Office: Secretary
Affiliated to the Hindu Council (Brent).

Virsad Union of UK
273 Balham High Road
London SW17 7BD

Brahma Samaj (Society) South London
131 Tranmere Road
Earlsfield
London SW18 3QP
Tel: 081-947-4709 (home)
Contact: L D Bhatt
Office: President
A membership group with two types of members: one

is an active membership among all types of Brahmins and the other is all Hindus at large who take part in the society's activities. The society is a social, cultural, religious and educational organisation which meets in hired halls to celebrate Hindu festivals.

Soaham Yogashram

90 Alma Road
London SW18

Vedanta Movement

13 Elsenham Street
London SW18 5UN
Tel: 081-874-6100 (home)
Contact: Mrs Iris Rafferty
Office: General secretary
Membership Group. The movement stands for the unity of all faiths; East-West cultural understanding; the realisation of brotherhood in society through spiritual communism; the blending of manual labour, intellectual work and spiritual activity; animal welfare and food reform on the basis of the unity of life, and a psycho-ethical system of spiritual practice which can be universally acceptable.

Hindu Association of Great Britain

8 Ashen Grove
London SW19

Shree Ganapathy Temple

125-133 Effra Road
Wimbledon
London SW19 8PU
Tel: 081-542-4141

Audichya Gadia Brahma Samaj Society (London)

85 Toynbee Road
Wimbledon
London SW20 8SJ

Hindu Association of Great Britain

76 Grand Drive
Raynes Park
London SW20

Nadiad Nagrik Mandal

18 Copse Hill
Wimbledon
London SW20

Sardar Patel Memorial Society

85 Toynbee Road
Wimbledon
London SW20 8SJ

LONDON (W POSTCODES)

Navkala

21 Hanway Place
London W1

Radha Krishna Temple

9/10 Soho Street
London W1V 5DA
Tel: 071-437-3662
Contact: Kasturi Majari dasi
Office: Secretary
Place of worship. An authentic Vedic style Temple with deities of Radha and Krishna, Jagannatha, Baladev, and Subhadra. The Temple is owned and run by ISKCON (the International Society for Krishna Consciousness) and is a base for their distribution of spiritual knowledge. The Society aims to cultivate pure loving devotion to God, incorporating all races/religions etc, based on the teachings of Vedic literature. Activities include deity worship, spiritual welfare, food distribution to the homeless and festival programmes for all important dates on the Vaisnava calendar. Visitors are welcome for daily worship, study and meditation from 4.30am-9.30pm. Group visits by prior arrangement. The centre can also provide guest speakers for schools, colleges and other community groups. Enquiries are welcome.

Iyengar Yoga Institute

223a Randolph Avenue
London W9 1NL
Tel: 071-624-3080
Contact: Mira Mehta
Office: Secretary
A yoga centre which aims to: advance public education in the classical teachings of the science of yoga; promote the advance for public benefit of the study and practice of yoga; support research into the therapeutic effects of yoga as a means of improving the mental and physical health of the community and to publish the useful results of such research. It has close liaison with the parent institute in Pune in India and classes are held at various levels. Activities include arranging training for teachers of yoga; workshops, lectures and seminars; liaising with similar bodies around the world and running a small library and bookstall.

Paramhansa Yogashram
33 Warrington Crescent
Maida Vale
London W9

Shanti Sadan Yoga Centre
29 Chepstow Villas
Notting Hill Gate
London W11 3DR
Tel: 071-727-7846
Fax: 071-792-9817
A meditation centre. "Shanti Sadan" is Sanskrit for "Temple of Inner Peace". It was founded in 1933 by Dr Hari Prasad Shastri, who died in 1956. His teachings are carried on here by his followers. These are on the philosophy and practice of Adhyatma Yoga, the Yoga of self-knowledge, as taught in the ancient Hindu classical texts, the Upanishads and Bhaghavad Gita and adapted to modern life. Lectures are held on Wednesdays and Fridays at 8.00pm during term time. The centre publishes over thirty books on Yoga and related subjects as well as the quarterly journal "Self-Knowledge". Lectures are also held at other venues in central London. Public lectures and meditation courses are free – there is a voluntary collection.

London Sevashram Sangha
99a Devonport Road
Shepherd's Bush
London W12 8PB
Tel: 081-749-272
Contact: Swami Nirliptanandaji
Office: Swami
Place of worship. It is a spiritual brotherhood of Sannyasis (monks), volunteer workers and devotees dedicated to the service of humanity. Founded in 1961 by Swami Purnandaji Maharaj, it is a registered charity and is non-sectarian, non-communal and non-political in outlook. There is a commitment to the exposition and interpretation of the philosophy of the Hindu scriptures as a guide to a sublime way of life and as a means to provide peace and spiritual tranquility and a consciousness of the self, in order to create a harmonious atmosphere in the present disturbed world society. The range of activities include: worship; guidance on meditation and philosophy of life, welfare advice and activities; Indian languages and drama; courses and lectures; interpreting service; youth activities; celebration of Hindu festivals and the publication of books.

Shree Akshar Purushottam Youth Organisation
143 Askew Road
London W12
Swaminarayan Hindus.

LONDON (WC POSTCODES)

Swaminarayan Hindu Mission
60 Bedford Court Mansions
Bedford Avenue
London WC1B 3AD

SOUTH EAST ENGLAND (SOUTH)

Lohana Community Association of Wandsworth
c/o 94 Croydon Road
Beckenham
Kent

Hindu Community
21 Woodlane Road
Brighton BN3 6HB

Medway Hindu Centre
71 Earnest Road
Chatham
Kent ME4 5PT
Contact: Mr R B Patel

Gurjar Hindu Union
29 Livingstone Road
Tilgate
Crawley
West Sussex CR10 5NS
Tel: 0293-548151
Contact: Mr U Nayee
Office: Honorary Secretary
Religious charity. It is presently in the process of building the first ever Hindu Cultural Centre with a Temple in the Southern part of the UK. This centre will cater for Sussex, Surrey and Kent. Activities include the celebration of Hindu festivals; sporting, religious and cultural activities, and close liaison with youth, schools and social services.

Swaminarayan Hindu Mission
17 Mendip Walk
West Green
Crawley
West Sussex RH11 7JZ

Tel: 0293-526825
Contact: Dhirajbhai K Patel

Bharatiya Sanskar Kendra
33 Goldwell Road
Thornton Heath
Croydon
Surrey CR4 6HZ
Tel: 081-681 1125
Contact: Mr Nitin Mehta

Global Sanskritik Cultural Society
24 Limes Road
Croydon
Surrey
Tel: 081-684-7298
Contact: Mr J Kharbanda
Office: Secretary

Hindu College London
c/o 50 Moreland Avenue
Croydon
Surrey CR0 6EA
Tel: 081-656-1835 (home)
Contact: Dr J C Sharma
Office: Principal
Educational charity. An educational institution in a collegiate, corporate and co-ordinating sense with a network of activities. It was set up to spread the knowledge and preserve the tradition of the Hindu Dharma and culture. The activities planned include Indian languages, music, art, culture and whatever else is associated with the Hindu way of life and the teaching of Hindu religion by correspondence worksheets and workshops to the second generation of Hindus in the UK, Europe and USA. A totally non-political organisation. The college aims to educate, publish, organise lectures and seminars and conduct examinations on the Hindu dharma and award certificates.

Hindu Swayamsevak Sangh
58 Greenwood Road
Mitcham
Croydon
Surrey CR4 1PE
Tel: 081-764-2805
Contact: Mr R A Shah

Oshwal Mahajanwadi
Corner of London Road and Campbell Road
Croydon
Surrey

Shree Radha Krishna Cultural Centre
London Road
Croydon
Surrey

Swaminarayan Hindu Mission
9 Gonville Road
Thornton Heath
Croydon
Surrey CR4 6DF
Contact: Sumanbhai Patel

Medway Hindu Sabha
361 Canterbury Street
Gillingham
Kent ME7 5XS
Tel: 0642-575654
Tel: 0634-403280
Contact: Mr S L Gupta
Office: Honorary Secretary
Place of worship. The main objective of the organisation is to promote the Hindu religion, help those who wish to embrace it and to explain the details and ideals of Hinduism. Members do Kirtan together, celebrate the main Hindu festivals and sort out family problems.

Sarvoday Hindu Association
c/o 243 Raeburn Ave
Kingston-upon-Thames
Surrey KT5 3DF
Tel: 081-390-3646
Contact: Mr H Desai
The association is concerned with the promotion of the welfare of the Asian community in and around Kingston.

Lohana Community (South London)
70 Heathfield Vale
Selsden
Surrey CR2 8AS
Tel: 081-651-4170 (home)
Contact: Narendra Chotai
Office: Secretary
The South London Lohana community is a membership group which has been established for seventeen years and promotes Indian culture and religion. A Gujarati school is also run in South London. Further details are given in a circular. Activities include the promotion of Indian culture and religion and a Gujarati school for youths.

Indian Welfare and Cultural Association Temple
130 Northumberland Road
Southampton
Hampshire

Swaminarayan Hindu Misssion
32 Basset Green Road
Southampton SU2 3DH
Tel: 0703-558678
Contact: Praful Patel

Vedic Society
75-165 Radcliff Road
Off Northam Road
Southampton SO2 0PS
Tel: 0703-632275
Contact: Secretary
Place of worship and religious and cultural organisation. A charity organisation classed as a Hindu Temple. Its approximate membership is five hundred and it is the largest purpose-built temple in the UK. Activities include worship, promotion of understanding between ethnic minorities, music classes, languages and reflexology.

Surrey Satsang Samiti
1 Newlyn House
Benhill Wood Road
Sutton
Surrey SM1 HHE
Tel: 081-643-0388
Contact: Jyoti Bhoyrul
Hymn singing organised regularly on Sunday afternoons.

Bhartiya Sanskar Kendra
33 Goldwell Road
Thornton Heath
Surrey

Lohana Union
21 Weybridge Road
Thornton Heath
Surrey

Surrey Gujarati Hindu Society
33 Galpins Road
Thornton Heath
Surrey
Tel: 081-674-8902 (home)
Contact: Rajni Patez
Office: Secretary
The society has been established since 1967 under Friendly Society Acts and its main activities are social, cultural and religious. It has no boundaries of caste or residence and is open to all Gujaratis. Other membership is accepted with approval of the committee. Its Annual General Meeting is held regularly in March/April and accounts are given to members. Accounts are also available for examination at the Public Record and the Registry of Friendly Societies.

Surrey Hindu Brotherhood
107 Broughton Road
Thornton Heath
Surrey

UK Valam Brahmin Association
68 Lucern Road
Thornton Heath
Surrey CR4
Contact: Mr B P Vyas
Office: President
Affiliated to the Hindu Council (Brent).

Greenwich Gujarati Samaj
46 Lulworth Road
Welling
Kent

Vishwa Hindu Parishad
40 Holmesdale Road
West Croydon
Surrey CR0 2LQ
Contact: R M Jhalla
Office: Secretary

Vishwa Hindu Parishad
45 Kidderminster Road
West Croydon
Surrey
Contact: Mr I M Patel
Office: Secretary

SOUTH WEST ENGLAND

ISKCON Bristol
KRSNA'S Shop
2 Perry Road
Bristol BS1 5BQ
Tel: 0275-853788
Contact: Minaketana
Office: Secretary
A small, colourful temple on the Clifton side of the City Centre. Programmes held every Sunday, 2.00pm-6.00pm with music, discussion and

vegetarian feast. Sunday school 2.00pm-4.00pm. Bhagavad-gita study course on Tuesday from 7.00pm-10.00pm. The centre arranges guest speakers from schools, colleges and interfaith groups. Small groups may also visit by prior arrangement.

Sanatan Deevya Mandal
163b Church Road
Redfield
Bristol BS5 9LA
Contact: Mr V Jethwa

Hindu Community Centre
64 Swindon Road
Cheltenham GL50 4AY
Tel: 0242-584250
Contact: President
A place of worship and community centre with daily worship and a multi-purpose hall downstairs which is used for marriage ceremonies, sports, and other activities. Activities include teaching of English and mother tongue language; sports and youth; classical dance teaching and musical instrument teaching.

Indian Association Cheltenham (Gloucestershire)
The Hindu Community Centre
64 Swindon Road
Cheltenham GL50 4AY
Tel: 0244-584250

Gloucester Hindu Centre
15 Cherston Court
Barnwood
Gloucester GL4 7LE
Tel: 0452-653314
Contact: Mr Lallu Patel
Office: Chair

Shree Kadwa Patidar Samaj (UK)
148 West Way
Broadstone
Poole BH18 9LN

Hindu Samaj, Swindon
33 Okebourne Park
Liden
Swindon SN3 6AH (home)
Contact: Mr P N Patel

Shree Lohana Mahajan
12 Thackeray Close
Liden
Swindon
Wiltshire

KEY TO TERMS IN HINDU ORGANISATIONAL TITLES

Note: This is not a complete glossary of significant Hindu terms. It is a guide to the meaning and/or background of some of the words used in the titles of Hindu organisations listed in this directory. More information on the italicised words can be tracked down elsewhere in the key and/or in the section on Introducing the Hindu Community by using the directory's Keyword Index.

Aarti

A variant Romanisation of *arti*. It means worship entailing the circling of light in front of the Temple's particular deity.

Aden

Aden in the Arabian Peninsula had a Gujarati Hindu community and its use in an organisation's title indicates this historical connection.

Adhyatmik

Meaning "spiritual".

Akshar

The name of one tradition within the *Swaminarayan* Hindu movement.

Andhra

Andra Pradesh is the name of one of the States of India. The term is sometimes used in the title of Telugu speaking Hindu organisations.

Anoopam

Hindi for "matchless" or "unique".

Arjuna

Sanskrit literally meaning "white". It is the name of the third of the five Pandava princes in the Hindu epic, the Mahabharata. He is called "white" because of the purity of his actions. Krishna acted as his charioteer on the battlefield of Kurukshetra and spoke the *Bhagavad Gita* to him on the first day of the battle in which he was originally unwilling to fight. Arjuna is seen among Hindus as an exemplary type of the spiritual seeker.

Arti

A variant Romanisation of *aarti* (see above).

Arya

Sanskrit for "Aryan". The Arya Samaj, founded by Swami Dayanand Saraswati, promotes a return to what it understands to have been the *Vedic* practice of worship without images.

Ashram

A Sanskrit word denoting a place of spiritual retreat, renewal and meditation. It can be anywhere that spiritual seekers gather and it might be a home, a monastery or another kind of building.

Aurobindo

Part of the name of Sri Aurobindo Ghose (or Ghosh), 1872-1950, a Hindu teacher who developed a system of what came to be called "integral *yoga*" which aimed to bring together the "ascent" of humanity to divinity with the "descent" of the divine into the material world. From 1920 onwards, he linked up with Mira Alfassa who later founded Auroville, in Pondicherry, India, where Aurobindo devotees live and where she is known simply as "the Mother".

Baba

A Hindi term of affectionate respect, used for elders and for some spiritual leaders.

Bajarang

Hindi for "healthy". Bajarangbali is a title of Hanuman, the monkey-headed god, servant of Rama.

Balak

Hindi for "child" or "boy".

Balaknathji

The name of a spiritual leader from the medieval period believed by his followers to be immortal and depicted as a semi-naked blue-skinned youth. He is worshipped by devotees and because of his emphasis on celibacy, females are prohibited from entering the sanctuary of his temples.

Bandhu

Hindi for "friend".

Bari

Hindi for "widow".

Bavis

Gujarati for "twenty-two".

Bhadran

The name of a town in Gujarat State, India.

Bawa

A variant Romanisation of *baba* (see above).

Bhagvad

Sanskrit word for "Lord" and found in the *Bhagvad Gita* (literally "Song of the Lord") a frequently referred to Hindu scripture.

Bhagwad

A variant Romanisation of *Bhagvad* (see above)

Bhagwan

Hindi for "God".

Bhai

Hindi for "brother".

Bhajan

Hindi for "devotional song".

Bhakti

Sanskrit/Hindi for "devotion". It is used to refer to those Hindu traditions which focus upon personal devotion to, and love of, God understood in terms of a supreme Personality. *Bhakti-Marga* is the Hindu path which entails devotion to a personal God.

Bhaktivedanta

Name of the Manor which is the headquarters of the International Society for Krishna Consciousness. A title for one who has realised the conclusion of the Vedas through devotional service, as in the name of Srila Bhaktivedanta Swami Prabhupada, the Society's founder.

Bharat

A Sanskrit and Hindi word for a king and saint in the *Bhagavata Purana* and also for his descendent *Bharata*, otherwise known as Arjuna (see above). India was originally named Bharatavarsha after him. Contemporary Indians refer to India as *Bharat*.

Bharata

A variant Romanisation of *Bharat* (see above).

Bharatiya

The Sanskrit and Hindi word for "Indian" - that which pertains to India.

Bhartiya

A variant Romanisation of *Bharatiya* (see above).

Bhavan

The Sanskrit and Hindi for "house".

Bhawan

A variant Romanisation of *bhavan* (see above).

Bodali

The name of a tribe.

Brahma

Sanskrit referring to the divine as creator of the universe. Brahma is one of the Hindu *trimurti* of Brahma, Vishnu and Shiva. Originally, Brahmanism was used as the name of one of the traditions of Hinduism, but which today is not as numerically significant as *Vaishnavism* and *Shaivism/Shaktism*. Brahma Samaj denotes Gujarati *Brahmin* (see below) caste organisations

Brahman

Pronounced as "Br*aa*hman", this refers to the priestly grouping among the four traditional *varna* of Hinduism (see below). Pronounced as "Brahman" it is the Sanskrit word for the eternal Absolute.

Brahmarishi

The title of a *Brahmana* who has performed great austerities to attain mystic powers and insight.

Brahmbhatt

A *Brahmin* surname.

Brahmin

A variant Romanisation of *Brahman* (see above).

Charotar

An area of Gujarat State in India and name of the community from that area.

Charotaria

That which pertains to *Charotar* (see above).

Chouis

Gujarati for "twenty-four".

Chovis

Variant Romanisation of *chouis* (see above).

Cutch

A part of the Indian state of Gujarat.

Darji

The name of an occupational *caste* associated with tailoring.

Dashashram

"Dash" is the Sanskrit/Hindi for "ten".

Deevya

Meaning "transcendental".

Depala

A name.

Dev

A male name and honorific title meaning "god".

Dham

A holy or sacred place.

Dharam

Hindi for "righteousness" and "religion" (see *dharma* below).

Dharma

The Sanskrit word literally meaning "intrinsic function", "holding" or "carrying" or that which sustains and determines the basic structures of existence, the basis of ethics, order and religion. Hindus call their religion the *Sanatana-Dharma*, the "eternal religion".

Dhamarj

The name of an Indian town.

Dhyanyoga

Dhyana is Sanskrit for "meditation" and "absorption" and used together with the word *yoga* it refers to one of the first three stages of Patanjali's classical system of *yoga* as a path by which *samadhi* can be attained.

Durga

Sanskrit meaning "unfathomable one". It is one of the oldest and most widely used names for the Divine mother, the consort of Shiva. Durga appears as the destroyer of ignorance. Durga also means "prison" and her role is also to keep conditioned souls in the material world.

Dwar

Meaning "gate".

Gadia

The name of a community.

Gadhia

Variant romanisation of *gadia* (see above).

Gam
Hindi for "village".

Ganapathy
Sanskrit variant name for Ganesha (or Ganesh), son of Shiva and Parvati. He is seen as a god of wisdom and as the remover of obstacles and bringer of success. He is celebrated in the Ganesh-Purana and is depicted as an elephant-headed god.

Ganati
Variant Romanisation of *gnati* (see below).

Gandhi
A Gujarati surname of a trading community. The name of Mohandas Karamchand Gandhi (1869-1948), known as the *Mahatma* (Sanskrit for "great soul"). Gandhi played a leading role in the Indian independence movement basing his actions upon the principles of *satyagraha* (Sanskrit literally meaning "holding fast to truth") and *ahimsa* (Sanskrit for "non-injury").

Gayatri
The Gayatri *mantra* is one of the most sacred of the verses of the *Rigveda*. Gayatri is also the name of the demi-goddess who presides over the mantra.

Geeta
Sanskrit/Hindi for "song". When used alone it usually refers to the *Bhagavad Gita* ("Song of the Lord"), although there are other *Gitas* like the *Ganesha- Gita*.

Gita
A variant Romanisation of *Geeta* (see above).

Gnati
Gujarati for "*caste*".

Guja
The name of a town in *Gujarat* (see below).

Gujarat
An Indian state on the west coast of India in which approximately seventy per cent of Britain's Hindus have ancestral origins.

Gujarati
Adjective referring to *Gujarat* (see above), especially used as a way of describing the mother tongue and ethnicity of people whose family roots are in Gujarat.
Gujerati

A variant Romanisation of *Gujarati* (see above).

Gujrat
A variant Romanisation of *Gujarat* (see above).

Guru
Sanskrit/Hindi for "teacher". It is especially used of a spiritual teacher or Master, although Hinduism traditionally recognises that one has different *gurus* in the four stages of life. One's first *gurus* are one's parents, then one's intellectual teachers, then one's spiritual Master, but also there is the god whom one worships who is one's ultimate *guru*. One's relationship with a *guru* should be characterised by trust in their wisdom.

Hare
It is the vocative form of *Hara*, another name for Radha (see entry below), the divine consort of Krishna and embodiment of *bhakti* (loving devotion). The word sometimes appears in the phrase "Hare Krishna Movement" as a way of referring to the International Society for Krishna Consciousness.

Haveli
Hindi for bungalow.

Hindi
The name of the official language of India and the mother tongue of many Hindus from the north of India. It is transcribed in the Devanagari script.

Istree
Hindi for "woman". It is often used in the title of women's organisations.

Iyengar
Used in the title of a form of *yoga* – *Iyengar Yoga*.

Jagriti
Hindi for "awake".

Jalaram
Appears in the name of Jalaram Bapa, a saintly trader in Virpur and devotee of Ram, especially revered by Gujarati Hindus.

Jan
Hindi meaning "people".

Jansari
The name of a community.

Jatiya
The name of a community.

Ji
A suffix used in conjunction with a name, denoting respect.

Kadwa
A Gujarati caste name for a section of the *Patidars* (see below).

Kala
Sanskrit for "art".

Kalaniketan
A place for performing arts.

Kali
Sanskrit meaning literally "the black one". It is the name of the consort of Shiva and and is the Divine Mother often represented either as dancing or in sexual union with Shiva. Kali particularly has devotees in West Bengal.

Kalyan
Hindi for "welfare".

Karamsad
The name of a town.

Kendra
Sanskrit for "centre", often used today of a place where Hindus meet.

Keshavashram
Keshav relates to Lord Krishna. For *ashram* see above.

Kisumu
A town in Kenya from which many Hindus came who migrated to Britain from East Africa.

Kripalu
Meaning "merciful".

Krishan
A variant Romanisation of *Krishna* (see below).

Krishna
Sanskrit meaning literally "dark blue" and also "all attractive". It is the name of the most celebrated Hindu deity who features in the *Bhagavad Gita* as the instructor of Arjuna (see above). In some Hindu traditions Krishna is seen as an *avatar* of Vishnu and in others, as the Supreme Deity Himself.

Krishnamurti
The name of a twentieth century philosopher.

Kshatriya
Sanskrit word for the second *varna* of Indian society. Often translated into English as "warrior", its duty was to protect the community. It is a term used by contemporary caste organisations within this community.

Kutch
A Roman alphabet variant of *Cutch* (see above) referring to an area of the Indian state of Gujarat.

Kutchi
An adjective referring to that which pertains to what orignates in *Kutch* (see above), for example, their culture or mother tongue.

Kutchhi
A variant Romanisation of *kutchi* (see above).

Lakshmi
Sanskrit for "fortune". The name of the consort of Vishnu, she is the goddess of fortune and prosperity. Although no temple is dedicated to her name alone, she is the object of much devotion among Hindus.

Laxmi
A variant Romanisation of *Lakshmi* (see above.)

Leuva
A variant romanisation of *Leva* (see below).

Leva
The name of a traditionally artisan *caste* associated with the *Patidars* and the *Patels,* many of whom follow the *Swaminaryan* (see below) movement.

Limbachaya
The name of a traditional "barber" occupational grouping.

Limbachia
A variant Romanisation of *Limbachaya* (see above).

Lohana

The name of a Gujarati *caste* traditionally associated with trading.

Luhar

The name of a *caste* traditionally associated with "blacksmithing".

Ma

Hindi for "mother", used of the leader of Auroville, founded on the basis of the teachings of *Sri Aurobindo* (see above). Also used as a title for any goddess.

Mahajan

The name of a *caste* based organisation which also means "great person".

Mahan

Sanskrit/Hindi for "great"

Mahatma

A title applied to Gandhi, meaning "great soul".

Maharashtra

The name of a state in India.

Mahila

Hindi for "woman".

Mandal

Hindi for "circle", often used as a way of describing a Hindu group or organisation.

Mandata

Variant romanisation of *Mandhata* (see above0.

Mandhata

A Gujarati *caste* name.

Mandir

Hindi for "temple".

Mandli

Hindi for "group" or "society", often used of Hindu organisations.

Matyia

The name of the Gujarati *caste* of Patels.

Mirpur

The name of a community from a district now in Azad Kashmir in Pakistan.

Mitra

Hindi for "friend", and also the name of the sun god and ruler of the day associated in the *Vedas* with Varuna, the ruler of the night.

Moksha

Sanskrit describing liberation from *samsara* and rebirth, seen by some Hindus as being the highest goal of life.

Muktyananda

The name of a Swami who lived 1908-1983. He followed *siddha-yoga*, the *yoga* of powers, and taught the identity of one's true Self with the Absolute Consciousness.

Murti

Hindi for the statues used in Hindu worship.

Murugan

The name of the son of Shiva (see below), brother of Ganesh (see above). He is particularly worshipped by Hindus from Tamil Nadu in India.

Nadiad

The name of a town in Gujarat.

Nagrik

Hindi for "municipal" or "citizen".

Nar

Sanskrit for "man".

Narayan

Sanskrit for "God", used of Vishnu.

Narayana

Variant Romanisation of *Narayan* (see above).

Nath

Hindi for "Lord". It is often found as part of a name, for example, Balaknath.

Nathji

See above for *Nath*. The suffix *ji* (see above) denotes respect.

Nav
Hindi for "new".

Navnat
Gujarati surname.

Nivas
Hindi/Sanskrit for "place of abode" or "residence".

Oshwal
The name of a Gujarati *caste* group.

Pancholi
A Gujarati surname and community.

Pandurang
The name of a Hindu saint.

Paramahansa
A spiritual title forming part of the name of Ramakrishna Paramahansa, a Bengali saint.

Parishad
Sanskrit/Hindi for "organisation", as for example, in Vishwa Hindu Parishad.

Parivar
Hindi for "family".

Patel
Name used by several Gujarati caste groups. It is often equivalent to *Patidar* (see below).

Patidar
The name of a Gujarati caste traditionally associated with agriculture.

Pij
The name of a town.

Pragati
Hindi for "progress".

Prajapati
Sanskrit for "Lord of creatures" or "Progenitor of creatures". It is used in the *Vedas* to refer to Indra and also other deities. The *Laws of Manu* refer to Prajapati as being *Brahman* in the role of the one who creates and sustains the universe. It is also a title used by a Gujarati *caste* traditionally associated with carpentry, members of which have names such as Mistry and Lad.

Prajnayama
Prajna is Sanskrit for "consciousness".

Pratinidhi
Hindi for "representative". Used, for example, in the organisational name Arya Pratinidhi Sabha, meaning "Hindu Representative Council" (see below for *sabha*).

Pravasi
Hindi for "traveller".

Punjabi
An adjective referring to that which pertains to the Punjab, a state in contemporary India. It is used of the mother tongue and culture of the people originating from this area which originally included land that is now part of the country of Pakistan.

Purnima
Hindi for "full moon".

Purushottam
Akshar Purushotam Sanstha is the name of one sector of the *Swaminarayan* movement.

Radha
The name of the eternal consort of Krishna (see above). Radha and Krishna are central in *Gaudiya Vaishnava* devotion where Radha is seen as the personification of Krishna's spiritual energy and the supreme form of devotion.

Rajput
Is the name of a *kshatriya caste* associated with the military.

Ram
Ram (or Rama) is the name of an *avatara* of Vishnu, appearing at the beginning of the *Treta Yuga* (the Hindu name for the second of the four ages, the current one being *Kali Yuga*). Rama is the hero of the *Ramayana* epic, the substantial authorship of which is attributed to the sage Valmiki (see below). He and his wife Sita are viewed as the ideal of husband and wife.

Rama
Alternative form of the name Ram (see above).

Ramakrishna
The name of a Bengali spiritual leader (1836-1886) worshipped by many as an *avatara* and who taught that

all religions lead to the realisation of God. One of his famous disciples was Swami Vivekananda. The Ramakrishna Mission is now a monastic order in the Shankara tradition of Hinduism, combining service to God with service to human beings in social activities for the sick, the homeless and other disadvantaged people. Vedanta Centres are founded by the Mission when monks visit at the invitation of local people.

Ramayan
Alternative version of the name *Ramayana* (see below).

Ramayana
Sanskrit for "the life story of Rama", the oldest epic in Sanskrit which is attributed to Valmiki. It consists of twenty-four thousand couplets arranged in seven *kanda* (or "chapters"). It tells the story of Rama and Sita, including Sita's abduction by Ravana, battle with demons, the return to Ayodhya, and their ascent into the spiritual realm.

Sabha
Hindi for "assembly", "conference" or "council".

Sadan
Hindi for "house".

Sahaja
Sanskrit for "natural". Truth is seen as being natural, whilst ignorance arises from the workings of the mind.

Sahit
Panjabi for "literature".

Sajeevan
Hindi for "alive".

Samaj
Sanskrit/Hindi for "society", as for example, in the organisation title Arya Samaj.

Samiti
Hindi for "committee".

Sanatan
Roman alphabet variant of Sanskrit/Hindi meaning "imperishable" or "eternal". Hindus call their religion *Sanatana Dharma* ("the eternal religion") to characterise their belief in its revealed and universal nature.

Sanatana
Variant Romanisation of *Sanatan* (see above).

Sanathan
Variant Romanisation of *Sanatan* (see above).

Sandesh
Hindi for "message". Used in the name of a magazine.

Sangh
Variant Romanisation of *sangha* (see below).

Sangam
Hindi for "confluence" or "joint".

Sangathan
Hindi for "jointly".

Sangha
Sanskrit/Hindi for a "crowd" or "group". Usually used in the Hindu context of a group of seekers who gather around a *guru* (see above) for teaching and spiritual enlightenment.

Sangit
Hindi for "music".

Sanskar
Refers to a "purificatory process".

Sanskritik
Sanskrit for "perfect" and "cultured". The language of Sanskrit is not a contemporary conversational language, but it is the sacred language of Hinduism in which all its major texts are composed. It has its own alphabet called *Devanagari*, from *deva* (meaning "god") and *nagari* (meaning "city"). Sanskrit is therefore thought of as the language that is spoken in the cities of the demi-gods.

Sansthan
Hindi for "institution".

Sant
Panjabi description of a charismatic religious leader.

Sardar
Panjabi for "chief", often used as equivalent of the title "mister".

Sarvoday

Hindi for "uplift of all". It is a term promoted by *Mahatma* Gandhi.

Sarvodaya

Variant Romanisation of *Sarvoday* (see above).

Sat

Sanskrit for "truth".

Satavis

Gujarati for "twenty-seven".

Satsang

From the Sanskrit *sat* (see above) meaning "truth" and *sang*, meaning "company" or "group". It is used in Hindi and Panjabi to describe a devotional group.

Sattavis

Variant Romanisation of *satavis* (see above).

Satya

Variant Romanisation of *sathya* (see above).

Seva

Hindi for "service". It can include reference to purely devotional service or to humanitarian service.

Sevak

Hindi for "one who performs service".

Sevashram

An *ashram* (see above) devoted to service.

Sewa

Variant Romanisation of *Seva* (see above).

Shakha

Sanskrit meaning "branch". It is used to describe a school of the *Vedas* which were originally transmitted orally and had a variety of *shakhas* or "schools" associated with each line of oral transmission.

Shakti

Sanskrit/Hindi for "power", "force" or "energy". It is the name for primal energy, venerated under different personal names in India - for example, Kali and Durga - as the consort of Shiva. Shakti is of particular importance in the *Tantra* path of Hinduism.

Shanti

Sanskrit for "peace".

Shikha

Hindi for "hair".

Shiva

Sanskrit literally meaning "the kind, friendly one", Shiva is the name of the third of the Hindu *trimurti* of Brahma, Vishnu and Shiva. Shiva is seen as the destroyer of ignorance. His symbol is a *linga* and he is often portrayed together with his wife Shakti whose symbol is a *yoni*, representations of the male and female sexual organs respectively. Their union is understood to have a transcendental meaning.

Shree

Sanskrit for "eminent one". An honorific title of respect used in front of the names of gods, saints, or teachers. Shree Nathji refers to a black representation of *Krishna* (see above), especially worshipped by the *Pushtimargis*.

Shri

Variant Romanisation of *Shree* (see above).

Shyam

Sanskrit for "dark" – an epithet for *Krishna* (see above).

Siddha

Sanskrit for "perfect" or "complete". In the *Puranas*, a *siddha* is a being of great power.

Sidhant

Hindi for "principle".

Sojitra

The name of a town.

Soni

The name of a Gujarati and Panjabi *caste* traditionally associated with goldsmithing.

Sorathia

The name of a Savrasta community in Gujarat.

Sorthia

Variant Romanisation of *sorathia* (see above).

Sri

Variant Romanisation of *shree* (see above).

Subhag
Hindi for "beautiful".

Swami
Sanskrit for "sir" or "lord". In general, it appears as an honorific title before the name of a teacher or holy person, especially those who are *sunnyasis* or renunciants.

Swaminarayan
Literally meaning "Lord God", it is the name of a Hindu movement (see "Introducing the Hindu Community") followed by a significant number of Gujarati Hindus.

Swayamsevak
Hindi for "self-service" or "self-help". It is part of the title of the Swayamsevak Sangh, a twentieth century organisation of Hindu activists, which stresses self-discipline.

Tamil
The name of a people, language and culture originating in the South Indian state of Tamil Nadu.

Tantra
Sanskrit for "context" or "continuum". It describes the magical strand of Hinduism which focuses on the divine as *Shakti* (see above). There are two *Tantric* (see below) paths – the *Vamachara* (left hand path) and the *Dakshinachara* (right hand path). The former is a dangerous path of freedom from normal conventions which can only be undertaken under close supervision. The latter is a path of self-discipline. In both the emphasis is on the feminine aspects of the divine and followers are guided by *Tantric* texts.

Tantric
That which pertains to the *Tantra* (see above).

Uttersanda
The name of a town.

Valam
The name of a town.

Vanik
Gujarati surname for a trading or merchant *caste*.

Vanza
The name of an occupational grouping traditionally related to tailoring.

Vedanta
From the Sanskrit *veda*, meaning "knowledge" and *anta*, meaning "end". Hence *Vedanta* means the "conclusion of the *Vedas*", which are seen as eternal. Their quintessence is known as the *Uphanishads* which focuses especially on the relationship between *atman* and *Brahman* (see "Introducing the Hindu Community"). The *Vedanta* has several main branches (see "Introducing the Hindu Community").

Vedic
That which pertains to the *Vedas* (see above).

Vidhyala
Variant Romanisation of *vidyala* (see below).

Vidya
Sanskrit meaning "knowledge". *Apara-vidya* is intellectually acquired knowledge, whilst *paravidya* is spiritual knowledge.

Vidyala
Sanskrit for "school", from the Sanskrit *vidya* (see above).

Vikram
The name of a Hindu king and an era of time.

Vishwa
Variant Romanisation of *Vishva* (see below).

Vishva
Sanskrit for "universal". Used in the title of the organisation Vishwa Hindu Parishad, meaning Universal Hindu Organisation, a twentieth century activist organisation.

Vishwakarma
Sanskrit for "all creating". In the *Rig Veda*, the activity of creation is celebrated in two hymns in which the world is described as being made from primordial matter. It is the name of the divine as architect and in the *Puranas*, Vishwakarma is seen as the inventor of the sciences and of mechanics. He is a patron deity of a number of originally artisan castes who use his name in the title of their organisations.

Visva
Varainat Romanisation of *Vishwa* (see above).

Wanza
Variant Romanisation of *vanza* (see above).

Yamuna

The Sanskrit for the North Indian river also known as the Jumna or Jumnu, which is a tributary of the River Ganges. *Pushtimargis* and *Vaishnavas* worship Yamuna along with Shree Nathj (or Shrinathji) and Valabhacharya.

Yoga

Sanskrit meaning "joining". In a religious context it is used to describe the pathways used for seeking union with the divine including *karma yoga* (path of selfless action), *bhakti yoga* (path of devotion), *raja yoga* (royal yoga), *kundalini yoga* (tantric yoga), *jnanana yoga* (abstract knowledge). There is also *hatha yoga* which consists of the physical exercises that help the aspirant to other forms of *yoga*.

Yogashram

See *yoga* and *ashram* above.

Yuvak

Hindi meaning "youth".

THE JAIN COMMUNITY

INTRODUCING THE JAIN COMMUNITY

JAINS IN THE UNITED KINGDOM

Migration

Most Jains now living in the United Kingdom can trace their historical and ethnic origins back to the Gujarat area of India. Some migrated directly from India in the 1950s; others came in the 1960s and 1970s via the East African countries in which they or their forebears had previously settled, such as Kenya, Uganda and Tanzania.

Distribution

Approximately 30,000 people in the UK follow the Jain religion. Worldwide, there are approximately 8,000,000 Jains. Many live in and around the Greater London area and in Leicester. Other Jain communities are to be found in Manchester, Coventry, Northampton, Wellingborough and Luton.

Jains are not recorded as a separate category in the running totals of certified places of worship in England and Wales kept by the Register General. There are only two Jain places of worship recorded in this directory.

ORIGINS AND DEVELOPMENT OF JAINISM

The Tirthankaras

Jainism began in India. The term *Jain* means a follower of the *Jinas* (Spiritual Victors), human teachers who through their own efforts are believed to have attained *kevalajnana* (omniscience or infinite knowledge). These teachers were also known as the *Tirthankaras*, literally meaning "ford-makers", or those who help others to escape *samsara*, the cycle of birth and death. It is believed that in the present cosmic cycle there have been twenty four *Tirthankaras* who have taught others the beliefs of the religion known as Jainism.

Mahavira

The twenty-fourth *Tirthankara*, Vardhamana, usually called *Mahavira* (the Great Hero), is believed by Jains to have been born in 599 BCE into a noble family in the area of what is now the contemporary state of Bihar, in India. When he was thirty years old, he left home on a spiritual quest and after twelve years he is believed to have attained *kevalajnana*. Shortly after this, eleven men came to the place where *Mahavira* was staying to hear his sermon and became his *ganadharas* (chief disciples).

During the next thirty years, it is thought that his followers grew to about fifty thousand male and female ascetics and approximately half a million lay people. At the age of seventy-two, *Mahavira* died and attained *nirvana*, the state of bliss beyond life and death.

Jainism in India

At first, the followers of Jainism lived throughout the Ganges valley area of India. At around the time of the Emperor Ashoka (250 BCE) most Jains migrated to the city of Mathura on the Yamuna River. Later on, many travelled west to Rajasthan and Gujarat and south to Maharashtra and Karnataka, where Jainism rapidly grew in popularity.

SOURCES OF JAIN BELIEFS AND PRACTICES

Shruta

Jain scriptures are known as the *shruta*. The canonical literature called the *Agamas* or *Siddhanta* (doctrine) represents the teaching of *Mahavira*. The Jain scriptures consist of some sixty texts and are divided into three main groups of writings - the *Purvas* (Old Texts), the *Angas* (Limbs) and the *Angabahyas* (Subsidiary Canon). A majority of these texts are written in *Ardhamagadhi*, an ancient Magadhan language.

The *Purvas* consist of twelve books and are believed to constitute the teachings of the *Tirthankaras* as handed down in oral tradition. Jains in the *Shvetambara* tradition (see below) believe that all this material was lost. Jains in the *Digambara* tradition (see below) claim that some of the material from these oral teachings is the basis for their early treatise, *Shat Khanda-Agama* (the Scripture in Six Parts).

The *Angas* also consist of twelve books and the collection comprise of such major texts as the *Acaranga Sutra* and the *Bhagavati Sutra*. The *Angas* contain materials about doctrinal matters, ecclesiastical law, and narratives for the laity. *Digambaras* have traditionally maintained that these texts are no longer extant in their original form.

The *Angabahya* (Subsidiary Canon) is composed of a group of texts which were composed at a later period by mendicant authors. They contain narratives for the instruction of the laity, material on confessional rites, rules of discipline for monks and nuns, and Jain cosmology. The most well-known and popular of these is the *Kalpa Sutra* of the *Shvetambaras*, which contains the biographies of *Mahavira* and other *Tirthankaras*.

Commentaries

In addition to the canon itself there are extensive commentaries written in subsequent times by the *acharyas* (teachers or scholars). These include metaphysical and ethical discussions which are written in *Sanskrit* in both prose and verse form. The *Tattvartha Sutra*, written in the second century BCE by Acharya Umasvati, belongs to this group of texts. This text is viewed by contemporary Jains as being very important and as providing the basis for Jain education.

KEY JAIN BELIEFS

Anekantavada

Jainism adheres to an understanding of truth called *anekantavada* (non-onesidedness). This is the belief that no one perspective on an issue contains the whole truth. In the Jain view, any event or proposition should be viewed from four points of view. These points of view are according to: *dravya* (substance); *kshetra* (place); *kala* (time); and *bhava* (condition). Ideally, this should result in a non–dogmatic approach to the doctrines of other religions.

Human Place in the Universe

According to the Jain scriptures, space is infinite but only a finite portion is occupied by what is generally known as the *loka* (universe). Everything within this universe, whether *jiva* (sentient) or *ajiva* (non-sentient) is viewed as eternal, although the forms which a thing may take at a given time are transient and changeable.

Human beings are believed to inhabit the middle of the universe, with the heavens above and the hells below containing other forms of life. Jains believe that there never was a time when this uncreated, eternal universe did not exist, therefore they do not believe in a creator god. They believe that all living beings have an individual *jiva* or *atman* (soul) which occupies the body which, in turn, is viewed as being a conglomerate of atoms.

Ajiva (non-soul) is everything in the universe that is insentient, including all matter, the principles of motion and rest, time and space. At the time of death, the *jiva* is believed to leave the body and instantaneously to occupy a new body. The goal of Jainism is to achieve *moksha* or *nirvana* which is release from this beginningless cycle of birth and death.

Karma

In Jain understanding all *jivas* are equal in their potential capacity for infinite knowledge, energy and bliss. However, during the soul's beginningless embodied state, these inherent qualities are obscured in varying degrees by different amounts and types of *karma*. From a Jain perspective, *karma* is understood in material terms as a form of subtle matter.

As a result of volitional actions undertaken through body, speech and mind, the *karma* adheres to the *jiva*. This accumulated *karma* is seen as the cause of the *jiva's* bondage in the cycle of birth and death. The ultimate aim of life is to emancipate the *jiva* from *karmic* matter by exhausting all previously bound *karma* and guarding against the accumulation of any new *karma*. It is believed that this can be achieved by leading an ascetic life of disciplined conduct according to Jain principles.

Jain teaching sees *karma* as being of eight main types which determine the state of an individual's existence and what they can hope to attain. The four principal *karmas* are: *mohaniya* (*karmas* which delude insight and conduct); *jnanavaraniya* (*karmas* which cloud and obscure knowledge); *darshanavaraniya* (*karmas* which obscure perception); and *antaraya* (*karmas* which restrict energy). The four subsidiary *karmas* are *vedaniya* (*karmas* which produce feeling); *nama* (*karmas* which cause the formation of the body); *ayu* (*karmas* which determine the longevity of life); and *gotra* (*karmas* which determine family environment).

The amounts and types of *asravas* (*karmic* particles) bonded to the *jiva* determine the type of body which the *jiva* inhabits. Life forms are grouped in a hierarchy based on the number of senses which they possess. The lowest forms of life, including trees and plants, have only the sense of touch.

Higher on the evolutionary scale are animals with two, three or four senses, for example, insects and birds. The highest level of beings, which are human beings and some animals, have five senses including rationality and *manas* (intuition). Even beings with only one sense can experience pleasure and pain through the sense of touch.

Moksha

It is believed that it is only from the human state that one can achieve *moksha* or *nirvana*, the liberation from the cycle of birth and death. Through a variety of religious practices, the *jiva* progresses from a state of inadequate perception of the world to the attainment of omniscient knowledge.

At this stage, such a person is called an *arhat* or an *arihanta* (meaning "worthy of worship"). At the time of death, the *jiva* of an *arhat* attains total emancipation from all *karmic* matter and instantaneously rises to the summit of the universe where, motionless, it exists forever. Such a *jiva* is designated a *siddha* (a Perfected Being). In order to achieve *moksha* it is necessary to have the qualities known to Jains as the *Three Jewels* (see below).

TRADITIONS IN JAINISM

There are two main groups of Jain ascetics, the *Shvetambara* and the *Digambara*. These terms are also used to describe their lay followers. The majority of Jains worldwide, and in the UK, are *Shvetambara*. The two groups differ in some of their beliefs and practices, the differences of which emerged in the third and fifth centuries CE.

Shvetambara

The *Shvetambara* (white-robed) monks and nuns wear three pieces of white clothing and carry a set of begging bowls, a small woollen whisk-broom, a walking stick and a blanket, with the whisk being used to aid in avoiding harm to insects.

A group of the *Shvetambaras*, known as the *Sthanakvasis*, and a sub-group of the latter called *Terapanthis*, additionally wear a *muhpatti* (piece of cloth) over the mouth to avoid their breathing in and harming minute living beings. Among the *Sthanakvasis*, all foods and other necessities are supplied by lay followers. Only strained and boiled water which contains no living organisms, is drunk.

Mendicant leaders of the *Terapanthi* community have introduced a practice of renunciants spending a few years in training to teach the Jain religion. These young novices, called *samanas* (male novices) and *samanis* (female novices), are encouraged to visit Jain communities in India and overseas and in recent years have been very active in educational work. It is estimated that there are over two thousand five hundred monks and five thousand nuns in this group.

Digambara

The *Digambara* (sky-clad) monks renounce all forms of property including clothes and begging bowls. They are allowed to carry only a peacock-feather whisk-broom and a gourd containing washing water. *Digambara* nuns, however, are clothed in a white sari. The nuns are highly revered by the community and in all other matters obey the same regulations as *Digambara* monks, including eating and drinking only once a day in the home of a Jain layperson.

Because of the severity of their mendicant rules there are probably no more than a few hundred *Digambara* monks and nuns living in India today. Because of the restrictions on travel which operate for these ascetics (as a result of the possibility of harm being caused to living beings by mechanised forms of transport), the day-to-day leadership of the community rests upon lay scholars who visit the *Digambara* community outside of India as well as upon advanced laymen called *bhattarakas* who can be distinguished by their ochre-coloured robes.

JAIN LIFE

Three Jewels

Jains seek to live according to the so-called Three Jewels: right faith (the essentials of Jainism); right knowledge (of how *jiva* and *karma* operate); and right conduct adhering to the five *vratas*. Jains believe that conduct befitting the attainment of higher stages of personal evolution or enlightenment involves, for lay people, adhering to the five *anuvratas* (minor vows).

For monks and nuns, the vows are the *mahavratas* (great vows) which are a more restrictive interpretation of the same principles that inform the *anuvratas* for the laity. The principles are *ahimsa* (non-violence), *satya* (truthfulness), *asteya* (not stealing), *brahmacharya* (chastity) and *aparigraha* (non-materialism).

Ahimsa

For lay people, *ahimsa* involves not killing. For monks and nuns this includes not hurting, mentally or physically, any living creature including even the smallest life forms.

For most Jains in the UK, the principle of *ahimsa* influences their diet which is strictly vegetarian. Jain scriptures permit the consumption of dairy products such as milk, curds, and *ghee* (clarified butter) but prohibit meat, eggs, butter, root vegetables, figs, honey and alcohol since it is believed that partaking of any of these prohibited items would destroy many lives.

Jain ascetics must not eat after sunset or before sunrise and some laity also observe these restrictions. Various reasons are given for this, but the principal one is that Jains believe that after sunset, tiny organisms are developed which might sit on the food, not be seen and then be eaten, thus violating the principle of *ahimsa*, albeit unintentionally. The principle of *ahimsa* also restricts employment of Jains to those occupations that do not harm humans or animals.

Satya

Satya (truthfulness) is enjoined in order not to harm another by speech; *asteya* (not stealing) is the principle of not taking what belongs to another.

Brahmacharya

Brahmacharya (chastity), for lay Jains, means avoiding sexual promiscuity whilst for monks and nuns it entails complete sexual celibacy.

Aparigraha

Aparigraha (non-materialism) is concerned with the Jain belief that one should not attach importance to material things.

Tapas

In addition to the five *anuvratas*, many Jains also on occasion voluntarily undertake *tapas* (practices of austerity) such as eating only one meal a day or fasting from sunrise to sunset, either for a day or for a week.

JAIN WORSHIP

Personal Puja

Jains may offer *puja* (worship) three times a day – before dawn, at sunset, and at night, by chanting *mantras* (litanies). The most important of these *mantras* is the *Panca-namaskara-mantra* saying, "I pay homage to the *arhats* (the living omniscient beings), *siddhas* (the perfected beings), *acharyas* (the Jain mendicant leaders), *upadhyayas* (Jain mendicant teachers) and *sadhus* (all other Jain ascetics)". The second important ritual is *pratikramana,* a confession of trans- gressions against one's religious vows committed knowingly or unknowingly.

Mandirs

In addition to worshipping in their home shrines, many lay Jains also worship at *Shvetambara* or *Digambara mandirs* (temples). These *mandirs* often contain statues or pictures of one or more *Tirthankaras* or images of all the twenty-four *Tirthankaras* depicted in meditation, either standing or seated in the lotus posture. Devotion to these images inspires Jains and puts them in the proper frame of mind for spiritual activities.

Before coming into a place of worship Jains purify themselves with a bath. Shoes and leather objects are left outside. At the entrance to the *mandir* a worshipper puts a saffron mark on his or her brow and utters the word *Nisihi* to put aside all worldly cares. Using rice grains, a decoration is made on a low table beside the door. To the chant of *mantras*, worshippers bathe the images of the *Tirthankaras*, offer flowers and incense, and wave *arati* (lamps) in front of them. *Shvetambara* monks and nuns may also visit *Shvetambara mandirs*. In temples, there are sometimes designated laymen who perform religious rituals.

There are some *Shvetambaras* who do not worship in community temples. *Sthanakvasis* and *Terapanthis* do not participate in the temple rituals described above since they claim that veneration of images is not sanctioned in the Jain scriptures and they emphasis *bhavapuja* (mental worship). They perform their religious rites in *upashraya* (meditation halls).

In Leicester, there is a purpose-built Jain Temple which provides places of worship under one roof for all the major traditions of Jainism. In addition to the main *Shvetambara* temple, there is a also a *Digambara* Temple and a *Sthanakvasi upashraya*, a room dedicated to monks and a meditation room dedicated to Shrimad Rajchandra, the spiritual mentor of Mahatma Gandhi. The Oshwal Centre in North London has a temple in a separate building from its community hall.

JAIN CALENDAR AND FESTIVALS

Jain Calendar

Jains date the era of *Mahavira,* known as the *Vira-nirvana-samvat,* from the year of his death in 527 BCE. However, except for special events in Jain history, they have traditionally used the *Vikramasamvat* calendar which is also used among Hindus. Both calendars are lunar.

Jain festivals

The following are the most significant Jain festivals:

Mahavira Jayanti
(March/April)

Marks the anniversary of the birth of *Mahavira.*

Akshaya-tiritiya
(April/May)

Means "the immortal third" and celebrates the first time that alms were given to Jina Rishabha, the first *Tirthankara* of this cosmic cycle.

Shruta-pancami
(May/June)

Or *Guru-pancami,* meaning "Teacher's Fifth", is celebrated by the *Digambaras* on the fifth (*pancami*) day of May/June. Among *Shvetambaras* this day is known as *Jnana-pancami* (Knowledge-Fifth) and is observed in October/November. It commemorates the day on which the *shruta* (Jain scriptures) were written down. At this time, copies of the scriptures are displayed in Jain *mandirs.*

Paryushana-parva
(August/September)

Marks the most important religious period in the rainy season in India during which Jain monks and nuns find a fixed place of residence instead of moving from place to place as at other times of the year. During this period lay people often observe special vows. Among *Shvetambaras,* the portion of the sacred *Kalpa Sutra* which contains the life of *Mahavira* is recited.

The *Digambaras,* call this season *Dasha-lakshana-parva,* meaning "the Festival of the Ten Virtues", namely forgiveness, humility, honesty, purity, truthfulness, self-restraint, asceticism, study, detachment, and celibacy. During the festival, each day is devoted to a discourse on one of these virtues. The final day is the holiest in the year and is marked by the celebration of *Samvatsari-pratikramana.* This is an annual ceremony of confession in which all Jains participate, requesting forgiveness from relatives and friends for offences of thought, word or deed by uttering the words "*micchami dukkadam*" (meaning "may my transgressions be forgiven").

Vira-Nirvana
(November)

Marks the death and *nirvana* of *Mahavira.*

Karttika-purnima
(December)

Marks the end of the rainy season retreat for monks and nuns. At this time, they resume their travels on foot. It is the end of the Jain religious year.

JAIN ORGANISATIONS

Jain Organisations

There are both national and local Jain organisations in the UK and they are known by such common Indian terms as *mandal* (the Hindi word literally meaning "circle"), *samaj* (the Hindi word meaning "society") and *sangh* (the Hindi word for "group" or "gathering"). Local groups may be open to general Jain membership or may be specific to certain social groupings such as *Oshwal* or *Navnat, Oshwal* having originally been an Indian trading caste.

There are also interest groups which deal with issues of particular concern to Jains, for example, the Young Indian Vegetarians. Some may be more specific in their membership as with the National Association of Vanik Associations, representing Vanik social groupings. Jain Samaj Europe and the Institute of Jainology act in a co-ordinating role for many Jain individuals and organisations in the United Kingdom, Europe and throughout the world.

Personnel

The Jain community is composed of four groups of people: *sadhus* (male ascetics or monks), *sadhvis* (female ascetics or nuns), *shravakas* (laymen) and *shravikas* (laywomen). *Sadhus* and *sadhvis* dedicate themselves exclusively to the pursuit of *moksha*. They renounce their family and all their possessions and take the *mahavratas* (Five Great Vows) at an initiation ceremony known as *diksha*. *Pujaris* (priests) can be found in Jain Temples who officiate for the temple rituals. At the Leicester Jain Centre there are two part-time *pujaris*.

BIBLIOGRAPHY

Acharya Bhuvanbhanusoorishwarji, *Handbook of Jainology*, Sri Vishvakalyan Prakashan Trust, Mehsana, 1987.

Banerjee, S R, *Chhotdal Jain's Jaina Bibliography* (2 volumes), Vir Sewa Mandir, New Delhi, 1982.

Bhargava, D, *Jain Ethics*, Motilal Barnarsidass, Delhi, 1968.

Bhattacharya, B C, *The Jaina Iconography*, Motilal Banarsidass, Delhi, (2nd edition), 1974.

Bhattacharyya, N, *Jain Philosophy: Historical Outline*, Munshiram Manoharlal, New Delhi, 1976.

Dundas, P, *The Jains*, Routledge, London, 1992.

Ghosh, A, *Jain Art and Architecture* (3 volumes), Bharatiya Jnanypith, New Delhi, 1974–1975.

Jain, J P, *Religion and Culture of the Jains*, Bharatiya Jnanpith, New Delhi, 1975.

Jain, M U K, *Jain Sects and Schools*, Concept Publishing, Delhi, 1975.

Jain Samaj Europe, *Mahavira Darshan and Rituals: Special Issue of The Jain*, April 1992.

Jaini, P S, *The Jaina Path of Purification*, University of California Press, Berkeley, 1979.

Jaini, P S, *Gender and Salvation: Jaina Debates on the Spiritual Liberation of Women*, University of California Press, Berkeley, California 1991.

Kapashi, V, *In Search of the Ultimate*, V K Publications, Harrow, 1984.

Maratt, P, *Jainism Explained*, Jain Samaj Europe Publications, Leicester, 1985.

Nahar, P C, and Gosh, J C, *Encyclopaedia of Jainism*, Sri Satguru Publications, Delhi, 1986.

Sangave, V S, *Jaina Community: A Social Survey* (2nd edition), Popular Prakashan, Bombay, 1980.

Satyaprakash (ed), *Jainism: A Select Bibliography*, Indian Documentation Service, Gurgaon, 1984.

Sogani, K C, *Ethical Doctrines in Jainism*, Jaina Samskrita Samrakshaka Sangha, Sholapur, 1967.

JAIN UK ORGANISATIONS

The organisations listed in this section include head offices of organisations with branches throughout the country and organisations which aspire to serve the Jain community at a UK wide level.

Federation of Jain Organisations in UK
11 Lindsay Drive
Kenton
Middlesex HA3 0TA
Tel: 081-204-2871
Contact: Mr Vinod Kapashi
Office: Co-ordinator
A co-ordinating organisation in formation, promoting unity and brotherhood. The Federation organises lectures and seminars, circulates information to other organisations and collects and publishes informative materials to widen the knowledge and better understanding of Jain ideology.

Institute of Jainology
Unit 18, Silicon Business Centre
26-28 Wandsworth Road
Greenford
Middlesex UB6 7JZ
Tel: 081-997-2300
Fax: 081-997-4964
Contact: Mr Nemu Chandaria
Office: Co-ordinator
The organisation was founded in 1983 at the World Jain Conference held in London. It aims to: promote greater understanding of the Jain faith among the people of the world and to render Jain philosophy and teachings more accessible to all by developing, translating, publishing and distributing Jain texts. This is being carried out in association with the International Sacred Literature Trust which has a ten year programme for translating the Jain scriptures into English. The Institute also contributes to care and protection of the natural environment in accord with the Jain Declaration on Nature and in this connection works with the World Wide Fund for Nature and other organisations with an ecological concern in undertaking practical projects. The Institute also aims to establish research bodies, Jain Centres and Temples and to provide libraries and reading rooms as well as other facilities to meet for discussions, lectures, seminars and facilities for cataloguing for easy reference available literature on Jain philosophy. In this connection it is working with the British India Library to prepare a catalogue of Jain manuscripts outside of India and has established a Jain Education Board for teaching Jainism in the UK. Current attendance at such classes is over one thousand Jain youth. It also intends to collect and publish information on places of worship, meditation and study in India and elsewhere and to organise celebrations of important religious events in the Jain calendar. It publishes a quarterly newsletter called "Ahimsa" which is circulated

worldwide. The Institute is associated with several Jain organisations worldwide and is affiliated to the Inter Faith Network for the UK.

Jain Academy
69 Rowley Fields Avenue
Leicester LE3 2ES
Tel: 0533-891077
Fax: 0533-827410
Aims towards the advancement of the Jain religion particularly but not exclusively by the provision of an Academy for the study of Jainism and the dissemination of Jain values. It organises education for the Jains in the UK, especially young Jain school children and their teachers as well as learning at the academic level by organising undergraduate, postgraduate, distance learning and certificate courses at various universities. It invites scholars and research students from the UK and abroad. It has established a Council for the Jain Academy which includes prominent academics and Jain leaders from various parts of the UK. It has planned a three year Undergraduate Modular course, BA (Hons) in Jain Studies under the School of Arts and BSc/BA (Hons) Combined Studies at De Montfort University, Leicester. It has made arrangements with an Indian University for sending research scholars every year. It is negotiating co-operation with other important Indian Universities. Dr L M Singhvi, the present High Commissioner of India is guiding the Academy as Honorary President; Professor Richard Gombrich of Oxford University as Academic advisor; Dr Paul Marett as Honorary Director and Dr Natubhai Shah as Chairman.

Jain Samaj Europe
69 Rowley Fields Avenue
Leicester LE3 2ES
Tel: 0533-891077
Fax: 0533-827410
Contact: Dr Natubhai Shah
Office: President
A national organisation with branches in Leicester and London. It has national and overseas membership. It was established in 1973 as Jain Samaj Leicester and was expanded as Jain Samaj Europe in 1980. It has established a Jain Centre, an exciting development with marble frontage, fifty-two hand carved pillars, a dome and ceilings of sandstone, mirrored walls, stained glass windows, auditorium, library and office facilities. The Jain Centre is a sign of unity for Jains containing as it does a place of worship and study for all sects of Jains, perhaps for the first time in the world. It is also the first place in the Western world with consecrated

images. It has become a major tourist attraction in Leicester. It has established a Museum and initiated a Jain Academy, which has been responsible for the starting of an Undergraduate three year modular BA course in Jain Studies at the De Montfort University, Leicester. Jain Samaj Europe represents Jainism at national and international levels and undertakes activities for the promotion and dissemination of Jain values and their understanding and also for the religious needs of the Jain community. It has initiated the Jain-Christian Association, the Leicestershire Ahimsa Society for Care of Nature (LASCON), Pathshala (Sunday school) for Jain children, and study courses in London, Leicester and other areas. It also invites Jain scholars for the benefit of all Jains in the UK. It takes part in inter-faith activities and is in membership with the Inter Faith Network for the UK and the Leicester Council of Faiths.

Mahavir Foundation Ltd
18 Florence Mansions
Vivian Avenue
Hendon
London NW4 3GY
Tel: 081-205-2932 (home)
Contact: Indu Kumar Doshi
Office: Secretary
Membership group and representative body. The foundation encourages and promotes the principles of Mahavira and the faith of Jainism for the benefit of all humanity, such as non-violence and vegetarianism. Activities include worship and education in Lord Mahavira's philosophy of non-violence.

National Council of Vanik Organisations (UK)
37 Baron's Court
Church Lane
Kingsbury
London NW9 8AD
Tel: 081-205-6673 (home)
Contact: D R Shah
Office: General Secretary
National organisation which represents all Vanik organisations in the UK. It sponsors social activities and helps in co-ordinating the work of Vanik organisations.

Navnat Vanik Association of the United Kingdom
43 Burgess Avenue
London NW9 8TX
Tel: 081-205-0856 (home)
Contact: Mr Bhupendra J Shah

Office: General Secretary

The organisation exists for the promotion and understanding of the Hindu and Jain religions. Its principles are non-violence, human and animal welfare and the preservation of nature. Its activities are religious, cultural and social.

Oshwal Association of the UK

7 The Avenue
Wembley
Middlesex HA9 5SJ
Tel: 071-904-0055 (home)
Fax: 081-450-6755
Contact: Mr Rati Shah
Office: Secretary

The Association engages in religious programmes to promote Jain philosophy through social welfare, cultural, educational, youth and environmental concerns. There is a Jain Temple at the Oshwal Centre, Potters Bar, Hertfordshire.

Shree Digamber Jain Association

Shree Digamber Jain Centre
The Broadway
Wealdstone
Harrow
Middlesex HA3 7EH
Tel: 081-965-9990 (daytime)
Tel: 081-428-3005 (evening)
Fax: 081-961-8730
Contact: L B Shah

The association aims to facilitate the practice of Digamber Jain Religion by reading, discussions or meditations and as defined and proclaimed by Tirthankar Mahavir and further as recorded, depicted and explained in the Scriptures by Shree Kund Kund Acharya and as practised and preached by Param Pujya Sadgurudev Shree Kanjiswami at Songadh, Saurastra, India.

JAIN CENTRES AND LOCAL ORGANISATIONS

NORTH EAST ENGLAND

NORTH WEST ENGLAND

ENGLISH EAST MIDLANDS

ENGLISH WEST MIDLANDS

SOUTH EAST ENGLAND (NORTH)

LONDON (N)

LONDON (NW)

LONDON (SW)

SOUTH EAST ENGLAND (SOUTH)

There are a variety of forms of local Jain organisations in the UK that are reflected in this directory. There are only two temples, but there are also a number of organisations which operate from premises that are either owned or hired, whilst other groups are run from and/or meet in the homes of members.

NORTH EAST ENGLAND

Yorkshire Jain Foundation
14 Ancaster Road
West Park
Leeds LS16 5HH
Tel: 0532-751483 (home)
Contact: Professor K V Mardia
Office: President
Membership group. The Foundation aims to promote Jain values. It meets regularly to discuss the theory and practice of Jainism in a very broad context. Various publications have been planned and a library of Jain books is being contemplated: "Jain Thoughts and Prayers" is the latest publication of the Foundation. Other activities include youth activities and general welfare work.

NORTH WEST ENGLAND

Jain Social Group - Midlands and North
4 Spinney
Cheadle
Cheshire SK8 1JA
Tel: 061-439-4188
Contact: Mr Piyush Mehta
Office: Secretary
A group which mainly organises social and charitable activities and serves a welfare function.

Jain Samaj Manchester
219 Seymour Grove
Stretford
Manchester M16 9QS
Tel: 061-428-7617 (home)
Contact: Dr Naresh Shah
Office: President
A religious body with four hundred members living in Manchester and Cheshire. All the members follow the Jain religion. The organisation helps fellow members to worship, runs youth and women's activities and encourages children to learn their mother tongue as well as study religious literature.

ENGLISH EAST MIDLANDS

Jain Centre
32 Oxford Street
Leicester LE1 5XU
Tel: 0533-543091
Contact: Administrator
A place of worship and the first traditional Jain temple in the western world. The centre attracts visitors and

devotees from a wide area and is recognised as a major attraction in the city of Leicester. Its foundation stones were laid in 1983 and its images were consecrated in 1988. Virtually all the interior furnishings have come from India. The centrepiece is a group of fifty-two carved sandstone columns surrounding a central dome and marble images of three Tirthankaras. Places of worship are provided for all the major traditions of Jainism, as well as a meditation room dedicated to Shrimad Rajchandra, the spiritual mentor of Mahatma Gandhi. The ground floor of the centre includes an auditorium, kitchen and dining area, library and offices. A museum has also been set up to help interpret Jainism to the temple's many visitors. It has showcases, models and display panels to introduce Jain history, beliefs and way of life and it will be used as a Resource Centre for the Jain Academy and students of the adjoining De Montfort University who are undertaking Jain Studies courses. The temple is managed by Jain Samaj Europe. As well as being a place of worship, the Jain Centre is a base for activities which seek to promote Lord Mahavir's message of non-violence, reverence for life, forgiveness and brotherhood in the modern world and particularly in the city of Leicester. It is generally open to visitors from 2.00pm–5.00pm, Mondays to Fridays, but at other times to devotees only. Those wishing to bring visiting groups should contact the Administrator first and then confirm this in writing. The temple is maintained by the Jain community. Donations from visitors go towards its upkeep and are much appreciated.

Oshwal Association of the UK

20 Woodgreen Walk
Leicester LE4 7UN
Tel: 0533–760820 (home)
Contact: Mr N A Zakharia
Office: Secretary
The Association engages in worship, welfare, youth and social activities.

Oshwall Association of the UK - Northamptonshire

12 Stonehill Court
The Arbours
Northampton NN3 3RA
Tel: 0604–416040
Contact: Mr Anil P Shah
Office: Chairman

ENGLISH WEST MIDLANDS

Jain Ashram

322 Hampstead Road
Handsworth
Birmingham B20 2RA

Jain Sangh Birmingham

679 Shirley Road
Hall Green
Birmingham B28 9JX
Tel: 021–777–4668 (home)
Contact: Mr N V Parekh
Office: President

Vanik Samaj - Coventry

17 Poitiers Road
Cheylesmore
Coventry CV3 5JY
Tel: 0203–413033
Contact: Mr Kishore Shah
Office: Secretary
A small social and religious group consisting of twenty families who follow the Jain faith and also Vaniks (business community) who follow the Hindu faith. The group is very informal. Activities include celebration of social and religious functions. Meditation and devotional gatherings are held each month.

SOUTH EAST ENGLAND (NORTH)

Jain Association of the United Kingdom

4 Whitchurch Close
Edgware
Middlesex HA8 6PE
Tel: 081–952–5757 (home)
Contact: Mrs Prabal Jain
Office: Secretary

Bhakti Mandal

41 Bethecar Road
Harrow
Middlesex HA1 1SD
Tel: 081–952–6193 (home)
Contact: Mrs Prafula Shah
Office: Secretary

Oshwal Association of the UK - North West London

213 Kenton Lane
Kenton
Harrow
Middlesex HA3 8TL

Tel: 081-907-9258 (home)
Contact: Mr Ashok M Shah
Office: Chairman

Digambar Association of the United Kingdom
12 Clonard Way
Hatchend
Middlesex HA5 4BU
Tel: 081-965-9990 (home)
Contact: Laxmichand Shah

Oshwal Association of the UK
21 Ashton Gardens
Hounslow
Middlesex TW4 7BU
Tel: 081-570-6886 (home)
Contact: Mr Chunilal P Shah
Office: Chairman

Jain Sangh - East London and Essex
167 Eastern Avenue
Ilford
Essex IG4 5AW
Tel: 081-551-1907 (home)
Contact: Mr V Gandhi
Office: Secretary

Oshwal Association of the UK - East London and Essex
18 Carlisle Gardens
Ilford
Essex IG1 3SN
Tel: 081-518-6658 (home)
Contact: Mr Chandulal H Shah
Office: Chairman

Oshwal Association of the UK - Luton
51 Marlborough Road
Luton LU3 1FF
Tel: 0582-450304 (home)
Contact: Mr Chandrakant P Shah
Office: Chairman

Jain Meditation Centre UK
68 Chervil Beanhill
Milton Keynes MK6 4LQ
Tel: 0908-606015 (home)
Contact: S D Kothari
Office: Co-ordinator

Oshwal Association of the UK
12 Stonehill Court
The Arbours

Northampton NN3 3RA
Tel: 0604-416040 (home)
Contact: Mr Anil P Shah
Office: Chairman

Oshwall Centre
Cooper's Lane Road
Northaw
Hertfordshire EN6 4DG
Tel: 0707-643839
Contact: Manager or Administrator

Aden Vanik Association of the UK
9 Cedar Drive
Garston
Watford WD2 6RR
Tel: 0923-893421 (home)
Contact: Mr Subash Bakhai
Office: President

LONDON (N POSTCODES)

Digambar Jain Visa Mewada Association of the UK
12 Templars Crescent
London N3 3QS
Tel: 081-349-1963 (home)
Contact: Mr Navin Shah
Office: President

Oshwal Association of the UK - North London
18 Avondale Road
London N3 2ES
Tel: 081-346-5015 (home)
Contact: Mr Laxmichand D Shah
Office: Chairman

Oshwall Association of the UK - North East London
81 Evesham Road
London N11 2RR
Tel: 081-361-9728 (home)
Contact: Mr Narendra D Shah
Office: Chairman

LONDON (NW POSTCODES)

Jain Vishwa Bhararati
148 Hendon Way
London NW2 2NE
Tel: 081-458-5653 (home)
Fax: 081-458-0120
Contact: Mr M L Baid

Office: President

The organisation is a membership group which propagates the practice and philosophy of Jainism. This involves the study of Jain scriptures, the practice of meditation (Prekhsya Dhyan) and science of Living (Jivan Vigyan). Its main field of work is human values with special emphasis on non-violence, peace and respect for all faiths. Visits and discourses from ovserseas scholars and Samans/Samanies (mainly from India) are organised. The organisation has a close affinity with Jain Vishwa Bharati Institute (Deemed University), Ladnun, Rajasthan, India; Anuvrat Vishwa Bharati/Global Organisation (Anuvibha), Jaipur, Rajasthan, India; and Anekant International, Kathmandu, Nepal.

Navayug Jain Pragati Mandal

119 Church Hill Road
London NW2 5EH
Tel: 071-267-8580 (home)
Contact: Mr Dinesh Shah
Office: Secretary

Jain Samaj Europe - London Branch

2 Mount Road
Hendon
London NW4 3PU
Tel: 081-202-0469
Contact: Mr K C Jain
Office: London Area Chairperson

Part of a national organisation with branches in London and Leicester. It has both a national and an overseas membership. The London branch organises activities for the promotion and dissemination of Jain values and their understanding and also for the religious needs of the Jain community, including for London members and also for other Jains in the UK. These activities include lectures, celebrations, dance, drama and other cultural activities and coach trips to the Jain Centre in Leicester. It provides information on Jainism and the activities of Jain Samaj Europe and acts as a base for co-ordination with other Jain and inter-faith organisations. It sends Jain representatives to wider community organisations and institutions.

Jain Social Group - London

18 Wykeham Road
Hendon
London NW4 2SU
Tel: 081-908-0833 (home)
Contact: Mr Pramod Punater
Office: Secretary

International Mahavir Jain Mission

10 Alexander Avenue
London NW10 3QS
Tel: 081-459-0775 (home)
Contact: Ms Pushap Jain
Office: Chairperson

LONDON (SW POSTCODES)

Vanik Association of the UK

71 Pretoria Road
Streatham
London SW16 6RL
Tel: 0707-813977
Contact: Mr Mracdula Shah

SOUTH EAST ENGLAND (SOUTH)

Vanik Samaj of the United Kingdom

92 Osbourne Road
Brighton
West Sussex BN1 6LU
Tel: 0273-555053 (home)
Contact: Mr B C Mehta
Office: Secretary

Jain Social Group - South London

Hill Side
Bishops Walk
Croydon
Surrey CR0 5BA
Tel: 081-655-1499 (work)
Tel: 081-681-0886 (home)
Contact: Mr Bharat Vora
Office: President

Young Jains

1 Aurelia Road
Croydon
Surrey CR0 3BE
Tel: 081-944-6534 (work)
Tel: 081-689-8814 (home)
Contact: Mr Sailesh Shah
Office: President

A youth organisation which exists to create a better understanding and awareness of Jain philosophy, practice and culture. It is also dedicated to the promotion of Jainism in the Western world, where not much is known about it. Activities include youth and welfare.

Oshwal Association of the UK (South London)
37 Florida Road
Thornton Heath
Surrey CR7 8EY
Tel: 081-764-8928
Contact: Mr J M Shah
Office: Secretary
A place of worship and community group having a community centre with an in-house temple on Campbell Road which was built and opened in 1991. The Association engages in social, religious and cultural activities.

Young Indian Vegetarians
226 London Road
West Croydon
Surrey CR0 2TF
Tel: 081-655-4498
Contact: Mr N Mehta

KEY TO TERMS IN JAIN ORGANISATIONAL TITLES

Note: This is not a complete glossary of significant Jain terms. It is a guide to the meaning and/or background of some of the words used in the titles of Jain organisations listed in this directory. More information on the italicised words can be tracked down elsewhere in the key and/or in the section on "Introducing the Jain Community" by using the Directory's Keyword Index.

Aden
Aden in the Arabian peninsula had a Jain community and its usage in an organisation's title indicates this historical connection.

Ashram
A word of Sanskrit origin meaning a "hermitage", although in the modern Jain context it usually means a place of spiritual rest and retreat and/or a school where religious instruction is offered.

Bhakti
Hindi for "devotion."

Bharati
Meaning "belonging to *Bharat*", in other words, India.

Digambar
Alternative Romanisation of *Digambara*, the name of a Jain sect, the monks of which renounce all possessions including clothes.

Mahavir
The title of the twenty-fourth *Tirthankara* of the Jain religion (599–527 BCE).

Mandal
Hindi for "circle" or "group".

Mewada
"Group" or "community"

Navayug
"New era"

Navnat
Literally means "nine *castes*" and refers to a Jain merchant *caste* from Gujarat, India.

Oshwal
The name of a Jain merchant caste in Western India.

Oshwall
Variant Romanisation of *oshwal* (see above).

Pragati
"Progress".

Samaj
Gujarati or Hindi for "society", often used of organisations or associations.

Sangh
Hindi for a "group" or "union", often used of organisations.

Shree
Sanskrit for "eminent one". A honorific title of respect.

Vanik
A merchant *caste*.

Visa Oshwal
A section or sub-group of the *Oshwal* community.

Vishwa
Meaning "world" or "universe".

ERRATA

The following typographical and other errors affect the sense or accuracy of the text and should be amended:

Page 6   Under "The Sikh Community", the page range should be 564-568.

Page 11   At the bottom of the second column, last paragraph, add the missing line "...drafting the Introductory materials and Keys and in ...".

Page 33   Final paragraph, under "Clothing", line 2 should read "...should not be informal".

Page 40   In the second column, the figure for Christians should be 37,600,000 and for Buddhists 130,000.

Page 134   In the second column, under the heading Jodo, the second line should read "The True School of the Pure Land."

Page 228   Add at the beginning of the third paragraph in the second column "Worldwide there are estimated to be about 721,000,000 Hindus."

Page 232   Final paragraph in the second column: delete Shaivites and insert "Vaishnavites are..."

Page 300   The second half of the entry under "Satya" should be a separate paragraph with the heading "Asteya".

Page 319   Amend the first heading in the second column to read "...and Batmitzvah".

Page 390   Paragraph 4, line 2 should read "(authority and trust...)".

Page 391   Amend the first heading in the first column to read "Jamaat-i-Islami".

Page 395   In the penultimate paragraph the word "strong" should read "strongest" and the final word of this sentence should read "them".

Page 451   The Muslim Women's Association is no longer at this address and phone number.

Page 526   In the second column, amend the first line in the last paragraph to read "..Bhai Nandlal...".

Page 579   In the second column, amend the second line to read "...Zoroastrian Trust Funds of Europe."

Page 587   In the address in the third paragraph, second column, the organisation's name should read "Church of Jesus Christ of Latter-day Saints".

Page 588   In the first paragraph under "Namdharis", the second date should be "1812" not "1712".

     ...d the first line in the first column to read "..Sant Khalsa.."

     ...the Index, the

THE JEWISH COMMUNITY

INTRODUCING THE JEWISH COMMUNITY

JEWS IN THE UNITED KINGDOM

There are approximately 15,000,000 Jews worldwide. The Jewish population of the UK is estimated at around 300,000.

Jews have been present in the UK for many centuries. They were expelled by Edward I in 1290. Then, following the English Civil War, Menasseh ben Israel of Amsterdam successfully campaigned for the readmission of Jews to England, soon after which they began to return.

Sephardi and Ashkenazi

The Jewish community in the UK is composed of both *Sephardi* and *Ashkenazi* Jewish communities. *Sephardi* Jews came originally from Spain and Portugal. They have the longest continuous communal history in the UK, having been present in an organised form since the mid-seventeenth century.

However, the majority of Jews in the UK today are descendants of two waves of immigration by *Ashkenazi* Jews of Central and East European origins who migrated to England for economic reasons or who fled from persecution in the Russian Empire between 1881-1914, and from 1933 onwards during the Nazi persecution in Germany and other European countries. Since 1956 small numbers of Jewish immigrants have arrived from Arab and East European countries.

Geographical Spread

At present, the largest concentration of British Jews is in the Greater London area, with the largest provincial Jewish populations to be found in Manchester, Leeds and Glasgow. Other sizeable Jewish communities are those to be found in Birmingham, Bournemouth, Brighton, Liverpool and Southend.

Two-thirds of the Jewish community are affiliated to a synagogue. Of these, about eighty per cent belong to *Orthodox* (see below) synagogues and twenty per cent to the *Progressive* sector (see below) of *Reform* and *Liberal* synagogues. The Registrar General's list of certified places of worship records 354 Jewish places of worship in England and Wales and this directory includes details of 320 synagogues in the UK.

Languages

In most parts of the UK Jewish community English is used as the normal language for day-to-day communication, but Hebrew and Yiddish are also used. Hebrew is the language of the Bible and of modern Israel and is the universal language which binds together Jews in the *Diaspora*. It is the main language of worship and many Jewish children learn it in *Heder* (synagogue-based classes).

Yiddish is a Jewish language of Eastern European origin which was originally a Judeo-German dialect with a number of Slavic and Hebrew words. Yiddish is used conversationally in a number of *Chasidic* (see below) communities. However, many other Jews cannot conduct complete conversations in Yiddish and in modern Jewish circles, it is generally spoken only amongst the older generation of *Ashkenazi* Jews. More recently, however, there has been a concern to prevent the language dying out and organisations have been set up to propagate Yiddish language and literature.

Ladino was the lingua franca of *Sephardi* Jews of Spanish origin and is based on Castillian Spanish. Judaeo-Arabic has been spoken among Jews originally from Arabic lands.

ORIGINS AND DEVELOPMENT OF JUDAISM

Patriarchs

The origins of Judaism are set out in the Hebrew Bible. Abraham is traditionally considered to be the first of three *avot* (forefathers) of the kinship group which are seen as ancestors of the Jewish people. When Abraham died, the leadership of this growing community was passed on to Isaac, his son, who, in turn, passed it on to his son Jacob. The name Israel, which was given to Jacob, is also used to describe the Jewish people as a whole.

Moses and the Israelites

Judaism centres on faith in one God and the belief that God made fundamental revelations to the Jewish people through Moses at Mount Sinai around 1300 BCE, after Moses had led them out of enslavement to the Pharaohs in Egypt.

Following the death of Moses, Joshua became leader and led the conquest of the land of Canaan which the Israelites believed had been promised to them by God through Abraham. After the conquest the land was divided into twelve areas for the twelve tribes of Israel descended from the sons and grandsons of Jacob (Reuben, Simeon, Judah, Issachar, Zebulun, Benjamin, Dan, Naphtali, Gad, Asher, Ephraim, and Manasseh). The terms Jew and Judaism derive from the name Judah, one of the twelve sons of Jacob.

Kingdoms and Exile

In 1030 BCE Saul was appointed to be King. He was later succeeded by King David, to be followed by King Solomon who erected a great temple in Jerusalem. In time, two kingdoms developed, the Southern Kingdom of Judah with Jerusalem as its capital and the Northern Kingdom of Israel. Both Kingdoms were eventually defeated and occupied by invading armies. In 586 BCE, the Temple was destroyed in the Babylonian invasion and many Jews were exiled to Babylon. Eventually, some of the Jews returned to Jerusalem and rebuilt the Temple which was again destroyed in 70 CE by the Romans.

Due to the new exile which followed, the Jewish community was scattered far and wide, but in the centuries that followed Jewish culture flourished. By the end of the fifth century the *Talmud* (see below) was completed and *rabbinic law*, commentary and Biblical interpretation have been enriched in every generation. From philosophy to mysticism and religious poetry, a rich and diverse cultural tradition has been created and development continues in the contemporary world.

Diaspora, Holocaust and Israel

Today there are Jewish communities in many countries. Following the Holocaust of European Jewry in which six million Jews were systematically killed, the State of Israel was founded in 1948. Jewish communities outside of Israel are collectively known as the *Diaspora*, and UK Jews are thus one of the many *Diaspora* communities.

SOURCES OF JEWISH BELIEFS AND PRACTICES

Tanakh

Judaism is derived from the Jewish scriptures as interpreted by the *rabbis* (teachers) past and present. The Jewish scriptures are known as the *Tanakh*, which is an acronym of the names of the initials of its three constituent sections: *Torah*, *Nevi'im* and *Ketuvim*. The *Torah* (teaching) is referred to within the community as the *Chumash* (from the Hebrew word meaning five) and consisting of the five books of Moses (Genesis, Exodus, Leviticus, Numbers and Deuteronomy).

These books contain what are believed to be God's revelation to Moses on Mount Sinai, and have six hundred and thirteen commandments dealing with questions of ethics, spirituality, dietary regulations and other matters reflecting every aspect of communal and social life.

The *Nevi'im* (from *navi* meaning prophet) consist of the books of the prophets such as Isaiah, Jeremiah and the related historical books of Joshua, Judges and Kings covering the period up to the rebuilding of the Temple.

The remaining Biblical books are included in the *Ketuvim* (writings). Psalms and the Song of Songs are major sources of Jewish liturgy and spiritual expression and the Book of Ruth and the Book of Esther are particularly well-known among Jewish readers.

Talmud

The *Tanakh* is complemented by the *Talmud* which was compiled by *rabbinic* scholars in the centuries following the destruction of the second Temple by the Romans in 70CE. It was completed in the fifth century. *Orthodox* Jews believe that it includes material previously revealed at Sinai, together with the *Torah*, and transmitted by oral tradition down the generations.

The *Talmud* has two components, the *Mishnah* and the *Gemara* (both being words for learning or study). The *Mishnah* is primarily a summary of religious and civil law. It is divided into six orders, each of which is named after the first main word in its section and contains a varying number of volumes or tractates: Seeds, which contains materials on prayers and agricultural laws; Festivals, which deals with matters related to the Sabbath (see below) and festivals; Women, which includes law on marriage and divorce; Damages, which contains civil and criminal law; Holy Things, which includes laws of sacrifice and Temple ritual; Purification, which contains laws relating to personal and religious purity.

The *Gemara* is a commentary and discussion of the *Mishnah*, comprising analysis, debate and clarification of legal source material. The text is an edited record of the argumentation and disputes of the scholars, retaining the thrust and parry of the *rabbinic* colleges. The *Gemara* also contains a wide range of narrative material, including historical anecdote, allegory, prayer, religious discussion and ethical guidance.

The non-legal material in the *Talmud* is known as the *Aggadah* (an Aramaic word derived from the Hebrew word for narrative). The legal material is known as *Halacha* (see below), from a Hebrew root meaning "to go"; *Halacha* is the practice or "way" of the tradition.

Midrash

Another important literary genre of Jewish religious tradition is *Midrash*. The *Midrash* consists of rabbinic interpretation of the Bible and includes moral teachings, legends and parables from a variety of great *rabbis*. The earliest texts date perhaps from 400–500 CE, but they reflect generations of literary development. The latest collections are 1100–1200 CE and major anthologies were made between 1200–1500 CE.

Halacha

The life of the Jewish community is focused around the interpretation and practice of the *Halacha* (Jewish law). There is a whole battery of texts which are used as the basis for legal decisions including the sixteenth century *Shulchan Aruch* and the commentaries of Jacob ben Asher and Moses Maimonides. A *Beth Din* is a court of law which rules according to *Halacha* and which members of the Jewish community approach for rulings on issues in personal and social life such as divorce and conversion to Judaism.

KEY JEWISH BELIEFS

Shema

The *Shema* (hear) is a daily prayer composed of three passages in the *Torah*. It contains the basic affirmation of the Jewish faith. Its first line is a clear injunction to absolute monothesim (belief in one God): "Hear O Israel, the Lord is our God, the Lord is One" (Deuteronomy 6 v3).

The one God created the world, extending justice, compassion and love to all women and men. Whilst God's ways can be known, God is also awe-inspiring in his transcendence and His ultimate essence lies beyond human cognition. God is seen as both King and Father, worshipped in awe, yet close to His people in intimacy and devotion.

Torah and Mitzvot

The *Torah* is the revelation of God's will that includes the *mitzvot* (commandments) which encompass every aspect of life. The *mitzvot* enable men and women to sanctify their daily lives and bring holiness into the world. Jews emphasise the obligations of love and reverence for God who created heaven and earth.

Study of the *Torah* is a passionate and sacred task that is central in the religious life. Prayer is of great significance and *sabbaths* and festivals are set aside for celebration and devotion. *Torah,* prayer, *sabbaths* and festivals infuse the mundane with the transcendent and the eternal.

Humanity

The world is understood to be a creation of God and must be treated accordingly. Humanity is made in the Divine image and love of one's neighbour is the great principle of social life and the founding inspiration of the Jewish community. Justice and compassion are Divine attributes that Jewish people are obliged to realise in all aspects of their lives. Sin and spiritual estrangement are profound and ever-present but the compassion and grace of God permit atonement and a return to the ultimate purity of human nature. The High Holy Days of the Jewish year are devoted to penitence, prayer, charity and forgiveness.

Kingdom of God

Jews have traditionally hoped for the establishment of God's kingdom on earth. Also, traditionally, this has been connected with a belief in a *Mashiah* (Anointed One), or *Messiah*.

There are different Jewish understandings of the concept of *Mashiah*. In the original sense of "anointed one", the term covers Jewish kings such as David and Solomon. The traditional belief is that a special person will reveal himself and the Jewish community will be gathered from its exile around the world and re-establish itself in the ancient land where the Temple will be rebuilt and never again be destroyed. The Kingdom of God will be established on earth for everyone. The dead will be resurrected, which some understand in a physical sense, whilst others think it refers to the spiritual continuity of the soul.

Another perspective, often found among *Progressive* Jews, is that there will be no individual *Mashiah* but rather a new Messianic era without war and conflict.

Eretz Yisrael

The land of Israel is of great importance to Jews and the concept of *Zionism* is found in both a religious and political sense. Religious *Zionists* see redemptive significance in the development of the state of Israel and view the ingathering of the Jewish exiles as a manifestation of Divine providence.

Some *Orthodox* groups (mainly in Israel itself) oppose this viewpoint and deny that a secular state can have religious significance. As a modern political movement *Zionism* is the movement to secure a Jewish homeland in Palestine which was officially begun by Theodore Herzl who, in the nineteenth century, founded the World Zionist Organisation which is now based in Israel.

TRADITIONS IN JUDAISM

There are a number of different Jewish traditions present in the UK. Estimates based on synagogue membership figures suggest that approximately eighty per cent of UK Jews are affiliated to a synagogue. Many Jews have moved between traditions. Some people brought up in *Orthodox* communities join *Progressive* synagogues in later life and vice versa.

Orthodox

The *Orthodox* Jewish community affirms the authenticity of revelation and accords the Bible and its Rabbinical interpretations full authority in determining law, life and religious practice. The *Torah* is believed to have been revealed by God and to contain God's unchanging words. *Orthodoxy* understands itself as representing the mainstream of Judaism in historical continuity with the Jewish inheritance.

Chasidic

Within the orbit of *Orthodoxy* is the *Chasidic* movement. The word *Chasidic* come from *Chasid*, which literally means "the pious". *Chasidic* groupings originated in the *Shtetls* (Jewish settlements) of Central and Eastern Europe. Today, the term *Chasidic* generally refers to those whose theology is influenced more by mystic spirituality than by intellectual orientation.

Chasidic Jews are also sometimes called the *Charedim* or the *Ultra-Orthodox*, although not all *Charedim* and *Ultra-Orthodox* are *Chasidic*. The distinction between *Ultra-Orthodox,* whether

Chasidic or not, and *Orthodox* more generally speaking is that the *Ultra-Orthodox* seek to exclude modern culture from their lives and tend to reproduce in minute detail the cultural ways of previous generations.

Some groupings are influenced by the body of Jewish mystical philosophy known as the *Kabbalah* which consists of teachings that were transmitted within select circles of disciples. The most important Kabbalistic text is the *Zohar*, which is a commentary on the *Chumash* that was completed in fourteenth century Spain.

Progressive

Progressive Jews believe that the *Torah* was inspired by God, but written down by humans according to God's will. Thus it is open to challenge and revision and subject to the need of reinterpretation. Revelation is viewed as progressive because God's will is seen to be constantly unfolding. *Progressive* Jews make a distinction between those parts of Judaism that have eternal significance and absolute value, for example, the *Shabbat* and the pursuit of justice, and those that are temporary and relative, such as gender distinctions in Jewish law.

The *Reform* movement began in the early nineteenth century as an attempt to create a Judaism consistent with the modern world. The *Liberal* movement was first established in Germany and the USA as an offshoot of the *Reform* movement. Its adherence considered sincerity of heart to be paramount in Judaism and believed that rituals should be relatively unimportant. They therefore reformed the synagogue services and belief and practice in the light of modern knowledge and circumstances.

Conservative

Established at the beginning of the twentieth century, *Conservative* Judaism is often said to be half-way between *Orthodox* Judaism and *Progressive* Judaism. Conservative Jews wish to maintain Jewish traditions whilst recognising the influence of contemporary issues on practice. So, for example the *Shabbat* liturgy may be very similar to that used in *Orthodox* congregations, but men and women may sit together in the *synagogue* during services. *Conservative* Jews attempt to comply with as much of the *Torah* as is practicable in modern society, but they may accept the inevitability, for example, of driving to synagogue on the *Sabbath* now that members may live further away.

In the UK, *Conservative* Judaism has a national organisation known as the Masorti Assembly of Synagogues which has local constituent synagogues. This movement is closely related to American Conservative Judaism and attempts to wed a commitment to the *Halacha* with an historical approach to its application.

JEWISH LIFE

In *Orthodox and Reform* Judaism a Jew is traditionally understood to be any person born of a Jewish mother or a person who has converted to the Jewish faith. In *Liberal* Judaism having a Jewish father may also qualify a child for membership of the community, if the child has had a Jewish upbringing.

Circumcision and Brit

A number of ceremonies mark transitional points in Jewish life. It is believed that God entered into a *Brit* (a covenant forming a permanent relationship) with the Jewish community, first through Abraham and then through Moses at Sinai. The Jewish people are therefore sometimes referred to by others as "the chosen people".

Where an idea of "chosenness" appears within Judaism, it is a reference to the belief that the Jews have been "chosen" to live within a covenantal relationship with God with its implications of a certain way of living. Jews believe that this covenantal relationship gives no advantage to them above others, but rather an extra responsibility to live in accordance with God's laws, and to contribute to the world's moral order.

As a sign of God's covenant with Abraham, Abraham was required to *circumcise* himself and his two sons (Isaac and Ishmael). Because of this

Jewish law asserts that a male Jew should normally be *circumcised* on the eighth day of his life. The ceremony is known as *Brit Milah* and is carried out by a trained *Mohel* (circumciser) usually in the home with family and friends present at the ceremony. There is no equivalent ceremony for girls.

Barmitzvah and Batmitvah

Prior to the age of thirteen male Jews do not carry responsibility for *mitzvot* (the commandments), but at thirteen years old they take a new position within the community.

The ceremony which marks this is called *Barmitzvah* (son of commandment) and it involves the young man reading, in Hebrew, from the weekly portion of the *Torah* scroll, usually during the Saturday morning service in the synagogue. After the service the family of the boy who has become *Barmitzvah* may provide *Kiddush* for the congregation, presents are given to the boy, and some families may have a party for family and friends.

In *Progressive* Judaism there is also a *Batmitzvah* (daughter of commandment ceremony) for thirteen year old females which is in the same form as the *Barmitzvah* ceremony. In some *Orthodox* circles girls celebrate a *Batmitzvah* at the age of twelve, the traditional coming of age for females, whereas others may participate in a communal *Bat Chayil* ceremony usually held at the age of thirteen. The ceremony often takes place on a Sunday and girls take part in it as a group with their peers. *Psalms* and special readings are recited.

In *Progressive* Judaism there is also a ceremony called *Kabbalat Torah*, which takes place at the age of sixteen and marks the culmination of the young person's religious education.

Shabbat

The *Shabbat* (or *Sabbath*) is central to the rhythm of Jewish individual, family and communal life. It is observed as a day of worship, rest and peace. Saturday, on which it is observed, is believed to correspond to the seventh day of the creation on which God rested from creating the earth.

Shabbat begins about half an hour before sunset on the Friday evening and ends at nightfall on the Saturday night in line with the statement in the scriptural *Book of Genesis* that "there was evening and morning", implying that a day is deemed to begin on its preceding night. The time varies from week to week, starting later in summer and earlier in winter. Exact times are available in the Jewish press. *Shabbat* is concluded with *Havdala*, a ceremony of separation making the transition from the *Shabbat* to the working week, often performed at home after the last *Shabbat* services.

During *Shabbat* it is forbidden for Jews to engage in any activities which are considered as work. This is the general rule which has been interpreted in different ways by different Jewish traditions. For example, *Orthodox* Jews may not drive their cars on *Shabbat* as this entails making a spark in the engine which is seen as synonymous with starting a fire, which in turn is considered to be work. *Progressive* Jews, however, do not deem this as work and therefore do drive. The general exception to these *Shabbat* rules, as in all other areas of Jewish life, is where there is danger to life, in which case the laws of the *Shabbat* are set aside and precedence is given to saving lives.

Kashrut

Judaism has a series of important food regulations known as *kashrut*. Animals, birds and fish might be either *kosher* (permitted) or *treif* (forbidden). *Treif* is a Yiddish word, derived from the Hebrew *terephah*, which refers to an animal torn by a wild beast. Acceptable animals for consumption are all those with split hooves which chew the cud such as sheep, cows and deer. Pigs, rabbits and horses are unacceptable. All fowl other than birds of prey are acceptable. For example, chicken is acceptable but hawk is not. Eggs are considered *kosher* if they are from *kosher* fowl. Fish without both fins and scales are unacceptable – in other words, salmon is acceptable but prawns are not.

Fruit and vegetables are all acceptable and are considered *parve*, which means that they are neither milk nor meat products and can be eaten with both (see below). Food which contains, or has been cooked in, products from non-acceptable animals would be unacceptable to Jews. For example, chips cooked in non-*kosher* animal fat are not acceptable.

For meat to be *kosher* it must have been humanely slaughtered by a *shochet* (a qualified slaughterer) working under the supervision of the *Beth Din*. *Shechitah* (which is slaughter according to Jewish law) involves the draining of blood from the animal by slitting its throat.

Once killed, the meat from the animal must then be *kashered*. This involves the meat being soaked and salted or, in certain cases such as liver, broiled, in order to remove excess blood. The prohibition against consuming blood comes from the view that blood represents life and so, for example, eggs with blood spots should also not be eaten.

Jewish law prohibits the mixing of milk foods with meat foods. This derives from biblical prohibitions against boiling a kid in its mother's milk. Separate sets of kitchen utensils are used for the two types of food and a time lapse is practised between eating one type of food and the other. Glass (although not pyrex) can be used for both types of food. Fish may be served with milk but it is not eaten together with meat. The extent to which these food laws are observed varies from person to person. If intending to provide food for Jewish guests it is wise to check first about any requirements.

Women

In terms of gender traditions and expectations, in the personal domain there is a practice of married women attending a *mikveh* (ritual bath). *Halachically*, a woman is believed to become ritually unclean by the process of menstruation. According to *Halacha*, before marriage, after menstruation, and after childbirth, women should visit a *mikveh*. *Progressive* Jews view the practice of visiting the *mikveh* as an option rather than as a necessity.

In *Progressive* Judaism both women and men have equal opportunity to take part in religious ceremonies: they can form a *minyan* (see section on worship), carry the *Torah*, and become *rabbis*. In the *Orthodox* sector women do not to take on these roles, but many *Orthodox* synagogues employ women in an administrative capacity and as teachers.

Women, and especially mothers, are seen to have a key role in Jewish life because of their roles in the family which is at the centre of the practice of Judaism and, in particular, of many of its festivals and celebrations. In the legal domain distinctions of gender roles as specified in Jewish law are no longer recognised as binding in *Progressive* Judaism. They are, however, still upheld in *Orthodox* Judaism. For example, when a marriage breaks down a woman cannot remarry until she has been given a *get* (religious divorce) by her husband and a man normally cannot remarry until a woman has accepted a bill of divorce from him.

JEWISH WORSHIP

Shabbat Worship

The most regular and well attended forms of communal worship on *Shabbat* are *Kabbalat Shabbat* (first *Shabbat* service at dusk on Friday evening) and *Maariv* (the evening service said every day including Friday night), as well as *Shakharit* and *Musaf* on Saturday morning.

The service on a Saturday morning usually lasts one to two hours in *Progressive* synagogues and between two and three hours in *Orthodox* synagogues. In the *Orthodox* community the entire service, except the *rabbi's* sermon and the prayer for the Royal Family, is conducted in Hebrew.

Progressive Jewish congregations often say other prayers in English, although the extent of English usage varies from congregation to congregation. In *Progressive* synagogues, but not in *Orthodox* ones, the service may be accompanied by musical instruments, although in some *Orthodox* synagogues there may be unaccompanied choral singing.

During the *Shabbat* morning service a portion of the *Torah* (Pentateuch) is read. The *Torah* is divided into *Sidrah* or *Parashah* (fifty-four weekly portions) to be read each consecutive Saturday in the synagogue. In an *Orthodox* synagogue a minimum of seven men are called to read from the *Torah*.

Following the reading of the *Torah* the *Haftarah* (an excerpt from the *Nevi'im* which is considered to be relevant to the *Torah*) is read. After the service *Kiddush* is said. This is the prayer proclaiming the holiness of the *Sabbath* and festivals and is recited before meals on those days over a cup of wine. The congregation usually stays for biscuits and cake and a chat.

Special children's services are held in many larger synagogues, to encourage children to be able to take an active role in the service when they are older. Above all, *Shabbat* is a family-orientated time with special meals and time for the whole family.

In the *Orthodox* community formal communal prayers can only be said when a *minyan* (group of ten or more *Orthodox* males) has been convened. Communal worship can take place anywhere and not necessarily in a synagogue. An example of this is where collective prayers are said at the home of a bereaved person during the seven days of mourning immediately after a death. This is known as *sitting Shivah*. It is not necessary for a *rabbi* to officiate at communal prayers and any person familiar with them may lead them.

Traditionally, during worship all males and married women should cover their heads as a sign of respect when addressing God. Some Jews keep their heads covered at all times in recognition of the continual presence of God. The traditional means for doing this is, for Jewish men, the small "skull cap" known as a *kippah* (in Hebrew) or a *Yarmulkah* (in Yiddish). Some *Ultra-Orthodox* women cover their heads at all times with a *sheitel* (wig). In principle, any form of headcovering is acceptable for either sex.

Three daily prayers are stipulated. These are *Shaharit* (morning service), *Minhah* (afternoon prayers) and *Maariv* (evening prayers). The *Siddur* (prayer book - derived from the Hebrew word meaning "order") contains prayers for communal services, for private prayer and for special occasions and travellers.

The various Jewish traditions have different authorised Prayer Books for use in their synagogues. Prayers are mainly in Hebrew with the English translation given in prayerbooks on the opposite page. Prayer books open from right to left, as in all Hebrew texts, since Hebrew is written from right to left. There are special prayer books for the pilgrim festivals and for the high holy days, known as *Mahczorim* (from the Hebrew word meaning cycle).

Synagogue

The principal place of Jewish communal worship is the *synagogue* which *Ashkenazi* Jews usually refer to by the *Yiddish* word *Shul*.

Due to the *Orthodox* rule of walking to the synagogue, *Orthodox* synagogue buildings have moved from inner city areas where Jews first settled to the suburbs of towns and cities where the main Jewish communities are now established. The synagogue is a building where worship occurs, but is also a central place of administration for cultural activities and education. Synagogues are self-financing and may have a *Heder* (room) which is a school for Jewish education, where children can gain religious knowledge and learn Hebrew. The synagogue might also offer adult Jewish education. In the larger synagogues, services are held most mornings and evenings.

In *Orthodox* synagogues men and women are separated and women usually sit in a gallery above the men's section where the men carry out the service. Sometimes, where there is no gallery, the women are seated behind the men with a short curtain or partition separating the two, and in some very small house synagogues women and men worship in different rooms.

Inside the synagogue, a range of symbols and objects may be seen. The *Magen David* (Shield of David) is a six pointed star which is a modern Jewish symbol of no particular religious significance. The *Menorah* is an seven-branched candlestick of a type dating back to the Temple

in Jerusalem prior to its destruction by the Romans.

A *mezuzah* (literally meaning door post) is a hollow box, usually made out of wood or metal, containing a parchment scroll containing two sections of scripture (Deuteronomy 6 v. 4–9 and Deuteronomy 11 v. 13-21) which constitute the first paragraphs of the *Shema*. This may be found on the internal doors of a synagogue and is also found on the doorposts of many Jewish homes. It signifies the sanctity of home and communal life. A *mezuzah* is to be found situated in the top third of the right hand doorpost of every room in a building except the toilet and the bathroom.

The *Bimah* is a raised platform in the centre of the synagogue, from which the Torah is read. Most synagogues also have a pulpit from which the sermon is preached. A *Chazzan* (see section on "Personnel") leads congregational prayer. The *Aron Kodesh* (Holy Ark) is an alcove or cupboard with wooden or ornate door panels which contains the Torah scrolls. In Western countries it is usually on the East wall of the synagogue which is the direction of Jerusalem. It has an embroidered curtain across it, known as a *Parochet*. A *Ner Tamid* (everlasting light) is a lamp hung in front of the *Aron Kodesh*, reminding the congregation of the eternal presence of God.

The *Sefer Torah* is a hand–written scroll of the *Torah*. It is read four times a week, on Monday and Thursday mornings, Saturday morning and Saturday afternoons. It is also read on holy days. The *Torah* scroll is kept inside a velvet cover and is usually decorated with metal breastplates and adornments. It has an honoured place in Jewish worship, especially at the festival of *Simchat Torah*. The sanctity of the *Sefer Torah* is underlined by the use of a *Yad* which is a long pointer in the shape of a hand used by the reader so that the place may be kept without touching the parchment.

Clothing and Prayer

Tephilin (phylacteries) are worn on the forehead and left arm particularly by male *Orthodox* Jews over thirteen years old. They consist of two strap–on leather boxes which enclose parchment sections of the scriptures, the wearing of which is believed by the *Orthodox* to be in accordance with scriptural commandment. *Tephilin* are worn for morning prayers, but not for *Shabbat* or festival prayers.

Tallitot are traditional prayer shawls, often with black or blue stripes. *Tzitzit* are the fringes which are sewn on to the four corners. Traditional style prayer shawls are usually made of wool. Some *Orthodox* Jewish men may wear the fringes, known as *Arba Kanfot* (meaning "four corners"), at all times on a vest under their clothes. In *Progressive* Jewish communities women are often encouraged to wear a prayer shawl if they take a leading role in corporate worship, but they are not obliged to do so.

JEWISH CALENDAR AND FESTIVALS

Calendar

According to the Jewish calendar the year 1993 is the year 5753. This year appears on Jewish legal documents such as marriage certificates, on Jewish periodicals and on grave stones. A combined lunar and solar calendar is used, where each month is the equivalent of twenty-nine or thirty days, and a year is usually three hundred and fifty-four days. In a nineteen year cycle an extra month is inserted in years three, six, eight, eleven, fourteen, seventeen and nineteen of the solar cycle.

Festivals

Because months are based on the moon, no fixed date can be given in the Gregorian calendar for Jewish festivals. With regard to the festivals mentioned below, the period of duration given is that followed by *Orthodox* Jews. *Reform* Jews may celebrate these festivals for a day less. The reason for this is that prior to mathematical calculation of the new moon, festivals were originally given an extra day in order to ensure their observance on the correct date, as a new moon could fall on one of two days. *Progressive* Jews believe that now the new moon can be accurately calculated the addition of extra day is no longer needed and this has always been the practice in the State of Israel.

Jewish festivals always begin in the evening and are grouped into three types. These are: the *Yamim Noraim* (Days of Awe); the *Shalosh Regalim* (Hebrew literally meaning "three foot festivals") which are the three festivals that have an agricultural and historical significance and in which it was traditional for every Jew to go to Jerusalem; and there are the minor festivals.

The *Yamim Noraim* are:

Rosh Hashanah
(September/October)

Two days of judgement and penitence. The *Shofar* (ram's horn) is blown in the synagogue to remind people of their sins and to call them to spiritual awareness. It begins the Jewish year and the ten days of repentance which culminate in *Yom Kippur.*

Yom Kippur
(Day of Atonement)

A fast day devoted to prayer and worship, recollecting the sins of the past year and seeking forgiveness for them. The first two days and last day (*Yom Kippur*) are days during which no work may be done.

The *Shalosh Regalin* are:

Sukkot
(September/October)

This is the festival of *Tabernacles* which commemorates the wandering of the children of Israel between Egypt and Canaan and God's protection during this period. There is a practice of building *sukkot* (temporary huts) onto the sides of houses or in gardens. This practice is intended to recall how the Jewish ancestors lived in the wilderness. Normally, the UK climate prevents Jews living in the *sukkot* for the entirety of the festival, but Jewish families may have their meals in them. *Sukkot* can often be seen on the sides of synagogue and Jewish communal buildings.

The festival has a harvest connection which is acknowledged by taking four types of plant and parading them around the synagogue: a *lulav* (palm branch), an *etrog* (citron), two *aravot* (willow branches) and three *hadassim* (myrtle branches). In the *Diaspora*, *Sukkot* is a nine day period with the first two and last two days as festival days. The final day is *Simchat Torah*.

Simchat Torah (the rejoicing of the Torah)

Celebrates the completion and recommencement of the annual cycle of readings from the *Torah* in the synagogue.

Pesach
(March/April)

Pesach occurs at a time when the first fruits of barley would have been offered as sacrifice in the Temple when the barley harvest was gathered. It is an eight day period and the first two and last two days are celebrated as festivals. It commemorates the Exodus from Egypt, and God's redemption of the Jewish people.

As a reminder that the Hebrews had no time to wait for bread to rise before they had to leave Egypt, no *chametz* (leavened products) are consumed at this time. Such foods must be removed from the home, either by eating them beforehand or by giving them away. Prior to the festival the house is scrupulously cleaned in order to remove any crumbs of *chametz*. *Matzot* (unleavened bread) is consumed during the festival period. A spare set of kitchen utensils may be used for the duration of the festival.

The home ceremony centres around the *seder* meal which, in the *Diaspora*, takes place on the first two nights of the festival. The order of service surrounding this meal is found in the *Haggadah* (*Seder* service book) which utilises verses from the *Torah* and from *Midrashic* commentaries in order to tell the story of the Exodus.

Shavuot (Pentecost)
(May/June)

This festival commemorates the Israelites' receiving of the *Torah* at Mount Sinai and pledging allegiance to God. On the night before the festival many Jews stay awake all night studying the *Torah* in preparation for the anniversary of the revelation on the next day. The *Book of Ruth* is read during *Shavuot*. This festival lasts for two days and is the harvest festival of Mediterannean first fruits such as olives, dates, grapes, and figs. Dairy foods are eaten on *Shavuot*.

Minor festivals and additional fast days:

There are other festivals which form a part of Jewish life, but at which times there are no restrictions on work:

Chanukah
(December)

This festival commemorates the rededication of the Second Temple in Jerusalem by the Maccabees in 168 BCE after it had been desecrated by the Hellenists. *Rabbinic* legend recounts that only one jar of oil with the High Priest's seal on it was found which was fit for use to light the Temple *menorah* (seven-branched candlestick), but by a miracle the little jar lasted for eight whole days. Some families give gifts to children at this time. *Chanukah* lasts for eight days, and for each day one more candle on the *Chanukiah* (a nine-branched candelabrum) is lit at home and in the synagogue. It has a lamp for each of the eight days with an additional serving light. Sometimes large *Chanukiot* are erected outside the synagogue and in city squares.

Purim
(February/March)

Is the day which commemorates the story found in the *Book of Esther* concerning the saving of the Jews of the Persian empire from the evil government minister Haman. On this day children dress up and the synagogue service includes readings from the *Book of Esther* with the worshippers booing and hissing whenever Haman's name is mentioned. Presents are given to friends as well as gifts to the poor. It is a time marked by fancy dress parties and general merry-making.

Yom Ha'atzma'ut
(May)

Israeli Independence day is celebrated by a service in many, though not all, synagogues.

Tishah Be-Av
(July/August)

This day commemorates the destruction of the Temple in 586BCE and again in 70CE and is a fast day.

There are also a number of other fasts which are observed by Jews to varying degrees. For example, the day before *Purim* is the *Fast of Esther*.

JEWISH ORGANISATIONS

General Organisations

The main national representative organisation for British Jews is the Board of Deputies of British Jews which was founded in 1760. Every synagogue and national communal organisation is entitled to send delegates to the Board. It deals with matters affecting the status and rights of British Jews and has a number of Committees to deal with particular issues (for example, Defence and Group Relations, Israel and Foreign Affairs). It also has a Community Research Unit and a Central Enquiry Desk.

There are several other national representative organisations which are more specific in nature, such as the League of Jewish Women and the Anglo-Jewish Association. There are also fifteen local Jewish Representative Councils around the UK in the areas of sizeable Jewish population. These Councils include both religious and community organisations. In terms of specifically religious organisations, there are national synagogue groupings with affiliated synagogues, for example, the United Synagogue, the Reform Synagogues of Great Britain and the Union of Liberal and Progressive Synagogues.

There are other national religious organisations with a more specific nature, for example the Initiation Society which trains and authorises

people to circumcise in the *Orthodox* tradition, and the National Council of Shechita Boards which deals with issues concerning *shechita*. There are are also many local religious organisations including local *shechita* boards and *kosher* meals-on-wheels services.

There are a range of national and local organisations which are particular to the Jewish community but do not as such serve a religious function. These include various welfare organisations like Jewish Care and the Jewish Marriage Guidance Council. There are political organisations and also *Zionist* cultural groups and charitable refugee support groups.

There are several communal educational organisations and *Yeshivot* (plural of *Yeshiva*, a place of advanced Jewish learning, primarily concerned with Talmudic study). Whilst *Yeshivot* do offer ordination to those studying within them who wish to serve in the *Rabbinate*, there are also academic Colleges which specifically serve this need. In *Orthodox* Judaism there is Jews' College in London and in *Progressive* Judaism, the Leo Baeck College. In addition, there are many local and national organisations promoting Jewish education and culture in general including historical societies, musical groups, youth groups and Holocaust remembrance organisations.

There is a whole range of multi-national Jewish organisations. For example, there is a Conference of European Rabbis of which all Orthodox *rabbis* are entitled to membership. The Reform Synagogues of Great Britain and the Union of Liberal and Progressive Synagogues are constituent members of the World Union of Progressive Judaism which aims to foster the growth and practice of *Progressive* Judaism.

Further details of all Jewish organisations can be found in Massil, J (ed), *The Jewish Year Book*, Jewish Chronicle Publications, London, 1993.

Orthodox Organisations

The oldest *Orthodox* synagogue still in use in the UK is Bevis Marks *Sephardi* synagogue in London, which was built in 1701. There are a number of organised groupings of *Orthodox* synagogues. The spiritual leader of many *Orthodox Ashkenazi* Jews is the *Chief Rabbi* who is appointed by the Chief Rabbinate Council consisting of representatives of the Orthodox United Synagogue, established in 1870. Other *Orthodox* groupings are the smaller Federation of Synagogues and the Union of Hebrew Congregation Synagogues.

The best known *Chasidic* group in Britain is part of a world movement known as *Lubavitch*. The *Lubavitch* feel a particular obligation to persuade people to become religiously observant and to prevent the assimilation of Jews into secular culture. *Chasidic* Jews are concentrated in London and Greater Manchester with smaller numbers in other places where there are large Jewish communities. They follow the teachings of Israel ben Eliezer also known as the Baal Shem Tov who lived in the seventeenth century in Poland, and took a mystical approach to Judaism.

Reform and Liberal Organisations

There are two *Progressive* Jewish traditions in the UK: *Reform* Judaism and *Liberal* Judaism. *Reform* Judaism is the larger of the two traditions and originally the *Liberal* movement was more radically different from the *Orthodox* community than was *Reform* Judaism. Now, however, the initial distinction between *Liberal* and *Reform* Judaism has diminished and the communities have, to a significant degree, converged in their practice. *Rabbis* for both communities are given the same training at Leo Baeck College in London. Most UK *Progressive* Jews live in London, the South of England, Manchester and Leeds.

The *Reform* movement has its own *Beth Din* (established in 1948), cemeteries, day school and a major cultural centre in North London. It is organised nationally in the Reform Synagogues of Great Britain and is represented in many communal bodies such as the Board of Deputies of British Jews and the Jewish Welfare Board. The first *Reform* synagogue in the UK was the West London Synagogue opened in 1840.

The *Liberal* movement began in the UK in 1902 with the foundation of the Jewish Religious Union. The first *Liberal* Jewish congregation was set up in 1910 in London and was called the *Liberal* Jewish Synagogue. Since 1944 the name of the *Liberal* movement's national representative organisation has been the Union of Liberal and Progressive Synagogues.

Independent Synagogues

In addition to the formal groupings a number of independent synagogues exist in UK Judaism, of both *Orthodox* and *Progressive* traditions.

Personnel

The *rabbi's* role within the Jewish community is to teach and to preach, to take on pastoral duties and advise on Jewish law. All *rabbis* in the *Orthodox* sector are male whilst the *Progressive* sector has both men and women *rabbis*. *Rabbis* are often, but not always, salaried by the congregation. A synagogue minister can sometimes be referred to as *Reverend* which often implies that the minister does not have *rabbinic* ordination.

A *Dayan* is a judge in Jewish law who serves on the *Beth Din* and administers Jewish law in cases brought before it. In an *Orthodox Beth Din*, *Dayanim* are permanent salaried members, whilst in the *Reform Beth Din*, *rabbis* serve in rotation as *Dayanim*. A *Chazzan/Cantor* is a singer who leads the synagogue services and, in *Orthodox* synagogues, is male. *Progressive* synagogues tend not to have *Chazzanim* (plural of *Chazzan*), preferring to have a choir to assist the *Rabbi* during services. A *Sofer* (scribe) is a person who writes *Torah* scrolls, *tephillin*, and *mezuzot* by hand, using a quill pen on parchments. The *Chevra Kaddisha* (holy brotherhood) is a Jewish burial society responsible for washing and shrouding Jewish corpses and for looking after the needs of the bereaved.

Chassidic groupings are led by *Rebbes*. The *Rebbe* is a charismatic spiritual leader. The office of *Rebbe* is hereditary, often, but not always, being passed down to the eldest son.

Many synagogues have a committee structure. Some medium sized synagogues have part-time Secretaries and some large synagogues full time

Secretaries who can be approached as a first point of contact with the community.

BIBLIOGRAPHY

Alexander, P S (ed), *Textual Sources for the Study of Judaism*, Manchester University Press, Manchester, 1987.

Cohn-Sherbok, D, *The Jewish Heritage*, Blackwell, Oxford, 1988.

Cohn-Sherbok, D, "Judaism in Modern Britain: A New Orientation", in Badham, P (ed), *Religion, State and Society in Modern Britain*, Edwin Mellen Press, Lampeter, 1989, pp 209-224.

Close, B E, *Judaism*, Hodder and Stoughton, London, 1991.

Cooper, H and Morrison, P, *A Sense of Belonging: Dilemmas of British Jewish Identity*, Weidenfeld and Nicolson, London, 1991.

Cross, C, *What is Judaism ?*, Board of Deputies of British Jews (Central Jewish Lecture and Information Committee), London, 1974.

de Lange, N, *Judaism*, Oxford University Press, Oxford, 1987.

Epstein, I, *Judaism: An Historical Perspective*, Pelican, Harmondsworth, 1959.

Friesel, E, *Atlas of Modern Jewish History*, Oxford University Press, Oxford, 1990.

Gilbert, M, *Jewish History Atlas*, Weidenfeld and Nicholson, London, 1969.

Gilbert, M, *Holocaust Atlas*, Board of Deputies of British Jews, London, 1978.

Gletzer, N N (ed), *The Judaic Tradition*, Behrman, New York, 1969.

Gubbay, L and Levy A, *Ages of Man: A Plain Guide to Traditional Jewish Custom, Practice and Belief in Modern Times*, DLT, London 1985.

Kushner, T (ed), *The Jewish Heritage in British History: Englishness and Jewishness*, Frank Cass and Company, London, 1992.

Lawton, C, *The Jewish People: Some Questions Answered*, Board of Deputies of British Jews (Central Jewish Lecture and Information Centre), London, 1983.

Massil, S W, (ed), *The Jewish Year Book*, Jewish Chronicle Publications, London, 1993.

Neusner, J, *Between Time and Eternity: The Essentials of Judaism*, Dickenson Publishing Company, Californnia, 1975.

Pearl, C and Brookes, R S, *A Guide to Jewish Knowledge*, Jewish Chronicle Publications. London, 1965.

Romain, J, *Faith and Practice: A Guide to Reform Judaism*, Reform Synagogues of Great Britain, London, 1991.

Sacks, J, *The Persistence of Faith*, Weidenfeld and Nicholson, London, 1991.

Schmool, M and Cohen, F, *British Synagogue Membership in 1990*, Board of Deputies of British Jews (Community Research Unit), London, 1991.

Seltzer, RM, *Jewish People, Jewish Thought*, Collier Macmillan, London, 1980.

Turner, R, *Jewish Living*, Jewish Chronicle Publications, London, 1982.

Union of Liberal and Progressive Synagogues, *Affirmations of Liberal Judaism*, London, 1992

Unterman, A, *The Wisdom of the Jewish Mystics*, Sheldon Press, London, 1976.

Unterman, A, *The Jews: Their Beliefs and Practices*, Routledge and Kegan Paul, London.

Waterman, S and Kosmin, B, *British Jewry in the Eighties*, Board of Deputies of British Jews (Community Research Unit), London, 1986.

Williams, B, *The Making of Manchester Jewry: 1740-1875*, Manchester University Press, Manchester, 1976.

JEWISH UK ORGANISATIONS

The Jewish Community has a large range of organisations operating at a UK level. This directory has included those with a specifically religious focus or basis. There are, however, a wider number of communal groups and bodies, contact details of which can be obtained from Massil, S (ed), *The Jewish Yearbook 5753-5754*, Jewish Chronicle Publications, London, 1993.

Advisory Committee for the Admission of Jewish Ecclesiastical Officers

5 Mapesbury Road
London NW2 4HZ
Tel: 081-451-0233
Contact: Cedric Lauder
Office: Honorary Secretary
Representative committee set up in 1932 at the request of the Home Office to advise on employing non-British citizens as religious functionaries and also student permits for ecclesiastical colleges. It represents all branches of the Jewish community in liaison between the community and the Home Office. It is administered from the office of Jews' Temporary Shelter.

Agudas Harabbanim (Association of Rabbis of Great Britian)

273 Green Lanes
London N4 2EX
Tel: 081-802-1544

Agudas Israel of Great Britain

97 Stamford Hill
London N16 5DN
Tel: 081-800-6688

Agudath Hashochtim V'Hashomrim of Great Britain (Cattle Section)

33 Elm Park Avenue
London N15 6AR
Contact: S B Spitzer
Office: Honorary Secretary

Agudath Hashochtim V'Hashomrim of Great Britain (Poultry section)

25 Rostrevor Road
London N15
Contact: S Leaman
Office: Honorary Secretary

Anglo-Jewish Association

Woburn House
(5th Floor)
Upper Woburn Place
London WC1H 0EP
Tel: 071-387-5937
Contact: Mrs. E. Salasnik
Office: General Secretary
The association is a forum for all sectors of Anglo-Jewry, and its membership includes people from all religious viewpoints within Judaism, as well as those from a wide spectrum of political opinion. Members share in, and are in sympathy with, the

educational, cultural and human rights objectives of the Association. It aims to act as forum for all sectors of the Anglo-Jewish community; to promote and defend the human rights of people of all creeds and to protect persecuted Jews in all parts of the world and to help under-privileged Jews from all countries to establish themselves in life through higher education. It works by: representations to the Government and the Crown, as a privileged body of the Crown; at the United Nations through its founding membership of the Consultative Council of Jewish Organisations; through work in the Council of Europe; through specialised reports on racial and religious discrimination and by grants from educational and charitable trusts to help Jewish students in higher education.

Assembly of Masorti Synagogues

766 Finchley Road
London NW11 7TH
Tel: 081-201-8772
Fax: 081-201-8917
Contact: Gail Miller
Office: Administrator
Representative body.

Association of Adath Yisrael Synagogues

40 Queen Elizabeth's Walk
London N16 0HH
Tel: 081-802-6262

Association of Jewish Communal Professionals

17 Arden Road
London N3 3AB
Tel: 081-346-3121
Contact: Honorary Secretary

Association of Jewish Ex-Servicemen and Women

Ajex House
East Bank
London N16 5RT
Tel: 081-800-2844
Fax: 081-880-1117
Contact: Mr Harry A Farbey
Office: General Secretary
A welfare organisation which looks after the welfare of needy Jewish ex-servicemen and women and their dependents.

Association of Jewish Friendship Clubs

Woburn House
Upper Woburn Place
London WC1H 0EP
Tel: 071-387-8980
The association organises clubs with physical and mental recreation facilities and other objectives to benefit the sixty plus age group.

Association of Jewish Refugees in GB

Karminski House
9 Adamson Road
London NW3 3HX
Tel: 071-483-2536
Contact: L. Lassman
Office: Administrator
The association offers mutual aid and welfare, mainly to Nazi-era refugees.

Association of Jewish Sixth Formers

Hillel House
1/2 Endsleigh Street
London WC1H 0DS
Tel: 071-388-3776

Association of Jewish Teachers

c/o The Education Department
Board of Deputies of British Jews
Woburn House
Tavistock Square
London WC1 0EZ
Tel: 071-387-3952

Association of Jewish Women's Organisations in UK

Woburn House
Upper Woburn Place
London WC1H 0EP
Tel: 071-387-7688
Contact: Mrs Denise Williams
Office: Honorary Secretary
A forum for the major Jewish women's organisations in the UK for the exchange of ideas and information. It seeks to promote unity across the spectrum of religious belief and to further communal understanding. It encourages women to seek wider representation on communal bodies.

Association of Jewish Youth

AJY House
128 East Lane
Wembley
Middlesex HA0 3NL
Tel: 081-908-4747
Fax: 081-904-4323
Contact: Martin Shaw
Office: Executive Director

To promote the mental, physical and spiritual well-being of young Jews and to foster the highest standards of citizenship and loyalty. It works by means of a centralised programme of sporting and cultural events; by voluntary youth service; by providing a consultancy and advice service to affiliated groups; by training professional and voluntary personnel centrally and locally; and by providing general and specific information.

Association of Ministers (Chazanim) of Great Britain

9 Marlborough Mansions
Cannon Hill
London NW6 1JP
Tel: 071-431-0575 (home)
Contact: Rev S I Brickman
Office: Chairperson
Membership group.

Association of Orthodox Jewish Professionals of GB

53 Wentworth Road
London NW11 0RT

Association of United Synagogue Women

Woburn House
Upper Woburn Place
London WC1H 0EZ
Tel: 071-387-4300
Contact: Mrs S Cohen
Office: Administrator

Beth Din (Court of the Chief Rabbi)

Adler House
Tavistock Square
London WC1H 9HP
Tel: 071-387-5772
Fax: 071-388-6666
Contact: Jeremy Phillips
Office: Registrar
A judicial and supervisory body dealing with certain aspects of Orthodox Judaism, including dispute resolution; religious divorces, adoptions and conversions; and supervision of Jewish dietary requirements.

Bachad Fellowship (Friends of Bnei Akiva)

2 Hallswelle Road
London NW11 0DT
Tel: 081-458-9370
Fax:: 081-209-0107

Contact: Arieh Handier
Office: Chairman
Bnei Akiva is an educational youth organisation.

B'nai B'rith Hillel Foundation

Hillel House
1-2 Endsleigh Street
London WC1H 0DS
Tel: 071-388-0801
Fax: 071-383-0390

B'nai B'rith Youth Organisation

1-2 Endsleigh Street
London WC1H 0DS
Tel: 081-387-3115

Board of Deputies of British Jews

Woburn House
Tavistock Square
London WC1H 0EZ
Tel: 071-387-3952
Fax: 071-383-5848
Contact: Mr Neville Nagler
Office: Chief Executive
The elected representative body for the British Jewish community. It offers a forum for examining issues affecting the Jewish community and undertakes activities on behalf of the community, promoting good relations with the wider society and securing recognition of social and legal rights for Jewish people. Activities include protection of rights and countering bias; projecting the Jewish community; research and liaison with public bodies, minority and other religious groups. Affiliated to The Inter Faith Network for the UK.

Burial Society

Woburn House
Upper Woburn Place
London WC1H 0EZ
Tel: 071-387-7891
Burial society of the United Synagogue.

Campaign for the Protection of Shechita

66 Townshend Court
Townshend Road
Regents Park
London NW8 6LE
Tel: 071-722-8523

Central Council for Jewish Social Service

Stuart Young House
221 Golders Green Road
London NW11 9DW

Tel: 081-458-3282
Contact: Daphne Band
Office: Administrative Director

The council aims to provide a discussion forum for Jewish social service delivery organisations, to give practical advice and information to individual agencies and the community as a whole, and to facilitate consultation, co-operation and co-ordination of welfare services. The Central Council is the recognised negotiating body and the official voice of the Jewish community on social work matters. It provides support and back-up facilities to affiliated organisations including a comprehensive directory of Jewish social services covering the UK; a course of study for the development of Jewish communal leaders; conferences on major themes; the community's only co-ordinated plan for disaster response, providing immediate assistance as well as long term support and counselling; a newsletter called "Central Line" and a Jewish social service ombudsman.

Centre for Jewish Education

Sternberg Centre for Judaism
80 East End Road
Finchley
London N3 2SY
Tel: 081-343-4303
Fax: 081-349-0694
Contact: Michael J Shire
Office: Director

A central agency for education. The centre aims to bring about the development of life-long Jewish education in synagogues through the provision of education for all ages; enhanced quality of education; the setting of a higher priority for educational planning; trained teachers, head teachers, rabbis and educational leaders; and innovative educational resources. It provides training programmes, educational conferences and workshops; curriculum materials in Hebrew and Jewish studies; three learning and resource centres; educational consultants; family/community educational training and programmes and support for the development of education in communities.

Chavurah Movement

1 Ashbourne Grove
Mill Hill
London NW7 3RS
Tel: 081-959-3129 (home)
Contact: Rabbi Larry Tabick
Office: Co-ordinator

A co-ordinating body which serves the UK Chavurot (fellowship groups), both Synagogue-based and independent. Chavurot run worship and study groups mainly for adults.

Chief Rabbinate

Adler House
Tavistock Square
London WC1N 9HN
Tel: 071-387-1066
Contact: Rabbi Dr Jonathan Sacks
Office: Chief Rabbi

All congregations which contribute to the Chief Rabbinate Fund come under the jurisdiction of the Chief Rabbi, although this jurisdiction is also recognised by other congregations, both in Britain and overseas, who seek his guidance on questions of ecclesiastical law and religious life and are represented by him on public and ceremonial occasions.

Committee for the Welfare of Iranian Jews in GB

17 Arden Road
London N3 3AB
Tel: 081-346-3121

Founded in 1981, the Committee aims to assist and advise Jewish refugees and immigrants from Iran.

Commonwealth Jewish Council

Somerset House
37 Fortess Road
London NW5
Tel: 071-267-7991
Fax: 071-267-6394

Conference of Anglo-Jewish Preachers

Adler House
Tavistock Square
London WC1H 9HP

Council of Reform and Liberal Rabbis

Manor House
80 East End Road
London N3 2SY
Tel: 081-349-4731
Fax: 081-343-0901
Contact: Chairman

A representative organisation which aims to facilitate mutual understanding between the Assembly of Rabbis of the Reform Synagogues of Great Britain and the Rabbinic conference of the Union of Liberal and Progressive Synagogues and to represent both vis-a-vis the major organisations of Anglo-Jewry such as the Board of Deputies of British Jews and the Chief Rabbinate. It mainly organises joint meetings of the two Rabbinic bodies and issues statements.

Dvar Yerushalayim (London Jewish Academy)
24 Templers Avenue
London NW11 0NS
Tel: 081-455-8631

Federation of Synagogues
65 Watford Way
London NW4 3AQ
Tel: 081-202-2263
Fax: 081-203-0610
The Federation was founded in 1887 and includes Orthodox Jewish congregations not affiliated to the United Synagogue.

Friends of Sephardi and other Jewish Refugees
New House
67-68 Hatton Gardens
London EC1N 8JY
Tel: 071-242-4556
Tel: 071-242-2418
Contact: Sidney L Shipton
Office: Honorary Secretary
The charitable arm of the Sephardi Federation of Great Britain and the Commonwealth. The objects of the organisation are to relieve poverty, advance learning and the Jewish religion among Jews in all parts of the world and, where practicable, to give consideration to the needs of Sephardi Jews.

Guild of Jewish Journalists
103 Highfield Avenue
London NW11
Tel: 081-455-9425
Contact: John Lewis
Office: Honorary Secretary

Holocaust Educational Trust
BCM Box 7892
London WC1N 3XX
Tel: 071-222-6822
Contact: Greville Janner
Office: Chair

Initiation Society
47 The Ridgeway
London NW11
Tel: 081-455-2008
Contact: Dr M Sifman
Office: Medical officer

To train Mohalim and supply Mohalim in cases where required by maintaining a list of Mohalim practising in the British Isles and registered with the Society.

Institute of Jewish Affairs
79 Wimpole Street
London W1M 7DD
Tel: 071-935-8266
Fax: 071-935-3252
Contact: Anthony Lerman
Office: Director
The Institute of Jewish Affairs researches problems affecting Jews and the Jewish communities worldwide and makes its research available to Jewish leadership, the media, politicians, clergymen and academics. Its activities include publication, lectures, seminars and conferences.

Institute of Jewish Education
44a Albert Road
Hendon
London NW4 2SJ
Tel: 081-203-6799
A Teachers' Resource Centre. The Institute serves teachers in full-time and supplementary Jewish education and includes an early childhood department. It runs nationally accredited courses including NNEB and PPA for early childhood and in-service courses for teachers. Curriculum support materials, for example on Jewish festivals, are produced. There is also a fortnightly newsletter and a magazine called "The Jewish Educator".

Institute of Jewish Studies
University College
Gower Street
London WC1E 6BT
Tel: 071-380-7171
Fax: 071-387-8057
Established in 1953 by the late Professor Alexander Altmann, located within the Department of Hebrew and Jewish studies at University College, London, while retaining its autonomous status. It is funded by the private sector. Its programme of activities are dedicated to the academic study of all branches of Jewish civilisation, past and present, including series of public lectures, seminars, symposia, major international conferences, research projects and publications, especially of its conference proceedings. It brings together scholars, students and academic institutions from all sections inside and outside the University of London and the scholarly scene in and outside the UK and worldwide. It is open and free of charge, to all who are interested. In 1994, an

international conference on Jewish Religious Identity and Intellectual History will be held in celebration of the fortieth anniversary of the Institute's foundation.

International Jewish Vegetarian Society

Bet Teva
853–855 Finchley Road
Golders Green
London NW11 8LX
Tel: 081-455-0692
Contact: S Labelda
Office: Honorary Secretary

Jewish After Care Association

East London Synagogue
Rectory Square
London
E1 3NG
Tel: 071-790-3679

Jewish Aids Trust

HIV Education Unit
Colindale Hospital
Colindale Avenue
London NW9 5HG
Tel: 081-200-0369
Contact: Ms Rosalind Collin
Office: Director
A welfare organisation which works within the Jewish community to: raise awareness of the implications of HIV/AIDS; provide counselling for those infected or affected by HIV/AIDS; give support and practical help and to provide education for all youth, students, parents and Jewish social services.

Jewish Association for the Mentally Ill

Elscot House
Arcadia Avenue
London N3 2JU
Tel: 081-343-1111
Fax: 081-343-3355
Contact: Mrs Sheila Cohen
Office: Chairperson
The association consists of parents, carers, sufferers and professionals in the field. It aims to promote a greater understanding of the problems of the mentally ill, to alleviate suffering and to create facilities to meet needs.

Jewish Book Council

Woburn House
Upper Woburn Place
London WC1H 0EP
Tel: 071-387-3081

Jewish Care

Stuart Young House
221 Golders Green Road
London NW11 9DQ
Tel: 081-458-3282
Fax: 081-455-7185
Contact: Melvyn Carlowe
Office: Chief Executive
A voluntary social welfare organisation which provides services for elderly, mentally ill, visually impaired, and physically disabled people and their families. It provides services throughout the country including residential homes, day centres, hostels, social work teams, specialist services, day care units, counselling, sheltered housing and mental health care.

Jewish Committee for H M Forces

Woburn House
Upper Woburn Place
London WC1H 0EP
Tel: 071-387-3081
To provide for the religious needs of Jewish members of H M Forces.

Jewish Council for Community Relations

33 Seymour Place
London W1N 6AT
Tel: 081-445-0896
Contact: Edie Friedman
Office: Director
Membership group formed to combat prejudice and racism and to promote equal opportunities for all in Britain's multi-racial society. The Council develops Jewish anti-racist educational materials for schools and youth clubs; trains teachers and youth leaders on the use of these materials; campaigns on refugee and immigration issues; provides practical assistance to refugees and works with other communities to combat racism.

Jewish Crisis Helpline (Miyad)

c/o 23 Ravenshurst Avenue
London NW4 4EE
Tel: 081-581-999
Contact: Jeffery Blumenfeld
Office: Director
National helpline which responds to anyone who needs to talk to someone in confidence about an issue or a problem which is bothering them. The helpline is open from twelve noon to twelve midnight Sunday to Thursday and on Fridays before Sabbath commences and Saturday night after Sabbath ends. It

provides a sympathetic and listening ear to young or old for any problem or issue a caller wishes to speak about.

Jewish Deaf Association
90-92 Cazenove Road
London N16 6AB
Tel: 081-806-6147
Fax: 081-806-2251
Contact: Mrs Pat Goldring
Office: Executive Director
A national organisation which provides cultural, welfare and spiritual guidance for Jewish deaf and hard of hearing people. It is a "cradle to the grave" organisation providing a Day Centre for elderly deaf people, a social club for all ages, and sign language classes which take place under the auspices of the Hackney Adult Education Centre. The Association has recently opened an Advisory and Resource Centre which is open to people of all faiths. The Honorary Chaplain, Reverend Michael Plaskow, is available to give any spiritual guidance members may need.

Jewish Educational Development Trust
Adler House
Tavistock Square
London WC1H 9HN
Tel: 071-387-1066

Jewish Feminist Group
Box 39
Sister Write Bookshop
190 Upper Street
London N1

Jewish Guide Advisory Council
115 Fracklyn Gardens
Edgware
Middlesex HA8 8SB
Tel: 081-958-6440 (home)
Contact: Mrs N Mitchell
Office: Chair

Jewish Historical Society of England
33 Seymour Place
London W1H 5AP
Tel: 071-723-4404
Contact: C M Drukker
Office: Honorary Secretary
A membership group and cultural organisation with around eight hundred members, mostly in the UK but also overseas. The society organises lectures on Jewish history (monthly from September/October to

June/July) and every two to three years publishes the texts of many of the lectures with some occasional papers and book reviews.

Jewish Lads and Girls Brigade
Camperdown
3 Beechcroft Road
London E18 1LA
Tel: 081-989-8990
Fax: 081-518-8832
Contact: Charles Kay
Office: Secretary
A national voluntary youth organisation. The Brigade, founded in 1895, is established to train its members and other Jewish young people to be good Jews and good citizens.

Jewish Lesbian and Gay Helpline
BM Jewish Helpline
London WC1N 3XX
Tel: 071-706-3123
A group of Jewish lesbians and gay men, all volunteers, who give their time freely to staff and manage the line, attend training meetings, develop educational materials and programmes, and run outreach sessions. The helpline is open for calls every Monday and Thursday from 7.00pm-10.00pm. Information of interest is provided to Jewish lesbians and gay men, including all the latest news and forthcoming events, groups in the UK for women and men, social meetings and religious services, worldwide contacts including groups in Europe, Israel and USA. Details of international conferences, a list of helpful Rabbis and other referrals including alternative Jewish organisations are available.

Jewish Marriage Council
23 Ravenhurst Avenue
London NW4 4EE
Tel: 081-203 6311

Jewish Refugees Committee of the Central British Fund for World Jewish Relief
Drayton House
30 Gordon Street
London WC1H 0AN
Tel: 071-387-3925
Contact: Mrs Patricia Pitchon
Office: Administrator
A charitable organisation established to assist Jewish refugees who came to the UK during the years of Nazi persecution from 1933-39 and those who emerged from the concentration camps of Europe after 1945. It aims to give every possible help to today's refugees

wherever they may come from. It provides elderly refugees with a certain amount of financial help to cover daily living and major household items to enable them to spend the remainder of their lives in relative comfort and dignity. Recent refugees are helped with their asylum applications and given initial financial assistance to cover rent, food, transport and English classes. Several associated charitable trusts provide additional financial assistance. It supplies copies of personal records from its Archive for refugees requesting them as well as issuing letters of confirmation of arrival in the UK for Austrian pension purposes.

Jewish Scout Advisory Council
9 Graham Lodge
Graham Road
London NW4 3DG
Tel: 081-202-8613
Contact: P Russell
Office: Honorary Secretary

Jews Against Apartheid
24 Thornbury Avenue
Isleworth
Middlesex TW7 4NQ
Tel: 081-568-0971 (home)
Contact: Shalom Menahem Charikar
Office: Chair
A membership group based on Jewish ethics and history which publicises events in South Africa, especially the violation of basic human and political rights. Jewish history is the main source of the group's inspiration and Jewish religious festivals, particularly Passover, are occasions for joint activities with other groups for raising awareness and doing charitable and welfare work connected with events in South Africa.

Jews' College, University of London
44a Albert Road
London NW4 2SJ
Tel: 081-203-6427
Fax: 081-203-6420
Contact: Simon Goulden
Office: Executive Director
Jews' College has served the community since 1855 providing its Rabbis, teachers and an educated laity. Part of the University of London, it has become known as a resource centre both for Britain and internationally. Maintaining its Orthodox ethos, it seeks to widen and deepen the level of Jewish Studies. In addition to its degree programmes it has a number of voational courses for the Orthodox Jewish ministry and teacher training.

League of Jewish Women
Woburn House
Tavistock Sqaure
London WC1H 0EZ
Tel: 071-387-7688
The League has local groups in different parts of the country. It aims to unite Jewish women of every shade of opinion who are resident in the United Kingdom; to intensify in each Jewish woman her Jewish consciousness and her sense of responsibility to the Jewish community and the community generally; to stimulate her personal sense of civic duty and to encourage her to express it by increased service to the country.

Leo Baeck College
The Manor House
80 East End Road
Finchley
London N3 2SY
Tel: 081-349-4525
Fax: 081-343-2558
Contact: John Olbrich
Office: Registrar
The College trains Reform and Liberal Rabbis and is the only centre for Jewish-Christian-Muslim relations in the United Kingdom. It has close contacts with many Islamic organisations in Britain and promotes annual Jewish-Christian-Muslim conferences in Bendorf, Germany. It also arranges visits to Muslim colleges and holds regular events which Christians and Muslims attend.

Leo Baeck Institute
4 Devonshire Street
London W1N 2BH
Tel: 071-580-3493
Contact: Dr Arnold Paucker
Office: Director
An historical research institute founded in 1955 for the purpose of research into the history and culture of Central European German-speaking Jewry. It publishes a year book, symposium volumes and monographs and organises conferences and seminars.

Link Psychotherapy Centre
110 Cholmley Gardens
Fortune Green Road
London NW6 1UP
Tel: 081-349-0111
Contact: Eduardo Pitchon
Office: Chair
A group of professional psychotherapists that have come together to provide psychotherapy (mental care)

to families, children, and adults in the Jewish community. All specialise in psychoanalytical psychotherapy and do both individual and group work. Group members are non-affiliated and cover the whole spectrum of the community.

Lubavitch Foundation

107-115 Stamford Hill
London N16 5RP
Tel: 081-800-0022
Contact: Rabbi N Sudak
Office: Principal
The national headquarters of an organisation which has several local branches in Britain. Lubavitch began in eighteenth century Russia as a Jewish educational movement, known also as Chabad. This word is an acronym of the Hebrew words for "Wisdom, Understanding, Knowledge". The goal of Chabad-Lubavitch is to spread spiritual awareness among Jews (through Jewish observance and more profound Torah study) and also among non-Jews (through promoting knowledge of the seven Noachite laws). It is led by Rabbi Menachem Mendel Schneerson in New York, a seventh generation descendent of the founder of the movement and renowned author and sage. The organisation provides for worship, schools, adult education, publications and a library.

Maimonides Foundation

BCM Box 5905
London WC1N 3XX
Tel: 071-222-6822
Contact: Grenville Janner QC MP
An umbrella framework based in the Jewish community and designed to develop contact between the Jewish community and other faiths, nationalities and ethnic origins.

Manor House Centre for Psychodynamic Counselling

Sternberg Centre for Judaism
80 East End Road
London N3 2SY
Tel: 081-349-4525
Provides counselling and psychotherapeutic training for voluntary and professional workers in the community.

National Council of Shechita Boards

P.O. Box 579
Adastra House
401/405 Nether Street
London N3 1YR
Tel: 081-349-9160

Fax: 081-346-2209
The organisation aims to centralise information on all matters relating to the performance and administration of Shechita; to act as a liaison between the Shechita boards and the communities, and the various Government Ministries and other organisations affecting Shechita, and the kosher meat and poultry industry.

Noam (Noar Masorti)

766 Finchley Road
London NW11 7TH
Tel: 081-201-8773
Fax: 081-201-8917
Contact: Joel Levy
Office: Director
The youth organisation of the Assembly of Masorti Synagogues, a group devoted to the promotion of non-fundamentalist traditional Judaism. It runs informal camps, clubs and events for young people aged five to twenty years.

Operation Judaism

95 Willows Road
Birmingham B12 9QF
Tel: 021-440-6673

Oxford Centre for Post-Graduate Hebrew Studies

Yarnton Manor
Yarnton
Oxford OX5 1PY
Tel: 0865-77946

Rabbinical Commission for the Licensing of Shochetim

Adler House
Tavistock Square
London WC1H 9HP
Tel: 071-387-5772
The Commission aims to provide a licensing body for Shochetim and consists of the Chief Rabbi (chair); a member of the Spanish and Portuguese Synagogue, London (vice-chair); three members appointed by the London Beth Din; two members appointed by the London Federation of Synagogues; one member appointed by the Union of Orthodox Hebrew Congregations (London); and two members appointed by the Board of Deputies of British Jews to represent regional congregations.

Rabbinical Council of the Provinces

Adler House
Tavistock Square
London WC1H 9HN
Tel: 071-387-1066

Rabbinical Council of the United Synagogue

98 Anthony Road
Borehamwood
Hertfordshire WD6 4NB
Tel: 081-207-3759 (home)
Fax: 081-207-0568
Contact: Rabbi A Plancey
Office: Chairperson
A representative organisation originally established to represent the interests of rabbis serving the United Synagogue. It has since branched out to be involved in a wide area of initiatives within the United Synagogue and the wider community.

Reform and Liberal Association of Mohalim

Sternberg Centre
The Manor House
80 East End Road
London N3 2SY
Tel: 081-349-4731

Reform Synagogues of Great Britain

The Manor House
80 East End Road
Finchley
London N3 2SY
Tel: 081-349-4731
Fax: 081-343-0901
It has local congregations throughout the country. The national body includes the Assembly of Rabbis; the Rabbinical Court (Beth Din); the Reform Synagogue Youth (RSY-Netzer); Reform Synagogues Guilds; and the Reform Foundation Trust. The Reform movement began in nineteenth century European Judaism and it aims to: promote a living Judaism; interpret the Torah in accordance with the spirit and needs of the present generation; and, through a positive, constructive and progressive view of Jewish tradition, to raise and maintain a high standard of Jewish religious life throughout the country.

Reform Synagogues of Great Britain Youth Department

Manor House
80 East End Road
London N3 2SY
Tel: 081-349-4731

Fax: 081-343-0901
Contact: Ms Stevie Dee
Office: Youth Director
A national voluntary youth agency. It aims to meet the educational, social, developmental, and spiritual needs of Jewish young people aged nine to twenty-three years and to informally educate in a way which enables and empowers young people to make informed choices within an equal opportunity perspective. The agency imbues young people with a love of Reform Judaism and Reform Zionism and offers them Jewish life options.

Sabbath Observance Employment Bureau

Woburn House
Upper Woburn Place
London WC1H 0EP
Tel: 071-387-3036

Scottish Jewish Archives Committee

Garnethill Synagogue
125-127 Hill Street
Glasgow G3 6UB
Tel: 041-649-4526 (home)
Contact: Harvey L Kaplan
Office: Director
The Committee is a research and enquiry resource which runs the Scottish Jewish Archives Centre and collects and displays material relating to the history of the Jewish community of Scotland.

Sephardi Federation of Great Britain and Commonwealth

New House
67-68 Hatton Gardens
London EC1N 8JY
Tel: 071-242-4556
Fax: 071-242-2418
Contact: Sidney L Shipton
Office: Executive Director
Membership organisation which deals with the religious, cultural and social welfare of all Sephardi communities. It establishes seminaries to train spiritual leaders and teachers and provides aid to Israel for the rehabilitation and training of Sephardi immigrants. It co-operates with Jewish communities of all origins and tendencies to strengthen the Jewish people's unity.

Small Communities Committee of the Jewish Memorial Council

c/o Second Floor
Woburn House
Tavistock Square
London WC1H 0EP

Tel: 071-387-3081
Contact: Revd Malcolm Weisman
Office: Secretary
A communal organisation which provides from the cradle to the grave for the welfare of members of the Jewish faith in small congregations generally without their own Rabbi. The Minister serves all such communities as well as those Jews who are beyond the reach of any synagogue.

Social Action Forum
Manor House
80 East End Road
London N3 2SY
Tel: 081-349-4731/071-580-1663
Fax: 081-343-0901/071-436-4184
Contact: Vicky Joseph and Steve Miller
Office: Co-ordinator
A joint forum of the Reform Synagogues of Great Britain (RSGB) and the Union of Liberal and Progressive Synagogues (ULPS) representing over sixty Synagogues in the UK. The Social Action Forum is the umbrella organisation under which all social action programmes of the two bodies are undertaken. It brings together religious and lay representatives of Synagogues, youth movements, associated bodies and interested individuals to share ideas and plan forthcoming projects in relation to social justice issues such as racism, homelessness, human rights, business ethics, environmental issues, third world issues and disability. It can also be contacted via ULPS, Tel: 071-580-1663.

Society for Jewish Study
15 Sunny Hill Court
Sunningfields Crescent
London NW4 4RB
Tel: 081-203-1352
Contact: Alex Minn
Office: Secretary

Spiro Institute for the Study of Jewish History and Culture
c/o King's College
University of London
Kidderpore Avenue
London NW3 7ST
Tel: 081-431-0345
Fax: 071-431-0361
Contact: The Director
An educational institute with charitable status. In order to break down prejudices and to promote dialogue between different religions and ethnic groups and create understanding between them the Institute offers courses in general schools and at Universities for teachers of all grades. There are specially designed programmes for young people and adults. Its aim is to promote self-awareness and to strengthen Jewish identity whilst establishing contact with other groups. It teaches Jewish history and culture, Hebrew and Yiddish, Jewish drama, art and literature.

Sternberg Centre for Judaism
The Manor House
80 East End Road
London N3 2SY
Tel: 081-346-2288
The Centre provides a national centre for the promotion of Jewish religious, educational, cultural and intellectual matters by means of the work of bodies located in the Centre: the Advancement of Jewish Education Trust; the Akiva School; the Centre for Jewish Education; the Council of Reform and Liberal Rabbis; the Heimler Foundation, Manor House Society; the London Museum of Jewish Life; Leo Baeck College; Michael Goulston Educational Foundation; Pro-Zion; the Reform Synagogues of Great Britain and the Masorti New North London Synagogue.

Student and Academic Campaign for Jews of the former Soviet Union (SACSJ)
16 Western Park
London N8 9TJ
Tel: 081-348-6957 (home)
Contact: Adam Rose
Office: Chairperson
A campaign group which supports a Jewish youth cultural and training centre in Kiev, Ukraine. In addition it provides campaign ideas and advice to UK students and youth campaigners for full freedoms of emigration and religious expression for Jews of former Soviet states.

Synagogue Secretaries' Association
Edgware Synagogue
Edgware Way
Middlesex NW8 8YE
Contact: L Ford
Office: Chair

Tay Sachs and Allied Diseases Association
17 Sydney Road
Barkingside
Ilford
Essex IG6 2ED
Tel: 081-550-8989

Trades Advisory Council

c/o Board of Deputies
4th Floor
Woburn House
Tavistock Square
London WC1H 0EZ
Tel: 071-387-3952
The council aims to remove causes of friction in industry, trade and commerce and discrimination in the workplace, where these threaten good relations in which Jews are concerned. It works by offering arbitration and conciliation facilities in disputes, and by offering advice to employees suffering impediment by breach of the Code of Practice for good race relations laid down by the Commission for Racial Equality.

Traditional Alternatives

3 First Avenue
London NW4 2RL
Tel: 081-203-9044
An educational foundation with a number of organised activities exploring the role of women in modern Orthodoxy.

Tzedek (Jewish Action for a Just World)

26 Goodwyns Vale
London N10 2HA
Tel: 081-883-7453
Fax: 081-203-6232
Contact: Steve Miller
Office: Co-ordinator
A poverty relief and educational charity founded in 1990 by a group of young Jews to provide a Jewish response to global poverty. It provides financial support to overseas projects; organises short-term overseas work placements; and lively, participatory, educational and fund-raising events. It provides speakers and resources for all age groups, and is especially interested in inter-faith contacts and networking.

Union of Jewish Students

Hillel House
1-2 Endsleigh Street
London WC1H 0DS
Tel: 071-387-4644
Fax: 071-383-0390

Union of Liberal and Progressive Synagogues

21 Maple Street
London W1P 6DS

Tel: 071-580-1663
Fax: 071-436-4184
Contact: Sharon Silver-Myer

Union of Maccabi Associations

Gildesgame House
73a Compayne Gardens
London NW6 3RS
Tel: 071-328-0382

Union of Orthodox Hebrew Congregations

40 Queen Elizabeth's Walk
London N16 0HH
Tel: 081-802-6226
Contact: Rabbi Joseph Dunner
Established in 1926 as a congregational association for Orthodox Jews of primarily Central and Eastern European origin and including many of the Hasidic congregations.

United Synagogue

Woburn House
Tavistock Square
London WC1H 0EZ
Tel: 071-387-4300
Fax: 071-838-4934
Contact: Jonathan M Lew
Office: Chief Executive
The headquarters and executive offices of the synagogue group. It is mainly concerned with synagogue activities.

World Organisation of Jews from Arab Countries (British section)

14-16 Cockspur Street
London SW1 5BL
Tel: 071-242-4556

Youth and Hechalutz Department

Balfour House
741 High Road
London N12 0BQ
Tel: 081-446-2277
Fax: 081-343-9037
Contact: Arik Hatzor
Office: Director
Educational agency. The UK branch of an Israel based organisation promoting knowledge and understanding of Israel. This is done through education and long term and short term programmes in Israel.

JEWISH SYNAGOGUES AND LOCAL ORGANISATIONS

SCOTLAND

WALES

NORTHERN IRELAND

NORTH EAST ENGLAND

YORKSHIRE AND HUMBERSIDE

NORTH WEST ENGLAND

ENGLISH EAST MIDLANDS

ENGLISH WEST MIDLANDS

EAST ANGLIA

SOUTH EAST ENGLAND (NORTH)

LONDON (E)

LONDON (N)

LONDON (NW)

LONDON (SE)

LONDON (SW)

LONDON (W)

SOUTH EAST ENGLAND (SOUTH)

SOUTH WEST ENGLAND

A variety of forms of local Jewish organisations are listed in this directory. These include synagogues; welfare bodies; representative bodies; student societies and houses; *yeshivas*; and other educational institutions with the general exception of schools.

SCOTLAND

Aberdeen Hebrew Congregation
74 Dee Street
Aberdeen AB1 2DS
Tel: 0224-582135
Contact: Ms Sandra Shrago
Office: Honorary Secretary
Place of worship. A small community synagogue welcoming all shades of Judaism. It provides facilities for worship and a Sunday school for infants and juniors.

Dundee University Jewish Society
c/o Synagogue
9 St Mary Place
Dundee
Tayside

Edinburgh Hebrew Congregation
4 Salisbury Road
Edinburgh
Lothian
Tel: 031-667-3144
Tel: 031-667-9360 (home)
Contact: Rabbi Shalom Shapiro
Office: Minister
The Edinburgh Town Council and Burgess Role, Minutes of 1691 and 1717, record applications by Jews for permission to reside and trade in Edinburgh. Local directories of the eighteenth century contain Jewish names and there is some reason to believe that there was an organised Jewish community in 1780. This synagogue was consecrated in 1932 and renovated in 1980. Contact can also be made through Dr I Leifer, Tel: 031-668-2910.

University Jewish Society
c/o Societys' Centre
Room 6
21 Hill Place
Edinburgh
Lothian

Board of Jewish Education
28 Calderwood Road
Glasgow G43 2RU
Tel: 041-637-7409

Board of Shechita
29 Queensferry Street
Glasgow
Strathclyde
Tel: 041-429-0867

Garnethill Synagogue

129 Hill Street
Glasgow G3
Tel: 041-332-4151
Contact: Mrs Rhoda Livingston
Office: Secretary
An Orthodox synagogue with Saturday morning worship at 9.45am to which visitors are welcome. It is the first centrally located purpose-built synagogue in Glasgow. It is also the home of the Scottish Jewish archives. Parties of visitors can be taken round. Applications should be made in writing, giving alternative dates.

Giffnock and Newlands Synagogue

Maryville Avenue
Giffnock
Glasgow
Strathclyde
Tel: 041-638-6600

Glasgow Jewish Representative Council

Resource Centre
222 Fenwick Road
Glasgow G46
Contact: Ephraim Borowski
Office: Honorary Secretary
The Council acts as a forum for discussion of matters of concern to the Glasgow Jewish community and acts as the voice of the community in its interactions with the wider community and other religious or ethnic groups within it.

Glasgow Jewish Resource Centre

222 Fenwick Road
Giffnock
Glasgow G46 6UE
Tel: 041-620-2194
Contact: Dorothy Zolkwer
Office: Director
A library and information centre which holds extensive information on Judaism, the Holocaust and Israel for the use of the community and, in particular, all educational establishments. Its activities centre around youth and community and informal education.

Glasgow New Synagogue

147 Ayr Road
Newton Mearns
Glasgow G77 6RE
Tel: 041-639-4083
Contact: P Kraven
Office: Honorary Secretary

Jewish Blind Society Centre

49 Coplaw Street
Glasgow G42
Tel: 041-423-2288

Jewish Hospital and Sick Visiting Association

49 Coplaw Street
Glasgow G42
Tel: 041-423-8916

Jewish Teenage Centre

Jewish Education Centre
Maryville Avenue
Glasgow
Strathclyde
Tel: 041-638-6609

Jewish Welfare Board

49 Coplaw Street
Glasgow G42
Tel: 041-423-8916

Langside Hebrew Congregation

125 Niddrie Road
Glasgow G42
Tel: 041-423-4062

Lubavitch Foundation

8 Orchard Drive
Giffnock
Glasgow
Strathclyde
Tel: 041-638-6116

Netherlee and Clarkston Hebrew Congregation

Clarkston Road
Clarkston
Glasgow
Strathclyde
Tel: 041-644-3611 (home)
Contact: Mrs B J Mann
Office: Secretary

Newton Mearns Synagogue

14 Larchfield Court
Newton Mearns
Glasgow G77 5BH
Tel: 041-445-2231
Contact: Kenny Davidson

Queen's Park Synagogue
Falloch Road
Glasgow G42 9QX
Tel: 041-632-1743

United Synagogue Council
Queens Park Synagogue
Falloch Road
Glasgow
Strathclyde
Tel: 041-632-1743

Yeshiva
Gliffnock Synagogue
Maryville Avenue
Glasgow
Strathclyde
Tel: 041-638-2030
Contact: I Jesner
Office: Chair

Youth Council
Glasgow Jewish Resource Centre
Hebrew College
Maryville Avenue
Glasgow
Strathclyde
Tel: 041-620-2194
Contact: Ms L Wellins
Office: Chair

WALES

Cardiff New Synagogue (Reform)
Moira Terrace
Cardiff CF2 1EJ
Tel: 0222-223042 (home)
Contact: Rabbi Elaina Rothman
Place of worship. A constituent member of the
Reform Synagogues of Great Britain dedicated to
living Judaism. Activities include educational, social
and charitable work.

Cathedral Road Synagogue
Cathedral Road
Cardiff
South Glamorgan

Hillel House
17 Howard Gardens
Cardiff
South Glamorgan
Tel: 0222-481227

Kashrus Commission
9 Green Lawns
Penylan
Cardiff
South Glamorgan
Tel: 0222-483096
Contact: I N Cohen
Office: Chair

Union of Jewish Students
c/o Hillel House
17 Howard Gardens
Cardiff
South Glamorgan
Tel: 0222-481227

Newport Synagogue
3 Queen's Hill Crescent
Newport
Gwent
Tel: 0633-262308
Contact: Honorary Secretary
A place of worship. The synagogue is self-contained
with a function room and class rooms. It is an
Orthodox Hebrew congregation mainly following
the tenets of the United Synagogue. The synagogue
has its own cemetery, burial society and charitable
organisations.

Swansea Hebrew Congregation
17 Mayals Green
Mayals
Swansea SA3 5JR
Tel: 0792-401205
Contact: H M Sherman
Office: Chair

NORTHERN IRELAND

Belfast Hebrew Congregation
49 Somerton Road
Belfast BT15
Tel: 0232-77974
Tel: 0232-779491 (home)
Contact: Mrs Norma Simon
Office: Honorary Secretary

Jewish Community Centre
49 Somerton Road
Belfast
Tel: 0232-777974

Jewish Ladies Guild
45 Glandore Avenue
Belfast
Tel: 0232-777795
Contact: Mrs B Danker
Office: President

NORTH EAST ENGLAND

Beth Midrash Lemoroth
50 Bewick Road
Gateshead NE8
Tel: 091-4772620

Gateshead Hebrew Congregation
180 Bewick Road
Gateshead NE8
Tel: 091-4770111
Tel: 091-4773871 (home)
Contact: M Guttentag
Office: Senior Warden

Sunderland Talmudical College and Yeshiva
Prince Consort Road
Gateshead NE3 4DS
Tel: 091-490-0195
Contact: Rabbi S Zahn
Office: Principal

Yeshiva Lezeirim
Cambridge Terrace
Gateshead NE8
Tel: 091-4770744
Contact: Rabbi E Jaffe
Office: Principal

Middlesbrough Synagogue
Park Road South
Middlesbrough
Cleveland
Tel: 0642-819034
Contact: Lionel Simons
Office: Honorary Secretary

Jewish Students' Society
Hillel House
1 St George's Terrace

Jesmond
Newcastle-upon-Tyne NE2
Tel: 091-2812106

Jewish Welfare Society
Lionel Jacobson House
Graham Park Road
Gosforth
Newcastle-upon-Tyne NE3 4BH
Tel: 091-2840959
Contact: Mrs P Ashton
Office: Secretary

Newcastle Jewish Housing Association Ltd
c/o Lionel Jacobson
40 Graham Park Road
Gosforth
Newcastle-upon-Tyne NE3 4BH

Newcastle Reform Synagogue
The Croft
off Kenton Road
Gosforth
Newcastle-upon-Tyne NE3 4RF
Tel: 091-284-8621
Contact: Rabbi Moshe Yehudai
Office: Rabbi

United Hebrew Congregation
Graham Park Road
Gosforth
Newcastle-upon-Tyne NE3 4BH
Tel: 091-2840959

South Shields Hebrew Congregation
25 Beach Road
South Shields
Tyne and Wear
Tel: 091-5361987 (home)
Contact: Mr J Kersh
Office: Honorary Secretary

Centre for Advanced Rabbinics
2 The Oaks West
Sunderland SR2 8HZ
Tel: 091-565-9290

Sunderland Hebrew Congregation
Ryhope Road
Sunderland SR2 7EQ
Tel: 091-565-8093
Contact: Secretary

Whitley Bay Hebrew Congregation
2 Oxford Street
Whitley Bay
Tyne and Wear NG26 3TB
Tel: 0632-2521367 (home)
Contact: M A Sonn
Office: Honorary Secretary

YORKSHIRE AND HUMBERSIDE

Bradford Synagogue
Bowland Street
Bradford BD1 3BW
Tel: 0274-728925
Tel: 0274-544420 (home)
Contact: Mr T Dyson
Office: Honorary Secretary
Place of worship and social activities, including regular
services and study groups.

Darlington Hebrew Congregation Synagogue
Bloomfield Road
Darlington
County Durham
Contact: I Weiss
Office: Secretary

Sir Moses Montefiore Synagogue
Holme Hill
Heneage Road
Grimsby DN32 9DZ
Tel: 0472-342579 (home)
Contact: M M Lewis
Office: Secretary
Place of worship. A small community with services
held on a Friday evening, on the first Saturday of the
month, and on festivals as appropriate.

Harrogate Hebrew Congregation
St Mary's Walk
Harrogate
North Yorkshire
Place of worship. An Orthodox Jewish synagogue.

Hull Jewish Representative Council
4 Drydales
Kirkella
Hull HU10 7JU
Tel: 0482-658902
Contact: B Donn
Office: Honorary Secretary

Hull Reform Synagogue
Neve Shalom Synagogue
Great Gutter Lane West
Willerby
Hull
Humberside
Tel: 0482-656469
Contact: L M Sugarman
Office: Honorary Secretary
Place of worship. A full member of the Reform
Synagogues of Great Britain. Founded in 1962, the
congregation has now grown to over one hundred
persons. In March 1992 the congregation moved into
the new purpose-built Synagogue. Activities include
worship and youth activities.

Hull University Jewish Students Society
c/o Hillel House
18 Auckland Avenue
Hull
Humberside
Tel: 0482-48196
Tel: 0482-46370
Contact: Lindsey Rose
Office: Chair

Hull Western Synagogue
Limmaeus Street
Hull
Humberside

Old Hebrew Congregation
4 Drydales
Kirkella
Hull HU10 7JU
Tel: 0482-658902 (home)
Fax: 0482-658902 (home)
Contact: B Donn
Office: President
A congregation which no longer maintains its own
premises, but currently worships with the Hull
Western Synagogue. A site for a new Synagogue and
Community Centre has been purchased and it is
hoped that the congregations will soon move to the
new pemises as a United Congregation.

Beth Hamedrash Hagadol Synagogue
Street Lane Gardens
Leeds LS17 6HQ
Tel: 0532-692182
Contact: Mrs M Wilson
Office: Executive Officer
Place of worship. An Orthodox synagogue which also
runs religious seminars and a fortnightly leisure club.

Chaplaincy Centre

17 Queens Road
Leeds LS6 1NY
Tel: 0532-789597
Fax: 0532-667473 (home)
Contact: Rabbi Jonathan Dove
Office: Chaplain
The base for the Yorkshire and Humberside Chaplaincy Board, a multifaceted and dynamic organisation catering for the needs of all Jewish students. There is a full-time chaplain who ensures the welfare of Jewish students in the Yorkshire and Humberside region. There is a wide spectrum of activities including education, counselling, provision of religious activities and services, Union of Jewish Students activities as well as official functions such as liaising with Universities on matters such as exams on the Jewish sabbath and holidays and Jewish student matters in general.

Chassidishe Synagogue

c/o Talmud Torah
Sandhill Lane
Leeds LS17 6AQ
Contact J Lewis
Office Honorary Secretary

Etz Chaim Synagogue

411 Harrogate Road
Leeds LS17 7TT

Jewish Day Centre

26 Queenshill Avenue
Leeds LS17
Tel: 0532-692018
Contact: Jackie King
Office: Organiser

Jewish Education Bureau

8 Westcombe Avenue
Leeds LS8 2BS
Tel: 0532-663613
Fax: 0532-697318
Contact: Rabbi Douglas S Charing
Office: Director
An educational organisation which promotes the study of Judaism in schools, universities and colleges as part of Religious Education or Multi-cultural education. It also welcomes the opportunity for real dialogue between people of different faiths in today's multi-faith Britain. It runs in-service courses for teachers, school visits and produces a wide range of publications as outlined in a twice-yearly catalogue.

Leeds Jewish Welfare Board

311 Stonegate Road
Leeds LS17 6AZ
Tel: 0532-684211
Fax: 0532-664754
Contact: Sheila Saunders
Office: Chief Executive
A charitable trust and voluntary organisation. Leeds Jewish Welfare Board provides a wide range of social work and community care resources for the Jewish community in and around the Yorkshire area. Included are a family centre with residential facilities; the Queenshill Centre offering classes, activities and meals for the elderly, disabled and lonely; meals delivery service; social and community facilities for people with a learning disability and those with long term mental health problems.

Jewish Students' Association

c/o Hillel House
2 Springfield Mount
Leeds LS2
Tel: 0532-433211

League of Jewish Women

154 Street Lane
Moortown
Leeds
West Yorkshire
Tel: 0532-662072
Contact Mrs C Seaton
Office Honorary Secretary

Leeds Jewish Education Board (Talmud Torah)

2 Sand Hill Lane
Leeds LS17 6AQ
Tel: 0532-683390
Contact: Mrs Elana Fligg
Office: Secretary
An educational organisation concerned with the provision of religious Jewish education (Orthodox) to the Leeds Jewish community. It provides Sunday morning and after school weekday classes for children aged five to thirteen years and beyond. It services Jewish assemblies and withdrawal classes in non-Jewish schools with significant Jewish student populations. It also provides adult education.

Leeds Jewish Representative Council

Shadwell Lane Synagogue
151 Shadwell Lane
Leeds LS17 8DW
Tel: 0532-697520

Fax: 0532–370851
Contact: Jeffrey Hillman
Office: President
Representative body. An umbrella organisation acting on behalf of, and protecting, the interests of the Leeds Jewish community.

Leeds Kashrut Authority
151 Shadwell Lane
Leeds LS17 8DW
Tel: 0532–697520
Fax: 0532–370851
Contact: Barry Abis
Office: Admin Secretary
Food monitoring body. The authority maintains the correct standards of preparation of food in all aspects in keeping with Jewish law.

Makor–Jewish Resource Centre
411 Harrogate Road
Leeds LS17 7TT
Tel: 0532–680899
Fax: 0532–668419
A resource Centre which aims to inform people about all aspects of Israel and basic Judaism. There is a lending library for books, cassettes, videos on a wide range of Israeli/Jewish topics. Staff are able to help with ideas and material.

New Central Vilna Synagogue
7a Stainburn Parade
Leeds LS17 8AN

Queenshill Synagogue
26 Queenshill Avenue
Leeds LS17

Shomrei Hadass Congregation
368 Harrogate Road
Leeds LS17 6QB
Tel: 0532–681461

Sinai Synagogue
Roman Avenue
Leeds LS8 2AN
Tel: 0532–665256
Contact: Mrs S Gordon
Office: Honorary Secretary

United Hebrew Congregation
Shadwell Lane Synagogue
151 Shadwell Lane
Leeds LS17 8DW

Tel: 0532–696141
Contact: Mr M S Samuel
Office: Secretary
Place of worship. The synagogue was built seven years ago and offices are contained within the building along with a large and small function room. Morning and evening services held every day of the year.

Bradford Jewish Benevolent Society
Buckstone Court
Cliffe Drive
Rawdon LS19 6LL
Tel: 0274–504468
Contact: M Levi
Office: Treasurer

Jewish Centre Charitable Trust
Psalter House
Psalter Lane
Sheffield S11
Tel: 0742–552296

Jewish Welfare Organisation
275 Dobcroft Road
Sheffield S11 9LG
Tel: 0742–366800
Contact: M Ballin
Office: Honorary Secretary
Welfare organisation engaged in charitable and welfare work within the Jewish community.

Ladies' Benevolent Society
12 Clarendon Court
Carr Bank Lane
Sheffield S11 7FB
Tel: 0742–308902
Contact: Mrs J Flowers
Office: Honorary Secretary

Representative Council of Sheffield and District Jews
76 Dore Road
Sheffield S17 3NE
Tel: 0742–360984 (home)
Contact: Mrs Agnes Spier
Office: Honorary Secretary

Sheffield and District Reform Jewish Congregation
Sheffield
South Yorkshire
Tel: 0742–308433
Contact: Mr B C Rosenberg

Office: President
Services held alternate Friday nights. For further information please telephone.

United Hebrew Congregation
Wilson Road
Sheffield S11
Tel: 0742-662930
Contact: I Korklin
Office: Honorary Secretary

Bradford Hebrew Congregation
The Synagogue
Springhurst Road
Shipley
West Yorkshire BD18 3DN
Contact: Honorary Secretary

Synagogue
Top Storey of Bowman's Buildings
Aldwark
York
North Yorkshire

NORTH WEST ENGLAND

Blackpool Reform Synagogue
40 Raikes Parade
Blackpool
Lancashire FY1 4EX
Tel: 0253-23687
Contact: B Raven
Office: Honorary Secretary
Place of worship. A constituent member of the Reform Synagogues of Great Britain. Services are held on Friday evenings and Saturday mornings and on festivals.

Synagogue
Leamington Road
Blackpool
Lancashire

Hillcock Hebrew Congregation
Ribble Drive
Whitefield
Bury BL9 6RT
Tel: 061-773-0748 (home)
Contact: V Goldberg
Office: Honorary Secretary

Yeshurun Hebrew Congregation
Coniston Road
Gatley
Cheshire SK8 4AP
Tel: 061-428-8242
Fax: 061-491-5265
Contact: Dr Alan Unterman
Office: Minister
Place of worship. A modern Orthodox synagogue with a membership of approximately three hundred families. There is a religion school of over one hundred children, a lending library of Jewish books, youth activities, study groups, ladies guild, women's groups, burial society and communal cemetery. The synagogue holds twice daily services and employs a full time minister, part time cantor and an office administrator.

Hale and District Hebrew Congregation
Shay Lane
Hale Barns
Cheshire WA15 8PA
Tel: 061-980-8846

Adult Jewish Education Committee
c/o Harold House
Dunbabin Road
Liverpool L15
Tel: 051-722-5671
Contact: Clive Lawton
Office: Chairperson

Allerton Hebrew Congregation
Mather Avenue
Liverpool L18
Tel: 051-427-6848

Community Centre
Dunbabin Road
Liverpool L15 6XL
Tel: 051-722-5825

Greenbank Drive Synagogue
Greenbank Chambers
Greenbank Drive
Liverpool L17 1AF
Tel: 051-733-1417
Contact: Rev Chait

Hillel House
25 Arundel Drive
Liverpool L17 3BX
Tel: 051-733-2819

Jewish Women's Welfare Society

433 Smithdown Road
Liverpool L15 3JL
Contact: Mrs J Shoham
Office: Secretary
The society aims to help under-privileged, elderly and young unmarried mothers, financially if necessary, and to give aid and support.

Jewish Youth and Community Centre

Harold House
Dunbabin Road
Liverpool L15
Tel: 051-722-5671
Fax: 051-722-0212
Contact: E S Rosen
Office: Director
A youth and community centre which aims to provide for the social and cultural needs of the Merseyside Jewish community by offering a comprehensive programme of educational, religious, leisure and sporting activities for all age groups in a Jewish environment and atmosphere. The centre is a focal point for many Jewish constituent groups and other communal organisations. Orthodox practices and customs are strictly adhered to within the centre. Part of the ethos is to encourage young members and their families to participate together in the cultural and social events which celebrate the Jewish festivals. Activities include informal Jewish education programmes for young people and adults of all ages; cultural and sporting facilities for the Jewish community on Merseyside; a Kosher restaurant; book shop; gift centre and resource centre.

Liverpool Jewish Resource Centre

Harold House
Dunbabin Road
Liverpool L15 6XL
Tel: 051-722-3514
Fax: 051-722-0212
Contact: Mrs Naomi S Kingston
Office: Chairperson
A resource centre which is run under the auspices of the Merseyside Jewish Representative Council in collaboration with the Youth and Community centre which forms part of a network of resources. The aim is to provide the Jewish and wider community with any material relating to Judaism and Israel. There is a large selection of books, videos and cassettes available.

Liverpool Progressive Synagogue

28 Church Road North
Liverpool L15 6TF

Tel: 051-733-5871 (home)
Contact: Mrs N Golduck
Office: Honorary Secretary

Merseyside Amalgamated Talmud Torah

King David Primary School
Beauclair Drive
Liverpool L15
Contact: Mrs E Wolfson
Office: Chair

Merseyside Jewish Welfare Council

433 Smithdown Road
Liverpool L15 3JL
Tel: 051-733-2292
Fax: 051-734-0212
Contact: A Hurst
Office: Secretary
A communal body representing other organisations with a welfare and social work function. It provides advice and assistance for Jewish families; meals-on-wheels and home and hospital visiting. It supplies information, advice and a casework service to the general community and any other organisation which may be dealing with Jewish families.

Old Hebrew Congregation

Princes Road
Liverpool
Merseyside
Tel: 051-709-3431

Synagogue

2 Dovedale Road
Liverpool
Merseyside

Ullet Road Synagogue

101 Ullet Road
Liverpool L17
Contact: Arnold Cooklin
Honorary Secretary.

University Jewish Students' Society

c/o Students Union
Bedford Street
Liverpool L7

Beth Hamedrash Daesek Eliezer

74 King's Road
Prestwich
Manchester

Cheetham Hebrew Congregation
453 Cheetham Hill Road
Manchester M8 7PA
Tel: 061-740-7788

Cheshire Reform Congregation
Menorah Synagogue
198 Altrincham Road
Manchester M22 4NZ
Tel: 061-428-7746

Damesek Eliezer Synagogue
74 Kings Road
Prestwich
Manchester
Tel: 061-740-2486
Contact: Rabbi S Goldberg

Heaton Park Hebrew Congregation
"Ashdown"
Middleton Road
Manchester M8 6JX
Tel: 061-740-2767
Contact: Rev L Olsberg

Higher Crumpsall and Higher Broughton Hebrew Congregation
Bury Old Road
Manchester M8 6EX
Tel: 061-740-1210

Higher Prestwich Hebrew Congregation
Highbury House
445 Bury Old Road
Higher Prestwich
Manchester M25 5TY
Tel: 061-773-4800

Hillel House
Greenheys Lane
Manchester M15 6LR
Tel: 061-226-1061

Holy Law and South Broughton Hebrew Congregation
Bury Old Road
Prestwich
Manchester M25 8EX
Tel: 061-740-1634

Hulme Hebrew Congregation
Hillel House
Greenheys Lane
Manchester M15 6LR

Jewish Programmes Material Project (JPMP)
142 Bury Old Road
Manchester M8 6HD
Tel: 061-795-7050
Fax: 061-740-7407
Contact: Doreen Gerson
Office: Director
A resource centre. Its main activities revolve around youth and community work. It provides videos, books, audio visual programmes and a music library.

Jewish Social Services (Greater Manchester)
12 Holland Road
Manchester M8 6NP
Tel: 061-795-0024
Fax: 061-795-3688
Contact: Ivan Lewis
Office: Chief Executive
A registered charity and social welfare organisation providing a range of social services including professional social work support, home care, volunteer befriending scheme and financial assistance to vulnerable client groups of all ages.

Jewish Soup Kitchen
Rita Glickman House
Ravensway
Prestwich
Manchester
Tel: 061-795-4930
Contact: Mrs D Phillips
Office: Honorary Secretary
A meals on wheels service provided.

J T Tannenbaum Jewish Cultural Centre
Jubilee School
Bury Old Road
Manchester M8 6FY
Tel: 061-795-4000
Contact: M Kaye
Office: Administrator

Manchester Jewish Blind Society
Nicky Alliance Day Centre
Middleton Road
Manchester M8 6JY
Tel: 061-740-0111
Contact: M Galley
Office: Director

Manchester Jewish Marriage Council
Levi House
Bury Old Road
Manchester M8 6FX
Tel: 061-740-5746

Manchester Jews' Benevolent Society
Levi House
Bury Old Road
Manchester M8
Tel: 061-740-4089
Contact: S Leinhardt
Office: Honorary Secretary

Manchester Reform Synagogue
Jackson's Row
Albert Square
Manchester M2 5W0
Tel: 061-834-0415
Contact: N Franks
Office: Secretary

Morris Feinmann Homes Trust
178 Palatine Road
Didsbury
Manchester M20 8GA
Tel: 061-445-3533
Fax: 061-448-1755
Contact: Peter F Kurer
Office: Chairperson
A registered charity which takes care of elderly Jewish people and runs a residential/nursing home for sixty-four people.

North Manchester Reform Congregation (Sha'arei Shalom)
Elms Street
Whitefield
Manchester M25 6GA
Tel: 061-796-6736 (home)
Contact: Mrs L Tucker
Office: Honorary Secretary

Outreach Community and Residential Services
24a Bury New Road
Prestwich
Manchester M25 8LD
Tel: 061-798-0180
Contact: P Sutton
Office: Director

Prestwich Beth Hamedrash Synagogue
74 Kings Road
Prestwich
Manchester M25 8HU
Tel: 061-740-2486 (home)
Contact: Rabbi S Goldberg
Office: Minister

Sale and District Hebrew Congregation
14 Hesketh Road
Sale
Manchester M33 5AA
Tel: 061-973-3013
Contact: M Coppel
Office: Secretary

Sha'are Sedek Synagogue
Old Lansdowne Road
West Didsbury
Manchester M20 8NZ
Tel: 061-445-5731
Contact: Mrs D Stewart
Office: Secretary

Shechita Board
435 Cheetham Hill Road
Manchester M8 7PF
Tel: 061-740-9711
Contact: Y Brodie
Office: Administrator

South Manchester Synagogue
Wilbraham Road
Manchester M14 6JS
Tel: 061-224-1366
Contact: S L Rydz
Office: Administrator

United Synagogue
Meade Hill Road
Manchester M8 6LS
Tel: 061-740-9586
Contact: Reuben Wilner
Office: Secretary

Withington Congregation of Spanish and Portuguese Jews
Queenston Road
West Didsbury
Manchester M20 8WZ
Tel: 061-445-1943

Yeshiva (Talmudical College)

Saul Rosenberg House
Seymour Road
Higher Crumpsall
Manchester M8 6BQ
Tel: 061-740-0214
Contact: Revd G Brodie
Office: Secretary

Blackburn Hebrew Congregation

Orchard Road
St Annes-on-Sea
Lancashire FY8 1RT
Tel: 0253-728245
Contact: Rabbi R Fisher
Services held in homes and in St Annes on Holy days.

St Annes Hebrew Congregation

Orchard Road
St Annes-on-Sea
Lancashire FY8 1PJ
Tel: 0253-721831
Contact: P Davidson
Office: President

Synagogue

Orchard Road
St Anne's-on-Sea
Lancashire

Academy for Rabbinical Research (Kolel)

134 Leicester Road
Salford M7 0LU
Tel: 061-740-1960
Contact: Rev J Freedman
Office: Secretary

Adass Yeshurun Synagogue

Cheltenham Crescent
Salford M7 0FE
Tel: 061-740-4548
Contact: S Gluckstadt
Office: Honorary Secretary

Adath Israel Synagogue

Upper Park Street
Salford M7 0HL
Tel: 061-740-3905 (home)
Contact: Revd S Simon
Office: Secretary

Great and New (Stenecourt) Synagogue

Singleton Road
Holden Road
Salford M7 0NL
Tel: 061-792-8399
Contact E Levene
Office Secretary

Kahal Chassidim Synagogue (Lubavitch)

72 Singleton Road
Salford M7 0LU
Tel: 061-740-3632
Contact: S Topperman
Office: Secretary

Lubavitch Foundation

72 Singleton Road
Salford M7 0LU
Tel: 061-740-9514

Lubavitch Yeshiva

72 Singleton Road
Salford M7 0LU
Tel: 061-740-9264
Contact: Rabbi A Cohen
Office: Dean

Manchester Central Board for Hebrew Education and Talmud Torah

Emanuel Raffles House
57 Leicester Road
Salford M7 0DA
Tel: 061-708-9200
Contact: Mr S Pine
Office: Chairperson
An umbrella organisation which promotes Jewish education within the Manchester community. It runs Sunday Schools (including a Special educational Needs Unit) and religious assemblies in secondary schools. The organisation liaises with Local Education Authorities and Examination Boards on all Jewish educational matters and promotes Bible studies, especially for teenagers.

Manchester Council of Synagogues (Orthodox)

c/o The Synagogue
Leicester Road
Salford M7 0HH
Tel: 061-740-4830
Contact: M Green
Office: Secretary

Nefusot Yehudah Synagogue
Emanuel Raffles House
2 Upper Park Road
Salford M7 0HL
Tel: 061-795-4567
Contact: Dr D J Marshall
Office: Honorary Secretary

North Salford Synagogue
2 Vine Street
Kersal
Salford M7 0NX
Tel: 061-740-7958
Contact: Rabbi L W Rabinowitz

Ohel Torah Congregation
132 Leicester Road
Salford M7 0ES
Tel: 061-792-2413 (home)
Contact: S Spielman
Office: Secretary

Reshet Torah Education Network
4 Hanover Gardens
Salford M7 0FQ
Tel: 061-740-5735
Contact: Rabbi S M Kupetz

Spanish and Portuguese Synagogue
18 Moor Lane
Salford M7 0WX
Tel: 061-773-1344

Talmud Torah Chinuch N'orim
11 Wellington Street East
Salford M7 9AU
Tel: 061-792-4522
Contact: B Waldman
Office: Chair

Telzer and Kowner Synagogue
Ground Floor
134 Leicester Road
Salford
Greater Manchester

Zeuve Agudath Israel Synagogue
Ground Floor
35a Northumberland Street
Broughton
Salford
Greater Manchester

Preston Synagogue
31 Avondale Road
Southport
Merseyside PR9 0NH
Tel: 0704-538276 (home)
Contact: Dr C E Nelson
Office: Honorary Secretary

Southport Jewish Representative Council
7 Grange Road
Southport
PR9 9AB
Tel: 0704-532367
Fax: 0704-542075
Contact: Gillian L Mayer
Office: Honorary Secretary

Southport New Synagogue
Portland Street
Southport
PR8 1LR
Tel: 0704-535950
Contact: Julian Desser
Office: Honorary Secretary

Southport Synagogue
Arnside Road
Southport
Merseyside
Tel: 0704-32964
Contact: Mrs M Cohen
Office: Secretary

Synagogue
Jewish Convalescent and Aged Home
81 Albert Street
Southport
Merseyside PR9 9LN

Wallasey Hebrew Congregation
27a Falkland Road
Wallasey
Merseyside L44 8EN
Contact: L S Goldman
Office: Honorary Secretary

Whitefield Hebrew Congregation
Park Lane
Whitefield
Lancashire M25 7PB
Tel: 061-766-3732

Hebrew Synagogue
Falkland Road
Egremont
Wirral
Merseyside

ENGLISH EAST MIDLANDS

Jewish Communal Centre
Highfield Street
Leicester
Tel: 0533-540477

Jewish Students Society
c/o Students Union
Leicester University
Leicester

Leicester Progressive Jewish Congregation
12 Waveney Rise
Oadby
Leicester LE2 4GG
Tel: 0533-715584 (home)
Contact: Mr and Mrs J Kaufman
Office: Honorary Secretaries
Affiliated to the Union of Liberal and Progressive Synagogues, it holds regular services, mostly at the Friends Meeting House, Leicester. There is also a religion school, adult education and social activities.

Synagogue
Highfield Street
Leicester
Tel: 0533-700997 (home)
Contact: G J Louis
Office: Honorary Secretary

Hebrew Congregation
95-97 Overstone Road
Northampton
Tel: 0604-32822 (home)
Contact: Rev H Silman
Office: Minister

Nottingham Hebrew Congregation
Shakespeare Villas
Nottingham NG1 4FQ
Tel: 0602-472004
Contact: Rabbi Perez
Office: Minister
The place of worship and spiritual centre for Nottingham's Orthodox Jewish community.

Nottingham Jewish Welfare Board
35 Arnot Hill Road
Nottingham NG5 6LN
Tel: 0602-260245
Contact: Dr M Caplan
Office: Chair
An old-established welfare organisation run by donations from the local Jewish community. Together with its sister organisation, the Nottingham Jewish Women's Benevolent Society, the Welfare Board founded the Nottingham Jewish Housing Association. A residential home for the elderly has been established by voluntary donations, which has been operating successfully for about five years with up to twenty-five residents. The home observes Jewish dietary laws and provides facilities for observing Sabbath and festivals. Other activities include visiting the sick, aged and lonely; providing food parcels where neccessary and occasionally help is given in cases of sudden, urgent and unexpected financial hardship.

Nottingham Progressive Jewish Congregation
Nottingham Progressive Synagogue
Lloyd Street
off Mansfield Road
Sherwood
Nottingham NG5 4BP
Tel: 0602-624761
Contact: Rabbi Setti D Kunin
Office: Minister
A religious congregation committed to the principles of Progressive Judaism. The central activity is worship but other important activities include education (adult and child), celebration of festivals, social activities and taking part in the life of the local community. Contact can also be made through the Honorary Secretary, Helen Prins, Tel: 0602-608533 (home).

University of Nottingham Jewish and Israel Society
c/o Nottingham University
Nottingham NG7 2RD
Contact: Judith Jackson
Office: Chair
A student organisation of about thirty members engaging in religious, social and anti-racism activities. It has Friday night meals and other religious and social activities for any students that are interested, although the majority of members are Jewish. All events are held jointly with Nottingham Trent University Jewish Society.

Nottingham Trent University Jewish Societry
c/o Nottingham Trent University
Nottingham NG1 4BU

Women's Benevolent Society
8 Croft Road
Edwalton
Nottingham
Tel: 0602-231105
Fax: 0602-819959
Contact: Mrs Doreen Christie
Office: Chair
The society helps the Jewish elderly and needy with
financial and emotional support. Regular weekly visits
are organised.

ENGLISH WEST MIDLANDS

Birmingham Central Synagogue
133 Pershore Road
Edgbaston
Birmingham B5 7PA
Tel: 021-440-4044
Contact: Mr P Hartheimer
Office: Secretary
Place of worship. An Orthodox synagogue.

Birmingham Jewish Youth Trust
The Youth Centre
Hillel House
19 Sandhurst Road
Birmingham B13
Tel: 021-442-4459

Birmingham Progressive Synagogue
4 Sheepcote Street
(off Broad Street)
Birmingham B16 8AA
Tel: 021-643-5640
Contact: Mrs R Plotner
Office: Administrator

Birmingham Union of Jewish Students
C/o Hillel House
26 Somerset Road
Edgbaston
Birmingham B15

Hillel House
26 Somerset Road
Edgbaston
Birmingham B15
Tel: 021-454-5684

Jewish Welfare Board
1 Rake Way
Tennant Street
Birmingham B15 1EG
Tel: 021-643-2835
Fax: 021-643-5291
Contact: George Greenstone
Office: Director
A comprehensive welfare organisation with
professional social workers, housing management and
offering day centre activities. Its main client group is
the elderly, but social work responsibility is accepted
across the age spectrum. Recently constructed is a sixty
bed new residential home/nursing home for the
elderly and it also runs a meals–on–wheels service.

Lubavitch Centre
95 Willows Road
Birmingham B12 9QF
Tel: 021-440-6673

Pershore Road Synagogue
251 Pershore Road
Birmingham

New Synagogue
11 Park Road
Moseley
Birmingham B13 8AB
Tel: 021-449-3544

Synagogue
Blucher Street
Singer's Hill
Birmingham

Talmud Torah
Central Synagogue
133 Pershore Road
Birmingham B5 7PA
Tel: 021-440-4044

Coventry Synagogue
Barras Lane
Coventry CV1 3BU
Tel: 0203-220168
Contact: L R Benjamin
Office: Honorary Secretary
Place of worship attended by Orthodox Jews.

Leamington and District Progressive Jewish Group

12 Church Lane
Lillington
Leamington Spa
Warwickshire CV22 7RG
Tel: 0926-421300 (home)
Contact: Mrs J Heilbronn
Office: Honorary Secretary
A small local group attached to Birmingham Progressive Synagogue. Activities are services and discussions.

Solihull Hebrew Congregation

Monastery Drive
Solihull
West Midlands B91 3HN
Tel: 0564-775715 (home)
Contact: P Fiddler
Office: Honorary Secretary

Stoke-on-Trent Hebrew Congregation

Birch Terrace
Hanley
Stoke-on-Trent
Staffordshire
Tel: 0782-616417 (home)
Contact: H S Morris
Office: President

Synagogue

251 Pershore Road
Wolverhampton
West Midlands

Wolverhampton Hebrew Congregational Synagogue

Fryer Street
Wolverhampton WV1 1HT
Tel: 0902-752474
Contact: H Kronheim
Place of worship.

EAST ANGLIA

Beth Shalom Reform Synagogue

86 Union Lane
Cambridge CB4 1QB
Tel: 0223-67175
Contact: Jonathan Harris
A place of worship which holds regular services on a Saturday morning, twice monthly on a Friday evening and also services on high holy days; religion classes for members' children; adult education classes; social club for members; preparation for Bar/Bat Mitzvah; library of books of Jewish interest and religion; welfare to members including hospital visiting and visiting the house-bound.

Cambridge Traditional Jewish Congregation

3 Thompsons Lane
Cambridge
Contact: Dr D Stone
Office: Chairperson
Place of worship. The synagogue holds regular services in the traditional Orthodox manner, Jewish social activities and educational activities on mostly Jewish or connected topics.

Cambridge University Jewish Society

c/o The Synagogue
3 Thompson's Lane
Cambridge CB5 8AQ
Tel: 0223-354783
Contact: President

Cambridge University Progressive Jewish Group

1 Merton Street
Cambridge
Tel: 0223-64793
Contact: Rabbi Dr N R M de Lange
Office: Chaplain

Jewish Ladies' Society

3a Earlham Road
Norwich
Norfolk
Contact: Mrs E Griffiths
Office: Secretary

Synagogue

3a Earlham Road
Norwich NR2 3RA
Contact: Mr J Griffiths
Office: Honorary Secretary

Peterborough Hebrew Congregation

142 Cobden Avenue
Peterborough PE1 11L
Tel: 0733-571282
Contact: C Cunn
Office: Chairperson

Peterborough Liberal Jewish Community

82 Dogsthorpe Road
Peterborough PE1 3AH
Tel: 0733-898172

Contact: Pat Titman
Office: Secretary
The group is comparatively young and very small. Its main object is to hold services as often as possible, at the moment once a month. At present its activities are worship and a youth group. As the group expands other activities may be added.

Reformed Jewish Community
25 Sycamore Avenue
Peterborough PE1 4JW
The community has no official place of worship.

SOUTH EAST ENGLAND (NORTH)

South Bucks Jewish Community
The Friends Meeting House
Whielden Street
Amersham
Buckinghamshire
Tel: 0494–785942 (home)
Contact: c/o Mrs S Bijum
Office: Secretary
A Liberal Jewish congregation and synagogue. Its main activities are religious services and Jewish education for children.

Basildon Hebrew Congregation
3 Furlongs
Basildon
Essex
Tel: 0268–524947
Contact: M M Kochmann
Office: Chair
Religious congregation which meets for religious services.

Barking and Becontree United Synagogue
200 Becontree Avenue
Becontree
Essex
Tel: 081–590–2737
Place of worship.

Borehamwood and Elstree United Synagogue
Croxdale Road
Borehamwood
Hertfordshire WD6 4QF
Tel: 081–207–5227
Contact: B Winterman
Office: Administrator

Bushey and District United Synagogue
177–189 Sparrows Herne
Bushey
Hertfordshire WD2 1AJ
Tel: 081–950–7340
Contact: Rabbi Z M Salasnik
A place of worship established in the 1960s by young families who moved to Bushey. The area has continued to be popular for young couples and the synagogue's membership consists principally of families in the twenty-two to fifty-five age range and their children. In recent years, an increasing number of senior citizens have moved to Bushey. The synagogue caters for the complete age spectrum. The present building was completed in in 1984. Activities include worship, religion classes, kindergarten, youth clubs, senior citizens clubs and mother and toddler group.

Chelmsford Jewish Community
17 Taffrail Gardens
South Woodham Ferrers
Chelmsford
Essex CM3 5WH
Contact: S Keller
Office: Publicity Officer
A small Jewish community of about fifty families. Regular religious, social and cultural activities.

Chigwell and Hainault United Synagogue
Limes Farm Estate
Limes Avenue
Chigwell
Essex
Tel: 081–500–2451

Colchester and District Jewish Community
The Synagogue
Fennings Chase
Priory Street
Colchester
Essex CO1 2QB
Tel: 0206–45992 (home)
Contact: Norma B Stevenson
Office: Honorary Secretary
Place of worship. A purpose built synagogue which was established in 1969. There are approximately seventy-four families covering a wide geographical area. Activities include fundraising and a religion school on Sunday mornings, services every Friday at 8.00pm and on all high holy days and other festivals. The community has a good connection with the University of Essex where Israeli students study law. There is also a Ladies Guild.

Spec Jewish Youth and Community Centre

87 Brookside South
East Barnet
Hertfordshire EN4 8LL
Tel: 081-368-5117

Brady-Maccabi Youth and Community Centre

4 Manor Park Crescent
Edgware
Middlesex HA8 7NL
Tel: 081-952-2948

Edgware Adath Yisroel Synagogue

261 Hale Lane
Edgware
Middlesex
Tel: 081-905-4813
Contact: Rabbi Zvi Lieberman
Office: Minister
Place of worship. A small, warm and welcoming Orthodox Jewish community providing its members with all the communal activities and responsibilities. There is a great emphasis on Jewish learning for all. Youth activities, worship and study also take place.

Edgware and District Reform Synagogue

118 Stonegrove
Edgware
Middlesex HA8 8AB
Tel: 081-958-9782
Fax: 081-905-4710
Contact: The Secretary
Place of worship and community centre. A synagogue whose activities are aimed at promoting Judaism amongst the one thousand seven hundred families who belong to the synagogue. It runs prayer services, a day centre, a youth centre, a religion school, a kindergarten, and provides communal halls for various activities.

Edgware Jewish Family Service

Rectory House
Rectory Lane
Edgware
Middlesex HA8 7LF
Tel: 081-951-0166
Fax: 081-951-1915
A partnership between Jewish Care and Norwood Child Care working with the Jewish community to offer appropriate responses to the needs of Jewish individuals and families.

Edgware Masorti Synagogue

Brady Maccabi Centre
4 Manor Park Crescent
Edgware
Middlesex HA8 7NL
Tel: 081-958-6459

Edgware United Synagogue

Edgware Way
Edgware
Middlesex HA8 8JT
Tel: 081-958-7508

Yeshurun Synagogue

Fernhurst Gardens
Edgware
Middlesex

Hertsmere Progressive Synagogue

High Street
Elstree
Hertfordshire WD6 3BY
Tel: 081-953-8889
Contact: Honorary Secretary
Place of worship. A constituent synagogue of the Union of Liberal and Progressive Synagogues. The Synagogue serves approximately two hundred and fifty families living in the local and surrounding area. Regular services are held with a Rabbi. There is a religion school and educational and social activities.

Enfield and Winchmore Hill United Synagogue

53 Wellington Road
Bush Hill Park
Enfield
Middlesex
Tel: 081-363-2697
Tel: 081-367-2569 (home)
Contact: S Leon
Office: Honorary Secretary

Greenford Synagogue

39-45 Oldfield Lane
Greenford
Middlesex
Tel: 081-578-3196 (home)
Contact: R A Hyams
Office: Honorary Secretary

Harlow Jewish Community

Harberts Road
Hare Street
Harlow

Essex
Tel: 0378–424668 (home)
Contact: Mrs C Petars
Office: Honorary Secretary
A place of worship affiliated to the Reform Synagogues of Great Britian and Northern Ireland. Its catchment area includes Bishop's Stortford, Takeley, Hoddesdon, Hertford, and Epping. There are approximately eighty families on the membership list. Each year a student minister is appointed to attend to congregational needs, usually once a month. There is a fund operating with the aim of providing a full time minister. There is a ladies' guild, children's scripture classes and social functions.

Harold Hill and District Affiliated Synagogue
Trowbridge Road
Harold Hill
Essex
Tel: 04023–48904 (home)
Contact: Miss D Meid
Office: Honorary Secretary

Harrow and Wembley Progressive Synagogue
326 Preston Road
Harrow
Middlesex HA3 0QH
Tel: 081-904-8581
Contact: Mrs S Rose
Office: Secretary
Place of worship and a Progressive Jewish community which prides itself on being a caring, friendly community where visitors of all faiths are made to feel welcome. Shabbat services are held on Friday nights and Saturday mornings. The synagogue runs a religion school, welfare groups, friendship clubs, youth clubs and a whole range of social activities.

Middlesex New Synagogue
39 Bessborough Road
Harrow
Middlesex HA1 3BS
Tel: 081-864-0133
Contact: Mrs D Brogin
Office: Secretary

Neveh Shalom Community, David Ishag Synagogue
352-4 Preston Road
Harrow
Middlesex HA3 0QL
Tel: 081-904-3009
Contact: C Benson
Office: Honorary Secretary

Kol Chai - Hatch End Jewish Community
Woodridge Yard
Hatchend
Middlesex
Tel: 0923-825571
Contact: J Pentel
Office: Chair

Potters Bar United Synagogue
Meadowcroft
Great North Road
Bell Bar
Hatfield
Hertfordshire AL9 6DB
Tel: 0707-56202 (home)
Contact: Rev G Burns
Office: Minister

Hemel Hempstead United Synagogue
Lady Sarah Cohen Community Centre
Midland Road
Hemel Hempstead
Hertfordshire HD1 1RP
Tel: 0923-32007
Contact: H. Nathan
Office: Honorary Secretary

Elm Park United Synagogue
Woburn Avenue
Elm Park
Hornchurch
Essex RM12 5EA
Tel: 04024-42079
Contact: H Gaynor
Office: Administrator

Hounslow, Heathrow and District United Synagogue
100 Staines Road
Hounslow
Middlesex
Tel: 081-560-3633 (home)
Contact Mrs G Roth
Office Adminstrator

Barkingside Progressive Synagogue
129 Perryman's Farm Road
Barkingside
Ilford
Essex IG2 7LX
Tel: 081-554-9682
Contact: F Gold
Office: Secretary

Ilford Congregation (Ohel David)

Newbury Park Station
Ilford
Essex
Tel: 081–806–8109 (home)
Contact: D Elias
Office: Honorary Secretary

Ilford Federation Synagogue

14/16 Coventry Road
Ilford
Essex IG1 4QR
Tel: 081–554–5289
Contact: Mrs P Hacker
Office: Secretary

Ilford United Synagogue

84 Beehive Lane
Ilford
Essex IG1 3RT
Tel: 081–554–5969
Contact: Ms H R Michaels
Office: Administrator
Place of worship.

Lubavitch Centre

372 Cranbrook Road
Ilford
Essex
Tel: 081–554–1624

Newbury Park Synagogue

23 Wessex Close
Suffolk Road
Newbury Park
Ilford
Essex IG3 8JT
Tel: 081–597–0958

Ohel Jacob Beth Hamedrash

1st Floor
478 Cranbrook Road
Ilford
Essex
Contact: D Grant
Office: Honorary Secretary

Redbridge Jewish Youth and Community Centre

Sinclair House
Woodford Bridge Road
Ilford
Essex IG4 5LN

Tel: 081–551–0017
Contact: I A Berkoff
Office: Director

South West Essex Reform Synagogue

Oaks Lane
Newbury Park
Ilford
Essex IG2 7PL
Tel: 081–599–0936
Contact: Rabbi H Goldstein
Place of worship. It provides facilities for worship, education, youth activities and welfare work.

Jewish Residents Association

25 The Links
Kempston
Bedfordshire
Tel: 0234–853563
Contact: Mrs K Rapstone
Office: Secretary

Kenton United Synagogue

Shaftesbury Avenue
Kenton
Middlesex HA3 0RD
Tel: 081–907–5959
Contact: Mrs J Velleman
Office: Administrator

Buckhurst Hill Reform Synagogue (Sukkat Shalom)

P O Box 14
Loughton
Essex IG10 1QW
Tel: 081–508–2414 (home)
Contact: Cecil Dalton
Office: Chairperson
Place of worship and a constituent synagogue of the Reform Synagogues of Great Britain. It is a small congregation of one hundred and forty families, formed approximately twelve years ago. It is unique in as much as, although it has no building of its own, it employs a full-time Rabbi. It has a radical approach to traditional Judaism.

Judean Youth Club

c/o Synagogue
P O Box 215
Luton LU1 1HW
Contact: Mrs B Felson
Office: Chair

Luton Synagogue
PO Box 215
Luton LU1 1HW
Tel: 0582-25032
Contact: D Bailey
Office: Honorary Secretary

Maidenhead Synagogue
9 Boyn Hill Avenue
Maidenhead
Berkshire SL6 4ET
Tel: 0628-73012
Contact: Rabbi Dr Jonathan Romain
Office: Minister
A place of worship. The synagogue also acts as a Jewish communal centre with a wide range of religious, educational, social, cultural and welfare activities.

Milton Keynes and District Reform Synagogue
11 Fairways
Two Mile Ash
Milton Keynes
Buckinghamshire MK8 8AL (home)
Contact: Mr Zvei Friedman

Barnet and District Affiliated Synagogue
Eversleigh Road
New Barnet
Hertfordshire EN5 1NE
Tel: 081-449-0145
Contact: Mrs H Spillman
Office: Secretary

Eastern Jewry Community
Newbury Park Station
Newbury Park
Essex IG2
Tel: 081-806-8109 (home)
Contact: D Elias
Office: Honarary Secretary

Northwood and Pinner Liberal Synagogue
Oaklands Gate
Northwood
Middlesex HA6 3AA
Tel: 0923-822592
Contact: Mrs S Kempner
Office: Honorary Secretary
Place of worship. The synagogue has a membership of over five hundred and fifty families and is affiliated to the Union of Liberal and Progressive Synagogues. It seats three hundred and fifty people for services and is also used for social events. A wide range of religious,

educational and cultural activities take place at the synagogue. A religion school meets on the premises, for children of six to fifteen years and there are classes on Saturday or Sunday mornings at the choice of the parents as well as pre-school classes for younger children. Support is given to members who are sick or in need of help and visits are made to members in hospital. Several clubs for youth at different ages meet and a football team, a Brownie pack and Guide company meet on the premises.

Oxford Jewish Congregation
The Synagogue
21 Richmond Road
Oxford OX1 2JL
Tel: 0865-53042
Contact: The President
A place of Jewish worship, educational and cultural activities.

Oxford Progressive Synagogue
2a Northmoor Road
Oxford
Tel: 0865-512802 (home)
Contact: Mr. Michael Cross

Oxford University L'Chaim Students Shul
1st Floor
121 St Aldate's
Oxford

University Jewish Society
171 Iffley Road
Oxford
Tel: 0865-726037
Contact: J Montagu

Pinner United Synagogue
1 Cecil Park
Pinner
Middlesex HA5 5HJ
Tel: 081-868-7204
Contact: Mrs C Lipman
Office: Administrator
Primarily a place of worship, but also provides a youth and community centre for social, welfare and cultural activities.

Radlett and Bushey Reform Synagogue
118 Watling Street
Radlett
Hertfordshire WD7 7AA
Tel: 0923-856110
Contact: Mrs A Pyzer

Office: Honorary Secretary
Place of worship. Activities include worship, youth clubs, cubs and scouts.

Ladies Guild
343 Peppard Road
Emmer Green
Reading
Berkshire
Tel: 0734–472711
Contact: Mrs V Stein

Reading Synagogue
Goldsmid Road
Reading
Berkshire RG1 7YB
Tel: 0734–573954/0734–571018 (home)
Contact: Mrs L Creme
Office: Honorary Secretary

Thames Valley Jewish Progressive Community
Reading
Berkshire
Tel: 0734–500551 (work)
Tel: 0734–867769 (home)
Contact: Diz Edelman
Office: Chairperson

University Jewish Society
c/o Reading Hillel
82 Basingstoke Road
Reading
Berkshire
Tel: 0734–873282

Youth Centre Hanoar Hatzioni
10 St Davids Close
Caversham
Reading
Berkshire
Tel: 0734–477596

Clayhall United Synagogue
Sinclair House
Woodford Bridge Road
Redbridge
Essex
Contact: Mrs Fishman
Office: Secretary
Place of worship. Its main activities are worship and welfare. Visitors are welcome, but prior arrangement is neccessary for group visits.

Harold Hill Synagogue
Trowbridge Road
Harold Hill
Romford
Essex

Romford and District Affiliated Synagogue
25 Eastern Road
Romford
Essex
Tel: 0708 760286
Contact: B Shooter
Office: Administrator

Ruislip and District Affiliated Synagogue
Sheney Avenue
Ruislip Manor
Middlesex HA4 6BP
Tel: 0895 622059
Contact: A Barnett
Office: Administrator

Hebrew Congregation
Oswald Road
St Albans
Hertfordshire
Tel: 0727–825295 (home)
Contact: H Turner
Office: Honorary Secretary

Masorti Congregation
St Albans
Hertfordshire
Tel: 0727–48778
Contact: S Gess
Office: Secretary

Southend-on-Sea and District Jewish Representative Council
8 Earls Hall Avenue
Southend-on-Sea
Essex SS2 6PD
Tel: 0702–343114 (home)
Contact: D G Harris
Office: Chairperson
A central body to which other affiliated Jewish organisations appoint delegates. It aims to: speak for and represent the local Jewish community in all but religious matters; foster and enhance internal Jewish co-operation within the area and to safeguard and further the welfare, defence and security and reputation of the Jewish community.

Belmont United Synagogue
101 Vernon Drive
Stanmore
Middlesex HA7 2BW
Tel: 081-863-9783
Contact: Mrs C Fletcher
Office: Administrator

Stanmore and Canons Park United Synagogue
London Road
Stanmore
Middlesex HA7 4NS
Tel: 081-954-2210
Contact: Mrs B Dresner
Office: Administrator

Bushey and District Affiliated Synaogue
Police Station Lane
Watford
Hertfordshire

Watford United Synagogue
16 Nascot Road
Watford WD1 3RE
Tel: 0923-232168
Contact: Mrs C Silverman
Office: Secretary
Place of worship. The focal point for the Jewish community within the Watford area, where religious services are held. The synagogue is also used as a Kindergarten, a meeting place for Brownies and Hebrew classes for children.

Welwyn Garden City United Synagogue
Barn Close
Handside Lane
Welwyn Garden City
Hertfordshire AL8 6ST
Tel: 0707-33-8425
Contact: Mrs S Myeroff
Office: Honorary Secretary

Wembley United Synagogue
Forty Avenue
Wembley Park
Middlesex HA9 8JW
Tel: 081-904-6565
Contact: Mrs R Garfield
Office: Administrator

Colman Levene Talmud Torah (Orthodox)
Synagogue Office
Finchley Road

Westcliff-on-Sea
Essex SS0 8AD
Tel: 0702-344900
Contact: Rabbi Michael Harris
Office: Principal

Guild (Reform)
Southend and District Reform Synagogue
851 London Road
Westcliff-on-Sea
Essex
Tel: 0702-7116633

Jewish Lads and Girls Brigade
1 Hall Park Avenue
Westcliff-on-Sea
Essex
Contact: Mrs R Linton
Office: Secretary

Kashrut and Shechita Board
c/o Synagogue Office
Finchley Road
Westcliff-on-Sea
Essex SS0 8AD
Tel: 0702-344900
Contact: David Gordon
Office: Warden

Kosher Meals on Wheels Service
93 The Ridgeway
Westcliff-on-Sea
Essex
Tel: 0702-74230
Contact: Mrs H Davies
Office: Honorary Secretary

Southend and District Reform Synagogue
851 London Road
Westcliff-on-Sea
Essex
Tel: 0702-75809
Tel: 0702-338460 (home)
Contact: N Klass
Office: Chair

Southend and Westcliff Hebrew Congregation
Synagogue Office
Finchley Road
Westcliff-on-Sea
Essex SS20 8AD

Tel: 0702-344900
Contact: Rabbi Michael Harris
Office: Minister

Southend and Westcliff Hebrew Education Board

Synagogue Office
Finchley Road
Westcliff-on-Sea
Essex SS0 8AD
Tel: 0702-344900
Contact: Mr. Alan Gershlick
Office: Chair
An educational group which provides Hebrew education for the children of the Orthodox Jewish community in Southend and Westcliff by holding classes on Sundays and weekdays.

Southend and Westcliff Jewish Day Centre

Victoria Oppenheim House
1 Cobham Road
Westcliff-on-Sea
Tel: 0702-344263
Contact: Mrs C Mann
Office: Manager

Talmud Torah (Reform)

851 London Road
Westcliff-on-Sea
Essex
Tel: 0702-75809 (home)
Contact: Mrs Woods
Office: Principal

Westcliff and Leigh Synagogue

38 Ceylon Road
Westcliff-on-Sea
Essex

Youth Centre (Orthodox)

38 Ceylon Road
Westcliff-on-Sea
Essex
Tel: 0702-346545
Contact: D Jay
Office: Secretary

LONDON (E POSTCODES)

East London Central Synagogue

30-40 Nelson Street
London E1 2DE
Tel: 071-790-9809

Tel: 081-202-7571 (home)
Contact: A Berniger
Office: Secretary

Commercial Road Great Synagogue

262 Commercial Road
London E1

Congregation of Jacob

351-353 Commercial Road
London E1
Contact: A Segal
Office: Secretary

East London United Synagogue

52 Rectory Square
Stepney Green
London E1 3NG
Tel: 071-790-1077
Contact: S Mather
Office: Administrator

Ezras Chaim Synagogue

2 Heneage Street
London E1

Fieldgate Street Great Synagogue

41 Fieldgate Street
London E1
Tel: 071-247-2644

Great Garden Street Synagogue

7 Greatorex Street
London E1 5NF
Tel: 071-247-4436 (home)
Contact: L Gayer
Office: Secretary

Nelson Street Sephardic Synagogue

Nelson Street
London E1

Sandy's Row Synagogue

Sandy's Row
Middlesex Street
London E1 7HW
Tel: 071-253-8311
Contact: A Wilder
Office: Secretary

Settlement Synagogue

2 Beaumont Grove
London E1 4NQ

Tel: 071-790-6262
Contact: The Rabbi
Place of worship. The only synagogue which is both Reform and Liberal and probably the most active synagogue surviving in London's East End. Founded in 1919 in the Oxford and St Georges Jewish Settlement, the synagogue still continues a friendly, informal atmosphere combining traditionalism with modernism. Activities are religious, social and cultural, and there is also an interest in interfaith activities.

Stepney B'nai B'rith Clubs and Settlement
Beaumont Hall
2/8 Beaumont Grove
London E1 4NQ
Tel: 071-790-6441
Contact: Nicholas Collins
Office: Director

Teesdale Street Synagogue
68-70 Teesdale Street
London E2

United Workman's Synagogue
21-22a Cheshire Street
Bethnal Green
London E2

Bevis Marks Synagogue
St Mary Axe
London EC3
Tel: 071-626-1274

Highams Park and Chingford United Synagogue
Marlborough Road
Highams Park
London E4 9AZ
Tel: 081-527-0937 (home)
Contact: Mrs S R Benjamin
Office: Secretary

Aden Jews' Congregation
117 Clapton Common
London E5
Tel: 081-806-1320
Contact: M A Solomon
Office: Honorary Secretary

Beth Hamedrash D'Chassidey Belz
96 Clapton Common
London E5
Tel: 081-800-3741
Contact: Dayan J D Babad

Beth Hamedrash Torah Chaim Liege
145 Upper Clapton Road
London E5
Contact: Rabbi Y Meisels

Clapton Federation Synagogue
47 Lea Bridge Road
London E5
Tel: 081-806-4369
Tel: 081-806-7565 (home)
Contact: K Franklin
Office: Secretary

Springfield Synagogue
202 Upper Clapton Road
London E5 9DH
Tel: 0702-340-762 (home)
Contact: L Blackman
Office: Honorary Secretary

Stamford Hill Beth Hamedrash
50 Clapton Common
London E5
Tel: 081-802-4017 (home)
Contact: M Chontow
Office: Secretary

East Ham and Manor Park District Synagogue
26 Carlyle Road
London E6

Forest Gate Federated Synagogue
52 Claremont Road
London E7

West Ham and Upton Park Synagogue
93-95 Earlham Grove
Forest Gate
London E7 9AR
Tel: 081-534-1917
Tel: 081-554-8347 (home)
Contact: A C Gilbert
Office: Secretary

West Hackney Synagogue

233a Amhurst Road
London E8
Tel: 081-254-2128 (home)
Contact: C Pollock
Office: President

Hackney United Synagogue

Brenthouse Road
Mare Street
London E9 6AG
Tel: 081-985-4600
Contact: Mrs B Heumann
Office: Administrator

Yavneh Synagogue

25 Ainsworth Road
London E9
Tel: 081-530-5816 (home)
Contact: R I Jacobs
Office: Secretary

Leytonstone and Wanstead Synagogue

2 Fillebrook Road
London E11
Tel: 081-550-5391 (home)
Contact: S Pizer
Office: Secretary

Waltham Forest Hebrew Congregation

140 Boundary Road
London E17 8LA
Tel: 081-509-0775
Contact: D Magnus
Office: Secretary

Wanstead and Woodford United Synagogue

20 Churchfields
South Woodford
London E18 2QZ
Tel: 081-504-1990
Contact: Mrs S Braude
Office: Administrator

Woodford Progressive Synagogue

Marlborough Road
South Woodford
London E18 1AR
Tel: 081-989-7619
Contact: Mrs R Harris
Office: Honorary Secretary

LONDON (N POSTCODES)

Garden Suburb Beth Hamedrash

Jacob and Alexander Gordon House
5 The Bishops Avenue
London N2
Tel: 081-458-3765
Contact: Rabbi C Wilschanski

Hampstead Garden Suburb (United) Synagogue

Norrice Lea
London N2 0RE
Tel: 081-455-8126
Fax: 081-201-9247
Contact: Mrs M S Wolff
Office: Administrator

Finchley Synagogue

Kinloss Gardens
London N3 3DU
Tel: 081-346-8551
Contact: Mrs B Fireman
Office: Administrator
An Orthodox place of worship which comes under the umbrella of the United Synagogue and includes a community centre.

Ha-Makon

The Manor House
80 East End Road
Finchley
London N3
Tel: 081-904-2802 (home)
Contact: Robin
Office: Co-ordinator
A cultural and social group for Jewish people aged twenty-one to thirty-one years. The group is backed by no political, religious or other movement but is based on Jewish identity and young people and the idea that making friends is a good activity. It provides a broad range of debates, talks, discussions and basic art lessons. The group meets once a fortnight at the Manor House, 80 East End Road, Finchley, London between 8.00pm-10.30pm.

London Board for Shechita

P O Box 579
Adastra House
401-405 Nether Street
London N3 1YR
Tel: 081-349-9160

Manor House Society

Sternberg Centre for Judaism
80 East End Road
Finchley
London N3 2SY
Tel: 081-346-2288
Fax: 081-349-0694
Contact: Pam Lewis
Office: Administrator
The Manor House Society is a cultural venture which aims to bring a wide range of Jewish cultural and intellectual events within the reach of a large audience. Events which are regularly organised include: evening concerts, lunchtime recitals, art exhibitions, art classes, debates, poetry readings, children's workshops and entertainment.

New North London Synagogue

The Manor House
80 East Road
London N3 2SY
Tel: 081-346-8560
Contact: Rabbi Jonathan Wittenberg
Place of worship. Independent traditional Orthodox synagogue, founded in 1974. It is a constituent synagogue of the Assembly of Masorti Synagogues.

Finsbury Park United Synagogue

220 Green Lanes
London N4 2NT
Tel: 081-800-3526
Contact: H Mather
Office: Administrator

Highgate United Synagogue

Grimshaw Close
57 North Road
Highgate
London N6 4BJ
Tel: 081-340-7655
Contact: Mr Ben Soller
Office: Secretary
A place of worship for a small religious community.

Muswell Hill United Synagogue

31 Tetherdown
London N10 1ND
Tel: 081-883-5925
Contact: H Hankin
Office: Administrator

Palmer's Green and Southgate United Synagogue

Brownlow Road
New Southgate
London N11 2BN
Tel: 081-881-0037
Contact: M Lewis
Office: Administrator

Finchley Progressive Synagogue

54a Hutton Grove
London N12 8DR
Tel: 081-446-4063
Contact: Joan Shopper
Office: Administrator
Place of worship. A Progressive synagogue which is a constituent member of the Union of Liberal and Progressive Synagogues. It provides facilities for worship and education.

Finchley Reform Synagogue

Fallowcourt Avenue
Finchley
London N12 0BE
Tel: 081-446-3244
Contact: Rabbi Jeffrey Newman
The Synagogue provides a place for Jewish people to worship on the Sabbath and for the celebration of Jewish festivals. In addition it is a communal building in which various activities take place for non-members as well as members. Activities are religious and communal and include children's and adult education, social issues, youth activities, old-peoples club, fund-raising activities and kindergarten.

New Connexions

Finchley Reform Synagogue
Fallowcourt Avenue
London N12 0BE
Tel: 081-446-3244
Tel: 081-368-7638 (home)
Contact: Ms Janet Berenson-Perkins
Office: Director
A forum to explore spiritual ideas which is open to all faiths. Its activities include weekly meetings with programmes led by various invited professionals including lectures, discussion music, song, experiential workshops and prayer.

Woodside Park Synagogue

Woodside Park Road
London N12 8RZ
Tel: 081-455-4236
Contact: D Bruce

Office: Administrator
Place of worship. A constituent synagogue of the United Synagogue. It provides facilities for worship and ancillary services such as education.

Southgate and District Reform Synagogue
45 High Street
London N14 6LD
Tel: 081–882–6828
Fax: 081–882–7539

Southgate Progressive Synagogue
75 Chase Road
London N14 4QY
Tel: 081–886–0977
Fax: 081–882–5394
Contact: Rabbi Stephen Howard
Place of worship and community centre. A member of the Union of Liberal and Progressive Synagogues which provides a wide range of activities and programmes, both religious and secular. Facilities include a new architect-designed synagogue, community hall, offices, meeting rooms, classrooms and youth club building. Activities include worship, religious education, youth activities and social activities.

South Tottenham Synagogue
111 Crowland Road
London N15 6UL
Tel: 081–800–2731
Contact: H L Corb
Office: Administrator

Adath Yisroel Tottenham Beth Hamedrash
55/57 Ravensdale Road
London N16
Tel: 081–800–3978
Contact: Dayan A D Dunner

Ahavat Israel Synagogue D'Chasidey Viznitz
89 Stanford Hill
London N16
Tel: 081–800–9359
Contact: Rabbi F Schneelbalg

Beth Chodosh Synagogue
51 Queen Elizabeth's Walk
London N16
Tel: 081–800–6754

Beth Hamedrash Beis Nadvorna
45 Darenth Road
London N16 6ES
Tel: 081–806–3903
Contact: Rabbi M Leifer

Beth Hamedrash D'Chasidey Belz
99 Bethune Road
London N16
Tel: 081–802–8233

Beth Hamedrash D'Chasidey Gur
2 Lampard Grove
London N16
Tel: 081–806–4333

Beth Hamedrash D'Chasidey Ryzin
33 Paget Road
London N16
Tel: 081–800–7979

Beth Hamedrash D'Chasidey Sanz Klausenburg
42 Craven Walk
London N16

Beth Hamedrash D'Chasidey Square
22 Dunsmure Road
London N16
Tel: 081–800–8448

Beth Hamedrash of the Agudah Youth Movement
69 Lordship Road
London N16
Tel: 081–800–8873
Contact: M J Kamionka

Beth Hamedrash Ohel Shmuel Sholem
37 Craven Walk
London N16 6BS
Tel: 081–800–3868
Contact: Rabbi J Meisels

Beth Hamedrash Torah Etz Chayim
69 Lordship Road
London N16
Tel: 081–800–7726
Contact: Rabbi Z Feldman

Beth Hamedrash (Trisker) Synagogue
146 Osbaldeston Road
London N16
Tel: 081-806-3551

Beth Hamedrash Yetiv Lev O'Satmar
86 Cazenove Road
London N16
Tel: 081-800-2633
Contact: Rabbi C Wosner

Beth Sholom Synagogue
27 St Kilda's Road
London N16
Tel: 081-809-6224
Contact: Rabbi M Deutsch

Birkath Yehuda (Halaser) Beth Hamedrash
47 Moundfield Road
London N16 6DT
Tel: 081-806-8323 (home)
Contact: Rabbi M Lebovits

Commercial Road Talmud Torah Synagogue
153 Stamford Hill
London N16 5LG
Tel: 081-800-1618

Jacob Benjamin Elias Synagogue
140 Stamford Hill
London N16
Tel: 081-806-8109 (home)
Contact: D Elias
Office: Honorary Secretary

Kehal Chasidim Synagogue
Queen Elizabeth Walk
London N16 0HJ
Tel: 081-802-6226
Contact: Mr A Barnett
Office: Honorary Secretary

Kehillath Chasidim Synagogue
85 Cazenove Road
London N16

Lubavitch Synagogue
107-115 Stamford Hill
London N16
Tel: 081-800-0022
Contact: Rabbi N Sudak

Mesifta Synagogue
82-84 Cazenove Road
London N16

New Synagogue
Egerton Road
Stamford Hill
London N16 6UD
Tel: 081-800-6003

North London Progressive Synagogue
100 Amhurst Park
London N16 5AR
Tel: 081-800-8931
Contact: Mrs Yetta Freedman
Office: Secretary
Place of worship. A synagogue practising Progressive
Judaism. Its activities include worship and education.

Persian Hebrew Congregation
5a East Bank
Stamford Hill
London N16
Tel: 081-800-9261

Stanislowa Beth Hamedrash
93 Lordship Park
London N16
Tel: 081-800-2040
Contact: Rabbi M Aschkenasi

Walford Road Synagogue
99 Walford Road
Stoke Newington
London N16 8EF
Tel: 071-249-5604 (home)
Contact: S Raymond
Office: Secretary

Yeshiva Horomoh Beth Hamedrash
100 Fairholt Road
London N16 5HH
Tel: 081-809-3904
Tel: 081-800-2194 (home)
Contact: Rabbi E Schlesinger

Yeshuath Chaim Synagogue
45 Heathland Road
London N16
Tel: 081-800-2332
Contact: I Kohn
Office: Honarary Secretary

Yesodey Hatorah Synagogue
2/4 Amhurst Park
London N16

**Edmonton and Tottenham United
Synagogue**
41 Landsdowne Road
London N17
Tel: 081-808-1346

**Tottenham Hebrew Congregation and
Talmud Torah Classes**
366a High Road
London N17
Tel: 081-808-4698
Contact: Dr S S Cohen
Office: Secretary

**Bernhard Baron St. George's Jewish
Settlement**
120 Oakleigh Road North
London N20 9EZ
Tel: 081-446-3101
Contact: J Wosner
Office: Director

**Oxford and St George's North London
Jewish Centre**
120 Oakleigh Road North
London N20 9EZ
Tel: 081-446-3101

**Enfield and Winchmore Hill District Hebrew
Congregation**
53 Wellington Road
Enfield
London N21

LONDON (NW POSTCODES)

Cricklewood United Synagogue
131 Walm Lane
London NW2 3AU
Tel: 081-452-1739
Contact: K N Gamse
Office: Administrator

Dollis Hill United Synagogue
Parkside
Dollis Hill Lane
London NW2 6RJ

Tel: 081-452-7172
Contact: Warren Land
Office: Administrator

**Willesden and Brondesbury United
Synagogue**
143-145 Brondesbury Park
London NW2 5JL
Tel: 081-459-1083
Contact: Mrs J Questle
Office: Administrator

Belsize Square Synagogue
51 Belsize Square
London NW3 4HX
Tel: 071-794-3949
Contact: Thomas Tausz
Office: Honorary Secretary

Hampstead Reform Jewish Community
c/o 63 Ornan Road
London NW3 4QD
Tel: 071-794-8488 (home)
Contact: Mr Michael Teper
Office: Chairperson
Place of worship. A small friendly Reform synagogue
based in the Hampstead area. It meets regularly on
Friday evening, Saturday morning and all festivals.
There is a social programme as well and all visitors are
welcome.

Sanz Klausner's Synagogue
31 Broadhurst Gardens
London NW3

South Hampstead Synagogue
20/22 Eton Villas
Eton Road
London NW3 4SP
Tel: 071-722-1807

Beth Hamedrash Hendon
3 The Approach
London NW4 2HU
Tel: 081-202-5499
Contact: Rabbi D Halpern

Hendon Adath Yisroel Synagogue
11 Brent Street
London NW4 2EU
Tel: 081-202-9183
Contact: N Hammond
Office: Secretary

Hendon Reform Synagogue

Danescroft Avenue
Hendon
London NW4 2NA
Tel: 081-203-4168
Contact: Mrs M Djora
Office: Secretary

Hendon United Synagogue

Raleigh Close
Wykeham Road
London NW4
Tel: 081-202-6924
Fax: 081-202-1720
Contact: Mrs Nicole Monk
Office: Membership Secretary
Place of worship. A vibrant community with about eighteen hundred members. Activities include a kindergarten, mother and toddler group, Hebrew classes, daily services, lectures, functions and day centre. The Synagogue cares for the very young to the very old and has various social, cultural and educational committees.

North Hendon Adath Yisroel Synagogue

31 Holders Hill Road
London NW4 1NE
Tel: 081-203-0797 (home)
Contact: A H Ehreich
Office: Secretary

Ohel Israel (Skoler) Synagogue

11 Brent Street
London NW4

Yakar Educational Foundation

2 Egerton Gardens
Hendon
London NW4 4BA
Tel: 081-202-5551/2
Fax: 081-202-9653
Contact: Rabbi Saul Zneimer
Place of worship. An Orthodox synagogue.

Hampstead Adath Yisroel Congregation

10a Cranfield Gardens
London NW6

Hampstead United Synagogue

1 Dennington Park Road
West Hampstead
London NW6 1AX
Tel: 071-435-1518
Contact: Mr D Cohen

Office: Administrator
Place of worship. The synagogue was founded in 1892 as an Orthodox congregation owing its allegiance to the Chief Rabbi. It has facilities for worship and cultural activities.

Mill Hill Reform Synagogue

51 Hale Drive
London NW7
Contact: Mr M Casale
Office: Chair

Mill Hill Synagogue

Station Road
Mill Hill
London NW7

Mill Hill United Synagogue

Brockenhurst Gardens
London NW7 2JY
Tel: 081-959-1137
Contact: Mrs M Vogel
Office: Administrator

Liberal Jewish Synagogue

28 St Johns Wood Road
London NW8 7HA
Tel: 071-286-5181

New London Synagogue

33 Abbey Road
London NW8 0AT
Tel: 071-328-1026

St John's Wood Synagogue

37/41 Grove End Road
St Johns Wood
London NW8 9HA
Tel: 071-286-3838
Place of worship.

Kingsbury United Synagogue

Kingsbury Green
London NW9 8XR
Tel: 081-204-8089
Contact: Mrs M Lazarus
Office: Administrator

Ahavath Shalom (Neasden) Synagogue

Clifford Way
London NW10

Beth Abraham Synagogue
46 The Ridgeway
London NW11
Contact: Rabbi C Schmahl

Beth Hamedrash Divrei Chaim
71 Bridge Lane
London NW11
Tel: 081-458-1161
Contact: Rabbi Chaim A Z Halpern

Beth Shmuel Synagogue
171 Golders Green Road
London NW11
Tel: 081-458-7511
Contact: Rabbi E Halpern

Beth Yisachar Dov Beth Hamedrash
2/4 Highfield Avenue
London NW11
Contact: Rabbi G Hager

Binah Centre (Jewish Special Education Service)
Highfield Road
Golders Green
London NW11 9LU
Tel: 081-905-5161
Fax: 081-905-5096

Bridge Lane Beth Hamedrash
44 Bridge Lane
London NW11 0EG
Contact: Rabbi S Winegarten

Finchley Road Synagogue
4 Helenslea Avenue
London NW11
Tel: 081-455-4305
Contact: Rabbi S Rubin

Golders Green Synagogue
41 Dunstan Road
London NW11 8AE
Tel: 081-455-2460
Contact: Mrs R Sliw
Office: Administrator

Machzikei Hadath Synagogue
Highfields Road
London NW11

Tel: 081-204-1887 (home)
Contact: R Shaw
Office: Honorary Secretary

New Essex Masorti Congregation
c/o Assembly of Masorti Synagogues
766 Finchley Road
London NW11 7TH
Tel: 081-554-0158 (home)
Contact: Avrom Pearl
Office: Vice-Chair
Congregation practising traditional Judaism with a modern approach, under the auspices of the Assembly of Masorti Synagogues. Men and women sit together and women take part in the service. Activities include worship and education.

North Western Reform Synagogue
Alyth Gardens
Finchley Road
London NW11 7EN
Tel: 081-455-6763
Contact: Mrs Mavis Ashleigh
Office: Administrator
Place of worship and also a community centre providing social and educational activities for all ages throughout the congregation.

Ohel David Synagogue
Lincoln Institute
Broadwalk Lane
Golders Green Road
London NW11
Tel: 081-806-8109
Contact: D Elias
Office: Honorary Secretary

Ravenswood Foundation
17 Highfield Road
Golders Green
London NW11 9DZ
Tel: 081-905-5557
Fax: 081-209-1618
Contact: Norma Brier
Office: Executive Director
A Jewish organisation providing welfare services for Jewish and non-Jewish children and adults with learning difficulties and their families. This provision includes a range of residential homes which include a Village community in Berkshire where residents live in chalet-style homes, homes in the community in London and group homes. Also provides a recreational service offering "integrated" activities for three to twenty-one year olds and an employment

project in catering and gardening. There is a group of qualified social workers who offer support to both users and families.

Sinai Synagogue
54 Woodstock Avenue
London NW11 9RJ
Tel: 081-455-6876 (home)
Contact: C Cohen
Office: Secretary

LONDON (SE POSTCODES)

Catford and Bromley United Synagogue
6 Crantock Road
London SE6 2QS
Tel: 071-698-3025
Contact: Rabbi J H Rochman

Woolwich and District Synagogue
81 Marlborough Lane
Charlton
London SE7
Tel: 081-856-0845
Contact: J M Gaus
Office: Secretary
Place of worship and the centre for all Jewish activities in the area. Primarily concerned with worship, but also embraces cultural, educational and social activities and concern for the welfare of the community
.

LONDON (SW POSTCODES)

Chelsea Affiliated Synagogue
Smith Terrace
Smith Street
Chelsea
London SW3 4DL
Tel: 081-450-6266
Contact: M Friedmann
Office: Administrator

Westminster Synagogue
Rutland Gardens
Knightsbridge
London SW7 1BX
Tel: 071-584-3953
Contact: Mrs M R Henriques
Office: Secretary

South-West London Synagogue
104 Bolingbroke Grove
Wandsworth Common
London SW11 1DA

Tel: 071-228-7665
Contact: Mrs S Isaacs
Office: Administrator

New Wimbledon and Putney District Synagogue
The Clubroom
Toland Square
Eastwood Estate
Roehampton Lane
London SW15
Tel: 081-788-0176 (home)
Contact: J Leigh
Office: Honorary Secretary

South London Liberal Synagogue
Prentis Road
Streatham
London SW16 1QB
Tel: 081-769-4787
Contact: Rabbi Neil S Kraft
Place of worship. Part of the Union of Liberal and Progressive Jews. Activities include worship services every Friday and Saturday and on festivals; social and cultural activites; religion school; adult education and youth activities.

South London United Synagogue
45 Leigham Court Road
London SW16 2NF
Tel: 071-677-0234
Contact: Mrs A Gabay
Office: Administrator

Wimbledon and District Reform Synagogue
44-46 Worple Road
London SW19 4EJ
Tel: 081-946-4836
Conatct: Mrs F Solomon
Office: Administrator

LONDON (W POSTCODES)

Central Synagogue
Great Portland Street
36 Hallam Street
London W1N 5LH
Contact: Mrs C Jowell
Office: Secretary/Administrator
Orthodox synagogue. All communications to the Secretary/Administrator.

Evening Institute for the Study of Judaism

Union of Liberal and Progressive Synagogues
The Montagu Centre
109 Whitfield Street
London W1P 5RP
Tel: 071-580-1663
Open to the general public. Lecturers include Rabbi
Dr Charles Middleburgh; Rabbi Hillel Avidan, MA;
Rabbi Neil Kraft, BA; and Rabbi Dr John Rayner.
Cost of participation is £16.00 for a term or £30.00
for two terms. The courses of the Institute are designed
for those who wish to brush up their knowledge of
Judaism or who want to pursue their own specific
Jewish intellectual interest a litle further, and also for
those Jews and non-Jews who know nothing at all
about the subject but want to learn a little of the faith
and culture of Jewish life. A range of courses take place
on Monday evenings, with the first part of the evening
devoted to a study of Jewish topics (7.15pm–8.05pm)
and the second part to the study of Hebrew
(8.15pm–9.15pm.)

London Jewish Medical Society

The Medical Society of London
11 Chandos Street
London W1M 0EB
Contact: Dr J Schwartz
Office: Honorary Secretary
A learned society for doctors, senior medical students
and members of allied professions, such as
pharmacology and psychology.

Jewish Blind and Physically Handicapped Society

118 Seymour Place
London W1H 5DJ
Tel: 071-262-2003
Fax: 071-262-8185
Contact: Malcolm Jozin
Office: Honorary Secretary
A registered charity (No: 259480) which provides
modern sheltered housing (self-contained flats) with
communal facilities, amenities and welfare services for
Jewish blind, partially sighted and disabled persons,
couples and families. The Society co-operates with
other voluntary organisations, hospitals and local
authorities.

West Central Liberal Synagogue, London

21 Maple Street
London W1P 6DS
Tel: 071-636-7627
Contact: Mr M Cohen
Office: Honorary Secretary

West End Great Synagogue

21 Dean Street
London W1V 6NE

West London Synagogue of British Jews

34 Upper Berkeley Street
London W1
Tel: 071-723-4404
Contact: M Ross
Office: Director

Western Charitable Foundation

32 Great Cumberland Place
London W1H 7DJ
Tel: 071-723-7246
Contact: Sidney Jaque
Office: Chair

Western Marble Arch United Synagogue

32 Great Cumberland Place
London W1H 7DJ
Tel: 071-723-7246
Contact: Martin Frey
Office: Administrator

New West End Synagogue

St Petersburgh Place
London W2 4JT
Tel: 071-229-2631
Fax: 071-229-2355
Contact: Peter Hartman
Office: Administrator

Ealing United Synagogue

15 Grange Road
Ealing
London W5 5QN
Tel: 081-579-4894
Contact: Mrs S Hayman
Office: Administrator

Hammersmith and West Kensington United Synagogue

71 Brook Green
Hamersmith
London W6 7BE
Tel: 071-602-1405
Contact: S M Fainlight
Office: Administrator

Communal Centre

Montefiore Hall
2 Ashworth Road
London W9 1JY
Tel: 071-289-2573

Lauderdale Road Synagogue

Lauderdale Road
Maida Vale
London W9 1JY
Tel: 071-286-2153
Contact: Rabbi A Levy

Spanish and Portuguese Jews' Congregation

Lauderdale Road Synagogue
2 Ashworth Road
London W9 1JY
Tel: 071-289-2573
Sephardic Jews originate from the old Spanish community, expelled in the fifteenth century. The community developed a number of unique customs, continued by Sephardim in dispersion.

Holland Park Synagogue

St James Gardens
London W11 4RB
Tel: 081-603-7961
Contact: Mrs Z Fineburgh
Office: Secretary
A Spanish-Portuguese Synagogue.

Notting Hill Synagogue

206 Kensington Park Road
London W11 1NR
Tel: 081-952-4354 (home)
Contact: H Lamb
Office: Secretary

Ealing Liberal Synagogue

Lynton Avenue
Drayton Green
Ealing
London W13 OEB
Tel: 081-997-0528
Contact: Mrs D Stern
Office: Administrator

SOUTH EAST (SOUTH)

Bognor Regis Hebrew Congregation

Elm Lodge
Sylvan Way
Bognor Regis

West Sussex
Tel: 0243-823006 (home)
Contact: J S Jacobs
Office: Honorary Secretary

Brighton and Hove Jewish Representative Council

103 Tivoli Crescent North
Brighton
East Sussex BN1 5NA
Tel: 0273-558559
Office: Honorary Secretary
Representative body. Work includes communal welfare and youth activities.

Bromley and District Reform Synagogue

28 Highland Road
Bromley
Kent BR1 4AD
Tel: 081-460-5460
Contact: Rabbi S Rothschild
Place of worship.

Crawley Progressive Jewish Congregation

44 Brighton Road
Crawley
RH10 6AT
Tel: 0293-34294
Contact: Mrs L Bloom
Office: Honorary Secretary

East Grinstead and District Jewish Community

7 Jefferies Way
Crowborough
East Sussex TN6 2UH
Tel: 0892-653949
Contact: E Godfrey
Office: Warden

Croydon and District Synagogue

30 Elmwood Road
Croydon
Surrey
Contact: Mrs L Hanover
Office: Honorary Secretary

Synagogue

Thorpe Lee House
Egham
Surrey

Eastbourne Hebrew Congregation

22 Susans Road
Eastbourne
East Sussex BN21 3HA
Tel: 0435-866928
Fax: 0435-865783
Contact: Mrs M J Mindell
Office: Honorary Secretary
Place of worship. This synagogue will celebrate its seventy-fifth birthday in 1993. Although now a small, elderly community, services are held every Saturday morning at 10.00am and on all Jewish festivals. There is also a Ladies Guild.

Brighton and Hove Hebrew Congregation

The Synagogue
31 New Church Road
Hove
East Sussex BN3 4AD
Tel: 0273-327785
Contact: M Shaw
Office: Honorary Secretary

Brighton and Hove Independent Talmud Torah

31 New Church Road
Hove
East Sussex BN3 4AD
Tel: 0273-776170
Contact: Mrs Margaret Book
Office: Administrator
Education establishment which runs classes for the purpose of teaching the Jewish faith (traditional) from five to fifteen year olds. It also runs a Jewish Teenage Centre (Sundays) and GCSE classes in Religious Studies.

Brighton and Hove Jewish Centre

Ralli Hall
81 Denmark Villas
Hove
East Sussex BN3 3TH
Tel: 0273-202254
Contact: Norina Duke
Office: Administrator
Community and youth centre. A meeting and activity centre for all sectors of the Jewish community. Facilities include a fully equipped gym, a teenage/disco room, a snooker room with full size tables, table tennis tables, kosher meat and milk kitchens, and a large hall with stage lighting and sound equipment. The centre provides activities for youth, senior citizens clubs, amateur theatrical groups and meeting and function rooms.

Brighton and Hove New Synagogue (Reform)

Palmeira Avenue
Hove
East Sussex BN3 3GE
Tel: 0273-735343
Contact: M Phillips
Office: Honorary Secretary

Brighton and Hove Progessive Synagogue

6 Lansdowne Road
Hove
East Sussex BN3 1FF
Tel: 0273-737223
Contact: Judy Gabriel
Office: Administrator
Place of worship. A house of prayer and worship for all non-Orthodox members of the Jewish faith, including those with a non-Jewish partner who are equally welcome. Visitors from other faiths are always welcome but are requested to make arrangements by telephone prior to this. Activities include worship; study and a religion school for children; social and welfare activities. Services are held Friday at 8.15pm and Saturday at 11.00am and on all festivals.

Hove Hebrew Congregation

Holland Road
Hove
East Sussex
Tel: 0273-732035
Contact: Sol Farrell
Office: Secretary

Jewish Welfare Board

2 Modena Road
Hove
East Sussex
Tel: 0273-722523
Contact: Mrs J Markham
Office: Honorary Secretary

Lubavitch Foundation

15 The Upper Drive
Hove
East Sussex
Tel: 0273-21919
Contact: Rabbi P Efune
Office: Director

Torah Academy

31 New Church Road
Hove
East Sussex

Tel: 0273-28675
Contact: Rabbi P Efune
Office: Rabbi

Kingston Liberal Synagogue
Rushett Road
Long Ditton
Surrey KT7 0UX
Tel: 081-398-7400
Contact: Rabbi Danny Rich
Place of worship. A Liberal synagogue serving the local community. There are around three hundred and twenty members, a full time Rabbi and a friendly and caring congregation. It was established in 1967 and is well respected in the area. The synagogue organises religious services, social activities and activities for youth.

Chatham Memorial Synagogue
Sutton Place
Sutton Road
Maidstone
Kent ME15 9DU
Tel: 0622-53040
Contact: c/o Dr C Harris

Margate Synagogue
Albion Road
Cliftonville
Margate
Kent
Tel: 0843-221891 (home)
Contact: B Gradus
Office: President

Jewish Community Centre
The Thicket
Southsea
Portsmouth PO5 2AA
Contact: Mrs D Clannachan
Office: Secretary

Jewish Ladies Benevolent Society
The Thicket
Southsea
Portsmouth PO5 2AA

Portsmouth Synagogue
The Thicket
Southsea
Portsmouth PO5 2AA
Tel: 0705-824391
Contact: Rev A Dee

Sir Moses Montefiore Synagogue
Honeysuckle Road
Ramsgate
Kent

Thanet and District Reform Jewish Community
239a Margate Road
Ramsgate
Kent CT12 6TE
Tel: 0843-603241 (home)
Contact: David Mirsky
Office: Chair

Reigate and Redhill Jewish Community
59 Gatton Road
Reigate
Surrey
Tel: 07372-42076
Contact: M J Kemper
Office: Chair

Richmond Synagogue
Lichfield Gardens
Richmond-on-Thames
Surrey TW9 1AP
Tel: 081-940-3526
Fax: 081-940-3526
Contact: P Lamb
Office: Secretary
Place of worship. An Orthodox Jewish synagogue under the auspices of the United Synagogue. Activities include worship, religion classes, day centre and a teenagers centre.

Jersey Jewish Congregation
Route Des Genets
St Brelade
Jersey
Tel: 0534-482429 (home)
Contact: Secretary
Place of worship. An Orthodox Jewish synagogue which serves as a place of worship and the centre for many religious and social events. Activities include worship, fund-raising and a Ladies Guild.

Southampton and District Jewish Society
42 Ripstone Gardens
Highfield
Southampton
Hampshire
Tel: 0703-550442
Contact: Mrs L Trichter
Office: Chair

Southampton Synagogue

Mordaunt Road
Inner Avenue
Southampton
Hampshire
Tel: 0703-453197 (home)
Contact: C Freeman
Office: Secretary

Staines and District United Synagogue

Westbrook Road
South Street
Staines
Surrey TW18 4PR
Tel: 0784-254604
Contact: Mrs P D Fellman
Office: Secretary

Sutton and District Affiliated Synagogue

14 Cedar Road
Sutton
Surrey SM2 5DA
Tel: 081-642-5419
Contact: Miss A Stern
Office: Administrator

North West Surrey Synagogue

Horvath Close
Rosslyn Park
Oatlands Village
Weybridge
Surrey KT13 9QZ
Tel: 0932-855400
Contact: Rabbi Fred Morgan
Office: Minister

Place of worship and study. The aim is to provide a centre for the local Jewish community as well as to make links with the wider community; to enrich the spiritual life of members and to increase the well-being of society through social-action projects. Activities include Jewish worship and study, social and cultural activities, youth programmes, programmes for the retired and the elderly, welfare activities and links, visits of school parties and non-Jewish groups.

South Hampshire Reform Jewish Community

5 Kings Head Yard
Little Minster Street
Winchester
Hampshire SO23 9SY
Tel: 0962-855836
Fax: 0962-840558
Contact: D Habel
Office: Chair

Place of worship. A community of Progressive Jews holding regular services and providing religious education. A number of social activities are held during the year and evening adult education meetings are arranged each month.

SOUTH WEST

Bristol Jewish Liaison Committee

88 Gloucester Road
Bristol BS12 2QN
Tel: 0454-419877 (home)
Contact: H Harris
Office: Honorary Secretary

Bournemouth District Jewish Representative Council

59 Fitzharris Avenue
Bournemouth BH9 1BY
Tel: 0202-523550 (home)
Contact: Mrs T Lurie
Office: Secretary

Bournemouth Hebrew Congregation

Wootton Gardens
Bournemouth BH1 1PW
Tel: 0202-557433
Contact: Mrs R Bloom
Office: Secretary/Administrator

Bournemouth Reform Synagogue

53 Christchurch Road
Bournemouth
Dorset

Friendship Club

6 Wilfred Road
Bournemouth BH5 1NB
Tel: 0202-21255 (home)
Contact: S Mazin
Office: Honorary Secretary

Jewish Association for Cultural Studies

2 Southwood Avenue
Bournemouth BH6 3QA
Tel: 0202-417416
Contact: Mr E Williams

Jewish Care

Braemar Royal
Grand Avenue
Southbourne

Bournemouth
Dorset
Tel: 0202-423246

Lubavitch Centre
Chabad House
8 Gordon Road
Boscombe
Bournemouth
Dorset
Tel: 0202-36615

Bristol and West Progressive Congregation
43 Bannerman Road
Easton
Bristol BS5 ORR
Tel: 0272-541937
Contact: J Grandfield
Office: Honorary Secretary

Bristol Hillel
8 Alma Vale
Bristol BS8
Tel: 0272-737177

Bristol Jewish Liaison Committee
88 Gloucester Road
Rudgeway
Bristol BS12 2QN
Tel: 0454-419877 (home)
Contact: Mr H Harris
Representative body. A meeting place for all Jewish factions who get together to discuss items for the common good and when necessary to promote a Jewish viewpoint for the media.

Bristol Synagogue
9 Park Row
Bristol BS1
Tel: 0272-23538
Contact: Mrs Y Sanders
Office: Honorary Secretary

Bristol University Jewish Society
University Union
Queens Road
Bristol BS8 1LN
Contact: Chairperson

Exeter Hebrew Congregation Synagogue
Synagogue Place
Mary Arches Street
Exeter EX4 3BA

Tel: 0392-51529
Contact: Ellis Weinberger
Office: President
Place of worship. An independent Jewish congregation welcoming all Jewish people and their partners to find their way to be part of the community. Activities include worship, social events, hospital and prison visiting. There is a burial society and a Sunday school.

Hebrew Congregation
Catherine Street
Plymouth PL1 2AD
Tel: 0752-664995
Contact: Mrs Reva Joseph
Office: Honorary Secretary

Bournemouth University Jewish Society
Bournemouth University
Wallisdown Road
Poole
Dorset BH12 5BB
Tel: 0202-524111

Swindon Jewish Community
4 Lakeside
Swindon
Wiltshire
Tel: 0793-521910
Contact: M Vandervelde
Office: Chair

Torquay and Paignton Synagogue
Abbey Road
Torquay
Devon

Torquay Synagogue
"Son Bou"
7 Broadstone Park Road
Livermead
Torquay TQ2 6TY
Tel: 0803-607197 (home)
Contact: c/o E Freed
Services are held on the first Saturday of each month.

KEY TO TERMS IN JEWISH ORGANISATIONAL TITLES

Note: This is not a complete glossary of significant Jewish terms. It is a guide to the meaning and/or background of some of the words used in the titles of Jewish organisations listed in the directory. More information on the italicised words can be tracked down elsewhere in the key and/or in Introducing the Jewish Community, by using the directory's Keyword Index.

Abraham

The name of the first of the *avot* (forefathers) of the Hebrew people.

Adath

A construct of the Hebrew word *edah*, *adath* is the Hebrew for "congregation" or "community of".

Agudah

Hebrew meaning "union" or "association", a group bound by a common purpose.

Agudas

Ashkenazi pronunciation of a construct of the Hebrew word *agudah*, it means "union of" or "association of."

Ahavat

A construct form of the Hebrew word *ahavah*, meaning "love".

Akiva

The name of a major Jewish *rabbi* and martyr (c. 50-135 CE).

Ari

The name of a major sixteenth century mystic and *Kabbalist* (from *Kabbalah*).

Baeck

The surname of Leo Baeck, a twentieth century German *Liberal* rabbinic leader, after whom a *Progressive* College for the training of *rabbis* and the study of Judaism is now named.

Beis

Ashkenazi pronunciation of a construct of the Hebrew word *bayit*, it means "house of", in other words, "home".

Belz

The name of a Ukrainian town near Lvov with a Jewish settlement from the beginning of the sixteenth century CE onwards. It was the spiritual centre of the Belzer *Chasidim* before the Holocaust. The *Chasidim* are known by the name of their town of origin.

Bernhard Baron

Surname of Bernhard Baron, an industrialist in the USA and the UK (c. 1850-1929 CE) who was a philanthropist, especially with regard to Jewish causes including endowment of the Jewish Settlement that bears his name.

Beth
Sephardi pronunciation of the Hebrew for "house", often used of a "group" or "gathering of people."

Bevis Marks
Bevis Marks is the name of the London location of a major *Sephardi* synagogue. The name itself has no Jewish connection.

Binah
Hebrew meaning "understanding".

Birkath
Hebrew meaning "blessing of".

B'nei
Hebrew meaning "sons of" or "children of". Used in the name of the major Jewish organisation *Bnei B'rith* (see below), which has branches throughout the world and was founded in the USA in 1843 CE.

B'rith
Hebrew meaning "covenant". Hence, *B'nei B'rith* means "children of the covenant".

Chaim
Hebrew meaning "life" or "health".

Chasidim
Hebrew plural of the Hebrew word *chasid*. It is the collective name of the Jewish groups which emphasise the mystical tradition in Judaism and are part of a broad movement initiated in the eighteenth century CE by Baal Shem Tov.

Chasidische
Yiddish meaning "pertaining to *Chasidim*" (see above).

Chavurah
Hebrew meaning "fellowship".

Chayim
Variant Romanisation of *chaim* (see above).

Chazanim
Hebrew meaning "cantors", the plural of the Hebrew word *chazan* meaning "cantor".

Chinuch
Hebrew meaning "education".

D'Chasside
Meaning "of the *Chasidim* of".

David
Biblical name of the major Jewish king and psalmist.

Din
Meaning "law", found in the name of *Beth Din*, a rabbinical court.

Dor
Hebrew meaning "generation".

D'var
Hebrew meaning "word of".

Eliezer
The name of a Biblical servant of the Patriarch Abraham.

Etz
Hebrew word meaning "tree".

Emet
Hebrew meaning "truth".

Ezras
A construct form of *ezrah*, which means "help".

Falashas
A term sometimes used to describe Ethiopian Jews.

Gur
Polish *Chasidic* centre of the Gerer *Chasidim* before the Holocaust.

Hadass
Ashkenzi pronunciation of *hadath*, meaning "the faith".

Hadath
Hebrew word meaning "the faith", with *ha* being the definite article.

Hagadol
Hebrew meaning "the great", with *ha* being the definite article.

Hamakon
Hebrew literally meaning "the place", with *ha* being the definite article. Often used as a name for the Divine.

Hamedrash
Hebrew meaning "the learning" or "the study", with *ha* being the definite article. Hence *Beth Hamedrash* is literally a "house of study," (see *beth*) in other words a synagogue/study centre.

Harabbanim
Hebrew meaning "the *rabbis*", with *ha* as the definite article.

Haramah
Hebrew meaning "the high" or "the exalted", with *ha* as the definite article.

Hashochtim
Hebrew meaning "the slaughterers", with *ha* as the definite article and used of those who slaughter animals according to the *shechita* regulations.

Hatorah
Hebrew for "the *Torah* ", with *ha* as the definite article. *Torah* literally means "teaching" and refers to the five books of Moses believed to have been revealed at Mount Sinai as well as their accompanying oral interpretation and tradition.

Hebrew
Original language of the *Torah* and of modern Israel. It is also used in *Orthodox* synagogue services and in parts of *Progressive* synagogue services.

Hechalutz
Hebrew meaning "the pioneer". It is used of those who developed the land of Israel in the pre-1948 period.

Hillel
The name of a major rabbinic leader of Pharisaic Judaism in the first century BCE, often used in the names of centres for Jewish students.

Holocaust
The name given to the systematic genocide of Jewish people in Europe during the Second World War.

Ishah
Hebrew meaning "woman".

Ishmael
The name of the Biblical brother of Isaac, who are both the sons of Abraham.

Jacob
Jacob is the third Biblical patriarch, the son of Isaac, and the father of the twelve tribes of Israel.

Kashrus
Ashkenazi pronunciation of the Hebrew word for "dietary laws".

Kashrut
Sephardi pronunciation of the word *kashrus,* (see above).

Kahal
Hebrew meaning "congregation".

Kehillath
A construct of the Hebrew word *kehillah* meaning "community", *kehillath* means "community of ...".

Kolel
The Hebrew word for a centre of advanced *rabbinic* (from *rabbi*) study.

Kollel
Hebrew for "voice", or "voice of".

Kosher
The word which describes food and its preparation which conforms with Jewish dietary laws.

Lemorot
Meaning "for women teachers".

Lezeirim
Meaning "for young men".

Liberal
A Jewish grouping originating in nineteenth century Germany which believed that the tradition had to be adapted to the demands of modern culture.

Liege
The name of the town in Belgium from which the community in question originated.

Lev
Hebrew literally meaning "heart", often used as a name.

Lubavitch
The name of a Lithuanian *Chasidic* centre which was the origin of the contemporary *Lubavitch* group in Judaism.

Maccabi
The name of the second century BCE Jewish leader Judah ha-Maccabi who defeated the Hellenist Syrians. Now used in the name of Jewish sports and athletic groups derived from his name.

Machzikei
Hebrew for "strengtheners" or "upholders of", used in *Machzikei Hadas* meaning "Upholders of the Faith".

Masorti
Hebrew for "traditional" and used in the name of the contemporary Jewish group who combine traditional practice with an acceptance of modern scholarly analysis of the Biblical texts. It is the British equivalent of the American *Conservative* Judaism tradition.

Mesifta
Aramaic for "place of study" equivalent to the Hebrew term *yeshiva*.

Midrash
The name given to a body of rabbinic interpretation of the *Torah*.

Mohelim
The plural of the Hebrew word *mohel*, it describes those who perform *milah* which is circumcision.

Moses Montefiore
The name of a famous leader of Anglo-Jewry in the nineteenth century.

Nadvorna
The name of an *Chasidic* centre in Galicia.

Nefusot
Hebrew for "scattered ones".

Neve
Hebrew for "meadow".

Noam
Hebrew literally meaning "pleasant".

Noar
Hebrew for "youth".

Noraim
Plural of the Hebrew word *nora* which means awe-inspiring and is used of the High Holy Days of Judaism, as in the Hebrew *Yamian Noraim*.

Nusach
Hebrew word for liturgical text or "chant". Jews from different areas or sects have different *nuschaot*. These range from different tunes for chanting, through different words in common prayers, to different prayers and orders of service.

Orthodox
The name of the majority Jewish tradition in the United Kingdom, the major organised form of which is the United Synagogue led by the *Chief Rabbi*.

Ohel
Hebrew literally meaning "tent" or "tent of".

Progressive
The collective name covering both *Liberal* and *Reform* Judaism and which is used to describe the attempt, beginning in the nineteenth century, to adapt the tradition in keeping with modern "progressive" developments.

Rabbi
Hebrew for "teacher".

Rabbinate
The name of a representative body of *rabbis*, or "teachers".

Rabbinical
The name of a body of *Rabbis* (see above).

Rabbinics
The study of the teaching of the *rabbis* (see above).

Reform
The name of one of the *Progressive* traditions of Judaism organised in the UK as the Reform Synagogues of Great Britain.

Representative Council

The name given to the body operating at a local level in a number of cities with significant Jewish populations, on which all communal bodies may be represented.

Reshet

Hebrew for "network".

Rashey

A construct plural of the Hebrew singular *rosh, rashey* means "heads of ...".

Ryzin

A Ukrainian *Chasidic* centre.

Sabbath

The Jewish day of rest, celebration, renewal, devotion to the *Torah* and family observed from Friday sunset to Saturday sunset, during which time no work is done except in the case of alleviating suffering or other similar emergencies.

Sanz-Klausenberg

Eastern European towns which were centres of pre-Second World War *Chasidim*. Sanz is in Galicia and Klausenberg is in Romania.

Sedek

Hebrew for "righteousness".

Sephardi

Sepharad is the Hebrew word for Spain. *Sephardi* is the word for Jews of Spanish, and later also of Oriental, origin.

Shechita

The slaughtering of animals for consumption in accordance with Jewish law.

Sha'arei

Hebrew literally meaning "gates of".

Shalom

Sephardi pronunciation of the Hebrew word for "peace", often used in a greeting.

Shem

The name of one of the sons of Noah from whom the Semitic peoples are believed to be descended and from which the English words "semite" and "semitic" are derived.

Shochetim

The plural word for "religious slaughterers."

Sholom

An alternative *Ashkenazi* pronunciation of *shalom* (see above).

Shomrei

Hebrew literally meaning "guardians of".

Sinai

The mountain upon which it is believed that the *Torah* was revealed to Moses.

Sir Moses Montefiore

The name of a major nineteenth century leader of Anglo-Jewry.

Skoler

The name of a group of *Chasidim* originating in Skolai, Galicia.

Spanish and Portuguese

The name of synagogues set up by and for those people and their descendents who were expelled from the Iberian peninsula in the 15th century CE.

Spiro

Robin Spiro is the name of the man who founded the Spiro Institute, an adult Jewish educational institute.

Stanislowa

The name of an *Chasidic* group which originated in Stanislaw, Russia.

Sternberg

The surname of Sir Sigmund Sternberg who endowed the Sternberg Centre named after him.

Synagogue

The name for a Jewish place of worship.

Talmud

A very important collection of law, narrative, history, allegories and moral, philosophical and religious discussion

Talmudical

Meaning "concerned with the *Talmud*" (see above).

Tay Sachs

The name of a rare hereditary disease found in *Ashkenazi* Jewry. An organisation is dedicated to supporting sufferers from the disease.

Torah

Hebrew word meaning "instruction". Technically, it refers to the part of the Jewish Bible comprising of the first five books of Moses. Colloquially, it includes all Jewish learning.

Trisker

The name of *Chasidim* originating in Trisk in the Ukraine.

Tzedek

Variant Romanisation of *sedek* (see above).

United Synagogue

The name of the major modern *Orthodox* synagogue grouping in the UK, the leader of which is the Chief Rabbi.

V'Hashomrim

Hebrew literally meaning "and the guardians". The *shomer* ensures that dietary laws are observed in restaurants and similar establishments.

Vishnitz–Monsey

Vishnitz is the name of the town of origin in Hungary of a group of *Chasidim*. Monsey is an American branch of the group based in Monsey, New Jersey.

Yakar

Hebrew literally meaning "precious".

Yavneh

A major centre of *rabbinic* (from *rabbi*) learning after the destruction of the Temple by the Romans. It is in central Israel.

Yehudah

The Hebrew word for "Judah", a Biblical name of one of the sons of Jacob from whom the kings are believed to have been descended. Later, it was also the name of a kingdom in Southern *Eretz Yisrael* and an area of *Eretz Yisrael*. It is also the word from which the English word "Jew" is derived.

Yerushalayim

Hebrew for the city of "Jerusalem" in Israel.

Yeshiva

A centre for *Talmudic* (from *Talmud*) study.

Yeshuath

Hebrew literally meaning "salvation of".

Yeshurun

A Biblical synonym for Israel.

Yesodey

Hebrew for "foundations of".

Yetiv

Aramaic word for "settled" or "tranquil".

Yisachar

The Hebrew of the Biblical name Issachar.

Yisrael

The Hebrew word for "Israel". This was an alternative name for Jacob, earned after the story of his struggle with an angel. Hence, "children of Israel" and "Eretz Yisrael", name of the modern State of Israel.

Yisroel

Variant Romanisation of *Yisrael* meaning Israel.

THE MUSLIM COMMUNITY

INTRODUCING THE MUSLIM COMMUNITY

MUSLIMS IN THE UNITED KINGDOM

Migration

There has been a significant Muslim presence in Britain since the early nineteenth century when Muslim seamen and traders from the Middle East began to settle around major ports. For example, Yemeni Muslims settled in South Shields and established a Muslim community there and similar communities grew up around the ports of Liverpool and Cardiff.

The first mosques in the United Kingdom were established in Liverpool and Woking around the end of the nineteenth century. More settlement occured when Muslims were de-mobbed from military service in the British army after the first World War. The size of the community significantly increased with the arrival in the 1950s and 1960s of workers from the Indo-Pakistan subcontinent, seeking employment in the mills and factories of industrial Britain where there was a shortage of workers in the aftermath of the Second World War. In recent years, Muslim refugees have also arrived from countries such as Somalia and Bosnia.

With a global Muslim population of around 961,500,000, it is estimated there are around 1,500,000 Muslims in the UK, based on recent extrapalations from the 1991 Census. However, some work being done within the community suggests the possibility of a significantly higher figure. In England and Wales the Registrar General lists 487 mosques which are certified as places of worship and this directory includes records of 650 mosques in the UK.

Approximately two thirds of the Muslims in the UK have ancestral origins in the Indo-Pakistan subcontinent, coming to Britain either directly or via earlier migrations to East Africa and the Caribbean. The remaining one third of the Muslims in the UK have ethnic and national origins in a variety of other countries and regions, such as Cyprus, Malaysia, Iran and the Arab world.

Communities became established and continued to thrive and grow, particularly in the West Midlands, West Yorkshire, Lancashire, Greater London and Glasgow. Currently, Muslim communities can be found in most major towns and cities.

Ethnic Backgrounds

The ethnic backgrounds of the Muslim community in the UK are quite diverse and therefore a number of different languages are spoken among Muslims. Knowledge of Arabic is considered very important as this is the language of the *Qur'an* (see below). In addition to English, Urdu, Malay, Gujarati, Hausa, Bengali, Turkish, Panjabi, Farsi, Pushto and Arabic are among the most commonly used languages among Muslims in Britain today. The community includes a number of converts from the indigenous population who have become Muslims in adult life.

ORIGINS AND DEVELOPMENT OF ISLAM

Revelation

According to Muslim belief, the last Prophet of Islam was the Prophet Muhammad (571CE-632CE), who received a series of revelations from God (in Arabic, *Allah*.) All those who believed in Muhammad as the last of the prophets and in the revelation to him which forms the *Qur'an*, were moulded into an *Ummah* (world community) irrespective of their place of origin, language or colour of skin.

These revelations are believed to have come to Muhammad through the Angel Gibreel (Gabriel) over a period of twenty-three years. It is stressed by Muslims that Muhammad did not bring a new faith. As the "seal of the prophets" he is understood to complete the succession of prophets, renewing and completing the teachings of Abraham, Moses and Jesus who are seen as being among the greatest of the prophets.

Muslims believe that essentially the same message, guiding people to the right path, was communicated by God through all the prophets. Because people kept disobeying and corrupting the code of guidance which the prophets preached, other prophets were sent to restate the original message. Muslims therefore affirm the *Torah* brought by Moses and the Gospel or *Injil*

of Jesus, although they believe that these have been corrupted from their original purity. Muhammad is thus seen as the last of the prophets, correcting error and calling people back to the ways of Allah.

Prophet Muhammad and the Ummah

Muhammad was born in the Arabian city of Makka (Mecca) and, at the age of forty, began to receive God's revelations. Thirteen years later, together with the infant Muslim community, Muhammad migrated from Makka to Madina, five hundred kilometres away. This migration is known as the *Hijra*. The formative significance of this event in Islamic history can be seen from the fact that the Muslim dating system (which is based on a lunar calendar) begins from *Hijra* onwards and therefore, in English, dates in the Muslim calendar are expressed as "AH" (after *Hijra*).

Caliphate and Imamate

Following the death of the Prophet Muhammad the *Caliphate* (from *khalifa* meaning viceroy) was established to provide leadership for the Muslim community. Among *Sunni* Muslims (see below), the first four *Caliphs*, Abu Bakr, 'Umar, 'Uthman and 'Ali are often called *al-khulafa ar-rashidun* (the rightly guided *Caliphs*) because their exemplary lives are viewed as being appropriate to the nature of the office of *Caliph*. Initially, the *Caliph* was elected by the community, although Abu Bakr appointed 'Umar.

After the first four *Caliphs* the office became de facto hereditary, with confirmation by the *ulama* (religious scholars). However, after the death of Muhammad the Muslim community had a dispute concerning the location of authority in the community, which led to the development of the *Sunni* and *Shi'a* traditions of Islam (see below).

The name *Shi'ite* comes from the phrase *shiat 'Ali* (the party of 'Ali). This group of people advocated the appointment of 'Ali ibn Abi Talib as successor to the Prophet instead of Abu Bakr. After 'Umar's death following his appointment by Abu Bakr, 'Ali was offered the office on certain conditions, but an arbiter awarded the function to 'Uthman. Following 'Uthman's assasination 'Ali was elected as the Fourth *Caliph*, but was himself killed. His son Hasan was elected *Caliph* but gave up the office under threat of attack from another group.

Upon Hasan's death his brother Husayn led a revolt to re-establish the legitimacy of the *Caliphate*. Husayn was betrayed and killed and this event became the foundation of developing themes of suffering and persecution to be found in the *Shi'a* tradition of Islam. Reverence for 'Ali and his successors led to the development of the *Shi'a* idea of the *Imamate* in which descendents of Ali have a special sanctity and role in the spiritual leadership of the community.

Development and Diversity

From its origins in Arabia, Islam spread towards the Indian sub-continent after 750CE, and also into Africa and Europe. The European presence of Islam has a long history in the Balkans, Greece, Sicily, and Spain. In Spain, for example, after its initial establishment by military force, Islamic culture spread through the land influencing many aspects of life and thought, developing peacefully alongside Christian and Jewish culture, until the Muslims were expelled by the Christian monarchs King Ferdinand and Queen Isabella in 1452.

During the Moghul empire (1550-1707CE) Islam made deep inroads into India. From India, Islam spread to Malaysia, Indonesia and the Philippines. The partition of the Indian sub-continent in 1947 resulted in the creation of the Muslim majority state of Pakistan, the Eastern part of which, in 1971, became the independent country of Bangladesh.

SOURCES OF MUSLIM BELIEFS AND PRACTICES

Qur'an

The *Qur'an* is the fundamental source of guidance for Muslims. They regard it as the pre-eminent "sign" or "miracle" of God and as the final and ultimate source of guidance which is permanent and unchangeable in spite of the way society changes in terms of values and standards. It can be applied in each age in the way most suitable to the conditions of that age and is a guide to ethics, human relationships, social justice, political principles, law, trade and commerce.

The text of the *Qur'an* is divided into *surahs* (or chapters) which are of varying lengths and are not in chronological order. The opening *surah*, called the *Fatiha*, is a key prayer of Muslims and a summary of Islamic belief which must be read in Arabic in the context of the observance of every *salat* (Muslim obligatory daily prayers - see below).

Because it is viewed as the actual words of God, the learning and recitation of the *Qur'an* is a central duty and joy for believers. It is believed to have been originally revealed in Arabic, an understanding of which is therefore seen as essential for penetrating its true meaning. It is thus considered preferable to read it in its original Arabic version although translations (or more strictly, in Islamic understanding, what are understood only as interpretations) are available in English and many other languages.

Shari'ah

The framework within which Muslim life has evolved is the *Shari'ah* (law). The sources of *Shari'ah* are the *Qur'an*, the *Sunna*, *Ijma* and *Qiyas*.

The *Sunna* is the example of the Prophet and his way of life which acts as a model for Muslims to emulate. The *Hadith* are the traditions about this which contain accounts of the words and actions of Muhammad and his companions that have been gathered into generally recognised collections of material.

Ijma is the practice of reaching consensus of approval for particular aspects of *Shari'ah*. Where Islamic legislation is unclear about a situation, experts who are knowledgeable about the Muslim holy texts propose clarifications which must gain their consensus agreement for it to become an accepted principle.

Ijtihad (*Sunni* term for the exercise of judgement) or *'aql* (*Shi'a*) is the concept of reasoning or intelligence. Rational discussion and debate is therefore very much at the heart of Islam. One form of reasoning which is often employed is that of *Qiyas* (or analogy). In the use of *Qiyas* analogies are drawn between situations in the *Qur'an*, *Sunna* and *Hadith* and contemporary circumstances, in order to determine the application of the *Shari'ah* to novel situations.

Schools

Among the *Sunni* Muslims there are four recognised *madhahib* (schools or orientations) whose scholars have the task of discerning the way of applying the *Shari'ah* in various contexts. These are the *Hanafi*, the *Hanbali*, the *Maliki* and the *Shaf'i*. They are all recognised as having developed out of the *usul al-fiqh* (foundations of sacred law).

Different schools have come to predominate in various areas of the world and so the *Hanafi* school is predominant in India and most parts of the former Turkish Empire, the *Maliki* school in West Africa and the Arab West, the *Shafi* in Indonesia, Malaysia and the Phillipines. The *Shafi* is also important in Egypt where the first two schools can also be found. The *Hanbali* school is found only in Saudi Arabia and Qatar. This latter school, in fact, understands itself to be *ghayr muqallidun* (not attached to tradition) and therefore not a school at all but upholders of early Islam.

Muslims in Britain with ethnic or ancestral backgrounds in these various areas of the world might therefore be expected to follow the relevant predominant school. Each school recognises the others as being orthodox, but Muslims are always within one school or another since the mixing of these traditions is not encouraged. The *Shi'a* tradition of Islam also has a number of schools, the most widespread of which is the *Ja'fari* school of the *Twelvers* (see below).

KEY MUSLIM BELIEFS

Monotheism

Islam is strictly monotheistic. God, *Allah*, is believed to be one and unique and is spoken of in masculine terms although the Divine Reality is believed to be beyond the limitations of human gender. He is merciful and powerful, omniscient and omnipresent. He is in control of events in history and on the Day of Judgement. He created the universe and sustains it and has prescribed Islam as the correct way of life for the people he has created, although humans have a choice as to whether they follow this way or not.

Becoming a Muslim

In order to become a Muslim a person must accept and declare that there is "no god except God" and that "Muhammad is his messenger". This declaration of faith is known as the *Shahada*. Three basic tenets underlie Islam: the unity of God; Muhammad as the seal of the prophets, through whom the *Qur'an* was revealed; and human accountability before God on the Day of Judgement.

Although Muhammad is viewed as the "seal" of the prophets and therefore the final prophet, Islam recognises that God has sent prophets to all peoples and sees *Qur'anic* revelation as consistent with what has been given before but which has been corrupted by the disobedience of the peoples who received these revelations.

The Five Pillars of Islam

The essentials of Muslim practice are summarised in the "Five Pillars of Islam": These consist of:

Shahadah

The declarattion of faith which states that there is no god except God and Muhammad is his messenger.

Salat

Which is ritual prayer five times a day (see section on worship).

Zakat

The welfare due which consists of two and a half per cent of a Muslim's total annual wealth that must be donated to the service of the needy. An additional *Zakat* is due at the end of *Sawm* (fasting) during the month of *Ramadan* and this is known as *Zakat al-Fitr*.

Ramadan

A month of fasting and spiritual discipline (for details see section on "Muslim Calendar and Festivals").

Hajj

Pilgrimage to Makka which involves visiting the *Ka'bah* (the House of God) believed to have been built around four thousand years ago by Abraham. For those who can afford it, the *Hajj* is a requirement at least once in a lifetime.

Goal and Purpose of Human Life

The purpose of human life is to exercise *khilafa* (orthauity and trust to rule) over the world in a responsible way and to live in accordance with God's creative will to which human beings are recalled in the revelations of *Torah*, *Injil* and *Qur'an*, as well as through all the other prophets of God. How each person individually responds to the will and revelation of God is believed to determine their eternal destiny. Belief in the Day of Judgement, when an individual's actions will be placed on the scales of good and evil, acts as a powerful reinforcement for personal responsibility of each human being.

TRADITIONS IN ISLAM

There are two principal traditions within Islam – *Sunni* and *Shi'ia*. There is also an aspect of Islam known as *Sufism* which either *Sunni* or *Shi'a* Muslims might embrace.

Sunni

Ninety per cent of the world's Muslims are *Sunni* Muslims. They recognise the first four "rightly guided" *Caliphs* and *Qur'an*, *Sunna*, *Qiyas*, and *Ijma* as the four sources of the law. Within the *Sunni* branch of Islam there are a range of movements and groupings which have particular emphases or concerns. They are not, however, as organisationally clear-cut as, for example, Christian denominations and there may well be cross-membership of the various tendencies. In the UK, the majority of these groupings are of South Asian origin and are organised in a variety of *Sunni* Muslim traditions.

Barelwis

Barelwis were founded in Bareilly in India by Maulana Ahmad Raza Khan (1856-1921). They give a particularly high respect to the person of the Prophet Muhammad as a model and inspiration for Muslim life. They venerate *pirs* (spiritual guides) who are looked to for guidance. In *Barelwi* mosques singing or chanting of any kind is not permitted as part of worship.

Deobandis

Deobandis follow a movement founded in India in 1867 which is named after a training college for Indian Muslim religious scholars called Deoband. It promotes an interpretation of Islam as expounded by religious scholars of Deoband in which the emphasis is much more on the personal rather than the social aspects of the religion. Thus, they are generally non-political.

Tablighi Jamaat

Tablighi Jamaat (also known as *Tehrik-i-Iman*) was founded in India in 1927 by Maulana Muhammad Ilyas (1885-1944), a student of Deoband. The movement is non-political; it attempts to encourage other Muslims to practice Islam on a more fervent and regular basis and it substantially overlaps with the *Deobandi* movement.

Ahl-e-Hadith

Ahl-e-Hadith is a movement whose followers are sometimes known to outsiders as *Wahabis*. It claims to follow the *Deobandi* tradition in a more rigorous way by accepting only the teachings of the *Qur'an* itself and the earliest teachings in the *Hadith*. It rejects any regulations which are not from these sources.

Jamati-i-Islami

Jamaat-i-Islami operates as a political as well as a religious grouping. It was founded in India in 1941 by Sayyid Abul A' la Maududi (1903–1979). It favours a return to the following of traditional Muslim doctrine in the face of the secular influences of Western civilisation.

Shi'a

About 10% of Muslims worldwide are *Shi'a*. *Shi'a* is an Arabic word which literally means follower or associate. *Shi'a* believe that Muhammad instituted from within his family (the descendents of Ali and Fatima, the Prophet's daughter) a succession of individual *Imams* (spiritual leaders) to guide the community. The *Shi'a* concept of the *Imam* should not be confused with the general use of the term by Muslims to describe their local prayer leaders (see section on personnel).

In common with other Muslims *Shi'as* believe that the process of revelation was completed with the coming of Muhammad, but they differ from other Muslims in believing that *Imams* or *Hujjah* (Proofs of God) are specially selected by God and have the authority to interpret the *Qur'an* and to provide guidance to the believers.

Twelvers and Seveners

All *Shi'a* Muslims agree that Ali was the first *Imam*, but thereafter there are differences of view concerning the succession.

A minority are known as the *Seveners*, whilst the majority are known as the *Twelvers* (or *'Ithna Asheries*). The *Twelvers* believe in a series of twelve *Imams*, the last of whom, Muhammad Al-Muntazar (who was last seen in 873CE), is believed by them to have been the *Mahdi* (Guided One). All Muslims expect the coming of a descendant of the Prophet before the end of time in order to establish justice on the earth. The *Twelvers* believe that the *Mahdi* is alive although currently invisible, waiting for God's command to reappear.

Shi'as also differ from *Sunnis* with regard to a number of festivals which are observed (see section on festivals) and, in addition, they value pilgrimages to the shrines of their Imams and saints – in particular those of Imam Ali (in Najaf) and Imam Husayn (in Karbala) in Southern Iraq. Hussayn, the grandson of the Prophet, was killed in Karbala in confrontation with the armies of the Ummayyad *Caliph*, Yazid, whom Hussayn believed had departed from the ideals of the Ummah and its leadership. He is thus seen by *Shi'a* Muslims as an inspiration to all who suffer and struggle against injustice.

Ismailis

Ismailis are a *Shi'ia* Muslim group who accept the leadership of the first six *Imams*, but thereafter claim the primacy of the elder son of the sixth *Imam*, Ismail. Among the *Ismailis* are the *Nizaris* who are also known as the *Agha Khanis*. They believe in the Aga Khan as their living *Imam* and believe that he will, in turn, choose a member of his family to succeed him.

There are also *Bohras*, a group which emerged out of the *Musta'lian Ismailis*. The *Nizari* and the *Musta'lian Ismailis* disagreed over two opposing claimants to the *Imamate*. Both the *Nizaris* and the *Bohras* are *Seveners*.

Tasawwuf

Tasawwuf (*Sufism*) is the name for the mystical strand of Islam which can be found in both the *Sunni* and *Shi'a* traditions of Islam.

The word is thought to come from the Arabic *suf* (wool) which characterised the simple clothing worn by early ascetics. *Sufism* traces its origins back through *silsilahs* (lines of spiritual initiation) and is led by spiritual authorities known as *shaykhs* or *pirs* who advise the initiates of the *Sufi* Orders in their quest for an intimately spiritual relationship with God.

Sufism involves a commitment to the practical and readily accessible aspects of Islam based on the Shari'ah, but also emphasises the inner, spiritual knowledge of God, focusing on God as the Absolute Reality. As aids to their spiritual development, the members of *Sufi* Orders engage in various practices such as meditation, chanting the names of God, and ritual dancing. There are many worldwide *Sufi* Orders including, for example, the *Naqshbandi*, the *Qadiris*, and the *Chisti*.

MUSLIM LIFE

Shari'ah

The basic Muslim beliefs are put into practice by the way of life given by God, revealed through the Prophet Muhammad and known as the *Shari'ah*. The *Shari'ah* is not only concerned with ritual matters but also governs and regulates conduct in all areas of life, for example attitudes to prayer, economics, family life, and the behaviour of rulers.

Jihad

Jihad, the striving to protect, promote and live by the message of the *Qur'an* through words and actions, is also a central belief in Islam. It involves *Da'wah*, which is the task of spreading the message of Islam through invitation issued by means of words and deeds; creating satisfactory social conditions for Islam to be practised freely; increasing the self-discipline of people who are already Muslims so that they become better Muslims; and, in limited circumstances, defending Islam by force of arms if necessary.

This last aspect is only one dimension of *jihad* although outside of the Muslim community *jihad* is often mistakenly assumed to mean only this. It does not include imposing Islam by force on non-Muslims because the *Qur'an* forbids compulsion in matters of religion.

Halal

Food laws are also an important part of Muslim values and ethics. The *Qur'an* does not allow consumption of the meat of pigs and carnivorous animals. This includes pork products and foods which contain the by-products of pigs (such as ice cream containing pig-fat). All marine animals which do not have fins or scales are also forbidden by Muslim law, with the exception of prawns.

Alcohol is also prohibited under Islamic law and any drinks or foods which contain alcohol in any amount are unacceptable. Other meats are also *haram* (unlawful) unless the animal has been ritually slaughtered. Ritual slaughter involves prayers during slaughter, and a method of butchery which allows the blood to flow from the animal's body. Meat which is lawful is known as *halal* meat.

When *halal* meat is not available for consumption by Muslims, *kosher* meat (slaughtered according to the Jewish *shechita* method) is permissible for *Sunni* Muslims (although not for Shi'a 'Ithna Asheries) or a vegetarian meal will suffice. Foods which contain the by-products of non-*halal* meat are also considered unlawful, for example cheese which contains a non-*halal* animal product such as rennet.

During the month of *Ramadan* (see section on festivals below) Muslims should consume no food or drink between dawn and sunset although exceptions are made for children, the sick, pregnant women, people who are very old and travellers.

Gender and Family

According to Muslim understanding the *Shar'iah* confers equal dignity on both women and men. Men and women have the same religious duties, and in some cases the same legal rights, as in the possibility of owning property in their own right. However, there are also gender differentiations of rights and responsibilities with regard to social roles which are believed to be divinely revealed in the *Qur'an*.

In Islam, marriage and procreation is viewed very positively and celibacy is discouraged. Traditionally, the role of a man is believed to involve financial support of his wife and family (irrespective of his wife's wealth), and the protection of female family members including wife, daughters and, if his father is deceased, his mother as well.

Physical contact with people of the opposite sex outside of the same family is discouraged. The practice of restricted contact between Muslim women and men who are not family members is often referred to by the Asian term *purdah*. This may involve a variety of methods, for example wearing a veil (this is a social custom which originates in the Middle East), remaining within the home as much as possible, separate seating where mixed company occurs, and men and women generally socialising separately. Many Muslim women cover their faces from the sight of men other than their husbands and other male members of their family.

There are a variety of interpretations of how the basic value of modesty is best fulfilled in terms of particular items of clothing. Some Muslims understand a simple headscarf as sufficient to fulfill the demands of modesty in this regard, whilst others wear the *hijab* which is a covering that almost completely encloses the head and face.

Muslims believe that it is a human duty to marry and that the ideal family structure is based on monogamy which is the normal practice among Muslims in the UK. However, under the terms of the *Shari'ah* polygamy is considered lawful in certain circumstances. These include infertility of the first wife, or permanent physical or mental infirmity of the first wife.

Under Islamic law a man may take up to four wives, although the regulations regarding such marriages are such that polygamy is often a practical impossibility. These regulations include that a man must have the means to provide for each wife and that he must treat each wife absolutely equally, in financial and social terms. According to English law polygamous marriage is accepted as valid, if the marriage took place in a country where polygamy is permitted.

MUSLIM WORSHIP

Salat

The main form of *'ibadah* (worship) is that of *salat* (Arabic for the five times a day obligatory prayers) or *namaz* (Urdu). The exact times at which prayer takes place vary throughout the year.

Prayer time-tables are published with details of the times, and these can often be found on display in mosques. Generally speaking, prayer takes place at around the following periods of the day: *Fajr* (dawn), *Zuhr* (midday), *Asr* (late afternoon), *Maghrib* (after sunset), and *Isha* (late evening). Prayers are obligatory from puberty onwards, except for women who are menstruating or in the post-natal period. People who are not fully conscious or under the influence of medicinal drugs are also exempted from prayers.

Friday is the day for congregational prayers. Most male Muslims attend the mosque for this *Salat al-Jum'ah* which is mandatory for them. It is optional for women and, in practice, a majority of Muslim women do not attend this. *Wudu* (ablutions or ritual washing) must take place prior to all prayers. This includes washing hands, face, mouth, nose, arms (up to the elbows), and the feet (up to the ankles).

During prayer, worshippers face Makka, the *qiblah* (direction) of which is marked by the *mihrab*, a small recess on the wall of the mosque which often contains a copy of the *Qur'an* and which indicates the direction of Makka. In the UK, this direction is towards the South East. A Muslim can pray in any clean place and use a prayer mat if he or she cannot reasonably attend a mosque. Muslim employees, schoolchildren and students ideally require the opportunity to conduct their obligatory prayers whilst at work or in school or college.

Mosques

The first mosques were established and financed by the personal efforts of individuals living in the area. For example, the first mosque in Birmingham was established in 1941 by two Yemeni Muslims who were concerned to make arrangements for Muslim prayers, burial rites, and religious education for children. Thus the mosque served Muslim needs which were not being met in the wider community.

At present many mosques are buildings which

were formerly private residences, or even rooms in houses which are still used as private residences. Others are housed in public buildings which had former uses, for example, as warehouses or churches. Recently, however, a number of purpose built mosques have been built.

Within the Muslim community mosques are known by a number of terms, the most common being *masjid* and *jami' masjid*. The latter term is often used among South Asian Muslims to refer to a "central mosque". Among Arab Muslims, *jami'* is often used on its own to refer to *mosques* in general. *Masjid* means "a place of prostrations". No images, paintings or decorations which represent living beings are to be found inside mosques. In some mosques, however, Arabic calligraphy may be observed on the walls and perhaps some geometrical patterns.

There are no seats in a mosque but the floor is carpeted. Music is not played although in some mosques there may be congregational chanting. There is a *minbar* (pulpit) to one side of the *mihrab* from which the Imam delivers sermons on Fridays and at festival times. Visitors may also notice the Muslim symbol of the crescent moon and star.

Although every mosque is, in principle, open to all Muslims, mosques may in practice be predominantly used by specific Muslim tendencies or national groupings. As a result, particular dominant languages are used for instruction and general communication, although the language of the prayers themselves is always Arabic. The dominant language can sometimes be recognised from the name of an organisation, for example, the Urdu Society Mosque in Burnley, Lancashire.

Whilst it is rare for followers of different Islamic movements to worship together regularly at the same mosque, mosques of different types sometimes join together to form Councils of Mosques, such as the Bradford Council of Mosques.

Mosques provide a number of services like the channelling of *Zakat* to the poor; providing *imams* to visit Muslims who are sick in hospital or who are inmates in prison; educational

facilities (see below); and instruction in the Urdu and Arabic languages. In addition to this, many mosques are now registered for solemnisation of marriages, and some mosques have installed morgues ensuring that Muslims can perform Islamic burial rites for their fellow Muslims.

Muslim women often do not regularly attend mosques for worship. When they do so, they usually sit separately, for example, in a room upstairs which is, nevertheless, considered as part of the mosque although in some mosques women are permitted to worship behind the men on the same floor. In some cases women are not allowed to worship in mosques but only to attend for cultural events and special occasions.

MUSLIM CALENDAR AND FESTIVALS

Calendar

The Muslim calendar is a lunar one, with each year composed of twelve months and each month of twenty-nine or thirty days.

As such, the Muslim year is eleven days shorter than the solar calendar, and this means that festival dates move through the solar year and cannot be conclusively dated a long way in advance since they depend upon the sighting of the new moon for the start of a new month.

The first day of the Muslim year is the anniversary of the *Hijra* with which the Muslim calendar begins. This marks the Prophet Muhammad's original migration from Makka to Medina that led to the creation of the Muslim community. Most of the year 1993CE is therefore the year 1413 according to the Muslim calendar.

Eid al-Fitr

Is a festival which occurs at the end of the month of *Ramadan* during which the revelation of the *Qur'an* began. Between one and two days leave from work is usually taken to participate in this festival.

Eid al-Adha

Is a three day festival which marks the end of the

Hajj and occurs on the tenth day of the *Zill Hajj* month. It celebrates the supreme example of sacrifice and submission exhibited by the Prophet Abraham, as well as the declaration by God of the completion of the final divine revelation in the *Qur'an*.

Ramadan

Is the name of the ninth month (which is either twenty-nine or thirty days long) of the lunar year. During this time Muslims should abstain from eating, drinking and sexual intercourse from before dawn to sunset. These daylight abstentions are deemed by Muslims to reflect devotion for God as the person abstains for God alone. Fasting is also seen as increasing self-discipline and patience, decreasing selfishness and lending a sense of solidarity between Muslims and equality before God.

There are, however, some categories of people who can be exempt from the requirements of fasting. These include children who are below the age of puberty and people who are mentally unfit during *Ramadan*. They do not have to fast nor do they have to compensate in any way for missing the fast. People travelling long distances may temporarily break the fast and should make up for this by fasting a day at another time for each day they have missed; people whose health would be severely affected by fasting may fast in compensation at another point in the year for an equivalent length of time.

Those who will not recover from the risk of ill health may offer a poor Muslim a meal or the financial equivalent for each day of fasting missed, and pregnant women and women who are breast feeding are not bound to fast. Women who are menstruating must not fast. They must make up for each day they do not fast by fasting at another point in the year.

First of Muharram

Marks the Islamic New Year.

'Ashurah

Is a *Shi'a* commemoration marking the martyrdom of Imam Husayn, the grandson of the Prophet Muhammad. This is the tenth day of the month of Muharram in the Islamic calendar. It is the occasion for "passion plays" and a ritual of self-beating through which *Shi'as* express their identity with the suffering of the martyrs.

Milad al-Nabin

Is a celebration of the birthday of the Prophet on the twelfth day of *Rabi 'al-Awal*, the third month of the Muslim calendar. It is particularly important among *Barelwis* in view of their special veneration of the Prophet.

Lailat al-Baraat

Takes place fifteen days before *Ramadan* and celebrates the belief that on this night the fate of humankind is ordained for the next year.

Lailat al-Qadr

Occurs on the twenty seventh night of fasting in *Ramadan* and marks the day when the *Qur'an* began its descent to earth and was first revealed to Prophet Muhammad.

MUSLIM ORGANISATIONS

The composition of the Muslim community in the UK is varied and can be considered from a number of different perspectives including groupings with an ethnic/national component and movements within the two main traditions within Islam, the *Sunni* and the *Shi'a*. Individual Muslims might identify themselves with one or more of these groupings at the same time. The Deobandi and Tablighi Jamaat are numerically the strong of the Muslim movements in the UK and there is some overlap between the

The general background to the various Muslim movements has already been described in the earlier section on "Traditions in Islam".

395

Barelwis

This tendency is particularly numerous amongst communities where Muslims are, or have been, minorities (for example those originally from East Africa or Gujarati Indians). Two national organisations linked to the *Barelwi* movement are the Jamaat Ahl-e-Sunnat and the World Islamic Mission.

Deobandi

The *Deobandi* movement is represented in different parts of the country but is at its strongest in Lancashire and West Yorkshire. Two organisations with links to this movement are the Jamiat-e-Ulama of Briatain and Darul Uloom College in Bury.

Tablighi Jamaat

The *Tablighi Jamaat* movement in the UK is centred in Dewsbury but has substantial activity elsewhere in West Yorkshire, Lancashire and the Midlands. Their organisations and mosques can also be found elsewhere in Britain.

Ahl-e-Hadith

This is a numerically small group in the UK and is mainly concentrated in Birmingham.

Jamaat-i-Islami

There are several organisations who have a relationship to Syed Maududi's (1903-1979) thinking. Maududi was an idealist, thinker and founder of *Jamaat-i-Islami* in 1941. Such organisations include the UK Islamic Mission, which has several branches throughout the UK. The movement tended mainly to function amongst migrants from Pakistan. After the emergence of Bangladesh, Bengali Muslims established their own *Dawat-ul-Islam* movement in 1976. Later, the Islamic Forum of Europe was also formed by young Bangladeshis to serve the intellectual needs of Bangladeshi youth.

Sufi Orders

Many of the international *Sufi* orders have branches in most UK towns and cities with a substantial Muslim presence. There are also a number of *Sufi* Centres associated with specific orders. *Sufi* Orders are generally *Sunni* rather than *Shi'a* in composition. There are also a number of western *Sufi* organisations.

Other National and Regional Organisations

Several organisations with an international membership have a presence in the UK, such as the Muslim World League, which was established in Makka in 1962 and has an office, library and prayer hall in London.

There are a range of federations and councils of Islamic organisations at both regional and national levels. Regionally, these include the Bradford Council for Mosques and the Lancashire Council of Mosques. Nationally, they include the Council of Mosques (UK and Eire), the Imams and Mosques Council and the Union of Muslim Organisations. These have some overlap in terms of membership, but none has yet established itself as a generally accepted and authoritative national council.

In addition to the general organisations, which are related to particular movements within Islam, there are also a range of Muslim organisations in the UK which are functionally orientated towards a major concern for the Muslim community. For example, the UK Action Committee on Islamic Affairs have a particular interest in the law and the Muslim community.

Educational Organisations

There are a range of educational bodies which operate on a national level and serve a variety of functions. For example, there is the Muslim College in London which trains *imams*; the Islamic Foundation in Leicester, an education, research and training organisation founded in 1973 which produces literature and runs courses on Muslim belief and practice for non-Muslim professionals working in a multi-cultural context, and the Muslim Community Studies Institute in Leicester which carries out research and produces publications on Muslim life in both Muslim societies and Western societies.

There is, in addition, the Muslim Education Co-ordinating Council UK in London which monitors and advises on the teaching of Muslim children in Local Education Authority Schools; the Muslim Educational Trust, which caters for the educational needs of Muslim children; the Islamic Academy in Cambridge, an educational research organisation; and the Muslim Education Forum, which brings together a range of these bodies in an informal network designed to co-ordinate their activities.

Madrassahs are *Qur'anic* schools which are local in nature and are usually attached to a mosque. Children attend in the evenings after day school. Both male and female children attend such lessons where they read and learn sections of the *Qur'an* which in turn necessitates the learning of Arabic. They also learn the rituals and practices of Islam.

There are also a few private Muslim day schools which provide a full time educational service for Muslim children. Many Muslim organisations wish to see the establishment of Muslim schools with voluntary aided status. At the time of writing, however, none have been granted this by the Department for Education.

Dawah

Islam is centrally concerned with announcing the revelation that Muslims have received and with inviting others to embrace that revelation through membership of the *Ummah*.

There are therefore a number of organised *Dawah* initiatives in the UK, the aim of which is to spread the Muslim faith throughout the UK. Some are local independent organisations. Others are affiliates of national organisations such as the UK Islamic Mission, which has branches and affiliated mosques nationwide. Some missionary groups aim to spread the word of Islam to non-Muslims, whilst others focus on drawing back Muslims who have drifted away from their faith.

Youth

Among Muslim youth are local independent groups of Muslim youth and also local groups affiliated to national organisations such as Young Muslims UK and the Federation of Student Islamic Societies (FOSIS). The National Association of Muslim Youth, based in Leicester, has branches throughout the country. Together with Young Muslims and FOSIS, workshops and "camps" are organised for Muslim youth.

Community Groups

Local Muslim community groups are usually attached to the mosque and are therefore normally also related to a particular Muslim movement or they are composed of a group with certain ethnic origins, such as the various Pakistan Muslim Welfare Associations. They have a welfare and cultural role and may be eclectic but have sub-groups for certain sectors of the community, for example youth groups and women's groups. In recent years some Muslims have begun to form explicitly political organisations. An example of this is the Islamic Party of Britain which was set up in 1989 and is led mainly by white converts to Islam. There is also the Muslim Parliament which is organised by the Muslim Institute and aspires to represent Muslim opinion within British social and political life.

Personnel

In terms of Muslim personnel, the *imam* (or *Maulvi* or *Maulana*) is the leader of the prayers. *Imam* is an Arabic word meaning "the one who stands in front." In principle, this can be any Muslim who is well versed in the *Qur'an*. Among *Sunni* Muslims, there is no hierarchy of ordained clergy. The *imam* may also act as a spokesperson for the community. Frequently, however, having arrived in adulthood from the area of the world where the majority of the members of a mosque community have their ethnic origins, the *imam* may only have a poor command of the English language, and the chairperson or secretary of the Mosque Committee therefore tends to represent the community in the outside world.

Fuquha are legal experts of the religious law which is in force in Muslim countries. *Pirs* or *shaykhs* are spiritual guides from the Sufi orders. *Ulama* is a term denoting religious scholars in general.

Individual mosques are usually controlled by Mosque Committees which generally include a president and secretary. Committee membership elections are normally held annually. The mosque committee co-ordinates funding for the mosque and connected Muslim organisations and is also responsible for appointing an imam.

BIBLIOGRAPHY

Abdalati, H, *Islam in Focus*, American Trust Publications, Indianapolis, 1975.

Abdul-Fadl, M, *Introducing Islam from Within*, Islamic Foundation, Leicester, 1991.

Ahmad, K, *Islam: Basic Principles and Characteristics*, Islamic Foundation, Leicester, 1974.

Ahmad, K, *Islamic Perspectives,* Islamic Foundation, Leicester, 1979.

Awan, B A "Islam", in Tiptaft, N, *Religion in Birmingham*, Norman Tiptaft Ltd, Warley, 1972.

Badawi, Z, *Islam in Britain*, Ta-Ha Publishers Ltd, London, 1981.

Barton, S W, *The Bengali Muslims of Bradford*, Community Religions Project, University of Leeds, Leeds, 1986.

Coulson, N J, *A History of Islamic Law*, Edinburgh University Press, Edinburgh, 1964.

Daftari, F, *The Ismailis: Their History and Doctrine*, Cambridge University Press, Cambridge, 1990.

Darsh, S M, *Muslims in Europe*, Ta-Ha Publishers, London, 1987.

Glasse, C, *The Concise Encylopaedia of Islam*, Stacey International, London, (2nd edition), 1991.

Henley, A, *Caring for Muslims and their Families:*

Religious Aspects of Care, National Extension College, Cambridge, 1982.

Islamic Foundation, *Islam: The Essentials*, Islamic Foundation, Leicester, 1974.

Jafri, SHM, *The Origins and Development of Shi'a Islam*, Oxford University Press, London.

Joly, D, "Making a place for Islam in British Society: Muslims in Birmingham", in Gerholm T and Lithman, Y F, *The New Islamic Presence in Western Europe*, Mansell, London, 1990, pp. 32-52.

Joly, D and Nielsen, J S, *Muslims in Britain: An Annotated Bibliography, 1960-1984*, Centre for Research in Ethnic Relations, University of Warwick, Warwick, 1985.

Kettani, M A, *Muslim Minorities in the World Today*, Mansell, London, 1986.

McDermott, M Y and Ahsan, M M, *The Muslim Guide: For Teachers, Employers, Community Workers and Social Administrators in Britain*, Islamic Foundation, Leicester, 1980.

Maududi, A A, *The Islamic Law*, Islamic Publishers, Lahore, 1960.

Mawdudi, A, *Islam: A Historical Perspective*, Islamic Foundation, Leicester, 1974.

Momen, M, *An Introduction to Shi'i Islam: The History and Doctrines of Twelver Shi'ism*, London, Yale University Press.

Nadwi, S A H A, *Muslims in the West: Message and Mission*, Islamic Foundation, Leicester, 1982.

Nasr, S H, *Ideals and Realities of Islam*, George Allen and Unwin, London, 1966.

Nielsen, J S, *Muslim Immigration and Settlement in Britain Research Papers on Muslims in Europe No 21*, March 1984.

Nielsen, J S, *A Survey of British Local Authority Response to Muslim Needs*, Research Papers on Muslims in Europe No 30/31, June/September, 1986.

Nielsen, J S, "Muslims in Britain: Searching for an Identity", in *New Community*, Volume XIII, No 3, Spring 1987, pp 384-394.

Nielsen, J S, *Muslims in Western Europe*, Edinburgh University Press, Edinburgh, 1992.

Padwick, C, *Muslim Devotions*, SPCK, London, 1961.

Peach, C, "The Muslim Population of Great Britain", in *Ethnic and Racial Studies*, Volume XIII, No 3, 1990, pp. 415-419.

Rahman, T, *A Code of Muslim Personal Law, Volumes I & II*, Islamic Publishers, Karachi, 1978 and 1980.

Raza, M S, *Islam in Britain: Past Present and Future*, Volcano Press Ltd, Leicester, (2nd edition) 1992.

Rex, J, "The urban sociology of religion and Islam in Birmingham", in Gerholm, T and Lithman, Y G, *The New Islamic Presence in Western Europe*, Mansell, London, 1990, pp 206-218.

Robinson, F, *Varieties of South Asian Islam*, Research Paper No.8, Centre for Research in Ethnic Relations, University of Warwick, Coventry, 1988.

Schimmel, A, *Islamic Names*, Edinburgh University Press, Edinburgh, 1989.

Shaykh Haeri, F, *The Elements of Sufism*, Element Books, Dorset, 1990.

Trimingham, J S, *The Sufi Orders in Islam*, Oxford University Press, Oxford, 1971.

Wahab, I, *Muslims in Britain: Profile of a Community*, The Runnymede Trust, London, 1989.

MUSLIM UK ORGANISATIONS

The organisations listed in this section include both head offices of organisations with branches throughout the country and organisations which aspire to serve the Muslim community on a UK–wide level.

All Muslim Funeral Society
127 Kingsway
Luton
Bedfordshire LU1 1TS
Contact: Mr Abdul Shakur
Office: General Secretary
Membership group. Any Muslim living in England can become a member of the society by paying a membership fee. The society mainly functions to assist the deceased's family with funeral expenses.

AMANA
P O Box 2842
London W6 9ZH
Tel: 081–748–2424
Contact: Umar Hegedus & Khadijah Knight
AMANA exists to promote an understanding of Islam and its followers. It addresses both Muslims and non–Muslims providing well–grounded information and advice. AMANA focuses on Islamic issues that arise in Britain and Europe. Resources, training, speakers, consultancy and research can be supplied to schools, colleges, social services departments, health education authorities and employers.

Association of Muslim Schools of UK and Eire (AMS)
2 Digswell Street
London N7 8JX
Tel: 071–607 8839
Fax: 071–609–4943
Contact: Moeen Yaseen
The association will encourage the development of, and co–ordination between, full time Muslim Schools in the UK and Eire to advance the cause of Islamic education based on the Qur'an and the Sunnah; to improve the provision of effectiveness of these schools and to extend such development and co–ordination to other such associations overseas. Objectives include teacher training; curriculum development; resource development; public relations, parental involvement and community awareness; school management training; monitoring and inspection; voluntary aided and grant maintained status; school development; assessment, evaluation and accreditation.

Association of Muslim Youth and Community Workers
81 Melbourne Road
Spinney Hill North
Leicester LE2 0GW
Tel: 0533–515296
Contact: Mr Shams–uddeen Hassan
Office: Chair

A membership group which provides support and development for volunteer and professional Muslim youth and community workers in terms of influencing local government policy as this affects the Muslim community. It aims to make Muslim workers more aware of issues that affect the lives of the Muslim community in order to be more effective in tackling these issues and to liaise and negotiate with non-Muslim and other faith workers in effecting service delivery. It organises seminars and conferences to enable non-Muslim professionals to deal more effectively with the Muslim community.

Council of Mosques (UK & Eire)

46 Goodge Street
London W1P 1FJ
Tel: 071-580-4504
Mosques and Islamic organisations in the UK and Eire are members of the Council. Members can represent their organisations through any one office-bearer or through the imam. All members have the same status irrespective of their size or membership. It exists to: help in establishing new mosques; maintain the mosques of the United Kingdom and Eire and to activate the functions of the mosques which were being discharged in the early days of Islam. The council works by: helping to establish mosques in areas where there are none and by helping to maintain the sanctity of the mosques; combating ideological onslaughts and counteracting anti-Islamic attitudes; developing Islamic identities and by developing better understanding and good relations between the Muslim and non-Muslim communities. Affiliated to The Inter Faith Network for the UK.

Council of Representatives of UK Muslims

48 Wilberforce Road
London N4

Council for the Preservation of the Holy Places of Islam

34 Francis Road
Leyton
London E10
Tel: 081-588-0581

Dar-ul-Ehsan Publications

252 Almondbury Bank
Huddersfield
West Yorkshire HD5 8EL
Tel: 0484-541304 (home)
Contact: Dr Muhammad Iqbal
Office: Secretary
Charitable trust which aims to promote better

understanding of Islam and Muslims by all, especially non-Muslims, through publications on all aspects of Islam particularly the spiritual dimensions of the Faith. The publications, big or small, are distributed free of charge. However, this registered international religious charity accepts donations to cover the costs of administration and printing of new books.

Dawatul Islam Youth Group

52 Fieldgate Street
London E1 1DL
Tel: 071-247-3832
Fax: 071-247-0689
A voluntary youth organisation and youth section of Dawatul Islam UK and Eire. The group provides a unique opportunity to the youth of society to grow in Islam – the beautiful way chosen by the Creator. Its members aim to make a good society and use this life to earn an eternal life of success. The group aims to provide an alternative socialising platform to keep youngsters away from gang fights, drugs and other evil destruction. It aims to provide the youth with the opportunity to build their life on moral teaching and practice. Activities include welfare, training camps, conferences, sports, study circle and library.

Federation of Student Islamic Societies of the UK and Eire

38 Mapesbury Road
London NW2 4JD
Tel: 081-452-4493
Fax: 081-208-4161
Contact: T Othman
Office: Executive Director
Representative body founded by Muslim students in the UK and Eire in 1962 with the motto "And hold fast to the covenant of Allah and do not be disunited" (Qur'an 3:310). Since then it has played an important role as an independent organisation in serving Muslim students, carrying out da'wah work and supporting Muslims all over the world. The Federation organises conferences, training programmes and is a welfare association.

Guyana United Sad'r Islamic Anjuman

8 Hazledean Road
Craven Road
London NW10
Tel: 081-961-3814
Fax: 081-961-3814
Contact: Haji Abdool Hafiz Rahaman
Office: Vice President
A branch organisation representing Muslims in Georgetown in Guyana, the organisation was founded

in 1936 by a learned priest from India. Its main purpose is to unite and keep Muslims together and to spread the knowledge of Islam throughout Guyana. Today there are other branch offices in the USA and Canada. Muslims represent approximately ten per cent of the Guyana population which is approximately seventy thousand Muslims. The organisation manages two orphanages which look after around one hundred and fifty boys and girls. It aims to spread the Islamic faith among all mankind.

Idara Isha'at al Islam

15 Stratton Road
Gloucester GL1 4HD
Tel: 0452-306623
Contact: Mr E Y Bawa
Office: Trustee
An organisation established in 1974 and founder of Britain's first full-time Madrasah for girls in the UK. The family of seven, including five females, have memorised the Holy Qur'an, a unique family. Mr Bawa is an author of Islamic books for twenty-eight years and publishes books and magazines in English and Urdu and offers Muslim welfare in all fields. The sons and three sons-in-law are all *Maulvis* qualified at Arabic colleges.

Imams and Mosques Council (UK)

20-22 Creffield Road
London W5 3RP
Tel: 081-992-6636
Fax: 081-993-3946
Contact: Maulana Mohammad Shahid Raza
Office: Executive Director
An organisation of affiliated mosques, the Council is an independent, non-political organisation. It is a symbol of unity among mosques in Britain. It is an umbrella organisation to deal with various common problems faced by imams and mosques in the UK. It promotes better relationships among various faith communities through co-operating on religious and spiritual issues on a wider scale. Activities include training courses for imams, information desk on Islam, Shari'ah and specific Islamic issues, a pension scheme for imams, financial, education and advisory assistance to the mosques in the UK, and co-operation with inter- faith organisations. Affiliated to the Inter Faith Network for the United Kingdom.

Institute of Ismaili Studies

14-15 Great James Street
London WC1
Tel: 071-405-5328 (home)

Institute of Muslim Minority Affairs

46 Goodge Street
London W1P 1FJ
Tel: 071-636-6740
Fax: 071-255-1473
Contact: Hamid Ismail
Office: Resident Director
The primary purpose of the Institute is to encourage, support and pursue research in, and to extend the study and knowledge of, the conditions of life of Muslim minority communities wherever they reside.

IQRA Trust

24 Culross Street
London W1Y 3HE
Tel: 071-491-1572
Fax: 071-493-7899
Charitable trust and resource centre. The Trust works to promote greater understanding of Islam and to help Muslims participate in all levels of British society. It aims to provide clear, accurate and reliable information about the Islamic faith and the Muslim way of life. It provides training courses for teachers, health workers and social workers, runs a touring exhibition for schools and colleges and produces publications for teachers, pupils and professionals in a variety of fields.

Islamia Schools Trust

129 Salusbury Road
London NW6 6RG
Tel: 071-372-2171
Fax: 071-372-0655
An educational organisation to support educational plans and projects to advance the Islamic education of Muslims in the United Kingdom and Eire by means of the dispersal of funds.

Islamic Academy

23 Metcalfe Road
Cambridge CB4 2DB
Tel: 0223-350976
Fax: 0223-350976
Contact: Professor Syed Ali Ashraf
Office: Director General
An educational research organisation. The Academy was established in 1983 as a religious charity with the main aim of formulating Islamic concepts embracing all branches of knowledge to replace secularist concepts which are at present used for teaching different subjects. It is conducting research in educational philosophy for all branches of knowledge from an Islamic perspective; designing curricula from an Islamic point of view and getting text books written

accordingly; organising teacher education courses; working for the establishment of faith as the basis of education for a multi-faith, multi-cultural country; publishing the journal "Muslim Educational Quarterly" and books on Islam and Islamic education for both pupils and teachers.

Islamic Council of Europe

16 Grosvenor Crescent
London SW1X 7EP
Tel: 071-235-9832
Fax: 071-823-1590

Islamic Council on Palestine

46 Goodge Street
London W1P 1FJ

Islamic Council of Scotland

30 Clyde Place
Glasgow G5
Tel: 041-429-663
Contact: Mr Bashir Man

Islamic Cultural Centre

The London Central Mosque Trust Ltd
The Islamic Centre
146 Park Road
London NW8 7RG
Tel: 071-724-3363/7
Contact: Dr Al-Ghamdi
Office: Director General
Place of worship and study. Facilities for worship, studies, lectures, welfare, library service and bookshop, counselling, marriages and funeral prayers. Affiliated to The Inter Faith Network for the UK.

Islamic Educational Welfare Association

25 Evershot Road
London N4 3DG
Tel: 071-272-7031
Contact: Abdul Aleem Siddiqui
Voluntary organisation. It aims to: promote the Islamic faith and the imparting of religious knowledge to Muslims and non-Muslims in the UK; promote unity and good-will among Muslims living in the UK; provide moral and practical support to all Muslims; reform and purify the individual enabling him/her to develop a true Islamic personality; facilitate the up-bringing of Muslim children living in this country in accordance with Islamic principles; arrange meetings, discussions and conferences on matters of common interest; safeguard Islamic values and heritage of Muslims in the UK; demand female doctors for Muslim women in hospital; promote a

bond among Muslims and friendly relations between Muslims and non-Muslims; demand Halal meat for Muslim hospital patients; persuade ILEA to introduce full dress for Muslim girls and boys in schools; make matrimonial alliances among Muslim families in the UK and to provide Arabic and religious education for Muslim children.

Islamic Foundation

Markfield Conference Centre
Ratby Lane
Markfield
Leicester LE6 0RN
Tel: 0530-244944
Contact: Mr S F Ahmad
Office: Public Relations Director
An educational research organisation dedicated to making Islam a living reality in our age. For this purpose it aims to improve human communication and develop a better understanding of Islam among all people of the world, Muslim and non-Muslim, so as to galvanise man to the message of the ideal of One God and the unity of mankind, as brought by all the Prophets of God throughout the ages, last of whom was the Prophet Muhammad. Its activities include research and publications. Youth and women use facilities on the campus. Affiliated to the Inter Faith Network for the United Kingdom.

Islamic Propagation Centre International

481 Coventry Road
Small Heath
Birmingham B10 0JS
Tel: 021-773-0137
Fax: 021-766-8577
Contact: Mr S M Khan
Office: General Secretary
An organisation devoted to supplying information and literature on Islam. The group works to gain new members of the faith and engages in da'wah, in other words, the preaching of Islam.

Islamic Rights Movement

P O Box 139
Leicester LE2 2YH
Tel: 0533-706714
Fax: 0533-706714
Contact: Mr A Hussain
Office: Chairperson
Membership group. The Islamic Rights Movement takes an interfaith approach to human rights. It believes that all religions must unite to exert pressure on governments and raise the social consciousness of the people to safeguard human life; grant freedom of

thought and belief and not to imprison or torture people. The group mobilises non-Muslim inter-faith human rights organisations for an inter-faith approach to human rights. It also educates people in The Islamic Rights Charter through seminars and conference camps as well as publishing literature on Islamic human rights.

Islamic Sharia Council of UK and Eire

34 Francis Road
London E10 6PW
Tel: 081-558-0581
Fax: 081-881-3984
Contact: Dr Suhaib Abdul Ghaffor
Office: General Secretary
Semi-legal Court. The organisation was established in 1980 to cater for families in dispute to effect reconciliation and failing this, to dissolve the marriage Islamically. It aims to deal with basic issues concerning interest, insurance and disputes between parties and to try to settle resulting disputes concerning guardianship of, and access to, minors as well as to explain the way in which inheritance is divided.

Islamic Society for the Promotion of Religious Tolerance in the U.K.

20-22 Creffield Road
London W5 3RP
Tel: 071-935-3330
Contact: Hesham El Essawy
Office: Chairman

Islamic Texts Society

5 Green Street
Cambridge CB2 3JU
Tel: 0223-314387
Fax: 0223-324342
Contact: A R Azzam
Publishing house. A charitable company registered in the UK which aims to further an understanding of Islam in the West by publishing in English works of traditional importance to Islamic faith and culture.

Khaniqahi-Nimatullahi

41 Chepstow Place
London W2 4TS
Tel: 071-229-0769 (home)
Contact: Dr Javad Nurbakhsh

Jama't Ahl-e-Sunnat UK (Association of Sunni Muslims UK)

106 Leslie Road,
Forestfield
Nottingham NG7 6PR

Tel: 0602-790956
Contact: Maulana Syed Zahid Hussain
Office: President
An organisation of Imams and Ulama of the Sunni tradition representing the Barelvi movement. Mainly acts to liaise between mosques and Sufi organisations within the Barelwi circle and organises national and residential conferences on issues affecting the ideological attitude of Muslims in Britain.

Jamiat Ahl-e-Hadith UK

20 Green Lane
Small Heath
Birmingham B9 5DB
Tel: 021-773-0019
Fax: 021-766-8779
Contact: Maulana Abdul Hadi Umta
Office: General Secretary
The headquarters in this country of the Jamiat Ahl-e-Hadith.

Jamiat-e-Ulama of Britain (Association of Muslim Scholars of Islamics in Britain)

6 Victoria Crescent
Birkdale Road
Dewsbury
West Yorkshire WF13 4HJ
Tel: 0924-451857 (home)
Contact: Maulana Abdul Rashid Rabbani
Office: General Secretary
A national organisation of Muslim scholars, with links to the Deobandi movement. It conducts educational activities, provides advice to Muslims on Islamic observance and plays a role in building up relationships with other communities at local and national level in order to contribute to the welfare of society generally.

Linkers

134 Dalyell Road
London SW9 9UP
Maintains listings of Muslim organisations.

London Sufi Centre

21 Lancaster Road
London W11 1QL
Tel: 071-229-1064
Contact: Secretary
Place of worship. The Sufi Order of the West follows the teachings of Hazrat Inayat Khan who was the first Sufi teacher to introduce Sufism to the West in 1910. Through practices such as meditation, retreat and dance the group explores life's purpose and celebrates the interconnections of all religions in a monthly

service. There are networks of groups across Europe and North America currently headed by Pir Vilyat Khan. The London Centre is led by the representatives of the Sufi Order in England and is the main focus of this work in the UK. Activities include weekly teaching, meditation, and dance groups as well as group and individual retreats.

Malaysian Islamic Study Group - UK and Eire
90 St Thomas Road
Finsbury Park
London N4 2WQ
Tel: 081-345-2318

Memon Association UK
3 Weir Road
Balham
London SW12 8UW
Tel: 081-743-3233 (home)
Fax: 081-749-1442 (home)
Contact: Mr A A Yousuf
Office: Honorary General Secretary
The association aims to work towards the advancement of the religion of Islam and the education of Muslim children in accordance with the tenets and doctrines of the Sunni school of thought. It aims to financially assist members of the Muslim community in particular, and others in general, who are poor and needy. Its activities include the social well-being of members, youth projects, sports and education, women's cultural activities, publication of community journal, advice and counselling.

Message of Islam Movement
14 Lea Road
Greet
Sparkhill
Birmingham B11 3LU
Tel: 021-771-3680

Movement for Islamic Resurgence
11 Turpin House
Battersea Park Road
London SW11 5HR
Tel: 071-627-0425 (home)

Muslim College
20-22 Creffield Road
London W5 3RP
Tel: 081-992-6636
Fax: 081-993-3946
Contact: Dr M A Zaki Badawi
Office: Principal
Educational establishment. The College represents the assumptions of a more open and positive stance in the teaching of Islamic studies, combining the virtues of Western methodology with those of Muslim learning. It also aims to convey Islamic ideas in a way that will be comprehensible to the educated European. It offers courses on Islam and related studies, including a three year post-graduate Diploma in Islamic studies, advanced and elementary courses in classical and modern Arabic language, courses on Islamic history, Sufism and history of Islamic law in co-operation with the University of London.

Muslim Community Studies Institute
P O Box 139
Leicester LE2 2YH
Tel: 0533-706714
Contact: Mr Asaf Hussain
A research and consultancy organisation which aims to: create an understanding of Islam through publication of studies such as "Islam in Britain" and the "Sociology of Islam"; mobilise Muslim youth and women for active participation in community affairs and to raise the conscience and consciousness of Muslims by educating them in Islamic Human Rights through the subsidiary organisation The Islamic Rights Movement. It publishes studies on Muslims, Islam and the Muslim World through the publishing arm Volcano Press and it organises conferences and networking for youth, women and Muslim organisations.

Muslim Education Co-ordinating Council (UK)
7 Paul Gardens
East Croydon
Surrey CR0 5QL
Tel: 081-681-6087
Fax: 081-681-6087
Contact: Mr Nazar Mustafa
Office: Chairperson
Membership group and body representing other groups. It strives for the better education of Muslim children and for satisfaction of their religious and cultural needs and aims to raise educational and political awareness among young Muslims to be law abiding citizens of this country.

Muslim Educational Forum
93 Court Road
Balsall Heath
Birmingham B12 9LQ
Tel: 021-440-3500/8218
Fax: 021-440-8144
Contact: Mr Mohammad Khalid/Mr Yahya Yacob

Office: Administrative Officers

The Muslim Education Forum is a loose confederation of all the major Muslim education organisations in the UK. The General secretary is Mr Fazlan Khalid. It had its first meeting in January 1989 when it met to discuss the implications for Muslims of the provisions in the 1988 Education Reform Act.

Muslim Educational Trust

130 Stroud Green Road
London N4 3RZ
Tel: 071-272 8502
Fax: 071-281-3457
Contact: Mr G Sarwar
Office: Director
An educational charity which was established in 1966 in order to cater for the educational needs of Muslim children in Britain. In addition to providing teachers for Islamic studies classes in schools, the trust liaises with the Department for Education, Local Education Authorities and individual schools and teachers, as well as publishing books for their use.

Muslim Hands

141a Berridge Road
Forest Fields
Nottingham NG7 6HR
Tel: 0602-704490
Fax: 0602-704490
Contact: Sahibzada Syed Lakhte-Husanain
Office: Chairman
A Midland-based charity with the aim of providing relief to those in need around the world by monetary collections from around the country. Assistance is offered in monetary contributions, medical, food or clothing supplies and in long-term education schemes.

Muslim Information Service

233 Seven Sisters Road
London N4 2DA
Tel: 071-272-5170

Muslim Institute

6 Endsleigh Street
London WC1H 0DS
Tel: 071-388-2581
Contact: Kalim Siddiqui

Muslim Law (Shariah) Council

20-22 Creffield Road
London W5 3RP
Tel: 081-992-6636
Fax: 081-993-3946
Contact: Maulana Mohammed Shahid Raza

Office: Executive Secretary
The council consists of twenty-five religious scholars representing all schools of Muslim Law (Fiqh) in Britain. Primarily it provides services to the Muslims concerned with questions of personal status: marriage, divorce, inheritance, wills etc. It also gives Islamic legal opinion (fatwa) on any question put to it. Services also available to non-Muslims seeking expert information on Islamic law.

Muslim Parliament of Great Britain

6 Endsleigh Street
London WC1H 0DS
Tel: 071-3882581
Tel: 0494-786861 (home)
Fax: 071-383-5006
Contact: Dr M Ghaissudden
Office: Assistant Director
The Muslim Parliament was set up to try and co-ordinate the activities of all other Muslim groups and to present united demands to the government of the UK. Lobbying is done to secure Muslims' rights as citizens of the UK.

Muslim Schools Trust

78 Gillespie Road
London N5 1LN
Tel: 071-359-0280
A publishing trust, the main purpose of which is to produce literature in English on Islam, particularly about the life pattern and life-style of the Prophet Muhammad, in a rational and objective way. The first seven volumes of a twenty-five volume encyclopedia have already been collected, compiled and published.

Muslim Teachers Association

146 Park Road
London NW8 7RG
Tel: 071-724-3363
Contact: Mr S Syed
Office: Secretary
A Membership group which aims to unite all Muslim teachers and students in the UK into an Islamic brotherhood of co-operation and endeavour in accordance with the guidance of the Qur'an and the Sunnah of the Prophet. It represents the educational interests of Muslims at all official levels within the UK. Promotes and safeguards the welfare, morality and education of Muslim children. It provides relevant information to Muslim teachers, parents and students in order to solve their problems.

Muslim Welfare House

233 Seven Sisters Road
London N4 2DA
Tel: 071-263-3071/071-263-5381
Fax: 071-281-2687
Contact: M A Hasan
Office: General Secretary
Has the following subsidary departments: Muslim Information Services; Muslim Welfare House London Publishers; Muslim Welfare House Educational Centre; Muslim Welfare House Youth Club; Muslim Booshop (Muslim Information Centre, Tel: 071-272-5170). It has fourteen branches in major UK cities and localities and provides a range of services and activities to Muslims and non-Muslims alike including religious activities and services; social, sport and recreational services; educational services; information on Islam and publishing.

Muslim Women's Helpline

London
Tel: Helpline: 081-908-6715
Tel: 081-904-8193 Monday to Friday, 10-4
Tel: Administration: 081-908-3205 (Admin 10-4)
An independent organisation established by Muslim women to provide a caring helpline service to Muslim females who seek emotional support, a listening service, practical information, and advice on where to find help on a range of issues. Refers callers needing professional advice to Muslim specialists (eg legal advisers, doctors, welfare workers, psychologists). The service is confidential and non-judgemental. The Helpline also trains Muslim women in communication and counselling skills and offers face to face counselling when sought. In addition, it liaises with other Muslim and non-Muslim organisations in order to render and receive from them services which will benefit muslim women.

Naqshbandi Order

175 Warren Road
Washwood Hearh
Birmingham B8 2YD
Tel: 021-328-3478 (home)

National Association of Muslim Youth (UK)

Markfield Conference Centre
Ratby Lane
Markfield
Leicester LE6 ORN
Tel: 0530 244950
Fax: 0530-244946
Contact: Mohammed Dhalech
Office: Development Officer

A national youth organisation which aims to help young people through their leisure time activities to develop their physical, mental and spiritual capacities that they may grow to their full maturity. It also aims to develop a positive approach to youth work with young Muslims and to allow a networking facility to Muslim youth workers and groups.

National Muslim Education Council of UK

109 Campden Hill Road
Notting Hill Gate
London W8
Tel: 071-221-6608
Contact: Dr S A Pasha
Office: Secretary
An organ of the Union of Muslim Organisations which represents the educational interests of Muslim communities in the UK. It negotiates with the Department for Education to secure an Islamic curriculum in state schools and for the establishment of voluntary aided Muslim schools. Future projects include the setting up of an international Islamic University in the UK. The council produces publications and runs national conferences.

Popda Muslim Welfare Association

197 Walsall Road
Darlaston
West Midlands
Tel: 021-526-5830
Contact: Ismail Adam Mohammed
Office: Secretary
Membership group and representative organisation. The association is made up of Muslims from Sarikhurad, in Gujarat, India and aims to provide moral and financial support for the eradication of illiteracy, poverty and sickness in the Sarikhurad area of Gujarat, India. The association is now beginning to look with the same view towards its own membership within the UK.

Raza Academy

138 Nothgate Road
Edgeley
Stockport
Cheshire SK3 9NL
Tel: 061-477-1595 (home)
Contact: Mr M I Kashmiri
Office: Chairperson
The Academy is an organisation publishing literature on all Islamic topics. Its monthly journal "The Islamic Times" has been published for the past six and a half years. Its main aim is to publish and to educate young

Sunni Muslims on Islam and give a picture of events and activities around the world. It also organises conferences.

Shariat Council and Darul IFTA and Europe
98 Fernham Road
Rotherham S61 1AW
Tel: 0709-563677
Contact: Mufti Mohammed Aslam
Guidance group on religious matters and clarification of Islamic law. The organisation assists with any problems relating to religious queries or questions recognised nationally (especially Muslim family law).

S I Education Society
133 Rowan Road
London SW16 5HU
Tel: 081-679-7778
Fax: 081-679-6363
Contact: Moulana S S S Rizvi
Office: Patron
Educational organisation. An organisation devoted to multi-media education about the Islamic faith to all, especially youth. It produces a monthly magazine "The Minister" and an audio monthly magazine "The Voice". It runs a telephone system of teaching Islam (081-679-2188). It also runs Islamic camps, seminars, library, correspondance courses and religious classes. A video magazine "The Vision" is in production and the society hopes to begin religious broadcasts on local radio.

Somali Islamic Circle Organisation
16 Settles Street
London E1
Tel: 071-377-5003 (home)

South Indian Muslim Association (UK)
123 Burgess Road
East Ham
London E6 2BL
Tel: 071-471-9394 (home)
Contact: Mr A K Salim

Sri Lanka Islamic UK Association
62 Rose Glen
Colindale
Kingsbury
London NW9 LJS
Tel: 081-952-2105 (home)
Fax: 081-962-2105
Contact: A Azahim Mohamed
Office: General Secretary
Membership group. The organisation was formed in

1973 with the aim of getting Sri Lankan Muslims together. Today its membership covers over five hundred families. It is the only representative body for Sri Lankan Muslims in the UK. The association holds weekly classes for children and adults on Qur'an/Islamic Studies and monthly lectures on various subjects. Youth activities are also arranged.

Sufi Order of the West
London Sufi Centre for Holistic Studies
58 St Stephens Gardens
London W2
Tel: 071-221-3215

Ta Ha Publishers Ltd
1 Wynne Road
London SW9 0BB
Tel: 071-737-7266
Fax: 071-737-7267
A publishing house for books on Islam and related topics. It also sells books published by other companies. A mail order service is available.

UK Action Committee on Islamic Affairs
146 Park Road
London NW8 7RG
Tel: 081-794-2780
Contact: Mr Iqbal Sacranie
Office: Convenor
The committee has been formed to represent the views of the Muslim community, particularly on issues relating to the community and the law in Britain.

UK Islamic Education WAQF (UKIEW)
2 Digswell Street
London N7 8JX
Tel: 071-607-8839
Fax: 071-700-0320
Contact: Administrative Secretary
Aims to advance Islamic education and, in particular, the education of Muslims in the UK and Eire by raising and disbursing funds.

UK Islamic Mission
202 North Gower Street
London NW1 2LY
Tel: 071-387-2157
Fax: 071-383-0867
Contact: S T H Shah
Office: President
A charitable organisation which aims to: help the Muslim community in the UK to project its cultural identity; promote and encourage mutual appreciation

and friendly relations between Muslims and non-Muslims; and strengthen the bonds of brotherhood among the Muslim community.

UK Islamic Mission Central Office
148 Liverpool Road
London N1

Union of Moslem Families (UK)
55 Balfour Road
London N5 2HD
Tel: 071-226-0934
Contact: Faizullah Khan

Union of Muslim Organisations of UK and Eire (UMO)
109 Camden Hill Road
London W8 7TL
Tel: 071-221-6608
Contact: Dr Sayid Aziz Pasha
Office: General Secretary
Represents one hundred and eighty-three Muslim organisations and two million Muslims living in the UK and Eire. It campaigns for the rights of the Muslim community by organising national conferences, meeting MPs and organising fringe meetings at Party Conferences of the three major political parties in the UK. It negotiates on behalf of the Muslim community with various Governmental Departments and Local Authorities. The organisation's main concerns are education, youth, mosques and family law.

World Ahl Ul-Bayt (AS) Islamic League (UK)
57 Church Drive
North Harrow
Middlesex HA2 7NR
Tel: 081-954-9881
Tel: 081-868-9972 (home)
Contact: Mr Mohsin Jaffer
Office: Inter-Faith representative
Open to Shi'a personalities, well-known for their interest and endeavour in general Islamic affairs, and to Shi'a organisations throughout the world. The membership fee is £50 pa for individuals and £100pa for organisations. It aims to: co-ordinate the activities of various Shi'a organisations throughout the world; serve the Shi'a community in religious, economic, social and other matters; create better understanding between Shi'a and other Muslims and non-Muslim communities. It works by holding conferences, seminars and meetings; by publications in different languages and by participating with other organisations in matters of common interest. Affiliated to The Inter Faith Network for the UK.

World Council of Muslim Youth
47 Wellington Road
Edgbaston
Birmingham B15 2EP

World Federation of Khoja Shia Ithna Asheri Muslim Communities
P O Box 60
Wood Lane
Stanmore
Middlesex HA7 4LQ
Tel: 081-954-9881
Fax: 081-954-9034
Contact: Mr Mohsin Jaffer
A federation of groups of East African (mainly) Shi'a Ithna Asheries of Indian origin concerned with education (religious and secular) and welfare covering all groups.

World Islamic Mission (UK)
12 Dorchester Avenue
Prestwich
Manchester M25 8LH
Tel: 061-733-5257
Contact: Manlana Quamaruzzamon Azani
Office: Secretary general
Membership is open to Muslims, with about twenty-one thousand and eighty-seven current members. It aims to: make efforts for the propagation of Islamic teachings among Muslims and others and to establish good relationships with other Faith communities in order to restore social harmony and understanding. It works by: publishing books on Islam; holding public meetings; establishing schools, libraries and mosques and by publishing magazines. Affiliated to The Inter Faith Network for the United Kingdom.

Young Muslim Organisation UK - Central Office
54 Fieldgate Street
London E1 1ES
Tel: 071-247-7918
Contact: Mussadiq Ahmad
Office: Central President
National voluntary youth group. It seeks to train youth in developing to their full potential and to grow up as good citizens. It holds educational, social, cultural and sports programmes, regular study circles, seminars, training camps, outings and Summer youth camps.

Youth Adventure and Training
16 Stratton Road
Gloucester GL1 4HB

Tel: 0452-504147
Contact: Mohammed Dhaleih
Office: Co-ordinator
The organisation aims to: offer Muslim young people opportunities which are educative, designed to promote equality of opportunity, participative, enpowering and fun; enable young people, through these opportunities, to understand and act upon the personal, political, social, spiritual and economic issues which affect their lives, the lives of others and the communities of which they are a part.

Zahra Trust UK

PO Box 1021
London W2 4JQ
Contact: Mrs Aliya Haeri
Educational trust and publishing house. The Trust is dedicated to the dissemination of the original teachings of Islam and Sufism through books and taped discourse, aimed primarily at the contemporary audience, both Muslim and non-Muslim alike. It publishes books on the teachings of Islam, Sufis and the Qur'an.

MUSLIM MOSQUES AND LOCAL ORGANISATIONS

SCOTLAND

WALES

NORTHERN IRELAND

NORTH EAST ENGLAND

YORKSHIRE AND HUMBERSIDE

NORTH WEST ENGLAND

ENGLISH EAST MIDLANDS

ENGLISH WEST MIDLANDS

EAST ANGLIA

SOUTH EAST ENGLAND (NORTH)

LONDON (E)

LONDON(N)

LONDON (NW)

LONDON (SE)

LONDON (SW)

LONDON (W)

LONDON (WC)

SOUTH EAST ENGLAND (SOUTH)

SOUTH WEST ENGLAND

A variety of forms of Muslim local organisation are listed in this directory. These include mosques, centres, welfare bodies and student societies.

In some cases there are separate entries at the same address where a welfare association owns a mosque but receives a separate entry because its objectives and activities are wider than the mosque activities alone, or where a number of organisations with a particular sectional remit such as youth or women's work are based at the same address and are sometimes different parts of the same organisation.

SCOTLAND

Mosque and Islamic Association of Aberdeen
164 Spital
Aberdeen AB2 3JD
Tel: 0224–493764
Contact: Dr Ruhul Amin
Office: Chairman

Mosque
Friars-Vannell
near Burns Statue
Dumfries
Dumfries and Galloway

Islamic Association
18 Park Place
Dundee DD1 4HW
Tel: 0382–69950
Contact: c/o Mr I Jamal
Office: Secretary

Islamic Centre
112-114 Hill Town
Dundee
Tayside
Tel: 0382–28374

Jamia Masjid Tajdare - Madina
96 Victoria Street
Dundee DD1 2NR
Tel: 0382–24817
Contact: Mohamad Sadiq
Office: Secretary

Heriot-Watt University Islamic Society
Heriot-Watt University
Lord Balerno Building
Room 1.7
Riccarton
Edinburgh EH14 4AS
Tel: 031–451-3272
Fax: 031–449-5153
Contact: Hamayun Ahmad
Office: Vice President

Ismaili Community
2 Marchmont Street
Edinburgh
Lothian
Tel: 031–229-3344
Contact: Mr Nagib Jiwa

Livingston Mosque and Community Centre
1 Craig's Hill
East Road
Livingston
Edinburgh EH5 5DD
Tel: 0506–31936
Office: Makmood Ali

Mosque
8 Temple Park Crescent
Edinburgh EH11
Tel: 031–229-3844
Contact: Hafiz Abdul Hamid

Mosque and Islamic Centre
50 Potter Row
Edinburgh EH8 9BT
Tel: 031–667-0140
Contact: Abdul Rahman Al Matrodi

Mosque and Islamic Community Centre
12 Roxburgh Street
Edinburgh EH8 9TA
Tel: 031–556-1902
Contact: Hafiz Abdul Karim
Office: Imam
Place of worship. Activities include worship and a school for children aged six to sixteen years old to teach them Urdu and Arabic and Islamic studies.

Mosque Anwar-e-Madina and Community Centre
Zetland Hall
11 Pilrig Street
Edinburgh EH6
Tel: 031–554-9904
Contact: Mr Abdul Ghafoor
Office: Imam
Place of worship. A mosque run by the Executive Council of the Pakistan Association of Edinburgh and East of Scotland. The association is committed to inter-faith and understanding amongst people of different faiths in the area. It takes an active part in the activities of the local inter-faith association and in One World Week in Edinburgh. It provides facilities for worship and education (teaching of the Holy Qur'an and Urdu) and it also runs sports clubs for adults as well as youth.

Pakistan Association
11 Pilrig Street
Edinburgh EH6
Tel: 031–441-3443
Contact: Mr Jusuf Inayat

UK Islamic Mission
4 Gillespie Place
Edinburgh EH10

World Without Hunger Organisation
365 Lanark Road
Edinburgh EH13 0LY
Tel: 031–441-3443
Contact: Mr M Yousaf Inait OBE JP
Aims to create, establish and maintain an organisation to eradicate poverty, help victims of un-natural disasters all over the world, irrespective of race, colour, creed or religion; and to establish or maintain educational institutions and educational projects all over the world irrespective of race, colour, creed or religion. It is the first Asian charity established in Scotland.

Falkirk Islamic Centre
8 Burnhad Lane
Falkirk FK11
Tel: 0324–611018
Contact: Mr A Farooqi

Fife Islamic Centre
79 Wellesley Road
Methil
Fife KY8 3AD
Tel: 0333–421261
Tel: 0592–651920 (home)
Contact: Saeed Ahmed
Office: Secretary
Children are taught the Qur'an and Urdu daily and meet twice a week to play sport; there is an interpretation service from the centre and immigration advice is offered as appropriate; sponsorship and other official forms are available; and social events are organised (eg celebration of Pakistan Independence Day).

Al-Huda Islamic Centre
65 Albert Road
Glasgow G42
Tel: 041–423-7003
Contact: Maulana Naqui
Office: Imam
An Ithna Asheria mosque.

Asna Ashariyya Shia Mosque
19 Ashley Street
Glasgow G3
Tel: 041–332-9639
An Ithna Asheria mosque.

Dawat-ul-Islam Mosque

31 Oakfield Avenue
Glasgow G12 8LL
Tel: 041-334-5559

Glasgow Islamic Centre and Central Mosque

1 Mosque Avenue
Glasgow G5 9TX
Tel: 041-429-3132
Fax: 041-429-7171
Contact: President

A place of worship and community centre which aims to: provide religious, educational and cultural services to the Muslim community for their moral, social and cultural development; education to lead life in the British multi-cultural society as a true Muslim and as an ideal citizen; social welfare and advisory services to the Muslim community and support for the authorities at all levels in implementing equal opportunities policy for ethnic minorities in all socio-cultural sectors. Activities include children's education in religion, languages, and cultural education, youth development, adult education, guidance and resource services and cultural activities.

Injaman-Ehyae-Islam

275 Tantallon Road
Shawlands
Glasgow G41 3JW
Contact: Mr N S Naqshbandi

Kizra Central Mosque

138 Butler Biggins Road
Glasgow G42
Tel: 041-422-1154
Contact: Haji M Sarwar
Office: General secrtetary

Madrasa al-Arabia al-Islamia and Mosque

490 Paisley Road West
Glasgow G51
Tel: 041-427-2152
Contact: Dr M Sarwar
Office: President

Madrasa Taleem-ul-Islam

161 Nithsdale Road
Glasgow G41
Tel: 041-424-0787
Contact: Mr Mohammed Iqbal

Masjid-e-Noor

79 Forth Street
Glasgow G41 2TA
Tel: 041-429-3383

Masjid-i-Khizra

69 Albert Road
Glasgow G42
Tel: 041-423-1208
Contact: Mr Ghalam Rasool
Office: President

Masjidul al Furqan

19 Carrington Street
Glasgow G4 9AJ
Tel: 041-332-2811

Mosque

Langside
Govanhill
Glasgow G53

Muslim House

16 Queen Crescent
Glasgow G4 9BL
Tel: 041-332-5223
Contact: Mr Hassain Hemsy
Office: President

Pakistan Muslim Welfare Society

21 Maxwell Drive
Glasgow G41
Contact: Mr L Bhatti

Strathclyde University Muslim Students Society

c/o Students Union
90 John Street
Glasgow G1 1XW
Tel: 041-552-846 (home)
Contact: Abdul Rahim Leyman
Office: Secretary

Student representative society. The society's main objectives are to represent Muslim students in the University and cater for their particular needs as Muslims. The society has around one hundred members. There is a prayer room within the chaplaincy where daily prayers are held. Congregational prayers are held once a week on a Friday. Attempts are made to introduce Islam to the local communities through seminars and a discussion group is held for exploring topics related to the religion. The society also organises social events including outings and sports.

United Muslim Organisation, Strathclyde
26 Bank Street
Glasgow G12 8ND
Tel: 041-339-5513
Contact: Dr M S Kauser

Carfin Mosque
Chapelknowe Road
Carfin
Motherwell
Strathclyde

Jamia Islamia and Islamic Teaching Centre
Carfin
Motherwell ML1 4XE
Tel: 0698-62008
Tel: 0698-833493
Fax: 0698-834806 (home)
Contact: Ghulam Saqlain Siddiquie
Office: General Secretary
Place of worship and teaching centre. There is a mosque, conference room and kitchen. The organisation covers Lanarkshire, Monkland and East Kilbride. As well as facilities for worship, there is a teaching centre for Urdu, Arabic and English, a youth group, a women's organisation and welfare services.

Stirling Islamic Centre
39 Bannockburn Road
St Ninian
Stirling FK7 0BU
Tel: 0786-74324

Stirling University Islamic Society
c/o Stirling University Students Association
Robbins Building
Stirling University
Stirling FK9 4LA

WALES

University College of Wales Students Islamic Society
University College of Wales
Aberystwyth
Dyfed SY23 2AX

Bangor Islamic Centre
61 High Street
Bangor

Islamic Centre
Weston Hill
Barry

Bangladesh Muslim Association
13 Miskin Street
Cathays
Cardiff CF2 4AQ

Centon Mosque and Madresa
Tamilmul Quran
63 Severn Road
off Cowbridge Road
Centon
Cardiff
South Glamorgan
Tel: 0222-397640
Contact: G Mustaffa
Office: Imam

Darul Islah Waddawah
13 Deburgh Street
Cardiff CF1 8LB
Contact: Banuri Manzil

Islami Darasgah
68 Connaught Road
off Albany Road
Roath
Cardiff CF2 3PX
Tel: 0222-488454
Contact: H N K Khattak
Office: Secretary
Place of worship. Activities include worship and teaching Islam to children.

Islamic Centre (South Wales)
Alice Street
Butetown
Cardiff
South Glamorgan
Tel: 0222-460243
Contact: Sheikh Said Hassan Ismail
Office: Secretary
Place of worship. A purpose-built mosque with Minaret. There is a prayer room for women and class rooms for children. There are also ablution facilities, a kitchen for cooking and a small library. Lectures on Islam are given to school pupils and students, Eid celebrations are held, marriages are solemnised and education is provided for Muslim children.

Madina Mosque
163–167 Woodville Road
Cathays
Cardiff
South Glamorgan

Madrassa Taleemul Qur'an
60 Beecham Street
Riverside
Cardiff
South Glamorgan

Masjid-e-Abu Hurairah
2 Glyn Rhondda Street
opposite Cardiff University
Roath
Cardiff
South Glamorgan

Mosque
17 Peel Street
Cardiff
South Glamorgan

Mosque
60 Beauchamp Street
Riverside
Cardiff
South Glamorgan

Mosque (Islamic Fhikka Propieshtan)
37 Plantagenet Street
off Tudor Road
Riverside
Cardiff CF1 8RF
Contact: Muktar Ali
Office: Secretary
Tel: 0222-221309

Muslim Education and Family Welfare Society
Pennsylvania
249 Llanedeyrn
Cardiff CF1 7LW
Tel: 0222-731848
Contact: M A Fardoqui
Office: Chair

New Mosque
Penarth Road
Grange Town
Cardiff
South Glamorgan

Shah Jalal Mosque
3 Crews Road
Roath
Cardiff
South Glamorgan

UK Islamic Mission
21 Glenroy Street
Roath
Cardiff
South Glamorgan

Mosque
2 Albert Street
Haverfordwest
Dyfed
Tel: 0437-765791 (home)
Contact: Mr Islamadean
Office: Treasurer
Place of worship. The mosque was established in 1989 in an upstairs room of a house which has been converted for worship. There are washing facilities on the next floor. There is a spice shop next door where halal meats are sold and the key to the mosque is kept.

Alexandra Road Mosque
20 Alexandra Road
Newport
Gwent
Tel: 0633-257781
Contact: Mr M Mahmoud

Al-Noor Mosque
23a Harrow Road
Newport NP9
Tel: 0633-244395 (home)
Contact: Mr A R Mujahid

Al-Rahman Mosque
26 Ruperra Street
Newport
Gwent
Tel: 0633-255150
Contact: Mrs F Nasser

Anjumin Raza-e-Mustafa
15 Methuen Road
Newport NP9 0BN
Tel: 0633-244395
Tel: 0633-277166
Contact: Mr A R Mujahid
Teaches children Islamic studies.

Gwent Bangladeshi Association
12 Cedar Road
Mainsee
Newport NP9 0BA
Tel: 0633-212254
Tel: 0633-263847 (home)
Contact: Mr Tahir Ullah
Religious Centre.

Hussaini Mission
Commercial Street
Newport
Gwent

Islamic Society for Gwent
63 Stow Hill
Newport
Gwent
Tel: 0633-259005
Contact: Mr Ramzan
Office: Secretary

Jamia Mosque
183-186 Commercial Road
Newport NP9 2PF
Tel: 0633-215420
Tel: 0633-244395 (home)
Contact: Mr A R Mujahid

Mosque
c/o 70/72 Port Tennant Road
PO Box 18
Swansea SA1 8IF

Mosque & Islamic Community Centre
14 St. Helens Road
Swansea SA1 4AW
Tel: 0792-54532
Contact: Mr M Khan
Office: Imam

NORTHERN IRELAND

Islamic Centre Belfast
38 Wellington Park
Belfast BT9 6DN
Tel: 0232-664-465
Contact: Dr Mamoun
Office: President
Place of worship. A charitable organisation established
to promote the benefit of the Muslim community in
Northern Ireland and the Muslim community at large,
by promoting religion, advancing education, relieving

poverty and distress and by providing facilities for
protection of health and recreation with the aim of
improving the conditions of life of the Muslim
community. The centre has a mosque and small library
and provides facilities for daily worship, study
meetings on a weekly basis, seminars and Islamic
education for children. People of other faiths are
welcome.

NORTH EAST ENGLAND

Islamic Society of Darlington
41 Westmoreland Street
Darlington DL3 0NX
Tel: 0325-484880
Contact: Mohamed Sadiq
Office: Secretary
Mosque and community centre. Established about
seven years ago, it is the only Muslim organisation in
County Durham. It has a full time Imam and steadily
increasing membership. Prayers are held five times a
day. Children are taught Islamic studies and mother
tongue languages. There are facilities for holding
Islamic weddings.

Durham University Islamic Society
12 Renny Street
Gilesgate
Durham

Mosque
12 Rining Street
Kepier Court
Durham
Tyne and Wear

Mosque
4 Moyorswall Close
Durham
Tyne-and-Wear
Tel: 0386-7972

Muslim Welfare Association Hartlepool
94 Milton Road
Hartlepool TS26 8DS
Contact: Mr Karem Elahi

Abu-Bakr Mosque
9 Park Road South
Middlesbrough
Cleveland

Islamic Cultural Association South Bank

3 South Terrace
South Bank
Middlesbrough
Cleveland
Contact: Mr M Manzoor

Madrassa-Zia-ul-Qur'an

Bow Street
Middlesbrough
Cleveland
Tel: 0642-230408
Contact: Mr M A Khan
Office: Secretary

Masjide-e Jamia Al Madina

133a Waterloo Road
Middlesbrough TS1 3JB
Tel: 0642-245855
Tel: 0642-818617 (home)
Contact: M A Durrani
Office: General secretary
Place of worship. The building is a mosque, with its ground floor used as a Muslim Community Centre which hosts all Muslim community services, including Muslim women's groups learning sewing, English language classes, Quranic lessons and Islamic studies for under eighteens. This also includes the social and political activities of the Muslim community. Activities include looking after the interests of the Muslim community of Middlesbrough including the interests and needs of Muslim women. It has a special female Muslim social worker who is bi-lingual and can communicate with the local community.

Heaton Mosque

1 Rothbury Terrace
Heaton
Newcastle-upon-Tyne NE6 5XH
Tel: 091-265-4083
Contact: Secretary

Islamic Society Mosque

Newcastle University
Kings Walk
Off St Thomas Street
Newcastle-upon-Tyne NE1 7RU
Tel: 091-232-6889
Contact: Omar Yaqub
Office: President
A mosque and membership group which not only provides a place of worship but also a cultural centre with a library where the society, through limited resources, attempts to keep up to date books on different cultural aspects of Islam. There are social and cultural activities like trips, social gatherings, lectures, seminars etc.

Muslim Welfare House

Newcastle Branch
6 North Terrace
Spital Tongues
Newcastle-upon-Tyne NE2 4AD
Tel: 091-232-3055
Contact: Mahmoud
Office: Secretary
Charitable organisation. A cultural and educational independent charity devoted to the presentation of Islam and the service of Muslims in the educational and social fields and the communication media.

Muslim Womens Association of Newcastle

20 Cavendish Place
Newcastle-upon-Tyne
Tyne and Wear
Contact: Mrs Christine Ahmed

Newcastle Central Mosque

Malvern Street
off Elswick Road
Newcastle-upon-Tyne N4
Tel: 091-226-0562

Pakistan Muslim Association

Malvern Street
Newcastle-upon-Tyne NE4 6SU
Tel: 091-226-0562
Contact: Mr Z J Khan
Office: Chairperson
Place of worship. It provides facilities for religious celebrations and general welfare work. It is also used for social and religious gatherings such as weddings and annual celebrations.

UWAIS Foundation

126 Ladykirk Road
Fenham
Newcastle-Upon-Tyne NE4
Tel: 091-232-7639
Contact: Malik Chaudhry
A registered Muslim charity.

Alazhar Mosque

Laygate Lane
South Shields
Tyne and Wear
Tel: 091-454-0738

South Tyneside Bangladesh Muslim Cultural Association and Mosque

3-5 Baring Street
Off Ocean Road
South Shields
Tyne and Wear
Tel: 091-4542501 (home)
Contact: Syed F Hussain
Office: Chaiperson
Place of worship and community association. A mosque where all Muslims are welcome. Membership of the cultural association is limited to Bangladeshi Muslims who are residents of South Tyneside. Activities include worship, daily Qur'an and mother tongue classes.

Jamiat e Judullah

39 Hartington Road
Stockton-on-Tees
Cleveland TS18 1HD
Tel: 0642-679943
Contact: Mr M Hussain
Office: Secretary
Place of worship. The place is used daily by Muslims as a mosque for prayers. Activities include worship and daily classes in reading the Qur'an for children and others who wish to learn. Children are taught Urdu and general knowledge about Islam.

Masjid-e-Farooq-e-Azam

29 Hartington Road
Stockton-on-Tess
Cleveland TS18 1HD
Tel: 0642-679943
Tel: 0642-675020 (home)
Contact: M Hussain
Office: Secretary
Place of worship. A Muslim organisation covering local areas of Thornaby, Billingham, Yarm, and Stockton. The main activities are holding worship prayers and teaching children the Qur'an and mother tongue.

Stockton Mosque

10 Shaftsbury Street
Stockton-on-Tees
Cleveland
Contact: Mr M Iqbal

Thornaby Muslim Association

69 Oxford Road
Thornaby
Stockton-on-Tees
Cleveland
Contact: Mr H Farooq

Sunderland Mosque

75 Chester Road
Sunderland
Tyne and Wear
Tel: 091-565-8708
Contact: Mr Syed Jamil Miah

YORKSHIRE & HUMBERSIDE

Anjuman-Zinatul Islam

78 Taylor Street
Batley WF17 5BA
Tel: 0924-472216

Indian Muslim Welfare Society

Community Centre
Taylor Street
Batley WF17 5BA
Tel: 0924-420890
Fax: 0924-420890
Contact: Mr A Y Lunat
Office: President

Islamic Cultural Centre

Henry Street
Batley Carr
Batley
West Yorkshire

Islamic Jamat Khana

Bradford Road
Batley
West Yorkshire

Jama Masjid Mosque

1 Whitaker Street
Batley
West Yorkshire
Tel: 0924-472215

Madina Masjid

Purlwell Lane
Batley WF17 7NQ
Tel: 0924-472378
Tel: 0924-478330 (home)
Fax: 0924-420786
Contact: Dr Abdurehaman J Rajpura
Office: Chairman

Place of worship, membership group and representative body. Engages in social and religious activities. There are also GCSE classes in Islamic Studies.

Madrassa Noor ul Islam
Snowden Street
Batley WF17 7RS
Contact: c/o Mr A Bulbullia

Madresa Noor-ul-Islam and Mosque
39 Norfolk Street
Batley WF17 7SA

Madresa Noor-ul-Islam
18 Woodsome Estate
Batley WF17 7EB
Contact: Mr A S Patel

Mosque
206 Bradford Road
Batley Carr
Batley
West Yorkshire

Mosque
6 Oxford Street
Batley
West Yorkshire

Mosque
2-4 West Street
Batley
West Yorkshire

Mosque
90 Dark Lane
Batley
West Yorkshire

Mosque
79 Warwick Road
Batley
West Yorkshire

Mosque and Muslim Welfare Society
Hope Street
Batley
West Yorkshire

Abu Bakar Mosque
479 Leeds Road
Bradford BD3 9LD
Tel: 0274-668343

Al-Falah Islamic Youth Mission
Al-Falah Building
Richmond Road
Bradford BD7 1DR
Tel: 0274-724998
Tel: 0274-742736
Contact: Mohammed Iqbal
Office: Manager

Anjuman-e-Haideria
47/48 Southfield Square
Bradford BD8 7SL
Tel: 0274-391667
Contact: Syed Shamsher Kazmi
Office: General Secretary
Place of worship and education. A Shi'a Muslim organisation which provides facilities for religious gatherings including funerals and weddings. Children's education and worship are held for all Muslims but mainly Shi'a Muslims. The organisation aims to take any measure it considers neccessary concerning the well-being of the Shi'a sect and the co-existence of Islam. Day to day religious gatherings and prayers are held five times a day, lessons are provided for children in Arabic, Urdu and Islamic Studies according to the Shi'a Muslim faith.

Azad Kashmir Muslim Association
11 Farcliffe Place
Bradford BD8 8QD
Tel: 0274-498677 (home)
Contact: Mohammed Amin Qureshi
Office: General Secretary
The organisation's main concern is with domestic problems between families and others, mostly concerning Muslim family welfare. It was established twenty-five years ago and serves the Muslim community and other minority communities in the area including Sikhs and West Indians as well as the host community. It is well known for its charity work and works for deserving people and struggles for equality and justice for all.

Bradford Council of Mosques
6 Claremont
Bradford BD7 1BG
Tel: 0274-732479
Contact: Sher Azam
Office: President

Represents seventy-five thousand Muslims in the Bradford area. It is concerned with the promotion and maintenance of mosques and Islamic identity and good relationships with other faiths.

Bradford Khalifa Muslim Society
32 Bertram Road
Bradford BD8 7LN
Contact: Abdul Hamid Ismail
Office: Chairperson
Membership group. The organisation aims to work towards betterment and understanding between members and allieviate illiteracy, poverty and other disadvantages suffered by the ethnic minority community. It also aims to promote religious activities and the spread of Islam. It provides supplementary education, youth activities, training facilities for women and provides vocational training for the unemployed.

Bradford Muslim Sunnatwal Society
8 Fairfield Road
Toller Lane
Bradford BD8 8QQ

Dawatul Islam
14 Nesfield Street
Bradford BD3 0AN

Girlington Muslim Welfare Association
182a Durham Road
Bradford BD8
Tel: 0274-544358
Tel: 0274-542382

Hanifa Mosque
Carlisle Road
Bradford BD8

Hussainia Islamic Mission
All Saints Road
Bradford BD7 3AY

Islamic Centre Darul Islam Masjid and Madressa
10 Hanover Square
Bradford BD1 3BY

Islamic Cultural Centre
9 Ashgrove
Great Horton Road
Bradford
West Yorkshire

Islamic Educational Institute
9 Ambler Street
off Carlisle Road
Bradford BD8
Tel: 0274-487549

Islamic Madressah
45 Woodview
Bradford BD8 7AJ

Islamic Missionary College and Mosque
28 Shearbridge Road
Bradford BD7 1NX
Tel: 0274-729087
Tel: 0274-823044
Contact: L Hussain
Office: Trustee

Jamia Islamic Mosque
Cross Lane
Great Horton Road
Bradford
West Yorkshire

Jamia Masjid and Muslim Association of Bradford
30 Howard Street
Bradford BD5 0BP
Tel: 0274-724819
Contact: President Afsar Khan

Jamia Masjid Hanafia & Muslim Community Centre
12 Carlisle Road
Bradford
West Yorkshire
Tel: 0274-492539

Jamiyat Tabligh-ul-Islam
13 Jesmond Avenue
Bradford BD9 5DP
Tel: 0274-729087
Tel: 0274-823044 (home)
Contact: Mr L Hussain
Office: Trustee

Jamiyat Tabligh-ul-Islam
87-89 Ryan Street
Bradford BD5 7AP
Tel: 0274-729087
Tel: 0274-823044 (home)
Contact: Mr L Hussain
Office: Trustee

Jamiyat Tabligh-ul-Islam

St Lukes Church Hall
Victor Street
Bradford B9
Tel: 0274–729087
Tel: 0274–823044 (home)
Contact: Mr L Hussain
Office: Trustee

Jamiyat Tabligh-ul-Islam

564a Thornton Road
Bradford BD8 9NF
Tel: 0274–729087
Tel: 0274–823044 (home)
Contact: Mr L Hussain
Office: Trustee

Jamiyat Tabligh-ul-Islam

Roxy Buildings
Barkerend Road
Bradford BD3 9AP
Tel: 0274–729087
Tel: 0274–823044 (home)
Contact: Mr L Hussain
Office: Trustee

Jamiyat Tabligh-ul-Islam

2 Browning Street
Bradford BD3 9DX
Tel: 0274–729087
Tel: 0274–823044 (home)
Contact: Mr L Hussain
Office: Trustee

Jamiyat Tabligh-ul-Islam

54 Airville Road
Bradford
Tel: 0274–729087
Tel: 0274–823044 (home)
Contact: Mr L Hussain
Office: Trustee

Jamiyat Tabligh-ul-Islam

Hilton Road
Bradford
Tel: 0274–729087
Tel: 0274–823044 (home)
Contact: Mr L Hussain
Office: Trustee

Jamiyat Tabligh-ul-Islam

Toller Lane
Bradford 8
Tel: 0274–729087

Tel: 0274–823044 (home)
Contact: Mr L Hussain
Office: Trustee

Jamiyat Tabligh-ul-Islam (Central)

68–69 Southfield Square
Bradford BD8 7SN
Tel: 0274–729087
Tel: 0274–823044 (home)
Contact: Mr L Hussain
Office: Trustee

Madni Masjid

133 Newton Street
West Bowling
Bradford
West Yorkshire

Madressa Islam Talimuddin Blenheim Mosque

off Church Street
Bradford BD8 7PD
Tel: 0274–542027
Tel: 0274–493732 (home)
Contact: Mohamed Cassam Bham
Office: Secretary
Place of worship. A place where local people can get together and pray, teach, learn and solve community problems and especially deal with the unemployed.

Mosque

Steadiman Terrace
off Leeds Road
Bradford
West Yorkshire

Mosque

68 Stanacre Place
Bradford BD3
Tel: 0274–638348

Mosque and Bradford Muslim Welfare Society

62 St Margarets Road
Bradford BD7 3AE
Tel: 0274–575919
Contact: A H Pandor
Office: Secretary

Mosque and Tawakkulia Islamic Society

48 Cornwall Road
Bradford BD1 7JN
Tel: 0274–734563

421

Mosque (Jamiyat-ahl-Hadith)
5 Camden Terrace
Bradford BD8 7HX
Tel: 0274–728993

Mosque / Madresa Islamiya Talimud Din
Blenham Road
off Church Street
Bradford B8
Tel: 0274–542027

Jamiyat Tabligh ul-Islam
1-3 Burnett Place
Marsh Field
Bradford BD5 9LX
Tel: 0274–729087
Tel: 0274–823044 (home)
Contact: Mr L Hussain
Office: Trustee

Mosque (Madressa Terte ul Quran)
42 Woodview Terrace
Bradford BD9 7AJ

Mosque Nusrati Islam Mosque
94/98 Preston Street
Bradford BD7 1JE
Tel: 0274–724488

Shahjalal Islamic Society
149a Littlehorton Lane
Bradford BD5

Sufat-ul-Islam
154 Sunbridge Road
Bradford BD1 2HF

Surti Khalifa Sunatwal Society and Mosque
27 Ventnor Street
off Leeds Road
Bradford BD3 9JZ

UK Islamic Mission
3 Byron Street
Bradford BD3 0AD
Tel: 0274–306299

World Islamic Mission
28 Shearbridge Road
Bradford BD7 1NX
Tel: 0274–729087

Anwar-e-Madina Mosque
Crawshaw Street
Ravensthorpe
Dewsbury
West Yorkshire

Dewsbury Muslim Association
25 South Street
Savile Town
Dewsbury
West Yorkshire
Tel: 0924–454178
Contact: M M Artez

Gulzar-e-Madina Mosque
3 High Street
West Town
Dewsbury
West Yorkshire
Tel: 0924–430338
Contact: Mr M Bashir

Islamic Centre/Juma Masjid
200 Bradford Road
Batley Carr
Dewsbury WF13 2HD
Tel: 0924–461700

Madni Jamia Masjid
North Gate
Dewsbury
West Yorkshire
Tel: 0924–461700

Madressa Muslim Association
Pilgrim Drive
Dewsbury
West Yorkshire
Tel: 0924–430612

Markazi Mosque
2 Chapel Street
Savile Town
Dewsbury WF12 9NF
Tel: 0924–1427
Contact: Mr Yusuf Adam Patel
Place of worship.

Masjid-e-Umar and Madresa-e-Talimuddin
North View
Savile Town
Dewsbury WF12 9LF
Tel: 0924–455064

Contact: Mr M I Dedat
Office: Secretary
Place of worship and religious education. An establishment for practising and teaching of Islamic activities set up for the welfare of the Muslim community and a necessary base for wedding and funeral ceremonies as well as being a focal point for the Muslim population of the community. Its main activities are worship and the teaching and learning of Islam.

Masjid Ghausia

13 Warren Street
Savile Town
Dewsbury
West Yorkshire

Mosque

Jeremy Lane
Heckmondwike
Dewsbury
West Yorkshire
Tel: 0924-402602

Mosque

33 Battye Street
Heckmondwike
Dewsbury
West Yorkshire

Mosque

1 Stoney Bank Street
Scout Hill
Dewsbury WF13 3RJ
Tel: 0924-451085
Contact: Mr Mohammad Razaq
Office: Secretary

Mosque

North Road
Ravensthorpe
Dewsbury
West Yorkshire
Tel: 0924-461089

Mosque and Madresa-e-Taumuddin

10-11 Thornleigh
Savile Town
Dewsbury
West Yorkshire

Muslim Welfare Society, Madrassa and Mosque

24-26 Hope Street
Dewsbury WF13 2BT
Tel: 0924-463524

Zakaria Mosque/Savile Town Muslim Jamaat

2 Chapel Street
Savile Town
Dewsbury WF12 9NQ
Tel: 0924-1427
Contact: Mr Yusuf Adam Patel
A registered charity which caters for the religious and social needs of the community. Activities include Arabic and mother-tongue classes for children up to fifteen years old; arranging major religious ceremonies and festivals; advisory counselling on all socio-religious matters; wedding ceremonies; activities for youngsters; Muslim burials; participation in relief work for several relief organisations. The organisation also distributes food to the needy and unemployed from all denominations.

Doncaster Mosque Trust

Bentinck Close
St James Street
Doncaster DN1 3ST
Tel: 0302-368336
Tel: 0302-326350
Contact: Mr M M Mufti
Office: Secretary
Place of worship where any Muslim may come and pray. Youth activities also take place.

Pakistani Cultural Centre and Mosque

8 St Helens Road
Belle Vue
Doncaster DN4 5EH
Tel: 0302-361941
Contact: Mr S H Raza
Office: Secretary

Grimsby Islamic Society

79 Armstrong Street
Grimsby
South Humberside

Anjuman Islah-ul-Muslemeen

18 Rothwell Road
Halifax
West Yorkshire
Tel: 0422-380934

Contact: Dr Rahmat A Chaudhry
Educational establishment. A madrassa providing facilities for teaching Muslim children.

Central Mosque and Islamic Centre
3 Alfred Street
Halifax
West Yorkshire
Contact: Haji Mohammed Rafiq

Elland Mosque Association
26/34 Elizabeth Street
Elland
Halifax HX5 0JH
Tel: 0422-378808
Tel: 0484-515311
Fax: 0484-517985
Contact: F R Tariq
Office: Chairperson
A place of worship established in 1972. It is a coverted house which caters for the religious and cultural requirements of the Muslim community in Elland. Activities include religious and mother-tongue teaching.

Halifax Islamic Society
30 Parkinson Lane
Halifax HX1 3XL

International Islamic Mission and Madni Jamia Masjid
112-124 Gibbet Street
Halifax
West Yorkshire

Islamic Cultural Association
14 Milton Terrace
Halifax
West Yorkshire
Contact: Mr A H Shah

Jamiat Ahl-e-Hadith Mosque
124 Hanson Lane
Halifax
West Yorkshire

Madni Jamia Mosque
Gibbet Street
Halifax
West Yorkshire
Contact: Secretary

Markazi Jamia Masjid
49 Rhodes Street
Halifax
West Yorkshire
Tel: 0422-330041

Mehfil-e-ahl-Sukhan
27 Mayfield Avenue
King Cross
Halifax
West Yorkshire
Tel: 0422-346511
Contact: Mr Haji M Rafique

Mosque
10 Franklin Road
Halifax
West Yorkshire

Mosque and Bangladesh Muslim Association
117 Gibbet Street
Halifax
West Yorkshire
Tel: 0422-55218
Contact: Mr Siddat Ali

Muslim Youth Sports Club
4 Dean Street
Elland
Halifax
West Yorkshire
Contact: Mr Mohammed Aslam

Heckmondwike Mosque and Pakistan Muslim Welfare Society
Community Centre
Jeremy Lane
Heckmondwike
West Yorkshire WF16 9HN
Contact: Mr M B Jee
Office: General Secretary
A place of worship and community centre. The centre is run under the auspices of Ahle-Sunnat-Val-Jammat (Hanfiya) Barelwi grouping within the orthodox Sunni branch of Islam. People from other Muslim groupings are also permitted to become members though. Worship takes place for men and women (separately) and the teachings of Islam are promoted to Muslims and non-Muslims from within British society. Activities include Arabic, Urdu, Islamic prayers and the Qur'an is taught to children.

Anjuman Islamia Razvia

15 Percy Street
Fartown
Huddersfield HD2 2SB
Contact: Mr M Riaz

Anjuman Rai

39 Birkby Lodge Road
Birkby
Huddersfield
West Yorkshire
Contact: Mr Nisar-Ul-Haq

Bangladeshi Muslim Association

13 St Thomas Road
Lockwood
Huddersfield
West Yorkshire

Bilal Mosque

245 Yewhill Road
Lockwood
Huddersfield
West Yorkshire

Birkby/Fartown Jamia Mosque

27 Yew Street
Fartown
Huddersfield
West Yorkshire
Contact: Mr S Mohammed

British Muslim Solidarity in Huddersfield

155 Halifax Old Road
Birkby
Huddersfield
West Yorkshire

Ghosia Mosque

18 St Steven Road
Lockwood
Huddersfield
West Yorkshire

Huddersfield Council of Islamic Affairs

c/o Muslim Community Centre
Clare Hill
Off St Johns Road
Huddersfield HD1 5BS
Tel: 0484-435839
Contact: Mr B Ahmad
Office: Chairperson
A charitable trust and representative body for the Muslim residents of South Kirklees. An umbrella organisation which caters for the social, cultural and religious needs of its members, including the provision of places of worship and community centres, particularly for the younger generation, in order to provide an atmosphere and facilities to strengthen their faith.

Huddersfield Muslim Burial Council

2 Hall Avenue
Thornton Lodge
Huddersfield HD1 3NL
Tel: 0484-516544
Contact: Mr M Tariq
Office: Secretary
A body representing other Muslim groups. The organisation helps make provision regarding the private Muslim cemetry with the local authority and Muslim organisations. They also try to improve facilities for the Muslim communities regarding burial arrangements.

Islamic Cultural Centre

16a Springdale Avenue
Huddersfield
West Yorkshire

Islamic Socialist Movement

155 Halifax Old Road
Birkby
Huddersfield
West Yorkshire
Contact: Secretary

Jamia Masjid

32 Upper George Street
Huddersfield HD1 4AW

Madani Jamia Masjid

21 Bentley Street
Lockwood
Huddersfield
West Yorkshire
Contact: Mr Haji M Sarsar

Madani Jamia Masjid Association

73 Victoria Road
Lockwood
Huddersfield
West Yorkshire
Contact: Mr Abdul Aziz

Madni Masjid
Blond Street
Lockwood
Huddersfield
West Yorskhire
Tel: 0484–22444

Madressa Ghar-e-Hira
10b Thornton Lodge Road
Huddersfield
West Yorkshire

Majlis Ansarullah Huddersfield
72 St Johns Road
Birkby
Huddersfield HD1 5EY
Contact: Mr M M A Mehmood

Masjid-e-Noor
Crosland Road
Thornton Lodge
Huddersfield HD1 3JS

Masjid Omar
32 Blacker Road
Birkby
Huddersfield
West Yorkshire
Tel: 0484–541634

Mosque
Victoria Road
Lockwood
Huddersfield
West Yorkshire

Mosque
129 Old Halifax Road
Birkby
Huddersfield
West Yorkshire
Contact: Mr M Riaz

Mosque
1 Cobcroft Road
Fartown
Huddersfield
West Yorkshire

Mosque Omar
4 Arnold Street
Birkby

Huddersfield
West Yorkshire
Contact: Mr Ali Mushtaq

Muslim Funeral Association
45 Morley Lane
Milnsbridge
Huddersfield
West Yorkshire
Contact: Mr M Asad

Muslim Funeral Society
181 Manchester Road
Thornton Lodge
Huddersfield HD1 3TE
Tel: 0484–548298
Contact: Mr K Uddin
Office: President
Membership group. A self-help group which helps to arrange funerals for Muslims in the locality and to make arrangements for bodies to be sent to Pakistan.

Muslim Welfare Association
1 Lynndale Avenue
Birkby
Huddersfield
West Yorkshire
Contact: Mr Fazal Rahaman

Shah Jalal Mosque
85 Fenton Street
Lockwood
Huddersfield
West Yorkshire

Hull Mosque and Islamic Centre
Berkeley Street
Hull HU3 1PR
Tel: 0482–24833
Contact: Dr Ayyub

Islamic Society
Union Building
Hull University
Cottingham Road
Hull

Mosque
153 Boulevard
Hull HU3 3EJ
Tel: 0482–24833

Bangladesh Islamic Association
20 Clarendon Street
Keighley
West Yorkshire
Contact: Mr Toymus Ali

Jamia Mosque
70 Bradford Street
Keighley
West Yorkshire

Jamia Mosque
75 Emily Street
Keighley BD21 3EG
Tel: 0535-607039

Keighley Muslim Association
79 Devonshire Street
Keighley
West Yorkshire
Tel: 0274-482936
Tel: 0535-664945 (home)
Contact: Mr Zafar Iqbal

Madrasa
10-12 Belgrave Road
Keighley
West Yorkshire
Contact: M Iqbal

Madrassa Alenath
2 East Avenue
Keighley
West Yorkshire
Contact: Faiz Alam

Mosque
37 Victoria Avenue
Keighley BD21 3JL

Pakistan Muslim Association
c/o The Mosque
45 Asa Leigh Road
Keighley
West Yorkshire

Shahjalal Mosque and Bangladesh Islamic Organisation
Temple Row
Keighley BD21 2AH
Tel: 0535-603444
Contact: Mr Mohammed Tahir

Almadina Jamia Mosque
33 Brundell Grove
Leeds LS6 1HR
Tel: 0532-758615

Bangladesh Islamic Society
24 Birchwood Avenue
Leeds LS17 8PL

Bangladesh Islamic Society
27 Ellers Road
Leeds LS8 4JH

Jamia Masjid and Islamic Centre
46-48 Spencer Place
Leeds LS7 4BR
Tel: 0532-621300

Kashmir Muslim Community Centre and Mosque
1 Hardy Street
Leeds LS11 6BJ
Tel: 0532-714873

Khoja Sh'ia Ithna Asheri Mosque and Muslim Community of Metropolitan Leeds
168 Beeston Road
Leeds LS11 8BD
Tel: 0532-659073
Contact: Noorali Bhamamni
Office: Honorary Secretary
Place of worship and community centre. The organisation aims to provide religious education both to the elders and children of the community. These lectures give instruction in all aspects of Islamic philosophy and also on rules and regulations according to the Shi'a school of thought. It also provides social services to the members of the community. It is the organisation's objective to foster better understanding and harmony between the various communities in the United Kingdom. It is managed by a Management Committee which is elected by members.

Leeds Islamic Centre
46-48 Spencer Place
Leeds LS7 4BR
Tel: 0532-621300

Leeds Muslim Council
31-33 Brudenell Grove
Leeds LS6 1HR
Tel: 0532-752535

Leeds University Students' Mosque
Behind Grammar School
5 Bellvue Road
Leeds LS6

Masjid-e-al-Ameen
21 Leopold Street
Leeds LS7 4DA
Tel: 0532-621362

Masjid-e-Bilal and Muslim Community Centre
Harehills Place
Harehills Road
Leeds LS14 3DZ
Tel: 0532-480711
Contact: Ghulam Hussain
Office: Secretary

Masjid-e-Shah Jalal
27 Ellers Road
off Markham Avenue
Leeds LS8 4JH
Tel: 0532-481860

Masjid-e-Umar and Muslim Association
29 Stratford Street
off Dewsbury Road
Leeds LS11 6JG
Tel: 0532-709536

Mosque
45 St Martin's Gardens
Leeds LS7 3LD

Mosque
145 Spencer Place
Leeds LS7 4DU
Tel: 0532-621989
Mosque
29 Stretford Street
Leeds LS11

Mosque and Muslim Welfare Centre
2 Nancroft Terrace
Armley
Leeds LS12 2DQ

Muslim Centre
Conway Road
Leeds
West Yorkshire

Muslim Community and Education Centre
69 Woodsley Road
Leeds LS3 1DU

Muslim Women's Counselling Service
6 Baldovan Place
Leeds LS8

Omar Welfare House
5 St Johns Terrace
Leeds LS3 1DY
Tel: 0532-451306
Fax: 0532-342472
Contact: Dr Kadhem Al-Rawi
Office: Manager
The centre was established in 1981 serving the Muslim community and the students of Leeds University and Leeds Metropolitan University. It is situated close to the educational establishments in the city. It provides various activities including prayers, study circles, Arabic tuition for children and social events.

Pakistan Muslim Association
10 Nursery Lane
Leeds LS17 7HN

Pakistan Muslim Association
137 Gipton Wood Road
Leeds LS8

Jamiah Mosque and Community Centre
114a College Road
Rotherham S60 1JF
Tel: 0709-563631
Contact: Mr K M Shabbir

Jamiat-ahl-e-Hadith
Broom Grove
Rotherham S60 2TE
Tel: 0709 369715
Tel: 0709 360594 (home)
Contact: Mr N Ahmed
Office: Welfare Secretary
Place of worship. The organisation provides Qur'anic teaching, Urdu and Arabic reading and welfare advice as well as being a place of worship.

Jamiat-ahl-e-Hadith (Moorgate Mosque)
Moorgate Street
Rotherham S60 2EY
Tel: 0709-369715
Contact: Mr Hafiz Abdul Ghani

Mosque
46 Milton Road
Eastwood
Rotherham
South Yorkshire

Muslim Community Centre and Mosque
20 Mile Oak Road
Rotherham
South Yorkshire
Contact: Mr M Sardar

Rotherham Jamia Mosque
Chapel Walk
Rotherham
South Yorkshire
Tel: 0709-560038

Rotherham Mosque Trust
12 Davis Street
Rotherham S60 1JX
Contact: Mr Afzal

Bangladeshi Mosque
29 Gilliatt Street
Scunthorpe
South Humberside

Bangladesh United Muslim Society
56 Fox Street
Scunthorpe
South Humberside
Tel: 0724-853694
Contact: Mr A Noor

Jamia Mosque
107 West Street
Scunthorpe DN15 6JD
Tel: 0724-842772

Madrassa Taleem ul Quran Mosque
44 Percival Street
Scunthorpe DN15 6JD
Tel: 0724-852491

Mosque
107 West Street
Scunthorpe
South Humberside
Tel: 0724-842772

Scunthorpe Mosque Committee
56 Buckingham Street
Scunthorpe
South Humberside
Tel: 0724-846231
Contact: Mr M Ali

Anjuman-e-Haideriah
166 Psalter Lane
Sheffield S11
Contact: Mr N Sherazi

Anjuman-e-Haideriah
140 Steade Road
Sheffield

Arabic Mosque
275 Staniforth Road
Sheffield S9
Tel: 0742-446179

Association of Muslim Scholars of Islamic s in Britain (Jamiat -e Ulama of Britain)
54 Sheldon Road
Nether Edge
Sheffield S7 1GW
Tel: 0742-550318 (home)
Contact: Mr M Ismail
Office: Secretary
Contact point for the Association (which is a national organisation) in South Yorkshire and the Midlands.

Bangladesh Allya Mosque and Islamic Centre
16–18 Swarcliffe Road
Sheffield S9 3FA
Contact: Chairperson

British Muslim Association
53 Barncliffe Road
Sheffield S10 4DG
Contact: Mr M Rashid

Council for Islamic Affairs
71 Broad Oaks
Sheffield S9

Council of Mosques and Islamic Organisations in Sheffield
226 Darnell Road
Sheffield S9
Contact: Mr C M Walayat
Office: Secretary

Dar ul Aloom Siddiqia Mosque
24 Burngreave Road
Sheffield S3 9DD
Tel: 0742-701034
Contact: Chairperson

Elahi Mosque and Islamic Cultural Centre
305 Staniforth Road
Darnall
Sheffield
Tel: 0742-431270

Ghousia Mosque
Owler Lane
Sheffield S4
Tel: 0742-387966
Contact: Chairperson

Industry Road Mosque
13 Industry Road
Darnall
Sheffield S9 5SP
Tel: 0742-441500
Contact: Mr M Hayat Khan

Islamic Cultural Centre
36 St Lawrence Road
Sheffield S9
Contact: Mr Munshi
Office: Chairperson

Ittehad Committee
8 Brair Road
Sheffield S4
Contact: Mr S Khan

Jaime Masjid Trust
13 Industry Road
Sheffield S6
Tel: 0742-447686

Jamia Islamia Mosque
42 Earl Marshal Road
Sheffield S4
Tel: 0742-432475

Jamia Masjid Hanifa
372 Sheffield Road
Tinsley
Sheffield S9
Tel: 0742-443824

Jamia Mosque Committee
214 Darnall Road
Darnall
Sheffield S9 5AF
Contact: Mr M Siddique
Office: President

Jamiat Islah-ul-Muslimeem
c/o Makki Mosque
Plantation Road
Sheffield S8 9IJ
Tel: 0742-582348
Contact: Mr M Bostan

Jamiyate Tablige Islam
Bodmin Street
Sheffield S9 3TA
Tel: 0742-445618
Contact: Mr Hafiz M Rafique

Madni Islamic Community Association and Mosque
22 Wincobank Lane
Sheffield S4 8AA
Tel: 0742-442998
Contact: Mr Q M Siddique

Makki Masjid
Plantation Road
off Albert Road
Heely
Sheffield S8 9IJ
Tel: 0742-582348
Contact: Mr Obydur Rahman

Mosque
Shirland Lane
Sheffield
South Yorkshire

Muslim Butchers Association
c/o Raza Brothers
102 Attercliffe Common
Sheffield S9

Muslim Parents Association
244 Staniforth Road
Sheffield S9

Muslim Welfare House Sheffield
10–12 Severn Road
Sheffield S10 2SU
Tel: 0742-671969/666446

Fax: 0742-671969
Contact: Abdul Razak Bougara
Office: Chairperson
A charity organisation which was established a decade
ago. It consists of a praying area capable of catering for
up to two hundred and fifty people. There is also
limited accomodation for single persons. There is a
small library service, consisting of books, video tapes
and cassettes in many languages. There is a kitchen for
large catering and access for disabled people. The
centre facilitates the needs of the Muslim community,
promotes healthy relationships between Muslims and
non-Muslims and advances the education of the
community, especially in Islamic knowledge.

Pakistan Chhachhi Association
29 Firth Park
Firvale
Sheffield S5 6WL
Tel: 0742-444457 (home)
Contact: Mohammad Ilyas
Office: Chairperson
A membership group established in 1980. It aims to
help people whatever their problem is, for example,
to attend hospital, social security offices, police station
and court with people who cannot speak English.
There are members who can speake Urdu, Pushto,
Punjabi, Arabic and Hindi. The organisation also
provides help on the Islamic religion to both Muslims
and non-Muslims. Other activities take place
involving youth and the elderly.

Pakistan Muslim Welfare Association
Darnall Star Works
Darnall
Sheffield S9 5AF
Contact: Mr M Rafique
Office: Chairperson

Quba Culra Mosque
120 Worksop Road
Attercliffe
Sheffield S9
Tel: 0742-440235

Sheffield Islamic Centre and Madina Mosque
24–32 Wolseley Road
Sheffield S8 0ZU
Tel: 0742-585021
Tel: 0742-550391 (home)
Contact: Mr M Nazir
Office: Secretary
The centre provides a place of worship and Islamic
information, for men, women and youth. Activities

include Islamic education and conducting marriages
under Islamic law as well as an elderly day centre
facility for men and women. It holds seminars and
speeches on Islam.

Sheffield, Rotherham and District Council of Muslims
1 Derriman Glen
Silverdale Road
Sheffield S11 9LQ
Tel: 0742-360465
Contact: Dr A K Admani

Sheffield Sufi Association
184 Rutland Road
Sheffield S3
Contact: Mr Samir Gadi

Sheffield Sufi Group
16 Hartland Drive
Beighton
Sheffield
Contact: A Rosowsky

Tinsley Islamic Cultural Centre
372 Sheffield Road
Tinsley
Sheffield S9 1RQ
Contact: Mr M Ramzan

Uamni Masjid
Rothay Road
Sheffield S4
Tel: 0742-441165

UK Islamic Mission (Sheffield)
29 Firth Park Road
Sheffield S5 6WL
Contact: Mr Ilyas

Young Muslims Sheffield
10 Severn Road
Sheffield S10 2SU

Young Muslims Sheffield Girls Group
10 Severn Road
Sheffield S10 2SU

Muslim Religious Centre
25 Midland Street
Skipton
Yorkshire

Duke of York Street Mosque Committee
241 Doncaster Road
Wakefield WF1 5DA
Contact: Mr M Bashir

Jamia Swafia Mosque
Park Hill Lane
Eastmoor
Wakefield SF1 4NJ

Madressa Arabiaya Islamiya
18 Marsland Place
Wakefield
West Yorkshire
Contact: Mr Z Abedin

Markazi Jamia Mosque
12 Grange Street
Wakefield SF2 8TF
Tel: 0924–71469

Mosque
26 Katherine Street
off Eggbreg Road
Wakefield
West Yorkshire
Tel: 0924–71469

Mosque
3 Marsland Street
Wakefield
West Yorskshire

St Catherine Street Mosque Committee
169 Agbrigg Road
Wakefield WF1 5BN
Contact: Mr M Mughal

Wakefield Muslim Society
3 Benjamin Street
Wakefield
West Yorkshire
Contact: Mr M Younas

Mosque
62 Heslington Road
York
North Yorkshire
Tel: 0904–31098

UK Islamic Mission
3 Flavian Grove
Rawcliffe Lane

York
North Yorkshire
Tel: 0904–28834

York Mosque (UK Islamic Mission)
Bull Lane
Hull Road
York
North Yorkshire
Contact: Mr S Khan

York Muslim Association
75 Dodsworth Avenue
Heworth
York YO3 7TZ
Tel: 426261 (home)
Contact: Mr A Karbani

York University Islamic Society
c/o Students Union
Heslington
York Y01 5DD

NORTH WEST ENGLAND

Gousia Razvia Jamia Mosque and Islamic Centre
Higher Antley Street
Accrington BB5 0QH
Tel: 0254–389972
Contact: Mr M Iqbal
Place of worship. A place where any Muslim can come and pray and any other religious person can visit.

Hyndburn Council of Mosques
36 Washington Street
Accrington BB5 6TF
Contact: Mr Mirza Yousuf
Office: Chair

Madressah Talim-ul-Islam
50 Fountain Street
Accrington Lancashire BB5 0QP
Tel: 0254 231533
Contact: Mr M S Bhatti
Office: Chairperson
Educational establishment. The madrassah was founded in 1981 to teach Muslim children to read the Holy Qur'an and books about the religion, culture and history of Islam. There are also lessons in Asian languages like Urdu, and also Arabic. Classes are held in the evenings and there are three teachers. The

organisations does not receive grants. The Madrassah is used by about seventy-four children currently, between five and sixteen years and of both sexes.

Pakistan/Kashmir Death Committee
48 Portland Street
Accrington BB5 1RH
Contact: c/o Mr K Hussain

Raza Jamia Mosque
Grimshaw Street
Accrington BB5 0AZ
Tel: 0254-393454
Contact: Mr Haji F Ellahi
Office: Chairman

Raza Jamia Mosque and Islamic Centre
229 Blackburn Road
Accrington BB5 0AL
Tel: 0254-393454
Contact: Mr Haji F Ellahi
Office: Chairman

Dar-Uloom Qadiria Jilania
95 Burlington Street
Ashton-under-Lyne
Lancashire OL6 6HQ
Tel: 061-344-1006 (home)
Contact: Muhammed Zafar Iqbal Qazi
Office: Secretary
Religious organisation. Support is given in every aspect of community affairs including housing, social security, immigration, interpretation and attestation of translated documents through its related members who cover all areas of social welfare of the community in general and Muslim community in particular. Activities include Friday prayers – collectively performed with the congregation; mother tongue (Urdu) education is given to children and an elderly group has been organised which meets weekly as well as for a monthly lunch. In addition, religious, poetic, literary and national heritage events are held, together with an annual exhibition of aspects of Islamic calligraphy in Arabic and Urdu scripts, as well as other general artistic events.

Jamia Masjid
Newton Street
Penny Meadow
Ashton-under-Lyne
Lancashire OL6 6EJ
Tel: 061-330-0617

Madrassa Arbia Taleemul Qur'an and Mosque
Richmond Hill
Katherine Street
Ashton-under-Lyne
Lancashire OL7 0AL
Tel: 061-330-9837

Mossley Mosque Committee
81 Egmont Street
Ashton-under-Lyne
Lancashire
Tel: 04575-5507

Mosque
71 Stamford Road
Ashton-under-Lyne
Lancashire

Mosque
Wellington Street
Ashton-under-Lyne
Lancashire
Tel: 061-330-9837

Tameside Muslim Welfare Association Mosque
225 Stamford Street
Ashton-under-Lyne
Lancashire

Tameside Muslim Welfare Society
230 Oldham Road
Ashton-Under-Lyne
Lancashire
Contact: Mr Zikar-Ur-Rehman

Blackburn Council of Mosques
3 Wareham Street
Blackburn BB1 5PH
Tel: 0254-691212
Contact: Mr Ibrahim Chopdat
Office: Secretary

Cutchi Muslim Association
173a Burnley Road
Blackburn
Lancashire
Tel: 0254-60581
Contact: Mr J J Virmani

Dar Al Da'wa Al Islamiya (Islamic Propagation Centre)
69 Victoria Street
Blackburn BB1 6DN
Tel: 0254–675528
Contact: Mr Haji Mohammed Sadiq Chowdhry
Office: Chairperson
A membership group which provides free translations of Asian languages to mosques and groups and multi-lingual and calligraphy workshops. The centre has all kinds of artefacts and free literature on Muslim culture. It also works in an advisory capacity and provides welfare advice and assistance.

Hanfi-Sunni Circle and Mosque
48 Altom Stret
Blackburn BB1 7NE
Tel: 0254–52608

Hanfi Sunni Jamia Masjid and Hanfi Sunni Muslim Association
33a Randall Street
Blackburn BB1 7LG
Tel: 0254–52170
Contact: Malik Khadam Hussain

Hanfia Muslim Raza Mosque
40 Balaclava Street
Blackburn
Lancashire

Islamic Education Centre
44 Devonport Road
Blackburn BB2 1HW
Contact: Mr Mohammed Sabir

Islamic Lending & Reference Library
55 Whalley New Road
Blackburn BB1 6JY
Tel: 0254–681558

Islamic Religious Centre and Mosque
209 Preston New Road
Blackburn BB2 6BN
Tel: 0254–2607319
Contact: Yakood Fancy
Office: President

Islamic Welfare Association
25 Logwood Street
Blackburn BB1 9TU

Tel: 0254–583384
Contact: Mr Mohammed Hussain
Office: Secretary

Jame Masjid-e-Noor
71 Saunders Road
off Preston New Road
Blackburn BB2 6LS
Tel: 0254–698609
Contact: Raja Muhammad Sharif Qazi
Office: President
Place of worship. The mosque is linked to Blackburn UK Islamic Mission.

Jamia Ghosia Mosque
99 Chester Street
Blackburn
Lancashire
Tel: 0254–51080
Contact: M Aslam

Islamic Cultural Centre and Jamee Mosque
Cumberland Street
Blackburn BB1 1JP
Tel: 0254–662737
Contact: Ahmed Suleman Sidat
Office: Mosque President
A mosque where people pray as well and a study room for children studying Islam.

Lancashire Association of Muslims
c/o Comet Cash and Carry Company
Empire Building
Rendal Street
Blackburn
Contact: Mr A Patel

Madressa-e-Raza
Chorlton Street
Blackburn BB1 6NF
Contact: Mr Mohammed Patel

Madressa e Talimul-Islam
86 Stansfield Street
Blackburn BB2 2NG
Contact: Abdul Aziz Mulla

Madressa-Furkania
26 Providence Street
Little Harwood
Blackburn BB1 5PT
Contact: Secretary

Madina Mosque

19-23 Oak Street
Blackburn
Lancashire

Madni Mosque

19 Lancaster Place
Blackburn BB2 6GT
Tel: 0254-676618
Contact: Mr M A Sharif

Markazi Jamia Ghousia Masjid

98 Chester Street
off Audley Range
Blackburn BB1 1DR

Masjid-e-Aneesul Islam

Troy Street
off Whally Range
Blackburn BB1 6NY
Tel: 0254-583245
Contact: Mr A Patel

Masjid-e-Hidayah

50 Millham Street
Blackburn BB1 6EU
Contact: Imam Patel
Office: Imam

Masjide-e-Noor-ul-Islam and Islamic Education Society

108-110 Audley Road
Blackburn BB1 1TF
Tel: 0254-676989
Contact: Mr M Patel
Office: Vice President

Masjid-e-Rizwan

Newton Street
Blackburn BB1 1NE
Tel: 0254-263707
Contact: Mr B Mullah

Masjid-e-Sajedeen & Madrasah e Islamiah

Plane Tree Road
Little Harwood
Blackburn BB1 5PA
Contact: Mr I H Chopdat
Office: General Secretary
Place of worship and provider of religious education from age five onwards to Hifz Qur'an and Ketabs. It also provides welfare, the use of a hall for weddings and

gatherings, assistance in funeral arrangements. A future goal is to provide Muslim schools both for boys and girls on the basis of single sex education.

Masjid-e-Tauheedul-Islam

48-50 Millham Street
Blackburn
Lancashire

Masjidul-Momineen and Kokni Muslim Welfare Society

Ash Street
Little Harwood
Blackburn BB1 6LX
Contact: Secretary
Place of worship. The mosque is open for daily prayers to all Muslims. It can cater for two hundred and fifty people at once and has facilities for making Muslim funeral arrangements.

Mosque

19-21 Oak Street
Blackburn
Lancashire

Naqshbandia Aslamiyya Spiritual Centre

1-5 Cob Wall
Whalley Old Road
Blackburn BB1 5JJ
Contact: Mr Khaja Sufi

Religious Advice Centre

223-225 Whalley Range
Blackburn BB1 6NN
Tel: 0254-582141
Contact: Yunus U Patel
Office: Volunteer
Place of worship and membership group. The centre provides facilities for worship and for wefare activities. Multi-religious discussions are held and encouraged. Advice and counselling is offered on religious matters. It promotes activities for relations between Christianity and Islam. The centre aims to unite different major faiths, and to unite all Muslim schools of thought. There is a Bible and Qur'an reading circle.

Shi'a Islamic Centre

143 Preston New Road
Blackburn BB2 6BJ
Tel: 0254-26559 (home)
Contact: Nazir Hussain
Office: Secretary
Place of worship. The organisation aims to: propogate Islam according to the Holy Prophet Hazrat

Mohammed and his twelve Viceregents; provide a place of worship for the Shi'a community of Blackburn; provide a library for the use of members; publish and distribute literature and information on Islam according to the Shi'a faith and to provide religious education for children.

Surti Sunni Vohra Association

4 Norwich Street
Blackburn
Lancashire

UK Islamic Mission

Jame Masjid e Noor
71 Saunders Road
Blackburn BB2 6LS
Tel: 0254–698609
Contact: Raja Muhammad Sharif Qazi
Office: President
A membership group which aims to: establish a mosque and Islamic centre; provide facilities for congregational prayers and study of the Qur'an and Hadith and to run religious meetings. It also aims to: provide education and training for Muslim children and youth; set up reading rooms and libraries; spread Islam through literature, lectures and seminars; provide social and welfare services and to provide help and guidance for students. It is a registered charity. The organisation runs classes in the Qur'an, Islamic studies, Urdu language and other useful lectures at Juma prayers and other evenings.

Islamic Community Centre and Mosque Bina Mahal

100 Rigby Road
Blackpool
Lancashire

Anjuman Womens Group

c/o The Community Centre
High Street
Bolton
Lancashire
Contact: Ms C Forrest

Ashrafia Mosque

41 Park Road
Bolton BL1 4RX
Contact: Mr G H M Kotwal

Bolton Somali Muslims

48 Langdon Close
Bolton BL1 2QN
Contact: c/o Mrs J Ibrahim

Bolton Surti Sunni Vohra Muslim Association

c/o 98 High Street
Bolton BL3 6SZ
Tel: 0204–26489
Contact: Mr K Motala
Office: Manager

Canning Street Mosque

Canning Street
Bolton
Lancashire

Daubill Muslim Society and Masjid Al Rahman

2-14 Randal Street
Bolton BL3 4AQ
Tel: 0204–660177
Contact: President
Place of worship. A newly built mosque in the Daubhill area of Bolton, just five minutes drive from Bolton town centre. Mainly used for worship and community relations.

Farnworth Cultural Centre

118 Market Street
Farnworth
Bolton
Lancashire
Tel: 0204–793793
Contact: Mr Iftkhar Khan

Ghosia Mosque and Madrasha

81 Anburn Street
Bolton BL3 6TQ
Tel: 0204–64085
Contact: S Akuji
Office: Presient
Place of worship. A typical mosque and madrassa. There is a small building which consists of classrooms and a main prayer hall. It is mainly used for worship and providing Islamic education for children.

Macca Mosque Muslim Community Centre

Grecian Crescent
Bolton Crescent
Bolton BL3 6QU
Tel: 0204–24200
Contact: Mr Zahoor Raja
Office: Secretary
Place of worship and community centre. A voluntarily run centre which has provision for sports. It caters for around six thousand Muslims from Bolton and the surrounding areas. The mosque has a committee comprising of twenty-seven members from which

sub-committees are formed. All ages are catered for in some way or another. Activities include education, worship, youth, sports activities, weddings. Both religious and non-religious functions take place.

Madina Mosque
128 St George Road
Bolton BL1 2BZ
Tel: 0204–21691
Contact: Bashir Ahmed
Office: Secretary
Place of worship. The mosque provides facilities for worship and for children to learn the Urdu language and also to read the Qur'an.

Makki Mosque & Islamic Cultural Centre
Eskrick Street
Bolton
Lancashire

Masjid-e-Noor-ul-Islam
Prospect Street
Halliwell Road
Bolton BL3 6QP
Tel: 0204–393522
Contact: Mr Sabir Adam
Place of worship. The main function of the organisation is to provide its members with facilities for worship, marriage, funerals and other such activities. Islamic education is taught to children and Islamic scholars are regularly invited to give lectures on Islam.

Mosque
64 Lawrence Street
Farnworth
Bolton
Lancashire

Mosque
Dean Road
Bolton
Lancashire

Rehman Mosque
6 Broadhurst Court
Bolton BL3 6JB
Contact: Y A Patel

Sughra Mosque
Back Granville Street
Farnworth
Bolton BL4 7LD

Tel: 0204–73497
Contact: Mr Bashir Ahmed
Office: General Secretary

Taiyabah Mosque and Community Centre
31a Draycott Street
Bolton BL1 8HD
Tel: 0204–35997
Contact: Mr Master
Office: Secretary

Zakaria Mosque
20 Peace Street
Bolton BL3 5LJ
Tel: 0204–35002
Contact: Mr Ayoob Limbada

Jamiah Sultania Mosque
3-7 Bridge Street
Brierfield
Lancashire BB9 5PE
Tel: 0254–692764

Anjaman-e-Muhibban-e-Ahel-e-Bait Hussainia Mosque
37 Grey Street
Burnley BB10 1BA
Office: Imam
Place of worship and membership group. Activities include worship, welfare programmes, youth and womens activities, religious education and community languages.

Burnley Council of Mosques
3 Elm Street
Burnley BB10 1AJ
Tel: 0282–412107
Contact: Mr Mohamed Shareef Quadri
Office: Secretary

Burnley Funeral Committee
81 Gordon Street
Burnley
Lancashire
Contact: Mr A Khan

Darul Uloom
141 Leyland Road
Burnley BB11 3DN

Ghausiah Mosque
66–68 Colne Road
Burnley
Lancashire

Islamic Centre
38 Brougham Street
Burnley BB12 0AS
Contact: Mr G N Chaudhry

Jamia Masjid-e-Farooq-e-Azam
North St (off Colne Rd)
Duke Bar
Burnley BB10 1LU
Tel: 0282-22321
Contact: Mr Izat Khan

Jinnah Community Development Services
Islamic Central Hall
4 Brougham Street
Stonyholme
Burnley BB12 0AS
Tel: 0282-23296
Fax: 0282-23296
Contact: Mr M R Malik
Community development and advice centre. A fifteen year old advice service which has both full-time and part-time staff. Activities include advice on welfare rights and immigration, mediation with statutory bodies on behalf of clients, translation services and housing advice.

Lancashire Council of Mosques
41–43 Gordon Street
Burnley BB12 0AX
Tel: 0254-692289
Contact: Mr M Rafique Malik
Office: Secretary
Umbrella organisation which co-ordinates the activities of around fifty mosques, madrassas, and teaching centres, both religious and non-religious, with a special emphasis on social, educational and recreational activities, although wishing not to intefere with the independence of these organisations and centres. The council has initiated inter-faith dialogue and fully participates in consultative processes initiated by local authorities and central government departments. Activities include youth, elderly, under fives, worship, race and community relations.

Shah Jalal Mosque and Madrassah
112–114 Burns Street
Burnley
Lancashire

Tel: 0282-450269
Place of worship and welfare association. The Bangladeshi Welfare Association incorporates the Shah Jalal Mosque and the advice service. The advisory service is run for the local community, employing four full-time staff and is funded mainly through the local authority urban programme funding. The place of worship provides teaching for children of the Holy Qur'an, mother tongue (Bengali) and Arabic. Lectures on the Muslim Faith are held for the adult members of the community.

Stoneyholme Jamia Masjid
102 Rectory Road
Burnley BB12 0BP
Tel: 0282-422358
Tel: 0282-23296 (home)
Contact: Mr M S Qadri

UK Islamic Mission
52 Gordon Street
Burnley BB12 0AX
Tel: 0282-421430

Urdu Society Mosque
18 March Street
Burnley BB12 0BT
Contact: Mr Nasar Ullah Khan

All Jammu and Kashmir Muslim Conference
59 Shepherd Street
Bury
Lancashire
Contact: Mr A H M Younis Khan

Darul Uloom Muslim Training College
Holcombe Hall
Holcombe Brook
Ramsbottom
Bury BL8 4NG
Tel: 0706-825160
Contact: Mufti Shabbir

Islamic Centre
Church Street
Bury BL9 6AZ
Tel: 061-764-7306
Contact: Mr Liaqat Ali
Office: Trustee
Place of worship. Activities include worship for men, women and children, religious education for adults and children and celebration of religious festivals.

Islamic Cultural Association

108 Walmersley Road
Bury BL9 6DX
Tel: 061-797-7942 (home)
Contact: Mr M M Ali
Office: Chair
Membership group. The association aims to unite and co-ordinate the activities of Muslims in Bury and Radcliffe and provide a platform for representation at a national level to promote and safeguard the economic, social and cultural interests of the Muslim community in the UK. It also aims to promote and provide educational activities. Activities include adult religious education and welfare.

Khizra Mosque

55 Hurst Street
Bury
Lancashire
Contact: Mr M Aslma

Khizra Mosque

85 Warmersley Road
Bury
Lancashire
Tel: 061-764-1638

Mosque

67 Thompson Street
Masley Road
Bury
Lancashire

Mosque

32 Heywood Street
Bury
Lancashire
Tel: 061-764-0491

Mosque and Dar-ul-Uloom

Holcombe Hill
Holcombe
Bury BL8 4NG
Tel: 070-682-6106/8

Noor Islam

48 Birdgefield Street
Radcliffe
Bury
Lancashire

School of Religious Instruction

19 Hathaway Road
Sunnybank
Bury
Lancashire
Contact: Mr S M Z Hassan

Mosque

King Street
Botcher Gate
Near City Centre
Carlisle
Cumbria

Jamathana Islamia

The Paddock
Brookfield Road
Cheadle
Cheshire

Chester Islamic Society

8 Westlorne Street
Chester CH1 4AF

Islamic Prayer House

45 Egerton Street
Chester
Cheshire

Dawatul Islam Mosque

142 Lyons Lane
Chorley
Lancashire PR6 0PJ
Tel: 02572-68644
Contact: Mr Sajid
Office: Secretary

Mosque

30 Railway Street
Chorley
Lancashire

Madina Mosque

3 Chapel Street
Colne
Lancashire BB8 5AH

Shajalal Mosque

286 Walthall Street
Crewe
Cheshire

Mosque
21-23 Victoria Street
Darwen
Lancashire BB1 5JJ
Tel: 0254-774508
Contact: Mr Hamid Khan
Office: President

Mosque
Granwell Street
Farnworth
Lancashire

Mosque
64 Lawrence Road
Farnworth
Lancashire

Great Harwood Mosque and Mosque Committee
1 Park Street
Great Harwood
Near Blackburn BB6 7BP
Contact: Mr M Ashraf
Office: Secretary
Place of worship. Activities include prayer, teaching mother tongue and religious elderly group.

Madressa Islamia
44 Greaves Street
Great Harwood
Lancashire BB6 7DY

Mosque
24 Edmond Street
off Princess Street
Great Harwood
Lancashire

Mosque
21 Jackson Street
Hyde
Cheshire SK14 1BX
Tel: 061-368-1551

Islamic Society
53 Dale Street
Lancaster LA1 3AP
Tel: 0524-64131
Contact: Mr Abdul Patel
Office: Chairman

Lancaster Islamic Society Mosque
1/2 Hawerden Cottages
Off Hinde Street
Lancaster LA1 9DJ
Tel: 0524-64131
Contact: Mr I Patel
Office: Secretary

Masjide Tauheedul Islam
29 Bicknell Street
Lancaster
Lancashire
Tel: 0254-54318

Muslim Welfare Society and Raza Mosque
71 Blade Street
Lancaster LA1 1TS
Tel: 0524-32087
Contact: Mr I Sulliman
Office: Secretary
Place of worship. Activities include worship, evening classes for children to learn Qur'an reading and Urdu language. There is also a funeral service.

Al-Rahma Mosque and Liverpool Muslim Society
29/37 Hathersley Street
off Mulgrave Street
Liverpool L8 2TJ
Tel: 051-709-7504
Contact: Mr M A Ali

Islamic Society of Britain
119 Queen's Drive
Liverpool L18 1JL
Tel: 051-733-2940
Contact: Dr A Z Khan

Liverpool University Islamic Society
Islamic Prayer Room
Old Students Union
Brownlow Hill
Liverpool

UK Islamic Mission (Liverpool Branch)
119 Queens Drive
Liverpool L18 1JL
Tel: 051-733-2940
Contact: Dr A Z Khan

Anjuman-e-Hamidiyak

10 Tollgate Close
Longsight
Manchester M13 0LG

Anjuman-e-Taraqqi-e-Urdu

6 Birkdale Road
Manchester M8
Contact: Mrs Rizui

Bohra Mosque

2-4 Slade Lane
Longsight
Manchester

College of Islamic Studies

3 Woodlands Road
Cheetham Hill
Manchester M8
Tel: 061-773-5257
Tel: 061-740-3696
Contact: Qamaruzzaman Azmi

Dar-ul-Uloom Islamia Education and Cultural Society

1 Hawkhurst Road
Manchester M13 0SJ
Tel: 061-256-2812
Contact: Mr Bashir
Office: Trustee

Didsbury Mosque and Islamic Centre

271 Burton Road
Off Barlow Moor Road
West Didsbury
Manchester M20 8WA
Tel: 061-434-2254

Eccles and Salford Islamic Society

5 Liverpool Road
Eccles
Manchester M30 0WB
Tel: 061-789-2609
Contact: Sheikh Awadalla Youssef
Office: Imam

Place of worship. Open to all Muslims, the centre hopes to provide as much information and any service required by the community. Activities include worship, education, holding Islamic celebrations and ceremonies.

Hidayah Mosque

2 Seymour Place
off Humphrey Road
Old Trafford
Manchester M16
Contact: Maulana Abdulhai Patel

Hiduyutal Muslim Society

83 Humphrey Road
Old Trafford
Manchester M16

Hijaz Islamic Foundation

62 Richmond Avenue
Sedgley Park
Prestwich
Manchester M25
Tel: 061-773-5257
Contact: Naqar Azmi

Hijra Mosque

63 Humphrey Road
Manchester M16

Hijra School

28 Hall Lane
Manchester M23 8AQ
Contact: c/o Dr A M Mangood

Ibad ul Rahman Trust

3 Woodlands Road
Manchester M8 7LF
Tel: 061-740-3696
Tel: 061-643-5499 (home)
Contact: Dr Bashir Ahmad
Office: Trustee

Islamic Academy and Mosque

19 Chorlton Terrace
Off Upperbrook Street
Brunswick
Manchester M13 9TD
Tel: 061-273-1145
Contact: Mr Iqbal
Office: Imam

Place of worship and cultural centre. An organisation for the Muslim community of Lancashire. Established in 1975, it is housed in an old church building of listed status. As well as prayers five times a day and Friday prayers, it publishes the monthly magazine "Al Hilal" and many other books and pamphlets. It holds religious meetings and seminars and is a member of many City Council committees.

Islamic Society
c/o UMIST Students Union
Sackville Street
Manchester M60 1QD

Islamic Welfare Circle
c/o 127 Manley Road
Whalley Range
Manchester

Islamic Welfare Circle
c/o 28 Hanley Avenue
Stretford
Manchester
Contact: Mr A Ghandi Choudhury

Islamic Welfare Circle
c/o 29 Northleigh Road
Firswood
Manchester
Contact: Mr Azmat Ullah

Islamic Youth Movement
66 Woodlands Road
Cheetham
Manchester M8 7NF
Tel: 061-740-1665/0577
Contact: Mr Salam
Office: Chair
Youth organisation. It helps to organise indoor and outdoor sporting activities for young people and runs play schemes in the Easter and Summer holidays. Its aim is to support youngsters during their moments of stress and strain from living between cultures and also the generation gaps.

Itehad-ul-Muslimeen
92 Duncan Road
Manchester M13 0GU

Jamia Mosque and Ibadur Rahman Cultural Society
3 Woodlands Road
off Cheetham Hill Road
Cheetham
Manchester M8 7LF
Tel: 061-740-3696
Tel: 061-643-5499 (home)
Contact: Dr Bashir Ahmad
Office: Trustee
Place of worship.

Jamiat Ahle Hadith
125 Beresford Road
Manchester M13 0TA

Jamiat Al-Salfinata
289 Slade Lane
Levenshulme
Manchester

Ladies Islamic Circle
271 Burton Road
Manchester M20

Madina Masjid / UK Islamic Mission
2 Barlow Road
off Stockport Road
Levenshulme
Manchester M19
Tel: 061-224-5143
Contact: Mr S D Butt

Manchester Branch UK Islamic Mission
3 Walcott Close
Manchester M13 9AP

Manchester Council of Mosques
Eileen Grove
Rusholme
Manchester
Tel: 061-224-2156
Tel: 061-643-5499 (home)
Contact: Dr Bashir Ahmed
Office: Chairman

Manchester Muslim Welfare Association
180 Brook Lane
Levenshulme
Manchester M19
Tel: 061-225-5960

Masjid-e-Noor/Old Trafford Muslim Society
115-117 Stamford Street
Old Trafford
Manchester M16
Tel: 061-834-7268 (home)
Contact: A Chunara
Office: Chairperson/Secretary

Mosque
229 Clarendon Road
Whalley Range
Manchester

Mosque
25 Bellot Street
Manchester M8 7PQ

Mosque and Darul Uloom
81 Stamford Road
Longsight
Manchester M13 05W
Tel: 061-256-2812

Muslim Advice Centre
10 Greenhill Road
Manchester M8 7LG

Muslim Educational Society
c/o 272 Dickenson Road
Manchester M13 0YL

Muslim Society and Community Advisory Service
76 Moss Park Road
Stretford
Manchester

Muslim Youth Foundation
Clydesdale House
27 Turner Street
Manchester M4 1DY
Tel: 061-832 5352
Fax: 061-839-2104
Contact: Mr Ali Akbar
Office: Secretary
Membership group with place of worship. It aims to promote understanding of Islam and to practice its tenets in a European society through the development of good behaviour and conduct. Activities include recreational, religious, welfare and worship activities for male and female youth.

Muslim Youth Movement of Malaysia
63 Humphrey Road
Old Trafford
Manchester M16 9DE

North Manchester Central Moque
3 Woodlands Road
Cheetham Hill Road
Manchester M8 7LF
Tel: 061-773-5257
Tel: 061-740-3696
Contact: Dr Amanat Ali

Salford Mosque
4 Harris Avenue
Davyhulme
Manchester M31
Tel: 061-748-9261

Shah Jalal Mosque and Islamic Society
1a Eileen Grove
Off Platt Lane
Rusholme
Manchester M14 5WE
Tel: 061-224-2156

South Manchester Jamia Mosque
32 Upper Park Road
Victoria Park
Manchester M14 5RU
Tel: 061-224-4119

Sunni Muslim Association
20 Bridesoak Street
Cheetham
Manchester M8 7PN

Trafford Park Muslim Society
1100 Eleventh Street
Trafford Park
Manchester M17 1BS

UK Islamic Mission
371 Wilmslow Road
Fallowfield
Manchester M14 6AH
Tel: 061-224-5479

UK Islamic Mission - Madrassa Talim-ul-Islam
443 Cheetham Hill Road
Cheetham
Manchester M8 7PF
Tel: 061-740-0577

Young Muslim Organisation
c/o 81 Stamford Hill
Longsight
Manchester M13 05W

Young Muslims Sports Association
122 Egerton Road North
Whalley Range
Manchester M16

Young Muslim Sports Club

258 Barlow Moor Road
Chorlton-Cum-Hardy
Manchester M21 8HA
Contact: Mr Amman Khan

Zakariyya Mosque and Madrassa

22-24 Clarendon Road
Whalley Range
Manchester M16 8LD
Tel: 061-881-9860

Mossley Community Mosque

81 Egmont Street
Mossley
Lancashire
Contact: Shazidur Rahman

Anjuman Islahul Muslimin

7 Parrock Street
Nelson
Lancashire
Tel: 0282-696987
Contact: Rana Farooq Alam Khan

Ghousia Jamia Mosque

Every Street
Nelson BB9 7HG
Tel: 0282-694471
Contact: Mr Khan

Ilm-o-Adab Mission

13 Giles Street
Nelson BB9 9UD
Tel: 0282-603296
Contact: Mr A Salimee
Publishing organisation. The organisation aims to create awareness of Islam and other communities and tries to meet the needs of ethnic minority groups. It provides literature to promote understanding within the community. It publishes Islamic educational literature for all age groups and publishes a newspaper for the local area in Urdu and English.

Ithaad Community Hall (Unity Hall)

7 Cross Street
Nelson BB9 7EN
Tel: 0282-694700
Contact: Abdul Hafiz Malik
Office Secretary
A community centre built by the Ithaad organisation for the benefit of the community and open to all members of the community. Activities include sports and other social events, including youth and women.

Ithaad ul Muslimin

27 Hartington Street
Brierfield
Nelson
Lancashire

Jamia Masjid Ghousian

Clayton Street
Nelson
Lancashire
Tel: 0282-614976
Contact: Sufi M Nosherwan

Jamiat Ahle Hadith

21 Thursby Road
Nelson
Lancashire
Tel: 0282-690451
Contact: Mohammad Aslam

Jamnia Masjid Sultana

7 Bridge Street
Brierfield
Nelson
Lancashire
Tel: 0282-692764
Tel: 0282-698705 (home)
Contact: Raja Jemroze Khan
Office: President
Place of worship.

Markazi Bazami Ghosia and Mehria

26 Barkerhouse Road
Nelson
Lancashire
Contact: Iftikhar H Shah

Mosque

12 Howarth Street
Nelson
Lancashire
Tel: 0282-614976

Pendle Council of Mosques

41 Forest Street
Nelson BB9 7NB
Tel: 0282-694471
Contact: Mr Syed Akhtar Shah
Office: Chair

UK Islamic Mission Islamic Centre and Madina Masjid

4–8 Forest Street
Nelson BB9 7NB
Tel: 0282 694471
Contact: Mr Ghulam Hussain
Place of worship. A three story building. The first floor is used for prayers, the second and third for teaching Arabic, Urdu and Islamic studies to boys and girls in the evenings. Activities include worship for men, women and youth and a bookshop selling Islamic literature.

Asian Muslim Welfare Association

196 Waterloo Street
Glodwick
Oldham OL4 1ES
Contact: Shamim Akhtar Khan

British Pakistan Muslim Welfare Association

11 Brompton Street
Glodwick
Oldham OL14 1AB
Contact: Nadir Hussein

Coldhurst Mosque Committee

8 Rederse Street
Oldham OL1 2EH
Contact: Mr Miah

Glodwick Bangladesh Mosque Committee and Jallalabad Mosque

52 Orme Street
Oldham OL4 1RZ
Tel: 061-6260132
Tel: 061-6244565 (home)
Contact: Abdul Rahman
Office: Chairperson
Place of worship and membership group committee. It provides facilities for worship and religious teaching.

Hussaini Mosque

102 Greengate Street
Oldham
Lancashire

Hussania Islamic Mission

405 Park Road
Glodwick
Oldham OL4 1SQ
Tel: 061-620-6952

Islamic Centre

Stenfield Street
Couldhurst
Oldham
Lancashire

Jama Mosque

Derby Street
Werneth
Oldham
Lancashire

Jamiat-ahl-e-Hadith

23 Villiers Drive
Oldham OL8 1DY
Contact: M I Bhatti

Jamiat Ahle Hadith Mosque

11 Ross Street
Werneth
Oldham
Lancashire
Tel: 061-624-2555

Jamiat Tabligh-ul-Islam

397 Park Road
Glodwick
Oldham OL4 1SF
Contact: Mohammed Iqbal

Jamiat Tabligh-ul-Islam

371 Park Road
Oldham
Lancashire
Contact: Mohammed Iqbal

Madrassar Taleem ul Quran

201 Lees Road
Oldham OL14 1NW
Tel: 061-678-0593
Contact: Iftikhar Ahmed Naweed
Office: Secretary

Middleton Road Mosque

101 Mars Street
Oldham OL9 6QF

Minhaj-ul-Qur'an Movement UK

288 Manchester Street
Oldham OL9 6HB
Tel: 061-624-1425
Membership group. The Minhaj-ul-Qur'an Institute International was established in 1980 in Pakistan by the

eminent scholar Dr Prof Muhammad Tahir-ul-Qadri. The UK branch of the Institute was formed some seven years ago. Its fundamental aim is the unity of all people on one platform, the eradication of sectarianism, and the promotion of religious tolerance and harmony within society. The group is particularly concerned for youth, women and the elderly and is keen on developing a programme that will help youngsters to say no to a life of drugs and crime in general. A library service of religious books, audio and visual cassettes is provided.

Mosque
156 Middleton Road
Oldham OL9 6BG
Tel: 061-678-6748

Mosque
116 Manchester Road
Oldham OL9 7AX
Tel: 061-624-5448
Contact: President

Mosque
55 Middleton Road
Oldham
Lancashire

Nagina Mosque and Urdu School
74 Werneth Hall Road
Coppice
Oldham OL8 1QZ
Tel: 061-626-0522 (work)
Contact: Raja Zafer Iqbal
Office: General Secretary

Nusrat ul Islam Mosque and Urdu School
266 Waterloo Street
Glodwick
Oldham OL4 1ER
Contact: M Rafique

Nusratual Islamic Mosque
84 Hardy Street
Oldham OL4 1DL

Pakistan Cultural Association
8-10 Worcester Street
Werneth
Oldham
Lancashire

Tabligh-ul-Islam Mosque
87 Greengate Street
Oldham
Lancashire

UK Islamic Mission
44 Manchester Road
Werneth
Oldham OL9 7AP
Contact: A Butt

Werneth Mosque and Urdu School
48 Hereford Street
Oldham OL9 7RQ
Tel: 061-652-8018
Contact: Mr M Khan

Gujarat Sunni Muslim Community Centre
15 Eldon Street
Preston PR1 7YD
Tel: 0772-25658
Contact: G H Mulla
Office: Honorary General Secretary

Gujarati Sunni Muslim Society - Masjid-e-Noor
Noor Street
Preston PR1 1QS
Tel: 0772-881786
Contact: Secretary

Jama Masjid Preston Muslim Society
18 Clarendon Street
Preston PR1 3YN
Tel: 0772-57127
Contact: Mr Osman Monshi
Office: Honorary Secretary

Madrassa-e-Noorul-Islam
Noor Hall
Noor Street
Preston
Tel: 0772-827531
Contact: Hajji Ibrahim

Masjeed-e-Quba
17 Lex Street
Preston PR1 4XL
Tel: 0772-701970
Contact: Bashir Ahmed
Office: Secretary

Masjid-e-Aqsa Preston Hanfi Sunni Muslim Society

95-97 Fishwick Parade
Preston PR1 4XR
Tel: 0772-794644
Contact: Haji-Sandal Hussain
Office: General Secretary
Place of worship. Offers facilities for prayer, teaching children mother tongue (Urdu), and teaching about Islam, Qur'an and the Muslim faith.

Masjid-e-Raza

103-105 St Paul's Road
Preston
Lancashire
Tel: 0772-203578
Tel: 0772-827785 (home)
Contact: Ghulam A Kausar
Place of worship. The mosque was purpose built in 1971. There are about four hundred members. About one hundred and ninety children attend the mosque for religious studies and mother tongue learning. It is managed by a Management Committee of thirteen members and it is a self-funding organisation.

Medina Mosque

26-28 Fishwick Parade
Preston PR1 4XQ
Tel: 0772-788847
Contact: Musa Roked
Office: Secretary
Place of worship. The society associated with the mosque is known as the Preston Gujarati Muslim Society. It aims to advance the religion of Islam in accordance with the doctrines and beliefs of the Sunni Muslims and to promote cultural and educational activities for people living in the Fishwick and New Hall Lane area of Preston. The society is run by charitable donations. Worship is carried out and mother tongue teaching is given to children.

Preston and West Lancashire Council of Mosques

4 Varley Street
Preston
Lancashire
Tel: 0772-8844962
Contact: Mr Ibrahim Kabir
Office: Chair

Preston Muslim Cultural Centre

21 Fishergate Hill
Preston PR1 8JB

Quwwatul Islam Mosque and Preston Muslim Society

Peel Hall Street
Deepdale
Preston
Lancashire
Tel: 0772-54578
Contact: Secretary
Place of worship and education. It is used for worship, Islamic education for young children, training and gatherings for women and youth.

Bolton Bangladesh Association

8 Bury/Bolton Road
Radcliffe
Lancashire M26 0LD
Contact: Dr F R Bhuiyan

Islamic Centre

48 Bridgefield Street
Radcliffe
Lancashire
Tel: 061-724-5465

Pakistan Islamic Centre

18 Peter Street
Rawtenstall
Lancashire BB4 7NR
Tel: 0706-216603
Contact: Mohammed Safdar
Office: Chairperson
Place of worship. Activities include worship and welfare for the Muslim community and Urdu classes for youth as well as attempting to increase the cultural understanding for young people of Pakistani origin.

Shah Jalal Mosque and Cultural Centre

13A Longholme Road
Rawtenstall
Lancashire BB4 7NG

Al-Amin Teaching Centre

40 Corbet Street
Rochdale OL16

Al-Furqhan Mosque

17 Philip Street
Rochdale
Lancashire

Anjumane Ahle Sunnat Wal Jamaat
2 South Street
Rochdale
Lancashire
Tel: 0706-45095

Bilal Mosque
Bulwer Street
Rochdale OL16

Darul Munawar Islamic Teaching Centre
100-104 Durham Street
Rochdale
Lancashire

Dar-ul-Uloom Jamia Chishtiah
49-53a Milkstone Road
Rochdale OL11 1EB
Tel: 0706-50487
Contact: Hafiz A H Chishti
Office: General Secretary
Place of worship, teaching centre and book centre. Established in 1986, Jamia Chishtiah provides for the spiritual well-being of Muslims by regular Friday and daily prayers and celebration of Islamic holy days throughout the year. In addition a Muslim funeral service is offered. Starting in January 1994, there will be a full-time Islamic Studies course for students over sixteeen years of age in order for them to become qualified imams in this country. There is also Islamic education of children and adults and the provision of a comprehensive Islamic book centre. Associated with it is a Muslim Youth Movement whose activities, amongst others, include lectures and weekly study circles. Activities are run for the young, the old and for women.

Golden Mosque
Lower Sheriff Street
Rochdale OL12 6TG
Tel: 0706-48681
Contact: Mr Ghauri
Office: President

Idara Talimul Islam
43 William Street
Rochdale 0L11 1HW
Tel: 0706-45135
Fax: 0706-42517
Contact: Mr Mohd Anwar
Office: Chairperson

Islamic Youth Movement
25 Hare Street
Rochdale
Lancashire

Jalalia Mosque
66 Trafalgar Street
Rochdale OL1 6JL
Tel: 0706-46822

Madarsa Islamia and Urdu Centre, Rochdale
58 Morley Street
Rochdale
Lancashire
Tel: 0706-343551/351008
Contact: Mr MI Misbahi
Officer: Director
Place of worship, teaching and book centre. Also centre for various spiritual sessions and activities. Two daily teaching sessions are held for children and adults (male and female) in Islamic education and in preparation for GCSE and "A" levels in Urdu. Marriages are also conducted at the centre and religious advice is available for moslems in rochdale.

Madina Islamic Cultural Studies Centre
35 Whitworth Road
Rochdale OL12 0RA

Muslim Brothers Association
c/o 59 King Street East
Rochdale
Lancashire

Muslim Community of Wardleworth
12 Trafalgar Street
Rochdale
Lancashire

Neelie Masjid & Islamic Centre
25 Hare Street
Rochdale 0L11 1JL
Tel: 0706-48094
Tel: 0706-59307 (home)
Contact: M S Baleem
Office: Vice President

Rochdale Muslim Society
47 Norford Way
Bamford
Rochdale OL11 5QS
Contact: A Rauf
Membership group.

UK Islamic Mission

25 Hare Street
Rochdale OL11 1JL
Tel: 0706-48094
Contact: Mr M Baleem
Office: President
Place of worship and teaching centre. A socio-religious organisation which arranges daily prayers, Friday prayers and Eid prayers. The organisation also offers spiritual advice to the Muslim community, arranges lectures and teaching of the Qur'an every week and imparts religious education to youths and adults. Activities include worship (five daily prayers), evening classes (five days a week) for boys and girls of five to fifteen years old. Solemnisation of weddings and guidance on funerals and burials.

Masjid-e-Bilal and Islamic Centre

127 Blackburn Road
Haslingden
Rossendale BB4 5HN
Tel: 0706-25335
Contact: Mr Said-ul-Rahman

Mosque and Islamic Centre

4 Beaconsfield Street
Haslingden
Rossendale BB4 5TD
Contact: Mr M Rahman
Place of worship. Activities include prayers five times a day, mother tongue, Islamic teaching, funerals, age concern, religious events, festivals and a luncheon club for the elderly.

Muslim Welfare Association

30 Sandown Road
Haslingden
Rossendale BB4 6PL

Mosque

5 Gardener Street
Salford M6
Tel: 061-748-9261

Salford University Islamic and Cultural Association

15 Murray Street
Salford M7 9DX

Muslim Welfare Centre

69 Fox Street
Edgley
Stockport
Cheshire

Tel: 061-477-6592
Contact: Mr Abdul Khaliq
Office: Chairperson
Community centre. The only centre for the Muslim community in Stockport. At present the centre is used for religious education and mother tongue teaching, youth activities, mother and toddler group and English language lessons for adults and advice. The community is applying for permission to use the premises for worship.

Mosque

Eagle Street
Todmorden
Lancashire OL14 5HQ
Tel: 0706-6310
Contact: Gulzar Khan
Office: Secretary

Jamait-ul-Muslemeen

9 Arpley Street
Warrington
Cheshire
Contact: Mr N Mohammed

Mosque and Cultural Centre

43 Arpley Street
Warrington
Cheshire

Quwwatul Islam Mosque and Weston Muslim Society

Peel Hall Street
Weston
Cheshire MR1 6QQ

Islamic Cultural Centre

St James School
Clifton Street
Worsley Menses
Wigan WN3 5HN
Tel: 0942-495038

Mosque

Clifton Street
Pool Stock
Wigan
Lancashire

ENGLISH EAST MIDLANDS

Azad Youth Club

12a Saltergate
Chesterfield
Derbyshire
Tel: 0246-277284
Fax: 0246-277284
Contact: Aftab Saddiq
Office: Youth Leader
A membership group which meets at weekends to organise various trips and social evenings and other activities like camping and football. The club helps out members of the Muslim community.

Chesterfield Muslim Association

12a Saltergate
Chesterfield
Derbyshire S40 1UT
Tel: 0246-277284
Fax: 0246-277284
Contact: Mr Aftab Saddiq
Office: Co-ordinator
A membership group which represents the Muslim population of Chesterfield and North East Derbyshire. It has been in operation since 1987. Facilities provided include translation service, information and advice on immigration, help with DHSS regulations, Urdu and Arabic classes for young people and basic English for adults. The Association has also set up the Azad Youth Club, Chakswari Cricket Club and Women's Welfare Group.

Chesterfield Muslim Students

5 Shirland Street
Chesterfield
Derbyshire

Chesterfield Muslim Women Welfare Group

12a Saltergate
Chesterfield
Derbyshire S40 1UT
Tel: 0246-277284
Contact: Fiaz Bi
Women's membership group. A body of women (aged ten to sixty-five years old) who are mostly housewives. They create educational opportunities by learning more about the British way of life and learn new practical skills. The group's main aim is to combat isolation by giving each other a chance to air their views and speak out. English language classes are held in the evenings.

Derby Jamia Mosque

6 Rosehill Street
Derby DE3 8EX
Tel: 0332-44838/366461
Contact: Rehmat Khan
It aims to offer a place of worship, provide religious and language classes and celebrate religious festivals. It provides advice on welfare rights, a monthly luncheon group and daily Urdu and Arabic classes and organises cultural events under the auspices of the mosque. There is also a library and voluntary administrative support. The Young Muslim Organisation meets at the mosque every Friday evening.

Islamic Centre Derby

The Central Mosque
Sacheveral Street
Derby DE1 2JR
Tel: 0332-292021
Contact: Talib H Shah
Office: Secretary
A place where Muslims can worship and have their welfare and cultural needs catered for. Activities include worship, welfare and children's language and religious teaching.

Jamia Hanfia-Taleem-ul-Islam

26 Western Road
Derby DE3 6SE
Tel: 0332-204187
Contact: A Akbar
Office: Secretary
Place of worship. It is mainly for worship, but also provides an education centre where young children are taught moral and ethical education with the aim of developing their abilities for the benefit of the local community and to protect them from getting into crime. The organisation impresses on children that successful people in the eyes of God are those who lead their lives respecting moral standards explained in religion and help others with their needs. In this way the organisation aims to create good members of the community for tomorrow. It also provides help to the elderly in the community in various ways.

Jamiat Ahl-e-Hadith

7 Hastings Street
Derby DE3 6QQ
Tel: 0332-766237
Contact: Mr M L Bhatti
Office: Secretary
A place of worship and a madrasa (school) where the younger generation is taught Urdu and Arabic and about Islam. Activities include worship and teaching.

Madras Salfia Jamit-ahle-Hadith

7a Hastings Street
Derby DE3 6QQ
Tel: 0332-766237
Contact: Mr M Yousaf
Activities include teaching young children Urdu and Arabic languages, the ideology of Islam and mankind and celebration of religious festivals. Resources available are tape, administrative support and transport. Meetings are held as and when required.

Mosque

54 Dairyhouse Road
Derby DE3 8HL

Muslim Culture Association

54 Becher Street
Derby DE3 8NN
Tel: 0332-367439
Contact: Mr R T Khan

Muslim Women's Association

57 Muirfield Drive
Mickleover
Derby DE3 5SP
Tel: 0332-519212
Contact: Mrs Bajwa
The association aims to offer social and cultural help by encouraging Muslim women to meet and share their Muslim culture. Activities include welfare advice and celebration of religious feativals. Administrative support, translations and transport to members are available.

Pakistan Muslim Welfare Association

9 Madeley Street
Derby DE3 8EX
Tel: 0332-365845
Aims to establish a school for Muslim girls between nine and fifteen years of age and to advise members of Muslim community on welfare and cultural issues. Activities include sports and advisory and information services for members of the Pakistani community and organisation of social and cultural events. The following resources are available: translations, technical aids, signers, administrative support and transport.

Young Muslim Women's Group

c/o 11 Peartree Crescent
Derby DE3 8RN
Tel: 0332-766225
Contact: Ms Nina Akhter

A group of Muslim women who meet three times a week at the Madeley Centre to discuss topics which affect them.

Young Muslims Derby

c/o Madeley Centre
Rosehill Street
Derby DE3 8EX
Tel: 0332-47509
Contact: Shokat Ali
Membership is open to Muslim boys aged fourteen to twenty-five years. It aims to assist young Muslim boys in Derby and to educate them culturally as well as socially; to organise cultural and social events, as well as to provide English and Arabic classes, and welfare and educational advice. The following resources are available: voluntary administrative support, videos, exhibitions, and literature. Meetings are held once a fortnight.

Hinckley Muslim Association

1 Manor Close
Burbage
Hinckley
Leicestershire LE10 2NL
Tel: 0445-611480
Contact: Mr Manzoor Moghal
Office: President
Membership group. The association exists to promote the social, cultural and religious welfare of the Muslim community. It runs an evening supplementary school for Muslim children for teaching the Qur'an, Arabic and Urdu.

All Jammu and Kashmir Muslim Conference

4 Crowns Hill Rise
Leicester LE5 3DG
Tel: 0533-358511

Anjuman-e-Saifee

3-5 Wellington Street
Leicester LE1 6HH
Tel: 0533-470446
Contact: S H Jaffer A Kapasi
Office: Treasurer
Place of worship and community centre. Dawoodi Bohras are a group of believers on the basis of a voluntary acceptance of a faith and a code of beliefs, tenets, conduct and way of life, accepting the benevolent leadership of their head, his holiness, the Dai-al-Mutlaq. Activities include religious, social, cultural and sports activities for all the community members.

Association of Sunni Muslims
39 Farringdon Street
Leicester LE5 0EB

Beaumont Leys Muslim Association
47 Calder Road
Leicester LE4 0RF
Tel: 0533-353694
Contact: Mr Yusuf Subedar
Office: Chairperson
Offers language and religious instruction. Its activities involve children, community action, education, ethnic minorities, family and religious activities.

British Pakistan and Muslim Welfare Association
Jinnah Advice Centre
6 Beeby Road
Leicester LE5 3LE
Tel: 0533-741022

Dar-us-Salam Mosque
55-57 Upper Tichbourne Street
Leicester LE2 0QN
Tel: 0533-543887/540592
Tel: 0533-543257 (home)
Contact: C M Haque
Office: Chairman

Dawoodi Bohra Jamaat
3-5 Wellington Street
Leicester LE1 6HH
Tel: 0533-664668

Dawoodi Bohra Welfare Society
106 Jean Drive
Leicester LE4 0GF
Tel: 0533-832600
Contact: Mr D Kapasi
Office: Secretary
Registered charity. A small community which holds meetings and religious gatherings during the month of Ramadam and Muharram and monthly meetings all year round at a centre on Martin Street. Activities include charity work, youth activities, religious gatherings and prayers.

De Montfort University Islamic Society
Students Union
4 Newark Close
Leicester LE2 7BJ
Tel: 0533-555576

Evington Muslim Association
9 Kedlestone Road
Leicester LE5 5HX
Tel: 0533-735529

Federation of Muslim Organisations in Leicestershire
88 Sparkenhoe Street
Leicester LE2 0TA
Tel: 0533-623518
Contact: Mr Tarik Iqbal
Founded in 1983 with forty-two affiliated bodies. It promotes the needs of the Leicestershire Muslim community and helps to foster better relations with other communities. Activities include advisory, community action, elderly people, information, umbrella group, race relations and religious activities.

Gujarati Muslim Association
54 Frederick Road
Leicester LE5 5HE
Tel: 0533-510219

His Highness Prince Aga Khan Shia Imami Ismaili Jamat Khana
2 Westcotes Drive
Leicester LE3 0QR
Tel: 0533-546006
Tel: 0533-660620 (home)
Contact: A F Sayani
Islamic Centre
55 Barclay Street
Leicester

Jame Masjid (King Faisal Mosque)
Atkinson Street
off Asfordby Street
Leicester LE5 3QK
Tel: 0533-621963/460300
Contact: Mr I Omarji
Office: Secretary

Kokni Muslim Jamat
157 Beatrice Road
Leicester

Kokni Muslim Youth Club
43 Milverton Avenue
Leicester LE4 0HY

Ladies Islamic Circle
65 Stoughton Drive North
Leicester

Leicester Cutchi Jamat

9 Maifa Street
Leicester

Leicester Central Mosque

Conduit Street
Leicester LE2
Tel: 0533-738338
Contact: Mr Khan
Office: Managing Trustee
A newly purpose-built mosque and community centre in the heart of the city catering for the religious, social, spiritual and educational needs of the Muslims in Leicestershire. It is a place of worship, Islamic school and library; it arranges for funeral services, is registered for the solemnisation of marriages and is open to visits from schools and colleges. Inter-faith organisations are also welcome. regular educational programmes are held in English for ladies, youth and children. Weekly sessions of dhikr (remembrance of Lord) according to Sufi traditions. Elderly people meet on Fridays.

Leicester Mosque Trust

57 Upper Tichbourne Street
Leicester

Leicester Muslim Association

28 Melbourne Road
Leicester

Leicestershire Muslim Kokni Association

17 Gillbank Drive
Ratby
Leicester LE6 0NH
Tel: 0533-394471

Leicester Muslim Mosque

146 Berners Street
Leicester
Tel: 0533-622460

Madressa-e-Anjuman-e-Ghousai Asrafia

3-5 Evington Street
Leicester
Tel: 0533-546544 (home)
Contact: Aziz Thadha
Office: Chairman

Masjid al Bukhari and Muslim Education Centre

159-161 Loughborough Road
Leicester LE4 5LR
Tel: 0533-665506

Tel: 0533-665472
Contact: Gulam Omarji Makadam
Office: Chairperson

Masjid al Falah and Islamic Education Trust

3-9 Keythorpe Street
Leicester LE2 0AL
Tel: 0533-511833
Contact: Mr Ahmed Haji
Office: Secretary

Masjid-e-Noor and Leicester Muslim Society

146-152 Berners Street
Leicester LE2 0FU
Tel: 0533-622640
Tel: 0533-518688 (home)
Contact: Mr Ibrahim Bayat

Masjid Tabuk and Evington Muslim Centre

59 Stoughton Drive North
Leicester LE5 5UD
Tel: 0533-735529
Tel: 0533-737183 (home)
Fax: 0533-461611
Contact: Mohamed Seedat
Office: Secretary
Place of worship and religious school. All are welcome at the mosque.

Mosque and Islamic Centre

2a Sutherland Street
Leicester LE2 1DS
Tel: 0533-553867/854052
Contact: Mohammed Salim

Muslim Education Centre

159 Loughborough Road
Leicester LE4 5LQ
Tel: 0533-665506

Muslim Khatri Association

95 Rowsley Avenue
Leicester LE5 5JP

Muslim Ladies' Association

Flat 3
172 Evington Lane
Leicester LE5 6DH
Tel: 0533-735995

Muslim Welfare Trust
c/o 24 Wilson Street
Leicester LE2 0BB
Tel: 0533-517948

Muslim Youth Education Council
28 Bakewell Street
Leicester LE2 1GN

Pakistan Association Muslim Community
Muslim Community Centre
Old Boys School
Melbourne Road
Leicester LE2 0GU
Tel: 0533-25670
Contact: Mr R T Khan
Office: Chairperson
Religious and cultural association catering for the Pakistani community. Activities include accommodation, community action, education, ethnic minorities, immigration, religious and social activities.

Shia Ithna-Asheri Jama'at Mosque
127 Loughborough Road
Leicester LE4 5LQ
Tel: 0533-682828
Contact: Secretary

Sunni Muslim Jamat
14 Lanbourne Street
Leicester LE2 6HL
Tel: 0533-884508 (home)
Contact: Mr H S Majothi
Office: Chairperson
A religious organisation run mainly by women members. When required, halls are hired for religious, cultural and social activities. For worship, members use the nearest convenient mosque.

Surati Muslim Khalifa Society
127 Mere Road
Leicester LE5 5GQ
Tel: 0533-511120
Tel: 0533-625919 (home)
Contact: Mr Mustafa F Karim
Office: Co-ordinator
Membership group and place of religious education. The society aims to promote the advancement of the Muslim faith through religious education and to serve the local minority ethnic community. It promotes and manifests this by providing and maintaining a Muslim

school for religious studies. It also provides social and cultural activities for its members including youth and sports activities and a womens group.

UK Islamic Mission Leicester Branch
41 Gwendolen Road
Leicester LE5 5FL
Tel: 0533-730043
Tel: 0533-512928 (home)
Contact: Mr Sadiq Khokhar
Office: Chairperson
Branch organisation. Place of religious training and weekly meetings of groups of similar aims. Religious meetings are held to enhance God-consciousness amongst the members. Public meetings are organised on religious and social issues.

Young Muslim Association
31 Lambourne Road
Leicester

Omar Mosque and Islamic Society
85 King Street
Loughborough
Leicestershire LE11 1SD
Tel: 0509-214500

Young Muslims Loughborough
79 Empress Road
Loughborough
Leicestershire LE11 1RH
Tel: 0509-212942 (home)
Fax: 0509-210912
Contact: Mahboob-ur-Rashid Chowdhury
Office: President
Youth membership group and local branch organisation. It aims to mobilise youth in a coherent and organised manner to lead a life as effective individuals within the social environment and to help them realise their social responsibility whilst simultaneously developing their individual relationship with the Creator thereby helping to create a society that is God-conscious.

Al Jamat-ul-Muslimin of Bangladesh
8 St Georges Street
Regent Square
Northampton NN1 2TR
Tel: 0604-24930
Contact: Chairperson or Secretary
Place of worship and community centre. A community and religious organisation which was established in 1967. It represents the Bengali

community in Northampton. Activities include prayer, religious education, community activities, welfare and education of the Bengali community.

Institute of Islamic Studies
Norpak House
Harold Street
Northampton

Islamic Pakistani Community Centre
98a Colwyn Road
Northampton NN1 3PX
Tel: 0604–21125
Tel: 0604–585505 (home)
Contact: Mr Riaz Bhatti

Islamic Union
c/o Norpak House
Harold Street
Northampton

Mosque
43 Argyle Street
Northampton
Tel: 0604–57230

Islamic Centre
3 Curzon Street
St. Ann's Road
Nottingham NG3 6DG
Tel: 0602–580754

Islamic Education Centre
39 Bridlington Street
Hyson Green
Nottingham NG7 5LX
Tel: 0602–29106
Contact: Mr Abdul Ghafar

Jamiah Fatima Mosque
118a Berridge road
Forestfield
Nottingham NG7
Tel: 0602–244004
Contact: Manlana Syed Zahid Hussain
Office: Head Iman

Lenton Muslim Centre
56 Rothsay Avenue
Lenton
Nottingham NG7 1PY
Tel: 0602–470484
Contact: Mr Nazan Khan

Madni Masjid and Muslims Education Centre
289 Gladstone Street
Forest Fields
Nottingham NG5 1BS
Tel: 0602–691275
Tel: 0602–692566 (home)
Contact: Raza Ul Haq
Office: Chair

Madrassa Karimia
141 Berridge Road
Forestfield
Nottingham NG7 6HR
Tel: 0602–704490
Contact: Mr M Hussain

Madrassa-e-Islamia
58 Thurgarten Street
Nottingham NG2 4AG
Tel: 0602–502520
Contact: Mr Awangzaib

Meadows Muslim Action Group
Meadows Muslim Centre
Collygate Road
Lenton
Nottingham NG7 1PY
Tel: 0602–527134
Tel: 0602–528860 (home)
Contact: Mr M Ishaq
Open for every Muslim. It serves the religious, cultural and social needs of Muslims and is also open to non-Muslims. Activities are organised for children.

Muslim Welfare House
215 Derby Road
Lenton
Nottingham NG7 1QJ
Tel: 0602–412462

Muslim Youth Cultural Society
3 Cranmer Grove
Cranmer Street
Nottingham NG3 4HE
Tel: 0602–70325
Tel: 0602–525177 (home)
Contact: M Yasin

Pakistan Community centre
163 Woodborough Road
Nottingham
Tel: 0602–582973
Contact: Mr Masood

Islah-ul-Muslimin Muslim Community Centre and Mosque
Winstanley Road
Wellingborough
Northamptonshire
Tel: 0933-678030 (home)
Contact: Mr Ashrof Ullah Khan
Office: General Secretary

Mosque
Strode Road
Wellingborough
Northamptonshire

WEST MIDLANDS

Amir-e-Millat Mosque and Community Centre
144 Stoney Lane
Spark Hill
Birmingham B11
Tel: 021-449-6001

Anjuman Arian
321 Northfield Road
Harborne
Birmingham B17 0TS
Contact: Mr M S Mian

Anjuman e Naqeebul Islam Mosque
82 Washwood Heath Road
Satley
Birmingham B8 1RD
Tel: 021-328-4930

Anjuman-e-Taraqqi-Urdu
55 Langley
Olton
Birmingham

Anjuman Noor-ul-Islam and Mosque
33 Yewtree Road
Witton
Birmingham B6 6RT
Tel: 021-328-1297
Islamic education and cultural centre.

Association of Muslim Youth
31 Farm Road
Birmingham B11

Aston University Islamic Society
Students Union
Gosta Green
Birmingham B4 7ET

Bangladesh Islamic Centre
8 Mayfield Road
Lozells
Birmingham B19

Bangladesh Islamic Centre and Mosque
296 Burbury Street
Lozells
Birmingham B19

Bangladesh Welfare Association and Mosque
19-21 Alum Rock Road
Saltley
Birmingham B8 1LL
Tel: 021-328-4746
Contact: Mr A Rahman
Office: Vice President

Birmingham Anjumane Islam Mosque Trust
President Saddam Hussein Mosque
Trinity Road
Aston
Birmingham B6 6AG
Tel: 021-554-9157
Contact: Honorary Secretary
Place of worship. Caters for and looks after the welfare of Muslims. Activities include Islamic education for Muslim children in Arabic, Urdu and mother tongue, elderly Muslims and social and welfare work including immigration advice.

Birmingham Dawatul Islam
523-527 Coventry Road
Small Heath
Birmingham B20 1SB
Tel: 021-772-8408
Fax: 021-773-4340

Birmingham Islamic Society
63 Moor Green Lane
Moseley
Birmingham B13 8NE
Contact: Dr Ethisham

Central Mosque and Birmingham Mosque Trust
180 Belgrave Road
Highgate

Birmingham B12 0XS
Tel: 021-440-6150
Contact: Dr M Nasim
Office: Chair

Chashma-e-Rahmat Mosque
Oldbury Road
Smethwick
Birmingham B66
Tel: 021-552-8729
Contact: Hafiz Mohammed Miyas
Office: Iman

Confederation of Sunni Mosques Midlands
107 Golden Hillock Road
Small Heath
Birmingham B10 0DP
Tel: 021-622-1369
Contact: Raja M Saleem Akhtar
Office: Chairman

Council of Birmingham Mosques
15 Woodstock Road
Birmingham B13 9BB
Tel: 021-429-1193

Dawatul Islam Womens Group
527 Coventry Road
Small Heath
Birmingham B10 0LL

East African Muslim Association
55 Showell Green Lane
Sparkhill
Birmingham B11
Tel: 021-771-4511
Contact: Wali Din

Ghamkol
126 Durham Road
Sparkhill
Birmingham B11 4LQ

Handsworth Mosque and Islamic Centre
23 Booth Street
Handsworth
Birmingham B21 0NG
Tel: 021-551-3049
Contact: Alhaj Fazlur Rahman
Office: Secretary General
Place of worship. Muslims attend to say daily prayers
(Salat - five times a day). The Imam teaches children

and youth five evenings a week and also delivers
lectures to Muslim gatherings, especially before Friday
prayers at midday.

Haroonia Islamic Centre
74 College Road
Alum Rock
Birmingham

Imanbarra Mosque
3 Woodview Drive
Birmingham B15
Tel: 021-440-4124

IPCI - Islamic Propagation Centre International (UK)
481 Coventry Road
Birmingham B10 0JS
Tel: 021-773-0137
Fax: 021-776-8577

Islamia Ibadat Khan Association
62 Osbourne Road
Sparkhill
Birmingham B11

Islamic Centre
30 Anderton Road
Birmingham B1

Islamic College
14 Lea Road
Greet
Birmingham B11 3LU
Tel: 021-771-3680

Islamic Cultural Association and Study Centre
262 Washwood Heath Road
Birmingham B8 1JR
Tel: 021-328-3478
Contact: Sheikh Mahmood Rashid
Office: Chair
Linked to the Naqshbandi Sufi order.

Islamic Cultural Centre
Dyson Hall
Birmingham B6

Islamic Educational and Cultural Centre
129 Normandy Road
Perry Barr
Birmingham

Islamic Education Centre

232 Witton Road
Aston
Birmingham B6 6LB
Tel: 021-523-4256 (home)
Contact: Mr A Sabur Choudhury
Office: Chairperson

Place of worship and religious education. Founded in 1976, a freehold premises was donated by the chairperson for religious activities. The centre has no source of its own income and so depends on charity. It has a regular assembly of about one hundred worshippers and around one hundred and twenty-five children are receiving religious education and mother tongue teaching. All Muslim festivals and functions are performed at the centre.

Islamic Educational Centre and Mosque Trust

238 Charles Road
Small Heath
Birmingham B10 9AA
Tel: 021-773-1937

Islamic Library and Central Hanafiyah Mosque

28 Tennyson Road
Small Heath
Birmingham B10 0HA
Tel: 021-773-6094
Contact: Adil al-Farooqi
Office: Imam

Islamic Moroccan Association

5 St Benedicts Road
Small Heath
Birmingham B10 9DP
Tel: 021-772-4391
Contact: Hamid Mohammed

Islamic Resource Centre

93 Court Road
Balsall Heath
Birmingham B12 9LQ
Tel: 021-440 3500
Fax: 021-440-8144
Contact: Mr Y Yacob
Office: Manager

Community and education centre which provides an extensive advice service on various topics ranging from housing difficulties, welfare benefits, immigration, employment and training and educational advice on a daily basis. The centre is committed to providing equality of opportunity regardless of race, religion, sexual disability in all services and projects. Advice is free and confidential. Activities include welfare services, advice on employment, immigration, social and health issues and education and mother tongue teaching.

Islamic Society

Students' Union
University of Birmingham
University Road
Birmingham B15

Islamic Teaching and Community Centre

141 Nechells Park Road
Nechells
Birmingham B7 5PH
Contact: Mr M Bashir

Islamic Welfare Association and Mosque

62 Wills Street
Lozells
Birmingham B19
Tel: 021-523-0810
Contact: Taj Afzal

Jalalabad Association

12 Pugh Road
Aston
Birmingham B6 5LL
Contact: M A Islam

Jalalabad Mosque and Islamic Centre

24–26 Dartmouth Road
Selly Oak
Birmingham B29 6EA
Tel: 021-471-1556
Contact: Hira Miah
Office: Secretary

Jami Mosque and Islamic Centre

523–525 Coventry Road
Small Heath
Birmingham B10 0LL
Tel: 021-772-6408
Contact: Dr A S Abdur Rahim
Office: President

Place of worship and Islamic Centre. Its projects include a Dar-ul-Uloom (full time high school and college divisions); Madrassa-e-Hifzul Qur'an; evening and weekend Islamic school; mother tongue Bangla/Urdu School; Darse Qur'an/Darse Hadith and Tarbiah department; Lozells Islamic centre; Ulama Board UK; Bangladesh Islamic Consultative commitee; Young Muslims, Bangladesh Islamic organisation; Marriage registration; British Muslims Engineers and Scientists' Association; Women's group and Employment Training Scheme.

Jamia Islamia (Naqshbandia)
1 Willow Crescent
Cannon Hill
Birmingham

Jamia Islamia Sultan Bahu Trust
17-21 Ombersley Road
Balsall Heath
Birmingham

Jamia Mosque
27 Putney Road
Handsworth
Birmingham B20 3PP
Tel: 021-772-6408
Contact: Quari A Wafi
Office: President

Jamiat Ahl-e- Hadith
53 George Arthur Road
Birmingham B8

Jamiat-ul-Musalimin
28 Tennyson Road
Small Heath
Birmingham B10 9AR
Tel: 021-773-6094

Jamiate Nizame Islam
64 Somerville Road
Small Heath
Birmingham B10 9EN
Tel: 021-328-8466
Contact: Malik Fazal Hussain
Office: Director
Body representing religious groups and a membership group. Its aim it to unite Muslims and mobilise the Muslim Ummah. It is also an Islamic centre and place of worship. It publishes its work, holds seminars, carries out Dawah work for understanding of the concept of Muslim Ummah.

Kashif-ul-Uloom Mosque
2 Blake Lane
Bordsley Green
Birmingham B9
Tel: 021-771-3247

Khoja Shia Ithna-Asheri Muslim Jamaat
17 Clifton Road
Balsall Heath
Birmingham B12 8SX
Tel: 021-440-0643
Tel: 021-440-2448 (home)
Contact: Firoz Moti

King's Heath Mosque
113 Station Road
Birmingham
Tel: 021-444-5428

Kokni Muslim Association
14 Arden Road
Aston
Birmingham B6 5AP

Madina Masjid
Corner of Adderley Road and Ash Road
Saltley
Birmingham B8
Tel: 021-327-1123

Madrasa Talimud Qur'an
21 Wenman Street
Balsall Heath
Birmingham B12 9SP
Contact: Haji Mir Afzal Khan

Madrasah Muhy-ul-Islam
153 Albert Road
Aston
Birmingham

Madrassa Islamia
221 Alexander Road
Birmingham

Madrassa Islamia Taleem-ul-Quran
59 Kyrwicks Lane
Sparkbrook
Birmingham

Madrassa Naqshbanbdi
1a Asmolia
Bordeseley Green Road
Birmingham

Madressa Bhinat
44 Mayfield Road
Birmingham B13

Madressa Islamia Talimuddin Society

113 Station Road
King's Heath
Birmingham
Tel: 021-444-8988
Tel: 021-444-1425 (home)
Contact: Abdus Samad Esakjee
Office: Chairperson
Place of worship and membership group. It provides
a place for worship and ablutions and teaching Islam.
Activities include teaching children Urdu and Arabic,
prayer five times a day and special morning prayers on
Eid function, marriage arrangements, and general
lectures and teaching on Islam for all ages.

Markazi Jamiat Ahl-e-Hadith and Community Centre

20 Green Lane
Small Heath
Birmingham B9 5DB
Tel: 021-773 0019
Contact: Mr M Abdul Headi
Office: General Secretary

Maroof-e-Islam

183 Grove Lane
Handsworth
Birmingham B20 2HD

Masjid Adam and Madrasah Salfia

53 George Arthur Road
Saltley
Birmingham B8 1LN
Tel: 021-327-5168

Masjid e Noor

158 Frederick Road
Aston
Birmingham B6 6DG
Tel: 021-328-0156

Masjid-e-Noor

8 Towell Road
Kingstanding
Birmingham B44 8EA

Medina Mosque

17 Park Avenue
Hockley
Birmingham B18 5ND
Tel: 021-554-6717

Mehr-ul-Millat Mosque

21 Shakespeare Street
Sparkhill
Birmingham B11
Tel: 021-773-5966

Mosque

Dawlish Road
Bournbrook
Birmingham

Mosque

18 Speedwell Road
Birmingham B5 7PT
Tel: 021-440-1876

Mosque

58 Trinity Road
Aston
Birmingham B6

Mosque

6 Wittan Street
Birmingham B6

Mosque

44 Fantham Road
Aston
Birmingham B6
Tel: 021-523-9963

Mosque

239 Alum Rock Road
Alum Rock
Birmingham B8

Mosque

49 Couchman Road
Alum Rock
Birmingham B8

Mosque

Hob Moor Road
Small Heath
Birmingham B9

Mosque

22 Hugh Road
Small Heath
Birmingham B10

Mosque
6 Fullham Road
Sparkbrook
Birmingham B11

Mosque
89 Edgbaston Road
Balsall Heath
Birmingham B12
Tel: 021-558-4077

Mosque
40 Oakfield Road
Moseley
Birmingham B12

Mosque
8 Manfield Road
Lozells
Birmingham B19

Mosque
10 Holly Road
Handsworth
Birmingham B20 2DB
Tel: 021-523-7529

Mosque
129 Newcombe Road
Handsworth
Birmingham B21

Mosque
Stafford Road
Handsworth
Birmingham B21

Mosque
14 Linwood Road
Handsworth
Birmingham B21

Mosque
15 Ministead Road
Erdington
Birmingham B24 8PS
Tel: 021-328-4627

Mosque and Anjuman Khuddamuddin
11-15 Woodstock Road
Moseley
Birmingham B13 9BB
Tel: 021-449-1193

Mosque and Dar-ul-Uloom Islamia
107-113 Golden Hillock Road
Small Heath
Birmingham B10 0DP
Tel: 021-771-4534
Contact: Mr Saleem Akhtar

Mosque and Madrasa
84 Bordesley Green Road
Bordesley Green
Birmingham B9
Tel: 021-772-3387

Mosque and Madrassah Faiz-ul-Quran
298 Dudley Road
Birmingham

Mosque and Muslim Student House
517-519 Moseley Road
Birmingham B12

Mosque Ghausia and Community Centre
237 Albert Road
Aston
Birmingham B6 5LX
Tel: 021-327-1123
Contact: Mr M Azim
Office: President

Mosque Jamia and UK Islamic Mission
401-403 Alum Rock Road
Alum Rock
Birmingham B8 3DT

Muslim Association
19b Freer Road
Aston
Birmingham B6 6NE
Tel: 021-551-9171

Muslim Bazar Kallayan Somity
45 Gaddesby Road
Lings Heath
Birmingham B14 7EX

Muslim Centre
"Peace"
4 Goffs Close
Harborne
California Way
Birmingham B32 3XA
Tel: 021-426-5261 (home)
Contact: Mr Mutteeullah Dard

Office: Preacher

Membership group. A group of volunteers attempting to unite mankind with its Creator and to establish peace throughout the world. The group believes in all the Prophets including Abraham, Moses, Jesus, Krishna, Buddha, Confucious, Zoroaster, Muhammad, Ahmad and many others. Activities include lectures explaining Islamic teachings on every aspect of human religious tolerance to all ages and sexes.

Muslim Education Trust

55 Portland Road
Edgbaston
Birmingham B16 9HS
Tel: 021-454-0671
Contact: Dr Am Rajput

Muslim Foundation

122 Stamford Road
Handsworth
Birmingham B20 3PS
Tel: 021-356-3092
Contact: Mr H Zaman
Office: Chair

Muslim Liason Committee

Central Jamia Mosque
180 Belgrave Road
Birmingham B12 0XS
Tel: 021-440-5355
Contact: Mr M Y Qamar

Muslim Prayer House

19 Cromer Road
Birmingham B12

Muslim Prayer House

40 Oakfield Road
Balsall Heath
Birmingham B12

Muslim Prayer House

594 Coventry Road
Small Heath
Birmingham B10

Muslim Prayer House

66 Fentham Road
Aston
Birmingham B6

Muslim Prayer House and Community Centre

1 Willows Crescent
Balsall Heath
Birmingham B12 9NN
Tel: 021-440-3502
Contact: Mr Abdul Rahman

Muslim Welfare and Community Centre

61 Algernon Road
Edgbaston
Birmingham B16 0HX
Contact: Mr M Dad

Muslim Welfare Association

98 Walford Road
Sparkbrook
Birmingham B11 1QA
Tel: 021-772 2396
Contact: Qari Tassawar Ul-Haq
Office: Chairperson

Place of worship and representative body. Activities include information on Community welfare, worship, Islamic and mother tongue education, establishing Mosques and training for adults and children.

Muslim Welfare Society

31 Gladstone Road
Sparkbrook
Birmingham B11 1LP

Muslim Welfare Society and Parents Association

35 Selly Park Road
Selly Park
Birmingham B29 7PH
Contact: Mr M Rafique

Muslim Women's Centre

52 Mackenzie Road
Moseley
Birmingham B11 4EL

Noor-ur-Uloom Mosque

85 St Oswald Road
Small Heath
Birmingham B10 9RB
Tel: 021-773-7036
Contact: M Sadiq

Organisation of Muslim Women

Masjid Adam
53 George Arthur Road
Saltley
Birmingham B8 1LN
Tel: 021-327-5168

Paigham-e-Islam Trust

423 Stratford Road
Sparkhill
Birmingham B11 4LB
Tel: 021-773-8301
Contact: H M Idrees
Place of worship. A mosque, madrassa and a bookshop. It provides daily Islamic teaching to children, prayers five times a day, advice to schools, colleges and other interested parties regarding Islam and Asian culture.

Quwat-ul-Islam Mosque

97 Florence Road
Smethwick
Birmingham
Contact: A E Qureshi
Office: Chairperson
Place of worship. The organisation provides a service to the local Asian community in general and to Muslims in particular, to overcome their social welfare problems at the same time as fulfilling their religious needs by teaching Islamic studies to the local children and providing a place of worship. Activities include youth groups, discussion sessions, adult learning, sports activities, religious education for children and adults, worship and general community work.

Sadam Hussain Mosque

Birchfield Road
Perry Barr
Birmingham B20

Selly Park Muslim Welfare Society

1014 Pershore Road
Selly Park
Birmingham B29 7PX
Contact: Mr S A Malik

Small Heath Mosque

6 Johnson Close
Small Heath
Birmingham B8 2RF
Tel: 021-784-3930
Contact: Mr Ghani

Sparkbrook Islamic Centre

179-187 Anderton Road
Sparkbrook
Birmingham B11 1ND
Tel: 021-773-8651
Contact: Mr Mohammad Afzal
Office: Centre Manager
One of the largest Islamic Community Centres in the UK. Its activities include a mosque, community centre, youth activities, evening school, bookshop, library, holiday schemes, welfare work, elderly and women's work, Christian- Muslim dialogue and visits by groups.

Sparkhill Mosque and Islamic Centre

181 Woodland Road
Sparkhill
Birmingham B11 4ER
Tel: 021-778-5157

Sufi Centre (Naqshbandi Order)

38 Warwick Road
Birmingham B11 4QR
Tel: 021-772-8120
Contact: Sufi Abdullah Khan

Taiba Mosque and Islamic Educational Cultural Centre

9 Serpentine Road
Witton
Birmingham B6 6SB
Tel: 021-327-4204
Tel: 021-328-0837 (home)
Contact: Maulana Bostan Qadri
Office: President
Place of worship and membership group. It aims to provide Mosque worship for the Muslim community. Activities include welfare, community work, worship, youth and women.

UK Islamic Mission

30 Anderton Road
Sparkbrook
Birmingham B11 1NQ

Washwood Heath Muslim Centre and Madrassah Qasim Ul-Uloom

790 Washwood Heath Road
Washwood Heath
Birmingham B8 2JG
Tel: 021-327-7434
Contact: Qari Tassawar Ul-Haq
Office: Director
Place of worship, representative body and Muslim

school. The organisation runs a school of religious organisation, arranges meetings and lectures, and generally provides information. Activities include worship, Islamic education and support in Islamic affairs.

Young Muslim Organisation

523 Coventry Road
Small Heath
Birmingham B10 0LL
Tel: 021-772 3014
Contact: Dr Abdur-Rahim
Office: President

Zawyia Islamic Centre

126 Pershore Road
Edgbaston
Birmingham B5 7NY
Tel: 021-440-1347
Contact: Councillor S Abdi
Membership group. A body representing other groups. Activities include welfare, women, youth and an Indian bazaar.

Zawiya Mosque

294 Edward Road
Edgbaston
Birmingham B5 7PH
Tel: 021-440-5746
Contact: Sheikh Mohamed Kassam
Office: Sheikh Kassam
Place of worship. It is the oldest mosque in Birmingham, having been founded in the Indian bazaar in 1943.

Zia-ul-Quran Mosque

218-220 St Saviours Road
Alum Rock
Birmingham B8
Tel: 021-328-1584

Mosque

134 Princess Street
Burton-upon-Trent
Staffordshire
Contact: Afzal Quarashi

Mosque Committee

173 Uxbridge Street
Burton-upon-Trent
Staffordshire
Tel: 0283-51163
Contact: Mr Rafaqat Hussain
Office: Chairman

Muslim Community Education Centre

7-10 York Street
Burton-upon-Trent DE15 2XL
Tel: 0283-512026 (home)
Contact: Haji Mohammed Sadiq
Office: Chairperson
A religious organisation runs under the management of Jamiat-Ahl-e-Hadith (Burton branch). The organisation functions for education and welfare, including the teaching of the Qur'an and mother tongue language (Urdu).

Anjuman-e-Gujerati Mosque

260-261 Stoney Stanton Road
Foleshill
Coventry CV1 4FR
Tel: 0203-622774
Tel: 0203-550322 (home)
Contact: Yusuf Ismail Badat
Office: President

Anjuman-e-Gujerati Muslims

115 Leicester Causeway
Coventry CV1 4HL
Contact: Mr A Khalifa

Hillfields Mosque and Muslim Association

1-3 Berry Street
Hillfields
Coventry CV1 5JT
Tel: 0203-251184
Tel: 0203-555497
Contact: Mr Usmani
Office: Secretary
Place of worship and association. It was established by Indian Gujerati Muslims in 1977 as a registered charity. It is maintained by voluntary contributions by fund raising locally and in other cities. Activities include worship, religious education (including evening classes for about one hundred children), funeral and marriage facilities for Muslims. The general welfare of local Muslims is catered for.

Islamic Brotherhood

57 Leicester Causeway
Foleshill
Coventry CV1 4HL
Contact: Mr M Ayoub

Islamic Education and Cultural Society

59 Highland Road
Earlsdon
Coventry CV5 6GQ

Islamic Society
c/o Students Union
Coventry University
Priory Road
Coventry
West Midlands

Islamic Study Centre
159 Stoney Stanton Road
Coventry
West Midlands
Tel: 0203-229113

Jamia Mosque
Eagle Street
Foleshill
Coventry CV1 4GY
Tel: 0203-22169
Tel: 0203-419514 (home)
Contact: Mr M Ali
Office: Secretary

Masjid-e-Zeenat-ul-Islam
283-287 Stoney Stanton Road
Coventry CV1 4FR

Zeenut-ul-Islam Mosque
Cambridge Street
Coventry
Contact: Mr Y Badat

Anwar-ul-Quran Mosque and Muslim Community Centre
153 Walsall Road
Darlaston
West Midlands WS10 8BD

Bangladesh Islamic Society
134 Franchise Street
Darlaston
West Midlands
Contact: Ramzan Ali Choudhury

Bangladesh Islamic Society and Mosque
48 Cook Street
Darlaston
West Midlands

Darlaston Bangladeshi Muslim Organisation
197 Walsall Road
Darlaston
West Midlands
Contact: Abrus Miah

Mosque
59 Walsall Road
Darlaston
West Midlands

Mosque
51 Cobden Street
Fallingheath
Darlaston
West Midlands
Tel: 021-526-2988

Muslim Welfare Society (Darlaston and Wednesbury) and Masjid-e-Umar
Bills Street
Darlaston
West Midlands WS10 8BB
Tel: 021-526-6596
Contact: Mahmood Ebrahim Patel
Office: Honorary Secretary
A place of worship. The objects of this society are the development of the Islamic religion as practised by Sunni Muslims through the provision of a mosque. In addition, there is the advancement of the education of Muslim children in accordance with the tenets and doctrines of the Sunni sect of Islam.

Dudley Mosque
Birmingham Street
Castle Hill
Dudley
West Midlands
Tel: 0384-253951/233081
Contact: Mr M Hanif
Office: General Secretary
Place of worship. It exists for the spiritual and educational needs of Muslims in Dudley, and also the recreational, cultural and social needs, especially of the young people. It aims to foster good will and harmonious relations with other communities and organisations.

Ghausia Mosque and Welfare Association
c/o Lye Mosque
High Street
Lye
Dudley
West Midlands

Jamia Masjid & Islamic School Ahl-e-Hadith
29 Queen's Cross
Dudley
West Midlands DY1 1QU
Tel: 0384-258479

Tel: 0384–239417
Contact: Mr M Shabir
Office: General Secretary
Place of worship and education.

Lye Islamic and Welfare Association
92 Brook Street
Dudley
West Midlands

Muslim Community House
39 Claughton Road
Dudley
West Midlands DY2 7EA
Tel: 0384–233081
Contact: Mr G H Choudhary
Office: Chairperson
Resource agency. It provides advice, information and support to the Muslim community arranging social, cultural, religious and educational programmes. It supports self-help activities for the Muslim community including youth and children.

Muslim Youth Association
16 North Street
Dudley
West Midlands

Bengali Muslim Mosque and Community Centre
149/150 New John Street
Halesowen
Nr Birmingham B62 8HT
Contact: Mr Hiron Miah
Office: Chair
Place of worship. Activities include worship, religious education and mother tongue teaching.

Blackheath Islamic and Community Centre / UK Islamic Mission
314–318 Long Lane
Halesowen
Nr Birmingham B26 9LQ
Tel: 021–559-7314

Blackheath Jamia Mosque Trust
21 Vicarage Road
Halesowen
West Midlands
Contact: Mr Abdul Razzaq
Office: General Secretary

Blackheath Jamia Mosque Trust
143–150 Maltmill Lane
Blackheath
Halesowen
West Midlands

United Muslim Committee
14 Victoria Road
Halesowen
West Midlands

Mosque
48 Radford Avenue
Kidderminster
Worcestershire

Mosque
2 Radford Avenue
Kidderminster
Worcestershire

Mosque
Valley Road
Lye
West Midlands

Muslim Culture and Promotional Group
4 Abbots Way
Westlands
Newcastle-under-Lyme
Staffordshire ST5 2ET
Tel: 0782–615978 (home)
Contact: Mr F Y Khan
Office: Secretary
Membership group. It aims for the promotion and advancement of Muslim culture.

Muslim Society and Mosque
152 Edward Street
Nuneaton
Warwickshire CV11 5RA
Tel: 0203–327882

Nuneaton Muslim Society
The Mosque
Frank Street
Nuneaton
Warwickshire CV11 5RB
Tel: 0203–382372
Contact: Mr Y E Sidat
Office: General Secretary

Sandwell Muslim Education Association
130 Vicarage Road
Oldbury
West Midlands

Hanif Madressah
140 Mount Pleasant
Redditch
Worcestershire

Mosque
28 Easemore Street
Redditch
Worcestershire B98 8HA
Tel: 0527-63834
Contact: Mohammed Akram

Blackheath Bangladesh Association
34 Beeches Road
Rowley Regis
West Midlands B65 0BT
Tel: 021-561-2055
Contact: Mr Hiron Miah

Rugby Mosque
Grosvenor Hall
88 Grosvenor Road
Rugby
Warwickshire
Tel: 0788-543680

Cobridge Muslim Community Centre
4 Kirby Street
Cobridge
Stoke-on-Trent
Staffordshire
Contact: K Iqbal

Federation of Mosques
53 Mulgrave Street
Hanley
Stoke-on-Trent ST1 5EP
Tel: 0782-46765
Contact: Mr Raja
Office: Director

Ghausia Mosque
233 Waterloo Road
Stoke-on-Trent
Staffordshire
Tel: 0782-24451
Contact: R Fiyaz

Gilani Noor Mosque
2 Chaplin Road
Longton
Stoke-on-Trent ST3 4QS
Tel: 0782-335606
Contact: K Hussain

Islamic Centre
Bedford Road
Shelton
Stoke-on-Trent ST1 4PJ
Tel: 0782-280364
Contact: Mr Rana Muhammad Tufail
Office: Director
Place of worship and community centre. It caters for religious worship and the social, cultural and educational needs of the Muslims living in the benefit area.

Islamic Cultural Centre
16 York Street
Hanley
Stoke-on-Trent
Staffordshire
Tel: 0782-268122
Contact: Mr A Ahmed

Madina Mosque
273 Waterloo Road
Cobridge
Stoke-on-Trent
Tel: 0782-261429
Tel: 0782-267329 (home)
Contact: Mr Dean Merchant
Office: Chairperson
Place of worship. The Mosque is non-political and unbiased and is fully convicted to freedom of choice and the spread of religion through preaching. Activities include worship and Islamic education for children.

Muslim Defence Council
21 Furnace Road
Longton
Stoke-on-Trent
Staffordshire
Tel: 0782-341076
Tel: 0782-341076
Contact: Mr Habib Ullah Siddiqi

Muslim Funeral Society
5 Chatham Street
Shelton

Stoke-on-Trent ST1 4NY
Tel: 0782-269661
Contact: Mr M Akram

Muslim Youth Association
17 Rushton Road
Stoke-on-Trent
Staffordshire
Contact: Mr Mohammed Farooq
The Association aims to uphold Muslim youth activities and to provide information and help with jobs, health, housing.

Naqshabandia Mosque
18 Dyke Road
Hanley
Stoke-on-Trent
Staffordshire
Tel: 0782-287432
Contact: Mr A Akbar

Talim-ul-Qur'an and Mosque
1 Ashford Street
Shelton
Stoke-on-Trent
Staffordshire
Tel: 0782-416179 (home)
Contact: Mr Sadiq
Place of worship and religious education. The organisation's aim is to run the Mosque and meet the salery expenses of the two priests who are responsible for the religious education side. In addition to worship and welfare activities, an anual gathering is held and scholars address local people regarding issues like a Muslim's role in a multi-racial society etc.

Tunstall Mosque
2a Keele Street
Tunstall
Stoke-on-Trent
Staffordshire
Tel: 0782-813617
Tel: 0782-827677 (home)
Contact: Mr B Ali

Ghausia Mosque and Social Welfare Association
2a High Street
The Lye
Stourbridge
West Midlands DY9 8LF
Tel: 0384-893110
Contact: Mr R G Kham
Office: President

Place of worship and educational organisation. The Mosque is open all day seven days a week. There are also Arabic classes held for children.

Lye Islamic and Welfare Association
13c Vale Street
Amblecote
Stourbridge
West Midlands

Muslim Mosque Trust
119 Crescent Road
Hadley
Telford
Shropshire
Contact: c/o Mr Abdul Haliq

Pakistan Welfare Association and Mosque
47-49 Mill Bank
Wellington
Telford
Shropshire
Tel: 0952-55389

Kanz-ul-Iman Muslim Welfare Association
8 Peel Street
Tipton
West Midlands DY4 8RG
Tel: 021-557-6556
Contact: Mr M Arif

Mosque and Tipton Muslim Trust Association
17 Wellington Road
Tipton
West Midlands DY4 8RS
Tel: 021-557-2692
Contact: Mr Montaz Ali
Place of worship. It mainly serves the Bangladeshi community, but as a place of worship is open to any Muslim. It is a converted old house but the organisation plans to raise the resources to provide a purpose-built place of worship to improve the quality of life and provide a better environment and improve neighbourhood relations. Activities include worship, welfare and theological classes for Muslim children.

Tipton and Tividale Muslim Welfare Association
10 Gate Street
Tipton
West Midlands DY4 7SP
Tel: 021-520-5832
Contact: Mr R A Qayyum

Anjuman-e-Gosia Mosque

68 Selbourne
Chuckery
Walsall
West Midlands

Anjuman Isha'at Islam

110 Prince Street
Walsall
West Midlands
Contact: A Hussain

Anjuman-i-Ishaat e Islam

102–104 Wednesbury Road
Walsall
West Midlands

Bangladesh Islamic Cultural Association

9 Mount Street
Walsall
West Midlands
Contact: Jayfar Ali

Bangladesh Mosque (Bangladesh Islamic Cultural Association)

74 Wednesbury Road
Walsall WS1 3RR
Tel: 0922-20051
Tel: 0922 641073 (home)
Contact: Mr Kaisor Ali
Office: Secretary
Membership group. The mosque and centre provide a range of activities for the elderly, disabled, unemployed and young from the Bangladeshi community. The mosque is in the process of construction at the time of writing. Islamic classes are run for the elderly and evening classes are held for children between the ages of seven years and sixteen years. Besides the normal five prayer times a day special prayers are held on Friday. From time to time holiday projects are organised.

Ghausia Qasmia Trust

28 Little London
Walsall
West Midlands
Contact: M Yasin

Ghosia Quasmia Mosque + Darul Uloom

34–35 Mount Street
Walsall
West Midlands
Tel: 0922-34862

Islamic Society of Britain (Walsall Branch)

52a Milton Street
Walsall WS1 4JS
Tel: 0922-21659 (home)
Fax: 0922-32338 (home)
Contact: Mr Sohaib Siddiq
Office: President (Ameer)
The Islamic Society of Britain (Walsall) aims to introduce Islam in its pristine form, to invite everyone to its message and to campaign against all forms of injustice and oppression in order to create a just, caring and God-conscious society. To achieve this, weekly study circles, lectures, seminars, exhibitions, conferences on Islamic issues and social activities are held, creating greater Islamic awareness and respect towards others in the community.

Jame Ghosia

14 Selbourne Street
Chuckery
Walsall
West Midlands
Tel: 0922-31586

Jamia Mosque

Green Lane
Birchill
Walsall
West Midlands

Markazi Jamia Masjed Raza Committee

56 Florence Street
Walsall
West Midlands
Contact: A K Qadri

Mosque and Butts Muslim Community

22 Cannon Street
Butts
Walsall
West Midlands
Tel: 0922-640983

Mosque and Islamic Centre

4 Rutter Street
Caldmore
Walsall WS1 4HN
Tel: 0922-20982
Contact: Saeed Ur Rahman
Office: Imam
Place of worship and welfare. The doors of the centre are open around the clock to all members of the local community (Muslims and non-Muslims who wish to seek salvation in this life and the life here after). The

caretaker is resident and the centre is equipped with all possible and affordable facilities for the worship and welfare of all, regardless of age, gender or place of origin.

Mosque and Islamic Cultural Society

156 Wednesbury Road
Walsall
West Midlands
Tel: 0922-20618

Mosque and Madresa Talimuddin

38 Florence Street
Walsall
West Midlands
Tel: 0922-20982

Pakistan Muslim Welfare Association

62 Dalkeith Street
Birchill
Walsall WS2 8QB
Tel: 0922-640787

Pakistan Muslim Welfare Association

64 Farringdon Street
Birchills
Walsall
West Midlands
Contact: Ashiq Hussain
Place of worship. The association runs the central Mosque Birchills Street and community centre. It provides Islamic education and welfare for youth, women and the disabled through its voluntary work and fundraising.

Shah Jalal Mosque

32-33 Mount Street
Walsall
West Midlands
Tel: 0922-647624
Contact: Mr H Rahman
Office: Chairperson
Place of worship. The mosque was established in 1985 and has over two hundred and fifty members. Over three hundred children study religious education at the mosque.

UK Islamic Mission Walsall Branch

4 Rutter Street
Walsall
West Midlands
Tel: 0922-20982

Young Muslims Walsall

4 Rutter Street
Walsall WS1 4HN

Bangladesh Islamic Association

10-11 Lewisham Road
Smethwick
Warley
West Midlands B66 2BP
Tel: 021-558-8204
Contact: Mr M Uddin
Registered for marriages, and funeral prayers are offered. Hospital visitation, training for English as a second language and sewing classes are provided. Other religious duties and services are provided as necessary and educational liaison is offered with local authorities and welfare advice organisations.

Cradley Heath Muslim Association

43 Highgate Street
Cradley Heath
Warley
West Midlands B64 5RX
Tel: 021-559-6813
Tel: 021-0384-62049 (home)
Contact: Mr Basharat Ali

Islamic Centre and Library

273 Montague Road
Smethwick
Warley
West Midlands B66 4PS
Tel: 021-565-3782
Contact: Mr Fazlur Rehman
Office: Organiser

Muslim Mother Tongue Association Sandwell

290 Tat Bank Road
Oldbury
Warley
West Midlands
Tel: 021-552-7376
Contact: Mr S Akhtar

Muslim Mother Tongue Association

18 Holly Lane
Smethwick
Warley
West Midlands B66 1QN
Tel: 021-558-6982
Contact: Mr Allah Dad

Oldbury Mosque and Muslim Welfare Association

Formerly Oldbury Labour Club
Oldbury Road
Smethwick
Warley
West Midlands B66 1HN
Tel: 021-565-2666
Tel: 021-565-5062 (home)
Contact: Mr M Hanif
Office: General Secretary
Place of worship promoting the ideology of Islam and providing religious facilities to the Muslim community. Mother tongue and Arabic teaching facilities are also offered for children.

Pakistani Muslim Islamic Community Centre

205 Cheshire Road
Smethwick
Warley
West Midlands
Tel: 021-555-6047
Contact: Mr Mohammed Saeed

Rowley Regis Muslim Welfare Association

99 Beeches Road
Rowley Regis
Warley
West Midlands
Tel: 021-559-7954
Contact: Mr Umar Faruq

Sandwell Central Mosque Trust and Ittehad-ul-Muslemeen Sandwell

49 Barker Street
Oldbury
Warley
West Midlands
Tel: 021-552-6775/8679
Contact: Mr S J Shah

Sandwell Muslims Organisation

Formerly Oldbury Labour Club
Oldbury Road
Smethwick
Warley
West Midlands B66 1HN
Tel: 021-565-2666
Contact: Mr Ghulam Choudhary
Office: Project Organiser
A voluntary organisation acting in community development as a resource agency providing advice and information on matters relating to welfare rights, immigration and nationality law, taxation, housing and numerous other areas of social interest. An interpretation and translation service is also provided.

Sandwell Pakistan Muslim Welfare Association

46 Grange Road
Cradley Heath
Warley
West Midlands
Tel: 021-561-4250
Contact: Mr R G Khan

Sandwell Pakistan Muslim Womens Association

130 Vicarage Road
Oldbury
Warley
West Midlands B76 8HR
Contact: Mrs Uzra Butt

Sandwell Pakistan Muslim Womens Association

1 Rectory Gardens
Vicarage Street
Oldbury
Warley
West Midlands
Tel: 021-552-6775
Contact: Mrs Z Durrani

Smethwick Bangladeshi Muslim Welfare Association

253 Halfords Lane
Smethwick
Warley
West Midlands
Tel: 021-558-9449 (home)
Contact: Mr Assad Uddin
Office: General Secretary
Place of worship. The association provides for the teaching of Islam, congregational prayers, sermons and all relevant activities within the Islamic faith. Activities include worship and welfare.

Smethwick Pakistani Muslims Association

1-7 Corbett Street
Smethwick
Warley
West Midlands B66 3PY
Tel: 021-555-6047
Contact: Mr Mohammed Azad
Office: Chairperson
Mosque and community centre. The objects of the

association are to relieve the inhabitants of Smethwick who are in conditions of need, hardship or distress (particularly members of the Pakistani community living or resident therein). Activities include the provision of advice; facilities for education and cultural training and services for advancement of the Islamic religion.

Young Muslim Organisation (Smethwick)

2 Kimberley Road
Smethwick
Warley
West Midlands
Tel: 021-558-7581
Contact: Mr A Hannan
Office: President
A body representing Muslim youth. The main aim of the organisation is to unite Muslim youth, to guide them in understanding the Islamic faith, to educate and advise them and to help them with their social and welfare problems or any other counselling matters. Activities are arranged around the Smethwick area sometimes including sports. Advice and education is given regarding the welfare of youth.

Bangladesh Muslim Association

93 Vicarage Road
Wednesbury
West Midlands
Tel: 021-556 0491/2047
Tel: 021-502-2137 (home)
Contact: Mr Gous Ahmed

Wednesbury Bangladesh Muslim Welfare Association

9 Brunswick Park Road
Wednesbury
West Midlands
Tel: 021-502-0521
Contact: Mr Arju Miah

Bangladeshi Eshat-ul-Islam in UK

99 Edward Street
West Bromwich
West Midlands B70 8NT
Tel: 021-553 4567 / 021-558-7581
Contact: Mr M Younus

Bangladesh Islamic Centre

67 Dartmouth Street
West Bromwich
West Midlands B70 8BZ

Tel: 021-553-5598
Contact: Mr A Jalil
Office: Secretary

Islamic Centre of West Bromwich

19a Victoria Street
West Bromwich
West Midlands B70 8ET
Tel: 021-525-1742 (home)
Contact: Mr Haji Mohammad Khalid
Place of worship. A place for Muslims to come and pray. Help and understanding for the community is also provided. Other activities include religious education and mother tongue language classes for children.

Muslim Welfare Association

64 Beeches Road
West Bromwich B70 6HH
Tel: 021-236-0493
Contact: Mr N Malik

Sandwell Confederation of Bangladeshi Muslim Organisations

Bond Wolf House
312-314 High Street
West Bromwich B70 8EN
Tel: 021-500-5441
Contact: Mr Z S Chowdhury
Office: Development Officer
Umbrella organisation. It aims to: advance the social, religious, educational and cultural needs of the Bangladeshi community; work and assist Bangladeshi groups in their development and to set up and run self-help activities to overcome their difficulties and disadvantages; establish links and co-operation with Borough's statutory and voluntary organisations with a view to meet the needs of the community; act as a resource agent, providing advice, information and support to the Borough's Bangladeshi population; and in general to provide services to the Borough's Bangladeshi Muslim community.

West Bromwich Muslim Association

38 Trinity Road North
West Bromwich
West Midlands

Ahl-i-Summit Na Jama't

8 Haymarket
Pendeford
Wolverhampton
West Midlands

Jamia Mosque and Mosque Committee

197 Waterloo Road
Wolverhampton WV1 4RA
Tel: 0902-312232
Tel: 0902-715450 (home)
Fax: 0902-715450
Contact: Mr M Quazi
Office: Secretary
Place of worship and religious organisation. Activities include worship, religious education, social and cultural activities, teaching Arabic and the Holy Qur'an and welfare work.

Jamia Mosque and Muslim Community Centre

283 Newhampton Road West
Whitmore Reans
Wolverhampton WV1 0RS
Tel: 0902-752190
Tel: 0902-20717 (home)
Contact: Hajee Altaf-Hussain Chaudhury
Office: Chairperson
Place of worship. The organisation supports teaching centres at Dudley Road and Lime Street. The Council of Trustees comprises of forty people nominated by the general membership. The are currently about one hundred and twenty households in membership. Activities include prayers five times a day and at festivals and funeral arrangements and preparation of the body. Arabic and Urdu classes are provided for children and also Easter and summer play scheme for children of both sexes.

Pakistan Muslim Welfare Association

197 Waterloo Road
Wolverhampton WV1 4RA
Tel: 0902-312232
Tel: 0902-715450 (home)
Fax: 0902-715450
Contact: Mr M Quazi
Office: Secretary
Representative organisation. The organisation aims to look after the welfare, social and other needs of the community.

Penfield Mosque and Madresa

84 Lime Street
Wolverhampton
West Midlands

UK Islamic Mission

213 Newhampton Road East
Whitmore Reans

Wolverhampton WV1 4BB
Tel: 0902-711304
Contact: Mr M Hanif

Wolverhampton Muslim Trust

Glebe House
Dunstall Road
Wolverhampton
West Midlands
Tel: 0902-24360
Contact: Mr M Baig

Young Muslims Wolverhampton

213 Newhampton Road East
Wolverhampton
West Midlands

Al Medina Muslim Association

20 Middle Street
Worcester
Worcestershire
Tel: 0905-29532
Contact: A Sattar

Mosque and Muslim Community Centre

Tallow Hill
Worcester
Worcestershire

Mosque and Muslim Welfare Association

52 Shrub Hill Road
Worcester WR4 9EE
Tel: 0905-396044
Contact: Mohammed Riaz
Office: Secretary

EAST ANGLIA

Cambridge Muslim Welfare Society

c/o The Mosque
Mawson Road
Cambridge CB1 2DZ
Tel: 0223-240354

Islamic Texts Society

5 Green Street
Cambridge C32 3JU
Tel: 0223-314387
Contact: Batul Salazar
Publishing house. A charitable company registered in the UK which aims to further an understanding of Islam in the West by publishing in English works of traditional importance to the Islamic faith and culture.

Mosque
1 Mawson Road
Cambridge CB1 2BZ
Tel: 0223-350134

Mosque
175 Chesterton Road
Cambridge
Tel: 0223-50134

Mosque
17 Hills Road
Cambridge
Tel: 0223-54605

Council of Muslim Women
107 Newmarket Road
Flat 4
Norwich
Norfolk
Tel: 0603-485390

Norwich City College Islamic Society
Welfare Dept
Ipswich Road
Norwich
Norfolk NR1 3PU

Norwich Ihsan Mosque
Chapelfield East
Norwich
Norfolk
Tel: 0603-23337
Contact: A Abdullah

Norwich Muslim Community
c/o 11 The Laithes
Norwich
Norfolk
Tel: 0603-615008

Ismaili Community
65 Eyrescroft
Bretton
Peterborough
Cambridgeshire

Mosque
317 Cromwell Road
Peterborough
Cambridgeshire
Tel: 0733-51759
Contact: Mr Karamat Hussain

Pakistan British Social Association
104 Gladstone Street
Peterborough PE1 2BL
Contact: Mr G Y Kayai
Office: President
Tel: 0733-64325
A membership group concerned with welfare and the holding of religious festivals and other ceremonial days. It aims to: provide an advisory service to people in need; advance public education in the Islamic culture and religious heritage and to promote the social welfare of its members. It runs a weekly advice session every Sunday.

Shi'a Ithna Asheri Mosque
2 Burton Street
Peterborough PE2 5HD
Tel: 0733-62187
Tel: 0733-2377057 (home)
Contact: Mahmood Huda

Sunni Mosque
60 Cromwell Road
Peterborough PE1 2EB
Tel: 0733-67285

Sunni Mosque
104 Gladstone Street
Peterborough
Cambridgeshire
Tel: 0733-64325

SOUTH EAST (NORTH)

Mosque
33 Buckingham Road
Aylesbury
Buckinghamshire
Tel: 0296-33794

Islamic Society
32 Valley Road
Banbury
Oxfordshire OS16 9BH

Taybah Mosque
71 Castle Street
Banbury
Oxfordshire
Tel: 0295-50872

Barking Muslims Association
2 Victoria Road
Barking
Essex IG11 8PY
Tel: 081-591-0154
Contact: Haji Mohammad Siddique
Office: Chairman
The association can also be contacted through its
Secretary, M A Mirza, Tel: 081-591-4537.

World Islamic Mission (Greater London Branch)
70 The Lintons
Barking
Essex IG11 8NX
Tel: 081-591-1710
Contact: Mufti Younas Kashmiri
Office: President

Ghousia Razvia Mosque
3 Salisbury Avenue
Barking
Essex IG11 9XQ
Tel: 081-594-6519
Contact: Mr H M Siddique

League of British Muslims
32 Somerby Road
Barking
Essex

Majlis-e-Iqbal Islamic Education Society
33 Salisbury Avenue
Barking
Essex IG11 9XQ

Basildon Muslim Association
36 Gordons
Basildon
Essex SS13 3DZ
Tel: 0268-554234
Contact: Mr Sarfraz Sarwar
Office: Secretary
Place of worship. A house mosque for a Muslim
organisation in a very small Muslim community. The
organisation mainly serves Muslims who are new to
the area, and there are presently only around ten
families. It helps people settle and arranges purchase
of Halal meat and prayers.

Bedford Study Centre
15 Goldington Road
Bedford MK42
Tel: 0234-64161

Heraa Islamic Centre
135 Ford End Road
Bedford MK40 4LA
Tel: 0234-46265

Islamic Centre
30 Alexander Road
Bedford

Mosque
92 Ford End Road
Bedford

Mosque
10/12 Iddesleigh Road
Bedford MK40 4JU
Tel: 0234-350395
Contact: Cllr M S Khan
Office: Chair
Place of worship and membership group. A voluntary
group with a membership of over two hundred
people. The committee manages the day to day
running of the mosque and teaching of the Holy
Qur'an along with the Urdu language to children and
adults. It organises religious functions, festivals and
preaching seminars. It also runs an Advice Centre
which is open to everyone irrespective of race, religion
or creed.

Mosque and Community Centre
1-7 Westbourne Road
Bedford

Mosque and Cultural Centre
37 Alexandra Road
Bedford
Tel: 0234-47032

Chelmsford Mosque Committee
18 Burns Crescent
Chelmsford
Essex CM2 0TS

Mosque
6 Baddow Road
Chelmsford
Essex

Muslim Shia Ithna Asheri Jamaat of Essex
32 Ockelford Avenue
Chelmsford
Essex CM1 2AP
Tel: 0245-250059

Mosque
163 Bellenden Road
Chesham
Buckinghamshire

Islamic Society
Lancaster Hall
Cranfield Institute of Technology
Cranfield
MX43 0AL

Cultural and Islamic Society of Harrow
17 Ferncroft Avenue
Eastcote
Middlesex HA4 9JE
Tel: 081-868-6514 (home)
Contact: Mohammed Ajaz-Haque
Office: Social Secretary
Membership group. Social, cultural and religious activities are organised for the benefit of members. The organisation is funded through membership subscriptions and fund raising through social and cultural programmes. The Society also runs an Islamic school for children under the age of eighteen.

Indian Muslim Federation
70 Turner Road
Edgware
Middlesex

Islamic Centre - Edgware
1 North Parade
Mollison Way
Edgware
Middlesex

Muslim Students Society
Hendon College of FE
Silkstream Road
Edgware
Middlesex

UK Islamic Mission
14 Harcourt Avenue
Edgware
Middlesex

Enfield Mosque
228 High Street
Ponder's End
Enfield
Essex

Anjuman-e-Nau
108 Hill Rise
Greenford
Middlesex

Islamic School Greenford
61 Daryngton Drive
Greenford
Middlesex UB6 8BH

Muslim Association and UK Islamic Mission
21 Costons Avenue
Greenford
Middlesex

Harlow and Essex Muslim Cultural Association
10 Rosemount
Harlow
Essex
Contact: Dr Hoda
Office: Chairperson

Central Mosque
36/8 Station Road
Harrow
Middlesex
Tel: 081-861-2071

Edgware Islamic Centre
16 Glenalmond Road
Kenton
Harrow
Middlesex HA3 8JY

Harrow Central Mosque
145 Locket Road
Wealdstone
Harrow
Middlesex

Harrow Muslim Education Society
417 Pinner Road
Harrow
Middlesex
Tel: 081-427-1481

Shia Ishashri Community Building
Wilson Gardens
Harrow
Middlesex

Muslim Group
Birchwood Pavillion
Hatfield
Hertfordshire

Islamic Society
University of Hertfordshire Students Union
PO Box 109
College Lane
Hatfield
Hertfordshire AL10 9AB
Tel: 0707-268343/4
Contact: President
Membership group. A student body aimed at providing facilities for Muslims (for prayers and other needs) and also organising events to enlighten non-Muslims about Islam. It is affiliated to the Students Union and to the Federation of Student Islamic Societies in UK and Eire (FOSIS). It provides facilities for prayer within the University campus, arranges open days, talks, visits to mosques and get-togethers. It also liaises with the University authorities to improve facilities for Muslims on campus.

Islamic Education and Cultural Society
105 Park Lane
Hayes
Middlesex

Islamic Education Society
48 Balmoral Drive
Hayes
Middlesex UB4 0BX

Muslim Kumbar Womens Group
544 Uxbridge Road
Hayes
Middlesex
Tel: 081-561-5253
Contact: Mrs F Boliya
Office: President
Organises social functions and religious festivals.

Young Muslim Association
357 Station Road
Hayes
Middlesex

Quwwatul Islam/Markazi Jamia Mosque Mehria Ghosia
Hill Crest
150 St Albans Hill
Bennetts End

Hemel Hempstead
Hertfordshire HP3 9NH
Tel: 0442-43785
Contact: Mr Khadam Hussain
Office: President

Mosque
60 Cressex Road
High Wycombe
Buckinghamshire HP12 4TY
Tel: 0494-443925

Mosque
1 Hillview Road
High Wycombe
Buckinghamshire

Wycombe Islamic Mission and Mosque Trust
34-36 Jubilee Road
High Wycombe
Buckinghamshire HP11 2PG
Tel: 0494-520807
Contact: Mr M Hanif
Office: Secretary
Place of worship and education centre for Muslim children. A ten year old organisation, based in this purpose-built mosque. It has a full time religious officer who provides guidance to the community. The organisation caters for the religious, educational and social requirements of the Muslim community.

Hitchin Mosque
28 Florence Street
Hitchin
Hertfordshire SG5 1QZ
Tel: 0462-52067

Anjuman-e-Khwateen
28 Lansdown Road
Hounslow
Essex TW3 1LQ
Tel: 081-570 1394
Contact: c/o Mrs Ahsan Shah

Hounslow Jamia Masjid and Islamic Centre
235 Staines Road
Hounslow
Essex TW3 3JJ
Tel: 081-570-0938
Tel: 081-577-1858 (home)
Contact: Mr A K Qureshi
Office: General Secretary
Place of worship. Activities include daily worship, Islamic events, welfare and children's education.

Medina Islamic Mission and Islamic Centre Heathrow

35 Martindale Road
Hounslow
Essex TW4 7EW
Tel: 081-577-0647
Contact: Mr K M Ahmed
Office: President
A Sunni Muslim voluntary and welfare religious and cultural organisation. Its activities include Urdu and Arabic classes, religious teaching, sewing and knitting classes; assisting Muslims who face difficulties at the airport; arranging Eid prayers and social gatherings. It is a community centre for the elderly and for youth, for social and recreational activities.

Muslim Women's Association

157 Kingsley Road
Hounslow
Essex TW3

Young Muslim Association

122 Kingsley Road
Hounslow
Essex TW3 4AD

Hussaini Islamic Mission

38 Great South West Street
Hounslow West
Essex TN4 7NF
Tel: 081-570-3438

British Muslim Association

45 Springfield Drive
Barkingside
Ilford
Essex IG2 6PT
Tel: 081-518-2469 (home)
Contact: Mr M A Shah Siddique
Office: Secretary
Social and welfare organisation. It provides necessary help to needy people with regard to schooling, housing, health and immigration and nationality.

Idara Minhaj ul Quran

19 St. Thomas Garden
Ilford
Essex IG1 2PQ
Tel: 081-553-0498 (home)

Ilford Islamic Centre and Mosque

52-56 Albert Road
Ilford
Essex IG1 1HW

Tel: 081-478-3115
A religious and welfare organisation established in 1964. It moved to the present building in 1977, which was formerly a church hall. The organisation holds meetings and seminars and links with different faiths working in various spheres.

Ilford Muslim Welfare Association

1 Kingswood Road
Ilford
Essex

Mosque

17 Cambridge Road
Ilford
Essex

Mosque

119 St Albans Road
Seven Kings
Ilford
Essex

Mosque and Ilford Muslim Society

112 Balfour Road
Ilford
Essex IG1
Tel: 081-478-0347

Muslim Community Centre (League of British Muslims UK)

Eton Road
Ilford
Essex
Tel: 081-514-0706
Tel: 081-553-5363 (home)
Contact: Mr B Chaudhry
Office: Chairperson
Place of worship. A social, cultural and religious organisation. Its main purpose is to provide a meeting place for its members including a place for worship and to educate its members and other denominations for living harmoniously through social activities. It provides help for unemployed youths for job training in computer skills and keyboard skills. Regular indoor sports facilities are also provided to members. Regular advisory and counselling sessions are held for everyone.

Muslim Defence Council UK

17 Natal Road
Ilford
Essesx

Tel: 081-514-4436
Contact: Mr Raja Adalat Khan
Office: General Secretary

Pakistan Muslim Association of Barking and Ilford

75 Mayfair Avenue
Ilford
Essex

Redbridge and Chigwell Muslim Association

36 Woodford Avenue
Grants Hill
Ilford
Essex

Seven Kings Muslim Educational Trust

703 High Road
Seven Kings
Ilford
Essex
Tel: 081-599-6865

Hussaini Islamic Mission

19 Thornbury Road
Isleworth
Middlesex
Tel: 081-570-3438
Fax: 081-570-3438
Contact: Hojjatol Islam S M S Razavi
Office: Resident Alim
Place of worship and community centre. The mission serves the Shi'a Ithna Ashari Muslims of West London. It helps to provide Islamic services and holds Friday and other congregational prayers. A daily programme is held during the month of Ramadan. Gatherings are held to celebrate birthdays and commemorate the Martyrdom anniversaries of the Holy Prophet Mohammad and his twelve divinely appointed successors.

Anjuman-e-Haderiya

18 Brentwood Road
Luton
Bedfordshire

Bury Park Masjid Mosque

25 Bury Park Road
Luton
Bedfordshire
Tel: 0582-25412

International Islamic Propagation Mission

62 Maidenhall Road
Luton
Bedfordshire

Islamic Cultural Centre

25 Westbourne Road
Luton
Bedfordshire

Islamic Cultural Society and Mosque

2 Westbourne Road
Luton
Bedfordshire
Tel: 0582-34988

Lewsey Muslim Cultural Society

9 Sussex Close
Luton LU4 0UE
Tel: 0582-608500
Contact: Abdul-Khaleq Vazifdar

Luton Branch UK Islamic Mission

78 Selborne Road
Luton
Bedfordshire

Luton Islamic Society

100 Biscot Road
Luton
Bedfordshire

Luton Muslim Women's Association

207 Dunstable Road
Luton LU1 1BG

Masjid e Noor

20 Cromwell Road
Luton
Bedfordshire
Tel: 0582-410379

Mosque (UK Islamic Mission)

128-130 Oak Road
Luton LU4 8AD
Tel: 0582-27734

Obaid ul Rahman Islamic Society

123 Biscot Road
Luton LU3 1AN
Tel: 0582-455092

Pakistan Muslim Association
64 Dumfries Street
Luton
Bedfordshire

World Islamic Mission
156 Biscot Road
Luton
Bedfordshire
Tel: 0582-480881
Contact: Mohammed Iqbal

Noor ul Aslam Jamia al-Masjid
Holmanleaze
Maidenhead
Berkshire SL6 8AW
Tel: 0628-29423
Tel: 0628-24159 (home)
Contact: A R Malik
Office Chairperson
Place of worship and religious education. The mosque is managed by the Islamic Trust (Maidenhead) Ltd. It is purpose-built and modelled on the pattern of the holy mosque Al-Aqsa in Jerusalem and the Prophet's mosque in Medina. It has a green dome and towering high minaret. The mosque can accomodate about five hundred people. Prayers are held five times a day. Juma, congregational, prayer replaces the midday (Zohar) prayer. Classes are run at the mosque and various other locations to teach basic Islamic knowledge and the holy book Qur'an to about two hundred children. The trust is also responsible for solemnising marriages, arranging funerals and looks after other religious needs of the Muslim community in this area. Lectures by eminent Muslim scholars are arranged.

Bletchley Mosque
52 Duncombe Street
Bletchley
Milton Keynes
Buckinghamshire MK2 2LY
Tel: 0908-74380

Islamic Education Centre
73 Alston Drive
Bradwell Abbey
Milton Keynes
Buckinghamshire MK13 9HG
Tel: 0908-318633
Contact: Mrs Huda Khattab
Educational organisation. It runs a weekend madrassah for Muslim children in the Milton Keynes area as well as classes in Arabic, Qur'an and Islamic Studies, held in classrooms in a local school. Publishes the monthly magazine "USRA: The Muslim Family Magazine". Answers queries by mail and phone on various aspects of Islam, from Muslims and non-Muslims alike.

Jamia al-Karam
1a Bradwell Road
New Bradwell
Milton Keynes
Bukinghamshire MK13 0EJ
Tel: 0908-313804
Contact: Mr M I H Pirzada
Office: Managing Trustee
Place of worship. Activities include religious education and worship. It provides a boarding house for teenagers to learn more about the Arabic language and religion.

Mosque
Granby
Bletchley
Milton Keynes
Buckinghamshire
Contact: Mr Dalal

Mosque
52 Dunstable Street
Milton Keynes
Buckinghamshire
Tel: 0908-74380

Mosque and Community Centre
73 Alston Drive
Bradwell Abbey
Milton Keynes
Buckinghamshire MK13 9HG

Jamiat-e-Ulama-e-Pakistan (UK)
4 Davenham Avenue
Northwood
Middlesex HA6 3HN
Tel: 0923-823343
Contact: Mr S G Syedain
Office: Chief Organiser

Bangladeshi Islamic Education Centre and Mosque
57 Cowley Road
Oxford OX4 1HR
Tel: 0865-793118
Contact: Mr L Rahman
Office: Assistant Secretary
Place of worship and Islamic education. The organisation was established about five years ago and

is completely run by Bangladeshi Muslims without any grant. Its main aims and objects are to teach Islam to children and perform daily prayers. There are only a small number of Bangladeshi Muslims in Oxford so there are financial constraints although a full time imam is employed.

Islamic Books
62 Kelburn Road
Oxford OX4 3SH
Tel: 0865-777951
Contact: Sheikh Ahmad Bullock

Oxford Centre for Islamic Studies
St Cross College
Oxford OX1 3LZ
Tel: 0865-725077
Contact: Dr F A Nizami
Office: Director
An academic institution associated with Oxford University. It aims to promote a better understanding of Islam and of the Islamic World through research, publication and teaching. Research is undertaken including a Leverhulme Research Project to create an Atlas of Muslim history. Publications include the "Journal of Islamic Studies".

Oxford Mosque Society
10/11 Bath Street
Oxford OX4 1AY
Tel: 0865-245547
Contact: Mr Abdul Rashid
Office: General Secretary
Place of worship. Activities include religious education for girls and boys and prayers five times a day.

Oxford Muslim Welfare House and Mosque
2 Stanley Road
Cowley
Oxford OX4 1QZ
Tel: 0865-243149
Contact: Mr Aslam Khan

Oxford Brookes University Islamic Society
7 Warnerford Road
Oxford OX4 1LT
Tel: 0865-792250
Contact: Imran Abbasi

Oxford University Islamic Society
c/o St Cross College
Oxford OX1 3TU

Anjuman Ghulaman-e-Rasool
46 Palmer Park Avenue
Reading RG6 1DN
Tel: 0734-265132
Fax: 0734-352364
Contact: Mr A Q Butt
Welfare organisation.

Anjuman Muhibban-e-Rasool
15 Bulmershe Road
Reading RG1 5RM
Tel: 0734-597977
Contact: J M Banaras

Islamic Society
26 Apple Close
Tilehurst
Reading RG3 6UR
Contact: Mr A Razzak

Jamia Masjid
46 Alexandra Road
Reading RG1 5PF
Tel: 0734-61565
Contact: General Secretary

Jamiat Ahl-e-Hadith
100 Crescent Road
Reading RG1 5SN
Tel: 0734-669247
Contact: Mr R A Mir
Office: Chairman

Jamia Masjid
45 Chomley Road
Reading
Berkshire
Tel: 0734-67767
Contact: Mr A Q Khan
Office: President

Reading Branch UK Islamic Mission
325 London Road
Reading
Berkshire

Reading Islamic Centre
52 South Street
Reading RG1 4RA
Tel: 0734-504756
Contact: Mr Rana H Khan
Office: Secretary
Place of worship. A religious, social and cultural

organisation for the advancement of the religion of Islam; provision of educational facilities for the public in the learning of oriental languages; provision of scholarships, arrangements to partake in conferences, seminars and study tours and to cater for the social and cultural needs of the members. Activities include prayers and teaching of Arabic, Urdu and other languages.

Reading Muslim Womens Association

24 Shepherds House Lane
Earley
Reading
Berkshire
Tel: 0734-666606 (home)
Contact: Mrs Abdulla
Office: President
Women's membership group. The group believes that in order to appreciate other religions one should know about one's own religion. The aim is that Muslim women are active and know what is going on around them in order to become good citizens of this country. The group also holds cultural and social functions, including outings, for example, to Kew Gardens. Sewing classes, swimming and keep fit classes are also organised.

UK Islamic Mission Reading

4 Palmerstone Road
Earley
Reading RG6 1HL
Contact: Mr F Culasy
Office: General Secretary
Branch organisation. The Mission's main activities are the propagation of Islam and wefare.

Essex Islamic Educational Trust

67 Essex Road
Romford
Essex RM7 8BB
Tel: 0708-726901
Contact: Mr K A Siddiqui
Office: General Secretary
Its main activities are teaching the Arabic language; the religion of Islam; other languages; congregational prayers and preparation for GCSE in a range of subjects. There is also a gathering for ladies and adults and gatherings for cultural and religious festivals as well as educational visits.

Islamic Centre

141 Hatfield Road
St Albans
Hertfordshire

Tel: 0727-36272
Contact: The Secretary
Place of worship. The centre was established for the advancement of Islam and Islamic education. Its main activities are worship and daily classes for Muslim children.

Muslim Association

148 Hatfield Road
St Albans
Hertfordshire
Tel: 0727-30949

Islamic Trust and Jamia Mosque

35 Montem Lane
Slough SL1 2QW
Tel: 0753-30562

Jame Masjid Gousia

Diamond Road
Slough SL1 1RX
Tel: 0753-512994

Jamia Masjid Islamic Centre

83 Stoke Poges Lane
Slough SL1 3NY
Tel: 0753-225661

Khalifad-e-Rashida Movement

45 Warrington Avenue
Slough
Berkshire

Slough Islamic Trust

29 Diamond Road
Slough
Berkshire

Slough Mosque Committee

35 Ragstone Road
Slough
Berkshire

Central Jamia Mosque

12 Montague Way (Off King Way)
Southall
Middlesex UB2 5NZ
Tel: 081-574-5115
Contact: Mr G Syed
Office: Chairperson
A centre for Muslim worship, education and welfare. Prayers are held five times a day and the welfare organisation deals with all kinds of problems.

Mosque

103 Townsend Road
Southall
Middlesex
Tel: 081–574–6014

Muslim Women's Association

c/o Central Jamia Masjid
Montague Way
Southall
Middlesex
Tel: 081–574–5380
Contact: Mrs N Haq

West London Islamic Centre

120 North Road
Southall
Middlesex UB1 2JR
Tel: 081–574–8037
Contact: Mr A Vora
Office: General Secretary
Provides advice on and supports the social, cultural and welfare needs of the community, for example advice on housing, immigration, health and social security. Organises activities such as evening classes in mother tongue teaching, sports events, holiday outings and cultural events.

Mosque

53–54 Milton Road
West Cliff
Southend-on-Sea
Essex

Islamic Centre

Wood Lane
Stanmore
Middlesex HA7 4LQ
Tel: 081–954–9881
Fax: 081–954–9034
Contact: Mohsin Jaffer
Office: Chairperson
Place of worship. A Shi'a Muslim organisation which looks after the welfare of Muslims world-wide. The centre in Stanmore is open to visitors school parties and people from other institutions. People are shown around the centre and given talks on different aspects of Islam. Activities include worship, welfare, religious education, publication of religious books, and the running of a college of higher Islamic education.

Ismaili Jamat Khana

Corner of Cumberland Road and Lowther Road
Stanmore
Middlesex

Khoja Ashia Ithna-Asheri Muslim Community

Warren House
Wood Lane
Stanmore
Middlesex HA7 4LQ
Tel: 081–954–6247
Fax: 081–954–8028
Contact: Dr A G Lakha
Office: President
Membership group. It is a community organisation. The members of the organisation are East African Asians of the Khoja Shi'a Ithna-Asheri sect. It is a very close-knit community that meets regularly at least once a week. During religious festivals and certain months of the Islamic calendar meetings are held daily. Activities include youth, senior citizens, womens' group, sermons, weddings, funerals, religious festivals and celebrations.

Mosque Islamic Cultual Centre

26 Walker Road
Stevenage
Hertfordshire
Tel: 0438–313103

Islamic Educational Society

10 Cowley Mill Road
Uxbridge
Middlesex

Islamic Society

University of Brunel
Uxbridge
Middlesex UB8 3PH

Mosque

9 Cowley Mill Road
Uxbridge
Middlesex
Tel: 0895–35092

Anjuman-e-Jaafariyah

74 Kensington Avenue
Watford WD1 7RY
Tel: 0923–231257
Tel: 0923–237670 (home)
Contact: Syed Zulafkar Ali Shah
Office: Secretary
Anjuman-e-Jaafariyah is a charitable Islamic

institution, providing education and propagating information with respect to the teachings of the Holy Qur'an and the Holy Prophet, as related by the household of the Prophet, the Ahl-ul-Bait.

Mosque
Addiscombe Road Annexe
Addiscombe Road
Watford
Hertfordshire

Watford Jamia Mosque
Cambridge Road
Watford
Hertfordshire

Watford School of Arabic and Islamic Studies
492 Wippendell Road
Watford WD1 7QJ
Tel: 0923-245670
Fax: 0923-213377
Contact: Dr A Ghany Saleh
Office: Founder and Director
A charitable, voluntary Sunday school open to all members of the public, serving all members of the community regardless of nationality, religion, sex or age (above five years old). It is open 10.30am-2.00pm and its activities include teaching of the Arabic language and/or Islamic studies in a modern, enjoyable manner. GCSE and A Level courses are available and it is recognised by Cambridge and London Universities as an official examination centre. The centre also aims to build good Muslims and therefore good citizens by catering for the needs of whole individuals. It also intends to promote harmony within society through a friendly "family" atmosphere, lectures to the public, schools and places of worship, inter-faith talks, social events, exhibitions and services to the library, police etc.

An-Nisa Society
110 Thurlby Road
Wembley
Middlesex HA0 4RS
Tel: 081-900-0605 (home)
Contact: Khalida Khan
Office: Co-ordinator
Women's group. The society is run by Muslim women to campaign for and to provide faith-centred services and facilities. An-Nisa believes that the destruction of the family and the communities around it has led to social crisis. It believes that it is imperative to re-create strong family cells based on faith, personal responsibility and accountability. It's work therefore

centres on these concepts. Activities include education, social welfare, campaigning and other activities involving women, youths and children.

Islamic Guidance Society
24a District Road
Sudbury
Wembley
Middlesex HA0 2LD
Tel: 081-902-6215
Contact: Maulana M A Ovaisi
Office: Director

Islamic Welfare Association Mosque
106 Harrowdene Road
Wembley
Middlesex
Tel: 081-904-2260

Wembley Mosque and Islamic Centre
5 Stanley Avenue
near Alperton Station
Wembley
Middlesex
Tel: 081-902-3258

Southend Mosque and Southend Islamic Trust
191 West Road
Westcliff-on-Sea
Essex SS0 9DH
Tel: 0702-347265

Southend Muslim Association
The Mosque
Westborough Road
Westcliff-on-Sea
Essex

Southend Young Muslim Organisation
c/o Southend Islamic Trust
191-197 West Road
Westcliff-on-Sea
Essex

UK Islamic Mission
29 Highfield Gardens
Westcliff-on-Sea
Essex

Mosque
14 Wick Drive
Wickford
Essex

LONDON (E POSTCODES)

East London Mosque
92 Whitechapel Road
London E1 1JE
Tel: 071-247-1357
Fax: 071-377-9879
A large purpose-built place of worship.

Esha'atul Islam Mosque
16 Ford Square
off Commercial Road
Aldgate East
London E1 2HS
Tel: 071-790-0693
Contact: Mr Thohuruddin
Office: President
Place of worship and community organisation. Esha'atul Islam is a voluntary organisation established in 1983 to cater for local Bangladeshi and other Muslim religious and cultural needs. Local Muslims attend for daily worship, religious activities and social gatherings. Education is a major part of the activities and there are about two hundred and fifty pupils on the roll. More than fifteen hundred people use the services every week.

Holburn Islamic and Welfare Centre
4th Floor
1a Centre
1a Rosebery Avenue
London
E1 4RT
Tel: 071-278-3393 Ext. 127
Contact: Fazlul Karim Chowdhury
Office: Chairperson
Voluntary organisation. Activities include welfare, education and Islamic activities and activities for women and children.

Islamic Cultural Foundation
521 Commercial Road
London E1 0HQ
Tel: 071-790-1713

Islamic Society
Queen Mary College
Mile End Road
London E1

Jamia Masjid
59 Brick Lane
Aldgate East
London E1
Tel: 071-247-3507
Tel: 071-247-6052

Markazi Mosque
9-11 Christian Street
off Commercial Road
London E1 1SE
Tel: 071-481-1294
Tel: 071-488-4820 (home)

Mosque
16 Batty Street
London E1

Mosque
141 Leman Street
London E1

Mosque
39 Bournier Street
Spitalfield
London E1

Mosque
Duckett Street
Shandy Park
London E1

Tower Hamlets Islamic Service
28 Tunis House
Harford Street
London E1 4RP

Shair-e-Rabbani Islamic Centre
33 Granby Street
London E2 6DR
Tel: 071-739-6046

Dawatul Islam Coventry Cross Mosque and Islamic Centre
6 Broxbourne House
Devas Street
London E3 3LS
Tel: 071-515-6714

Mosque
Devon Street
3 Broxburne House
London E3
Tel: 071-987-2133

Mosque
14 Leonard Road
Chingford
London E4

Hackney Muslim Women's Council
101 Clapton Common
London E5
Tel: 081-809-0993 (home)

Madina Mosque Trust
2a Leabridge Road
Clapton
London E5
Tel: 081-985-8204

Medina Mosque
16 Mildenhall Road
London E5 9QP
Tel: 081-985-8204

Islamic Association (East Ham)
225 High Street North
London E6
Tel: 081-472-3069
Tel: 081-472-0522 (home)
Contact: S V Bax
Office: Secretary
Place of worship. It provides religious education for children, arranges religious functions and a pilgrimage service to Saudi Arabia. Information is provided on social services and immigration.

Islamic Centre (Upton Park)
175-177 Plashet Grove
Upton Park
London E6 1BX
Tel: 081-472-2957 (home)
Contact: Mr V A Patel
Place of worship. Offers facilities for worship, welfare, teaching and meetings.

Markaz-ud-Dawat-Wal Irshad Muslim Community Centre
177-179 Plashet Grove
East Ham
London E6

Masjid-e-Bilal and East London Islamic Centre
295 Barking Road
East Ham
London E6 1LB
Tel: 081-471-9355
Contact: Mr Afzal

Medina Mosque and Muslim Cultural Centre
225 High Street North
London E6 1JG
Tel: 081-472-3069
Contact: Mr L Hussain
Office: Secretary

Mosque
1 Canning Town
East Ham
London E6

Newham Muslim Citizens Association
81 Katherine Road
East Ham
London E6
Tel: 081-472-0018
Contact: Mr M Ahmad
Office: Secretary
Advice and information to the Muslim community.

Azeemia Foundation (UK)
Azeemi House
92b Hampton Road
Forest Gate
London E7 0NU
Tel: 081-555-4577
Contact: Mrs A Azeemi
Meditation and spiritual healing.

Bangladesh Shomity
52 Upton Park Road
Forest Gate
London E7 8LD
Tel: 081-471-0800
Contact: Mr M Ali
Advisory service and mother tongue language school.

Imamia Mission
519 Romford Road
Forest Gate
London E7 8AD
Tel: 081-472-3588
Contact: Mr Ali Naqui

Newham Muslim Council

72 Boleyn Road
Forest Gate
London E7 9QE
Tel: 081-472-1615
Contact: Mr Z Ali

Newham Muslim Womens Association

423 Romford Road
Forest Gate
London E7 8AB
Tel: 081-555-3784
Contact: Mrs Modi

Newham North Islamic Association Mosque and Community Centre

88 Green Street
London E7 8JG
Tel: 081-472-6887
Tel: 081-471-3677 (home)
Contact: Mr Shahan H Hussain
Office: General Secretary

Quwwat-ul-Islam Mosque and Islam Society

62-66 Upton Lane
London E7 9LN
Tel: 081-472-1072
Tel: 081-534-4248 (home)
Contact: Maulana Osman Adam

Dalston Mosque

160 Dalston Lane
London E8
Tel: 081-254 3266

Muridin al Haq

98 Greenwood Road
London E8 1NE

Turkish Mosque

9-15 Shacklewell Lane
London E8
Tel: 081-249-9172

UK Islamic Trust

9-15 Shacklewell Lane
London E8
Tel: 081-254-0431

Hackney Muslim Council

14 Warneford Street
London E9 7NG

Union of Muslims in Hackney

14 Warneford Street
London E9 7NG
Tel: 081-985-3258

Ahle Hadith Mosque

34 Francis Road
Leyton
London E10
Tel: 081-556-0558

Jamia Mosque

439-451 Lea Bridge Road
Leyton
London E10

Leytonstone Islamic Association

170 Church Road
London E10

Madrasa al-Tawhid

34 Francis Road
Leyton
London E10
Tel: 081-558-0581
Fax: 081-471-1894
Contact: Mohammed Idrees Sethi
Office: Secretary General
Place of worship. Regardless of any colour, race, faith or religion, everyone is welcome to learn or find out more about Islam. Worship takes place five times a day, daily classes for children (5.00-7.00pm), activities for youths and adults take place on Sundays.

Mosque

39 Beaconsfield Road
Leyton
London E10
Tel: 081-558-5601

Muslim Cultural Society

715 High Road
Leyton
London E10

Muslim Women's Welfare Association

School Annexe
Bickley Road
Leyton
London E10 7HL
Tel: 081-539-7478
Contact: Mrs Meher Khan
Office: Co-ordinator

Voluntary organisation. All ages are welcome to the organisation which provides advice and help on problems relating to housing, social services, marital, domestic problems, immigration, health, education and hobbies; creche facilities; discussion group; English language classes; video and toy library; social security benefit session; sewing classes; Urdu classes for children; keep fit classes; women's boutique; and a Summer holiday project.

Indian Muslim Federation
Trinity Close
London E11 4RP
Tel: 081-558-6399

Leytonstone Islamic Association
32 Barclay Road
London E11

Leytonstone Mosque and Islamic Association
Dacre Road
London E11 3AG
Tel: 081-539-7251

Anjuman-e-Islamia (Newham)
266-268 High St North
Manor Park
London E12 6SB
Tel: 081-472-5663
Office: Chairman
Mosque and cultural centre.

Manor Park Islamic Cultural Centre and Shah Jalal Mosque
724 Romford Road
Manor Park
London E12 6BT
Tel: 081-514-7772
Tel: 081-553-5826 (home)
Contact: Mr M Khan
Office: General Secretary
Place of worship. There are nine office bearers directly elected by the members every year to run the day to day functions of the mosque in accordance with the constitution. Activities include Islamic worship, Islamic teaching to children of five to sixteen years, religious gatherings, weddings and funerals.

World Islamic Mission (East London Branch)
28 Essex Road
Manor Park
London E12 6RE

Tel: 081-552-9050
Contact: Mr G Haider
Office: General Secretary

Alliance of Newham Muslim Associations
159 Plashet Road
Upton Park
London E13 0QZ
Tel: 081-470-5233
Contact: Mr M Farhat
An umbrella group for Muslim organisations in Newham.

British Muslim Association
56 Harold Road
Plaistow
London E13 0SQ
Tel: 081-471-2107
Contact: Mr M A Siddiqi

Canning Town Mosque and Welfare Association at the Muslim Community Centre
269 Barking Road
Plaistow
Canning Town
London E13 8EQ
Tel: 081-472-5096 (home)
Contact: Mr S Ali
Office: Secretary

Islamic Centre
72 Selwyn Road
Upton Park
London E13 0PY
Tel: 081-472-2745
Contact: Mr Naeem Khan

Islamic Voluntary Service (Newham)
205 Harold Road
Plaistow
London E13 0SE
Tel: 081-470-3674
Contact: Mr M Rafiq
Help and advice.

Masjid e Falah
510 Barking Road
Plaistow
London E13 8QE

Muslim Women's Welfare Association
83 Stopford Road
Plaistow
London E13 0NA
Tel: 081-471-7648
Contact: Ms S Sarwar

Islamic Community Centre
Limborough House
Thomas Road
London E14 7AW

Mosque
Limborough House
Wallwood Street
Burdett Estate
London E14

Mosque
Hale Street (cabin)
Poplar
London E14

Canning Town Muslim Association
22 Star Lane
London E16

Canning Town Islamic Centre
5 Market Place
Ordinance Road
London E16
Tel: 081-474-3674
Contact: Mr M Y Iqbal
Office: Secretary

Muslim Welfare Association Plaistow
40 Newham Way
Canning Town
London E16 4ED
Tel: 071-474-4936

International Muslim Movement
12 East Avenue
Walthamstow
London E17

Masjide Aqsa and Waltham Forest Muslim Welfare Society
79 Queens Road
Walthamstow
London E17
Tel: 081-520-2658
Contact: Mr Z A R Oomerjee

Office: Secretary
Place of worship. The welfare society was established twenty years ago to promote the religion of Islam and to provide and arrange for the religious education of Muslims, particularly children in the London borough of Waltham Forest. Activities include worship and welfare.

Muslim Advisory and Community Welfare Council
317 Markhouse Road
Walthamstow
London E17 8EE
Tel: 081-556-5750
Contact: M Salah-Ud-Din
Office: Secretary

Muslim Parents Association
c/o 13c Hoe Street
London E17

Waltham Forest Islamic Association
21/22 Verulam Avenue
London E17

Waltham Forest Pakistan Muslim Welfare Association
6 Exeter Road
London E17

LONDON (N CODES)

Islington Muslim Association
38 Northdown Street
London N1
Tel: 071-837-1771

Mosque
251 Pentonville Road
Kings Cross
London N1
Tel: 071-278-0877

UK Islamic Mission London Branch
148 Liverpool Road
London N1

Mosque and Islamic Centre
36 Long Lane
Finchley
London N3 2PU
Tel: 081-346-2160
Contact: Mr A H Mirza

Bazmi-i-Tafreeh

25 Evershot Road
London N4 3DG
Tel: 071-272-7031
Contact: Abdul Aleem Siddiqui

Voluntary organisation. The organisation was established in 1947 by Mr Chowdry Akbar Khan and is a multi-cultural, non-sectarian charitable body. It is dedicated to the unity of humankind in the UK. Activities are social, cultural and literary. It also aims to help handicapped, disabled and old people; visit the sick at home and in hospital; provide information on education, health and housing for newcomers in the UK; and provide the opportunity for employment to skilled and non-skilled people.

Muslim Community and Welfare Centre and North London Central Mosque

15 St. Thomas's Road
Finsbury Park
London N4 2QH
Tel: 071-359-1181
Contact: Mr I A Malik
Office: Co-ordinator

Welfare organisation and place of worship. One of the oldest Muslim welfare societies in the UK, founded in the 1960's. Initially, its basic aim was to render cultural and religious services to the Muslim residents in North London. Now it has embarked on a variety of useful and informative services to all ethnic minorities representing different faiths, cultural and linguistic groups. It is constantly broadening the sphere of its multi-cultural and multi-social services. It runs an advisory service, education classes, play group for under fives, home and hospital visits, women and girls activities, senior citizens lunch club, newsletter and cultural, social, religious and inter-faith meetings.

Muslim Welfare Centre

13 Leconsfield Road
London N5 2RX

Bangladesh Muslim Organisation

90 Sydney Road
London N8

Hornsey Mosque and Islamic Centre

385-389 Hampden Road
Hornsey
London N8

United Islamic Association

9 Willoughby Road
London N8

Islamic Society of the Faithful

70 Friern Park
North Finchley
London N12
Tel: 071-445-3769
Contact: Mr Nizar Boga
Office: President

Membership group. A charitable organisation run by dedicated people who are keen to have a deeper understanding of Islam. The organisation assists those in need of help; helps people with family problems; strives towards establishing educational needs of the young; meets every Friday evening to discuss the religion and its requirements; assists in marriage guidance and seeks to collect donations for the relief of poverty.

Islamic Community Centre

115 Clyde Road
London N15 4JS
Tel: 081-809-2137
Fax: 081-809-2137

Tottenham Mosque

115 Clyde Road
London N15 4JS
Tel: 081-809-2137

Aziziye Mosque and UK Turkish Islamic Association

117-119 Stoke Newington Road
London N16
Tel: 071-254 0046
Contact: Ahmet Ali
Office: Secretary

Place of worship. The largest Turkish Islamic organisation in North London. The organisation runs a place of worship and a general advice and counselling bureau. It aims to serve the needs of the community in every aspect. Activities include worship, religious and Qur'anic education, lessons in Turkish and Arabic classes, youth activities including sports, a women's group and general counselling and information.

British Muslim Council

22 Lynmouth Road
London N16 6XL

London Islamic Turkish Association

16 Green Lanes
London N16 9ND
Tel: 081-249-5417 (home)

Mosque
4 Linthorpe Road
London N16

North London Mosque
70–72 Cazenove Road
Stamford Hill
London N16
Tel: 081-806-6540

Stamford Hill Mosque
82 Foreberg Road
London N16

Turkish Mosque
1a Clissold Road
off Albion Road
Newington Green
London N16
Tel: 071-241-5425

United Kingdom Turkish Islamic Cultural Centre
5 Hayling Close
London N16
Tel: 081-254-0373

Al-Qur'an Society
101 Belmont Road
Tottenham
London N17 6AT
Tel: 081-881-3984
Tel: 081-889-6662 (home)
Fax: 081-881-3984
Contact: Dr Suhaib Hasan
Office: Chairperson
Membership group. An educational organisation where classes for young children are conducted regularly at the premises. A twenty lesson correspondence course is devised by the society. Anyone in the UK or abroad can join this course for a nominal registration fee. On completion, members are awarded with a certificate. Activities include publishing Islamic literature and holding classes of the Qur'an for children and youth; holding an annual conference on aspects of Islam.

London Islamic Cultural Society
42 Park View Road
Tottenham
London N17 9AT

Association of Muslim Ladies (Khawateen)
40 Church Crescent
Wetstone
London N20
Tel: 081-368-2120
Fax: 081-950-4978
Contact: Mrs Shahida Rehman
Office: Secretary
A voluntary organisation of women and youth taking part in religious, social and cultural activities. Contact can also be made through the Chairperson, Mrs Kausar Shakree on tel: 081-950-4978.

LONDON (NW POSTCODES)

Abrat Islamic Foundation
3-5 Dorset Square
London NW1 6PU
Tel: 071-724-7939 (home)
Place of worship and social activities. The organisation focuses on religious and cultural issues. It provides a meeting hall for Muslims for religious and cultural activities. At present, the organisation is awaiting planning permission to begin refurbishment. Activities for men, women, youths and children and cultural and religious teaching.

Dar Al-Shoura
68a Delaney Street
London NW1 7RY

Indian Muslims Relief Committee
P O Box 415
London NW1 2LD
Tel: 071-338-3678

Islamic Book Centre
120 Drummond Street
London NW1 2HL
Tel: 071-388-0710

Madina House
146 Gloucester Place
London NW1 6DT
Tel: 071-262-5314
Contact: Mrs N Ali
Office: Officer in charge
Residential children's home for Muslim children in need of care. It aims to provide a temporary home for children who, for whatever reason, are temporarily unable to live with their parents and thus to offer a stable, caring background based on Muslim principles and practices.

Mosque
35–46 Norfolk Square
Paddington
London NW1

Mosque
204a North Gower Street
Euston
London NW1
Tel: 081-387-8346

Central Mosque of Brent
Marley Walk
off Station Parade
London NW2
Tel: 081-450-9428
Contact: Raja M Riaz
Office: Chairperson
Religious organisation. It looks after the religious needs of the Muslim community of Brent.

Islamic Cultural House
107 Anson Road
London NW2

Mosque and Islamic Centre of Brent
33a Howard Road
London NW2 6DS

Memon Jammat
270 Kilburn High Road
London NW6

Muslim Womens Association
146 Park Road
London NW8

Hendon Islamic Centre
135 The Broadway
West Hendon
London NW9 7DY
Tel: 081-202-3236
Contact: Sayed M Kadri
Office: Secretary
Place of worship and community centre. In addition to religious and cultural activities, the centre runs Islamic religious classes.

Islamic Centre Edgware
63 North Way
London NW9 0RA
Tel: 081-204-2461

Kokni Muslim Cultural and Youth Organisation UK
83 Sheaveshill Court
Collindale
London NW9 6LT

Mosque
42 Beverley Drive
Queensbury
London NW9
Tel: 081-204-2006

Mosque and Islamic Centre
135 The Broadway
London NW9 7DY
Tel: 081-202-3236

Ghana Muslim Union
15 Exton Crescent
Stonebridge
London NW10

Stonebridge Islamic Group
27 Donavan Court
Exton Crescent
London NW10

Golder's Green Muslim Committee
17 Courtleigh Gardens
London NW11
Contact: Dr Mohammed

Kokani Muslims (Golder's Green)
127 Hamilton Road
Golder's Green
London NW11 9EG
Tel: 081-458-4677
Contact: Mr S A Kadiri
Office: General Secretary
Voluntary organisation and community centre. The organisation aims to: create and promote fraternity and complete co-operation amongst Kokani Muslims living within its jurisdiction; assist in making funeral arrangements and other ancillary matters on the death of a member or of the husband or wife of a member or his/her dependents; foster the educational, cultural and social advancement of the members and to co-operate with other Kokani Muslim organisations in the UK on matters of common interest and including all other Muslim organisations, national and international having similiar aims and objectives.

LONDON (SE POSTCODES)

Mosque
24 Newington Causeway
London SE1
Tel: 071-407-1602

Islamic Information Bureau
P O Box 914
London SE5 9TW
Tel: 071-733-7970 (home)
Contact: General Secretary
A voluntary organisation which aims to provide an information service on the teachings of Islam and in particular Twelver Shi'as; to represent the views and interests of the Muslim community; and to organise educational activities. The bureau operates mainly in the South London area and welcomes enquiries from any source, both from individual members of the public and from organisations.

Narool Islam Turkish Mosque
99 Cobourge Road
Off Old Kent Road
Peckham
London SE5
Tel: 071-703-0985

Lewisham and Kent Islamic Centre
283 Brownhill Road
Catford
London SE6 1AE
Tel: 081-698-4316
Tel: 081-467-2764 (home)
Contact: Dr S Saleem
Office: Secretary
Place of worship and cultural centre. The centre organises Islamic cultural activities and worship, and aims to cater for all ages and needs of the community. Activities include prayer five times a day, Arabic lessons six evenings a week, congregational prayer on Friday, lessons on the Qur'an on a Sunday and discussion sessions every Friday. Festivals are celebrated and mother tongue classes take place. The centre also organises visits to prisoners, hospital patients, arranges funerals, arranges matrimonial meetings and performs weddings.

Charlton Mosque
30 Ransome Road
Charlton
London SE7 8SR
Tel: 081-858-4479
Tel: 081-858-0209 (home)

Contact: Mr Asghar Hamid
Office: Chair
Place of worship. It also offers an advice service for welfare, passport and immigration matters, lectures arranged for non-Muslims, interfaith meetings and worship.

Greenwich Pakistan Muslim Welfare Association
53 Delafield Road
Charlton
London SE7

Muslim Council
16 Victoria Way
Charlton Road
London SE7
Tel: 081-215-5793
Tel: 081-853-4376 (home)

Pakistan Muslim Welfare Association and Mosque
12 Victoria Way
Charlton
London SE7 7QS
Tel: 081-858-2415
Contact: Mr Asghar Hamid
Office: Chair
Place of worship and advice.

Mosque and South East Muslim Association
51 Elm Grove
Off Rye Lane
Peckham
London SE15 5DB
Tel: 071-639-4589

Peckham Mosque
1 Peckham High Street
London SE15
Tel: 071-703-5995

Southwark Muslim Association
Bellenden Old School
Bellenden Road
London SE15
Tel: 071-732-8053

Southwark Muslim Women's Association
Bellenden Old School
Bellenden Road
London SE15
Tel: 071-732-8053

Greenwich Islamic Association
82 Admaston Road
Plumstead
London SE18

Greenwich Mosque and Islamic Centre
131 Plumstead Road
Woolwich
London SE18

Indian Muslim Federation
6 Tuam Road
Woolwich
London SE18
Tel: 081-855-8877

Mosque and Islamic Centre
131 Plumstead Road
Opposite the Bus Garage
London SE18 7DU
Tel: 081-854-4846
Fax: 081-854-0514

Bromley Muslim Council
11 High Street
Penge
London SE20 7HJ
Tel: 081-659-0640
Contact: Mr Khalid Sharif
The council organises religious and cultural activities
and takes part in multi-faith activities. Events that are
organised take place in hired public halls in the area.

South London Islamic Centre
19 Tremaine Road
London SE20 7UA
Tel: 081-659-1303 (home)
Contact: Mr Abdur Rahman Bazmi
Office: Convenor
A membership society which aims to provide
education and awareness of local Muslim inhabitants
in the religious, social and literary spheres of activities
and to foster good community and race relations at
large.

LONDON (SW POSTCODES)

Jama Mosque
15 Chesham Place
Knightsbridge
London SW1

Mosque
Pakistan Embassy
35 Lowndes Square
Knightsbridge
London SW1
Tel: 071-235-2044
Only Friday Juma.

Muslim Book Society
18 Eccleston Square
London SW1

Al Hilal Masjid
24 Brailsford Road
Tulse Hill
London SW2 2TB
Tel: 081-671 5574
Fax: 081-671-5574
Contact: Dr. Sayed Almohmoud Deewan
A religious organisation for social, cultural, literary and
religious activities.

South London Islamic Centre
c/o 45 Tierney Road
London SW2

Ahl-ul-Bayt Foundation
31 Draycott Place
Chelsea
London SW3

Ahl ul-Bayt Islamic Centre
11-13 Edgeley Road
London SW4 6EH
Tel: 081-627-2230
Shi'a Muslims.

Kensington Mosque
170 Old Brompton Road
London SW5 OBD
Tel: 071-373-0238
Contact: Chairperson
Place of worship. It provides facilities for worship and
welfare activities.

Al Muntada al Islami Education Centre
Bridges Place
off Parson's Green Lane
Fulham
London SW6

Burhani Community Centre
354 Lillie Road
London SW6
Tel: 071-229-6404 (home)
Contact: Dr Idris Zainuddin
Office: Chairperson

Islamic Society
Imperial College
Prince Consort Street
London SW7 2BB

Ismaili Centre
1 Cromwell Gardens
London SW7 2SL
Tel: 071-581-2071
Fax: 071-589-3246
Contact: Mr Shafik Sachedina
A cultural centre. In common with other Shi'a Muslims, the Ismailis affirm that after the Prophet's death, Hazrat Ali, the Prophet's cousin and son-in-law became the first Imam (spiritual leader) of the Muslim community and that this spiritual leadership (known as Imamat) continues thereafter by heredity through Ali and his wife Fatima (the Prophet's daughter). Succession to the Imamat, according to Shi'a doctrine and tradition, is by way of Nass (designation) which is the absolute prerogative of the Imam of the time to appoint his successor from amongst any of his male descendants. His Highness Prince Karim Aga Khan is the forty-ninth hereditary Imam of the Shi'a Imami Ismaili Muslims. The Centre provides wide ranging pastoral care and a place of worship for Shi'a Imami Ismaili Muslims.

Al-Furqan Charity Trust
1 Wynne Road
London SW9 0BB
Tel: 071-737-7266
Contact: Secretary
Youth centre.

Ansaru Allah Community
70 Fitzgerald House
Stockwell Park Road
London SW9 0UQ

Brixton Mosque
1 Gresham Road
London SW9

Islamic Community Centre
64 Cottage Grove
London SW9 9NQ

Khatme Nubuwwat Centre
35 Stockwell Green
Stockwell
London SW9 9HZ
Tel: 071-737 8199
Contact: M B Patel
Office: Secretary
Place of worship. Activities include worship and preaching of Islam.

Mosque
25 Bellfield Road
Brixton
London SW9
Tel: 071-274-1757

Battersea Mosque
75 Falcon Road
Battersea
London SW11 2PF
Tel: 081-228-4267

Islamic Cultural and Education Centre
5 Falcon Road
Battersea
London SW11
Tel: 081-228-4267
Tel: 081-223-1867 (home)
Contact: Hafiz Nisaruddin Ahmed

Balham Mosque
47-51 Balham High Road
Balham
London SW12 9AW
Tel: 081-675-7912
Contact: Mr Farooq Valimahomed
Office: Secretary
Place of worship. One of the largest centres for followers of mainstream (Sunni) Islam in the South London area. It provides facilities for religious activities and caters for the social and welfare needs of the Muslim population. Interfaith meetings are held. Induction courses on Islam are run for trainee teachers, police officers and social workers. It also represents the Muslim community on Islamic issues of concern in the wider community.

Knightsbridge Mosque
c/o 76 Hazelbourne Road
London SW12 9NS
Tel: 081-675-5529

Mosque

Gassiot Road
Balham
London SW12

Mosque

49 Lower Richmond Road
Putney
London SW15
Tel: 081-788-5554

Ksisli Jamaat Hyderi Islamic Centre

26 Estreham Road
Streatham
London SW16 5PQ
Tel: 081-769-7553
Contact: Secretary
Place of worship, education and lecture hall.
Membership is on a voluntary basis for members of the
Shi'a faith. The organisation is funded by donations
within the community. The organisation seeks
understanding and peace within our own community
and with other faiths in Britain. Activities include
education, welfare services, counselling, sports,
seminars and outings for the elderly, children and
regular lectures for all.

South London Islamic Centre

8 Mitcham Lane
Streatham
London SW16 6NN
Tel: 081-677-0588
Contact: Mr A R Lone
Office: Manager
Place of worship and community centre. The centre
is open to both male and female Muslims irrespective
of race, colour or nationality. It is funded solely by
donations from users and Muslims. Activities include
religious and moral education, mother tongue
teaching, advice centre, activities for women and
youths and a Muslim funeral service.

Idra-il-Jaaferiya Mosque

18a Church Lane
Tooting
London SW17
Tel: 081-672-5373
Contact: Asad Baig
Shi'a Muslims.

Islamic Education and Training Centre

30 Rowfant Road
London SW17 7AS
Tel: 081-675-0404

Islamic Education Centre

51 Gassiot Road
Tooting
London SW17
Contact: Mrs Sultanat Khan
Educational establishment. A small house owned by
the mosque and used by various teachers for religious
education for both young and old. The house is used
by men for worship and by women and children to
learn Qur'anic Arabic, comparative religion and Islam
as a way of life. Discussion groups meet to discuss
various matters such as religion, history and politics.

Memon Jamatt

37 Wonter Road
Tooting
London SW17
Contact: Mr I Sacranie

Muslim Women Welfare

18 Trinity Road
Tooting
London SW17 7RE
Tel: 081-767-6474
Contact: Co-ordinator
Women's Advice Centre. Practical advice is given in
such areas as welfare rights, housing, health care,
immigration and education. Recreational facilities and
creche are provided and volunteers assist those who
have language barriers.

Muslim Womens Group

72 Upper Tooting Road
Tooting
London SW17
Tel: 081-767-4894
Contact: Mrs Siddiqui

Muslim Youth Centre

64 Foulser Road
Tooting
London SW17
Tel: 081-767-4894
Contact: Waseem Siddiqui

Muslim Youth Organisation

72 Upper Tooting Road
Tooting
London SW17
Tel: 081-767-4894

Muslim Association (Greenwich)

6 Tuam Road
London SW18 2QU

Al-Medina Trust
161 South Park Road
Wimbledon
London SW19
Tel: 081-542-6269

Darul Aman Islamic Centre
54 High Street
Collierswood
London SW19 2JF
Tel: 081-543-5687

Education and Welfare Charitable Fund
59 Home Park Road
London SW19 7HS

Mosque
12 Melrose Avenue
Wimbledon Park
Wimbledon
London SW19
Tel: 081-946-4784

South Islamic Centre
106 Vineyard Hill Road
Wimbledon
London SW19
Contact: Mr M A Aziz

Wimbledon Mosque
262-270 Dunsford Road
Wimbledon Park
London SW19 8DS
Tel: 081-946 3350
Contact: Mr M A Hamid
Office: Chairperson
Place of worship. It is used as a place of worship and
centre for the Muslim community in Wimbledon and
the adjoining Boroughs. Activities include offering
salaat (prayer), providing facilities for teaching the
Qur'an and Hadith and basic principles of Islam,
promoting Islamic brotherhood, Qur'anic teachings
and Islamic tenets and thought and arranging seminars.

Muslim Women's Association
63 Coombe Lane
London SW20 0BD
Tel: 081-946-1052
Contact: Mrs Khanum Hassan
Office: President
A thirty year old organisation fulfilling a religious and
social function for women and families. Lectures are
given on many topics, monthly meetings are held,
during which the Qur'an is read and discussions on

various topics take place. The publication "The
Muslim Woman" is produced. The organisation
sponsors children abroad.

LONDON (W POSTCODES)

Dar al-Ifta
46 Goodge Street
London W1P 1FJ
Tel: 071-636-2080

Darul Muslimat
3 Dunraven Street
London W1Y 3FG
Tel: 071-499-4741

Islamic Society
University of Central London
Students Union
115 Cavendish Road
London W1

West End Mosque
10 Berwick Street
London W1
Tel: 071-437-8840

Islamic Arts Foundation
54 Bathurst Street
London W2 2SD

Mosque
71 Westbourne Road
Bayswater
London W2
Tel: 071-727-0729

Acton Mosque
40 Church Field Road
London W3

Larden Hall Mosque
Larden Road
Acton
London W3

Mosque
26 Churchfield Road
London W3

Hammersmith Imamwada
30-32 Southerton Road
Hammersmith
London W6

Mosque
121 Oakland Road
Hanwell
London W7
Tel: 081-579-2185

Mosque
3-5 Palace Gate
Kensington
London W8

Kensington Mosque
76 Goldborne Road
off Ladbroke Grove
London W10
Tel: 081-998-6646
Contact: Mr Bargach

Islamic Universal Association
20 Penzance Place
Holland Park Avenue
London W11 4PG
Tel: 071-602-5273/4
Contact: Mr Abdullah

Holy Party
62 St Stephen's Avenue
Shepherd's Bush
London W12 TD
Tel: 081-743-9699
Contact: Mr S B Khawaja

Mosque
112 Goldthon Road
London W12
Tel: 081-740-0463

Mosque
69 Tunis Road
London W12

Shepherd's Bush Mosque and Muslim Community Centre
302 Uxbridge Road
Shepherds Bush
London W12 7LJ
Tel: 081-740 0463
Fax: 081-742-9070

Contact: Dr Ahmed Badat
Office: Chairperson
Place of worship, cultural centre and religious school. Primarily a place of worship, the congregation consists of all different nationalities. The mosque holds daily classes in Islam for children aged four to fourteen years; adult classes are run at weekends; funeral services are arranged for the community and ceremonies are managed and gatherings are held during Islamic festivals.

LONDON (WC POSTCODE)

Islamic Environment Research Centre Ltd
53 Bedford Square
London WC1B 3DZ

Islamic Society
School of Oriental and African Studies
7 Malet Street
London WC1

Kings Cross Mosque and Islamic Centre
32 Wharton Street
London WC1 1TG
Tel: 071-833-2368

Islamic Society
London School of Economics
Houghton Lane
London WC2A 2AE

School of Islamic Sufism
3 Henrietta Street
London WC2E 8LU

SOUTH EAST (SOUTH)

East Sussex Islamic Association
41 Jameson Road
Bexhill
East Sussex
Contact: Mr Elzayat

Brighton Islamic Mission
PO Box 234
Brighton BN1 3QD
Tel: 0273-722438 (home)
Fax: 0273-540058
Contact: Dr Imam Abduljalil Sajid
Office: Chair
A friendly society. The mission was founded in 1980 to promote Islam as a way of life in the South of

England. The group meets on a weekly basis. It publishes and distributes books on Islam, has youth and womens sections, carries out welfare activities, holds public lectures and organises study circles.

Brighton Mosque
150 Dyke Road
Brighton BN1 5PA
Tel: 0273-505247
Tel: 0273-722438 (home)
Fax: 0273-540058
Contact: Dr Imam Abduljalil Sajid
Office: Imam
Place of worship and learning. A mosque, established in 1977 with the capacity to hold three hundred worshippers at once. The mosque receives five hundred visitors a week in addition to its representatives answering letters and telephone calls. All are welcome and Islamic literature is distributed to non-Muslims. About one hundred and seventy-five children attend weekly lessons in Islam.

Mosque
9 Charlotte Street
Brighton
East Sussex

Mosque
21a Bedford Place
off Western Road
Brighton BN1 2AA
Tel: 0273-25027
Contact: Imam Hanif
Office: Imam
Place of worship. It provides for worship, religious education for children and social ceremonies such as weddings, feasts and celebration and also runs activities for youth and children.

Muslim Community Centre
150 Dyke Road
Brighton BN1 5PA
Tel: 0273-505247
Tel: 0273-722438 (home)
Fax: 0273-540058
Contact: Dr Imam Abduljalil Sajid
Office: Director
Community organisation. The community centre was established in 1977 in order to help those individuals who are being discriminated against. It provides a translating and interpreting service to anyone who cannot communicate in English and represents him/her; offers advice on immigration,

education, employment, housing and welfare rights and represents clients in court and for other statutory bodies.

Students Islamic Society and Mosque
c/o Students Union
University of Sussex
Falmer
Brighton BN1 9QF
Tel: 0273-606755 (Ext 3322)
Contact: Secretary
Place of worship. A mosque with the capacity to accomodate around eighty people, both men and women. Wudu (ablution) facilities are available for both sexes. There is a library on Islam in Arabic and English and audio-visual material. Activities include worship for men, women and youth, lectures by outside speakers are arranged and are open to all.

Islamic Society
c/o Students Union
Kent University
Canterbury
Kent CT2 7NZ

Wessex Shi'a Ithna Asheri Jamat
42 Beechwood Close
Chandlers Ford
Hampshire S05 1DB
Tel: 0705-550142
Tel: 0329-662319 (home)
Contact: Jaffer Dharamsi

Kent Muslim Welfare Association
46a Salisbury Road
Chatham
Kent

Mosque
22b Chatham Hill
Chatham
Kent ME4 7AR
Tel: 0634-47409

Crawley Islamic Centre and Mosque
157 London Road
Crawley
West Sussex
Tel: 0293-528488
Contact: Mr Mohammad Hussain
Office: General Secretary
Place of worship. It serves the Muslim population of Crawley and district and provides facilities for worship, arranges religious education for Muslim

children, as well as an advisory service in the fields of welfare benefits, housing needs, immigration and nationality.

Jamiat Ul Muslemeen
20 Aston Court
Broadfield
Crawley
West Sussex
Contact: Mr K Mahmood

Jamiat ul Muslemeen + Quwatul Islam Masjid
1 Strachey Court
Webb Close
Crawley
West Sussex

Mosque
20 Selsey Road
Broadfield
Crawley
West Sussex
Tel: 0293-512555

Mosque
99 Fennell Crescent
Broadfield
Crawley
West Sussex
Tel: 0293-26895

Pakistani Muslim Welfare Association
32 Beckett Lane
Langley Green
Crawley
West Sussex
Tel: 0293-515341
Tel: 0293-517201 (home)
Contact: Mr M A Rajah

UK Islamic Mission
11 Aisla Close
Broadfield
Crawley
West Sussex

Ismalia Moslem Group
13 Keats House
Bexley Lane
Crayford
Kent

Croydon Mosque and Islamic Centre
525 London Road
Thornton Heath
Croydon
Surrey CR7 6AR
Tel: 081-684-8200/081-684-7512
Contact: S Mahmood
Office: Secretary General
Place of worship and community group. The mosque and cultural centre is the largest centre in the south of England. It is a place of religious education and worship, with lectures and discussions held regularly. New members are welcome and school visits are encouraged. Advice and imformation is offered on religious affairs, housing, youth education and sport and general issues concerning the welfare of the community. There is also an old age pensioners club.

Mosque
45 Wellesley Road
Croydon
Surrey
Tel: 081-684-7512

Muslim Association of Croydon
7 Stuart Road
Thornton Heath
Croydon
Surrey CR7 8RA
Tel: 081-683-3699(home)
Contact: Mr M H Rahman
Office: Secretary

Young Muslim Association
95 Beulah Road
Thornton Heath
Croydon
Surrey CR4 8JG
Tel: 081-653-0957
Contact: Mr J A Sharif (Jnr)

Sufi Way
Four Winds
High Thicket Road
Dockenfield
Surrey GU10 4HB
Tel: 0252-793990
Fax: 0252-793990
Contact: Wendy Rose-Neil
Office: Council member
Membership group. The Sufi Way was founded by Fazal Inayat Khan and is a non-sectarian organisation based on the teachings of his grand-father Hazrat Inayat Khan who brought Sufism to the West seventy

years ago. Its work includes spiritual and psychological development in the broadest sense and encompasses a wide range of activities to this end. Activities include spiritual and personal education and development with regular organised programmes and retreats.

Eastbourne Islamic Society
54 Seaside Road
Eastbourne
East Sussex

South-East Islamic Society
209 Kings Drive
Eastbourne BN21 2UJ
Contact: Taleb Dugahee
Office: Secretary

Minaret House
9 Leslie Park Road
East Croydon
Surrey CR0 6TN
Tel: 081-654-8801
Fax: 081-667-1280
Contact: Riadh El-Droubie
Educational organisation. It was established in 1967 for the promotion of Islamic studies as part of religious education in UK schools. The organisation publishes booklets and visual aid material to help teachers and students to undersatnd the true picture of Islam.

Portsmouth Muslim Society
90 Westbourne Avenue
Emsworth
Hampshire

Islamic Marriages Introductory Service & Counselling
1 Avondale Avenue
Esher
Kent KT10 0DB
Tel: 081-398-6020

Islamic Society
Farnborough College of Technology
Farnborough
Hampshire

Gillingham Mosque
114 Canterbury Street
Gillingham ME7 5UH
Tel: 0634-50878
Tel: 0634-251312
Contact: Syed Ikram Ali

Office: General Secretary
Place of worship. The mosque was established twenty-two years ago. It is a multi-purpose building for activities arranged by Kent Muslim Welfare Association (KMWA). Prayers are said five times a day with a service on Friday. The main hall can accomodate three hundred worshippers. There is a separate ladies wing, a fully equipped kitchen, a modest school, library and an office/meeting room. KMWA is registered for performing marriages at the mosque and also provides full voluntary service at the death of any Muslim.

Kent Muslim Welfare Association (KMWA)
114 Canterbury Street
Gillingham ME7 5UH
Tel: 0634-50878
Tel: 0634-251312
Contact: Syed Ikram Ali
Office: Secretary General
Welfare association of Sunni Muslims which aims to protect the social, moral and spiritual welfare of members in particular and all Muslims in general. It aims to organise worship, to provide welfare for women and youth, and to provide Islamic religious and cultural education for groups of all ages and both genders. It also provides Urdu and Arabic language teaching.

Gravesend and Dartford Muslim Association
14 Brandon Street
Gravesend DA11 0PL
Tel: 0474-351336
Contact: Mr M E Aslam
Office: Joint Secretary
Community organisation. Established in 1972, the organisation has grown in Gravesend and Dartford and aims to promote and liase with local authorities to establish Islam in Western society, and to uphold, teach, maintain the Islamic religion and worship.

Islamic Society
University of Surrey
Guildford
Surrey GU2 5XH

Mosque
24 Broad Acre
Oakfield
Guildford
Surrey

East Sussex Islamic Association
73 Parkstone Road
Hastings
East Sussex TN34 2NT

Sussex Muslim Ladies Circle
111 New Church Road
Hove BN3 4ED
Tel: 0273-722438
Fax: 0273-540058
Contact: Mrs Yasim Ahmed
Office: Secretary
Women's friendly society. The group was started in 1983 to promote understanding about women in Islam in Sussex. Members meet regularly each month. Get-together parties and study circles are organised. Literature on issues related to women in Islam is distributed and information is provided on various cultural traditions.

Sussex Muslim Society
8 Caburn Road
Hove BN3 6EF
Tel: 0273-722438
Fax: 0273-540058
Contact: Dr Imam Abduljalil Sajid
Office: Director
Representative body. The society was established in 1962 and represents fifteen places of worship and religious organisations in Sussex. The society is recognised in the locality as members sit on SACRE and other statutory bodies to represent Muslim view-points. The society has over two hundred individual members and over thirty-six organisational members. It is a registered charity. It publishes a quarterly bulletin, provides general advice and encourages better understanding between different faiths. Youth and womens groups are run.

Kingston Mosque
55/55a East Road
Kingston-upon-Thames
Surrey
Tel: 081-549-5315

Kingston Muslim Association
41 Wyndham Road
Kingston-upon-Thames
Surrey
Tel: 081-546-0607
Contact: Mohammed Anwar Malik

Kingston Muslim Women's Association
38 Gainsborough Road
New Malden
Kingston-upon-Thames
Surrey
Contact: Mrs H Syed
Office: President

UK Islamic Mission
2 Firtree Avenue
Mitcham
Surrey

UK Islamic Mission
60 Albert Road
New Malden
Surrey

Eastbourne Muslims Project
6 South Street
Eastbourne
Sussex
Contact: Mr Ilis Baig

Highbury Islamic Society
College of Technology
Dovercourt Road
Cosham
Portsmouth
Hampshire

Portsmouth Jamia Mosque & Islamic Centre
73-75 Marmion Road
Southsea
Portsmouth PO5 2AX
Tel: 0705-832541
Contact: The Secretary
Place of worship. The centre has two halls. It is run by an executive committee and employs two Imams and and part time teacher. There are facilities for one thousand people to pray together, funeral preparations, ablution facilities and the registering of marriages. Activities include lessons for both children and adults, hospital visiting, women's gatherings, marriage ceremonies and worship.

Mosque
Earlswood Road
Redhill
Surrey
Tel: 0737-60251

Mosque

8 Redstone Drive
Redhill
Surrey
Tel: 0737-67626

East Sussex Islamic Association (Hastings Mosque)

Mercatoria
St Leonards-on-Sea
East Sussex TN38 0EB
Tel: 0424-426232
Contact: Secretary
Place of worship. The object of the association is to help the individual to reform, purify and pursue his or her life in keeping with the Islamic methods. It is a voluntary non-political and non-sectarian association to help and guide the believers in Islam. Activities include the propogation of Islam, youth activities, Islamic education, worship, welfare and Islamic women's welfare.

Islamic Information Centre

38 Little Ridge Avenue
St Leonard's-on-Sea
East Sussex TN37 7LS
Tel: 0424-755355/812727
Public relations and information to non-Muslims.

Islamic Cultural Association

15 Merton Road
Highfield
Southampton
Hampshire
Contact: Mr B Rahman

Mosque

189 Northumberland Road
Southampton
Hampshire
Tel: 0703-35941

Mosque

Grove Road
Southampton
Hampshire

Razva Dar-ul- Allom

5 Rowland Buildings
near St Mary's Road
Southampton
Hampshire

UK Islamic Mission Southampton

186 Priory Road
St Denys
Southampton S02 1HS
Tel: 0703-321485
Contact: Mr Wasim Darr
Office: President

Majlis-e-Muhammadi

35 Warren Drive North
Surbiton
Surrey KT5 9LG (home)
Contact: Syed Shabbar
Setting up a helpline for Muslim young people in the Sutton, Kingston and Epsom areas. Also aims to initiate and organise interfaith seminars and discussions to acquaint Muslim youth with other religions and faiths.

Al-Muttaqiin

62 West Avenue
Wallington
Sutton
Surrey SM6 8PH
Tel: 081-686-1637
Contact: Brother Shafi Chowdhury
Office: Chairman
Al-Muttaqiin (The Careful Ones) is an Islamic organisation which aims to: raise awareness to take in all aspects of our lives against the influences of the Devil (Shaitaan) for the sake of Allah, the One and Only Lord we worship; study the Qur'an (the Divine Revelation) and the Sunnah (the practical lessons from the life of Mohammad) of the Final Messenger of Allah, Prophet Muhammad (Peace be upon him) for our guidance; encourage environmental consciousness and youth participation through weekend school and recreational activities; and to extend better understanding in the multi-faith, multi-cultural and multi-racial British society through the message of Islam (Peace).

Bangladesh Welfare Association

32 Mollison Drive
Wallington
Sutton
Surrey SM6 9BY
Contact: Mrs H J Kabir
Young women's group providing Islamic education to Bangladeshis.

British Islamic Academy

40 Park Lane
Wallington

Sutton
Surrey SM6 0TN
Tel: 081-395-1829
Contact: Dr M A Mannan

Muslim Cultural and Welfare Association

11 Park Hill Road
Wallington
Sutton
Surrey SM6 0SD
Tel: 081-647-9041 (home)
Contact: Mr Lal Hussain
Office: Secretary
Religious, cultural and welfare organisation. It aims to propagate Islamic teaching by organising lectures, social, cultural, educational and religious gatherings. Activities include organising Islamic festivals, organising a weekend school for mother tongue teaching and Qur'anic studies to young people and organising Friday prayers in rented accommodation.

Sutton Islamic Centre

62 Oakhill Road
Sutton
Surrey
Contact: Misdiq Zaida

Muslim Women Association of Croydon

61a Windmill Road
West Croydon
Surrey
Tel: 081-684-0599 (home)
Contact: Mrs N Sami

South London Muslim Association

76 Elmwood Road
West Croydon
Surrey CR0 2SJ
Contact: Mr M I Mohamed

Tehrik-i-Nizam-i-Qur'an and Sunnah

395 Sydenham Road
West Croydon
Surrey CR0 2EH
Tel: 081-689-3870 (home)
Contact: Mr H I Faryad
Office: Director

Jalat Jung Memorial House

Oriental Road
Woking
Surrey

Muslim Youth Movement

7 Kerry Terrace
Walton Road
Woking
Surrey

Shah Jehan Mosque and Woking Muslim Association

149 Oriental Road
Woking
Surrey GU22 7BA
Tel: 04862-60679

Islamic Society of Worthing

157 Tarring Road
Worthing
West Sussex
Tel: 0903-31192
Contact: S H Khan
Representative body. An organisation which helps everyone in knowing Islam in day to day life. Prior to buying this house two years ago the society was run from the Brighton Islamic Centre. The society is appealing for a bigger place for worship and Islamic practice. Activities relate to welfare, worship and women.

Worthing Islamic Social and Welfare Society

48 Lyndhurst Road
Worthing BN11 2DF
Tel: 0903-215845 (home)
Fax: 0903-211763 (home)
Contact: Mr A H Khabbazeh
Office: Chairperson
Place of worship and education. Activities include prayers and teaching Arabic, the Holy Qur'an and Islamic religion to children and adults.

SOUTH WEST ENGLAND

Bath Islamic Centre and Mosque

8 Pierrepont Street
Bath BA1 1LA
Tel: 0225-460922

Bath Sufi Healing Order

29 Grosvenor Place
London Road
Bath BA1 6BA
Tel: 0225-312694
Contact: Peggie Phillips
Office: Representative

Bournemouth Islamic Centre
48 St Stephen's Road
Bournemouth BH2 6JJ
Tel: 0202-557072
Fax: 0202-298681

Mosque
3 Stafford Road
off Christchurch Road
Bournemouth
Dorset

Students Islamic Society
48 Shaftsbury Road
Bournemouth BH8 8SZ

Bristol and Avon Muslim Association
10 The Old Co-Op
42 Chelsea Road
Easton
Bristol BS5 6AF
Tel: 0272-552686
Contact: Mr Saeed Anwar
Working for the benefit of the Muslim community of
Bristol and Avon.

Bristol University Islamic Society
c/o University Union
Queen's Road
Clifton
Bristol BS8 1LN

Dhar ul Ehsan Centre
564 Eighth Avenue
Bristol BS7 0QS
Tel: 0272-695581
Contact: Imdad Ali Poswal

Easton Masjid
St. Marks Road
Easton
Bristol BS5 6JH
Tel: 0272-510317
Contact: Mr Ashraf

Islami Darasagh Bristol
109 Lower Cheltenham Place
Monteplier
Bristol BS6 5LA
Tel: 0272-414301
Contact: Secretary
Study centre and place of worship. Established to
propagate the Word of Allah to all. The Muslim

community of Montpelier, St Warburghs and St Pauls
come together to offer collective and individual
prayers. Young people attend to learn mother tongue.

Jamia Masjid and Bristol Mosque Committee
Green Street
Totterdown
Bristol BS3 4UB
Tel: 0272-770944
Contact: Saeed Abdu Rahman
Office: Secretary
Place of worship. The central mosque for the Bristol
area provides facilities for the five daily prayers
required by the Islamic faith. Lectures, social
gatherings and religious celebratory feasts also take
place in the mosque throughout the year. The
mosque is open to interested groups who can arrange
visits via the secretary.

Mosque
109 Lower Street
Cheltenham Road
Bristol B6

Mosque
56 Goodwind Street
Bristol BS5

Taleem ul Islam Trust
28 Chelsea Park
Easton
Bristol BS5 6AG
Tel: 0272-558155

Mosque and Muslim Association
416–418 High Street
Cheltenham
Gloucester GL50 3JA

Thamesdown Islamic Association
19 Broomfield
Chippenham
Wiltshire

Mosque and Islamic Centre
15 York Road
Exeter EX4 6BA
Tel: 0392-50597

Islamic Trust Youth Section
18 Charles Street
Gloucester
Contact: Mr I Patel

Ismaili Muslim Group

87 Howard Street
Tredworth
Gloucester
Contact: Mr T A Uka

Jamia Mosque and Gloucester Islamic Trust

All Saints Road
Gloucester GL1 4EE
Tel: 0452-506870
Contact: Secretary
Place of worship. The trust caters for people who wish to pray and worship. It organises charity work and takes social responsibility for the community. It represents the Muslim community in various organisations. Activities include Islamic education for young children and various talks and lecures for colleges and schools, also does social welfare work and runs youth camps.

Khoja Shia Ithna Asheri Muslim Community of Gloucester

137 Eastgate
Gloucester
Contact: Husseini Imambara

Mosque and Muslim Welfare Association

44–46 Ryecroft Street
Gloucester G41 4LY
Tel: 0452-416830
Contact: Mr I Y Ginwalla
Office: Honorary Secretary
Place of worship. Established in 1961 for the benefit of all Muslims living in and around Gloucester. The association provides tuition to all Muslim children in Islamic education. The mosque is used five times a day for prayers and for lectures and visits by other communities. There is also a facility for washing, shrouding and burial of Muslims.

Khoja Shia Muslim Community of Gloucester

Wainsbridge
69 Bristol Road
Quedgeley
Gloucestershire GL2 6NE
Tel: 0452-524262
Tel: 0452-412041
Fax: 0452-309755
Contact: Mr B Najafi
Office: President
Organisation for worship. The organisation aims towards worship for all and trying to make people understand Shi'ism in its true sense. The group meets every Thursday night and as need be, religion is taught

to children and sermons are given. It aims to try to make children understand the necessity of religion in their lives.

Mosque

133 Broad Street
Swindon
Wiltshire
Tel: 0793-523831

Swindon Ismaili Community

32 County Road
Swindon SN1 2EW
Contact: Mr A A Moledina

Paksitan Muslim Association

2 Angler Road
Ramleaze
Swindon SN5 9SX
Contact: Mr Mohammad Salas Khan
Office: Representative
Voluntary welfare organisation. It teaches Urdu; organises social and welfare functions; gives advice to members of groups; interprets for elderly and disabled people; works to eliminate racial discrimination and to achieve equality of opportunity; works with local authorities/groups to promote relations and for multi–cultural education.

Thamesdown Islamic Association

12 Don Close
Greenmeadow
Swindon
Wiltshire
Tel: 0793-693569
Contact: Mr K A Nawaz

Torbay Islamic Centre

130 Avenue Road
Torquay TQ2 5LQ
Tel: 0803-211818

KEY TO TERMS USED IN MUSLIM ORGANISATIONAL LISTINGS

Note: This is not a complete glossary of significant Muslim terms. It is a guide to the meaning of some of the words used in the titles of Muslim organisations listed in the directory. More information on the italicised words can be tracked down elsewhere in the key and/or in "Introducing the Muslim Community" by using the directory's Keyword Index.

Abad
Arabic meaning "eternity" in the sense of "without end".

Abd
Arabic meaning "slave" or servant" referring to a state of dependence upon God and conformity to God's will. It is a title applied to the Prophet Muhammad and is also an element of many Muslim names.

Abel
Pertaining to *Abu* (see below). Correctly written as *Abul-*, meaning "father of.."

Abu
Arabic for "father".

Abu-Bakr
The name of the first *Caliph* (632-634) following the death of Muhammad. He was known as *al-siddiq* or "the faithful". His daughter Aishah was a favourite wife of the Prophet and he was thought to be one of the two people who transmitted the *tasawwuf* (esoteric *Sufi)* doctrines from Muhammad.

Adab
Arabic for "correctness", "propriety" or "good manners", concerning which the *Hadith* (see below) have much to say.

Adam
The name of the first man who is also believed by Muslims to have been the first prophet and the viceregent of God on earth. Unlike the angels, as the centre of creation, Adam was taught the names of all things. His failing was in seeking to make himself autonomous from God.

Aga Khan
The name and title of the Imam of the *Nizari* branch of the *Isma'ilis*. The title was first given in 1818 by the then Shah of Persia to Abu-l-Hasan Ali Shah. In 1841 the Aga Khan fled Persia after a rebellion against the Shah and via Afghanistan went to India. The present Aga Khan, Karim, is the fourth to have the title. In the belief of his followers he is also the forty-ninth *Imam* (see below) in unbroken line of succession.

Ahl
Arabic for "people".

Ahla
Pertaining to *Ahl* (see above).

Ahl-e-Hadith
Ahl-e-Hadith are Muslim groups with their origin in the Indian sub-continent who claim not to follow any *madhhab* or "school of law". Its origin is in the word *Ahl Al-Hadith* who did not engage in any speculation at the time of the Mu'tazilites and the Ash'arite reaction in the early years of Islam.

Ahlebait
Alternative Romanisation of *Ahl-ul-Bait* (see below).

Ahl-ul-Bait
Arabic for "people of the House". A term used for descendants of the Prophet through his daughter Fatima and his cousin and son-in-law 'Ali. In some countries a register is maintained of the Prophet's descendants who now number many thousands. The name is used in *Shi'a* organisations since they believe that 'Ali had a special intermediary role between God and the Muslim community which was inherited by Hussayn and his descendents in other generations.

Ahl-ul-Bayt
Variant Romanisation of *Ahl-ul-Bait* **(see above).**

Al-Azhar
Al-Azhar means "the glorious" and it is the name of the foremost centre of Sunni Muslim learning, founded in Egypt in 969CE.

Alim
Singular of *ulama* meaning a learned person, including imams, *muftis*, *qazis* and *maulvis*. The name *al-Alim* (Wise One) is also one of the ninety-nine most Beautiful Names of God.

Allah
Seen by Muslims as the supreme and true name of God which opens one to the reality of God. He is also known by ninety-nine other names known collectively as "The Most Beautiful Names."

Almadina
See *Madina* below.

Aloom
Variant Romanisation of *Uloom* (see below).

Alume
Variant Romanisation of *Uloom* (see below).

Aman
Arabic, depending on prounnunciation, meaning either "peace" or "safety" or "security", usually in the sense of what is achieved through belief.

Ameen
Al-amin was the name given to the Prophet Muhammad by the Quaraysh tribe before the revelation of the *Qur'an*. It means "trustworthy one" and is often used today of an organisational official in a position of trust.

Amin
Variant Romanisation of *Ameen* (see above).

Amir
Arabic meaning "ruler", "commander" or "chief". It is part of an honorific title applied to the *Caliphs*, namely, *Amiru al Mu'minin* meaning "Commander of the Faithful".

An
Variant Romanisation of the definite article *al* meaning "the".

Anjamin
Variant Romanisation of *Anjuman* (see below).

Anjuman
Arabic meaning "society", "association" or "organisation".

Anjumin
Variant Romanisation of *Anjuman* above.

Ansarullah
Arabic meaning "the helpers of Allah's cause," a common name for both Muslim individuals and associations.

Anwar
Plural of *noor* (see below) meaning "light". It is also one of the Names of God.

Aqsa
Al-aqsa means literally "the farthest (mosque)" and is the name given by the *Qur'an* to the Temple Mount in Jerusalem. It now refers to *Qubbat as-Sakhrah* (the

Dome of the Rock), which is also known as the Mosque of 'Umar. Muslims believe that from this rock the angel Gibreel carried the Prophet Muhammad through the heavens to the presence of God in *al-Isra* (the Night Journey) or *al-Mi'raj* (the Ascent).

Ar
Variant Romanisation of the Arabic definite article *al* meaning "the" (see above).

Arabia
The name of the *Arabian* peninsula. *Arab* means "nomad". Traditionally, north Arabians claim descent from a patriarch called 'Adnan, and from him, through Ishmael, son of Abraham. The south Arabians claim descent from a patriarch called Qahtan. By 636CE the peninsula had become Muslim following the beginning of the *Qur'an's* revelation in 612CE.

Arabiya
Variant Romanisation of Arabia (see above).

Arqam
The name of a Companion of the Prophet and an early convert to Islam who migrated to Madina because of persecution in Makka. He took part in the early struggles to establish Islam and lived to an old age. Before the conversion of 'Umar his house was one of the key meeting places for the early Muslim community and its site is now incorporated into that of the Grand Mosque in Makka.

Ashariyya
From *Ithna Ashariyya* (see below), the *Twelvers* of *Shi'a* Islam, founded by Ab al-Hasan 'Ali ibn Isma'il.

Asheri
Variant Romanisation of *Ashariyya* (see above).

Ashia
Variant Romanisation of *Ashariyya* (see above).

Ashrafia
From Ashraf, the name of a *Sufi* of Persian origin whose full name was Syed Mohammed Ashraf (1289-1405CE). He was the ruler of Samnan and became a *Sufi* and left his kingdom. He settled in Northern India at Kaccauchha where his tomb is. Many Muslims in the UK have contacts with his spiritual descendents.

Ashriia
Variant Romanisation of *Ashariyya* (see above).

Aslamiyya
Variant Romanisation of *Assalam* (see below).

Asna
Variant Romanisation of *Ithna* (see above).

Assalam
Arabic meaning "of peace", as in Dar Assalam, meaning "house of peace" and relating to Paradise.

Asrafia
Variant Romanisation of *Ashrafiya* (see above).

Azad
Meaning "free" or "independent."

Azam
Meaning "greater".

Aziza
From *Aziz*, one of the Names of God, meaning "mighty" or "powerful".

Aziziye
See *Aziza* above.

Bait
Part of *Ahl-ul-Bait* (see above).

Bakar
From Abu Bakr, the name of the second *Caliph*.

Bakr
Variant Romanisation of *Bakar* (see above).

Barkat
Variant Romanisation of the Arabic *barakat* meaning "blessing".

Bayt
See *Ahl-ul-Bait* above.

Bazar
Meaning "market".

Bazami
Meaning "circle" or "gathering".

Bazmi

Variant Romanisation of *bazami* (see above).

Bilal

The name of the first *muezzin* or "caller to prayer", Bilal was a black slave from Abyssinia who was an early convert to Islam, ransomed and freed by Abu-Bakr after his master had persecuted him for his beliefs.

Bina

Meaning "foundation" or "structure".

Bohra

A Muslim community originating from Gujarat in India. There are both Sunni and Shi'a Bohra groups in the UK.

Bukhari

The name of an important collection of 7,000 *Hadith* made by Abu 'Abdu'ilah Muhammad ibn Ismai'il ibn Abraham ibn al-Mughirrah al-Jufi al-Bukhari (810–870CE).

Chachhi

Variant Romanisation of *Cutchi* (see below).

Cutchi

Applying to those who originate in the Cutch or (Kutch) area of Gujarat State in India.

Dar

Arabic for "house".

Darasagh

Persian for *madrassah* (see below).

Darawi

The name of a *Sufi* renewer of Islam in Morocco, whose full name was Mulay-l-Arabi Darqawi (1737–1823CE). He left a strong influence among *Sufi* orders in Morocco.

Darqawi

A *Sufi* tradition.

Darul

Arabic meaning "house of..." or "place of..." giving *Darul-Islam* meaning "house of peace".

Da'wah

Arabic for "to call" and used in the context of calling people into the path of Allah and spreading the message of Islam.

Dawat

Alternative Romanisation of *da'wah* (see above). Used as part of the organisational name Dawatul Islam, meaning "the call of Islam."

Dawatul

Pertaining to *da'wah* (see above).

Da'watul

Pertaining to *da'wah* (see above).

Dawoodi

A branch of the *Bohra* (see above) community, originating in Western India. They are Ismaili Shi'as who believe in Dawood, son of Qutb Shah as a true successor of Dawood, son of Adjab Shah (d. 1588). The head of this group generally resides in Bombay.

Deral

Variant Romanisation of *darul* (see above).

Din

Arabic for "religion" and its practice. A specific religion is often known as a *millah* meaning "way".

Diwan

The base of a *Sufi* master.

Ehsan

Variant Romanisation of *Ihsan* (see below).

Ehyae

Meaning "revival", thus *Ehya-e-Islam* means "revival of Islam".

Eid

Part of the name of the two most important festivals of the Muslim calendar, *Eid-ul-Fitre* (festival of feast) and *Eid-ul-Adha* (festival of sacrifice).

Eshat

Meaning "propagation", "circulation" or "publicity".

Fahd

A male name which appears in the name of the King of Saudi Arabia.

Faisal

A variant Romanisation of the male name Faizul (see below).

Faiz

Meaning "bounty" or "grace".

Faizul

A male name which was the name of a former king of Saudi Arabia.

Falah

Arabic for the fulfillment of the aim of creation and the goal towards which a righteous life leads.

Farooq

A male name meaning "one who distinguishes between right and wrong". It was also a title of Umar, the second *Caliph* of Islam.

Furkania

Pertaining to *furqan*. A variant Romanisation.

Furqan

Arabic literally meaning "divider" in the sense of a criterion distinguishing one thing from another. It is the name of *Surah* 25 in the *Qur'an* and is also used of the *Qur'an* itself in terms of distinguishing between truth and unreality.

Ghamkol

A village in the Province of Sarhad in Pakistan, which is the centre of a *Sufi* tradition.

Ghar

Arabic for "cave". Ghar Hira is the name of the cave at the top of Mount Hira, to which the Prophet Muhammad used to retreat to meditate. The mountain is now called *Jabal an-Nur* (The Mountain of Light).

Ghausia

Ghaus Al-Azam (the great helper) was a title given to Shaikh Abdul Qadir Jeelani of Baghdad, a founder of the Qadiria Sufi Order. Many mosques and Muslim organisations in the UK and throughout the world adopt this name to show their respect for, and affiliation to, the Shaikh.

Ghousia

Variant Romanisation of *Ghausia* (see above).

Ghousian

That which pertains to *Ghausia* (see above)

Ghosia

Variant Romanisation of *Ghausia* (see above).

Gilani

Part of the name of Abdu'l-Qadir Gilani (1078-1166CE) who was a famous *Sufi* saint who founded the *Qadiri* school of *Sufism* .

Gosia

Variant Romanisation of *Ghausia* (see above).

Gosiah

Variant Romanisation of *Ghausia* (see above).

Gousia

Variant Romanisation of *Ghausia* (see above).

Gousiah

Variant Romanisation of *Ghausia* (see above).

Gujerat

The name of a state in north east India and of a city in the Province of Panjab, Pakistan.

Gujerati

That which pertains to Gujarat (see above).

Habibiyya

The name of a *Sufi* tradition, the word literally means "lover" or "friend".

Hadit

A variant Romanisation of *Hadith* (see below).

Hadith

Arabic literally meaning "speech" or "account", it refers to traditions which tell of the deeds and sayings of the Prophet Muhammad and his Companions. There are two basic kinds of *Hadith* : *hadith qudsi* (sacred Hadith) in which Allah is believed to be speaking through Muhammad and *hadith sharif* (noble Hadith) which are the Prophet's own actions and speech. After the *Qur'an,* the *Hadith* form another basis of *Shar'iah*. There are six well-established collections of *Hadith* although there are also others. *Shi'a* Muslims refer to *khabar* (news). Among *Sunni* Muslims, the authenticity of the *Hadith* is established through their *isnad* (chains of transmission), whilst for *Shi'a* Muslims the *khabar* are those of Ali and the *Imams* of *Shi'a* Islam.

Haideria

The name of a *Sufi* tradition.

Haideriah

Variant Romanisation of *Haideria* (see above).

Halal

Arabic literally meaning "released" (from prohibition). It refers to the meat of animals which have been slaughtered according to Islamic practice. Its opposite is *haram*.

Hanafia

One of the four orthodox *madhhab* (literally "movement", referring to the schools of law) recognised among *Sunni* Muslims. It was founded by Abu Hanifah (d. 767) and is predominant in most countries of the former Turkish Empire and in India, as well as among Muslims in the UK originating in those countries.

Hanfi

Variant Romanisation of *Hanafia* (see above).

Hanfia

Variant Romanisation of *Hanafia* (see above).

Hanif

Arabic literally meaning "one who is inclined" and it is the name used in the *Qur'an* for those who did not join in the idolatry of pre-Islamic *Jahilijjah* (Age of Ignorance). It is often used of Abraham.

Hanifa

Variant Romanisation of *Hanafia* (see above).

Haq

Arabic for "reality" or "absolute". It is a centrally important name of Allah.

Hefzul

Arabic for the memorisation of the *Qur'an* .

Heraa

Variant Romanisation of *Hira* (see below).

Hidayah

Arabic literally meaning "guidance" and the name of a *Sunni* book of law.

Hidayatul

Variant Romanisation of *hidayah* (see above).

Hijra

Arabic for "migration", it refers to the 622CE migration of Muhammad and a group of *muhajirun* (emigrants) from persecution in Makka to Yathrib, later called Madinat-an-Nabi (City of the Prophet) or Madina. From 637CE onwards, the Caliph Umar formalised into the Muslim calendar the Prophet's custom of dating events from the *Hijra* onwards.

Hilal

Arabic referring to the crescent of the moon, in other words, the new moon.

Hira

Ghar Hira is the name of the cave at the top of Mount Hira, to which the Prophet Muhammad used to retreat to meditate. The mountain is now called *Jabal an-Nur* (The Mountain of Light). It is a few miles from Makka and the opening of the cave faces Makka. It was on *Laylat al-Qadr* (The Night of Destiny), at the end of the month of *Ramadam*, that the *Qur'an* is believed to have descended to Muhammad.

Huda

Arabic meaning "guidance."

Hurairah

Arabic meaning "kitten". It pertains to the surname of Abu Hurairah, a famous companion of the Prophet Muhammed who gave him this title because he always had a cat with him.

Hussain

The name of the second son of 'Ali and Fatima (the daughter of the Prophet) and hence the grandson of the Prophet. He was killed in 680CE. Hussain's death was central to the development of the *Shi'a* tradition of Islam. It is commemorated in the *Shi'a Muharram* festival and re-enacted in *Ta'ziyah* (martyrdom plays) in the days preceding the 10th *Muharram* . The site of Hussain's tomb in Karbala, has been an important *Shi'a* place of pilgrimage.

Hussaini

That which pertains to Hussain (see above).

Hussainia
That which pertains to Hussain (see above).

Ibadah
Ibadah means "act of worship", from the Arabic *abada* meaning "to serve and *abd* meaning "slave".

Ibadat
Variant Romanisation of *Ibadah* (see above).

Ibadur
Variant Romanisation of *Ibadah* (see above).

Idara
Arabic meaning "organisation".

Idera
Variant Romanisation of *idara* (see above).

Idra
Variant Romanisation of *idara* (see above).

Ifta
A name for a religious or judicial opinion, also known as a *fatwa*.

Ihsan
Arabic literally meaning "to perform an action perfectly", it is used in the *Hadith* to describe sincere worship of God.

Il
Variant Romanisation of the Arabic definite article *al* meaning "the" (see above).

Ilm
Arabic meaning "knowledge".

Imam
Literally means "model" or "example". In *Shi'a* Islam it refers to people with special authority who are successors of the family of Ali and his wife Fatima. The various *Shi'a* groupings disagree over identification of the *Imam*. In *Twelver Shi'ism*, the *Imam* has absolute right to civil and political as well as spiritual authority. In *Sunni* Islam it refers to the leader of *salat*, although it is sometimes used an as honorific title.

Imama
Arabic literally meaning "the followers of the *Imam* ", in other words *Sh'ia* Muslims.

Imambarra
Arabic meaning literally "place of the Imam", it is used to designate some *Shi'ia* mosques.

Imami
Sometimes used as a description of *Shi'a* Muslims and also as an adjective describing their doctrines.

Imamia
The name given to the *Shi'a* Muslim followers of the *Jaffari* legal code and the Twelve *Imams* .

Injaman
Variant Romanisation of *anjuman* (see above).

Iqbal
Sir Muhammad Iqbal (1873-1938) was President of the Muslim League in pre-independence India and attempted to develop Islam and modernity.

Iqra
Arabic meaning "read !", which relates to the command to recite the *Qur'an* .

Irshad
Arabic meaning "guidance".

Ishaat
Variant Romanisation of *eshat* (see above).

Isha'at
Variant Romanisation of *eshat* (see above).

Islah
Arabic meaning "reform", often indicating a movement to improve worldly conditions.

Islahul
Variant Romanisation of *islah* (see above).

Islam
Islam literally means "surrender" and is the name of the religion followed by Muslims which is given in the *Qur'an* itself.

Islami
That which pertains to *Islam*.

Islamia
See *Islami* above.

Islamic

That which pertains to Islam.

Islamiah

See *Islami* above.

Islamiya

That which pertains to Islam.

Ismaili

The name of a group who are often considered to be part of *Shi'a* Islam. *Isma'ilis* began as an offshoot of *Twelver Shi'a* Islam. Ismail was the eldest son of Ja'far, the sixth *Imam* of the *Shi'tes*. Followers of Ismail came to be called *sab'iyyah* (*Seveners*), and among these *Seveners* various ways developed of recognising the Seventh Imam.

Isnah

Variant Romanisation of *ithna* (see below).

Issha'at

Variant Romanisation of *eshat* (see above).

Isshatul

Variant Romanisation of *eshat* (see above).

Itehad

Arabic meaning "unity".

Ithaad

Variant Romanisation of *Itehad* (see above).

Ithna

Ithna 'Ashariyyah means literally "*Twelvers*" from *ithna 'ashar*. It is part of the name of the *Shi'a* Muslim group which believes in a line of twelve *Imams*, with the Twelfth having been occulted in the nineteenth century and is expected to reappear as the *Mahdi*.

Ittehad

Arabic meaning "unity" or "federation".

Ittihas

Variant Romanisation of *ittehad* (see above).

Jafferia

The name applied to the followers of the *Jafferia* legal code.

Jafferiya

Variant Romanisation of *Jafferia* (see above).

Jaime

Variant Romanisation of *Jamia* (see below).

Jalal

Meaning "grandeur" or "eminence", it is the name of a *Sufi* whose tomb lies in Sylhet in Bangladesh. A number of Bangladeshi Muslim mosques in the UK are named after him.

Jalalabad

The name of a city in Northern India.

Jallalabad

Variant Romanisation of *Jalalabad* (see above).

Jamaat

Arabic meaning "association" or "society".

Jama'at

Variant Romanisation of *Jamaat* (see above).

Jama'nt

Variant Romanisatrion of *Jamaat (see above).*

Jamat

Variant Romanisation of *Jamaat (see above.)*

Jame

Variant Romaisation of *Jamia* (see below).

Jamia

Arabic meaning literally "meeting place" and used generally of mosques. Sometimes it is used specifically to refer to a central mosque in a geographical area.

Jamiah

Variant Romanisation of *Jamia* (see above).

Jamial

Variant Romanisation of *Jamia* (see above).

Jamiat

Variant Romanisation of *Jamaat* (see above).

Jamiyat

Variant Romanisation of *Jamaat* (see above).

Jamiyate

Variant Romanisation of *Jamaat* (see above).

Jammat

Variant Romanisation of *Jamaat* (see above).

Jammu

From Jammu Kashmir (see below).

Jamnia

Romanisation variant of *Jamia* (see above).

Jehan

Persian meaning "world".

Jinnah

Muhammad Ali Jinnah (1876-1948), the name of the President of the Muslim League in the India of the British Raj and the first President of the state of Pakistan in 1948.

Judullah

Arabic meaning "the army of Allah".

Juma

The name for Friday, the day on which special congregational prayers are held in mosques.

Kanz

Meaning a "treasure".

Karam

Meaning "generous" or "noble", it is the name of a spiritual and religious leader, Pir Karan Shah of Pakistan, whose followers can be found in the UK.

Kashif

Meaning "discover".

Kashmir

The name of a geographical area of the north east of the Indo-Pakistan sub-continent, part of which is in Pakistan and is known by Muslims as Azad Kashmir (see *Azad* above) and part of which is in the state of India.

Kerat

Variant Romanisation of *Qira't*, it relates to the reading of the *Qur'an* according to the science of recitation.

Khalifa

Arabic for "successor" or "viceroy". Adam, as the first man, was given *khilafa* and the word is also used of the first four "Rightly Guided" *Caliphs* of the early Muslim community, namely Abbu Bakr, 'Umar, 'Uthman and 'Ali. It is both a spiritual and a civil function. The insitution eventually became de facto hereditary with rival claimants.

Khalifad

See *khalifa* above.

Khalifate

The name of the institution within *Sunni* Islam in which community authority was vested.

Khan

A Turkish word for "prince" or "chief".

Khaniqahi

A name by which *Sufi* centres are sometimes known.

Khatme

Arabic meaning "conclusion" or "seal".

Khawateen

Arabic meaning "ladies".

Khizra

Meaning "green", often used in conjunction with the word *Gurbad* (tomb) since the colour of the Prophet's tomb is green.

Khoja

Term applied to converts to *Shi'a* Islam from the Gujarat area of India. They are mostly *Ismailis*, but some also joined the *Ithna Asheri* group and are strong in the UK.

Khuddam

Arabic meaning "servant".

Khuddamuddin

Arabic meaning "servant of the faith".

Khuddamul

Pertaining to *Khuddam* (see above).

Khwateen

Variant Romanisation of *Khawateen* (see above).

Kokani
Variant Romanisation of *kokni* (see below).

Kokni
Refers to people originating in Kokan, a region of India near Bombay. Many UK Muslims have their origins here.

Kumba
Meaning "family".

Li
Arabic meaning "to" or "unto".

Maarif
Arabic meaning "knowledge" or "insight".

Madani
Arabic for that which originates in *Madina* (see below).

Madina
The name of the city one hundred and eighty miles to the north of Makka, to which Muhammad and his followers migrated in 622CE. It is the second most sacred city for Muslims and contains the tombs of Muhammad and the first two *Caliphs* .

Madni
Variant Romanisation of *Madani* (see above).

Madrasa
Variant Romanisation of *Madrassah* (see below).

Madrassa
Variant Romanisation of *Madrassah* (see below).

Madrassah
Literally a "place of study". Traditionally, it is used of a school of higher study for students who had already memorised the *Qur'an*. It is now generally used in the UK to refer to Qu'ranic schools for children.

Madressa
Variant Romanisation of *Madrassah* (see above).

Madressah
Variant Romanisation of *Madrassah* (see above).

Mahal
The name given to the seat of a *Sufi sheikh* as a centre of learning.

Majlis
Arabic meaning literally "sitting" or "assembly". It is often used of a parliament or other representative assembly. It is also used of a *Sufi* gathering for prayer and singing which in India is known as *durbar*.

Majlusus
Variant Romanisation of *majlis* (see above).

Makka
The city in Saudi Arabia which is the direction in which Muslim prayers are made and for which Muslims undertake the *hajj*.

Makki
See *Makka* above.

Markazi
Arabic meaning "central".

Markazud
Variant Romanisation of *markazi* (see above).

Maroof
Meaning "generally recognised". It is a common male name among Muslims since in the *Qur'an* it is used of good things.

Masjeed
Variant Romanisation of *masjid* (see below).

Masjid
Arabic meaning literally a "place of prostrations", it is used of mosques which are places of worship of one God. It can either be an enclosed or an open space which is clean and into which Muslims should enter only in a condition of ritual purity. There are a range of architectural designs, but the prototype of a mosque was built by the Prophet at Quba' in Madina.

Masjide
Variant Romanisation of *masjid* (see above).

Medina
See *Madina* above.

Mehfil
Meaning "place of assembly" or "congregation".

Mehr
Meaning "kindness" or "affection", it is in the name of Pir Mehr Ali Shah of Golara in Pakistani Panjab. He was a *Sufi* leader of the *Chishtia* order and has a number of followers in the UK mainly among Muslims originating in Pakistan and Kashmir.

Mehria
Pertaining to the Pir Mehr Ali Shah (see above).

Memon
The name of an ethnic group from Western India and Malawi.

Milad
Arabic meaning "birth", as in *Milad un-Nabi* (the birthday of the Prophet).

Millat
Millat is a specific religion as distinct from *din* which refers to religion in general. *Millat* was particularly used in the Ottoman Empire to refer to different religious groups within the Empire.

Minaret
Derived from the Arabic *manarah* meaning "lighthouse", the word refers to the towers of many mosques from which *muezzin* (callers to prayer) make the *adhan* (call to prayer) five times a day.

Minhaj
Arabic meaning "road".

Mohammedi
That which relates to Muhammad, the Prophet of Islam who, according to tradition, was born in 570CE and died in 632CE. His name means in Arabic "the praised one" or "he who is glorified". Traditionally, every mention of his name is followed by *sall-al-Lahu alayhi wa-sallam,* meaning "God bless him and give him peace" although it is often sufficient to say *alayhi wa-sallam* (peace be upon him).

Mohammedia
See above. It may also signify adherence to the *Tariqah-i-Muhammadiyya* or *Jihad* Movement or to the *Ahl-e-Hadith.*

Mohi
A "reviver" or "revitaliser".

Mohiban
Variant Romanisation of *Mohibban* (see below).

Mohibban
Meaning "friends".

Mosque
The name given to a Muslim place of worship.

Muhibban
Variant Romanisation of *Mohibban* (see above).

Munir
Meaning "radiant" or "luminous".

Muntada
Meaning "a place of gathering".

Muntazar
Arabic meaning "the expected one", usually referring to "the *Hidden Imam* " of *Sh'ia* Muslim belief.

Muridin
Arabic meaning "disciples" and usually connected with a *Sufi sheikh* .

Muslamin
Variant Romanisation of the masculine plural of *Muslim* (see below).

Muslemeen
Variant Romanisation of the masculine plural of *Muslim* (see below).

Muslim
Arabic literally meaning "one who has surrendered to God", derived from the Arabic *salama* meaning "to surrender" and "to seek peace". The "s" in Muslim should be pronounced as in the English word "slim" and not as in "nose", as this latter pronunciation can sound like a word meaning "cruel" and could therefore be misunderstood and offensive.

Muslimat
Feminine plural of *Muslim* (see above).

Muslimeen
Masculine plural of *Muslim* (see above).

Muslimeem
Masculine plural of *Muslim* (see above).

Muslimin

Masculine plural of *Muslim* (see above).

Mustafa

Arabic meaning "the pure one", an alternative name by which Muhammad is known among Muslims.

Muttaqlin

Arabic meaning "careful ones".

Nabawut

Variant Romanisation of *nubuwwat* (see below).

Nabi

The title of a prophet who prophesies within a particular revelation. In the *Hadith* it is said, symbolically, that there have been one hundred and twenty-four thousand such prophets. Among these are two categories of *nabi*, a *bashir* being one who brings good news and a *nadhir* being one who brings a warning. *Nabi* is to be distinguished from *rasul* which means messenger and refers to a prophet who brings a new revelation rather than one who prophesies within a revelation.

Naqeebul

Pertaining to *Naqeeb* which means "leader".

Naqshbandia

Naqshbandia is a *Sufi* order founded by Muhammad ibn Muhammad Baha ad-Din Naqshband (1317CE-1389CE) of Bukhara. The observance of silence is a charcteristic of the order along with dhikr which is the invocation from the heart of the Divine Name.

Nau

Meaning "new".

Neelie

Meaning "blue colour".

Nimatullah

Meaning "gift of Allah", it is the name of a *Sufi*.

Nisa

Arabic meaning "women".

Nizama

Arabic meaning "order" or "system".

Nizame

Variant romanisation of *nizama* (see above).

Nizani

Variant romanisation of *nizama* (see above).

Noor

Arabic meaning "light". *Masjide-e-Noor* therefore means "mosque of light".

Noorul

Pertaining to *noor* (see above).

Nubuwwat

Arabic meaning "prophethood".

Nural

Variant Romanisation of *Noorul*.

Nusrat

Female name meaning "defender".

Nusrati

Pertaining to the *nusrat* (see above).

Nusratul

Pertaining to *nusrat* (see above).

O

Arabic meaning "he", "she" or "it".

Omar

'Umar ibn al-Khattab, the second *Caliph* and one of the main figures of Islam, before he became a Muslim originally set out to kill the Prophet and to dispute with his sister and her husband who had become Muslims. However, he let them recite to him verses from the *Qur'an* and these converted him. He was the first *Caliph* to bear the title *Amir al-Mi'minin* meaning "Commander of the Faithful". He was assassinated in 644 CE. Islam had spread rapidly during his *Caliphate* and most Islamic movements look back to this time as a model Islamic state, apart from the *Twelver Shi'as* for whom only the descendents of Ali and Fatima have a special place of honour.

Paigham

Paighambar is a Persian word for prophet, equivalent to both the Arabic *nabi* (see above) and *rasul*.

Pak

Meaning "pure". pertains to the name of the state called Pakistan.

Pratisthan

Malaysian word meaning "centre" or "department".

Qaafia

Meaning "rhyme".

Qamrul

Pertaining to *qamar*, meaning "moon".

Qasmia

A *Sufi* tradition of Pakistan.

Quawatul

Pertaining to *quuwat* meaning "ability" or "power".

Quawwatul

Variant Romanisation of *quauwatul* (see above).

Quba

The name of a village three miles outside of Madina where the Prophet Muhammad went after the *hijra* from Makka to Madina. The first mosque was erected here and was later called al-Taqwa (The Mosque of Remembrance).

Qul

Arabic meaning "say !", an injunction.

Qur'an

Arabic literally meaning "recitation". The *Qur'an* is the book at the centre of Islam and was revealed over a period of twenty-three years and recorded in the Arabic language.

Qusma

A Sufi tradition of Pakistan.

Rabbani

Pertaining to God – *rab* is an Arabic word for "lord " and is one of the names of God.

Rahimiyah

The name of a *Sufi* tradition.

Rahmah

Variant Romanisation of *rahman* (see below).

Rahman

Arabic literally meaning "mercy" from the Arabic root *rahima* meaning "to be mercificul". *Ar-Rahman*, meaning "the Merciful One" is, after the name of *Allah*, one of the most important and commonly used of the Names of God.

Rashida

Feminine Arabic form of *rashid* meaning "righteous".

Rashool

Variant Romanisation of *rasool* (see below).

Rasool

Arabic meaning "messenger".

Raza

The name of the founder of the *Barelwi* movement in Islam.

Razvi

Portaining to Raza, surname of Maulana Ahmed Raza Khan of Barielly in India (1856–1921 CE).

Razvia

Variant Romanisation of *Razvi* (see above).

Rehman

Romanisation variant of *rahman* (see above).

Risalah

The word describing the mission of a *rasul* or messenger, it is derived from the Arabic word *risalah* meaning "to send".

Rizwan

Meaning "delight" or "approval", the name of an angel.

Sahaba

Arabic for "the Companions of the Prophet".

Saifee

Relates to the followers of Saifuddin, a spiritual leader of the *Bohra Shi'a* Muslims.

Salam

Arabic meaning "peace".

Sanaullah
Meaning "admirer of Allah", a common male name among Muslims.

Shah
An honorific title for a leader.

Shair
Meaning "poet".

Shajalal
See "*Jalal*" above.

Shari'ah
From the Arabic root *shara'a* meaning "to prescribe". It refers to the Islamic way of life in the *Qur'an* and the *Sunnah* as interpreted, in *Sunni* Islam, by the four orthodox schools of the law.

Shi'a
From the Arabic word meaning "faction" or "party", its original use was in relation to the supporters of the *Caliphate* of Ali ibn Abi Jalib. Today it refers to the tradition of Islam which is organised in three main groupings, the *Ithna Ashariyya* (*Twelvers*), the *Isma'ilis* or *Seveners* and the *Zaydis* (*Fivers*) who are found in the Yemen.

Shomity
A Bengali word meaning "association".

Shoura
Meaning "advisory".

Siddiqia
Pertaining to Abu Bakr Siddiq (see Abu Bakr above).

Siraat
Arabic meaning "path".

Somity
Variant Romanisation of *shomity* (see above).

Sufat
Meaning "best friend".

Sufi
The name of the mystical tradition within Islam which emphasises its inner or esoteric aspects as well as its outer or exoteric forms.

Sughra
Feminine Arabic form of *saghir* meaning "small".

Sultana
A title for the wife of a *Sultan*.

Sultania
Variant Romanisation of *sultana* (see above).

Sunnat
Sunnah is the Arabic for "custom" and refers to the spoken or acted example of the Prophet Muhammad which shows Muslims how to live.

Sunnatwal
Arabic meaning "*Sunnah* (see above) and..."

Sunni
From the Arabic word *sunnah* meaning "custom", it refers to the majority of the global Islamic community who recognise the four *Caliphs* and are organised in one of four orthodox schools of law.

Sukhan
Persian word meaning "talk".

Surati
Alternative Romanisation of *Surti* (see above).

Surti
Denotes origination in Surat in Gujarat, India.

Tableeg
Variant Romanisation of *tabligh* (see below).

Tablig
Variant Romanisation of *tabligh* (see below).

Tabligh
Arabic meaning "preaching" or "message"

Tablique
Variant Romanisation of *tabligh* (see above).

Tabliquel
Variant Romanisation of *tabligh* (see above).

Tabuk
Name of a place where Muslims defeated Christians in a war during the time of the Prophet Muhammad

Tafreeh
Meaning "entertainment".

Taiba
Variant Romanisation of *taiyabah* (see below).

Taijdare
Meaning "king", a Persian title used of the Prophet Muhammad.

Taiyabah
Meaning "well disposed" or "pleasant", the word often appears together with Madina (see above).

Taleem
Variant Romanisation of *talim* (see below).

Taleemul
Arabic meaning "teaching of..."

Talim
Arabic meaning "teaching".

Talimud
Variant Romanisation of *taleemul* (see above)

Talimuddin
Arabic meaning "teaching the religion".

Talimul
Variant Romanisation of *Taleemul* (see above).

Tanzeem
Meaning "organisation".

Taraqqi
Arabic meaning "development" or "promotion". It usually refers specifically to various *Sufi* "ways" within Islam.

Tayabba
Variant Romanisation of *taiyabah* (see above).

Tayba
Variant Romanisation of *taiyabah* (see above).

Tehrik
Meaning "movement".

Telemuddin
Variant Romanisation of *talimuddin* (see above).

Tauheedul
Pertaining to *tawhid* (see below).

Tawakkulia
The name of a *Sufi* tradition.

Tawhid
The verbal noun in Arabic of *wahhada* meaning "to make one", referring to the Absoluteness and Unity of God.

Ul
Alternative Romanisation of the Arabic definite article *al-* meaning "the".

Ulama
Plural of *alim* meaning "learned" and referring to Muslim religious scholars who are competent to make judgements. In the *Shi'a* tradition of Islam such competent people are the superior *Mullahs*, the *Mujtahids*.

Ulami
Variant Romanisation of *ulama* (see above).

Uloom
Arabic plural of *Ilm*, meaning "knowledge" or "science", usually used in the sense of the religious sciences.

Umar
A variant Romanisation of the name of *Omar* (see above). The name of the Mosque of Omar, otherwise known as the Dome of the Rock, in Jerusalem.

Urdu
The national language of Pakistan.

Us
Variant Romanisation of the Arabic definite article *al-* meaning "the".

Usman
Variant Romanisation of *'Uthman*, the name of the third *Caliph* .

Vohra
Variant Romanisation of *Bohra* (see above).

Wal

Arabic meaning "and the…"

Watul

Variant Romanisation of *watul* (see above).

Zawiya

Variant romanisation of Wawiyah (see below).

Zawiyah

Arabic meaning "corner". In North Africa it tends to refer to a small mosque, but it also often refers to a *Sufi* meeting place for prayer and invocation of God's name.

Zawiyya

Variant Romanisation of *zawiyah* (see above).

Zinatul

Meaning "decoration".

Zeenutul

Variant Romanisation of *zinatul* (see above).

Ziyaul

Pertaining to *zia* meaning "brightness".

THE SIKH COMMUNITY

INTRODUCING THE SIKH COMMUNITY

SIKHS IN THE UNITED KINGDOM

Beginnings in the UK

Most Sikhs living in the UK are of Panjabi ethnic origin and many of these came directly to the UK from the Panjab, although a significant minority came via East Africa and other former British colonies to which members of their families had initially migrated. Many Sikhs served in the British Indian armies in the First and Second World Wars and thereafter a number of ex-servicemen migrated to Britain.

The size of the Sikh community in the UK is estimated to be around 400,000 and, as such, it is the largest Sikh community outside the Indian subcontinent, the global Sikh population being in the region of 19,000,000. Sikhs are mainly to be found in most large towns and cities in the UK but the largest communities are to be found in Birmingham, Bradford, Cardiff, Coventry, Glasgow, Leeds, Leicester, London (especially in Southall) and Wolverhampton.

A young Sikh prince, Dalip Singh, son of Maharajah Ranjit Singh, was the first Sikh to reside in Britain. He acquired the Elveden Estate in Norfolk and this place is now frequently visited by Sikhs, thus marking their early connections with the UK. Although a number of Sikhs settled in the UK in the 1920s and 1940s, the vast majority arrived in the 1950s and 1960s.

The first *Gurdwara* in the UK was opened in Putney in 1911 at the initiative of Sant Teja Singh and with funding from Maharaja Bhupinder Singh of Patiala. As the size of the UK Sikh community grew, the number of *Gurdwaras* opened increased. The Registrar General's list of certified places of worship gives 157 Gurdwaras in England and Wales and this directory records 180 Gurdwaras in the UK.

Migration and Ethnicity

Most Sikhs in the UK speak Panjabi and English. Almost all *Gurdwaras* run Panjabi classes and the community has gone to great efforts to transmit it to second generation children. It is held in great esteem and respect by Sikhs. Some Sikhs who came to the UK via East Africa may also be verbally fluent in Swahili. Panjabi speakers can communicate to some degree with Urdu and Hindi speakers as the three languages have some common vocabulary.

Gurmukhi is the script of the Sikh Scriptures, which is also used for writing the modern Panjabi language. Converts to the Sikh religion are welcome although conversion is not that common. This is essentially due to the fact that Sikhism is not an actively proselytising faith and in its outlook it accords respect to all other faiths.

The global Sikh population is estimated to be approximately eighteen to twenty million. Over eighty per cent of Sikhs live in the Indian province of Panjab. The older Panjab Province was partitioned in 1947 on the departure of British power from the sub-continent, when West Panjab became part of Pakistan and East Panjab part of India.

ORIGINS AND DEVELOPMENT OF SIKHISM

The Ten Gurus

Sikhs understand their *dharam* (the Sikh way of life), also known as *Gurmat*, to be an original, revealed religion which centres upon the teachings of the ten *Gurus* of Sikhism. The first *Guru* and founder of the faith, Guru Nanak Dev Ji (1469-1539) was born in the Panjab at a place called Talwandi, renamed Nankana Sahib in his honour and now a part of the state of Pakistan.

Sikhs believe that he was born in an enlightened state. Accounts of his early life illustrate that he was not only a precocious child, but also that he possessed divine charisma. When he was about thirty years old, he received the call to preach God's Word and over the next twenty-two years undertook four great journeys called *Udasi*. He travelled extensively within and beyond the Indian subcontinent, as far as Assam in the east, Sri Lanka in the south, Tibet and parts of Russia in the north, and the Middle East in the west, including Muslim holy places of Makka and Madina.

He preached a message of universal love, peace and brotherhood and emphasised worship of the one God. He never actively sought followers but taught that worship of God, in whatever

tradition one practised it, should be sincere and honest and not clouded by hypocrisy or ritualism. He eventually settled at Kartupur in the Panjab and founded a community of disciples who became known as Sikhs.

Guru Nanak Ji, as the founder of Sikhism was succeeded by nine other Gurus: Guru Angad Dev Ji (1504-1552); Guru Amar Das Ji (1479-1574); Guru Ram Das Ji (1534-1581); Guru Arjan Dev Ji (1563-1606); Guru Hargobind Ji (1595-1644); Guru Har Rai Ji (1631-1661); Guru Har Krishan Ji (1656-1664); Guru Tegh Bahadur Ji (1622-1675); and Guru Gobind Singh Ji (1666-1708). Sikhs believe that the ten *Gurus* who conveyed God's word were all spiritually one.

Although the word *guru* generally means a spiritual leader, to the Sikhs, when it is applied to their ten *Gurus*, its significance is much greater. The ten *Gurus* are seen as the divine Preceptors who conveyed God's Word. They are not, however, objects of worship.

After the line of the ten *Gurus*, Sikhism acknowledges no more human *Gurus*. The tenth *Guru*, Guru Gobind Singh Ji, vested spiritual authority in the *Guru Granth Sahib Ji* (the Sikh scriptures) and temporal authority in the *Khalsa Panth* (the Sikh community). Henceforth the living *Guru*, *Guru Granth Sahib Ji*, was to be the eternal *Guru*, believed to embody the Divine word. In 1699, Guru Gobind Singh Ji instituted *Amrit Pahul* (see below) for both men and women and in doing so completed the spiritual and temporal structure of the Sikh faith in the form of the *Khalsa Panth*.

History

Sikhism bestows upon its followers distinct religious beliefs and institutions together with its own language, literature, tradition and conventions. The early Sikh community faced considerable persecution in the Moghul Empire and later many Sikhs were martyred for their faith. However, the Sikh community in the Panjab eventually emerged as a temporal as well as spiritual community with its own military, economic and governmental structures and was a sovereign nation until the advent of the British Raj in the subcontinent.

Among the several towns founded by the Sikh *Gurus*, Amritsar, with the *Darbar Sahib* (commonly known among non-Sikhs as the Golden Temple) was developed by Guru Arjan Dev Ji who installed the *Guru Granth Sahibji* at its centre. Guru Hargobind Ji built the Akal Takhat in front of the *Darbar Sahib* declaring it the seat of temporal authority. The Sikh sovereign, Ranjit Singh, spent lavishly on buildings within its precincts, donating gold and other precious gifts.

SOURCES OF SIKH BELIEFS AND PRACTICES

Guru Granth Sahib Ji

The *Guru Granth Sahib Ji* is the most revered of the Sikh scriptures. The original version was known as the *Adi Granth*, *ad* meaning "first", both in time and importance and *Granth* meaning volume. It was compiled by Guru Arjan Dev Ji. It contains the *Gurbani* (teaching or utterance of the *Guru*) of the first five *Gurus* and the *Bhagat Bani*, verses from Hindu and Muslim saints which were compatible with Sikh teachings.

The original version contains five thousand five hundred and fifty one *shabads* (hymns) set to thirty *rags* (musical compositions) and nine hundred and seventy-five pages. Guru Arjan Dev Ji installed the *Adi Granth* in Amritsar in 1604. This original version is now often referred to as the *Kartarpur Bheer*, after the name of the place called Kartarpur in Panjab where it is kept. Guru Tegh Bahadur Ji's *shabads* were added later by Guru Gobind Singh Ji in 1706 at Damdama Sahib. This version is therefore known as the *Damadami Bheer* and in 1708 was given the status of *Guru* by Guru Gobind Singh Ji.

Guru Arjan Dev Ji installed the *Adi Granth* in Amritsar in 1604. Guru Tegh Bahadur Ji's *shabads* (hymns) were added later by Guru Gobind Singh Ji. All the *shabads* in the *Guru Granth Sahib Ji* are in verse and are set to musical compositions known as *rag*. Altogether, there are five thousand, eight hundred and seventeen

shabads set to thirty-one *rags*, in one thousand four hundred and thirty pages.

Dasam Granth

The *Dasam Granth* contains some writings of Guru Gobind Singh Ji and it was compiled by Bhai Mani Singh, who was the *granthi* (administrator) of the Darbar Sahib. It was completed in 1734. Both the *Guru Granth Sahib* and the *Dasam Granth* are written in the *Gurmukhi* script.

Rahit Nama

Rahit Nama consists of a set of principles according to which a Sikh's way of life should be conducted. It covers ethics relating to spiritual, moral and social discipline, reputed to be based on the injunctions of Guru Gobind Singh Ji and compiled by various Sikh theologians from the late seventeenth to the late nineteenth century. However, the *Gurbani* provides the fundamental guidelines and takes precedence in interpreting and following each *Rahit Nama*.

Rahit Maryada

Rahit Maryada is the Sikh Code of Conduct which is published by the Shromani Gurdwara Parbandhak Committee in Amritsar. It was first issued in 1936, but it was formally approved and adopted with some amendments in 1945. It is widely accepted as a standard, the Shromani Gurdwara Parbandhak Committee having been established in 1920 following the Gurdwara Reform Movement. Among its responsibilities are the organisation and administration (in accordance with Sikh tenets) of a large number of *Gurdwaras* in the Panjab, as well as hospitals and educational institutions.

Works of Bhai Gurdas and Bhai Nandlal

Expositions by Bhai Gurdas and Bhai Nandl, two Sikh theologians, are also highly regarded and are approved for reading and discourse in *Gurdwaras*, although they do not have the same status as the *Guru Granth Sahib Ji* and the *Dasam Granth*. Bhai

Gurdas (1551–1637CE) was a Sikh scholar and theologian of distinction to whom Guru Arjan Dev Ji dictated the *Adi Granth* when it was first compiled. His thirty-nine *vars* (theological and historical expositions in verse form) are often considered to be a key to understanding Sikh theology. The writings of Bhai Nandl (1633–1713), an eminent poet and a devout follower of Guru Gobind Singh Ji, are on Sikh philosophy.

KEY SIKH BELIEFS

Definitions

A Sikh is defined as one who believes in *Akal Purakh* (the one immortal God), the ten Gurus, the *Guru Granth Sahib Ji,* (the Sikh Scriptures) and the *Gurbani* (teaching of the ten *Gurus* as a unity). A Sikh also believes in the *Amrit Pahul* (the Sikh form of initiation) of the tenth *Guru* and adheres to no other religion. The *Gurbani* (also known as *Gurshabad*) is believed by Sikhs to be the Word of God.

God

The beliefs which are central to Sikhism include strict monotheism (belief in only one God). In Sikh understanding this one God is known to Sikhs by many names including Ram, Mohan, Gobind, Hari, Allah, and others. However, the two names traditionally used in worship, and especially in *Nam Japna* (the recitation of God's name), are *Satnam* and *Waheguru*. Sikhs believe that God has revealed himself continuously since before the advent of the ten *Gurus* and continues to do so since their departure by means of scriptures.

Sikhs believe that God is *nirgun* (transcendent) and also *sargun* (immanent) but can never be incarnate. It is believed God can be experienced but is beyond human comprehension. The *Mul Mantar* is a distillation of the fundamental belief of Sikhism that there is only one God.

Every section in the *Guru Granth Sahib Ji* begins with the *Mul Mantar*, which states that: "There is but One God, the Eternal Truth, the Creator, without fear, without enmity, not subject to time, immanent, beyond birth and death, self-existent: by the grace of the *Guru*, made known."

Sikhs believe that God created countless universes as an act of will. It is believed that creation evolved slowly: that from air came water, from water came the lower forms of life leading to plants, birds and animals and culminating in humans as the supreme form of created life on earth.

Goal of Life

It was taught by Guru Nanak Dev Ji that everything which happens is ultimately within God's will and that people should be obedient to God's will. This concept of the divine will or order is known as *hukam*. The Sikh belief is that a person is a small part of God. The person's soul exists from the time of its creation until the time at which it is re-absorbed into God. Until then a person's soul remains separate from God and the cycle of birth and death continues.

The highest form of life on this earth is the human and therefore a human life is the time when the cycle of transmigration can potentially be broken. The *karma* (actions and their consequences) of this life determine whether a person will achieve the union with God which Sikhism sees as the purpose of human existence. This liberation from the cycle of rebirth is known as *mukti*.

Barriers to the liberation of the soul are believed to include *maya*, an illusory, materialistic view of the world producing ignorance of one's own true nature and destiny and of God's will. This results in *haumai* (self-centredness), giving rise to *kam* (lust), *karodh* (anger), *lobh* (greed), *moh* (worldly attachment/obsessions) and *hankar* (pride), all of which block union with God.

There are also five stages to union with God. These are referred to as *Dharam Khand* (the region of realising one's spiritual duty), *Gian Khand* (region of divine knowledge), *Saram Khand* (region of wisdom and effort), *Karam Khand* (region of divine grace) and *Sach Khand* (region of truth).

Khalsa Panth

Sikhs believe in the collective identity of the *Khalsa Panth* as a society of equals irrespective of their background. *Khalsa* is synonymous with the Sikh community. The first five people to be initiated are known as the *Panj Pyare* (the five beloved ones).

These five, from wide-ranging backgrounds, volunteered from the crowd of around eighty thousand Sikhs summoned to Anandpur on 30th March 1699 by Guru Gobind Singh Ji, when the *Guru* asked who would offer his life to his Guru. The *Panj Pyare* were Daya Ram (of the *Khatri* caste), Dharam Das (*Jat*), Mohkam Chand (washerman), Himmat Rai (water carrier), and Sahib Chand (barber).

The *Panj Pyare* were all given the name *Singh* as a substitute for their original caste name on the basis that Sikhism recognises no castes. Guru Gobind Singh Ji then asked the *Panj Pyare* to administer *Amrit Pahul* to him in turn which was an instance when the *Guru* further emphasised equality with the *Khalsa Panth*.

The sharing of history, cultural values and religious tradition in the form of the *Khalsa Panth* has led members of the Sikh community to regard religious authority as emanating from the *Guru Granth Sahib Ji* occupying the central place in the *Darbar Sahib* in Amritsar, whilst political authority is thought to reside in the *Akal Takhat*.

TRADITIONS IN SIKHISM

Sikhs do not acknowledge groupings within Sikhism which could be classified as such on the basis of doctrinal schools. Organisations do, however, exist within the *Panth* to cater for various interests or to reflect particular aspects of Sikh life. An example is that of the *Sewa Panthi*, a group devoted to the service of humanity founded in memory of Bhai Kanayha. He was a Sikh who cared for wounded enemy soldiers in the same way as for Sikh soldiers, without any discrimination, and was highly praised for this by Guru Gobind Singh Ji. The *Guru* warmly embraced him when, in reply to a question, he stated that he saw no distinction between friend and foe but saw God residing in all.

There are other movements whose origins essentially lie in the revivalism of Sikh faith during its history. These are generally founded by Sikh individuals who are given the honorific title of *sant*.

Sants are those within Sikhism who, on the basis of their reputation for spiritual guidance and teaching, are respected and given this honorific title. They are expounders of the *Gurbani* and may hold significant influence within particular *Gurdwaras* or Sikh organisations.

SIKH LIFE

Ethics

Sikhs believe that in the course of everyday life God should always be remembered. Guru Nanak taught that truth is above everything but higher still than truth is truthful living. There are certain ethical principles which are intrinsic to Sikh belief and practice. Foremost amongst these are: *kirat karna* (earning a living by honest and approved means) and *vand chhakna* (sharing with the needy). *Seva* (service) to the community at large, or in helping to meet a particular need for the benefit of others is also an essential part of Sikh life.

The concept of equality was of central importance to Guru Nanak Dev Ji. He taught that all people are born with the opportunity to attain *mukti* whether they are rich or poor, male or female, high or low, educated or uneducated. What influences *mukti* is the *karma*, *maya* and *haumai* of individuals and the grace of the *Guru*. The ten Sikh *Gurus* did not believe in any caste distinctions and taught that every person is equal before God.

Equality

The Sikh concept of equality embraces women as well as men in both secular and religious life. This was historically decreed in the teachings and practices of the *Gurus*.

Women have played a significant role in Sikhism, for instance at the first *Amrit Pahul* ceremony in Anandpur in 1699. The wife of Guru Gobind Singh Ji took a leading role in the ceremony. Both women and men can be fully initiated into the Sikh religion and can act as a *granthi* (see section below) in a *Gurdwara*.

However, social and cultural conventions may influence gender roles in Sikh communities. For example, in cultures where modesty and domesticity are specifically associated with female roles and community leadership is a male role, these roles may prevail though perhaps be seen as different rather than as unequal.

Amrit Pahul

Amrit Pahul is the Sikh name for initiation into the *Khalsa Panth*. *Amrit* (the nectar of everlasting life) refers to the sweetened water used in *Amrit Pahul*. When coupled with adherence to the ethical principles of Sikhism this initiation is seen as the way to spiritual development and hence to the realisation of God's grace. The ceremony is for women as well as men and takes place at an age when the person can understand its significance. When married, women and men must undertake it together.

It can be conducted at any time when those undergoing the ceremony can understand its significance and can take place anywhere, providing only that it is in the presence of the *Guru Granth Sahib Ji* and that five members of the *Khalsa Panth* are present to officiate. The ceremony follows the same practice as the original *amrit* ceremony carried out by Guru Gobind Singh Ji. *Amrit* is prepared by mixing sugar with water stirring the ingredients with a *khanda* (double-edged sword), whilst certain passages from the scriptures are recited.

The initiate is also inducted into the Sikh code of discipline, takes the vows of the *Khalsa* and then is offered *Amrit* and has some of it splashed on the eyes and hair. The initiate must be in possession of the five symbols of the *Khalsa*.

A Sikh who has taken *amrit* is known as an *Amritdhari*. Sikhs who have not yet taken the five Ks are sometimes referred to as *Sahajdhari Sikhs*. This may include those who believe in Sikhism but have not yet decided to take *amrit* and those who have lapsed and would need to take it again if they were to return to the status of an *Amritdhari*. The term *Keshdari* is also often used for those Sikhs who wear uncut hair and turban but have not yet taken *amrit*.

Five Ks

Many Sikhs expect to be initiated at some stage in their life. Belonging to the *Khalsa* involves taking *amrit* and wearing the five articles of faith which distinguish individuals as Sikhs, commonly known as "the five Ks" because the Panjabi word for each begins with the sound of "k". The "five Ks" are:

Kesh (uncut hair)

This is usually tied up hair covered with a turban by men, although some women may also choose to wear it. The turban may be of any colour and is tied in a variety of styles. Only in certain cases do colours have particular meanings. Usually the style and colour of a turban signify personal preference only. The turban is not mentioned as one of the "five Ks", but it is seen as an essential and complementary adjunct to maintain the sanctity of the *kesh* and is treated by Sikhs with utmost respect. Historically, it is also a symbol of identity linked with royalty and responsibility.

Kangha

A small hair comb which should be worn in the hair. It is used to keep the hair clean and symbolises orderly spirituality.

Kara

A steel bracelet which serves as a reminder of the universality of God and is a symbol of spiritual allegiance and brotherhood, as well as a reminder to do good.

Kachhahera (or kachchha or kachha)

Is a knee length garment, tailored in a special manner, and usually worn under other clothes. It symbolises modesty and moral restraint.

Kirpan

A sword protects Sikh dignity and self-respect. It represents a readiness to fight in self-defence or in the protection of the weak and oppressed. Sikhs must never use the *kirpan* to fight for material gain. The *kirpan* most generally carried by Sikhs is about six inches long.

In short, the "five ks" have not only a moral and practical significance, but also a deep spiritual importance and the wearing of them is, for Sikhs, a sign of obedience to the will of God and of care for, and obedience to, the *Gurus* and their teachings.

Nam Japna

Nam Japna involves meditating on God and his attributes, reading and contemplating *bani* (passages) from the *Guru Granth Sahib Ji*. It is said by Sikhs to result in being *gurmukh* (God-filled and God-centred) as opposed to being *manmukh* (self-centred). *Nam Japana* can be a personal activity, although in congregational worship it can be facilitated by *kirtan*, the singing of hymns from the *Guru Granth Sahib Ji*, accompanied by music played on drums, harmoniums and other instruments. Although prayers can be said either individually or as a family, *sadh sangat* (congregational worship) is regarded as being very important to Sikh life.

Singh and Kaur

All Sikh men take the religious name *Singh* (meaning lion) and all Sikh women have *Kaur* (meaning princess) as their second names, for example, Paramjit Kaur (female), Mohinder Singh (male). This practice relates to the abolition of the caste system. It must, however, be noted that the name Singh does not necessarily mean that a person is a Sikh since this name was common in India before the rise of Sikhism. In addition, in the UK, some Sikh wives use their husband's name of Singh as a surname following Kaur. Sikhs will also often have a third name which may be derived from a place or a *got* (patriliniar) name.

Diet

Avoidance of tobacco, alcohol and other intoxicants is enjoined on Sikhs. With regard to meat, those Sikhs who eat meat must not eat *halal* meat (meat from animals killed according to Muslim law) and meat is only permitted for consumption if it is *jhatka*. This is where the animal is killed with one stroke instantaneously. Many Sikhs, however, are vegetarians.

Pilgrimage

Although pilgrimage does not constitute a religious duty for Sikhs, places associated with the Sikh *Gurus* are treated as places of pilgrimage. Many Sikhs going to the Panjab will also visit the *Darbar Sahib* and some may also visit other sites, particularly *Anandpur Sahib*. A visit to the birthplace of Guru Nanak Dev Ji at *Nankara Sahib* in Pakistan usually takes place in October/ November each year when several hundred Sikhs from the UK join their fellow Sikhs from the Panjab and other countries.

Birth, Marriage and Death

On the birth of a child, the naming ceremony is held in the *Gurdwara*. After a prayer from the family, the name of the child is taken from the first letter of the *vaak*, which is a passage of the *Guru Granth Sahib Ji* read after its random opening.

Sikh marriage is known as *Anand Karaj* (ceremony of bliss) and is not viewed simply as a social or civil contract. Rather it is believed that it is a spiritual state since living in this world and discharging family duties is advocated as the Sikh way of life. The marriage service involves the recitation of four stanzas called *Lavan* in the presence of the bride, the bridegroom and their relatives and friends. At the time of the recitation, the bride and bridegroom walk around the *Guru Granth Sahib Ji*. The ceremony concludes, as is usual with all Sikh ceremonies, with a collective prayer in the presence of the relatives and friends.

At death, Sikhs normally cremate the dead body. At the crematorium the granthi leads the mourners in the reading of *Kirtan Sohila* from the

Guru Granth Sahib Ji, and this is followed by a prayer. The family may also have a *sadhara panth* in memory of the departed soul.

SIKH WORSHIP

Gurdwara

The Sikh place of congregational worship is called the *Gurdwara*, meaning "doorway of the Guru". The *Gurdwara* is not only a place for formal worship, but it is also a centre for the provision of religious education including Panjabi classes, social activities such as youth clubs, women's groups, welfare provision, and elderly day centres. In keeping with the Sikh tradition of service *Gurdwaras* often provide temporary accommodation for the needy.

A *Gurdwara* is usually recognisable from the outside by the *Nishan Sahib* which is normally a triangular saffron flag on which is sewn the *khanda* (*Khalsa* emblem) made out of black cloth. The emblem consists of a symbolic two-edged sword surrounded by a circle outside of which are two further swords.

Before entering the hall of worship shoes must be removed and heads must be covered. Visitors should ensure that they are dressed modestly. No smoking or drinking of alcohol is permitted anywhere in a *Gurdwara* and nor should tobacco or alcohol be taken into the *Gurdwara*.

On entering the foyer of the *Gurdwara*, visitors may see pictures of Sikh martyrs and in the prayer hall itself there may be pictures of Guru Nanak Dev Ji and of Guru Gobind Singh Ji. On entering the prayer hall, Sikh worshippers kneel, touching the floor with their forehead before the *Guru Granth Sahib Ji*. At this time they also make an offering of money or fruit, milk or sugar. Respect shown in these ways to the *Guru Granth Sahib Ji* should not be mistaken for regarding the *Guru Granth Sahib Ji* as an object of worship which would be prohibited within Sikhism.

Although it is not religiously prescribed, traditionally men and women tend to sit separately on opposite sides of the prayer hall. Children normally remain with their mothers. Worshippers sit on the floor, which is normally carpeted, with their legs crossed. In the prayer hall, the focal point is the Guru *Granth Sahib Ji* which is placed upon a dais. The dais is a raised platform with a canopy above it. The *Guru Granth Sahib Ji* is placed on cushions and covered by *rumalas* (expensive cloths).

A Sikh is called upon to rise early and after a bath or shower to meditate on one God, and to say the morning set prayers of *Japji*, *Jaap Sahib*, *Savayye*, *Chaupai* and *Anand Sahib*. *Kirtan Sohila* is said before retiring for sleep. Prayers can be said individually, together with the family or with other Sikhs in a congregation. Some Sikh homes may have a separate room in which the *Guru Granth Sahib* is kept but, *diwan* (congregational worship) in the *Gurdwara* is regarded as particularly important.

Sadh Sangat

No single day of the week is holy for Sikhs but, for convenience, in the UK the *Gurdwara* is usually visited for *sadh sangat* on a Sunday. The *Gurdwara* is usually open daily and some Sikhs visit it every morning and evening. *Diwan* usually lasts between two and four hours. A typical Sikh religious service consists of *gurbani kirtan* (hymn-singing), a discourse on the divine name, followed by *Ardas* (a concluding corporate prayer) and concluded by *Karah Prashad* (see below) and the sharing of *langar* (see below). The *Ardas* ends with the invocation of God's blessing on everyone and not just on the followers of the faith. In the morning service *Asa di Var* is followed by *anand sahib* and a collective prayer by the congregation.

Most Sikhs also recite the *Japji*, a prayer composed by Guru Nanak which forms the first chapter of the *Guru Granth Sahib Ji*. More devout Sikhs also recite *Jap* (the tenth Guru's composition) and *Shabad Hazare* followed by the evening *Rehras* and late evening *Kirtan Sohila*. In the evening service, *Rehras* is usually followed by *Kirtan* and at the end of the service *Kirtan Sohila* is recited when the *Guru Granth Sahib Ji* is laid to rest, usually in a separate room.

Path

The *Path* is the liturgical reading of the *Guru Granth Sahib Ji*. On special occasions it is read from cover to cover by relays of readers. This form of reading is known as *Akhand Path* (which means "continuous reading") and takes two days and nights. It occurs at most Sikh festivals, when the *path* begins in the morning two days prior to the festival.

Saptah Path is another form of continuous *path* and takes seven days and nights. However, *Sahaj Path* is not continuous and is often undertaken when someone dies. While reading the *Guru Granth Sahib Ji* the reader or another person close by will wave over it a *chaur* sahib (a whisk made of white yaks' hair) as a sign of respect for the *Guru Granth Sahib Ji*.

Karah Prashad and Langar

Worship ends with the distribution of *Karah Prashad*. This is a sweet food made from semolina or flour, sugar, clarified butter and water which is served to every person present. *Karah Prashad* is blessed during *Ardas* at the end of worship and is therefore considered to be holy food. Its free distribution symbolises the central Sikh belief of the equality and unity of humankind and the repudiation of caste distinctions.

After the service *Langar*, a communal meal, is provided free of charge to all who attend the *Gurdwara*. The food provided, which has been blessed, will not contain meat, fish or eggs or their by-products so that vegetarians may partake of it. *Karah Prashad* and *Langar* both symbolise universal fraternity and equality. All eat together regardless of their social position.

SIKH CALENDAR AND FESTIVALS

Calendar

Most dates for Sikh festivals are calculated according to the lunar calendar and may vary from the Gregorian calendar within a period of fifteen days. A few festivals, notably *Vaisakhi*, are calculated by the *Vikrami* (North India) solar calendar, which is why the date of *Vaisakhi* remains almost constant in the Gregorian calendar. Sikh calendars and some Sikh authors use a dating system based on the first day of Guru Nanak Dev Ji's birth. This calendar is known as *Sammat Nanak Shahi*.

The approximate times of the occurrence of the festivals which are cited below refer to when they take place according to the Gregorian calendar.

Gurpurbs

Festivals are celebrated by means of *Akhand Path*, *Kirtan*, prayers, religious lectures, *Karah Prasad* and *Langar*. Those which specifically commemorate the birth or death of a *Guru* are known as *Gurpurbs*. The four major *Gurpurbs* which are celebrated in the UK are:

Guru Nanak Dev Ji's birthday
(November)

The celebration lasts for three days.

Martyrdom of Guru Tegh Bahadur
(November or December).

Guru Gobind Singh's Birthday
(December or January).

Martyrdom of Guru Arjan Dev
(May or June)

Other Sikh festivals include:

Installation of the Guru Granth Sahib Ji

This festival occurs in August-September. It celebrates the conferment of the Guruship on the *Guru Granth Sahib Ji* by Guru Gobind Singh three days before his death.

Vaisakhi

This celebrates the day in 1699 when Guru Gobind Singh Ji founded the order of the *Khalsa* by offering *amrit* to the *Panj Pyare*. This is nearly always celebrated on the 13th April, but very occasionally on the 14th April, due to the discrepancy between the Vikrami and Gregorian solar calendars. On this day Sikhs usually replace the *Nishan Sahib* which flies outside the *Gurdwara* with a new one. This is usually done in the context of a *nagar kirtan* (procession) carrying *the Guru Granth Sahib Ji* after *diwan*.

Diwali

Diwali is also celebrated among Sikhs. However, in the Sikh context it primarily commemorates Guru Hargobind Ji's return from imprisonment by the Moghul Emperor, Jehangir, in Gwalior fort, together with fifty-two Hindu kings for whose freedom the *Guru* had asked. It is thus a festival of deliverance, and is celebrated by the illumination of *Gurdwaras*. *Diwali* is also celebrated by Hindus, but for a different reason.

SIKH ORGANISATIONS

General Organisations

There are both national and local Sikh organisations. At present, there is no single national representative organisation for Sikhs in the UK, but there are various groups which operate nationally and may have local branches. A number of groups see themselves as specifically related to the political demand for an independent Sikh homeland of *Khalistan*.

Sikh organisations often serve several functions including youth and women's activities and education in addition to what are often understood to be more specifically religious functions. Other groups exist which serve the diverse needs of particular sections of the community, including literary, social, cultural or professional societies and associations, for example, the Sikh Cultural Society.

Social Groupings

Sikhism teaches that there are no distinctions between people and rejects the concept of caste (or *Zat*), which therefore has no religious significance for Sikhs.

The terms which appear in the titles of some *Gurdwaras*, such as *Ramgarhia* and *Bhatra*, are historically related to economic categories and are rooted in the history of the forebears of the families concerned. They do not necessarily define any contemporary economic or social status or who is allowed to attend a *Gurdwara*, although they may indicate who does actually attend.

Bhatras were historically traders. Many settled in British ports before the second World War and therefore some of the earliest gurdwaras were founded by *Bhatras*. They retain their own organisations in order to maintain their traditions and way of life.

Ramgarhias came from the *tarkhan* (artisan) grouping, though they also included some *Lohars* (blacksmiths) and *Raj* (bricklayers). It is now a Sikh grouping that takes its name from the defence of the Ramgarth fort in Amritsar, commanded, in the eighteenth century, by Jassa Singh. *Ramgarhias* were originally more urban than rural, although many became landowners and the British colonists encouraged groups of them to move to East Africa at the end of the nineteenth century to assist in the development of the transport network. From here, as a result of the Africanisation policies of the newly independent East African states, many migrated to the UK or arrived as refugees.

Personnel

Management Committees, consisting of honorary office bearers: president, secretary and treasurer usually run the *Gurdwara*. The people who serve on such committees are usually elected by the congregation every two years or so. Committees usually change on *Vaisakhi* day 13/14th April in the Gregorian calendar. There are also a number of *Gurdwaras* which are led by a *sant* (individual charismatic leader), for example, Guru Nanak Nishkam Sewak Jatha of the late Baba Puran Singh Karichowale in Birmingham.

Any adult Sikh is permitted to perform religious ceremonies but many *Gurdwaras* employ a *granthi*. A *granthi* is a professional reader of the *Guru Granth Sahib Ji* and is usually also responsible for its care. Although the word "priest" is sometimes used by people outside of Sikhism, Sikhism recognises no priesthood and all Sikhs are of equal status in terms of religion. Sikh leaders may therefore be called *Bhai* (brother).

Other waged personnel may include a caretaker and, sometimes, in the larger *Gurdwaras*, a community development worker. A *giani*, (expositor of the *Guru Granth Sahib Ji*) introduces religious discourses to the congregation. There is often a regular group of *ragis* (singers and musicians) to help with *diwan*.

BIBLIOGRAPHY

Babraa Kaur, D, *Visiting a Sikh Temple*, Lutterworth Educational, Guildford, 1981.

Ballard, R and C, "The Sikhs: The Development of South Asian Settlements in Britain," in J L Watson (ed), *Between Two Cultures*, Basil Blackwell, Oxford, 1977.

Beetham, D, *Transport and Turbans: A Comparative Study in Local Politics*, Open University Press, Milton Keynes, 1970.

Bhachu, P, *Twice Migrants: East African Sikh Settlers in Britain*, Tavistock, London, 1985

Bidwell, S, *The Turban Victory*, Sikh Missionary Society, Southall, 1980.

Cole, W O, "Sikhs in Britain", in Paul Badham, *Religion, State and Society in Modern Britain*, Edwin Mellen Press, Lampeter, 1989.

Cole, W O and Singh Sambhi, P, *Sikhism*, Ward Lock International, London, 1973.

Cole, W O and Singh Sambhi, P, *The Sikhs: Their Religious Beliefs and Practices*, Routledge and Kegan Paul, London, 1978.

Cole, W O and Singh Sambhi, P, *A Popular Dictionary of Sikhism*, London, 1990.

Helweg, A W, *Sikhs in England: The Development of a Migrant Community*, Oxford University Press, Delhi, (2nd edition), 1986.

Henley, A, *Caring for Sikhs and Their Families: Religious Aspects of Care*, National Extension College, Cambridge, 1983.

James, A, *Sikh Children in Britain*, Oxford University Press, London.

Knott, K, "Calculating Sikh Population Statistics" in *Sikh Bulletin* No. 4, West Sussex Institute of Higher Education, Chichester, 1987.

Loehlin, C H *The Sikhs and Their Scriptures*, Lucknow Publishing House, Lucknow, 1974.

MacLeod, W H (ed) *Textual Sources for the Study of Sikhism*, Manchester University Press, Manchester, 1984.

McCormack Kaur, M, *Brief Outline of the Sikh Faith*, Sikh Cultural Society of Great Britain, Edgware, London, 1987.

McCormack Kaur, M, *An Introduction to Sikh Belief*, Sikh Cultural Society of Great Britain, Edgware, 1987.

Shackle, C, *The Sikhs*, Minority Rights Group, London, 2nd edition, 1986.

Singh, G, *A History of the Sikh People, 1469-1978*, World Sikh University Press, New Delhi, 1979.

Singh, G, *The Sikh Festivals*, Sikh Cultural Society of Great Britain, Edgware, 1982.

Singh, K, *The Sikhs Today*, Orient Longman Ltd, Bombay, 1976.

Sikh Cultural Society of Great Britain, *The Sikh Gurdwaras in the United Kingdom*, Sikh Cultural Society of Great Britain, Edgware, 1989.

Singh Kalsi, S, *The Evolution of a Sikh Community in Britain*, Community Religions Project, University of Leeds, Leeds, 1992

Shergill N S, *International Directory of Gurdwaras and Sikh Organisations*, Nirpal Singh Shergill, London, 1985.

Singh Tatla, D & Nesbitt, E, *Sikhs in Britain: An Annotated Bibliography*, University of Warwick Centre for Research in Ethnic Relations, Coventry, (revised edition) 1993.

Wahiwala, R S (trans), *Sikh Code of Conduct*, Sikh Missionary Resource Centre, Birmingham.

SIKH UK ORGANISATIONS

The organisations listed in this section include both head offices of organisations with branches throughout the country and organisations which aspire to serve the Sikh community on a UK-wide level.

British Sikh Punjabi Literary Society

29 Europa Avenue
Sandwell Valley
West Bromwich
West Midlands B70 6TL
Contact: Mr S S Sangha
Office: National Convenor
Writers' association. The society was founded in 1985 to provide a forum for Panjabi writers whose faith is based in Sikh religious traditions, history, philosophy and culture. Since its highly successful conferences and events in the 1980s, many other educationalists, artists, writers and teachers felt encouraged to form associations and promote Sikh writings positively in Britain and to create new work fitting the contemporary needs. It arranges religious and cultural meetings, seminars and publications.

Degh Tegh Fateh

41 Dudley Street
Luton LU2 0NP
Tel: 0582-27725
Fax: 0582-27725
Contact: Harjeet Singh Sev
Office: Director
Suppliers of Sikh religious artefacts including books and musical instruments. It also gives advice on matters relating to the Sikh religion.

European Institute of Sikh Studies

116 Station Road
Harpenden
Hertfordshire AL5 4RH
Tel: 0582-766447
Contact: Dr Baljit Singh Bagga
Office: General Secretary
The Institute aims to produce and publish Sikh religious books and hymns of daily prayers in major European languages and to organise lectures, seminars, discussions and conferences on Sikh religion, history and problems facing the Sikh community in different countries. The first major project undertaken is the translation of "Guru Granth Sahib" (Sikh scripture) in modern English, in collaboration with International Sacred Literature Trust (Manchester). The Institute held Guru Nanak International Conferences in London in 1991 and 1992. The next conference will be held in October 1993. It also held two Sikh Youth conventions in 1991 and 1992 in London. The Instiutute has applied for charity status and has an approved constitution.

Gurbani Cassette Centre

68c Iffley Road
London W6
Tel: 741-9310
Contact: Secretary
The centre offers cassettes on the Sikh religion and its philosophy to the Sikh and non-Sikh community. It has a large cassette library specialising in preachings of the Sikh Gurus, Kirtan, Guru Granth Prayers, kirtan singing, hymns and spiritual instruction. It also has a unique collection of relics of historical importance.

New Approach Mission of Occidental Sikhism (NAMOS)

52 Beaconsfield Street
Forest Fields
Nottingham NG7 6FN
Tel: 0602-704088
Contact: Mr Biant Singh
Office: Volunteer worker
Information and educational organisation which aims to facilitate a greater understanding of Sikh Dharma (way of life) through education and training using updated resources giving a positive insight into Sikhism in Britain and the world. This is done in workshops and informal discussions and by working with statutory organisations as well as youth organisations and resource centres.

Panjabi Guardian and Multi-Lingual Publishers Ltd

129 Soho Road
Handsworth
Birmingham B21 9ST
Tel: 021-554-3995
Fax: 021-507-1065
Contact: Indarjit Singh
Office: Director
Publishing house. Established in 1988 to publish religious/cultural minority language works. Predominantly its work involves the promotion of minority languages (Panjabi in particular), religious dialogue, articles, letters and debates through the fortnightly journal the "Panjabi Guardian". The company also carries out translation, typesetting, publishing and printing work for voluntary, private and public agencies.

Sharomani Akali Dal Head Office

15 Manor Way
Southall
Middlesex UB2 5JJ
Tel: 081-571-2842
Contact: Sardar Bachittar Singh

Office: President
A national organisation with various branches in the UK. It is a Supreme Council of Sikhs representing the religious and political rights and rituals of the Sikh community which takes up issues with the Government and acts in religious, political and humanitarian social service to the community. Contact can also be made through the General Secretary, Gurcharan Singh, Tel: 081-578-7627.

Sikh Council for Interfaith Relations UK

43 Dorset Road
Merton Park
London SW19 3EZ
Tel: 081-540-4148
Contact: Mr Indarjit Singh
Office: General Secretary
Membership is open to all Sikh organisations and current membership is around twenty. It aims to develop and focus interest in interfaith dialogue in the Sikh community and to promote a greater understanding of Sikhism among non-Sikhs by producing suitable literature and disseminating information on interfaith dialogue and by holding meetings and seminars on interfaith worship. Affiliated to The Inter Faith Network for the UK.

Sikh Cultural Society of Great Britain

88 Mollison Way
Edgware
Middlesex HA8 5QW
Tel: 081-952-1215 (home)
Contact: Amar Singh Chhatwal
Office: General Secretary
The Society was founded in 1960. It publishes a wide range of literature on the Sikh religion and also the "Sikh Courier International".

Sikh Educational and Cultural Association (UK)

Sat-Nam Cottage
3 Compton Gardens
Kinver
Nr Stourbridge
Dudley
West Midlands DY7 6DS
Tel: 0384-873379 (home)
Contact: Mr K S Singh
Office: Chair
The association is a privately run voluntary centre which was established in 1972 to help various communities to become more informed about the Sikh faith and practice. It aims to disseminate information about the Sikh faith to individuals,

schools, colleges, universities and other interested bodies through the quarterly bulletin called "Sikhism - Way of Life" sent free. It also provides information to schools and colleges about the Sikh faith and talks to religious groups of various faiths and professionals such as police, prison govenors and others.

Sikh Human Rights Group

P.O. Box 45
Southall
Middlesex
Tel: 081-577-5834
Fax: 081-577-5834
The Sikh Human Rights Group is a formal group of concerned and dedicated persons with a sympathetic interest in human rights and the welfare of people as evaluated and taught in the humanitarian principles of Sikhism. Without holding a particular political position, the group supports and campaigns for human rights, welfare of people and a peaceful resolution of conflicts. The group focuses on the violation of human rights in the Panjab, India, but is interested in human rights issues across the world.

Sikh Missionary Society (UK)

10 Featherstone Road
Southall
Middlesex UB2 5AA
Tel: 081-574-1902
Contact: Harbans Singh Kular
Office: Honorary General Secretary
Religious charity which aims to spread the message of Sikhism among Sikhs and non-Sikhs. It provides basic information about Sikhism to anyone asking for it. It is a place from which the Sikh Ks can be obtained. It serves as a storehouse for information regarding Sikhism for the Sikh institutions in Europe in general and the UK in particular. Affiliated to The Inter Faith Network for the UK

Sikh Students Federation UK

110 Featherstone Road
Southall
Middlesex

SIKH GURDWARAS AND LOCAL ORGANISATIONS

A variety of forms of Sikh local organisations are listed in this directory. These include *Gurdwaras*, associations and centres.

SCOTLAND

Sri Guru Nanak Gurdwara
1 Nelson Street
Dundee DD1 2PN
Tel: 0382–23383
Contact: Secretary

Sikh Temple
1 Mill Lane
Leith
Edinburgh
Lothian
Tel: 031–553-7207
Contact: Jaswant Singh
Office: President
Place of worship for prayer and worship.

Central Gurdwara Singh Sabha
134–138 Berkeley Street
Glasgow G3 7HY
Tel: 041–221-6698
Contact: Parkash Singh
Office: Co-ordinator
A place of worship for the Sikh community which is the largest in Glasgow and in Scotland. It has a library and a cultural and welfare centre. Attached to it, but independent of it, is a multi-cultural day centre where a variety of social and cultural activities take place.

Guru Nanak Gurdwara
27 Otago Street
Kelvinbridge
Glasgow G12
Tel: 041–334-9125
Contact: Mr Bali
Office: President

Ramgarhia Association
27 Otago Street
Kelvinbridge
Glasgow G12
Tel: 041–334-9125
Contact: Mr Bali
Office: President

Shri Guru Tegh Bahadur Gurdwara Bhatra Sangat
32 St. Andrew's Drive
Glasgow G41 5SG
Tel: 041–427-2763
Contact: Granthi
Place of worship. A place for community use and religious gatherings for Sikhs. The Gurdwara

celebrates all the Sikh religious festivals in conjunction with the calendar for Sikhs which is sent from Amritsar. The main days are the birth of the founder Guru Nanak Dev Ji, Guru Gobind Singh Ji (the tenth Guru) and Baisakhi (birth of the Khalsa).

Singh Sabha Gurdwara
163 Nithsdale Road
Pollockshields
Glasgow G1
Tel: 041-423-8288

WALES

Nanak Darbar Bhat Sikh Temple
18 Copper Town
Adamstown
Cardiff
South Glamorgan

Sri Dasmais Singh Sabha Gurdwara Bhatra Sikh Centre
97-103 Tudor Street
Cardiff
South Glamorgan
Tel: 0222-224806
Contact: Waleiti Singh Balkar
Office: Secretary
Established since the 1950s, it is a registered as a place of worship and for the solemnisation of marriages. It is also a registered charity.

NORTH EAST ENGLAND

Darlington Sikh Temple
Louisa Street
Darlington DL1 4ED
Tel: 0325-461252
Contact: Mr A Singh Dawana
Office: President

Sikh Temple
23 Lorne Street
Middlesborough
Cleveland
Tel: 0642-250125
Contact: Mr G Singh
Office: Secretary

Gurdwara Sri Guru Singh Sabha
Tindale Close
Newcastle-upon-Tyne NE4 5SA

Tel: 091-273-4292
Contact: Surinder Bal
Office: Secretary

South Shields Sikh Temple
2 Dean Terrace
South Shields NE33 5JY
Tel: 091-232-4048

Guru Nanak Gurdwara and Sikh Community Centre
31 Allens Street
Thornaby
Stockton-on-Tees
Cleveland

YORKSHIRE AND HUMBERSIDE

Bradford Sikh Parents Association
24 Oakwood Grove
Bradford BD8 8QB
Tel: 0274-544932
Contact: Mr Sukhdev Singh
Office: Committee Member

Federation of Bradford Sikh Organisations
2 Luther Way
Bradford BD2 1EX
Tel: 0274-390069
Contact: Mr Mohinder Singh Chana

Gurdwara Amrit Parchar Dharmak Diwan
Harris Street
off Leeds Road
Bradford BD3
Tel: 0274-724853
Tel: 0274-667625 (home)
Contact: Pritam Singh
Office: President
Place of worship. The organisation aims to: teach Sikhism, the doctrine of the Holy Shri Guru Granth Sahib Ji and the teachings of the ten Gurus; propagate, encourage and arrange Amrit Parchar; discourage the use of alcohol and smoking and condemn obsolete customs and to encourage and arrange Panjabi education for both parents and children.

Guru Govind Singh Sikh Temple
Malvern/Ventnor Street
Off Leeds Road
Bradford BD3 9JN
Tel: 0274-727928
Contact: Mr Parmarjit Singh
Office: Secretary

Guru Nanak Charitable Trust UK
18 Usher Street
Bradford BD4 7DS
Tel: 0274–391912
Contact: Mr M S Bussan
Office: Secretary
Membership group which aims to advance the practice of the Sikh religion and to provide social, religious, cultural and educational activities for the community through organised religious services and opportunities for meeting members of other communities, as well as to provide for the care of the aged.

Guru Nanak Sikh Temple
Prospect Hall
Wakefield Road
Bradford BD4 7DS
Tel: 0274–723557
Contact: Sardar Piara Singh Nijjar
Office: President
Place of worship. The Gurdwara is open to everyone. As well as being a place of worship, the Gurdwara serves the local Sikh community and is a place for everyone to get together to discuss community problems. It is also used to educate youth and emphasis is placed on teaching young Sikhs their mother tongue.

Guru Nanak United Sikh Temple
64 Avenue Road
West Bailing
Bradford BD5

International Sikh Youth Organisation
30 Tyresal Green
Bradford BD4 8HQ
Contact: Mr S Singh

Ramgarhia Sikh Temple
Victoria Hall
Bolton Road
Bradford BD3 0ND
Tel: 0274–632761
Tel: 0484–530780 (work)
Contact: Mr Pal Singh Panesar
Office: Secretary

Guru Kalgidar Gurdwara
73 St James Street
Waterdale
Doncaster
South Yorkshire

Tel: 0302–369003
Contact: Mr Mehal Singh
Office: Secretary

Shri Guru Arjan Dev Gurdwara Sikh Temple
Cherry Tree Road
Hexthorpe
Doncaster
South Yorkshire

Guru Nanak Gurdwara
Prospect Street
Huddersfield HD1

Guru Nanak Sikh Sangat Sikh Temple
219 Keldergate
Deighton
Huddersfield HD2 1LF
Contact: Mr G Singh Gill

Huddersfield Sikh Temple Committee
12 Woodbine Road
Fartown
Huddersfield
West Yorkshire

International Sikh Youth Federation
195 Long Lane
Dalton
Huddersfield
West Yorkshire

Shree Guru Singh Sabha Sikh Temple
Hillhouse Lane
Fartown
Huddersfield
West Yorkshire
Contact: Mr Ajit Singh

Shri Guru Nanak Sangat
Guru Nanak Gurdwara
Prospect Street
Huddersfield HD1

Sikh Social Care
56 Imperial Road
Marsh
Huddersfield HD1 4PG
Contact: Mr Mohan Singh Sokhal

Sikh Temple
8 Bankfield Road
Huddersfield
West Yorkshire

Sikh Youth Association
144 Black House Road
Fartown
Huddersfield
West Yorkshire

Bhatra Sikh Community Centre
6 Grange Terrace
Chapeltown
Leeds LS7

Gurdwara Kalgidar Sahib, Bhatra Sangat
138 Chapletown Road
Leeds LS7
Tel: 0532-625427
Contact: President

Guru Nanak Nishkam Sewak Jatha (UK-Leeds)
78 Ladypit Lane
Beeston
Leeds LS11 6DP
Tel: 0532-760261
Tel: 0532-705680 (work)
Contact: Mr Sagoo
Office: Administrator
A registered charity, place of worship and a place for the solemnisation of marriages. It is active in inter-religious and Sikh-Christian dialogue and it encourages visits from schools, colleges and others in order to promote an understanding of Sikhism. Occasionally, speakers can be sent to other venues.

Guru Nanak Temple
62b Tong Road
Armley
Leeds LS12 1LZ
Tel: 0532-636525
Contact: Mr N Flora
Office: General Secretary

Leeds Association of Sikhs
1 Noorwood Mount
Pudsey
Leeds LS28 9HR

Pudsey Sikh Group
7 Sunnybank Lane
Pudsey
Leeds
West Yorkshire
Tel: 0274-666659
Contact: Secretary

Punjabi Sabha
c/o Leeds CRC
Centenary House
North Street
Leeds LS2 8JS

Ramgarhia Board Leeds
8/10 Chapeltown Road
Sheepscar
Leeds LS7 3AL
Tel: 0532-625427
Contact: Surinder Singh Sambhi
Office: Trustee
Place of worship and community centre. The Ramgarhia Board represents over five hundred Ramgarhia Sikhs in Leeds. Its aims and objectives are to promote religion, culture, education, leisure and sports and the welfare of the Sikh community by providing a place of worship and other buildings to hold different types of activities. Activities include social, leisure, and sports, including activities for youth, women and the elderly.

Ramgarhia Ladies Circle
c/o Leeds CRC
Centenary House
North Street
Leeds LS2 8JS

Sanatan Temple and Community Centre
281 Chapeltown Road
Leeds LS7 3AL
Tel: 0352-629073
Contact: Tarlok Singh Toor
Office: Secretary

Sikh Educational Advisory Service
9 Woodland Grove
Leeds LS7 4HQ
Tel: 0532-602484
Contact: Surinder Kaur
A complete and professional service is provided for the teaching of multi-cultural education in today's schools. The service offers courses, workshops and training tailor-made to meet the requirements of

Religious Education syllabi. It also supplies a wide range of resources and artefacts and specialises in story-telling from the Sikh tradition.

Sikh Study Centre
c/o Leeds CRC
Centenary House
North Street
Leeds LS2 8JS

Guru Nanak Gurdwara
22 Dale Street
Scunthorpe
Humberside

Guru Nanak Gurdwara
41 Normandy Road
Scunthorpe
Humberside
Tel: 0724-84136
Contact: Mr Jaswant Singh Dhinsa
Place of worship.

Sikh Temple
Ellesmere Road North
Sheffield S4
Tel: 0742-420108
Contact: Mr Kalsi
Office: President

Sikh Temple
120 Bushywood Road
Dore
Sheffield S17 (home)
Contact: Mr C S Hayre

NORTH WEST ENGLAND

Sikh Temple
8 Culshaw Street
Blackburn BB1 1JF
Tel: 0254-581965
Contact: Amarjit Singh Phind
Office: President

Guru Nanak Academy Liverpool
36 Merrilocks Road
Blundellsands
Liverpool L23 6UN
Contact: Dr Gopal Singh
Office: Director
Tel: 051-924-5848 (home)

An education and research establishment, founded in 1969, the organisation has published over one hundred papers in various journals across the world on religion related to science, human behaviour, healing, environment and ecology. Its activities include research and teaching of Sikh studies, publishing papers and books of a religious nature, holding worship group meetings and teaching meditation.

Dashmesh Sikh Temple
29 Esmond Road
Cheetham
Manchester M8

Gurdwara Dasmesh Sikh Temple
Heywood Street
Cheetham
Manchester

Raj Singh - Sikh History Family Project
Birley Centre
Chichester Road
Moss Side
Manchester

Shiri Guru Gobind Singh Gurdwara Mission Centre Registered (Sangat Bhatra Sikh Temple)
61 Upper Chorlton Road
Whalley Range
Manchester M16 7RQ
Tel: 061-226-7233
Contact: Parkash Singh
Office: General Secretary

Sikh Association
12 Sherbourne Street
Manchester M3 1EJ
Tel: 061-832-2241
Contact: Mr J S Kohli
Place of worship. Activities are mainly related to worship, but the organisation also provides mother tongue teaching, sports facilities and arranges youth camps. The association arranges talks to nurses, teachers, magistrates, police, school and university students.

Sikh Temple
107 Halliwell Lane
Cheetham Hill Road
Manchester M8

Sikh Union of Greater Manchester

31 Burford Road
Whalley Range
Manchester M16 8EW
Tel: 061-881-7067 (home)
Contact: Mr Ujjal D Singh
Office: Secretary
Membership group. An organisation based on broad principles of the Sikh religion and mainly benefiting Sikhs. It is available to deal with all aspects of social, religious, welfare, political and apolitical issues which affect the well-being of the Sikh community and its existence in the UK society.

Sri Guru Nanak Dev Ji Gurdwara

15 Monton Street
Moss Side
Manchester M14 4LS
Tel: 061-226-1131
Contact: Mr Manjit Singh
Office: Honorary General Secretary
Place of worship. The first established place of worship for the Bhatra Sikh community in Britain. It is also a focal point for the community to meet regarding social, religious and community issues.

Guru Nanak Gurdwara

Bhatra Singh Sabha
2 Clarendon Street
Preston PR1 3YN
Tel: 0772-251008
Contact: Mr Hazur Singh
Office: General Treasurer
Place of worship. The Gurdwara was established in around 1962. It was founded by the elders of the community volunteering the necessary funds to appropriate a property. It was the first Gurdwara in Preston and the surrounding districts. It is registered for the solemnisation of marriages. Activities include worship and welfare for the Sikh community.

Guru Nanak Cultural and Recreation Centre and Temple

2-10 Tunbridge Street
Preston PR1 5YP
Tel: 0772-798395
Contact: Mr Pritam Singh
Office: Trustee
Contact can also be made through the Secretary, Mr Amarjit Singh.

Sikh Association and Gurdwara

12 Sherborne Street
Strangeways
Salford
Lancashire
Tel: 061-832-2241
Contact: Kuldip Singh
Office: President

Guru Nanak Gurdwara Sikh Temple

Dover Road
Latchford
Warrington
Cheshire
Tel: 0925-418208
Contact: Mr P Singh
Office: General Secretary

ENGLISH EAST MIDLANDS

Guru Arjan Dev Gurdwara

Cromwell Road
Derby DE3 6TS
Tel: 0332-32539
Contact: Mr Chema
Office: President
Place of worship. A Sikh Gurdwara open to all people in the mornings (6.00-10.00am) and evenings (6.00-8.00pm) and all day at weekends. There is a free kitchen (langar) where everyone is welcome to a free vegetarian meal particularly at weekends. No one under the influence, or in possession of drugs is allowed in the Gurdwara complex.

Ramgarhia Sabha Sikh Temple

14 St James Road
Derby DE3 8QX
Tel: 0332-371811
Contact: Mr Mohan S Manku
Aims to: promote the interests and needs of the Sikh community in Derby; provide daily prayers and to promote harmonious relations with the indigenous community and organise cultural, social and religious activities. Its activities include Panjabi classes; a summer programme of activities for children and families; organisation of sports teams; celebration of various religious festivals; special programme of activities for women; liaison with schools; and Langar or dinner served every Sunday. Meetings held if and when required. Translations are available.

Sri Guru Singh Sabha

23-25 King Street
Kettering
Northamptonshire NN16 8QP
Tel: 0536-511447

Tel: 0536-515540 (home)
Contact: Mr S S Garcha
Office: Trustee

British Sikh Society

230 Loughborough Road
Leicester LE4 5LG
Tel: 0533-661293 (home)
Contact: Mr Sukhdev Singh Sangha
Office: Secretary
Membership group drawn mainly from the Sikh community. The society looks after the interests of its members and participates in local councils and local voluntary bodies to represent the Sikh community and in general ethnic minority interests. Activities are social, cultural and religious.

Federation of Sikh Organisations

106 East Park Road
Leicester LE5 4QH
Tel: 0533-769297 (office)
Tel: 0533-239179
Contact: Mr S Gurbinder Singh Sanra
Office: Co-ordinator
It acts as an umbrella body for Sikh groups in Leicestershire, including the Sikh Gurdwaras. It provides information, organises tasks and events on all aspects of Sikh culture, history and religion for the Sikh and the wider community. It makes relevant representations to local and national government and voluntary and statutory bodies.

Guru Amardas Gurdwara

219-227 Clarendon Park Road
Leicester LE2 3AN
Tel: 0533-701705
Contact: Mr Sukhdev Singh Sangha
Office: Secretary
A place of worship which opened in April 1992. It looks after the interests of the Sikh Community from the religious side, such as weddings, weekend services, services for births and deaths. The Temple welcomes visits from school parties and other groups.

Guru Nanak Gurdwara

8 Glossop Street
Leicester

Guru Nanak Gurdwara

9 Holy Bones
Leicester LE1 5LJ
Tel: 0533-517460
Contact: Jagpal Singh
Office: General Secretary

Place of worship and community centre. The Gurdwara is situated in the centre of Leicester and provides a traditional style of worship for the Sikh community. Activities cater for all age groups and include worship, education, recreation, sports and arts. There is also an information and help centre.

Guru Nanak Gurdwara

19-58 Gwendolin Road
Leicester LE5 5FL

Guru Nanak Gurdwara

5 New Walk
Leicester LE1 6TE

Guru Nanak Khalsa

45 Lanesborough Road
Leicester

Guru Tegh Bahadur Gurdwara

106 East Park Road
Leicester
Tel: 0533-760517
Contact: Mr Gurdip Singh
Office: General Secretary
A place of worship which caters for the spiritual needs of the Sikh community in Leicester. It holds a religious programme twice daily and also caters for marriages and death ceremonies. Sporting and cultural activities are held for men, women and children. There is a library and reading room. Panjabi and music classes are held for children every day.

Leicester Sikh Centre

219-227 Clarendon Park Road
Leicester LE2 2AN
Tel: 0533-701705
Contact: Mr Sukhdev Singh Sangha
Office: Secretary
The centre consists of different organisations and groups who operate in their own fields. The Sikh Parents Association deals with educational issues; the Sikh Womens Association looks after ladies affairs; the Sikh Elderly Project looks after elderly Sikhs; the Sikh Youth Project looks after youth and sports projects.

Leicestershire Sikh Education Forum

45 Newhaven Road
Evington
Leicester LE5 6JH

Ramgarhia Board
41 Ashover Road
Leicester

Ramgarhia Board Gurdwara
51 Meynell Road
Leicester LE5 3NE
Tel: 0533-760765
Contact: General Secretary

Seva Dal
91 Buller Road
Leicester

Shromani Akali Dal Longawal UK
69 Clumber Road
North Evington
Leicester LE5 4FS
Tel: 0533-767041 (home)
Contact: Mr Reshwel Singh
Office: General Secretary
A membership group of around one hundred and thirty members. The organisation offers religious, cultural and educational activities and advice to the Sikh community in general and youth in particular.

Sikh Culture, Welfare and Religious Society
10 Edward Avenue
Leicester LE3 2PB
Tel: 0533-896858

Sikh Education Council
14 Brightside Road
Evington
Leicester LE5 5LD
Tel: 0533-788835

Sikh Parents' Association
69 Clumber Road
Leicester LE5 4FJ
Tel: 0533-767041 (home)
Contact: Reshwel Singh
Office: Chairman
A membership group with three hundred families. Its main concern is to provide Panjabi education to children aged six to sixteen years in supplementary schools and to facilitate dialogue between parents, schools and the Local Education Authority.

Sikh Senior Citizen's Association
19 Staveley Road
Leicester LE5 5JU
Tel: 0533-730865

Sikh Welfare (Cultural Society)
19 Sommerville Road
Leicester LE3 2ET

Sikh Youth Missionary Project
78 Evington Lane
Leicester LE5 5PP
Contact: Kashmir Singh
Office: Secretary
To help Sikh youth maintain contact with their religion, language and culture. Activities include community action, counselling, education, ethnic minorities, race relations, religious activities and youth.

Sikh Temple (Gurdwara Sahib)
33/34 Clarence Street
Loughborough
Leicestershire
Tel: 0509-232411
Contact: Gurbakhsh Singh Liddar
Office: Committee Member
Place of worship and charity. The Gurdwara Sahib aims to advance the Sikh religion in accordance with the teachings of the Guru Granth Sahib and also to work closely with other charitable/voluntary organisations in furtherance of better understanding between people of different faiths/cultures. Activities include worship and welfare of communities in the Borough of Charnwood.

Sikh Gurdwara and Ramgarhia Community Centre
2 Craven Street
Northampton NN1 3EZ

Sikh Temple
53 Queen's Park Parade
Northampton

Sri Guru Singh Sabha
White Lodge
9 The Avenue
Dallington
Northampton NN5 7AJ

Sri Guru Singh Sabha
17-19 St Georges Street
Off Regent Square
Northampton NN1 2TN
Tel: 0604-34641
Contact: Mr Ujagar Singh
Office: President
Place of worship and community centre which provides facilities for worship, welfare, youth and elderly.

Bhatra Sikh Temple
36 Church Street
Lenton
Nottingham
Contact: Piara Singh
Office: General Secretary

Gurdwara Baba Budha Ji
24 Gladstone Street
Nottingham
Tel: 0602-780530
Contact: Sarabjit Singh Landa
Office: Liaison Officer

Gurdwara Nottingham
17 Berridge Road
Nottingham

Guru Nanak Darbar
4 Waterloo Road
Nottingham

Guru Nanak Dev Ji Gurdwara
1 Noel Street
Hyson Green
Nottingham
Tel: 0602-700750
Contact: Prithipal Singh
Office: President

Guru Nanak Sat Sang Gurdwara
60/62 Forest Road West
Nottingham NG7 4EP
Tel: 0602-781394
Contact: Malkiat Singh Matharu
Office: President
Place of worship. Activities include religious congregations, Panjabi language school, Panjabi music school, reciting and singing of religious hymns.

Sikh Community and Youth Services
27 Park Road
Lenton
Nottingham
Tel: 0602-507481
Fax: 0602-414303
Contact: Dr C S Syan
Office: Chairperson
Membership group and representative body. An advocacy and support group mainly for the Sikh community and for disadvantaged people. It is a community and youth organisation which has been based in Lenton, Nottingham, since its formation in 1988. Many projects at a national and local level have been successfully accomplished with the co-operation of local and national agencies. Activities are related to women, youth and other issues in the Sikh community.

Sikh Temple
16 Ebury Road
Sherwood Rise
Nottingham NG5 1BB
Tel: 0602-622132
Contact: Mr G S Sanghera
Office: Secretary
Place of worship. The Temple is open to its members for daily worship, to celebrate cultural and religious festivals and perform marriages according to the Sikh faith.

Sikh Temple Singh Sabha
97 Burford Road
Forestfield
Nottingham

Young Lions
c/o 1 Noel Street
Hyson Green
Nottingham
Tel: 0602-700750
Contact: Jagtar Singh
Office: President

ENGLISH WEST MIDLANDS

Akhand Kirtani Jatha Midlands
48 Mervyn Road
Handsworth
Birmingham B21 8DE

Babbar Khalsa House
153 Winson Street
Winson Green

Birmingham B18 4JW
Tel: 021-454-2996
Contact: Balbir Singh
Office: Jathedaar

Bebe Nanaki Gurdwara
89 Rookery Road
Handsworth
Birmingham B21
Tel: 021-551-3489
Contact: Mr Kulwant Singh
Office: General Secretary

Bhatra Sikh Singh Sabha Temple
221 Mary Street
Balsall Heath
Birmingham

Council of Sikh Gurdwaras in Birmingham
P O Box 2318
Hockley
Birmingham B19 2EZ
Tel: 021-523-4144
Fax: 021-515-4080
Contact: Gurdial Singh Atwal and Piara Singh Jheeta
Office: General Secretary and Chairman
The Council is an umbrella organisation established in 1989 with the objective of providing a representative body for all Sikhs in Birmingham. The Council aims to promote awareness of the Sikh religion and way of life; preserve and develop Sikh cultural heritage; and to develop and promote communication and good relations between persons of different faiths and racial groups.

Gurdwara Guru Nanak Bhatra Singh Sabha and Community Centre
248-150 Moseley Road
Balsall Heath
Birmingham B12
Tel: 021-440-2387
Contact: President

Gurdwara Nanaksar
Old Methodist Church
Waterloo Road
Smethwick
Birmingham B66 4JS
Tel: 021-558-9048
Tel: 021-420-1034 (home)
Contact: Bahadar Singh
Office: Sevadar
A place of worship which is open to people of all faiths to preach the message of Ik Onkar (One God, Father and Mother of all the beings of the world). The Gurdwara is open and accessible at all times. Worship takes place twice a day every day of the year. Meetings are held with people of all faiths encouraging mutual dialogue, creating mutual understanding and harmony. Other activities include increasing youths awareness of their faith and culture and the teaching of mother tongue, Sikh scriptures and Sikh Kirtan music.

Gurdwara Nishkam Sewak Jatha
14-20 Soho Road
Handsworth
Birmingham B21 9BH
Tel: 021-551-1123/4/5
Contact: Mr S Norang Singh
Office: President

Gurdwara Singh Sabha
Somerset Road
Handsworth Wood
Birmingham B20
Tel: 021-523-7201

Guru Nanak Gurdwara
130 High Street
Smethwick
Warley
West Midlands B66 3AP
Tel: 021-555-5926
The Gurdwara holds regular religious services and free kitchen for all; an Asian advisory service dealing with welfare rights, housing and immigration; kirtan classes, classes to enable one to read the scriptures; karate class and a community centre for the elderly.

Guru Nanak Gurdwara
629-631 Stratford Road
Sparkhill
Birmingham B11 4LS
Tel: 021-771-0092
Contact: Kashmira S Samar
Office: General Secretary

Guru Nanak Gurdwara
219 Mary Street
Balsall Heath
Birmingham B12

Guru Nanak Khalsa School
145a Soho Road
Handsworth
Birmingham B21 9ST
Tel: 021-551-1579

Guru Ram Das Temple

290 Balsall Heath Road
Birmingham B12

Guru Ramdas Singh Sabha Gurdwara

495 Moseley Road
Balsall Heath
Birmingham B12 9BX
Tel: 021-440-3653
Contact: Ram Singh
Office: General Secretary
Place of worship which promotes the teaching and philosophy of the Gurus. The organisation respects every religion as it is written in the Sikh Holy Book the Guru Granth Sahib. Everone is welcome to join prayer, visit or enquire. Activities include worship, welfare and Gurmukhi classes.

Khalsa Welfare Trust

Khalsa House
4 Holyhead Road
Handsworth
Birmingham B21 0LT
Tel: 021-554-8034
Contact: Mr B S Bawa
Office: President

Punjabi Cultural Society

145a Soho Road
Handsworth
Birmingham B21 9ST
Tel: 021-551-1579

Ramgarhia Circle

205 The Broadway
Perry Barr
Birmingham B20 3EU
Tel: 021-429-6823
Contact: Prem Singh Kalsi
Office: General Secretary

Ramgarhia Gurdwara

Unitarian Hall
27-29 Waverley Road
Small Heath
Birmingham B10 0HG
Tel: 021-773-8909
Contact: Mr Baldev Singh Ubbey
Office: General Secretary

Ramgarhia Sikh Temple

Graham Street
Birmingham B1 3LA
Tel: 021-235-5435

Tel: 021-236-2647
Contact: Mr G S Matharu

Shaheed Udham Singh Welfare Centre

346 Soho Road
Handsworth
Birmingham B21 8EG
Contact: Mr K S Sanghera

Sharomani Akali Dal Welfare and Sikh Centre

Khalsa House
535-537 Park Road
Hockley
Birmingham B18 5TE

Sikh Guild of Students

Aston University
Costa Green
Birmingham B4 7ES

Sikh Missionary Resource Centre

346 Green Lane
Small Heath
Birmingham B9 8DB
Tel: 021-772-5365
Contact: Ranjit Singh Wahiwala
Office: Honorary Secretary
A resource centre which was founded in 1984. It provides services and information to the community on a voluntary and independent basis. Students are provided with material help to assist them in their in their religious studies and projects. Activities include provision of resources; arranging religious and social seminars, youth camps, translating, typesetting in Asian languages, visiting of pensioners and immigration consultancy. Publisher of bi-lingual books on the Sikh religion (English/Panjabi).

Sikh Parents Association

629/631 Stratford Road
Sparkhill
Birmingham
Tel: 021-771-0092
Contact: Mr Samra
Office: General Secretary

Sikh Parents Association (South Birmingham)

86 Tetley Road
Sparkhill
Birmingham B11 3BT
Tel: 021-777-6391
Contact: Surjit Singh Khatra

Sikh Religious Symbols Action Committee
11 Apollo Way
Perry Barr
Birmingham B20 3ND
Tel: 021-356-7070
Contact: Bhai Madan Singh
Office: Chief Convenor

Sikh Sahit and Sabhyachan Kendra
145a Soho Road
Handsworth
Birmingham B21 9ST
Tel: 021-551-1579

Sikh Social History Project
Khalsa House
4 Holyhead Road
Handsworth
Birmingham B21 0LT
Tel: 021-554-8034
Contact: Harminder Singh
Office: Secretary

Sikh Temple
22 Goldshill Road
Birmingham B21

Sikh Welfare Mission
3 Hatfield Road
Lozells
Birmingham B19

Sikh Youth Centre
125 Soho Road
Handsworth
Birmingham B21 9ST
Tel: 021-523-0147
Contact: Mr Jagdish Singh
Office: Employment Co-ordinator

Sikh Youth Circle
47 Serpentine Road
Aston
Birmingham B6 6SB

Sikh Youth Service
Khalsa House
4 Holyhead Road
Handsworth
Birmingham B21 0LT
Tel: 021-554-8034
Contact: Balwinder Singh

Singh Sabha Bhatra Gurdwara
221 Mary Street
Balsall Heath
Birmingham B12 9RN
Tel: 021-440-2358
Contact: Mr N Singh
Office: Secretary

Sri Dashmesh Sikh Temple
305 Wheeler Street
Lozells
Birmingham B19 2BU
Tel: 021-523-6059
Contact: Kirpal Singh Dhillon
Office: General Secretary
Place of worship. Facilities for worship and marriages.

Gurdwara Ajit Darbar
Swan Lane
Coventry
West Midlands

Gurdwara Ajit Darbar Coventry UK
Lockhurst Lane
Foleshill
Coventry
West Midlands
Tel: 0203-662448
Contact: Mr S S Singh

Gurudwara Guru Hargobind Charitable Trust Sikh Temple
53 Heath Road
Coventry CV2 4QB
Tel: 0203-450260
Contact: Councillor Jaswant Singh Birdi
Office: Secretary General
Place of worship. A single storey building with a main hall, dining hall and kitchen. In addition to religious functions there is a ladies' Satsang every Monday and community activities.

Guru Nanak Sewak Jatha
128 De Montfort Way
Cannon Park
Coventry CV4 7DT
Contact: Mr A S Dhesi

International Sikh Brotherhood
24 Benthnell Road
Coventry
West Midlands

International Sikh Youth Federation

17 King George's Avenue
Foleshill
Coventry CV6 6FE
Contact: Mr G S Atwal

Nanak Parkash Gurdwara

71/81 Harnall Lane West
Foleshill
Coventry CV2 2GJ
Tel: 0203–220960
Contact: Mr G S Chohan

Nanaksar Gurdwara Gursikh Temple

224–226 Foleshill Road
Coventry CV1 4HW
Tel: 0203–220434
Tel: 0203–688609 (home)
Contact: Mr B S Pandher
Office: Secretary
Place of worship. The temple maintains religious worship, education and activities to advance the Sikh religion in accordance with the teachings of the ten Sikh Gurus. It aims to promote friendship and good will between members of the charity and with all other persons. It also operates classes for Sikh religious studies.

Ramgarhia Board

7 Pensilva Way
Primrose Park Estate
Coventry
West Midlands

Ramgarhia Gurdwara and Family Centre

1103 Foleshill Road
Foleshill
Coventry CV6 6EP
Tel: 0203–683048
Place of worship. Everybody is welcome at the morning, evening and Sunday noon services. Langar is served every morning and Sunday noon after services. There is also a family centre for the benefit of the public and sports and other activities are run.

Sharomani Akali Dal (UK)

38 Station Street East
Coventry
West Midlands

Shiromani Akali Dal

15 Park Street
Foleshill
Coventry CV6 5AT
Contact: Mr M S Dhillon

Sikh Cultural Society

305 Walsgrave Road
Coventry CV2 4BL
Tel: 0203–454523
Tel: 0203–457497 (work)
Contact: Dr G S Judge
Office: Secretary
The society was formed in the wake of the realisation that the educational and cultural needs of Sikh youth were not being adequately met by the existing Sikh Temples and institutions. Membership demands individual commitment to the Panjabi language and culture and to the Guru Granth Sahib, thereby establishing an effective voice within the Sikh community and the general British population and establishments. Activities include supporting and protecting the character, status and interests of Sikh culture and encouraging its study.

Sikh Mission

Khalsa House
19 St Luke's Road
Holbrooks
Coventry CV6 4JA
Tel: 0203–661442
Contact: D S Kundra
Office: Organiser
Membership group. The mission promotes and educates people on Sikhism.

Supreme Council of Sikhs

70-72 Humber Road
Stoke
Coventry CV3 1BA
Contact: Mr T S Shokar

Gurdwara Guru Teg Bahadur

7 Vicar Street
Dudley
West Midlands DY2 8RQ
Contact: Mr A S Shergill
Office: Chair

Shromani Akali Dal UK

12 Molyneux Road
Netherton
Dudley

West Midlands DY2 2DH
Contact: Mr R Singh
Office: President

Sikh Parents Association
20 Ravensitch Walk
Brierley Hill
Near Dudley
West Midlands DY5 2BY
Contact: Mr A S Kang

Sri Guru Nanak Singh Sabha Gurdwara
26 Wellington Road
Dudley
West Midlands
Contact: Mr A S Bedi
Office: General Secretary

Gurdwara Sahib Leamington and Warwick
96-102 New Street
Leamington Spa
Warwickshire CV31 1HL
Tel: 0926-424297
Contact: Shisham Singh Sahota
Office: General Secretary
Place of worship. It aims to: facilitate worship according to the Sikh religion; teach children the Panjabi language in the Gurmukhi script; keep good relationships with the other religious communities; help charities and look after old folks.

Shromani Akali Dal UK
89 Willes Road
Leamington Spa
Warwickshire

Shromani Akali Dal UK
19a Leam Street
Leamington Spa
Warwickshire

Sikh Community Centre
1 Mill Street
Leamington Spa
Warwickshire CV31 1ES
Tel: 0926-883129
Contact: Chanan Singh Aujla
Office: Manager
A community organisation which aims to: educate members of minority ethnic groups about their rights in society; highlight their rights; advise them on participating in everyday life; guide them to play an active part in the politics of the country they are living in and to highlight the facilities available from central and local government.

Gurdwara
84 Bracebridge Street
Nuneaton
Warwickshire CV11 5PB
Contact: c/o Mr G Singh

Guru Nanak Gurdwara
59-61 Park Avenue
Nuneaton
Warwickshire
Tel: 0203-386524
Contact: Mr J S Sekhon
Office: General Secretary
Place of worship. Previously a church which has now been converted into a Sikh Temple. There is a main hall with the capacity to accomodate about three to four hundred people, a dining hall and kitchen. Its opening hours are 6.00-9.00am and 5.00-8.00pm. The main service is held on every Sunday beginning in the early morning till noon. Activities include worship, womens get-togethers, wedding ceremonies and a community kitchen (Langar).

Guru Nanak Gurdwara
4 Craven Road
Rugby
Warwickshire CV21 3HY
Tel: 0788-543192
Contact: P S Atwal
Office: Secretary

Sikh Cultural Association UK
6 Hunscote Close
Shirley
Solihull
West Midlands B90 2NH
Contact: H Mudan

Guru Nanak Gurdwara
90 Tithe Barn Road
Stafford
Tel: 0785-58590
Contact: Nirmal Singh
Office: Priest
Place of worship. The only Sikh Temple in Stafford. All Sikh weddings take place there. Everone is welcome and children from different schools come to visit the Gurdwara. There are also facilities for children to learn Panjabi.

Guru Nanak Gurdwara

61 Liverpool Road
Stoke-on-Trent ST4 1AQ
Tel: 0782-415670
Contact: Ranjit Kaur Daliwal
Office: President

Ramgaria Sikh Temple

141 Whieldon Road
Fenton
Stoke-on-Trent ST4 4JG
Tel: 0782-44940
Contact: Mr Devgon

Sikh Cultural Association

92 Soames Crescent
Longton
Stoke-on-Trent
Staffordshire
Contact: Mrs D Singh

Sikh Womens Association

14 Boughey Road
Shelton
Stoke-on-Trent
Staffordshire
Contact: Mrs Dhillon

Guru Nanak Sikh Temple

Hadley Park Road
Hadley
Telford
Shropshire
Tel: 0952-251734
Tel: 0952-617515 (home)
Contact: Mr Malhi
Office: General Secretary
A place of worship which aims to: advance Sikhism
and worship according to the teaching of Guru Granth
Sahib Ji; hold congregation for the worship and
teaching of religious tenets and doctrines; perform
marriages according to the rites and rituals of the Sikh
religion and to celebrate the birthdays and martyrdom
days Shahidi Gurpurbs of the Sikh Gurus.

Gurdwara Guru Nanak Prakash

65-67 Walsall Road
Willenhall
Walsall
West Midlands
Tel: 0922-36485

Gurdwara Nanaksar

4 Wellington Street
Walsall
West Midlands
Tel: 0922-641040

Gurdwara Nanak Sar Temple

Pleck Street
Walsall
West Midlands

Guru Nanak Education and Community Service Board

156 West Bromwich Street
Walsall
West Midlands
Contact: Tara Singh

Guru Nanak Gurdwara

West Bromwich Street
Walsall
West Midlands
Tel: 0922-22199

Guru Nanak Sikh Organisation

212 Prince Street
Pleck
Walsall
West Midlands
Contact: Ranjit Singh Virk

Walsall Sikh Association

51 Bescot Road
Walsall WS2 9AD
Tel: 0922-29401 (home)
Contact: Harminder Singh Khera
Office: General Secretary
A membership group which aims to highlight the
needs of the Sikh community and create the means to
maintain Sikh identity within the Sikh community. A
group of well educated and well motivated people
who have identified a serious lack of provisions for the
Sikh community within the education system, health
system and the social service departments. It aims to
highlight and discuss the best ways to deal with these
enormous issues. It involves people from all walks of
life and facilitates and supports any of those groups
which are involved in voluntary community
development work. The association meets every three
months in the Gurdwara and participates in various
activities specifically involving youth, women and
elderly people.

Bhai Budha Dal Sandwell

64 Tiverton Road
Smethwick
Warley
West Midlands B67 3HX
Tel: 021-565-0043
Contact: Mr Bakshish Singh
Office: Chairman
Aims to look after the social recreational and welfare needs of the Asian elderly.

Desh Bhagat Committee

33 Birch Street
Oldbury
Warley
West Midlands
Contact: Mr B Singh

Gurdwara Amrit Parchar Dharmik Dewan

Birmingham Road
Oldbury
Warley
West Midlands
Tel: 021-552-3778

Gurdwara Nanaksar

Waterloo Road
Smethwick
Warley
West Midlands B66 4JS
Tel: 021-558-9048
Contact: Mr Gujar Singh
Office: Secretary

Nanaksar Satsang Sabha UK

111 Sycamore Road
Smethwick
Warley
West Midlands
Contact: Mr J Singh

Sharomani Akali Dal

23 Regent Street
Smethwick
Warley
West Midlands

Young Akali Dal Sandwell

144 West Bromwich Street
Oldbury
Warley
West Midlands (home)

Tel: 021-544-4939 (home)
Contact: Mr B Singh
Office: Secretary

Guru Nanak Gurdwara

Well Lane
Wednesfield
West Midlands

Sikh Temple

80 Hart Road
Wednesfield
West Midlands

Gurdwara Guru Har Rai Sahib

126-128 High Street
West Bromwich
West Midlands B70 8ND
Tel: 021-525-3275

Guru Nanak Gurdwara

8 Edward Street
West Bromwich
West Midlands B70 8NP
Tel: 021-553-1242
Contact: President

Shiromani Akali Dal/Sikh Community Support Association

49 Springfield Crescent
West Bromwich
West Midlands
Contact: Mr B Singh Rai

Guru Nanak Gurdwara

Vernon Street
Wolverhampton
West Midlands
Tel: 0902-26325

Guru Nanak Gurdwara

205-6 Lea Road
Penfields
Wolverhampton WV3 0LG
Tel: 0902-710289
Contact: Mr Pritam Singh
Office: Secretary

Guru Nanak Gurdwara

Arthur Street
Bilston
Wolverhampton WV14 0DG
Tel: 0902-492383

Contact: Mr R Karam
Office: General Secretary
A place of worship which preaches the Sikh religion and celebrates the birth and death of the Gurus throughout the year. Marriages and registrations take place all year round. Every Wednesday a special programme for women is held from 2.00–4.00pm. Every Sunday afternoon children aged from eight to sixteen years old learn the Panjabi mother tongue.

Guru Nanak Sikh Gurdwara

200–204 Cannock Road
Wolverhampton WV10 0AL
Tel: 0902-450453
Contact: Mr Gurmit Singh
Office: General Secretary

Guru Nanak Sikh Temple

Sedgley Street
Off Dudley Road
Wolverhampton
West Midlands
Tel: 0902-459413
Contact: Narinder Singh Chohan
Office: Secretary

Nanaksar Thath Isher Darbar

Mander Street
Wolverhampton WV3 OJZ
Tel: 0902-29379
Contact: Dr Sadhu Singh
Office: General Secretary

Ramgarhia Board and Temple

Westbury Street
Wolverhampton WV1 1JD
Tel: 0902-26885
Contact: Mr Lyall
Office: Secretary

Ramgarhia Sabha

334 Newhampton Road East
Wolverhampton WV1 4AD
Tel: 0902-25156
Tel: 0902-743207 (home)
Contact: Secretary

Sacha Sat Singh Mandal

6 Wanderers Avenue
Blakenhall
Wolverhampton
West Midlands

EAST ANGLIA

Cambridge Sikh Society

17 Woodcock Close
Impington
Cambridge CB4 4LD (home)
Tel: 0223-232519 (home)
Contact: Mr Amrik Singh Sagoo
The Society organises Sikh worship once a month in a hired hall.

Sangat Sikh Bhatra Temple

Great Yarmouth Road
Ipswich
Suffolk

Sikh Bhatra Temple

186 Cromwell Road
Peterborough
Cambridgeshire
Contact: Dr Singh
Office: President
Tel: 0733-65133

Sikh Gurdwara

Gladstone Street
Peterborough
Cambridgeshire
Contact: Kuldip Singh

SOUTH EAST ENGLAND (NORTH)

Gurdwara Singh Sabha

100 North Street
Barking
Essex IG11 8JD
Tel: 081-594-3940
Contact: Mr Gulshan
Office: Head Priest

Shiromani Akali Dal UK

100 North Street
Barking
Essex IG11 8JD
Tel: 081-517-0249

Guru Nanak Gurdwara

72 Ford End Road
Queens Park
Bedford
Contact: Mr Lal Singh Gill

Ramgarhia Sikh Society Gurdwara

33-39 Ampthill Street
Bedford MK42 9BT
Tel: 0234-342969
Contact: Mr Satnam Singh Riyait
Office: Secretary
Place of worship and community centre which serves the religious, cultural and social needs of the community. Activities include social welfare, education, music classes, sports and religious activities.

Ramgarhia Sikh Temple

69 Victoria Road
Bedford

Shri Guru Singh Sabha Gurudwara

46 Miles Road
Bedford

Edgware Gurdwara (Waltham Drive)

28 Highlands
Edgware
Middlesex
Tel: 952-5402

Sikh Temple

6 Maidstone Road
Grays Thurrock
Essex
Tel: 0375-376086
Contact: Sukhdev Singh
Office: Secretary

Sikh Divine Fellowship

132 Eastcote Avenue
Sudbury
Greenford
Middlesex UB6 0NR
Fax: 081-903-7143
Contact: Professor Harmindar Singh
Office: Secretary
Place of worship and membership group. Its main activities are worship and a theological discussion group.

Harlow Sikh Society

80 Greygoose Park
Harlow
Essex CM19 4JL
Tel: 0279-432177 (after 5.00pm) (home)
Contact: Mr D S Bawa
Office: Chair
Membership group. The organisation functions for people to meet together and follow religious and cultural pursuits. It welcomes people who are new in Harlow and need friends and also organises social events like discos and dances for the Sikh community. It aims to provide religious and moral support during illness, bereavement and weddings. It organises worship, celebration of Sikh festivals, gives talks in schools and liaises with other political, social and religious organisations.

Guru Nanak Sikh College

Springfield Road
Hayes
Middlesex UB4 0LT
Tel: 081-573-6085
Fax: 081-561-6772
The College was opened in January 1993 as a mixed, Independent College with about four hundred children enrolled from nursery to GSCE levels. It is hoped to add a sixth form at a later date. It is the first Sikh College in Europe and is founded by Sant Baba Amar Singh, the Chairman and spiritual Head of the the Nanak Sar Thath Ishar Darbar organisation worldwide.

Nirayana Enterprise

127 Norman Crescent
Heston
Middlesex TW5 9JN
Tel: 081-577-1448
Contact: Mr S S Dhanjal
It promotes understanding of Sikh philosophy through the Sikh Holy scripture, relaxation and meditation.

Sikh Association

223 West Wycombe Road
High Wycombe
Buckinghamshire

Sikh Temple

27 Kingston Road
High Wycombe
Buckinghamshire

Guru Singh Sabha Gurdwara

Radcliffe Road
Hitchin
Hertfordshire
Tel: 0462-432993
Contact: Mr Ajit Singh Sarai
Office: Secretary
Two congregations share the same Gurdwara.

Ramgarhia Gurdwara Society - Hitchin

Bearton Avenue
Hitchin
Hertfordshire
Contact: Mr G S Sahota
Office: General Secretary
Religious organisation and place of worship. The oldest Gurdwara established in the region. It is a registered charity. The main purpose of the society is to provide a place of worship for its members and the community and to arrange religious functions. The Gurdwara is a registered building for the solemnisation of marriages. It provides worship and welfare for the community.

Gurdwara Guru Nanak Nishkam Sewak Jatha (UK)

142 Martindale Road
Hounslow
Middlesex TW4 7HQ
Tel: 081-570-4774
Contact: Mr Grewal
Office: Trustee
A place of worship opened by the saintly Sant Baba Puran Singh of Kericho, Kenya and his followers. It aims to propagate religious teachings and meditation and to help needy people. It is open to all who believe in the Sikh faith. Activities include worship, Panjabi school and music classes.

Gurdwara Sri Guru Singh Sabha

Rear of 29-37 Hibernia Road
Hounslow
Middlesex
Tel: 081-577-2793
Contact: Mr Ranjit Singh
Office: President
Place of worship. Provides facilities for daily worship in mornings and evenings. The main religious congregations are on Sunday morning and for death ceremonies. Panjabi classes for children are run in the evenings. Religious teaching for young children is provided on a Sunday. The organisation also has a youth wing and has a women's wing called Guru Nanak Istri Satsang.

Sharomani Akali Dal

29 Waye Avenue
Cranford
Hounslow
Middlesex TW5 9SD
Tel: 081-897-9612

Sikh Art and Culture Centre

21 Montague Road
Hounslow
Middlesex TW3 1LG
Tel: 081-570-6734
Contact: Mr H S Dillon
The centre holds Panjabi language classes, vocal and instrumental music, folk dances. Exhibitions and displays of pictures, photographs and films are held on various cultures relating to ethnic minorities in this country. It celebrates cultural and religious festivals.

Sikh Art and Cultural Centre

93 Waye Avenue
Cranford
Hounslow
Middlesex TW5 9SQ
Tel: 081-759-0639

Sikh Study Centre (UK)

93 Waye Avenue
Cranford
Hounslow
Middlesex

Sri Guru Singh Sabha

48 Way Avenue
Cranford
Hounslow
Middlesex

East London Singh Sabha

3 Ashgrove Road
Goodmayes
Ilford
Essex IG3 9XE
Tel: 081-597-3644
Contact: Mr A S Sahotay

Punjabi Sabiacharik Sabha

22 Cranbrook Rise
Ilford
Essex IG1 3QN
Contact: Mr H S Desi

Redbridge Punjabi Sabhiacharik Sabha

293-97 Ley Street
Ilford
Essex IG1 4BN
Tel: 081-478-4962

Sikh Study Forum
85 Inglehurst Gardens
Redbridge
Ilford
Essex IG4 5HA
Tel: 081-550-5778
Contact: RS Dhesi

Nanaksar Sar Thath Ishar Darbar
7 Gernon Walk
Letchworth
Hertfordshire SG6 3HW
Tel: 0462-684153
Tel: 0462-686477 (home)
Contact: Resham Singh Johal
Office: Trustee
Part of a worldwide organisation which includes branches in the USA, Canada, New Zealand, Australia and Ireland and a big temple in Wolverhampton in the UK. It tries to give spiritual strength to the souls of people who go there to refrain from sex, anger, greed, worldly love and pride. People are encouraged to pray to God and do good deeds. It teaches that to love his people is to love God and that truth is evergreen. In addition to worship, the organisation helps to fund schools and hospitals, arrange free eye operations and run camps as well as other humanitarian work all over the world without any discrimination on the grounds of religion, creed or caste.

Guru Nanak Gurdwara
12-16 Portland Street
Luton
Bedfordshire
Tel: 0582-486571
Tel: 0582-455356 (home)
Contact: Mr Lakhbir Singh
Office: Secretary
Place of worship and membership group with a charitable organisation. It has five hundred members and looks after their social and religious interests. The place of worship consists of three houses joined together and includes a worship hall, toilets, dining room, kitchen, store-room, conference room, rest room and library. Activities include worship, welfare, youth, and women.

Sikh Missionary and Literary Society
392 Selbourne Road
Luton LU4 8NU
Contact: G S Lakra

Guru Nanak Satsang Sabha
31 Rutland Road
Maidenhead
Berkshire SL6 4HT
Tel: 0628-23507
Contact: Mr Harbans Singh Bhogal
Office: Secretary
A purpose-built Gurdwara which is also a resource centre for the Sikh religion. It is a member of an interfaith group and is affiliated to Maidenhead Community Consultative Council. Activities include worship, providing lectures and talks in schools, providing Religious Education and music classes and teaching mother tongue (Panjabi).

Singh Sabha
33 Lagen Square
Maidenhead
Berkshire

Ramgarhia Sabha
10 Hadrians Drive
Bancroft
Milton Keynes MK13 0PP

Sri Guru Singh Sabha
13 Stile Road
Headington
Oxford

Ramgahria Sabha
P O Box 107
Reading
Berkshire

Sri Guru Singh Sabha Gurdwara
30a Cumberland Road
Reading RG1 3LB
Tel: 0734 268353
Contact: Mr Amolak Singh Sokhi
Office: Secretary

Guru Nanak Punjabi Library
16 Arthur Road
Slough
Berkshire

International Sikh Brotherhood
32 Burlington Road
Slough
Berkshire

Ramgarhia Gurdwara
Woodland Avenue
Slough
Berkshire
Tel: 0753-525458
Contact: Mr I S Ghataura
Office: Secretary
Purpose-built in 1978.

Ramgharia Sabha
31 Chalvey Road East
Slough
Berkshire

Ramgharia Sabha
26 King Edward Street
Slough
Berkshire

Sharomani Akali Dal
31 Chalvey Road East
Slough
Berkshire

Sri Guru Gobind Singh Marg Gurdwara
76 Montague Road
Slough
Berkshire
Tel: 0753-579906

Sri Guru Singh Sabha Gurdwara
Waxham Court
Sheehy Way
Slough SL2 5SS
Tel: 0753-526828
Contact: Mr Tarbedi Singh Benipal
Office: General Secretary
Place of worship. The Gurdwara provides a place for
worship and educational facilities. It organises sports
activities, community kitchen and a Punjabi school
every Sunday. Also provides sewing classes, music
classes and the teaching of Sikh religious scriptures. All
these facilities are free of charge and anybody from any
community is welcome to use them and join in any
religious service which takes place every morning and
evening.

Dasmesh Sat Sang Sabha
6 Evelyn Grove
Southall
Middlesex
Tel: 081-843-1961

Guru Granth Gurdwara
45 Villiers Road
Southall
Middlesex
Tel: 081-574-1828
Contact: Dr N S Manget
Place of worship.

Ramgarhia Sabha Southall
53-57 Oswald Road
Southall
Middlesex UB 1HN
Tel: 081-571-4867
Contact: Jaspal Singh Bhambra
Office: General Secretary
Place of worship and cultural development. A Sikh
organisation managed by the Ramgarhia Community
resident in and around Southall. It provides facilities
for Sikh worship, social activities, education, sports
and leisure facilities for the young and old and, within
the constrains of a voluntary service, helps to deal with
the day to day problems faced by individuals.

Sharomani Akali Dal
30 Grodon Road
Southall
Middlesex

Sharomani Akali Dal
30 Hortus Road
Southall
Middlesex

Sri Guru Singh Sabha Gurdwara
Havelock Road
Southall
Middlesex
Tel: 081-574-8901
Fax: 081-893-5094
Contact: Bachittar Singh
Office: President
Place of worship. The largest Sikh Temple in the
Western Hemisphere.

Sri Guru Singh Sabha Gurdwara
2 Park Avenue
Southall
Middlesex UB2 4NP
Tel: 081-571-9687
Fax: 081-893-5094
Contact: Beant Singh
Office: General Secretary

Aims to promote the Sikh religion and also an understanding of all religions. Activities focus upon religion, youth and elderly.

Sikh Literary Society

217 Western Road
Southall
Middlesex

Watford Sikh Association

82 Valley Walk
Croxley Green
Watford WD3 3TE
Tel: 0923-220843
Contact: Mr S S Ahluwalia
Office: Secretary
Caters for the welfare and needs of the Sikh community in Watford.

LONDON (E POSTCODES)

Gurdwara Sikh Sangat

1a Campbell Road
Bow
London E3 4DS
Tel: 081-980-2281

Gurdwara Singh Sangat

Harley Grove
Bow
London E3 2AT
Tel: 081-980-8861

Ramgarhia Sikh Gurdwara

10-14 Neville Road
Forest Gate
London E7 9SQ
Tel: 081-471-0335
Tel: 081-472-3738 (home)
Contact: Mr R S Bansal
Office: General Secretary

Gurdwara Sikh Sangat

71 Francis Road
Leyton
London E10 6PL
Tel: 081-556-4732
Tel: 081-558-4755 (home)
Contact: Mr Harsharn Singh
Office: General Secretary
Place of worship. A centre of all social and cultural activities of the local Sikh community. Activities focus on worship and welfare.

Dashmesh Darbar Gurdwara

97a Rosebery Avenue
Manor Park
London E12 6PT
Tel: 081-471-2205/4
Tel: 081-597-9174 (home)
Contact: Mr Arvinder Singh
Office: President

LONDON (N POSTCODES)

Sikh Cultural Society of Great Britain

29 Elm Park Road
London N3 1EG
Tel: 071-346-4897
Contact: Mr B S Grewal

Sikh Sangha Gurdwara Society

68 Gloucester Drive
London N4
Tel: 081-800-9923

Singh Sabha Gurdwara

68 Gloucester Drive
London N4
Tel: 081-800-7233

Nanak Darbar North London

136 High Road
New Southgate
London N11 1PJ
Tel: 081-368-2484
Tel: 081-368-7104
Contact: Mr Surinder Singh Attariwala
Office: Honorary Secretary
Nanak Darbar, North London, was established in 1972 to cater to the needs of the Sikh community in North London. A religious service is held every Sunday from 11.00am-2.00pm. The Panjabi School has classes from 10.00-12.00 noon every Sunday. There is a music class once a week. The Elderly Luncheon Club has its activities twice a week.

Shiramani Akali Dal

62 Seymour Avenue
Tottenham
London N17

Maha Sabha (London)

9 Truro Road
Wood Green
London N22 4EH

LONDON (SE POSTCODES)

Sikh Temple
1 Thorncombe Road
Camberwell
London SE5

Greenwich Sikh Association
1 Calderwood Street
Woolwich
London SE18
Tel: 081-854-4233

Guru Nanak Darbar Gurdwara
Old Mill Road
Plumstead
London SE18

Ramgharia Gurdwara
Willmount Street
Masons Hill
Woolwich
London SE18 6ES
Tel: 081-854-1786

Gurdwara Baba Bhudda Sahib Ji
2 Shawbury Road
East Dulwich
London SE22

Nanak Community Centre
156 South Norwood Hill
South Norwood
London SE25 6AJ
Contact: R S Chana

LONDON (SW POSTCODES)

Southfields Sikh Association
1 Southbrook Road
Streatham
London SW16
Contact: Mr M Jaswant

Khalsa Centre
95 Upper Tooting Road
London SW17 7TW
Tel: 081-767-3196
Contact: Mr H S Arora
Office: Assistant Secretary
Place of worship and Sikh community centre with a membership of about three hundred families. It is situated on the main Upper Tooting Road. There is

a gathering of around one hundred and fifty to two hundred people every week to attend weekly congregations, solemnise and register marriages, celebrate birthdays and commemorate anniversaries of their loved ones. In the same building there is also a Khalsa Youth Centre offering youth activities.

Siri Guru Singh Sabha
74 Avarn Road
London SW17
Tel: 081-672-3852 (home)
Contact: Mr B S Chhabra

South London Sikh Gurdwara
142 Merton Road
London SW18 5SP
Tel: 081-870-7594

LONDON (W POSTCODES)

Ramgarhia Welfare Darvar
31 Hart Grove
Ealing
London W5

London Central Gurdwara (Khalsa Jatha)
62 Queensdale Road
Shepherd's Bush
London W11 4SG
Tel: 071-402-4696
Contact: Jasbir Singh Ghai
Office: President
Place of worship. On Wednesdays about one hundred and fifty people assemble for worship and on Sundays about five hundred people.

SOUTH EAST ENGLAND (SOUTH)

Guru Nanak Gurdwara
207 Lower Brook Street
Basingstoke
Hampshire RG21 1RR
Tel: 0256-473874

Sikh Temple
4 Kingshill Road
Basingstoke
Hampshire RG21 3JE

Sikh Sangat Gurdwara Association
Sydney Road
Chatham
Kent ME4 5BR

Tel: 0634-815934
Contact: Secretary
Place of worship.

Gurdwara Sri Guru Singh Sabha

27-29 Spencer Road
Crawley
Sussex RH11 7DE
Tel: 0293-530163
Tel: 0293-512890 (home)
Contact: Mr J P Singh
Office: Secretary
Place of worship. A registered charity funded by donations.

Sikh Union

41 Dovedale Crescent
Southgate West
Crawley
Sussex
Contact: Mr R S Bedi
Office: Secretary

Sri Guru Singh Sabha

63 Mill Road
Three Bridges
Crawley
Sussex

Nanak Community Centre

St James Road
Croydon
Surrey CR0 2BU
Tel: 081-688-8155
Contact: C S Dhanjal
Office: Chairperson
Place of worship. Worship and welfare facilities for Sikhs and others who have faith in the fundamental principles of Sikhism.

Sikh Prayers

124 Gonville Road
Thornton Heath
Croydon
Surrey
Tel: 081-684-8657
Contact: Mr P S Rekhi
Services once a month (on the third weekend) at St Jude's Church in Thornton Heath.

Sikh Temple

4 Edit Road
Croydon
Surrey

Guru Hargobind Sahib Sikh Temple

8 Highfield Road
Dartford
Kent
Tel: 0322-222951

Sikh Youth International

20 Mount Pleasant Road
Dartford
Kent
Tel: 0322-279664

Guru Nanak Durbar

31 Crabtree Manor Way
Belvedere
Erith
Kent DA17
Tel: 03224-32847
Tel: 081-311-3794 (home)
Contact: Secretary
A Sikh Temple registered for worship and marriages.

Kent Ramgarhia Darbar and Community Centre

63 Franklyn Road
Gillingham
Kent ME7 4DJ
Tel: 0634-576618
Contact: Mr Mohinder Singh Paddam
Office: Founder Member
Membership group. The organisation's main aim is to provide facilities for worship, welfare and education. Activities include teaching Panjabi to children, worship and the welfare of aged people.

Sri Guru Nanak Gurdwara

Byron Road
Gillingham
Kent
Tel: 0634-850921
Contact: Mr S S Sandhu
Office: President

Guru Nanak Darbar Gurdwara

Clarence Place
Gravesend
Kent
Tel: 0474-534121
Contact: Mr B S Sodhi
Office: General Secretary

Guru Nanak Day Care and Community Centre
11 The Grove
Gravesend
Kent

Guru Nanak Sandesh Parchar Board
20 Peacock Street
Gravesend
Kent DA12 1EF
Contact: Mr K S Sodhi

International Sikh Youth Federation
21 Brook Street
Northfleet
Gravesend
Kent
Contact: Mr Narinderjit Singh Thandi

Jugnu Bhangra and Youth
40 Singlewell Road
Gravesend
Kent
Contact: Mr Shaminder Singh Bedi

Kshatriya Sabha
28 Pelham Road
Gravesend
Kent
Contact: Mr G Singh

Shiromani Akali Dal
49 Milton Road
Gravesend
Kent

Sikh Cultural Society
10 Darnley Street
Gravesend
Kent

Sikh Gurdwara Committee
23 Wellington Street
Gravesend
Kent

Sikh Gurdwara Committee
55 Pelham Road South
Gravesend
Kent

Sikh Missionary Society
72 Peacock Street
Gravesend
Kent

Sikh Temple
4 Milton Avenue
Gravesend
Kent
Tel: 0474–567418 (home)
Contact: G S Talwer
Office: Secretary
The temple's main activities are worship, youth and welfare for the minorities in Gravesend. It also arranges interfaith meetings and a sports festival.

Sikh Community
24 Church Road
Hove
East Sussex BN3 2FN

Kingston Sikh Association
19 Douglas Rd
Tolworth
Kingston-upon-Thames
Surrey KT6 7RZ
Contact: c/o Mr Harcharan

Gurdwara Sabha
Cossack Street
Rochester
Kent ME1 2EF
Contact: Mr T S Sandhu

Medway Towns Gurudwara Sabha
39 Rose Street
Rochester
Kent

Guru Nanak Sar Gurdwara
5 Margate Road
Southsea
Portsmouth
Hampshire
Tel: 0705–824965 (home)
Contact: Kirpal Singh Digpal
Place of worship and community building promoting Sikh religion and ideals. Activities include a weekly prayer meeting and helping others as needed.

Gurdwara Nanaksar
3 Peterborough Road
Bevois Valley

Southampton SO2 0HY
Tel: 0703-226464
Contact: Mr Gill

Gurdwara Singh Sabha

Canbury Avenue
Southampton
Hampshire
Tel: 0703-333016
Contact: Mr Darshan Singh
Office: Secretary

Gurdwara Tegh Bahadur Sahib

8 Clovelly Road
Southampton SO2 0AU
Tel: 0703-226744
Contact: Mr Aqbal Singh
Office: Secretary
Place of worship. The organisation has two separate large rooms at the side of the building. Activities include advice on DSS and immigration, hiring out halls for meetings and other functions, youth, women, worship, welfare and a drop-in centre.

Shromani Akali Dal

c/o Gurdwara Nanaksar
3 Peterborough Road
Bevois Valley
Southampton SO2 0HY
Tel: 0703-226464

Sikh Community Council

Sikh Temple
3 Peterborough Road
Bevois Valley
Southampton SO2 0HY
Tel: 0703-226464

Singh Sabha Gurdwara

Onslow Road
Southampton
Southampton
Tel: 0703-226464

Sri Guru Sanagat Association

41 Derby Road
Southampton
Tel: 0703-226464

SOUTH WEST ENGLAND

Bristol Gurdwara Association

69 Sussex Place
Bristol BS2

Bristol Singh Sabha

c/o 491 Stapleton Road
Easton
Bristol BS5 6PQ
Contact: Mukhtyar Singh

Ramgharia Sikh Temple

81 Chelsea Road
Easton
Bristol BS5
Tel: 0272-554929
Contact: Mr Balwant Singh
Office: President

Sangat Singh Sabha Gurdwara

11 Summerhill Road
St George's
Bristol BS5
Tel: 0272-559333

Singh Sabha Sikh Temple

71-75 Fishponds Road
Eastville
Bristol B5 6SF
Tel: 0272-513968
Contact: Lakhinder Singh
Office: President

Guru Arjan Niwas Sikh Temple

46 Clifton Street
Exeter
Devon

Sikh Temple

North Street
Swindon SN1 3JX
Contact: Mr B S Nandra

KEY TO TERMS IN SIKH ORGANISATIONAL TITLES

Note: This is not a complete glossary of significant Sikh terms. It is a guide to the meaning and/or background of some of the words used in the titles of Sikh organisations listed in this directory. More information on the italicised words can be tracked down either elsewhere in the key or, in the section on "Introducing the Sikh Community", by using the directory's Keyword Index.

Ajit

Panjabi for "invincible". The first name of Ajit Singh, a son of the tenth *Guru*.

Akali

Panjabi for "timeless" or "deathless". *Akal* refers to God. Found within the term *Sharomani Akali Dal*, the name of a Sikh political party ("the Principal Party of God"), *sharomani* meaning "principal" and *dal* a "party" or organisation.

Akhand

Panjabi for "uninterrupted" or "continuous". An *akhand path* is a continuous reading of the *Guru Granth Sahib Ji* over forty-eight hours. The *Akhand Kirtani Jatha* is so called because of their practice of continuous singing of *kirtan* overnight.

Amrit

Panjabi for "nectar". It is the name for the sweet water blessed and used in the formal ceremony for initiating Sikhs into the *khalsa panth* .

Anand

Panjabi for "bliss" or "joy". It is used in *anand karaj* to refer among Sikhs to marriage.

Arjan

The first name of the Sikh's fifth *Guru*, Guru Arjan Dev, who was Sikhism's first martyr.

Ashram

Word of Sanskrit origin, used in English to denote a place of solace and spiritual rest and retreat.

Baba

Panjabi term of endearment and respect especially for older men such as grandfathers. A title given to eminent male Sikhs such as Baba Budha.

Babbar

Panjabi term for "a big lion" which was applied to *Babbar Khalsa*, members of a revolutionary movement in the Indian subcontinent in the 1920s. It now appears in the *Babbar Khalsa* and other similar organisations of Sikhs which aim to create a sovereign Sikh state.

Bebe

Title for a respected older woman usually carrying the sense of "mother." Found in the name of Guru Nanak Dev Ji sister, Bebe Nanaki, regarded as his first follower.

Bhagat

Panjabi for "devotee". In Sikh tradition it can refer to several persons belonging to the *bhagti* tradition, for example, Kabir, Farid, Namdev and others. It is also the name of the twentieth century Sikh freedom fighter killed by the British, named Bhagat Singh. *Desh bhagat* means "patriot".

Bhai

Panjabi for "brother". It is a title of respect for Sikh men, as in Bhai Gurdas. It is sometimes used of *granthis*.

Bhatra

The name of a Sikh endogamous community characterised by certain customs and traditionally by occupation. *Bhatra* Sikhs mainly migrated to Britain before the Second World War and *Gurdwaras* founded by them can be found especially in the seaports as well as in inland areas where they have settled in significant numbers.

Budha

Panjabi for "old man" or "man of wisdom". Part of the name of Baba Budha, a disciple of the first *Guru* whose life spanned those of the first six *Gurus*.

Changa

Panjabi for "good".

Dal

Panjabi/Hindi for "group" and used for "party" or "organisation", as in the Sikh political party *Akali Dal*.

Darbar

Panjabi for "court" or "hall" used in Ajit Darbar Gurdwara in Coventry and in *Dashmesh Darbar* (Court of the Tenth *Guru*).

Das

Panjabi for "ten" or for "servant". It is usually a part of a name, such as Guru Amar Das.

Dashmesh

Title of the tenth *Guru*, Guru Gobind Singh Ji.

Dasmais

Variant Romanisation of *Dashmesh* (see above).

Degh

Panjabi for a "large cooking pan". Also written in Roman script as *deg*. It is a part of the Sikh motto and prayer "*Degh Tegh Fateh*" - victory (*fateh*) to the cooking pan and the sword (*tegh*), reflecting the Sikh emphasis on providing free hospitality.

Des

Variant Romanisation of *desh* (see below).

Desh

Panjabi for "country". *Desh bhagat* means "patriot."

Dev

Panjabi for "God" and often appearing as part of male names as in Guru Nanak Dev Ji or Guru Arjan Dev Ji.

Dewan

Panjabi for "assembly" or "court". It is a term used for Sikh corporate worship (on the analogy of the Moghul Emperors' audience chamber). It can also be found in Roman script as *diwan*.

Dharam

Panjabi for "religion". Used, for example, *Dharam Parchar Sanstha* means "institution for preaching the faith."

Dharmak

Panjabi for "religious" or "pertaining to *dharam*". Also appears in Roman script as *dharmik* (see below).

Dharmik

Variant Romanisation of *dharmak* (see above).

Diwan

Variant Romanisation of *deewan* (see above).

Durbar

Variant Romanisation of *darbar* (see above).

Ekta

Panjabi for "unity".

Fateh

Panjabi/Persian for "victory", as in "*waheguru ji ki fateh*", meaning "victory to God".

Gobind

A title for God and the first name of the tenth *Guru*, Guru Gobind Singh Ji, a variant Romanisation of which is sometimes found as Govind (see below).

Govind

A variant Romanisation of *Gobind* (see above).

Granth

Panjabi for "volume". It is used in the name of the Sikh scriptures, the *Adi Granth* or *Guru Granth Sahib Ji*.

Gurbani

Panjabi for "*Guru's* utterance" or "*Guru's* speech" and refers to the *Guru Granth Sahib Ji*.

Gurdwara

Panjabi for "door of the *Guru*". It is used as the name for any building in which the *Guru Granth Sahib Ji* is installed although most often it is popularly used of a visibly religious building or place of Sikh worship.

Gurmat

Panjabi for "*Guru's* teaching" or "*Guru's* philosophy". It is the Sikh word for Sikhism.

Gursikh

Panjabi for "*Guru's* Sikh", a respectful title for an *Amritdhari* Sikh.

Guru

Panjabi for "teacher". In Sikhism the title is reserved for the ten human *Gurus* and the *Guru Granth Sahib Ji*.

Gurudwara

Variant Romanisation of *Gurdwara*.

Hai

Panjabi for "is", as in the words of Guru Gobind Singh, "*khalsa mero rup hai khas*", meaning "the *khalsa* is my very form".

Har

Meaning "Lord", it is a name part of the names of the seventh and eighth *Gurus*, Guru Har Rai and Guru Har Krishan.

Hargobind

Literally "Lord God", from Guru Har Gobind Ji, the sixth *Guru*.

Ishar

A name, meaning "God".

Istri

Panjabi for "woman", found for example in *Istri Sabha*, meaning "women's group".

Jatha

Panjabi for "band" or "squad", used of contemporary Sikh organisations such as *Akhand Kirtani Jatha*.

Ji

Suffix denoting respect, for example, Babaji.

Jugnu

A name, meaning literally "firefly".

Kalgidar

Literally "with a plume in his turban", a title for the tenth *Guru*, Guru Gobind Singh Ji.

Khalistan

Panjabi for "Land of the Pure". The name of the sovereign Sikh State for which some Sikhs are campaigning.

Khalsa

Meaning "pure" and "owing direct allegiance". The name for Sikhs as a collective group.

Khas

Panjabi for "special" or "particular", as in Guru Gobind Singh Ji's "*khalsa mero rup hai khas*", meaning "the *khalsa* is my very form."

Kirpal

Panjabi for "benevolent" and a name, as of Kirpal Singh, who is revered by his followers.

Kirtani

Variant Romanisation of *kirtini* (see below).

Kirtini

Panjabi for "those who sing *kirtan*" meaning singing Sikh hymns".

Kirtni

Variant Romanisation of Panjabi for "performing *kirtan*", meaning "singing Sikh hymns."

Kshatriya

The second, warrior grouping in the classical groupings of Indian society. Sanskrit word for *Khatri*, an urban grouping of Panjabi society.

Maha

Panjabi for "great".

Marg

Panjabi for "way" or "spiritual path".

Mera

Panjabi for "my", as in the words of Guru Gobind Singh, "*khalsa mero rup hai khas*", meaning "the *khalsa* is my very form."

Miri

Persian word relating to political power.

Nanak

Name of the first *Guru*, *Guru Nanak Dev*.

Nanaki

Name of Guru Nanak Dev Ji's sister, Bebe Nanaki, regarded as his first follower.

Nanaksar

Panjabi literally meaning "pool of Nanak". It is also a place in the Ludhiana District of the Panjab with a line of Sikh saints who have established a chain of *Gurdwaras* in Britain and elsewhere and is therefore found in the title of some *Gurdwaras* in Britain.

Nish

A Panjabi prefix meaning "without"

Nishkam

Panjabi for "without desire" in the phrase *nishkam seva*, meaning "service with no desire for reward", in other words, distinterested service. There is, for example, the *Nishkam Sevak Jatha* meaning literally "the band of selfless followers" which was set up by Sant Puran Singh.

Niwas

Panjabi for "house".

Panjab

Comes from the Persian for "five" and "water", in other words, the "Land of the Five Rivers" (tributaries of the River Indus). The Panjab is the name for a current State within India, the much larger area originally known as the Panjab having been divided between India and Pakistan in 1947 and the Indian state of Panjab having been further reduced in size since 1966. Also found written as Punjab in a variant Romanisation.

Panth

A collective term for Sikh society as in *Khalsa Panth*.

Parbandhak

Panjabi for "management" or "administrative". Part of the title of the Sikhs' main elected body, the *Shiromani Gurdwara Parbandhak Committee* in Amritsar and also used in the title of many Sikh organisations in the UK.

Parchar

Panjabi for "preaching".

Parivar

Panjabi for "family".

Parkash

A name meaning "manifestation". Used, for example, in the title of the Guru Nanak Parkash Gurdwara in Coventry.

Piri

Panjabi for "spiritual power".

Prakash

Variant Romanisation of *parkash* (see above).

Punjabi

A variant Romanisation for Panjabi (see above).

Rai

Part of the name of the seventh *Guru*, Guru Har Rai Ji.

Raj

Panjabi for "rule" or "dominion". "*Raj karega khalsa*", meaning "the *khalsa* will rule" is a Sikh rallying cry.

Ram

A name, which in the *Guru Granth Sahib Ji* is an epithet for God. In Hindu tradition, Ram is an incarnation of *Vishnu* (see introduction to the Hindu community). In Sikhism, the name is found as the first name of the fourth *Guru*, Guru Ram Das Ji.

Ramdas

Variant Romanisation of ran Das, the name of the fourth *Guru*.

Ramgarhia

A Sikh social and occupational grouping, originally of artisans. *Ramgarhias* took their preferred description from the title of an eighteenth century warrior whose title referred to a fortress in Amritsar.

Ravi

First part of the name of a mediaeval mystic *bhagat* and poet, Ravidas, some of whose compositions are in the *Guru Granth Sahib Ji* .

Rup

Panjabi/Hindi for "form", as in Guru Gobind Singh Ji's words,"*khalsa mero rup hai khas*", meaning "the *khalsa* is my very form."

Sabha

Panjabi for "assembly", often used of Sikh organisations.

Sabiacharik

Panjabi for "of civilised conduct" or "cultural".

Sacha

Panjabi for "true".

Sachkhand

Panjabi for "realm of truth", for example as part of the name of the the organisation Sachkand Nanak Dham International set up by Darshan Das.

Sahib

Panjabi/Urdu honorific ending and term of respect for individuals, sites long associated with Sikh history, the *Guru Granth Sahib Ji*, and the Sikh flag.

Samaj

Hindi for "society", often used of organisations.

Sandesh

Panjabi for "message".

Sang

Panjabi for "association" or "company".

Sangat

Panjabi for "congregation".

Sangha

Panjabi for "group" or "union", often used of organisations.

Sanstha

Panjabi for "institution" or "organisation".

Sat

Panjabi for "true".

Seva

Panjabi for "service".

Sewa

Variant Romanisation of *seva*, (see above).

Sewak

Panjabi for "one who gives voluntary service", for example in the *Gurdwara*.

Sharomani

Variant Romanisation of *shiromani* (see below).

Shere

Panjabi/Urdu for "lion", as for example in *Sher-e-Punjab* (Lion of Panjab).

Shiri

Variant Romanisation of *Shri* (see below).

Shiromani

Panjabi for "principal", as in the Shiromani Gurdwara Parbandhak Committee.

Shri

Prefix denoting respect, sometimes meaning simply "Mr", sometimes used in the title of a *Guru* , as in Shri Guru Nanak Dev.

Sri

Variant Romanisation of Shri (see above).

Shromani

Variant Romanisation of *shiromani* (see above).

Tegh

Panjabi/Persian for "sword", used in the first name of the ninth *Guru*, Guru Tegh Bahadur.

Takht

Panjabi for "throne", quite often relating to one of the five principal Sikh "seats of authority" or centres where important decisions are made relating to Sikhism.

Udham

Panjabi meaning "effort" and the name of Udham Singh who killed Sir Michael O'Dwyer in 1940 following the 1919 massacre of Sikhs carried out by General Dyer during O'Dwyer's governorship of the Panjab and praised by him.

THE
ZOROASTRIAN
COMMUNITY

INTRODUCING THE ZOROASTRIAN COMMUNITY

ZOROASTRIANS IN THE UNITED KINGDOM

Origins

The first Zoroastrian who was known to have visited Britain came in 1723 and the first Indian firm to open for business in Britain was run by a *Parsi* family called Cama and Company and began in 1855.

The Zoroastrian community is thus a relatively long-established community in Britain. It was from the *Parsi* (see section on "The Parsis" below) community that the first three Asians to serve as Members of Parliament, of whom the first was Dadabhai Naoroji, for the Liberals, in 1892.

Migration

There have been five main later phases of Zoroastrian migration to the UK. It was between the two world wars that the *Parsi* Zoroastrian community became established in the UK. The second phase of migration was from India in the 1950s, immediately following Indian independence. The third was from India immediately prior to the introduction, in the 1960s, of tighter immigration controls on migration from New Commonwealth countries. The fourth was of *Parsis* from East Africa (mainly Tanzania, Kenya and Uganda), and also Aden, following the introduction in the late 1960s and early 1970s of Africanisation policies in these newly independent states. In the fifth phase, Iranian Zoroastrians also came to Britain from Iran after the fall of the Shah in the early 1980s.

There are currently around 6,000 Zoroastrians in the UK. The Registrar General's list for England and Wales does not record Zoroastrian places of worship in a separate category and there is only one place of worship in the UK recorded in the directory, this being the room at Zoroastrian House. Globally, there are approximately 150,000 Zoroastrians, mainly in Iran, India (mainly Bombay and Gujarat state), Pakistan, Britain, North America and Australia.

Zoroastrians with family roots in India, whether directly from India or via East Africa, have *Parsi* Gujarati as their mother tongue. Zoroastrians with an Iranian family background, Persian or Farsi is their mother tongue, although most of the young generation are fluent in English. Zoroastrian prayers are said in the ancient Iranian languages of Avestan and Pahlavi.

ORIGINS AND DEVELOPMENT OF ZOROASTRIANISM

Zarathushtra

The term Zoroastrianism comes from the Greek form (Zoroaster) of the name Zarathushtra, who is the founder of the religion. The religion is also known as *Zarathushtrianism* from the Iranian form of his name, or as *Mazdayasni Zarathushtri* after Ahura Mazda (the Wise Lord), the supreme Creator of the spiritual and physical world.

The precise dates of Zarathushtra's life are subject to considerable debate. Estimates range generally from 1,700BCE to 600BCE, with some of the Zoroastrian community arguing for an earlier date of 6000BCE and many academics for a second millenium one.

Zarathushtra lived in Eastern Iran and was a priest of the old religion of the country. Zoroastrians believe that his life was characterised by ordeals and that at a young age he went to live a solitary life of meditation in the countryside.

It is believed that his first vision came to him at the age of thirty. He spent the following forty-seven years of his life spreading a message in which he denounced the *daevas* (the former gods of some of the Indo-Iranians which Zarathushtra saw as demonic spirits); he proclaimed worship of Ahura Mazda as the source of *asha* (truth, righteousness, order, justice) and *vohu manah* (good mind); and he called people to the threefold ethic of *humata* (good thoughts), *hukhta* (good words) and *hvarshta* (good deeds).

His teaching was accepted by the Iranian king Vishtaspa of the Kayanian dynasty, although he faced considerable opposition to his teaching aroused by supporters of the existing polytheistic religious structures.

History and Influence

For over a thousand years the religion flourished in Iran. Precisely how Zoroastrianism became the imperial religion of three successive Iranian Empires is unclear, but in various forms of development it became the religion of: the Achaemenids (559-331 BCE); the Parthians (third century BCE - 224 CE); and the Sasanians (224-652CE), who were defeated by the Arabs. Just prior to the Achaemenid period the *Magi*, whom Herodotus identifies as a priestly group from the Medes in the North West of Iran, seem to have adopted Zoroastrian beliefs and to have played a part in developing the religion's unifying role within the Empire.

It was during these years that Zoroastrianism is believed to have influenced post-exilic Judaism under the Archaemenid Emperors Cyrus and Darius. Zoroastrianism is also thought to have influenced Greek philosophers such as Plato, Pythagorus and Aristotle as well as the *Mahayana* Buddhism of Emperor Ashoka in the East.

The Parsis

In the tenth century CE some Zoroastrians from Khorasan, a province in North Eastern Iran, left Iran following the Arab conquest, seeking their own religious and economic freedom. They became established at Sanjan in Gujarat, North West India, in 936CE. This community became known as the *Parsis* or *Parsees*, Pars being the name of a province of Iran. Those remaining in Persia became known as the *Irani Zardushtis*, or simply as *Iranis*. Over the next thousand years many more Zoroastrians emigrated to India due to religious persecution in Iran, and because of this, many Zoroastrians consider India as their adopted homeland..

SOURCES OF ZOROASTRIAN BELIEFS AND PRACTICES

Oral Transmission

The main body of Zoroastrian scripture is known as the *Avesta* and it historically consisted of twenty-one books, the contents of which were originally transmitted for many centuries from generation to generation in an oral tradition and were only written down by the fifth or sixth century CE in a specially composed Avestan alphabet. Only about one eighth of these texts survive in their original form. These include the *Gathas* (hymns) of Zarathushtra.

Zoroastrian Scriptures

The Zoroastrian scriptures may, in their present form, be classified into five divisions:

Yasna and Gathas

Act of worship, consisting of prayers and praises. It is divided into seventy-two chapters, which include the *Gathas*. The *Gathas* are The Divine Hymns of Zarathushtra and are metrical compositions which are used in the Zoroastrian *Yasna*. The *Gathas* are written in the ancient *Avestan* langauge and are difficult to translate today since some words in the *Gathas* only appear in these sources and nowhere else. Sometimes, therefore, one can only gain an approximate sense of their meaning.

The *Gathas* are now divided into five sections. consisting of seventeen hymns in all: *Ahunavaiti Gatha* (*Yasna* chapters 28-30); *Ushtavaiti Gatha* (*Yasna* chapters 43-46); *Spenta-Mainyu Gatha* (*Yasna* chapters 47-50); *Vohukshathra Gatha* (*Yasna* chapter 51); *Vahishtoisht Gatha* (*Yasna* chapter 53).

The Yashts

These contain prose and verse addressed to individual *yazatas/yazads* (adorable beings worthy of worship).

The Vendidad (or Videvdat)

This is the "Law Against the Demons", which specifies in detail the laws of purity, and also contains divergent material such as the account of creation; the geography of *Airyana Vaeja* (the Aryan expanse); the legend of a golden age; legal matters; and the Revelation of Zarathushtra.

Visperad

This contains invocation and offerings of homage to "all the Lords" (*Vispe Ratavo*). It is a collection of supplements to the *Yasna*.

Khordeh Avesta

A short extract from the entire *Avesta* which consists of: *Nyayeshes*, which are praises to the elements - *Khorshed* (sun), *Meher* (the heavenly light and contract), *Mahabokhta* (the moon), *Avan* (water) and *Adar* (fire); the *Afrinagan* and *Afrins*, which are blessings; the *Gahs*, which are prayers to the five parts into which a day is divided; and the *Sirozah*, which contains twenty-two *Yashts*, invoking Zoroastrian *Yazatas*.

In addition, there are many texts written in the Pahlavi language, mostly in the ninth century CE, which reflect the later growth of the religion and its encounter with Judaism, Christianity, Islam and Buddhism.

KEY ZOROASTRIAN BELIEFS

Ahura Mazda

Zoroastrians believe that Zarathushtra introduced, for the first time in human history, the importance of the *Vohu Manah* (Good Mind). He taught human beings to think and reflect with a clear, rational mind, in order to dispel ignorance and blind faith.

Ahura Mazda (the Wise Lord or the Lord of Wisdom) is seen as the One Supreme, All-Knowing, ever-present, Creator of Asha (truth) and Vohu Manah (Good Mind). This All-Wise, Uncreated, eternally Good and perfect Ahura Mazda is seen as a friend to all and, in Zoroastrianism, is never to be feared by human beings.

Ahura Mazda is deemed to be extremely powerful, although in the world of conflict, not omnipotent. Zoroastrians believe that if Ahura Mazda was truly omnipotent then it would be within His power to prevent the forces of evil from attacking and afflicting His creations, and this is not the case.

It is because of Ahura Mazda's relative

non-omnipotence that chaos, misery, suffering, disease, death and all the negative states are believed to exist in the world.

Ahura Mazda's power and greatest strength lies in his omniscience. The role of humankind is to make Ahura Mazda truly omnipotent through the cumulative power of good thoughts, good words and good deeds when, at the end of time, evil will be made totally ineffective and redundant.

Angra Mainyu (The Destructive Spirit)

In Zoroastrianism the origin of evil is seen as being other than in Ahura Mazda. In Zoroastrian belief, had Ahura Mazda created evil, He would be deemed to be imperfect, as is the nature of evil. Zoroastrians maintain that a perfect, All-Wise Being cannot create that which is imperfect. If Ahura Mazda had created evil, then He could not be worshipped as a God or as a perfectly good Being. By ceasing to be perfectly good He would cease to be God.

Evil is therefore seen as coming into existence as a state of excess or deficiency in Ahura Mazda's otherwise good creations. It is a state of moving away from Ahura Mazda, in the same way that darkness does not orignate from light but is the result of moving away from light. Evil is seen as parasitical on the principle of good and as having no part in goodness. Rather, it opposes good and is therefore irreconcilably opposed to Ahura Mazda.

The Purpose of Creation

Ahura Mazda, through omniscience, is believed to have created the world in order to tempt evil from its spiritual existence into the physical world. The Wise Lord knew that He could then trap evil in the physical creations in which humanity, His finest creation, would be able to destroy the forces of evil through the conscious ethical weapon of good thoughts, good words and good deeds.

The Seven Good Creations

The sky, waters, earth, plants, cattle, humans, and fire form the world of the seven primary creations. Zoroastrians believe that Ahura Mazda was aided in fashioning this world by the guardians of the seven creations who collectively came to be known as the *Amesha Spentas* (Bounteous Immortals). They also form the ethical framework which is based upon the recognition, by humanity, of the attributes of Ahura Mazda.

Spenta Mainyu is the guardian of humanity and the attribute of the Bounteous Spirit; Vohu Manah is the guardian of cattle and the attribute of the Good Mind; Asha Vahishta is the guardian of fire and the attribute of Best Order/Truth and Righteousness; Kshathra Vairya is the guardian of sky and the attribute of the Desirable Power/Dominion; Spenta Armaiti is the guardian of earth and has the attribute of Bounteous Devotion; Haurvatat is the guardian of water and has the attribute of Wholeness; Ameretat is the guardian of plants and has the attribute of Immortality.

The *Amesha Spentas* all have Pahlavi names as well where Vohu Manah is known as Bahaman; Asha Vahishta is known as Ardibehesht; Kshathre Vairya is known as Shahrevar; Spenta Armaiti is known as Aspandarmad; Haurvatat is known as Khordad; Ameretat is known as Amardad. They are also believed, in their turn, to have evoked *Yazatas* which are referred to as the adorable being worthy of worship.

Yazatas

The concept of *Yazatas/Yazads* is a unique on in Zoroastrianism since they are not seen as individual gods nor are they regarded as angels.

The origins of the *Yazadas* are pre-Zoroastrian. They later became anthropomorphised and were seen as fulfilling a dual role. First, they were seen as furthering the well-being of the seven good creations of Ahura Mazda. Secondly, they are believed to help human beings to realise the inherent nature of Ahura Mazda which encompasses an all-embracing happiness stemming from Wisdom.

Therefore, for example, Asha Vahishta, who is the guardian of fire, is assisted by Adar Yazad who is the *Yazata* for fire and Haurvatat, the guardian of the waters, is assisted by Tir Yazad who is the *Yazata* for the rains. Each Amesha Spenta is assisted by three or four *Yazatas*, as can be clearly seen in the Zoroastrian calendar.

The Role of Humanity

Humanity is seen as being Ahura Mazda's most conscious creation because of the *Vohu Manah* and is therefore His agent in the combat against the forces of evil. Ahura Mazda has given humanity the freedom to choose between the forces of good and evil. Human beings, therefore, are the makers of their own destiny according to the choices they make. Hence, at death, they are responsible and held accountable by the creator, Ahura Mazda, for all their thoughts, words and actions.

Some of the choices which confront human beings in this cosmic battle between good and evil are between good thoughts, good words and good deeds and bad thoughts, bad words and bad deeds; between happiness and despair; between optimism and pessimism; between joy and misery; between moderation and deficiency or excess; between truth and falsehood; between order and chaos; between light and darkness; between charity and greed; between life and death.

Zoroastrians believe that it is the *urvan* (soul) - the immaterial essence or directing principle of human beings - that enables human beings to make the choice between the forces of truth and of falsehood. The soul is believed to operate on the basis of wisdom, innate reason, intellect and will, all of which are understood to be filtered through conscience.

The Concept of Death and Afterlife

In Zoroastrianism, death is seen as the negation of life. Therefore, it is deemed to be the work of evil whose inherent nature is to wreak havoc and destruction upon Ahura Mazda's good creations.

On the morning after the fourth day after death, it is believed that the urvan (soul) is judged at the Chinvat Bridge (Bridge of the Separator). Depending on whether its thoughts, words and deeds were good or evil, the urvan either ascends to the House of Song (heaven) or falls down into the abyss of the House of Deceit (hell) which, in Zoroastrian texts is pictured as cold and damp.

Resurrection, Last Judgement and Frasho-keriti

After death, the sould and the spirit continue to exist in heaven or hell until the end of time. At the end of time, it is believed that evil will be completely destroyed by the *Saoshyant* (Saviour). The Last Judgement of all *urvans* will then take place by passing through "an ocean of molten metal", starting from Gayomard (seen, in Zororastrianism, as the first human being) and also includingd Zarathushtra and the *Saoshyant*.

The good urvans, which are like Zarathushtra, will feel the "molten metal" as "cool milk", while the imperfect will be cleansed before joining the blessed. It is then believed that this will be followed by a resurrection of the body which will once again meet its spiritual counterpart, the urvan.

Time will cease to exist and world will return to its original perfect state of total goodness and harmony known to Zoroastrians as *Frasho-keriti* (Making Wonderful). It is at this point that Ahura Mazda will truly become all-powerful, as evil will have been completely vanquished and made ineffective within the world.

ZOROASTRIAN LIFE

Zoroastrian Ethics

Zoroastrians are urged to live life to the full and to enjoy the good creation. Fasting and celibacy are seen as weakening human beings and lessening their power to struggle against evil. Moderation is encouraged. Zoroastrian ethics enjoin an active, industrious, honest and charitable life. *Asha* (truth/righteousness) is the central principle of Zoroastrian ethics and includes within it all virtues, and is to be used in conjunction with *Vohu Manah* (the Good Mind).

Initiation

Navjote (Gujarati for "new birth") or *Kushti*

Bastan (Farsi for "tying the *kushti*") are the names for the initiation ceremony of Zoroastrianism. The actions of a child born of Zoroastrian parents are held to be the responsibility of its parents until the child has undergone this ceremony. Although in earlier times the ceremony took place at the age of fifteen, it now usually takes place for both males and females between the ages of seven and eleven, before puberty, although exceptionally it can be later with the permission of the officiating priest. Friends and relatives of the child attend the ceremony which is a combination of prayer, ritual and celebration.

Before the ceremony can begin the initiate is given a ritual purificatory bath and is then invested with the *Sudreh* and *Kushti* (see below) and recites the *Fravarane* which is a declaration of faith said daily by Zoroastrians. The *Fravarane* begins with the words: "Come to my aid, O Mazda ! I profess myself a worshipper of Mazda, I am a Zoroastrian worshipper of Mazda." It praises good thoughts, good words and good deeds, and ends by ascribing all things good to Ahura Mazda.

Sudreh and Kusti

The *sudreh* and *kushti* are to be worn at all times by Zoroastrians. The *sudreh* is a sacred shirt which is always white and made of muslin or cotton cloth in order to represent the plant kingdom. At the bottom of its v-shaped neck there is a one inch square pocket which contains a slit. This pocket is known as the *gireban* or *kisseh-kerfeh* (pocket of good deeds).

The white of the shirt symbolises purity and the pocket reminds Zoroastrians that they should be filling up their lives with good deeds, but also that whatever good a person does, it is only one square inch compared to Ahura Mazda's goodness. There is also a *girdo*, which is a large pouch at the back of the *sudreh* and represents a storehouse for future good deeds.

The *tiri* is a small vertical dart coming out of the hem of the *sudreh*. There is also a small triangular patch on the opposite side of the *tiri* which symbolises the threefold Zoroastrian teaching of good thoughts, good words and good deeds. The

sudreh is always worn next to the skin and is seen as "the garment of *vohu manah* (good purpose)".

The *kushti* is a sacred cord which is worn over the *sudreh*, and is passed three times around the waist and knotted at the front and back. It symbolises "the advantageous path". It is woven from seventy-two threads of fine lambs' wool (representing the animal kingdom) which symbolise the seventy-two chapters of the *Yasna* (liturgy). The *kushti* is sanctified by special prayers at every stage of the weaving. Both *sudreh* and *kushti* are seen as a protection against evil.

By constantly wearing the *sudreh-kushti* the Zoroastrian is always in touch with the seven creations of Ahura Mazda: the sky above, the earth below, the water within, plants and animals represented in the *sudreh* and *kushti*, humankind in him or herself, and fire which is the divine spark of life itself. Hence Zoroastrians have always been environmentally conscious.

Namah

Namah (*namaz* in Pahlavi) is the general Avestan term for prayer which is seen as a spiritual weapon in the struggle with evil. For devotional purposes the twenty-four hours in a day are divided into five *Gah* (times): *Havani* (from Sunrise to noon); *Rapithwin* (from noon till 3.00pm); *Uzerin* (from 3.00pm to sunset); *Aiwisruthrim* (from sunset to midnight); *Ushahin* (from midnight to sunrise).

To prepare for prayer, Zoroastrians wash hands, face and feet, untie the *kushti* and stand, holding it before Ahura Mazda, focusing on the sun, fire, or even artificial light if no natural light is available, as a symbol of *asha*. Prayer is then offered to Ahura Mazda and the *kushti* is retied. The *Ashem Vohu* prayers consisting of three lines is the first prayer taught to all Zoroastrian children and is concerned with asha. It is followed by the twenty-one word *Ahunavar* or *Ahuna Vairya*, which in the Zororastrian scriptures is said to have been recited by Ahura Mazda when He created the world. This prayer is deemed to be the most powerful instrument of prayer in warding off evil.

Death

Upon death, the body is believed to become polluting since dead matter is understood to be within the realm of Angra Mainyu and could be harmful to the living. Because of this, it is believed that disposal should be carried out as quickly as possible and in a way which is least harmful to the living.

Disposal into rivers or the sea is believed to pollute the water and disposal by burial may pollute the land. In India and Pakistan, the customary system is therefore one which Zororastrians view as ecologically sound and consists of exposure in a *dokhma* (a confined building), also known colloquially as the "Tower of Silence", where the body is rapidly consumed by scavenging vultures and the bones are destroyed by the action of lime in a deep pit. Due to the presence of evil, entry to the *dokhma* is restricted to a select few and only a few are still in use in both India and Pakistan.

In Iran this practice has been discontinued. In the UK, when bodies are not flown back to India, they are buried at the Zoroastrian cemetery at Brookwood in Surrey, established since 1863

ZOROASTRIAN WORSHIP

Places of Worship

Traditionally, Zoroastrian places of worship are known as Fire Temples because a consecrated fire burns perpetually inside them. This was not the case in Zarathushtra's own time, but it was introduced during the times of the Achaemenid kings in around the fifth century BCE, although the reverence for fire within the Aryan tradition pre-dates Zoroastrianism itself.

Before entering the worship hall, Zoroastrian men and women must bathe, remove shoes, cover their heads when praying, and then perform the *kushti* ritual. There is a consecrated chamber where the fire is housed and into which only priests may enter. *Parsi* Zoroastrian worshippers may bow before the fire and take some cold ash to place on their forehead as a gesture of humility.

Fire

Fire (*Atar* or *Adur/Adar*) is used in many Zoroastrian ceremonies and many individual Zoroastrians keep an oil lamp burning in their homes.

This centrality of fire in Zoroastrian worship has led some people to describe Zoroastrians as "fire worshippers". This is, however, a misunderstanding. Zoroastrians do not worship fire but worship Ahura Mazda and venerate the *Amesha Spentas* and the *Yazatas*. Fire is seen as the creation of *Asha* and is considered a sacred force because it is a source of light and warmth as well as a symbol of truth and righteousness.

Fire energy is understood to be the source of all other energies and of life itself throughout the universe. Using fire in worship is believed to help Zoroastrians to develop the five senses of sight, hearing, smell, taste, and touch and through these to feel the presence of *Ahura Mazda*. This philosophy lies behind the *Atash Nyayesh* (Litany of Fire).

ZOROASTRIAN CALENDAR AND FESTIVALS

Calendar

The Zoroastrian view of time is a linear one which has a specific end in view with the restoration of all things to a state of wholeness and perfection.

The current Zoroastrian dating system began with the date of the coronation and designation of the last Zoroastrian monarch of Sasanian Iran, Yazdegird III, whose reign commenced in 631 CE. The letters "AY" are used to denote the year, making 1993 CE the Zoroastrian year 1362 AY.

The annual calendar is composed of twelve months with thirty days in each month. The twelfth month, however, also has five additional *Gatha* days making a three hundred and sixty-five day annual calendar. Traditionally, one month was added every one hundred and twenty years in order to synchronise this calendar with the solar calendar consisting of three hundred and sixty-five and a quarter days.

In the Zoroastrian calendar, the names of the

months correspond with the names of the *Amesha Spentas* and the *Yazatas*. Zoroastrianism views all days as special, but it does have a cycle of festivals.

With regard to the dates and times of these festivals the *Shahenshahi* calendar first adopted by the *Parsis* originally came one month after the Iranian *Kadmi* (ancient) calendar. Then the *Fasli* (seasonal) calendar was adopted by some *Parsis* in the diaspora and this calendar is now also observed by many Iranians too. The *Fasli* calendar has dates which are fixed in alignment with the Gregorian calendar.

There are therefore three calendars which might be found in use amongst Zoroastrians. When festivals are celebrated according to the other two calendars they have dates which vary in relation to the Gregorian calendar.

The majority of Zoroastrians in the UK follow the *Shahenshahi* calendar, although it should be noted that most Zoroastrians in the UK and the world tend to celebrate festivals such as New Year in all three calendars, therefore giving Zoroastrians a reason for additional celebration since happiness is seen as being part of Ahura Mazda's good creation.

Festivals

Religious festivals, of which there are various kinds, play a central role in the devotional life of Zoroastrians.

Gahambars (seasonal festivals)

Are a series of six festivals devoted to the *Amesha Spentas* and to the creation of sky, water, earth, plants, animals and people. These festivals traditionally lasted for five days each. They are holy days of obligation during which prayers are recited, and on the final day a communal feast is held.

The first *Gahambar*, called *Maidyoizaremaya*, is linked with the sky. The second, *Maidyoishema*, is linked with the waters. The third, *Paitishahya*, is linked with the earth. the fourth, *Ayathrima*, is linked with plants. The fifth, *Maidhyairya*, is linked with cattle, and the sixth *Gahambar*,

Hamaspathmaedaya, is a special festival in honour of humanity's creation.

The cycle is then completed by the observance of *No Ruz* (see below) which is devoted to fire. The dates of the *Gahamabars* vary according to which calendar is used and all vary in relation to the Gregorian calendar:

The principal observance at the *Gahambars* is the *Yasht-i Visperad* (the Service of All the Lords of Creation) which is a three hours long service commencing at sunrise and giving thanks for the creations and sanctifying them with rituals and sacred words.

No Ruz
(New Year's Day – Spring Vernal Equinox, 20th/21st March)

Is associated with the seventh day of creation and, in particular, fire and is focused on remembrance of the first incursion of evil into the world and the time of the final *Frashegird* (Making Wonderful). It is marked by the wearing of new clothes, the holding of festivities, and the giving and receiving of presents. The *Shahenshahi No Ruz* is celebrated in August.

Khordad Sal
(6th day after Nohoz)

Celebrates the birth of the Prophet Zarathustra. Among Iranian Zoroastrians the festival is known as *Zad Ruz-e Ashoo Zartosht*.

Zarthosht no Diso
(11th day, 10th month)

Marks the anniversary of Zarathushtra's death .

Muktad
(26th day, 12th month)

This is the name given to the final ten days of the year observed in *Parsi* custom. Among Iranian Zoroastrians only the last five days before *No Ruz* are observed. These days are in honour of the *Fravashis* and are usually marked by prayers and sacramental meal in honour of them.

During the last five days of *Muktad*, the five *Gathas* are recited and ceremonies are performed in Zoroastrian homes and Fire Temples. Vases of flowers are put around homes and Fire Temples to commemorate relatives that have died and prayers are recited in remembrance of them and for asll the souls of humanity since it is believed that the souls of the dead pay visits at this time. The Iranian Zoroastrians also call the first five days of this period *Panje-kas* (the Lesser Pentad) and the last five days *Panje-mas* (the Greater Pentad).

Jashans

Each day and month in the Zoroastrian calendar is dedicated to an *Amesha Spenta* or *Yazata*, except for *Fravardin* which is connected with the first month and the nineteenth day. In addition to obligatory days of observance outlined above there are other festival days when the particular days and months dedicated to the *Amesha Spentas* and the *Yazatas* coincide. Marking these days is not obligatory, but it is considered meritorious. The *Jashans* include:

Tiragan (or *Tir roj*, or *Tir mah*)
(13th day, 4th month)

A festival devoted to Tir, the yazata of rain and fertility. The festival overlaps with the second seasonal gahamba and on this day, people splash each other with water.

Mehergan (or *Meher roj* or *Meher mah*)
(16th day, 7th month)

It is an autumnal festival, dedicated to the *yazata* Meher, who is associated with justice and with the sun.

Ava roj nu Parab (or *Ava roj* or *Ava mah*)
(10th day, 8th month)

Celebrated as the birthday of the waters. Special food offerings and prayers are made on this day in which Zoroastrians go to water and give thanks for its purification and nourishment of the world.

Adar roj nu Parab (or *Adar roj* or *Adar mah*)
(9th day, 9th month)

Celebrated as the birthday of fire on which, traditionally, food is not cooked in the house and thus fire is allowed to rest whilst Zoroastrians give thanks for the warmth and light which come from it throughout the year. Special prayers are offered next to the house fire.

Sadeh
(26th day, 9th month)

An open air mid-winter festival celebrated with bonfires and held one hundred days before *No Ruz*. It celebrates the discovery of fire by Hoshang Shah of the Pishdadian dynasty.

Jashan ceremonies include the representation of the sevenfold creation by means of the display of a variety of objects. The sky is represented by a piece of metal; water is contained in a beaker; the objects are placed on the carpeted ground of the earth; plant life is represented by flowers and fruits; animal life by milk; humanity by the officiating priests; and spiritual fire by physical fire, fed by sandelwood and incense. Each of these items is ofered with specific prayers to their spiritual counterparts among the *Amesha Spentas* who are, in turn, believed to bless the offerings which are then shared by those present.

ZOROASTRIAN ORGANISATIONS AND PERSONNEL

Organisations

The first Zoroastrian organisation in the UK was established in 1861 and was known as the Religious Fund of the Zoroastrians of Europe. Later, having become The Incorporated Parsee Association of Europe, it obtained rented premises for meetings and worship and in 1925 purchased a building. In 1969 this organisation, by then known as the Zoroastrian Association of Europe (Incorporated), purchased a centre in West Hampstead, London. Since 1978, the organisation has been known as The Zoroastrian Trust Funds of Europe (Incorporated).

Although there are small numbers of

Zoroastrians elsewhere in Britain and Europe, the Zoroastrian Trust Funds for Europe (Incorporated) headquarters and centre is in London and is the focus for most Zoroastrian activity in the country. The building known as Zoroastrian House is used for worship and other community activities.

Personnel

A *Dastur* (high priest) or a *Mobed* (authorised priest) officiates at Zoroastrian ceremonies and may be helped by *Ervad Sahebs* (assistants to the high priest). When officiating, Zoroastrian priests are dressed in white and wear the traditional *padan* (piece of white cloth) over their mouths, in order not to pollute the fire while praying. The ceremony for initiation into the priesthood takes over a month and there are also different grades of initiation. However, in the UK since there is no consecrated fire temple in which this initiation can take place, the *Ervad Sahebs* (priests) are only part-time and voluntary.

BIBLIOGRAPHY

Berry, N, "Parsis: the Jews of India", in *New Society*, 22.1.88, pp. 14–16.

Boyce, M, *A History of Zoroastrianism, Volume I*, E J Brill, Leiden, 1976.

Boyce, M, *A Persian Stronghold of Zoroastrianism*, Clarendon Press, Oxford 1977.

Boyce, M, *Textual Sources for the Study of Zoroastrianism*, Manchester University Press, 1984.

Boyce, M, "The Sacred Writings of Zoroastrianism" in Hayward, M (ed), *Shap Mailing on World Religions in Education 1984*, Shap Working Party/Commission for Racial Equality, London, 1986,

Boyce, M, *Zoroastrians: Their Religious Beliefs and Practices*, Routledge and Kegan Paul, London, 1984.

Boyce, M, Grenet, F, and Beck, R, *A History of Zoroastrianism, Volume III*, E J Brill, Leiden, 1990.

Boyce, M, *Zoroastrianism: Its Antiquity and Chronic Vigour*, 1985 Columbia University Iranian Lectures, 1992.

Green, J, "Death with dignity: Zoroastrianism", in *Nursing Times*, 12.2.92, pp. 44–45.

Hinnells, J, *Zoroastrianism and the Parsis*, Ward Lock Educational, London, 1981.

Hinnells, J "Death in Zoroastrian Belief and Practice", in Owen Cole, W, (ed), *Shap Mailing on World Religions in Education 1982*, Shap Working Party/Commission for Racial Equality, London, 1982.

Hinnells, J and Writer, R, "Zoroastrians in Britain", in Hayward, M, (ed), *Shap Mailing on World Religions in Education 1986*, Shap Working Party/Commission for Racial Equality, London, 1986, pp. 21–22.

Hinnells, J, and Writer, R, *Living Flame: Zoroastrians in Britain*, Manchester University Press (in preparation).

Kulke, E, *The Parsees in India: A Minority as Agent of Social Change*, Weltforum-Verlag, Munich, 1974.

Mehta, T, "Worship: A Zoroastrian Perspective", in Hayward, M (ed), *Shap Mailing on World Religions in Education 1985*, Shap Working Party/Commission for Racial Equality, London, 1986,

Mistree, K, *Zoroastrianism: An Ethnic Perspective*, Bombay: Zoroastian Studies, 1982.

Traditional Mazdayasni Zoroastrian Anjuman, *Zoroastrian Calendar*, Newport Beach, California (annual).

Williams, A V, *Zoroastrianism and Christianity*, Macmillan, London, 1992.

Zaehner, R, *Zurvan: A Zoroastrian Dilemma*, Oxford University Press, Oxford, 1955.

Zoroastrian Studies, *Zoroastrianism at a Glance*

ZOROASTRIAN UNITED KINGDOM ORGANISATIONS

The two Zoroastrian organisations listed in this section, whilst based in the UK and having a UK role, also have a role beyond the UK itself.

World Zoroastrian Organisation

135 Tennison Road
South Norwood
London SE25 5NF
Contact: President
The organisation aims to: establish and maintain contact between Zoroastrians worldwide; advance the Zoroastrian religious faith; relieve poverty among persons of the Zoroastrian religion; establish charitable homes and provide grants for further education and medical treatment. It also aims to publish and assist in the publication of literature relating to the religion and history of Zoroastrians and to promote the study of, and research into, the Zoroastrian faith, its history and cultural evolution. Annual seminars are held.

Zoroastrian Trust Funds of Europe

Zoroastrian House
88 Compayne Gardens
London NW6 3RU
Tel: 071-328-6018
Contact: Secretary or Librarian
Place of worship. It is a communal centre for religious activities of Zoroastrians in the UK and Europe and is registered as a place of worship and for the solemnisation of Zoroastrian marriages. The organisation was established in 1861 by the likes of Dr. Dadabhai Naoroji who subsequently, in 1892, became the first Indian Zoroastrian to be elected as a member of the British Parliament. Since then it has served the Zoroastrian community's cultural and religious needs in this country. The association is a registered charity and helps the community with medical and educational grants and loans. It has over one thousand one hundred members and has regular contact with the inter-faith movement. As Zoroastrian House is staffed by volunteers, at non-office hours and at weekends, contact can be made with the following people:
Kersey Jasavada, Tel: 081-540-5401 (home);
Rusi Dalal, Tel: 081-997-2076 (home);
Malcolm Deboo, Tel: 071-286-1285 (home);
Jehangir Sarosh, Tel: 0923-241349/211168 (home)
Affiliated to the Inter Faith Network for the UK.

ZOROASTRIAN LOCAL ORGANISATIONS

NORTH EAST ENGLAND

NORTH WEST ENGLAND

ENGLISH WEST MIDLANDS

SOUTH EAST ENGLAND (NORTH)

LONDON (E)

LONDON (N)

LONDON (SW)

SOUTH EAST ENGLAND (SOUTH)

Since the Zoroastrian community in the UK is not very numerous or geographically widespread a range of contacts are given for each local Zoroastrian community. These are then organised according to the various regions into which the local sections of the directory are divided.

NORTH EAST ENGLAND

North East Zoroastrian Community (Newcastle-upon-Tyne Contact)
37 Kingsley Avenue
Melton Park
Gosforth
Newcastle-upon-Tyne NE3 5QN (home)
Tel: 091-236-3053 (home)
Contact: Kersi Fanibunda

North East Zoroastrian Community (County Durham Contact)
15 St Charles Road
Spennymoor
County Durham DL16 6JY (home)
Tel: 0388-815983 (home)
Contact: Jeerogi Kotwall

NORTH WEST ENGLAND

North West Zoroastrian Community (Darwen contact)
11 Prospect Avenue
Darwen
Lancashire BB3 1JQ (home)
Tel: 0254-705304 (home)
Contact: Maneck Mehta

North West Zoroastrian Community (Manchester contact)
5 Craigweil Avenue
Didsbury
Manchester M20 0JQ (home)
Tel: 061-445-7554 (home)
Contact: Burjor Avari

North West Zoroastrian Community (Sale Contact)
32 Noris Road
Sale
Cheshire M33 3QR (home)
Tel: 061-973-3535 (home)
Contact: Taraneh Zomorrody

North West Zoroastrian Community (Stalybridge contact)
48 Bank Road
Carrbrook
Stalybridge
Cheshire (home)
Tel: 0457-835486 (home)
Contact: Cyrus Jokhi

**North West Zoroastrian Community
(Timperley Contact)**

121 Wood Lane
Timperley
Cheshire WA15 7PG (home)
Tel: 061-980-1921 (home)
Contact: Shireen Khambatta

ENGLISH WEST MIDLANDS

**Zoroastrian Community of the Midlands
(Birmingham Contact)**

15 Pickwick Grove
Moseley
Birmingham BL3 9LL (home)
Tel: 021-777-55786 (home)
Contact: Mini Pochkhanawala

**Zoroastrian Community of the Midlands
(Coventry Contact)**

One Grange Road
Balsall Common
Coventry CV7 7AD (home)
Tel: 0676-33472 (home)
Contact: Thirty Kotwal

SOUTH EAST ENGLAND (NORTH)

Zoroastrians of Harrow (Harrow Contact)

11 Imperial Court
Imperial Drive
Rayners Lane
Middlesex HA2 7HU (home)
Tel: 081-429-1602 (home)
Contact: Rustom Bhedwar

Zoroastrians of East London (Ilford Contact)

104 Mortlake Road
Ilford IG1 2SY (home)
Tel: 081-478-8828 (home)
Contact: Filly Maravala

Zoroastrians of Harrow (Pinner Contact)

47 Rose Court
Nursery Road
Pinner
Middlesex HA5 2AR (home)
Tel: 081-868-2715 (home)
Contact: Mahiar Ardeshir

LONDON (E POSTCODES)

Zoroastrians of East London

109 Chestnut Avenue
London E7 0JF (home)
Contact: Keki Kanga

LONDON (N POSTCODES)

North London Zoroastrian Association

1 Salisbury Mansions
St. Ann's Road
London N15 3JP (home)
Contact: Faridoon Madon

LONDON (SW POSTCODE)

Zoroastrians of South London

22 St. Matthews Road
London SW2 1NJ (home)
Tel: 071-733-0925 (home)
Contact: Mrs Gul Rusi Billimoria
The organisation was founded in 1986. Its main
objects are to advance the Zoroastrian religious faith
amongst the Parsee/Iranee Zoroastrian community of
South London and to make and maintain contact with
them. It currently has approximately one hundred and
fifty members and membership is by annual/life
subscription. Non-members are welcome but pay
extra charges for some functions. Zoroastrians living
outside of South London are also welcome to join and
the organisation makes every endeavour to liaise with
other Zoroastrian organisations to ensure there is no
clash of interest and members can attend the functions
of more than one organisation. Activities involve
monthly social/cultural gatherings.

SOUTH EAST ENGLAND (SOUTH)

Zoroastrians of South London

West Wickham Contact
217 Pickhurst Rise
West Wickham
Kent BR4 0AQ (home)
Tel: 081-777-5778 (home)
Contact: Behram Kapadia

SOME OTHER
RELIGIOUS GROUPS

SOME OTHER RELIGIOUS GROUPINGS

INTRODUCTION

As noted in the earlier chapter on "Using the Directory", the directory's focus on nine world religious communities does not cover all expressions of religious life in the UK. The present chapter is therefore included in order to provide some outline information about, and signposting for making contact with, some of the other forms of UK religious life which do not appear in detail within the other chapters. There were , however, some religious traditions not currently included in this chapter which themselves requested not to be included.

Most of the traditions included in this chapter have some historical or doctrinal relationship with one or more of the nine traditions that form the main subject-matter of the directory. However, the precise nature of these relationships is often a disputed one, particularly from the perspective of the majority traditions covered in the earlier chapters.

The directory does not attempt to adjudicate on these disputes, resulting as they do from conflicting and often mutually exclusive self-understandings. But by placing these traditions in this section the directory is acknowledging the existence of the issues involved. It is also providing the reader with some information about the distinctive beliefs and practices of the traditions concerned of which it is important to be aware in order to avoid misunderstanding.

Only one tradition included in this chapter presents itself as being entirely independent of the traditions covered in the earlier chapters, and that is *Paganism*. Whilst some forms of *Pagan* organisation may be relatively modern and thus might be characterised as an aspect of the *New Religious Movements* which are not covered in this directory, *Pagans* in general understand themselves as representing the historically indigenous religious traditions of the UK. It therefore seemed important to include some information on *Pagan* traditions within the directory even though these are entirely distinct from the nine religious traditions on which the directory principally focuses.

It should, however, once again be stressed that this chapter is not an attempt to provide comprehensive information on religious movements, traditions and groups other than these nine traditions and communities. For this reason, after an introduction to the traditions concerned, only a single UK contact point is provided. This does not, however, imply that there might not be other UK-wide points of contact.

In this chapter, acknowledgement should be recorded of consultative assistance from the following people: on the Brahma Kumaris, to **Sister Maureen** of the Brahma Kumaris World Spiritual University; on the Church of Christ, Scientist, **Mr Anthony Periton** of the Christian Science Committee on Publication for Great Britain and Ireland; on the Church of Jesus Christ of Latter-day Saints, **Mr Bryan Grant** of the Public Affairs Office of the Church of Jesus Christ of Latter-day Saints, Europe North area; on the Jehovah's Witnesses, **London Office** of The Watch Tower Bible and Tract Society of Pennsylvania; on the Namdharis, **Mr Vasdev Singh Bamrah** and **Mr Surjit Singh Jeet** of the Namdhari Sangat UK (Sant Khalsa Spiritual Institute of Namdhari Sikhs in the United Kingdom); on the Sant Nirankaris, **Mr S Singh** of the Sant Nirankari Mandal UK; on Pagans, **Dr Vivianne Crowley** of the Pagan Federation; on the Ravidassis, **Dr Charan Singh Bunger** of the Shri Guru Ravidass Sabha UK; on the Sathya Sai Baba Followers, **Mr D Amirthanandan** of the Sri Sathya Sai Centre; on the Valmikis, **Dr Davinder Prasad** of the Maharishi Valmik Sabha, Coventry.

With regard to New Religious Movements and the Metaphysical, New Age, Occult and Spiritualist groups which are not generally within the scope of this directory, directory users are referred to the bibliography below and to INFORM. They could also consult a directory that contains good coverage of such groups and was researched with assistance from INFORM: Ward, G (series ed); Dandelion, B P (Associate editor for the United Kingdom); and Poggi, I (Associate Editor for Ireland), *Volume I: United Kingdom and Ireland, of the Religions Directory International: A Comprehensive Guide to the World's Religions, Churches, Denominations, Temples, Synagogues, Religious Organisations and Spiritual Groups*, Apogee Books, Detroit, Michigan, 1990.

INFORM (Information Network Focus on Religious Movements)

Houghton Street
London WC2A 2AE
Tel: 071-995-7654

Bibliography

Adams, D, *The New Times Directory*, Routledge and Kegan Paul, London, 1982.

Annett, S, *The Many Ways of Being: A Guide to Spiritual Groups and Growth Centres in Britain*, Abacus, London, 1976.

Brady, K, *The London Guide to Mind, Body and Spirit*, Brainwave, London, 1988.

Barker, E (ed), *New Religious Movement: A Perspective for Understanding Society*, Edwin Mellen Press, Toronto, 1982.

Beckford, J, *Cult Controversies: The Social Response to the New Religious Movements*, Tavistock, London, 1985.

Clarke, P (ed), *The New Evangelists: Recruitment, Methods and Aims of New Religious Movements*, Ethnographica, London, 1987.

Davis, C M, *Mystic London*, Lovell, Adam and Wesson and Co, New York, n.d.

Dyson, A, and Barker, E (eds), *Sects and New Religious Movements*, Bulletin of the John Rylands University Library of Manchester, Manchester, 1988.

Needleman, J, and Baker, G, *Understanding the New Religions*, The Seabury Press, New York, 1978.

Rodway, H, *The Psychic Directory*, Futura, London, 1984.

Wallace, R, *The Elementary Forms of New Religious Life*, Routledge and Kegan Paul, London, 1983.

Wilcock, J, *A Guide to Occult Britain*, Sidgwick and Jackson, London, 1976.

BRAHMA KUMARIS

The Brahma Kumaris World Spiritual University is a movement based upon the teachings shared by a Sindhi businessman of Hindu religious background born as Dad Lekhraj and later known by the spiritual name of Prajapita Brahma.

It is believed that Prajapita Brahma received a vision that the transformation of the world as we know it will be followed by the establishment of an earthly paradise from which competition, hunger, the pain of death and inequalities (especially between men and women) would be abolished.

The movement believes in the soul as the eternal identity of the human being which uses the costume of the body to express itself. The human soul also goes through birth and rebirth, but always in human form. God is believed to be the Supreme of all souls, an unlimited source of light, love and peace.

The movement sees the universe in a cyclic process of creation, degeneration and re-creation which could compared to the Hindu framework of *yugas* or ages. The recreation of a paradise at the end of each cycle is through the understanding and imbibing of fundamental spiritual truths that are universal to most faiths.

The movement's world headquarters are in Mount Abu, Rajasthan, India. There are local *Brahma Kumari* Centres throughout India and in sixty-two countries around the world. There are forty centres in the UK.

Students at the centres practice *Raja Yoga* meditation, the experience of the consciousness of the soul and the awareness of the eternal relationship with the Supreme Soul. Courses are offered in meditation and spiritual understanding. Other courses and activities include Positive Thinking, Stress Management and workshops on Inter-Personal Skills. Workshops and classes are also held in hospitals, prisons, in business, and for other special interest groups.

Early morning meditation classes are held daily and on Thursday mornings, food is offered to God which is then shared with everyone who is present. Regular students of the Brahma Kumaris are vegetarian, abstain from tobacco and alcohol and are celibate.

Most centres outside of India are run by people who are working and who devote their free time to teaching meditation. At larger centres, some full time teachers are required who would then lead a "surrendered" spiritual life. There is no membership, but people attend centres as regular students and also help with teaching and other duties, sometimes within a few months of studying.

The *Brahma Kumaris* are a Non-Governmental Organisation affiliated to the United Nations and also have consultative status with the United Nations Economic and Social Council and UNICEF. In this capacity they have organised two international projects: the Million Minutes for Peace and Global Co-Operation for a Better World, which reached one hundred and twenty-nine oountries.

Brahma Kumaris World Spiritual University

Global Co-Operation House
65 Pound Lane,
London NW10 2HH
Tel: 081-459-1400
Fax: 081-451-6480

Bibliography

Babb, L A, *Redemptive Encounters: Three Modern Styles in the Hindu Traditions*, University of California Press, Berkeley, 1986.

CHRISTIAN SCIENTISTS

The *Christian Science* movement was founded by Mary Baker Eddy, born in New Hampshire, in the United States, in 1821. The Church of Christ, Scientist, was incorporated with a charter in 1879. It sought to restore what it understood to be original Christianity and particularly the lost element of its healing ministry. In 1908, Mary Baker Eddy founded the daily newspaper, *The Christian Science Monitor*, which is still published today.

Christian Science understands its authority to be drawn from the *Bible*, and its complete teachings are set out in the textbook *Science and Health With Key to the Scriptures* by Mary Baker Eddy. A Christian Scientist's understanding of God and humanity is based on the first chapter of Genesis where it is recorded that God made humanity in "his own image" (Genesis 1:27). God, Spirit, is understood to be all-powerful, ever-present Mind, the source of all good. His creation is seen as spiritual, entirely good and free from sin, suffering and death.

Christian Scientists believe they find freedom and redemption from sin by acknowledging their God-given identity. They look to Jesus Christ as the Way-shower, the Exemplar for humanity, and they seek to follow his teachings and example. They understand Jesus as exemplifying the Christ, his God-given nature. They accept Jesus' virgin birth, crucifixion, resurrection and ascenscion.

The movement is organised in branch churches which are each expected to maintain a *Reading Room* in which *Christian Science* literature may be read, borrowed or bought.

On Wednesday evenings at *Christian Science* churches *Testimony Meetings* are held where people testify about the healings which they have experienced. The movement has *Practioners* who devote their lives full-time to practising the church's healing methods.

Church of Christ, Scientist

108 Palace Gardens Terrace
London W8 4RT
Tel: 071-221-5650
Fax: 071-229-8922
Contact: Mr J Anthony Periton
Office: Manager for Great Britain and Ireland

Bibliography

The Christian Science Publishing Society, *A Century of Christian Science Healing*, The Christian Science Publishing Society, Boston, 1966.

CHURCH OF JESUS CHRIST OF LATTER-DAY SAINTS

The *Mormons*, as they are often popularly known, are officially named The Church of Jesus Christ of Latter-day Saints. They claim to be a Christian Church and assert that there are three basic Christian positions.

The first is that of the Churches claiming an unbroken line of Apostolic Succession such as the Roman Catholic and Eastern Orthodox Churches. The second is that of those Churches which claim a *Reformation* was necessary to restore the doctrinal integrity of the Church. The third is the position of The Church of Jesus Christ of Latter-day Saints which is that there was an apostasy, but that what was necessary was a divine *restoration*, not a human *reformation*. Mormons claim that they are that *Restored Church* in these, the *Latter-days*, using the term *saints* in the *New Testament* sense to indicate a believer (as distinct from someone who has been canonised as a saint).

The Church was founded in Fayette, New York, USA by Joseph Smith who became its first president. He claimed that his mandate came from God, through an event which members call the *First Vision*. This event took place in 1820 and Mormons believe that it consisted of the appearance of God the Father and His Son, Jesus Christ to the young Smith.

In 1827, Smith published *The Book of Mormon: Another Testament of Jesus Christ*. This the Church uses as scripture alongside the *Bible* in its King James version. Two other volumes are accepted as scripture: the *Doctrine and Covenants* and the *Pearl of Great Price*.

The Church formally came into existence in 1830. Its first foreign mission was to Britain, in 1837, and its oldest continuous branch anywhere in the world is in Preston, Lancashire. By 1993, its worldwide membership was nine million, with one hundred and sixty thousand British members.

The worldwide governing body of the Church is the *First Presidency* (the President and two counsellors). They are assisted by *The Council of the Twelve Apostles* and by *The Councils of the Seventy*. Worldwide, the Church is organised into *stakes* (the equaivalent of a *diocese*), *wards* (organised local units), and *branches* (embryonic wards).

Government is through *priesthood*, with two orders: the *Aaronic Priesthood* (for males judged worthy of age twelve and upwards) and the *Melchizedek Priesthood* (a higher order for men aged eighteen and over).

The Church is well known for its missionary work. Many members (usually nineteen to twenty-one year old men) dedicate two years of their lives to serve as unpaid missionaries wherever they are sent. Members are encouraged to live by a health code known as *The Word of Wisdom*. This encourages healthy living and discourages the use of stimulants such as alcohol, tea and coffee.

The Church has *chapels* for regular public worship, but its *temples* are reserved for sacred ordinances and are entered only by members in good standing. Temples exist throughout the world, including one in Lingfield, Surrey and one planned for Chorley, Lancashire.

The *family* is viewed as of critical importance and its ultimate expression is believed to be found in temple ordinances for both the living and the dead. Members go there to receive their *endowment*, which is a course of instruction on the gospel and the meaning of life. Husbands and wives, previously married in a civil ceremony, go there to be *sealed*. This means the extension of the marriage vows beyond this life and "for time and all eternity". Parents are sealed to their children also.

Mormons believe that temple blessings may be offered to those of their family who have died. Following genealogical research, they extend the offer of baptism through New Testament-style proxy baptisms (I Corinthians 15 v 29). Proxy sealings are also performed. Throughout, though, the right to choose remains. Deceased ancestors have the full right to accept or reject ordinances performed on their behalf. Such baptisms are not recorded on membership records. *Mormons* refer to this proxy work as a "labour of love", offered freely, without compulsion.

Mormons differ from other Christian Churches in a number of other ways: they do not accept the teaching of the *Trinity* and affirm that the Godhead of Father, Son and Holy Ghost is made up of three separate and distinct Beings. They also teach that the Father and the Son have physical bodies. They believe in continuing revelation; that their Church *President* is a *prophet* who receives revelation from God.

The Church believes in good interfaith relationships and co-operates with other Churches in worthwhile social and humanitarian projects designed to relieve suffering and uphold Christian values. Because of what it perceives to be its unique position as the divinely-inspired restored Church it does not, however, participate in ecumenical councils, believing that ecumenism can lead to doctrinal compromise.

Church of Jesus Christ of the Latter-day Saints

751 Warwick Road
Solihull
West Midlands B91 3DQ
Tel: 021-711-2244, Ext 202
Fax: 021-709-0180
Contact: Mr Bryan J Grant
Office: Director of Public Affairs

Bibliography

Arrington, L J and Britton D, *The Mormon Experience: A History of the Latter-Day Saints*, Allen and Unwin, London, 1979.

Hinckley, Gordon B, *Truth Restored*, The Church of Jesus Christ of Latter-day Saints, 1979.

Ludlow, D H (editor), *Encyclopaedia of Mormonism*, Macmillan, New York, 1992.

Smith, J F, *Essentials in Church History*, Deseret News Press, Salt Lake City, 1942.

JEHOVAH'S WITNESSES

The *Jehovah's Witness* movement was founded by Charles Taze Russell, born into a Presbyterian Christian family in Pennsylvania,

North America, in 1852. After a period of religious scepticism, between 1870 and 1875 he became deeply enagaged in the study of the *Bible* with a group of six people.

He issued a pamphlet entitled *The Object and Manner of the Lord's Return*, arguing for the spiritual nature of Christ's second coming. In 1879, he founded *Zion's Watch Tower and Herald of Christ's Presence*. The Zion's Watch Tower Society was established in 1881 and, in 1884, the Society was granted a legal charter for "the dissemination of Bible truths in various languages" by means of publications.

Russell then produced a seven volume series of doctrinal works now known as *Studies in the Scriptures*. At a convention of the Society in 1831, a motion was adopted that they should from then on be known as *Jehovah's Witnesses* and the emphasis of the movement's activity moved increasingly towards witness in the streets and on the doorsteps of people's homes.

The local unit of *Jehovah's Witness* organisation is the *congregation* or *company* which meets in what are known as *Kingdom Halls* and are led by *company servants*. The *congregations* or *companies* link together into *Zone Assemblies*. These are led by *Zone Servants* who in turn report to *Regional Servants*.

Jehovah's Witnesses base their religious authority upon an appeal to the Bible in their *New World Translation*. In distinction to the historic Christian Churches, and on the basis of the *New World Translation* of the Bible, Jesus is viewed as "a god", but not as "Jehovah God". He is seen as the first creation of Jehovah. The spirit is also seen only as an active force of Jehovah and *Jehovah's Witnesses* therefore reject the doctrine of the *Trinity* which is found in the historic Christian Churches.

Jehovah's Witnesses refuse to salute the flag of any nation; they do not vote or hold political office although they are allowed to pay taxes. In times of war, they take a strict position of neutrality, eschewing even non–combatant military service.

Jehovah's Witnesses

Watch Tower House
The Ridegway
London NW7 1RN
Tel: 081–906-2211
Fax: 081–906-3038

Bibliography

Beckford, J, *The Trumpet of Prophecy: A Sociological Study of Jehovah's Witnesses*, Basil Blackwell, Oxford, 1975.

Watchtower Bible and Tract Society, *Jehovah's Witnesses in the Divine Purpose*, Watchtower and Bible Tract Society, 1959.

NAMDHARIS

The word *Namdhari* means "one who has the name of God in his or her heart". *Namdharis* understand themselves as Sikhs who adhere strictly to the teachings of the Sikh *Gurus*. At the same time, it is fundamental to their beliefs that Guru Gobind Singh did not die in 1708, but lived until 1712. *Namdharis* also believe that *Guru* Gobind Singh did not confer Guruship upon the *Adi Granth*, but rather upon *Satguru* Balak Singh and a line of *Gurus* following after him. This distinguishes them from the Sikhs who believ that there were only ten human *Gurus*.

The *Namdhari* movement began in India as a reform and protest movement with regard to the Sikh community of the day. They also played a significant role in the struggle against the British Raj.

Namdharis are strict vegetarians and do not use alcohol or tobacco. They wear turbans with a flat band across them. Worship and meditation are central to *Namdhari* life. Sometimes, their intensity of the chanting of hymns has led *Namdharis* to cry out for God, and because of this *Namdharis* have sometimes been called *Kukas*, from the word *kooks*, meaning "shriek" or "cry".

Namdhari Sangat UK (Sant Khals Spiritual Institute of Namdhari Sikhs in the United Kingdom)

96 Upton Lane
Forest Gate
London E7 9LW
Tel: 081-471-6826
Contact: Contact can be made through the Publicity Secretaries, Mr Surjit Singh Jeet, Tel: 081-555-7656, or Mr Vasdev Singh Bhamrah, Tel: 0902-332964

Bibliography

Ahluwalia, M M, *Kukas: The Freedom Fighters of Punjab*, Allied Publishers, New Delhi, 1965.

Cole, W O, and Sambhi, P Singh, *A Popular Dictionary of Sikhism*, Curzon Press, London, 1990.

Kalsi, S Singh, *The Evolution of a Sikh Community in Britain: Religious and Social Change Among the Sikhs of Leeds and Bradford*, Community Religions Project Monograph Series, University of Leeds Department of Theology and Religious Studies, Leeds, 1992.

Singh, K, A *History of the Sikhs, Volume II, 1839-1974*, Oxford University Press, Delhi, 1977.

Singh Sanehi, S, "Nature of Guruship According to Namdhari Tradition", in McMullen, C O (ed), *The Nature of Guruship*, Christian Institute for Sikh Studies, Batala, 1976.

Singh Sanehi, S, "Kukas as they live", in Webster, C B, *Popular Religion in the Punjab Today*, ISPCK, Delhi, 1974, pp. 30-35.

PAGANS

Paganism is not a single, structured religion. It has its roots in the ancient traditions of nature spirituality which sought to live in harmony with the cyclical and rythmic patterns of nature. The *Pagan* vision of the Divine includes both the male and the female. *Pagan* traditions pre-date Christianity and should be clearly distinguished from *Satanism* which is a deliberate inversion of Christianity.

There are a diversity of traditions in which some *Pagans* follow their own inspirations whilst others are trained in particular disciplines. These traditions include *Druidry*, *Odinism* (*Asatru*), *Men's Traditions*, *Shamanism*, *Women's Traditions* and *Wicca* (*Witchcraft*).

With regard to *Druids*, there are several different *Orders*. Many draw upon the Celtic traditions, but not all *Druid Orders* are *Pagan*. A Council of British Druids meets and discusses matters of common concern.

Odinism is found in many forms but is centred around the Aesir, the sky gods of Scandanavian tradition, and the Vanir, the Gods of earth and agriculture, both of which were part of the pre-Christian *Pagan* traditions of Northern Europe. Some *Pagans* within these *Northern Traditions* prefer to use the word *Asatru* rather than *Odinist*.

A number of *Men's groups* have been formed within *Paganism* to celebrate male spirituality by exploring male mysteries and initiatory cults, either ancient or modern.

Shamanism is extremely diverse, with some *Shamans* describing themselves as *Wiccan* (see below), *Druidic* or *Women's Mystery Shamans*. Others, however, emphasise the specifically *Shamanistic* nature of their path which emphasises the reality of the spirit world and the *Shaman's* role as an intermediary with this world or as a guide through it.

Women's spirituality has always been respected in all *Pagan* traditions where women are *Priestesses* in their own right and the vision of Goddess has always been present. Some *Pagan* women work within existing traditions whilst others have established their own traditions.

Wicca, also known by the name of *Witchcraft* or, simply, the *Craft*, is an initiatory path into communion with the powers of Nature and the human psyche aiming for spiritual self-transformation, in which men are intiated as *Priests* and women as *Priestesses*.

In Britain, there are four main traditions - *Gardnerian*, *Alexandrian*, *Traditionalist* and *Hereditary*. *Gardnarians* claim lineage from Gerald Gardner who was central in the modern revival of the *Craft*; *Alexandrians* identify with Alex and

Maxine Sanders who developed Gardner's ideas; *Traditionalists* claim their methods pre-date *Wicca's* twentieth-century revival and have been passed down to them; *Hereditaries* claim traditions passed on through relations of blood and marriage in particular families.

Pagan Federation

BM Box 7097
London WC1N 3XX
Tel: 0691-671066

Bibliography

Adler, M, *Drawing Down the Moon*, Beacon Press, Boston (revised edition), 1986.

Carr-Gomm, *Elements of the Druid Tradition*, Element, 1991.

Crowley, V, *Wicca: The Old Religion in the New Age*, Aquarian Press, 1989.

Crowley, V, *The Phoenix From the Flame: Pagan Spirituality in the Western World*, Aquarian Press, 1994.

Harding, E, *Women's Mysteries*, Rider, 1984.

House of the Goddess (ed), *Key: Information to Unlock the Door of the Pagan Community*, House of the Goddess, London (new edition), 1993.

Hutton, R, *The Pagan Religions of the British Isles: Their Nature and Legacy*, Blackwell, 1993.

Jones, P and Matthews, C, *Voices From the Circle*, Aquarian, 1990.

Matthews, C, *Voices of the Goddess*, Aquarian, 1990.

Matthews, J (ed), *Choirs of God: Revisioning Masculinity*, Mandala Books, 1991.

Pagan Federation, *Pagan Federation Information Pack*, Pagan Federation, London, (second edition), 1992.

Pennick, N, *Practical Magic in the Northern Tradition*, Aquarian, 1989.

Starhawk, *The Spiral Dance*, Harper and Row, New York, 1989.

RAVIDASSIS

Guru Ravidass was born in a low-caste in Benares (now Varanasi), the sacred city of the Hindu religion, in northern India in the first quarter of the fifteenth century. At this time, the religious situation in India was highly complex and the tyranny of high-caste society towards poor and low-caste people was very strong.

Guru Ravidass was one of the prime exponents of the *Bhakti* Movement, a socio-religious programme which aimed to reform society through the preaching of " *bhakti* (devotion) to God" and "equality of humankind" and that through this, God was accessible to all. Against this background, Guru Ravidass struggled for justice, equality and social freedom. This philosophy inspires *Ravidassis* to contribute to the creation of a classless society where all may live with equal rights and freedom.

Ravidassis who are settled in the UK strictly follow the teachings and philosophy of Guru Ravidass and worship *Guru Granth Sahib* since forty-one hymns composed by Guru Ravidass are included within it. There are approximately twenty-one *Ravidassi* religious associations in the UK called *Sabhas*. Each has its own *Gurdwara* are is governed by the umbrella organisation Shri Guru Ravidass Sabha UK.

Ravidassis celebrate Guru Ravidass's birthday as a major event, but they also show devotion and hold celebrations on the birthdays of the Sikh *Gurus* and other prominent saints.

Guru Ravidass Sabha UK

Head Office
Shri Guru Ravidass Bhawan
Handsworth
Birmingham B21 9EN
Tel: 021-554-8761
Tel: 021-554-1570 (home)
Tel: 021-523-9593 (priest)
Contact: Dr C S Bunger
Office: General Secretary

Bibliography

Cole, W O, and Sambhi, P Singh, *A Popular*

Dictionary of Sikhism, Curzon Press, London, 1990.

Juergensmeyer M, *Religion as Social Vision: The Movement Against Untouchability in 20th Century Punjab*, University of California Press, California, 1982.

Kalsi, S Singh, *The Evolution of a Sikh Community in Britain: Religious and Social Change Among the Sikhs of Leeds and Bradford*, Community Religions Project Monograph Series, University of Leeds Department of Theology and Religious Studies, Leeds, 1992.

Nesbitt, E, "Pitfalls in Religious Taxonomy: Hindus and Sikhs, Valmikis and Ravidasis," in *Religion Today*, Volume VI, 1, 1990, pp. 9-12.

Nesbitt, E, *My Dad's Hindu, My Mum's Side are Sikh: Issues in Religious Identity*, ACE Research and Curriculum Paper, Charlbury National Foundation for the Arts Education, Warwick, 1991.

Webster, C B, *Popular Religion in the Punjab Today*, ISPCK, Delhi, 1974.

SANT NIRANKARIS

Sant Nirankaris understand themselves as a spiritual regeneration movement which originated in the Panjab and advocates the supremacy of one God - Nirankar, meaning "The Formless Being".

They believe in the Fatherhood of Nirankar and the brotherhood of humankind regardless of race, colour, creed or religion. They do not subscribe to casteism and believe in equality and responsible living in accordance with the guidelines given by a living *Guru* (spiritual Teacher and Guide) who is Baba Hardev Singh.

The movement is known as Sant Nirankari Mission or Nirankari Mission/Universal Brotherhood. *Nirankaris* are thus worshippers of Nirankar and respect all religions. Its largest following is in India where the followers come from various religions, stations and walks of life. Its international headquarters is in Delhi which is also the seat of its spiritual Head Teacher.

In the UK the Mission is a registered charity in the name of Saint Nirankari Mandal UK and there are twenty-two branches.

Sant Nirankari Mandal UK

217-218 Cheshire Road
Smethwick
Warley
West Midlands B67 6DG
Contact: Mr S Singh
Office: General Secretary

Bibliography

Kalsi, S Singh, *The Evolution of a Sikh Community in Britain: Religious and Social Change Among the Sikhs of Leeds and Bradford*, Community Religions Project Monograph Series, University of Leeds Department of Theology and Religious Studies, Leeds, 1992.

Seekree, H S, "The Sant Nirankaris", in Webster, C B, *Popular Religion in the Punjab Today*, ISPCK, Delhi, 1974, pp. 26-29.

SATHYA SAI BABA FOLLOWERS

The Hindu tradition is a broad and varied one in which a variety of new forms have developed and emerged, often related to individual leaders seen as *gurus*. Members of the Sai Baba Fellowship are followers of the living *guru* Sathya Sai Baba, born in India in 1926, as Satyanarayana. In 1940, he claimed to be the reincarnation of Shiroli Sai Baba who was a much revered holy person who had lived some years before in the town of Shirdi in Maharashtra.

Sathya Sai Baba's reputation grew rapidly on the basis of a series of remarkable happenings believed by his followers to be miracles. In 1963, he revealed that he was also the Hindu deities Shiva and Shakti in an embodied form. His followers believe that he has come to initiate the *Sai Age* and call him *Bhagwan* (meaning God). His message is presented as universalistic and non-sectarian in scope.

In India, there is a main *ashram* at Puttaparthi in Andhra Pradesh, where Sathya Sai Baba was born. The *ashram* is known as Prashanti Nilayam. In the UK devotees gather regularly for *bhajans* (singing of devotional songs), often in private houses. Many of the *bhajans* are addressed to Sathya Sai Baba himself and are followed by a period of silent meditation. The movement is based on spiritual education and selfless service activities.

Sri Sathya Sai Centre

62 Herns Lane
Welwyn Garden City
Hertfordshire AL7 2AH
Tel: 0707-326314
Contact: Mr D Amirthanandan
Office: Information Officer

Bibliography

Babb, L A, *Redemptive Encounters: Three Modern Styles in the Hindu Tradition*, University of California Press, Berkeley, 1986.

Bowen, D, *The Sathya Sai Baba Community in Bradford: Its Origin and Development, Religious Beliefs and Practices*, Community Religions Project Monograph Series, University of Leeds, Leeds, 1988.

Kanu, V, *Sai Baba - God Incarnate*, Sawbridge Enterprises, London.

Krystal, P, *Sai Baba - The Ultimate Experience*, Aura Books, Los Angeles, California.

Mason, P and Laing, R, *Sai Baba, The Ebodiment of Love*, Sawbridge Enterprises, London.

Rao, M N, *Sathya Sai Baba-God as Man*, Sathya Sai Baba Society, Trustin, California.

Ruhela, S P, and Robinson, D, *Sai Baba and His Message: A Challenge to Behavioural Sciences*, Vikas, Delhi, 1976.

Hislop, J S, *Conversation with Bhagavan Sri Sathya Sai Baba*, Sri Sathya Sai Education and Publication Foundation, Bangalore, 1978.

VALMIKIS

The *Valmiki* community derives its name from the Maharishi Valmiki Ji who wrote the world famous Hindu holy book, the *Ramyana*. *Valmikis*

believe that they lived in India before the Aryan invasion and had a very rich and developed culture. The foundation of their social life was based upon the philosophy of *dharma, karma* and non-violence and the society was not divided into castes. Hence, *Valmikis* do not recognise the caste system as formulated in the Hindu scriptures called *Manu Smriti*.

The main themes of the *Holy Ramayana* are based upon kingly obligations, parental authority, filial duty, wifely devotion, brotherly love, friendly loyalty, love and care for the environment and the whole creation. These are the values which are believed to reflect the spirit of the times and community to which the *Holy Ramayana* belonged. They also still form the basis of the *Valmiki* way of life here in the UK and all over the world.

Maharishi Valmik Sabha

St Luke's Road
Holbrooks
Coventry CV6 4JA
Tel: 0203-662845 (home)
Contact: Dr Davinder Prasad

Bibliography

Nesbitt, E, "Pitfalls in Religious Taxonomy: Hindus and Sikhs, Valmikis and Ravidasis," in *Religion Today*, Volume VI, 1, 1990, pp. 9-12.

INTER-FAITH ACTIVITY
IN THE UK

INTER-FAITH ACTIVITY IN THE UK

THE MEANING OF "INTER-FAITH"

"Multi-faith", "inter-faith" and "inter-religious" are now commonly used terms, but ones with varying connotations. When a society (or a particular event) is described as "multi-faith" what is usually meant is simply that it includes a diverse range of religious groups, and the stress is on the existence of this variety.

The term "inter-faith" puts the emphasis on a *relationship* between religions and the people who belong to them. Some people are concerned that a closer interaction between people of different religions will lead to a blurring of their distinctive religious identity. This can be heightened when "interfaith" appears as a single word, which may conjure up a vision of some new syncretistic religion (meaning, taking elements from various religions and putting them together in a new pattern with the intention of forming a new religion).

In practice, the experience of the vast majority of people involved in inter-faith activity is that it strengthens rather than weakens their sense of their own religious identity, while encouraging greater understanding and respect for that of other people.

As with all new developments, those who promoted the development of inter-faith relations were initially viewed with some suspicion by other members of their own religious communities. However, while inter-faith organisations have traditionally welcomed people with a wide variety of perspectives, the majority of those involved in inter-faith activity today are committed members from the mainstream of their religious communities.

The term "inter-faith" is in common use. However, the term "inter-religious" may also be employed, sometimes interchangeably with "inter-faith". Often, though, "inter-religious" is used to denote the simple state of encounter between different religions in a pluralist context whereas "inter-faith" tends to be used in circumstances which involve "dialogue" between the religions.

THE GROWTH OF INTER-FAITH ACTIVITY

For many centuries there has been contact of varying kinds between people of different religions. However, as an organised development, inter-faith activity in modern times can be traced back to the World's Parliament of Religions held in Chicago in 1893. This brought religious leaders such as Vivekananda and Paramahansa Yogananda to the attention of the Western world.

In this country, one of the earliest significant initiatives was the Religions of the Empire Conference, held in 1924 in conjunction with the British Empire Exhibition and was organised by Sir Denison Ross. The diplomat Sir Francis Younghusband took a prominent part in this and, in 1936, convened the World Congress of Faiths which subsequently established itself as a continuing inter-faith organisation.

In the last two to three decades the development and spread of organised inter-religious activities in Britain has accelerated, largely in response to the immigration, during the 1950s, 1960s and 1970s, of significant communities of diverse religious belief and practice.

The long-standing presence of the Jewish community and the more recent establishment of significant communities of Hindus, Muslims, Sikhs and others within British society has presented new challenges for the more established religious communities and social organisations, and also for the newer communities themselves.

In the earliest days, one of the main needs was simply for information about one another's beliefs and practices and a good deal of inter-faith activity was oriented towards this aim. This remains a continuing need, but since these earlier days inter-faith activity has expanded and developed in a variety of ways with differing goals, participants and forms of organisation as people from various communities of faith have responded to the challenge of a multi-faith society.

The Inter Faith Network for the United Kingdom's *Statement on Inter-Religious Relations* has drawn attention to the variety of motives which exist for inter-faith activity: "Some will see the impulse towards inter-religious relations as springing from the imperatives of their religion; some understand these relations primarily as a means towards social harmony; some as a route for securing greater social and religious acceptance; some as a means through which they can share their faith; and some in order to gain a better understanding and appreciation of another religious tradition."

Some inter-faith organisations are primarily based on individual membership (eg the World Congress of Faiths) whilst others link institutions and organisations (eg the Inter Faith Network for the United Kingdom). Some inter-faith work is specifically geared to social and political issues (eg that of the World Conference on Religion and Peace) while in other cases the focus is on prayer and worship (eg the Week of Prayer for World Peace).

Inter-faith activity can involve all the major religions or it can revolve around particular relationships. So, for example, the World Congress of Faiths organises multi-lateral events whereas the Council of Christians and Jews focuses principally on the special issues which arise in the relationships between Christians and Jews in the light of their past history. Increasingly, a range of bodies whose main focus is not in itself upon inter-faith relations are building an inter-faith dimension into their work in recognition of its growing significance and relevance to a wide range of causes and activities.

THE INTER FAITH NETWORK: AN INSTITUTIONAL LINK

The Inter Faith Network for the United Kingdom was established in 1987. It links seventy organisations in four categories of affiliation: representative bodies from within the main world religious communities in this country (eg the Council of Churches for Britain and Ireland, the National Council of Hindu Temples, the Buddhist Society); national inter-faith organisations (eg the Council of Christians and Jews and the World Congress of Faiths); local inter-faith groups (eg the

Wolverhampton Inter-Faith Group and the Leeds Concord Interfaith Society); and study centres and academic bodies concerned with the study of religions and the relationships between them (eg the Community Religions Project of Leeds University and the Religious Education Council).

The aim of the Network is "to advance public knowledge and mutual understanding of the teachings, traditions and practices of different faith communities in Britain, including an awareness both of their distinctive features and of their common ground and to promote good relations between persons of different religious faiths."

The Network provides information and advice on inter-faith matters and on establishing contacts with religious communities in Britain. It holds regular national and regional meetings and has organised seminars on particular issues and projects, for example the blasphemy laws.

It is a forum for information, exchange and meeting to promote mutual understanding; it is not a body which seeks to represent the views and positions of its affiliated organisations to others. On occasion, however, its officers have issued statements in relation to important issues and events which have a direct bearing on inter-religious relations in the UK, such as the Gulf War.

It has also produced a *Statement on Inter-Religious Relations*, endorsed by all of its affiliated organisations, which is the first broadly based multi-lateral statement of its kind in Britain. In 1993 it issued a short code of conduct on *Building Good Relations Between People of Different Faiths and Beliefs*, also endorsed by all its affiliated organisations, together with a longer document entitled *Mission, Dialogue and Inter-Religious Encounter*. The Code is reproduced in an annexe to this chapter.

The Network's association with the Multi Faith Directory Research Project which led to the publication of this directory is part of its aim to encourage and facilitate the contact between different religious communities and their members.

WORLD CONGRESS OF FAITHS: THE INTER FAITH FELLOWSHIP

The World Congress of Faiths (WCF) was founded in 1936 on the initiative of Sir Francis Younghusband who, on a military-diplomatic mission to Tibet in 1903, had a mystical experience of the unity of all peoples. He convened a "Congress" of people of different religious traditions from Britain and from overseas which met at University College, London, in July 1936 and led to the setting up of a continuing organisation.

Its aims are to create understanding and a sense of unity between the religious traditions of the world and among the various religious communities, but not to promote a new, syncretistic religion. The organisation is based on individual rather than organisational membership and is open to "seekers" as well as to those who are firmly rooted in a particular religious tradition.

The WCF sponsors a range of conferences and lectures and also publishes the journal, *World Faiths Encounter*. In conjunction with other organisations it is hoping to establish an International Interfaith Centre in Oxford.

OTHER INTER-FAITH ORGANISATIONS

International Association for Religious Freedom

The International Association for Religious Freedom (IARF) has a claim to be the oldest inter-faith organisation in the world. It dates back to the 1900 International Council of Unitarian and other Liberal Religious Thinkers and Workers. In origin, it was a grouping of those religious believers who were committed to "free" or liberal religious values, rather than being a campaigning body for religious liberty.

Its historical roots lie in the Unitarian and Free Christian movements and these continue to contribute significantly to its work. From the beginning it was open to all who shared a commitment to liberal religious values. This is reflected in its present name, adopted in 1969, which does not link it specifically either to the

Unitarian or to the wider Christian tradition.

Today, the IARF's membership also includes organisations from a range of religious communities (eg a number of Japanese Buddhist organisations and the Ramakrishna Mission). The aims of its British Members' Group are: "to support the international organisation in encouraging free, critical and honest affirmation of one's own religion: religion which liberates and does not oppress; the defence of freedom of conscience and the free exercise of religion in all nations."

World Conference on Religion and Peace

Following a long history of attempts to convene a world inter-faith conference for peace the World Conference on Religion and Peace (WCRP) met in Kyoto, Japan, in 1970.

At this event it was agreed to form an organisation which would engage in at least four programmes: (a) to initiate inter-religious seminars and conferences at all levels in order to create a climate for the peaceful resolution of disputes among and within nations without violence; (b) to encourage the establishment of national and regional committees for peace; (c) to develop an inter-religious presence at the United Nations and other international conferences, through which the influence of religion could be directly exerted to resolve conflicts; (d) to encourage the further development of the science of inter-religious dialogue for peace.

A European Committee of WCRP was formed in 1975 following the 1974 meeting of the WCRP International's Louvain Assembly in Belgium. The United Kingdom and Ireland Chapter was also formed at this time. As its name suggests, the WCRP is centrally concerned with the resources for peace which the religions can offer in terms of their traditions and communities. This also involves dialogue between the religions aimed at overcoming conflict rooted in religious differences. The international body has consultative status in the United Nations Economic and Social Council.

Standing Conference of Jews, Christians and Muslims in Europe

In 1971 the Standing Conference of Jews, Christians and Muslims in Europe was formed as a result of the concerns of European Christian and Jewish leaders that their communities should have greater knowledge of each other and of the increasingly significant Muslim presence in Europe. There is a common agenda for dialogue among these three religions in Europe which arises from their common Abrahamic, monotheistic and historical inheritance.

The Standing Conference was formed with four main aims: to help educate ministers of religion; to provide better information about the three religions; to encourage religious minorities in their search for identity in a European setting; and to improve relations between religious minorities and the wider society. Branches now exist in Germany, the Netherlands and the UK. It organises regular gatherings in Bendorf, Germany.

CHRISTIAN-JEWISH RELATIONS

Apart from the Christian community the Jewish community is the world religious community which has had the longest substantial and settled presence in the UK. It is therefore not surprising that organisations specifically concerned with Christian-Jewish relations have a particularly strong historical and contemporary profile in the UK. Because of the history of relations between the Jewish and Christian traditions, they have a particular agenda to address.

In earlier centuries in Britain, as elsewhere in European Christendom, Jews suffered outbreaks of violence and episodes of expulsion. As was also the case with non-Anglican Christians, there were legal restrictions on the full participation of Jews in British social life which continued into the nineteenth century and Jewish-Christian relations were generally characterised by mutual suspicion.

An early attempt at the organised promotion of better Christian-Jewish relations was the establishment, in 1927, of the London Society for Jews and Christians. This emerged from an initiative of the Social Service Committee of the Liberal Jewish Synagogue and the Society continues to hold regular meetings today.

In 1942, partly as a response to the situation of Jews in Nazi Europe, a Council of Christians and Jews (CCJ) was formed. From the outset it secured significant support from within the religious and political establishment of the UK.

As set out in its present Constitution, its aims are: "to educate Christians and Jews to appreciate each other's distinctive beliefs and practices and to recognise their common ground; to eradicate the roots of discrimination and prejudice, especially anti-semitism, but also all forms of intolerance and racial or religious hatred; to promote the fundamental ethical teachings which are common to Christianity and Judaism." There are now over fifty local branches around the country which are linked to the national Council.

In 1946 an international conference of Christians and Jews was held at Lady Margaret Hall in Oxford and it was decided to plan for an International Council of Christians and Jews (ICCJ). Its tasks became all the more urgent as the full truth emerged concerning the Holocaust of European Jewry in the Nazi death camps.

For various reasons the Council did not formally meet until 1975 in Hamburg, Germany, although from 1962 onwards an International Consultative Committee of organisations concerned with Christian-Jewish co-operation was in existence. The CCJ in this country is a member organisation of the ICCJ, which holds regular international conferences and seminars.

LOCAL INTER-FAITH ACTIVITY

In the last two to three decades a range of local multi-lateral inter-faith organisations and initiatives have sprung up in towns and cities throughout Britain. This directory records sixty-two of such groups in the UK.

Although many local inter-faith bodies are affiliated to The Inter Faith Network this is not true of all. Those which are affiliated are not branches of the Network but are independent entities in their own right which in most cases were in existence before the Network was established. They have a variety of histories, self-understandings and methods of working.

The organisation's name can sometimes be indicative of this variety. Some adopt the word "group" in their titles (eg the Derby Multi-Faith Group). This generally signifies a more informal form of organisation and an individual membership rather than an attempt to be a corporate and representative body.

On the other hand, there are those which call themselves a "council" (eg the Leicester Council of Faiths and the Birmingham Inter-Faiths Council). These tend to be more formally structured and attempt to maintain a balanced representation from among the principal religious traditions. They often have a role in representing the concerns of their local religious communities to the local authorities and other public bodies.

Some of the local organisations (eg the Tyne and Wear Racial Equality Council Inter Faith Panel and the Medway Inter-Faith Group) originate in the work of local Racial Equality Councils. Consequently, these groups have a particular concern for the promotion of better community relations and an anti-racist stance figures significantly in their self-understanding.

Other local groups place a particular emphasis on individual fellowship and meeting (eg the Birmingham Fellowship of Faiths) and may also include in their membership people who are spiritual seekers. Still others have an accent on common action in pursuit of agreed social goals (eg Rochdale Interfaith Action which has had a particular concern for immigration issues).

There are also groups which have been formed in areas with less local cultural diversity but which aim to promote a greater understanding within their area of inter-faith issues (eg the Beaminster One World Fellowship). As with the local branches of the Council of Christians and Jews, some groups (eg the Nottingham Christian-Muslim Forum) focus on a specific bi-lateral relationship in recognition that this can have a particular agenda.

In practice most local inter-faith groups or

councils embrace a variety of motivations and explore various ways to relate more effectively and relevantly to the needs and challenges of their religiously diverse local communities.

RELIGIOUS COMMUNITIES AND INTER-FAITH RELATIONS

UK religious communities have been giving increasing attention to relationships with people belonging to other religious traditions. For example, in succession to the former British Council of Churches Committee for Relations With People of Other Faiths, the new Council of Churches for Britain and Ireland has within it a Commission for Inter-Faith Relations, and a number of its member Churches have their own committees which focus on inter-faith issues. These various bodies have produced material on issues which arise for Christians in a multi-faith society in both theological and social terms.

Within the Sikh community, a Sikh Council for Inter Faith Relations has been formed and other religious communities are developing ways of relating to the other religious groups whom they live alongside.

In some areas, local inter-faith activity has been generated by an initiative for outreach on the part of a particular religious community (eg the Westminster Interfaith Programme of the Roman Catholic Archdiocese of Westminster). Quite often, local developments have been initiated by Christians as ways of building links with the more recently arrived communities in their area.

For some religious groupings the search for religious unity is central to their self-understanding. They therefore have a particular emphasis on relations between different religions although their view of this relationship will naturally be grounded in their particular tradition's perspective.

These groupings include, for example, the Baha'is, who proclaim the "oneness" and hence the underlying unity of religions. They also include the Unification Church, which understands itself as working for the unification of human life and has sponsored the Global Congress of the World's Religions and a number of other inter-faith initiatives. A variety of "New Age" groups also put particular emphasis on the unity of humanity and its spiritual dimension and reflect this in their activities.

INTER-RELIGIOUS CO-OPERATION IN SOCIAL AND POLITICAL ACTIVITY

Increasingly, individuals and groups who are motivated by their religious commitments to pursue particular social and political issues have formed multi-faith coalitions for this purpose. For example, in the 1980s a Faith Alliance produced a Manifesto for Human Rights and Racial Justice that was signed by various leading British religious figures.

There have also been inter-religious initiatives in relation to the homeless, the disabled and refugees. In addition, there have been a variety of initiatives at the local level, for example in defence of individuals and families under threat of deportation from Britain.

In recent years there has been a noticeable growth of inter-religious activities within organisations that are not themselves constituted on the basis of religious faith, but which want to engage people from various religious traditions in support of their organisations' goals, in recognition of the more religiously plural nature of British society.

Many of the organisations involved in this development are concerned with issues of peace and justice and of the environment. For example, the United Nations Association Religious Advisory Committee has, for many years, produced briefing papers and other materials to support religious communities in observance of worship and vigils for United Nations Day.

The Amnesty International Religious Bodies Liaison Panel has furthered Amnesty's aims among the religious communities by holding an annual conference, producing relevant materials on religions and human rights, and by seeking the support of religious communities and leaders, both nationally and locally, for Amnesty campaigns.

Among the Panel's publications have been

pamphlets on *Religions and the Death Penalty*, and *Arguments for Human Rights from the World's Religions*. The Multi-Faith Committee of the Anti-Apartheid Movement has worked to engage followers of the different religions in the struggle against apartheid. It has sponsored conferences and produced a leaflet on religious responses to apartheid.

The Fellowship of Reconciliation, whose international organisation dates back to 1919, has both national and international branches. It is a pacifist organisation with Christian roots, but is now open to people of all faiths. Various Gandhian organisations are active for peace, and invite participation from all religious traditions in line with the openness which Gandhi himself displayed. The World Wide Fund for Nature is very active in ecology and inter-religious concerns and has sponsored inter-faith events concerned with ecology and produced books and booklets on ecology and the world religions.

WOMEN AND INTER-FAITH INITIATIVES

There have sometimes been difficulties in securing the participation of women in inter-religious activities and organisations, especially in events or activities organised on a representative basis and particularly where these have been at national level.

In the majority of religious communities it is men, rather than women, are in the positions of power and leadership. Within some religious communities there are reservations about joint activity involving both men and women. At the local level, though, women have often been the driving force in developing inter-faith activity.

In 1991 The Inter Faith Network, together with the Women's National Commission, jointly sponsored a multi-faith seminar for women which was held in the Cabinet Office. A second Conference was held by the Network in 1992 and plans are being made for a continuing link between women involved in inter-faith dialogue.

INTER-FAITH PRAYER AND WORSHIP

One of the first public inter-faith services in Britain was Sir Francis Younghusband's memorial service at St Martin-in-the-Fields, London, in 1942. Another early example was the service sponsored by the World Congress of Faiths at the Memorial Hall, Farringdon Street, London, in connection with the Coronation of Queen Elizabeth II who had requested that people of all religions should pray for her.

The Week of Prayer for World Peace is an annual event which seeks to engage people of all religious traditions in common prayer for peace. It was initiated in 1974 and is observed during the week in October which precedes One World Week itself. One World Week itself is sponsored by the Christian Churches and development agencies, although people of other religious traditions also participate in it, especially at the local level.

It is intended that religious communities should see the Week of Prayer for World Peace as a preparation for the subsequent week of action. A simple leaflet is prepared and distributed with prayers and readings from various religions of the world. Specifically religious events are organised across the UK in connection with both Weeks.

Inter-faith prayer and worship has always been a more controversial and difficult activity than common action towards agreed social goals or engagement in theological dialogue. There are those in all religious communities who have reservations about participation in shared worship or prayer while others will feel that they can take part on particular occasions without compromising their integrity.

The terms "inter-faith worship" and "inter-faith prayer" have been used to describe many different kinds of activity. For example, among Roman Catholic Christians in the UK a distinction has sometimes been drawn between being together to pray, each in one's own tradition, and praying together, which would be seen by many as syncretistic. Members of other religious communities have sometimes been invited simply to be present as guests of a particular community at a special event, for example, at the enthronement of the current Archbishop of Canterbury.

There have been moves to include, in a representative way, members of different religious groups within the community at national events, such as the Commonwealth Day Observance now held annually at Westminster Abbey, or in civic services at local level. Special meetings have been held to pray together at times of crisis, for example when Christians, Muslims and others met at the time of the Gulf War to pray together for peace. Special events have been organised to express concern for refugees, political prisoners, the homeless or the environment.

These inter-faith gatherings have taken different forms. On some occasions those present have been invited to listen respectfully to prayers and readings from different traditions, delivered in turn by members of them. Sometimes the focus has been on shared silence. At other times, those present have been invited to share what is said or sung, whilst taking care that what is contributed does not contradict or offend the beliefs or practice of the participants. It has often proved easier to organise events where people of various traditions are present at the service of another tradition and perhaps offer a reading or prayer, but basically within the framework of the normal pattern of prayer and worship of the organising and host group.

In schools, there is a legal requirement for collective worship, and in responding to the more varied religious backgrounds of their pupils, many schools have tried to develop materials which draw upon a variety of religious traditions.

The 1988 Education Reform Act introduced a statutory requirement that the majority of these acts of "collective worship" should be "wholly or mainly of a broadly Christian character", which many have felt was a backward step within the context of a multi-faith society. However, even this position does still leave scope for a variety of approaches. For example, schools can apply to their local Standing Advisory Council on Religious Education for a "determination" to vary this requirement in particular cases as when,

for example, a majority of the pupils at a school are from other than Christian backgrounds.

EDUCATION AND INTER-RELIGIOUS CONCERNS

The educational system and educational institutions have been a major arena for the development of inter-religious activity in the United Kingdom, but also for tensions and sometimes conflict.

Religions have a major concern with education and some of the Christian Churches as well as the Jewish community have had a significant institutional and financial stake in the publicly-funded educational system in England and Wales, as have the Churches in Northern Ireland. In England and Wales, the Anglican and Roman Catholic (and to a lesser extent the Methodist) Churches have been involved through the existence of voluntary aided and voluntary controlled schools in England and Wales, as has the Jewish community. Significant sections of the Muslim community are pressing for a similar recognition to be given to a number of what are, at the time of writing, private Muslim schools.

Inter-religious activity has developed in educational institutions partly because education itself involves a spirit of enquiry. Because of the role of schools in dealing with the coming generation, educators have had to confront issues that arise from the growth of religious plurality due to the educational system's pivotal role in shaping attitudes and values.

At the level of compulsory education, the legally supported place of Religious Education in the school curriculum and the especially sensitive nature of the subject, coupled with the local level determination of its contents through Agreed Syllabus Conferences and more recently through Standing Advisory Councils on Religious Education, has meant that much inter-religious discussion, debate and activity has been focused in this area.

There has been tension and debate over the nature of the study and practice of religion in education between those who wish to maintain the special position of Christianity and are concerned that too much attention to the multi-faith dimensions of society's life will lead to a dilution of the traditional place of Christianity, and those who believe that both the educational syllabus, and the practice of collective worship in schools, should develop in ways which reflect the increasingly multi-religious nature of British society. Organisations such as the Religious Education Council, the Standing Conference on Inter-Faith Dialogue in Education and the Shap Working Party on World Religions in Education have been involved in giving guidance on these issues.

In higher education institutions a number of informal inter-faith groups (eg the Stirling University Inter Faith Group) have been formed to bring together students from different religious backgrounds, often including students from overseas.

TOWARDS THE FUTURE

In its beginnings inter-faith activity was often seen as a "fringe" activity undertaken by people who were less central to their own religious tradition. But it is increasingly being seen as an important and necessary part of the life and witness of all religious communities in a multi-faith society. At both local and UK levels, new initiatives are constantly emerging and many secular bodies are also developing their consultative processes and their activities to take account of Britain's increased religious diversity.

The Inter Faith Network's Code of Practice, *Building Good Relations with People of Different Faiths and Beliefs* provides a framework within which religious communities can find helpful and constructive ways of living side by side and working together for the positive benefit of all, with mutual integrity.

BIBLIOGRAPHY

Abe, M, *Buddhism and Christianity*, Macmillan, London, (forthcoming).

Alexander, P S, *Judaism and Christianity*, Macmillan, London, (forthcoming).

Amnesty International, *Arguments for Human Rights from the Worlds' Religions*, Amnesty International, London, undated.

Amnesty International, *Helping Amnesty's Work: Ideas for Religious Bodies*, Amnesty International, London, undated.

Amnesty International, *Religions and Death Penalty: The Case for Abolition*, Amnesty International, London, undated.

Anees, M A; Abedin, S Z; Sardar, Z, *Christian-Muslim Relations: Yesterday, Today, Tommorow*, Grey Seal, 1991.

Barrows, J H, (ed) *The World's Parliament of Religions*, Parliament Publishing Company, Chicago, 1893.

Bayfield, T and Braybrooke, M, *Dialogue With a Difference: The Manor House Group Experience*, SCM Press, London, 1992.

Braybrooke, M (ed), *Inter-faith Worship: A Report of a Working Party*, Galliard, London, 1974.

Braybrooke, M, *Interfaith Organizations: An Historical Directory, 1893-1979*, Edwin Mellen Press, Lampeter.

Braybrooke, M, *Pilgrimage of Hope: One Hundred Years of Interfaith Dialogue*, SCM Press, London, 1992.

Braybrooke, M, *Time to Meet: Towards a Deeper Relationship Between Jews and Christians*, SCM, London, 1990.

Braybrooke, M, *Children of One God: A History of the Council of Christians and Jews*, Valentine Mitchell, London, 1991.

British Council of Churches, *Can We Pray Together?*, British Council of Churches, London,

Brockington, J, *Hinduism and Christianity*, Macmillan, London, 1992.

Brockway, A, *The Theology of the Church and the Jewish People*, World Council of Churches, Geneva, 1988.

Brown, S, *Meeting in Faith: Thirty Years of Christian-Muslim Conversations Sponsored by the World Council of Churches*, World Council of Churches, Geneva, 1989.

Cole, W O and Sambhi, P Singh, *Sikhism and*

Christianity: A Comparative Study, Macmillan, London, (forthcoming).

Council of Churches for Britain and Ireland, *In Good Faith: The Four Principles of Interfaith Dialogue*, Council of Churches for Britain and Ireland, London, 1992.

Coward, H (ed), *Hindu-Christian Dialogue: Perspectives and Encounters*, Orbis, New York, 1989.

D'Costa, G, *Faith Meets Faith: Interfaith Views on Interfaith*, BFSS Religious Education Centre, 1988.

Hare, W L (ed), *Religions of the Empire: A Conference on Some Living Religions Within the Empire*, Duckworth, London, 1925.

Houston, G W, *The Cross and the Lotus: Christianity and Buddhism in Dialogue*, Motilal Banarasidass, New Delhi, 1985.

Ingram, P O and Streng, F J, *Buddhist Christian-Dialogue: Mutual Renewal and Transformation*, University of Hawaii Press, Honolulu, 1986.

Inter Faith Network for the United Kingdom, *Statement on Inter-Religious Relatioons*, Inter Faith Network for the UK, London, 1991.

Inter Faith Network for the United Kingdom, *Building Good Relations With People of Different Faiths and Beliefs*, Inter Faith Network for the UK, London, 1993.

Inter Faith Network for the United Kingdom, *Mission, Dialogue and Inter-Religious Encounter*, Inter Faith Network for the UK, London, 1993.

Islamic Foundation, *Christian Mission and Islamic Da'wah: Proceedings of the Chambesy Dialogue Consultation*, The Islamic Foundation, Leciester, 1982.

Jack, H A, *World Religions and World Peace*, Beacon Press, Boston, 1968.

Jack, H A (ed), *Religion for Peace: Proceedings of the Kyoto Conference on Religion and Peace*, New Delhi, Gandhi Peace Foundation and Bharatiya Bhavan, 196

Jack, H A (ed), *Religion in the Struggle for World Community*, World Conference on Religion ands Peace, New York, 1980.

Jack, H A, *A History of the World Conference on Religion and Peace*, New York, 1993.

Marty M and Greenspahn, F, *Pushing the Faith: Proselytism in a Pluralistic World*, Crossroad, 1991.

Millard, D, (ed.), *Faiths and Fellowship: The Proceedings of the World Congress of Faiths*, held in London, July 3rd-17th, 1936, JM Watkins, London, 1937.

Moayyad, H, (ed), *The Baha'i Faith and Islam: Proceedings of a Symposium, McGill University, March 23rd-25th, 1984*, Association for Baha'i Studies, Ottawa, 1990.

Momen, M, *Hinduism and the Baha'i Faith*, George Ronald, Oxford, 1990.

Novak, D, *Jewish-Christian Dialogue: A Jewish Justification*, Oxford University Press, Oxford, 1989.

O'Neill, M, *Women Speaking Women Listening: Women in Interreligious Dialogue*, Orbis, New York, 1990.

Peacock, A, *Fellowship Through Religion*, World Congress of Faiths, London, 1956.

Palmer, M; Nash, A; and Hattingh, I, (eds), *Faith and Nature: Our Relationship With the Natural World Explored Through Sacred Literature*, Century, London (undated).

Simpson, B and Weyl R, *The International Council of Christians and Jews*, International Council of Christians and Jews, Heppenheim, 1988.

Taylor, J H and Gebhardt, G (eds), *Religions for Human Dignity*, World Conference on Religion and Peace, Geneva, 1986.

Townshend, G, *Christ and Baha'u'llah*, George Ronald, Oxford, 1957.

Weller, C F (ed), *World Fellowship: Addresses and Messages by Leading Spokesmen of all Faiths, Races and Countries*, Liversight Publishing Company, New York, 1935.

Wednte, C W, *The Wider Fellowship: Memories, Friendships and Endeavours for Religious Unity, 1844-1927*, Beacon Press, Boston, 1927.

Wigoder, G, *Jewish-Christian Relations Since the Second World War*, Manchester University Press,

Manchester, 1990.

Williams, A V, *Zoroastrianism and Christianity*, Macmillan, London, 1992.

Yates, G, (ed), *In Spirit and in Truth, Aspects of Judaism and Christianity: A Jewish Christian Symposium*, Hodder and Stoughton, London, 1934.

BUILDING GOOD RELATIONS WITH PEOPLE OF DIFFERENT FAITHS AND BELIEFS

In Britain today, people of many different faiths and beliefs live side by side. The opportunity lies before us to work together to build a society rooted in the values we treasure. But this society can only be built on a sure foundation of mutual respect, openness and trust. This means finding ways to live our lives of faith with integrity, and allowing others to do so too. Our different religious traditions offer us many resources for this and teach us the importance of good relationships characterised by honesty, compassion and generosity of spirit. The Inter Faith Network offers the following code of conduct for encouraging and strengthening these relationships.

As members of the human family, we should show each other respect and courtesy. In our dealings with people of other faiths and beliefs this means exercising good will and:

- Respecting other people's freedom within the law to express their beliefs and convictions

- Learning to understand what others actually believe and value, and letting them express this in their own terms

- Respecting the convictions of others about food, dress and social etiquette and not behaving in ways which cause needless offence

- Recognising that all of us at times fall short of the ideals of our own traditions and never comparing our own *ideals* with the other people's *practices*

- Working to prevent disagreement from leading to conflict

- Always seeking to avoid violence in our relationships

When we talk about matters of faith with one another, we need to do so with sensitivity, honesty and straightforwardness. This means:

- Recognising that listening as well as speaking is necessary for a genuine conversation

- Being honest about our beliefs and religious allegiances

- Not misrepresenting or disparaging other people's beliefs and practices

- Correcting misunderstanding or misrepresentation not only of our own but also of other faiths whenever we come across them.

- Being straightforward about our intentions

- Accepting that in formal inter faith meetings there is a particular responsibility to ensure that the religious commitment of all those who are present will be respected.

All of us want others to understand and respect our views. Some people will also want to persuade others to join their faith. In a multi faith society where this is permitted, the attempt should always be characterised by self-restraint and a concern for the other's freedom and dignity. This means:

- Respecting another person's expressed wish to be left alone

- Avoiding imposing ourselves and our views on individuals or communities who are in vulnerable situations in ways which exploit these

- Being sensitive and courteous

- Avoiding violent language, threats, manipulation, improper inducements, or the misuse of any kind of power

- Respecting the right of others to disagree with us

Living and working together is not always easy. Religion harnesses deep emotions which can sometimes take destructive forms. Where this happens, we must draw on our faith to bring about reconciliation and understanding. The truest fruits of religion are healing and positive. We have a great deal to learn from one another which can enrich us without undermining our own identities. Together, listening and responding with openness and respect, we can move forward to work in ways that acknowledge genuine differences but build on shared hopes and values.

INTER FAITH
UK ORGANISATIONS

The organisations included in this section are either organisations formed by individuals and groups in two or more religious traditions, or are sections of secular organisations, formed in order to engage the religious communities more effectively on a multi-faith basis in meeting the organisations' aims and objectives.

Amnesty International Religious Liaison Panel
99–119 Roseberry Avenue
London EC1R 4RE
Tel: 071-814-6200
Fax: 071-833-1510
Human rights organisation. The panel draws its membership from members of different religions. It campaigns against infringements of human rights.

Anti-Apartheid Movement, Multi-Faith Committee
13 Mandela Street
London NW1 0DW
Tel: 071-387-7966

Calamus Foundation
18 Eaton Square
London SW1 9DD
Tel: 071-235-0302 (home)
Fax: 071-245-6821
Contact: Mrs Saba Risaluddin
Office: Trustee
Informal membership group. A Muslim-led, pan-Abrahamic organisation, dedicated to building bridges of understanding between Muslims, Jews and Christians and to identifying areas of common concern where breakthroughs can be achieved by dialogue and joint action. It is a registered charity and is active in interfaith work. It sees women and diversity as important themes in its work.

Council of Christians and Jews
1 Dennington Park Road
London NW6 1AX
Tel: 071-794-8178/9
Fax: 071-431-3500
Contact: Mr Paul Mendel
Office: Director
A membership group which aims to educate Christians and Jews to appreciate each other's distinctive beliefs and practices, to recognise their common ground and to combat all forms of discrimination, especially anti-semitism. CCJ also uses its skills in the broader field of community relations and inter-faith dialogue. It seeks to eradicate all forms of prejudice, intolerance and discrimination between people of different religion, race or colour and to promote the fundamental ethical teachings which are common to Judaism and Christianity. CCJ is not a missionary organisation, neither is it a political organisation: the aim is to promote dialogue. It does this by: encouraging friendly meeting; educational work; monitoring the media; community education

and by working with other organisations. CCJ is a national organisation with fifty-five branches all over the British Isles and Her Majesty the Queen is its Patron. Affiliated to The Inter Faith Network for the UK.

Fellowship of Reconciliation

40-46 Harleyford Road
London SE11 5AY
Tel: 071-582-9054
Fax: 071-582-9180
Contact: Director
A national organisation committed to peace-making and effecting change through nonviolent means. It totally rejects war as a means for resolving conflict. Although an ecumenical Christian organisation, it has constructive dialogue with other faiths and is part of an international fellowship which is multi-faith. The Fellowship of Reconciliation (Charity No: 207822) runs education programmes, produces literature and campaigns on issues relating to the promotion of non-violence.

Gandhi Foundation

Kingsley Hall
Powis Road
Bow
London E3 3HJ
Tel: 081-981-7628
Tel: 081-668-3161 (home)
Contact: Surur Hoda
Office: General Secretary
Membership group. Its purpose is to promote knowledge of M K Gandhi and to demonstrate the relevance of his teaching to many of the issues of our time. One of the activities is to hold an interfaith service each year on 30th January which is the date of the assassination of Gandhi.

Inter Faith Network for the United Kingdom

5-7 Tavistock Place
London WC1H 9SS
Tel: 071-388-0008
Contact: Brian Pearce
The Network links a range of national representative organisations from within the religious communities of the UK; national inter-faith organisations; local inter-faith groups from around the country; and academic study centres and educational bodies concerned with religious traditions and the relationships between them. Its goals are: the promotion of dialogue between different religious traditions; the exchange of information and experience; provision of guidance and information on

inter-faith matters; preparation of resource material; development of links between academic and other institutions; organisation of conferences and the maintainance of international links. It does not attempt to replace existing organisations but is a service organisation for them, providing a central point of reference for information. It has published a Handbook of Affiliated Organisations. The Network is not based on individual membership but its services can be used by anyone seeking information or advice in the inter faith field. Its affiliated organisations are:

Representative Bodies:
Afro-West Indian United Council of Churches
Arya Pratinidhi Sabha (UK)
Baha'i Community of the United Kingdom
Board of Deputies of British Jews
Council of Churches for Britain and Ireland
  Commission for Inter Faith Relations
Buddist Society
Council of African and Afro-Caribbean Churches
  (UK)
Council of Mosques (UK and Eire)
Friends of the Western Buddhist Order
Imams and Mosques Council (UK)
Islamic Cultural Centre
Jain Samaj Europe
Maha Bodhi Society of Sri Lanka (UK)
National Council of Hindu Temples
Roman Catholic Committee for Other Faiths of the
  Bishops' Conference of England and Wales
Sikh Council for Interfaith Relations (UK)
Sikh Missionary Society
Swaminarayan Hindu Mission
Vishwa Hindu Parishad (UK)
World Ahl ul-Bayt (AS) Islamic League
World Islamic Mission
Zoroastrian Trust Funds of Europe

Inter Faith Organisations:
Council of Christians and Jews
International Association for Religious Freedom
  (British Members' Group)
London Society for Jews and Christians
Standing Conference of Jews, Christians and Muslims
  in Europe.
World Conference on Religion and Peace (UK and
  Ireland Chapter)
World Congress of Faiths

Local Inter Faith Groups:
Birmingham Fellowship of Faiths
Birmingham Inter-Faith Council
Bradford Concord Inter Faith Society

Bristol Interfaith Group
Cambridge Inter-Faith Group
Cardiff Interfaith Association
Coventry Inter Faith Group
Derby Open Centre Multi-Faith Group
Dudley Council of Faiths
Edinburgh Interfaith Association
Glasgow Sharing of Faiths Group
Harrow Inter-Faith Council
Kirklees and Calderdale Inter-Faith Fellowship
Leeds Concord Inter-Faith Fellowship
Leicester Council of Faiths
Manchester Inter Faith Group
Newham Association of Faiths
Nottingham Inter-Faith Group
Oxford Round Table of Religions
Peterborough Inter-Faith Council
Reading Inter-Faith Group
Redbridge Council of Faiths
Richmond Inter-Faith Group
Tyne and Wear Racial Equality Council Inter Faith
  Panel
Walsall Inter Faith Group
Waltham Forest All Faiths Group
Wellingborough Multi-Faith Group
Wolverhampton Inter-Faith Group

Educational and Academic Bodies:
Bharatiya Vidya Bhavan
Centre for the Study of Islam and Christian-Muslim
  Relations
Centre for the Study of Judaism and Jewish -Christian
  Relations
Community Religions Project, University of Leeds
Institute of Jainology
Islamic Foundation, Leicester
Multi Faith Centre, Birmingham
Religious Education Council
Religious Resource and Research Centre, University
  of Derby
Shap Working Party on World Religions in
  Education
Standing Conference on Inter-faith Dialogue in
  Education
Study Centre for Christian-Jewish Relations (Sisters
  of Sion)

Inter Faith Women's Link
c/o Inter Faith Network for the UK
5-7 Tavistock Place
London WC1H 9SS
Tel: 071-388-0008
Fax: 071-387-7968
Contact: Dr Harriet Crabtree

An informal "network" of women from different faith communities who wish to be in dialogue with one another is in the process of formation. Details about this can be obtained from the office of the Network.

International Association for Religious Freedom (British Members' Group)
41 Bradford Drive
Ewell
Epsom
Surrey KT19 0AQ (home)
Tel: 081-393-9122
Contact: Revd Peter Godfrey
Office: Chapter President
The British Members' Group of the International Association for Religious Freedom (IARF) was started in 1962 and its aims are to support the international organisation in encouraging free, critical and honest affirmation of one's own religion which liberates and does not oppress; the defence of freedom of conscience and the free exercise of religion in all nations. A weekend conference is usually held in September and an annual newsletter is published. Members also receive the IARF journal "The World". At the Unitarian Annual Meetings each April a programme is organised for those taking part in the Donate-One-Meal Campaign. Affiliated to The Inter Faith Network for the UK.

Jain-Christian Association
69 Rowley Fields Avenue
Leicester LE3 2ES (home)
Tel: 0533-891077
Contact: Dr Natubhai Shah
The association aims to promote the value of a religious and spiritual view of life with proper regard for the integrity of each tradition. It promotes the aims of peace, non-violence, reverence and kindness to all creation. It initiates meetings, conferences, discussion and action in furtherance of the above objectives. The membership is open to followers of either traditions. Members study and share each other's traditions and beliefs, especially areas held in common, without seeking to influence or proselytise. It has organised various meetings and a successful Jain-Christian Conference on Reverence for Life in June 1992 at the Jain Centre in Leicester where the Archbishop of York and Dr L M Singhvi, High Commissioner of India, were keynote speakers. It has helped to promote co-operation between the Jain Samaj Europe and the Diocese of Leicester in establishing a joint appointment of a full time Officer as Jain Centre Administrator and Inter-Faith Chaplain. The Venerable David Silk, Tel: 0533-704441 is also a contact person.

Linking Up

Manchester BSR
27 Blackfriars Road
Salford
Lancashire M3 7AQ
Tel: 061-832-5208
Fax: 061-839-3500
Contact: Mr Harshad Chauhan
Office: Project Officer

An independent national initiative offering a free advisory and consultancy service to faith communities in urban priority areas that want to contribute positively to local economic development in urban priority areas.

Network

P O Box 1993
New Barnet
Hertfordshire EN5 5DH

Support group for people in mixed Jewish and non-Jewish relationships

Standing Conference of Jews, Christians and Muslims in Europe

Blackfriars
36 Queen's Drive
Glasgow G41 8DD
Tel: 041-423-2971
Contact: Father Gordian Marshall OP

The Standing Conference is an organisation in which Jews, Christians and Muslims in Europe work together in dialogue. It consists of a number of individuals who are members of the three faiths, living in various countries of Europe, who take initiatives in setting up dialogue opportunities. There is no formal membership structure or a subscription fee. It aims to remove ignorance, identify and combat prejudice and create an atmosphere of trust in which members of the three faiths can work together, respecting and supporting the proper identity of each. It tries to introduce new people to dialogue and to encourage those with experience, by setting up meetings and conferences in Britain and other European countries (particularly at Bendorf in the Federal Republic of Germany). Such meetings give opportunities for exchange of information, discussion of religious and social problems facing the member communities, joint study of religious texts and traditions, and experience of each other's forms of prayer. Affiliated to The Inter Faith Network for the UK.

United Nations Association Religious Advisory Committee

3 Whitehall Court
London SW1
Tel: 071-930-2931
Tel: 081-458-3532 (home)
Fax: 071-930-5893
Contact: Ms B R Scharf
Office: Honorary Secretary

A body of members of different faiths who are invited to join in their personal capacity rather than as representatives or delegates. All are concerned to support the United Nations as a means of peace and a defender of human rights and religious freedom. Regular quarterly meetings are held to discuss issues of concern and prepare materials for religious celebrations of United Nations Day, 24th October.

Week of Prayer for World Peace

60 Childcross Road
Rainham
Gillingham
Kent ME8 7SN
Tel: 0634-363631
Contact: Revd Jonathan Blake

Acts to promote each year a week of special prayer for peace and justice in which members of all faith communities are invited to be involved. Produces and distributes leaflets containing scriptures, stories and prayers set for each day of the week, drawn from the world's spiritual traditions.

World Conference on Religion and Peace (UK and Ireland Chapter)

c/o International Institute for Peace and Global
 Responsibility,
Institute of Education,
University of London
20 Bedford Way
London WC1H 0AL
Tel: 071-652-1925
Fax: 071-652-1925
Contact: Mr Tom Daffern
Office: Secretary

The World Conference on Religion and Peace (WCRP) UK and Ireland Chapter is a growing membership group with a mailing list of one hundred and eighty. It brings together representatives of all Faiths to promote respect for each other's faiths and to work together for peace and unity within the human family. It does this by: meetings, chiefly in London, but now extending into other areas of the UK; a flourishing Youth Group which organised a Youth Peace Bus journey to Moscow and back in 1987 (of which journey a video is now available); co-operation with other peace groups within Britain and by maintaining close links with the international WCRP in Geneva and its United Nations office in New York (WCRP is a recognised Non-Governmental Organisation within the UN system). The WCRP International holds international Assemblies every four years, to which the UK and Ireland Chapter sends an inter-faith delegation. The UK and Ireland Chapter produces a regular newsletter with information on inter-faith activities for peace and justice. Affiliated to The Inter Faith Network for the UK.

World Congress of Faiths

2 Market Street
Oxford OX1 3EF
Tel: 0865-202744
Fax: 0865-202746

Membership group open to both individuals and groups. It is a national organisation with international links in many countries. Membership is open to all who seek improved relationships between people of different faiths. The organisation works at both a practical grassroots level and at theoretical/academic levels, identifying the values religions have in common and working to increase mutual understanding and respect in areas of difference. Activities take place in the field of inter-religious relations, working to improve understanding of inter-faith issues through a programme of conferences and other events. It publishes the journal "World Faiths Encounter" which covers and reflects upon inter-faith activity in Britain. Affiliated to The Inter Faith Network for the UK.

Wyndham Place Trust

Keeley House
22-30 Keeley Road
Croydon
Surrey CR0 1TE
Tel: 081-686-7171
Fax: 081-680-5895
Contact: Mrs Fiona Shipley
Office: Secretary

An educational organisation which brings together people of various vocations and specialisations, and those associated with a range of political and religious opinions and engages in research and educational activities.

INTER-FAITH LOCAL ORGANISATIONS

SCOTLAND

WALES

NORTH EAST ENGLAND

YORKSHIRE AND HUMBERSIDE

NORTH WEST ENGLAND

ENGLISH EAST MIDLANDS

ENGLISH WEST MIDLANDS

EAST ANGLIA

SOUTH EAST ENGLAND (NORTH)

LONDON (E)

LONDON (NW)

LONDON (SE)

LONDON (SW)

LONDON (W)

SOUTH EAST ENGLAND (SOUTH)

SOUTH WEST ENGLAND

Generally speaking, the organisations included in this section are groups which are not based in any one single religious community, but involve two or more religious traditions.

SCOTLAND

Dundee Inter-Faith Group
International Women's Centre
49 Lyon Street
Dundee DD4 6RA
Contact: Ms Janet Brown
Affiliated to the Inter Faith Network for the UK.

Edinburgh Inter Faith Association
17 Falklands Gardens
Edinburgh EH12 6UW (home)
Tel: 031-539-1583 (home)
Contact: Dr James Russell
Office: Secretary
Current members include Baha'is, Brahma Kumaris, Buddhists, Christians, Hindus, Jews, Muslims and Sikhs. Subscription is £15.00 p.a. for faith traditions and £5.00 p.a. for individual membership. Its patron is the Lord Provost of Edinburgh; eminent members of various faith communities are its co-chairs; and representatives from various faith communities are on its committee. The aims of the association are to: bring together the faith communities of Edinburgh in deeper dialogue and co-operation; increase the sharing and understanding between citizens of Edinburgh; educate the citizens of Edinburgh about the presence and importance of the faith communities in our midst; promote interfaith and intercultural awareness and understanding in the schools of Edinburgh; see interfaith co-operation in Edinburgh as linking into global co-operation between different faiths for the creation of a better world. Affiliated to The Inter Faith Network for the UK.

Glasgow Sharing of Faiths Group
International Flat
20 Glasgow Street
Glasgow G12 8JP
Tel: 041-339-6118
Contact: Ms Rosemary Eldridge
Office: Convenor
It aims to promote friendship and understanding amongst members of religious faiths present in Glasgow. The group organises an annual exhibition of seven religious faiths for schools throughout the Strathclyde region. Affiliated to The Inter Faith Network for the UK.

Stirling University Inter-Faith Group

Chaplaincy Centre
Stirling University
Stirling FK9 4LA
Tel: 0876-473171
Contact: Niall Leighton
Office: Secretary

WALES

Cardiff Interfaith Association

225 Lake Road West
Cardiff CF2 5QY (home)
Tel: 0222-750857 (home)
Contact: Dr Iraz Zamiri
Office: Chairperson
Includes representatives of Baha'i, Buddhist, Christian (Church of England, Roman Catholic, Baptist, German Lutheran, and Quaker), Hindu, Muslim, Raj Yoga, Reformed Jewish, Sikh, Theosophist and Unitarian religious traditions. In addition, some attenders are humanists, seekers and agnostics, and there is a representative of the United Nations Association. It exists to bring people of different religious backgrounds together. It endeavours to foster fellowship and friendship and is a non–political, non–proselytising society. It works through a programme of events in which members are enabled to share their aspirations and beliefs and discover their common ground. This includes talks, workshops, social events and an annual service. An annual programme leaflet is produced. Affiliated to The Inter Faith Network for the UK.

Newport Interfaith Group

15 Bryngwyn Road
Newport NP9 4JS (home)
Tel: 0633-267367 (home)
Contact: Mrs Ingrid Wilson
Office: Secretary
A group of ordinary people who come together approximately every six weeks to share their ideas in a spirit of fellowship and mutual respect for each other's beliefs. Activities include discussions, friendship and visits. A public event is held annually to create further opportunities for bringing people of different faiths or none close together.

Swansea Inter-Faith Group

"The Gables"
48 King Edward Road
Brynmill
Swansea SA1 4LN (home)
Tel: 0792-648366 (home)

Contact: Mr Trevor McGairl
Office: Co-chair
A membership group which meets at the Swansea Friends Meeting House six times a year. Activities focus on inter-faith communication and mainly speakers are arranged with question and answer time to encourage ecumenism.

NORTH EAST ENGLAND

Tyne and Wear Community Relations Council Inter Faith Panel

4th Floor, MEA House
Ellison Place
Newcastle-upon-Tyne NE1 8XS
Contact: Mr Hari Shukla
The panel is a representative committee, but all other meetings are open to everyone who is interested. It exists to encourage and maintain contact between different religious groups and individuals involved in interfaith activities in order to create better understanding and working relationships and to combat racism. It does this by: regular meetings of the Panel; visits to different places of worship; open meetings on interfaith subjects and by occasional day conferences. Affiliated to The Inter Faith Network for the UK.

YORKSHIRE AND HUMBERSIDE

Bradford Concord Inter-Faith Society

5 Scholemoor Road
Bradford BD7
Tel: 0274-727525
Tel: 0274-576189 (Home)
Contact: Ms Molly Kenyon
Office: Secretary
A voluntary interfaith association with regular monthly meetings for discussions, seminars and visits to places of worship. Affiliated to The Inter Faith Network for the UK.

Kirklees and Calderdale Inter-Faith Fellowship

65 Grosvenor Road
Dalton
Huddersfield HD5 9JB (home)
Tel: 0484-429490 (home)
Contact: Mr Khosro Deihim
A membership group which aims to create opportunities for inter-faith dialogue and increasing mutual understanding between the different faith communities of Kirklees, Calderdale and adjacent areas. It plans and executes local inter-faith events of a

social, spiritual and educational nature and publishes and circulates an occasional bulletin called "Inter-Faith Matters" which has no subscription charge. Affiliated to The Inter Faith Network for the UK.

Harrogate Interfaith Concord

24 Woodpark Drive
Knaresborough
North Yorkshire HG5 9DL
Tel: 0423-862726
Contact: Mrs K Margham
Office: Secretary
It aims to foster understanding between faith groups in the area. The group meets once a month on alternate Mondays and wednesdays at the green House, 5 Station Parade, Harrogate.

Leeds Concord (Inter-Faith Fellowship)

19 Gledhow Park Drive
Leeds LS7 4JT (home)
Tel: 0532-629140 (home)
Contact: Dr Peter Bell
Office: Secretary
Open to members of all faiths in Leeds. The present membership is composed of Jews, Christians, Muslims, Hindus, Sikhs, Buddhists, Baha'is and Brahma Kumaris. Membership subscriptions are £5.00 p.a. (waged) or £6.50 p.a. for husband/ wife/family member, £1.50 p.a. (unwaged), Church/faith groups £10.00 p.a., High Schools £8.00 p.a., and Primary Schools £5.00 p.a. It exists to promote inter-faith dialogue and sharing among the Leeds faith communities and their members, in order to further mutual knowledge and understanding, respect, friendship and co-operation, and to give support to the development of a just and caring society in the city, region and wider community. It also aims to support religious and social education in the schools and further and higher education centres in the city and region. It works by means of an ongoing programme of: open meetings, conferences, inter-faith and community events, young people's and women's meetings, joint meetings and events with other organisations concerned with social justice and peace; the work of the Resources Centre with in-service courses for teachers; consultations and conferences for various groups; supportive work in schools; the organisation of school visits to places of worship; exhibitions; and advisory and liaison work for individuals and organisations. Regular mailings are sent to members, communities and churches. Papers are available from the Concord Environmental Committee and the Resources Centre which publishes details of courses and lists of addresses and maps relating to faith community organisations in Leeds. Affiliated to The Inter Faith Network for the UK.

York Interfaith Group

c/o York RE Centre
University College of Ripon and York St John
Lord Mayor's Walk
York Y03 7EX
Tel: 0904-616587

NORTH WEST ENGLAND

Northwest Standing Conference on Inter-Faith Dialogue in Education

1 Saint Pauls Close
Clitheroe
Lancashire BB7 2NB (home)
Tel: 0200-24719 (home)
Contact: Colin Scott
Office: Secretary

Merseyside Inter-Faith Group

81 St Mary's Road
Huyton
Liverpool L36 5SR (home)
Contact: Ms Vida Barnett
A small group whose activities include discussion of issues, topics, media programmes and videos by members of different faith groups. Affiliated to The Inter Faith Network for the UK

Manchester Inter-Faith Group

St Margaret's Rectory
Rufford Road
Whalley Range
Manchester M16 8AE (home)
Tel: 061-226-1289 (home)
Contact: Revd Robert Boulter
Open to anyone of any faith in Greater Manchester. It exists to foster appreciation of people's religious beliefs and practices through dialogue, social events and support of interfaith work in the Greater Manchester area. It does this by open meetings, occasional forums, work with schools and colleges, and with hospitals and police. Termly mailings are sent to all members. Affiliated to The Inter Faith Network for the UK.

Rochdale Interfaith Action

445 Bury Road
Rochdale OL11 5EU
Tel: 0706-58491 (home)
Contact: Mr Stanley Hope

Office: Member

A membership group which aims to foster friendship, understanding, mutual respect and sharing between Muslims and Christians and to work together to promote a concern for social and racial justice in the community. Monthly open meetings are held to promote dialogue and learning together. It arranges occasional conferences, interfaith gatherings and other opportunities for meeting. It encourages participation by local mosques and churches and individual Muslims and Christians and supports the right to family life of the Asian community in the face of divisions caused by immigration law and practice. Affiliated to The Inter Faith Network for the UK.

ENGLISH EAST MIDLANDS

Derby Open Centre Multi-Faith Group

Derby Open Centre
43 Peartree Road
Derby DE3 6PZ
Tel: 0332-271744
Contact: Ms Janine Shrigley
Office: Contact person

Membership group and resource centre. It aims to promote understanding and good relationships between people of different racial, cultural and religious groups. It is committed to a non-racist approach to education alongside a multi-cultural curriculum which combats racism. It organises workshops on various cultures and religions and also visits to places of worship in the inner-city for schools all over Derbyshire. Affiliated to The Inter Faith Network for the UK.

Leicester Council of Faiths

27 Tudor Road
Leicester LE3 5JF (home)
Tel: 0533-622628 (home)
Contact: Revd Michael Ipgrave
Office: Secretary

A representative organisation consisting of leaders of all the major faith traditions in the city, appointed by their communities. Its concern is to promote understanding between different faiths and to provide a forum for considering and acting upon matters of shared concern. Routine briefings are conducted through a committee elected by an annual general meeting with at least one member from each tradition. Open meetings and study groups are convened. Affiliated to The Inter Faith Network for the UK.

Leicester Inter Faith Council

c/o 50 Launeston Road
Stoneygate
Leicester LE2 2AQ
Tel: 0533-700654
Contact: Aramish Mambouby
Office: Chairman

Regular inter-faith activities.

Lincoln Inter Faith Group

2 Thornton Close
Hillcroft
Washingborough
Lincoln LN4 1HQ (home)
Tel: 0522-790838 (home
Contact: Revd F Amery

Loughborough Inter-Faith Group

Charnwood United Reformed Church
66 Nottingham Road
Loughborough
Leicestershire LE11 1EU
Tel: 0509-261651
Contact: Ms Daphne Beal

Northampton Interfaith Group

42 Gordon Street
Northampton (home)
Contact: Mr P Galbraith

Nottingham Christian-Muslim Forum

Department of Theology
University of Nottingham
Nottingham NG7 2RD
Tel: 0602-515853
Fax: 0602-515887
Contact: Dr Hugh Goddard

Nottingham Inter-Faith Group

6 Rockford Road
Nottingham NG5 1JX (home)
Tel: 0602-783675 (home)
Contact: Ms Margaret Gardner
Office: Secretary

Open to individuals of all faiths in the Nottingham area. It exists to promote friendship and sharing between faith communities in the multi-ethnic, multi-faith city of Nottingham and to encourage dialogue and respect for each other's faith and justice and understanding in our community. It works by monthly meetings at different faith centres and by work with other voluntary organisations and schools. A monthly mailing is sent to members. Affiliated to The Inter Faith Network for the UK.

Wellingborough Multi-Faith Group

Victoria Centre
Palk Road
Wellingborough
Northamptonshire NN8 1HR
Tel: 0933-27400
Contact: Ms Cynthia Bailey

The group, which meets on the fourth Tuesday of each month includes members of a wide variety of belief systems/religious organisations and enquirers of no particular religious pursuasion. It exists to promote understanding between people and to educate members about each other's beliefs. Meetings take the form of discussions, guest speakers or visits to places of worship. The group is affiliated to The Inter Faith Network for the United Kingdom.

ENGLISH WEST MIDLANDS

Birmingham Fellowship of Faiths

104 Witherford Way
Selly Oak
Birmingham B29 4AW (home)
Contact: Mr Richard Spencer
Office: Chairperson

A "grassroots" membership group which aims to promote mutual understandng between people of different world faiths. Activities include discussions, visits, arts events, talks, dialogue and music for all ages. Meetings are open to anyone. Affiliated to The Inter Faith Network for the UK.

Birmingham Inter-Faiths Council

141 Arden Road
Smethwick
Birmingham B62 (home)
Tel: 021-565-1535 (home)
Contact: Vince Murray
Office: Secretary

Membership group. A formally constituted body representing the major religious groups in Birmingham. It has a membership of about one hundred individuals and an active Executive Committee. A quarterly newsletter is published and monthly events are organised. The council is run by voluntary workers and brings together Sikhs, Hindus, Muslims, Christians, Baha'is, Buddhists and Jews living in Birmingham. It engages in educational and social activities, youth events and acting as a voice on matters of concern to people of faith. Affiliated to The Inter Faith Network for the UK.

Coventry Inter Faith Group

12 Marlborough Road
Coventry CV2 4EP (home)
Tel: 0203-442400 (home)
Contact: Revd Jean R Clark

A membership group which promotes inter-faith understanding through informal meetings for conversation, listening to invited speakers and visiting places of worship. Affiliated to The Inter Faith Network for the UK.

Dudley Council of Faiths

c/o Dudley One World Resource Centre
Hillcrest School
Hill Street
Netherton
Dudley
West Midlands
Tel: 0384-873379 (home)
Contact: K S Singh
Office: Secretary

Aims to: help the people of Dudley to learn more about the great faiths of the world and, more importantly, meet and make friends with their adherents; give religious expression to the multi-cultural society of Dudley and draw out the implications of mutual acceptance; provide a reminder of the principles of human dignity and religious truth which uphold society and to emphasise the positive contribution which each faith brings. It works closely with the Dudley Racial Equality Council and offers its services in particular cases of community anxiety and strife. It arranges for public lecture series; annual inter-faith celebrations; mutual visits to places of worship and multi-cultural youth camps Affiliated to The Inter Faith Network for the UK.

Leamington Spa Inter-Faith Group

78 Lewis Road
Leamington Spa
Warwickshire CV31 1UQ (home)
Tel: 0926-420811 (home)
Contact: Revd Marjorie Warnes

Walsall Interfaith Group

16 Biscot Drive
Walsall WS2 9DF (home)
Tel: 0922-613927 (home)
Contact: Revd Hilary Smart
Office: Secretary

An informal group which has been open to any individual or community seeking to promote dialogue and better understanding between people of different faiths. Membership subscription is £5.00 p.a.

(organisations), £2.00 p.a. (waged individuals), 50p p.a. (unwaged individuals). It has aimed to: encourage and promote understanding and friendship between the people of Walsall; work for racial harmony and peaceful co-existence; promote dialogue about religious faith, belief and customs and to endeavour to help minority groups where problems arise requiring local government co-operation or knowledge of community resources. It is not currently active, but the Secretary is a contact and information point for anyone who wishes to develop its work again. Affiliated to The Inter Faith Network for UK.

West Bromwich Interfaith Group

Churchfields High School
Church Vale
West Bromwich
West Midlands (home)
Tel: 021-588-8452
Contact: Miss Ann Gray
Office: Chair

A group of religious leaders and others who meet regularly to plan a programme of multifaith activities for the community at large. The aim is to promote knowledge and understanding and respect among and between people of all faiths. Activities include visits and speakers.

Wolverhampton Inter-Faith Group

The Inter-Faith Centre
43 Princess Street
Wolverhampton WV1 1HD
Tel: 0902-27601
Tel: 0902-341948 (home)
Contact: Mrs Ivy Gutridge
Office: Acting Secretary

A membership group which aims to create opportunities for people of all faiths to meet and to promote dialogue and mutual respect for one another's faith, justice, community service and understanding in the community. The Executive Committee organises about nine events each year, such as conferences, meetings or visits to communities of faith as well as a service of prayer. There is opportunity for smaller groups to meet and share experiences of faith and culture. The group is involved in community health, racial issues, police liaison, multi-faith education and peace issues. Affiliated to The Inter Faith Network for the UK.

EAST ANGLIA

Cambridge Inter-Faith Group

47 Priam's Way
Stapleford
Cambridge CB2 5DT (home)
Tel: 0223-842007 (home)
Contact: Mr David Yarham
Office: Convenor

A membership group which exists to promote friendship and understanding between members of the various religions represented in the Cambridge area. It seeks to overcome the misconceptions which so often provide the basis for prejudice, and to provide a forum wherein people of different faiths may share the insights of their own religions and may thus learn from one another. Meetings are usually bi-monthly on topics of religious interest, and feature invited speakers and/or discussions. Affiliated to The Inter Faith Network for the UK.

Ipswich Inter-Faith Group

Suffolk College
Rope Walk
Ipswich IP4 1LT
Tel: 0473-255885
Fax: 0473-230054
Contact: Cynthia Capey
Office: Secretary

Peterborough Inter-Faith Council

18 West Street
King's Cliffe
Peterborough PE8 6XA (home)
Tel: 0780-470022 (home)
Contact: Ms Lesley Mathias
Office: Chairman

Mainly designed for representatives from the various faiths, but Friends can also be associated with the work of the Council as non-voting members. The Council currently includes people of various Christian denominations and people from the Hindu, Sikh, Baha'i, Orthodox Jewish, and Muslim (Sunni, Shi'a and Ismaili) traditions. The membership fee for both Council members and Friends is £5.00 p.a. It exists to encourage understanding and co-operation between different communities of faith in Peterborough. It does this by holding meetings; discussion groups; inter-faith worship events as part of United Nations Day celebrations; liaison with schools, libraries and the public at large; visiting others' places of worship and sharing their celebrations. Affiliated to The Inter Faith Network for the UK.

SOUTH EAST ENGLAND (NORTH)

Bedford Inter Faith Group

4 Oberon Court
Shakespeare Road
Bedford MK40 2EB
Tel: 0234–262178
Contact: Bryan walker
Office: Chairman
Has operated informerly for the past ten years and more formally for the past two years.

Mid Essex Inter Faith Group

98 The Street
Little Waltham
Chelmsford
Essex CM3 3NT (home)
Contact: Jane Howarth
Office: Honorary Secretary
The group aims to foster fellowship and understanding between the various faiths, respecting the contribution and spiritual insights of each. It acts as a resource and a network, holds meetings and arranges visits.

Redbridge Council of Faiths

The Lodge
Coppice School
Manford Way
Chigwell
Essex IG7 4AL
Tel: 081–500–4736
Contact: Mr Peter Baker
Office: Chairman
Membership group. The Council's aims are to help enjoy each others' religious experiences in a mutual sharing and to work towards overcoming the evils of racism and sectarianism which divide the world. The Council maintains an association with various voluntary organisations throughout the borough. It organises public events relating to culture, recreation, education, civic, industrial and spiritual experience ranging from visits to places of worship to seminars, inter-faith services, concerts by both children and adults. Affiliated to The Inter Faith Network for the UK.

Maidenhead Community Consultative Council

c/o Community Consultative Council
14 Delmont Park Road
Maidenhead
Berkshire SL6 6HT
Tel: 0628–21414
Contact: Mike Bruton

High Wycombe Inter-Faith Group

Merlin House
Medmenham
Marlow
Buckinghamshire SL7 2HJ
Tel: 0491–571216 (home)
Contact: Ms J Beresford
Office: Chair
An interfaith organisation which aims not to convert but to understand in order to be more sensitive to cultural difference and to respect those who differ and learn from them. The group members learn about each other's faith, pray together and runs some social events, lectures and small groups.

Oxford Round Table of Religions

The Old Rectory
Middleton Stoney
Oxford OX6 8RZ (home)
Tel: 0869–89–317 (home)
Contact: Mr S K Vadivale
Office: Chairperson
Membership is open to anyone, and there is no membership fee. Current members include people from the Baha'i, Buddhist, Christian, Hindu, Jewish, Muslim, Quaker, Sikh and Unitarian traditions. It exists to educate each other about each other's religious tradition and to provide support in the organisation of events of inter-faith worship. It does this by monthly discussion meetings with speakers of the different faiths and by participating in events of inter-faith worship wherever possible. In addition, it acts as a resource centre for schools and other organisations that require access to the representatives of the different faiths. Affiliated to The Inter Faith Network for the UK.

Reading Inter-Faith Group

Lukers
Theale
Reading RG7 5AH (home)
Tel: 0635–34400 (home)
Contact: Mr Hugh Boulter
Office: Treasurer
A membership group which aims to enable members of different religious groups to: learn about religious beliefs, practices and traditions in order to create friendship, harmony and understanding; enter into dialogue and celebrate a common commitment to spiritual values; share in occasions at which others' worship is experienced and others' ceremonies are witnessed. Up to eight events per year are held focusing on a theme. The programme follows the

academic year and often includes an outing and a picnic, the latter held locally. Affiliated to The Inter Faith Network for the UK.

Watford Inter-Faith Association

17 Swiss Avenue
Watford WD1 7LL (home)
Tel: 0923-231224 (home)
Contact: Mrs Mary Fudge
Office: Secretary
A membership group which seeks to promote understanding and trust, dialogue and co-operation among members of all faith communities in Watford. It arranges public meetings and house meetings to learn about and discuss matters of common concern and to explore areas of both agreement and difference.

LONDON (E POSTCODES)

Waltham Forest All Faiths Group

12 Connaught Road
Chingford
London E4 7DL (home)
Tel: 081-524-1029 (home)
Contact: Ms Judith Law
Office: Secretary
An inter-faith group consisting of individual members from a variety of different faiths. The All Faiths Group has been meeting regularly since the Summer of 1982 and is open to anyone who wishes to have the opportunity of getting to know people of other faiths and learning more about their beliefs and practice. The group consists of Baha'is, Buddhists, Christians, Hindus, Jews, Muslims and Sikhs. It meets every two months in different venues so that members find out where the community buildings of the various faith groups are. Meetings provide a chance to share with, and learn from, people of other faiths and are not for argument or debate. Recent meetings have looked at topics such as "Religion and Equality", "Religion and Politics", and "Bereavement". Affiliated to The Inter Faith Network for the UK.

Newham Association of Faiths

267 Central Park Road
East Ham
London E6 3AF (home)
Tel: 081-470-5527 (home)
Contact: Ms Doris Sadeghi
Open to individuals of all faiths living or working in Newham, and also to religious groups established in the Borough who support the aims and purposes of the Association as printed in the Constitution. It exists to: foster better understanding and relationships

between the people of different faiths in our community; promote public awareness of issues which relate to justice, peace and welfare in the community and to defend religious freedom and tolerance for all faith groups in Newham. The association provides a programme of events which are open to members of the general public. Newsletters and occasional mailings are sent to mebers together with an annual programme of events. Affiliated to The Inter Faith Network for the UK.

LONDON (NW POSTCODES)

London Society of Jews and Christians

Liberal Jewish Synagogue
28 St Johns Road
London NW8 7HA
Tel: 071-286-5181
Contact: Rabbi David Goldberg
A membership group founded in 1927 as the forerunner of the National Council of Christians and Jews. It has always maintained a steady nucleus of loyal members committed to its founding ideals, which are as important and relevant today as they were over sixty years ago. These are to give the opportunity to Jews and Christians to confer together on the basis of their common ideals and with mutual respect for their differences of belief. Four or five meetings are held a year on topics of mutual interest. Affiliated to The Inter Faith Network for the UK.

LONDON (SW POSTCODES)

Faith, Asylum, Refuge

48 Great Peter Street
London SW1P 2HB
Tel: 071-222-1313
Contact: Mr Michael Feeney
Office: Director
Its aim is to encourage and assist the faith communities of London to extend hospitality to refugees and asylum seekers by stimulating practical support and assistance and promoting awareness of their needs. Membership is open to all local faith communities and all Christian agencies and congregations interested in, concerned about, and actively supportive of refugees in the London Boroughs.

South London Inter-Faith Group

82 Toynbee Road
London SW20 8SR (home)
Tel: 081-542-9618 (home)
Contact: Mr Eric Bramsted
Office: Secretary

A membership group which seeks to promote a greater understanding between different faith communities in South London by organising visits, talks and discussions. There are about one hundred and fifty people on the mailing list and attendance at visits and meetings varies between twenty and forty.

LONDON (W POSTCODES)

Westminster Interfaith

Heythrop College
Kensington Square
London W8 5HN
Tel: 071-795-4211
Fax: 071-795-4200
Contact: Fr Michael Barnes SJ
Office: Director

An agency of the Roman Catholic Diocese of Westminster which aims to respond to the Second Vatican Council and the Popes with regard to interfaith relations. The agency exists to promote greater understanding, co-operation and respect between Christians and people of other faiths and thus combat discrimination at all levels. It also aims to help Christians deepen their own faith by promoting a greater awareness of other faiths through dialogue, prayer and action. The activities of Westminster Interfaith include: organising of a variety of seminars, courses, lectures and study days; developing of a network of contacts across the faiths; publication of a regular newsletter and the promotion of interfaith dialogue in formal and informal ways, notably through the annual London Multifaith Peace Pilgrimage, held in June of each year.

SOUTH EAST ENGLAND (SOUTH)

Surrey Inter-Faith Group

4 Cromwell Place
Cranleigh
Surrey GU6 7LS (home)
Contact: Ms Joyce Spath

Richmond Inter-Faith Group

12 Hillmont Road
Hinchley Wood
Esher
Surrey KT10 9BA (home)
Tel: 081-398-3706 (home)
Contact: Revd A McClelland
Office: Secretary

Membership is open to all at £3.00 pa (individuals) and £7.50 pa (groups). At present the group includes eight faiths: Christian, Hindu, Muslim, Jewish, Baha'i, Sikh, Buddhist, Brahma Kumaris and also includes agnostics. It exists to promote better understanding of each other's faith by: dialogue; discussion; speakers; visits to places of worship; co-operation with other bodies such as the United Nations Association. Notices of meetings are sent out regularly and incorporate news of local inter-faith activities. Affiliated to The Inter Faith Network.

Gillingham Interfaith Group

35 Cecil Avenue
Gillingham
Kent (home)
Contact: Mrs E Hill

Discussion group which meets every month or so at the Chatham Unitarian Church. The group aims to facilitate mutual understanding between different faiths. Members of both Christian and non-Christian faiths are normally present at meetings.

Medway Inter-Faith Group

548 City Way
Rochester
Kent ME1 2TW (home)
Tel: 0634-409606 (home)
Contact: Sirjit Singh Marway
Office: Secretary

Open to anyone interested in inter-faith matters. At present it has Muslim, Bah'ai, Christian, Sikh and Hindu members. There is no membership fee. It exists to promote greater understanding and friendship between members of different faiths. Meetings are held to discuss each other's religious beliefs or to plan future events, for example: Any Questions Evenings; debates on "Interfaith leads to a strengthening of individual religious identity" and visits to one another's place of worship at festival times. Affiliated to The Inter Faith Network for the UK.

Harrow Inter-Faith Council

19 Culverlands Close
Green Lane
Stanmore
Middlesex HA7 3AG
Tel: 081-954-6525 (home)
Contact: Miss Pat Stevens
Office: Secretary

The council consists of up to four members of each faith (although others may be co-opted), and at the moment includes Baha'i, Buddhist, Christian, Jain, Jewish, Muslim, Sikh, Hindu and Zoroastrian members. An associate membership is open to anyone who is in sympathy with the aims of the council and wishes to support its work. Events other than council meetings are open to all individuals of any faith. There is no membership fee, but Associate Members are asked to make an annual donation. It exists to: promote dialogue about faith while honouring the integrity of the individual; encourage and promote understanding and friendship between people of differing faith; work for harmony and peaceful co-existence in the local community and to oppose prejudice where it exists; understand problems experienced in the practice of any faith within the community and to work together for their solution. It does this by means of bi-monthly Council meetings; bi-monthly "Faith and Culture" evenings; monthly discussion group; by work in schools; membership of the Standing Advisory Council on Religious Education and through exhibitions and displays for local schools and the public in the Teacher's Centre and local library. Affiliated to The Inter Faith Network for the UK.

SOUTH WEST ENGLAND

Bath Inter-Faith Group
45 Brooklyn Road
Larkhall
Bath BA1 6TF (home)
Tel: 0225-422252 (home)
Contact: Mrs Shelagh James
Office: Honorary secretary
Membership group. All members of Bath Interfaith group desire interfaith dialogue in a spirit of mutual understanding, for it is important that we should not separate ourselves from others by opinion, doctrine or dogma. Activities include talks, discussions, joint worship on special occasions.

One World Fellowship
56 The Green
Beaminster
Dorset DT8 3SD (home)
Tel: 0308-862004 (home)
Contact: Mary Moorhead
Office: Secretary
Membership group open to everyone of any religious faith or none. The Fellowship exists to promote understanding among people of different faiths and outlooks, and between all people and the natural world. It operates as an independent group with the support of local Anglican and Catholic clergy. Monthly meetings are open to non-members as well as members and are, for talks and discussion on a variety of topics. Occasional other events and visits are organised. It is concerned to develop relationships with other like-minded groups.

Bristol Inter Faith Group
2 Court Road
Frampton Cotterell
Bristol BS17 2DE (home)
Tel: 0454-772138 (home)
Contact: Mrs June Ridd
Office: Secretary
A membership group and forum for communication between religious groups in order to to enable people of different backgrounds to meet and, as far as possible, experience something of backgrounds and cultures different from their own. The group fosters positive attitudes within and between religious groups and the wider secular world. The group has a committee formed mainly by representatives of religious communities. It organises an annual inter faith service. Activities and events are hosted by religious communities. Affiliated to The Inter Faith Network for the UK.

Exeter University Interfaith Group
2 College Road
Shebbear
Nr Beaworthy
Devon EX21 5HH
Tel: 0409-281403
Contact: Mrs Sandy Martin
Office: President
Meetings four or five times termly: lectures, visits etc, everyone welcome.

Plymouth Interfaith Group
21 Dale Road
Plymouth PL4 6PH (home)
Contact: Arezoo Farahzad
Office: Secretary

Swindon Interfaith Group
120 York Road
Swindon
Wiltshire (home)
Contact: Mr Mike Thomas

RESOURCES

OTHER RELEVANT DIRECTORIES, HANDBOOKS AND BOOKS

GENERAL INFORMATION

BAHA'I

BUDDHIST

CHRISTIAN

HINDU

JAIN

JEWISH

MUSLIM

SIKH

ZOROASTRIAN

NATIONAL RELIGION

LOCAL RELIGION

ETHNIC MINORITY

This section lists a number of useful general overviews of religious traditions or a specific dimensions of religious life as found in a variety of religions, together with other relevant directories and handbooks on the religions covered in the directory.

GENERAL RELIGION

There are a wide range of general works available giving overviews of religions or specific dimensions of religious life. Some of these are listed below:

Al-Faruqi, I (ed), *Historical Atlas of the Religions of the World*, Macmillan, New York, 1974.

Appleton, G (ed), *The Oxford Book of Prayer*, Oxford University Press, Oxford, 1985.

American Theological Library Association, *Index to Book Reviews in Religion: An Author, Title, Reviewer, Series and Annual Classified Index to Reviews of Books Published in and of Interest to the Field of Religion*, American Theological Library Association, Evanston, Illinois, annual (since 1989).

American Theological Library Association, *Religion Index One: Periodicals*, American Theological Library Association, Evanston, Illinois, semi-annual (since 1949).

American Theological Library Association, *Religion Index Two: Multi-Author Works*, American Theological Library Association, Evanston, Illinois, annual (since 1976).

Barley, L; Field, C; Kosmin, B; and Nielsen, J, *Reviews of United Kingdom Statistic Sources Volume XX, Religion: Recurrent Christian Sources, Non-Recurrent Christian Data, Judaism, Other Religions*, Pergamon Press, Oxford, 1987.

Bishop, P, *Words in World Religions*, SCM, London, 1979.

Bishop, P (ed), *The Encyclopaedia of World Faiths*, Orbis, New York, 1987.

Carman, J and Juergensmeyer, N (eds), *A Bibliographic Guide to the Comparative Study of Ethics*, Cambridge University Press, Cambrdige, 1991.

Carmody, D and J, *Prayer in World Religions*, Orbis, Maryknoll, New York, 1990.

Cole, W O and Morgan, P, *Six Religions in the Twentieth Century*, Hulton Educational, London, 1984.

Coward, H, *Sacred Word and Sacred Text: Scriptures in World Religions*, Orbis, New York, 1991.

Eliade, M (ed), *The Encylopaedia of Religion* (sixteen volumes), Collier Macmillan, London, 1986.

Hinnells, JR (ed), *The Penguin Dictionary of Religions*, Penguin, London, 1984.

Hinnells, J R (ed), *A Handbook of Living Religions*, Viking, London, 1984.

Hinnells, JR (ed), *Who's Who of World Religions*, Macmillan, London, 1991.

Holm, J, *Keyguide to Information Sources on World Religions*, Mansell, London, 1991.

King, U, *Women in the World's Religions*, Paragon, New York, 1987.

Lea, E and Jesson A (compilers), *A Guide to the Theological Libraries of Great Britain and Ireland*, Association of British Theological and Philosophical Libraries, London, 1986.

Lurker, M, *Dictionary of Gods and Goddesses, Devils and Demons*, Routledge and Kegan Paul, London, 1987.

Prickett, J (ed), *Living Faiths: Initiation Rites*, Lutterworth Press, London, 1978.

Prickett, J (ed), *Living Faiths: Death*, Lutterworth Press, London, 1980.

Prickett, J (ed), *Living Faiths: Marriage and the Family*, Lutterworth Press, London, 1985.

Schumacher, S and Woerner, G (eds), *The Rider Encyclopaedia of Eastern Philosophy and Religion: Buddhism, Hinduism, Taosim, Zen*, Rider, London, 1989.

Sharma, A (ed), *Women in World Religions*, State University of New York Press, Albany, New York, 1987.

Smart, N, *The World's Religions: Old Traditions and Modern Transformations*, Cambridge University Press, Cambridge, 1989.

Smart, N and Hecht, R (eds), *Sacred Texts of the World: A Universal Anthology*, Macmillan, London, 1982.

Sutherland, S; Houlden, L; Clarke, P; Hardy, F (eds), *The World's Religions*, London, 1988.

Whitaker, *Religious Books in Print: A Reference Catalogue*, Whitaker, London, annual (since 1984).

Zaehner, R (ed), *The Hutchinson Encyclopedia of Living Faiths*, Hutchinson, London (4th edition), 1988.

BAHA'I

There is no generally available publication giving details of Bahai'i groups in the UK. However, the Baha'i Community of the UK (27 Rutland Gate, London, SW7 1PD, Tel: 071-584-2566) maintains up-to-date listings of all Spiritual Assemblies and Local Groups.

BUDDHIST

Swain, J (ed), *The Buddhist Directory*, Buddhist Society, London, 1991.

CHRISTIAN

Most of the Christian Churches and some of the organisations listed in this directory have their own directories or handbooks. Those listed below are therefore only those directories which cover a number of Churches or types of Christian group:

Brierley, P (ed), *UK Christian Handbook 1994/95,* Christian Research Association, London, 1994 (forthcoming).

Brierley, P (ed), *The Irish Christian Handbook*, MARC Europe, Kent, 1992.

Byrne, L (ed), *Directory of Women's Organisations and Groups in Churches and Ecumenical Bodies in Britain and Ireland*, Council of Churches for Britain and Ireland, London, 1992.

Centre for Caribbean Studies, *A Handbook of the Afro-West Indian United Council of Churches*, Centre for Caribbean Studies, London, 1984.

Douglas, D *The Handbook of the International Ministerial Council of Great Britain 1990*, International Ministerial Council of Great Britain, Watford, 1990.

Gerloff, R "Appendix 5:I, List of Black Independent and Related Churches (including Councils of Churches) in Britain" in, *A Plea for British Black Theologies: The Black Church Movement in Britain in its Transatlantic Cultural and*

Theological Interaction, Volume II, Peter Lang, Franfurt-am-Main, Germany, 1992, pp 863-1055.

Orthodox Parish of St John the Baptist, *Directory of Orthodox Parishes and Clergy in the British Isles 1988/9*, Stylite Publishing, Welshpool.

HINDU

There is no generally available Hindu publication listing Hindu religious groups nationally, although lists have appeared in some general publications. The International Society for Krishna Consciousness maintains a database of Hindu groups. There are a wide range of handbooks pertaining to specific caste organisations, but these are not generally publicly available.

JAIN

There are no publicly available Jain directories or handbooks. However, the Institute of Jainology (Unit 18, Silicon Business Centre, 26-28 Wandsworth Road, Greenford, Middlesex, UB6 7JZ, Tel: 081-997-2300) does try to maintain an up-to-date database of Jain groups.

JEWISH

S Massil (ed), *The Jewish Year Book, 5753-5754*, Jewish Chronicle Publications, London, 1993.

MUSLIM

Ali, M, *The Mosques in the United Kingdom and Eire and Prayer Time Table*, Ambala Sweet Centre, London, 1991.

Linkers, *List of Mosques, Islamic Centres and Islamic Associations in the UK*, Linkers, London 1993 (updated regularly by Linkers, 134 Dalyell Road, London, SW9 9UP).

Muslim Education Trust, *List of Mosques and Islamic Centres in Britain*, Muslim Education Trust, London, 1988.

Rahman, G (ed), *The Directory of Mosques, Islamic Centres and other Muslim Organisations in the*

United Kingdom and Ireland, Council of Mosques UK and Eire, London, undated.

SIKH

Shergill, N S, *International Directory of Gurdwaras and Sikh Organisations*, N S Shergill, London, 1985.

Sikh Cultural Society of Great Britain, *The Sikh Gurdwaras in the United Kingdom*, Sikh Cultural Society of Great Britain, London, 1989.

ZOROASTRIAN

There is no generally available Zoroastrian directory or handbook. However, the Zororastrian Trust Funds for Europe try to maintain details of the Zoroastrian community in the UK.

NATIONAL RELIGIOUS

In addition to handbooks and directories covering particular religions, there are a number of publications which have a more general coverage. Some of these are listed below:

Clarke, F (ed), *Interfaith Directory*, International Religious Foundation Incorporated, New York, 1987.

Inter Faith Network for the UK, *A Handbook of Affiliated Organisations of the Inter Faith Network (3rd edition)*, Inter Faith Network for the UK, London, 1993.

Office of Population and Censuses and Surveys, *The Official List, Part III - Certified Places of Worship*, Office of Population and Censuses and Surveys, General Register Office, London, 1981.

Ward, G (ed), *Religions Directory International: A Comprehensive Guide to the World's Religions, Churches, Denominations, Temples, Synagogues, Religious Organisations and Spiritual Groups, Volume 1: The United Kingdom amd Ireland*, Apogee Books, Detroit, Michigan, 1990.

Whiteaker, S (ed), *The Good Retreat Guide: 1991*, Rider Publications, London.

LOCAL RELIGIOUS

Many local and regional directories and listings exist. Details of these can often be obtained through local Racial Equality Councils, local Councils for Voluntary Service, or local libraries (the latter of which sometimes also have computerised listings available for public perusal and print-out). Examples of some of those which are published in the more permanent form of booklets and pamphlets are given below:

Blyth, H (ed), *Places of Worship in Oxford*, Advisory Centre for Multi-Cultural Education, Oxford, 1989.

Brent Council Education Department, *Brent Religious Education, Now and Tomorrow*, Brent Council Education Department, Brent, 1988.

Capey, C (ed), *Faiths in Focus in Ipswich and Suffolk: A Collection to Celebrate the Centenary of the World's Parliament of Religions, held in Chicago in 1893*, Ipswich, 1993.

Hertfordshire County Council Education Department, *Faith Communities Handbook (Hertfordshire)*, Hertfordshire County Council Education Department, Hetfordshire, 1991.

King, T (ed), *Places of Worship in Birmingham*, City of Birmingham Education Department and the Regional R E Centre at Westhill College, Birmingham.

Leeds City Council Department of Education, *Directory of Faith Communities in Leeds*, Leeds City Council Department of Education, Leeds.

Mead, J (ed), *Visiting Places of Worship in Waltham Forest*, Multi-cultural Development Service, Waltham Forest.

Publicity Unit of the Chief Executives Department of the Metropolitan Borough of Trafford, *Places of Worship in the Metropolitan Borough of Trafford*, Publicity Unit of the Chief Executives Department of the Metropolitan Borough of Trafford, Trafford, undated.

Warwickshire County Council Education Department, *A Directory of Places of Worship and Useful Contacts and Addresses for Teachers of Religious Education in Warwickshire*, Warwickshire County Council Education Department, Warwick.

Willows, H (ed), *A Guide to Worship in Central London*, London Central YMCA, London, 1988.

Wolverhampton Inter Faith Group and Wolverhampton Multi-Cultural Support Team, *Directory of Places of Worship in Wolverhampton*, Wolverhampton Inter faith Group and Wolverhampton Multi-Cultural Support Team, Wolverhampton, 1989.

ETHNIC MINORITY

There are a number of ethnic minority directories which are not primarily concerned to cover religious groups but do, in fact, provide useful contact information for them.

At the local level there are many such directories and listings, details of which can often be obtained through local Racial Equality Councils, local Councils for Voluntary Service, or local libraries. The directories listed below are restricted to some which aim to give UK-wide coverage:

Asian Times, *The Ethnic Minorities Directory: A Commercial and Social Directory of African, Asian and Caribbean Communities in Britain*, Hansib Publishing, London, 1993.

O'Maolain, C, *Ethnic Minority and Migrant Organisations, European Directory: 1991*, Joint Council for the Welfare of Immigrants, London, with the Centre for Research in Ethnic Relations, Warwick University, Coventry, 1991.

Patel, C B, *Who's Who of Asians in Britain*, New Life Publications, London, 1988.

Sachar, J S, *Asian Who's Who International: 1990/91*, Asian Observer Publications, Ilford.

SOME MULTI-RELIGIOUS RESOURCE ORGANISATIONS

There are a wide range of organisations which can give further advice on the religious traditions and organisations covered within this volume. A few of these are listed here in order that directory users can followup information and ideas. Those listed are organisations which can provide information spanning two or more religious traditions. In the chapter on the individual religious communities there are a number of entries relating to resource organisations operating on a UK and local basis with respect to particular religious traditions.

Alister Hardy Research Centre

Westminster College
Oxford OX2 9AT
Tel: 0865-243006
Fax: 0865-251847
Contact: Professor Lawrence Brown
Office: Director
The purpose of this Centre is to explore systematically the spiritual, transcendent or religious and other experiences, of individuals and groups and the ways they affect people's lives. Membership is open to anyone who is interested in supporting the Centre's research into there questions. For more information, write to the director

Bradford Interfaith Education Centre

Listerhills Road
Bradford BD1 1HD
Tel: 0274-731674
Fax: 0274-731621
Contact: David Fitch
Office: Centre co-ordinator
A resource and training centre for religious and cultural education established in 1986 to support Religious Education and Collective Worship in Bradford LEA schools. The centre now provides training courses and other services for schools, colleges and other institutions covering a wide area. Centre staff from local Christian, Muslim, Hindu and Sikh communities are available for talks or consultation and to lead guided visits to places of worship. The Centre houses a library and artefacts service, teaching areas, a shop and refreshment facilities. Its trails include a variety of shops and restaurants.

BFSS National RE Centre

West London Institute of Higher Education
Lancaster House
Borough Road
Isleworth
Middlesex TW7 5DU
Tel: 081-568-8741
Fax: 081-569-9198
The Centre aims to encourage and help teachers in school and church to provide enlightened religious education that develops understanding and respect. It mounts an annual programme of in-service courses in religious education, multicultural education and personal, moral and social education. It houses a large collection of teaching resources, including recent publications, videos, slides and poster materials, artefacts and religious objects.

Community Religions Project

Department of Theology and Religious Studies
University of Leeds
Leeds LS2 9JT
Tel: 0532-333646
Contact: Dr Kim Knott
Office: Co-Ordinator

Research centre. The project works to promote the academic study of contemporary religions in Britain. The recent emphasis on the project has been on the religions of Britain's ethnic minority groups, though the original aim, which continues to be kept in mind, was to encourage the study of all religions, particularly those in the West Yorkshire area. Within the overall aim of promoting this, the Community Religions Project is committed to exploring the appropriate methods for such study and suitable means of information dissemination. The project operates a policy of encouraging rigorous and objective scholarship, and welcomes students of all religious backgrounds who are willing and able to work in such a context. A secondary aim of the project is to collect data (for example, scholarly articles, papers and books) on contemporary religions in Britain which can be consulted by those engaged in research and teaching. Affiliated to The Inter Faith Network for the UK.

Centre for the Study of Islam and Christian-Muslim Relations

Selly Oak Colleges
996 Bristol Road
Birmingham B29 6LQ
Tel: 021-472-4231
Fax: 021-472-8852
Contact: Dr Jorgen Nielsen
Office: Director

An academic institution founded in 1976 and linked to the University of Birmingham and the Selly Oak Colleges. It is a joint venture between Muslims and Christians. Its aim is to analyse, explain and help resolve tensions, both at the theological and the communal levels. It seeks to bridge traditional distrust by bringing people of both communities together, and to bridge the divide between the academic world and the practical world of everyday life. It offers an extensive teaching programme at postgraduate level. It provides courses on Islam and Christianity for professionals working in multicultural and multi-religious situations all over the world. It advises and consults with local, national and international working groups, seminars and policy making bodies. It works with Church and Muslim agencies, political, educational and community groups, and professional and other informal groups. It produces publications on Islam and Christian-Muslim relations. Affiliated to The Inter Faith Network for the UK.

Centre for the Study of Judaism and Jewish-Christian Relations

Selly Oak Colleges
Central House
Bristol Road
Birmingham B29 6LQ
Tel: 021-472-4231
Contact: Rabbi Dr N Solomon
Office: Director

The centre promotes the advancement of education by promoting the study of: the beliefs, practices and histories of Jewish, Christian and other living faith communities; ways of promoting improved mutual understanding among the people of these communities; the causes of conflict between the people of these communities and suggestions for the resolution of such conflicts; the teaching and carrying out of research and study of the aforementioned subjects and the provision of an environment in which people of these traditions can work together in matters of mutual concern. It does this by means of lectures, courses, conferences and publications. Courses are open to those suitably qualified. Members of the general public are invited to become subscribers. A postgraduate Diploma of the Centre is validated by the University of Birmingham and MPhil and PhD theses are supervised. It is affiliated to The Inter Faith Network for the UK.

Centre for the Study of Religion and Education in the Inner City

Chapel Street
Salford M3 7AJ
Tel: 061-832-3709
Contact: Trish Hardy

INFORM

Houghton Street
London WC2A 2AE
Tel: 071-955-7654
Office: Director

INFORM stands for Information Network on Religious Movements. It aims to provide help, in the form of accurate and unbiased information about new religious movements, and about available counselling. It is committed to the preservation of a person's freedom of belief as defined in Articles two and eighteen of the Universal Declaration of Human Rights and as elaborated by the European Covention on Human Rights and Fundamental Freedoms. At the same time, it is aware that the actions of some members of some of the movements can give cause for legitimate concern, and it believes that such actions ought to be investigated as rigorously as possible. It works by: providing information on the beliefs, practices, membership, organisation and whereabouts of particular movements and on individuals and agencies which provide counselling, advice or support for any problems which arise as a result of direct or indirect association with a movement. It undertakes original research; maintains the network; arranges regional training seminars or workshops; provides speakers; acts as a recognised and independent body. There are no members as such, but INFORM is directed by a Board of Governors which consists of fifteen Directors, six of whom are nominated by nominating bodies. These nominating bodies are: the British Sociological Association, Sociology of Religion Study Group; the Church of England; the Roman Catholic Church; the Free Church Federal Council; the Home Office; and the British Association of Counselling.

Inter Faith Network for the UK

5-7 Tavistock Place
London WC1H 9SS
Tel: 071-388-0008
Fax: 071-387-7968

The Network links seventy organisations with an interest in relations between the different faith communities in Britain. It provides an information and advice service which everyone may use. Full details will be found in the entry for the Network in the section on national inter-faith organisations.

International Consultancy on Religion Education and Culture (ICOREC)

9a Didsbury Park
Manchester M20 0LH
Tel: 061-434-0828
Fax: 061-434-8374
Contact: Mr Martin Palmer
Office: Director

ICOREC is an interfaith, intercultural consultancy actively engaged in promoting greater understanding and appreciation of the variety of faiths and cultures of the world. Consultants are drawn from all the major faiths and represent a wide cross section within each faith. ICOREC has consultants around the world as well as a home team based in the UK, and particularly at its Manchester headquarters. Activities range from providing photographs for publication to initiating and organising international interfaith events, from compiling essential teachings of each faith to writing interfaith philosophical studies, from producing educational materials with and for a specific faith to running cross-faith studies.

Multi-Faith Centre

198-200 Hagley Road
Edgbaston
Birmingham B16 9PQ
Tel: 021-455-8848
Contact: Dr Mary Hall
Office: Executive Director

The Multi-Faith Centre is a Registered Charitable Company with Directors representing the Hindu, Muslim, Sikh, Buddhist, Jewish and Christian traditions. The teaching Team are also members of the six traditions. The centre was initiated in 1981 following a three year intensive research project in which fourteen communities participated, involving one hundred and fifty-six people of Anglican, Baptist, Buddhist, German Evangelical Lutheran, Hindu, Jewish, Methodist, Muslim, Pentecostal, Quaker, Roman Catholic, Sikh and United Reformed traditions. The project was successful in testing and developing an educational methodology for interfaith and intercultural dialogue and representatives of each tradition involved founded the Multi-Faith Centre. The aim of the Centre is to provide "Education by Encounter", with a permanent Team of multi-faith, multi-cultural educators and resource personnel from their communities. Over the years the staff have become genuine partners in discovery, in out-reach, in building up a climate of understanding, compassion and respect for others in order to promote harmony in our pluralistic world. The team designs and implements a variety of programmes to meet the specific needs of particular groups such as teachers, social workers, health workers, prison officers/chaplains, church personnel and university groups. The Centre offers facilitating services for several Councils of Churches in Europe and other European organisations. Affiliated to The Inter Faith Network for the UK.

National Society's Religious Education Centre

23 Kensington Square
London W8 5HN
Tel: 071-937-4241
Fax: 071-938-2004

Regional Religious Education Centre

Westhill College
Selly Oak
Birmingham B29 6LL

Religious Education Resource Centre

315 Woodlands Road
Glasgow
G3 8AG
Tel: 041-357-3929

Religious Education Council

1 Raffin Park
Datchworth
Hertfordshire SG3 6RR (home)
Tel: 0438-812416 (home)
Fax: 0438-812416 (home)
Contact: Mrs Gwen Palmer
Office: Chairperson
A national body which provides a forum for exploring concerns and issues related to religious education, and takes appropriate action on behalf of member bodies to promote the interests of Religious Education nationally. Membership is composed of a wide range of faith communities and professional Religious Education associations. It is not open to individual membership. The Council meets twice a year and its Executive more frequently. Priority has been given to responding to events and public statements impinging on the future of Religious Education., and to the production of reports on particular aspects of Religious Education. Revd. Dr. Stephen Orchard, Tel: 0332-296655 and Fax: 0332-43253 is the Secretary of the Council and another contact person for it. Affiliated to The Inter Faith Network for the UK.

Religious Resource and Research Centre

The University of Derby
Mickleover
Derby DE3 5GX
Tel: 0332-622222 Ext 2102
Tel: 0332-360235 (home)
Contact: Mr Paul Weller
Office: Head of Centre
The Centre is jointly sponsored by the University of Derby and the Church of England Diocese of Derby and has a Steering Committee with membership from a range of religious communities. Its work is conducted on an inter-faith and inter-disciplinary basis and it issues a bi-annual mailing to a network of individuals who are interested in the work of the centre. It is affiliated to The Inter faith Network for the UK.

It has an academic role in research and teaching within the institution and the locality, as well as a central service role on matters of religious belief and practice within the University. In its central service role it took the lead in drafting a University Code of Practice on Religious and Equal Opportunities. It worked jointly with The Inter Faith Network for the UK to produce *Religions in the UK: A Multi Faith Directory*. *Newsvalues*, the newsletter of the National Association for Values in Education and Training, is produced from the Centre. It also services the University's Theology Society and organises a range of events and conferences including a recent jointly-sponsored conference with the World Congress of Faiths on the theme of "A Good Death". Centre staff also contribute to the University's MA in Religious Pluralism programme, of which the Head of Centre is course leader. This programme is intended to meet the needs of students from a wide variety of disciplinary or religious backgrounds who recognise that within a multi-faith society it is becoming ever more important in the religious, educational, social service, health, commercial and industrial sectors, to gain an understanding of, and critical engagement with, the issues posed by religious pluralism. The programme focuses upon exploring the problematic and contested nature of religious pluralism and equipping course members both practically and theoretically to engage with the issues which it poses.

Shap Working Party on World Religions in Education

c/o National Society Religious Education Centre
23 Kensington Square
London W8 5HN
Tel: 071-937-4241
Fax: 071-938-2004
Contact: Dr P Williams
Office: Secretary
A membership group which promotes study of the world religions in education. It is concerned to ensure that the study of peoples' world views, beliefs, values and practices is given due attention throughout our educational system and especially in the school curriculum at all age phases. It does this through conferences, consultations, publications and by Working Party members being available to provide help and advice to enquirers. It also produces the annual journal World Religions in Education and the Shap Calendar of Religious Festivals. Affiliated to The Inter Faith Network for the UK.

St Mungo Museum of Religious Life and Art Gallery and Museum

2 Castle Street
Glasgow G4 0RH
Tel: 041-553-2557
Fax: 041-552-4744

Britain's first museum on the religions of the world. Open seven days, free.

Standing Conference on Inter-Faith Dialogue in Education

88a Brondesbury Villas
Kilburn
London NW6 6AD (home)
Tel: 071-798-1827
Tel: 01-328-6793 (home)
Contact: Ms Angela Wood
Office: Conference Organiser
Open to all interested individual and groups. There is no membership fee. It exists to: confirm that the understanding of a person's faith is fundamental to respect for her or him as human being; welcome our multicultural society with joy and hope and to repudiate every form of racism; support religious education as a developmental process by which all children, wherever they live, will have the opportunity to learn about the ideals and insights which inspire all peoples; stimulate teachers to recognise the enrichment of our society by the presence of many faiths and cultural traditions and to encourage educational institutions and authorities to promote interfaith dialogue for deeper and more sensitive understanding. SCIFDE meets three times a year nationally and encourages regional meetings at different times. National interfaith conferences are held, concerned with education in school and community, including Religious Education. Conference themes have included "Work, Rest and Play", "Woman", "Story", and "Bridges and Barriers". Affiliated to The Inter Faith Network for the UK.

Study Centre for Christian-Jewish Relations (Sisters of Sion)

17 Chepstow Villas
London W11 3DZ
Tel: 071-727-3597
The Centre is autonomous with no special membership framework. It aims to provide a place for the study of Judaism and the Jewish roots of Christianity and to provide a meeting ground for Christians and Jews in the spirit of the Second Vatican Council. Lectures and short courses are offered on Judaism and its links with Christianity and visitors are welcome to refer to its specialist library and educational materials. A series of pamphlets has been published and is available from the Study Centre. There are close links between the Centre and other organisations involved in Jewish-Christian and inter-faith dialogue. Affiliated to The Inter Faith Network for the UK.

Welsh National Centre for Religious Education

University College of North Wales School of
  Education
Deniol Road
Bangor
Gwynedd LL57 2UW
Tel: 0248-382761
Fax: 0248-382952
Contact: Reinallt A Thomas
Office: Director
A large resource centre including bookshop which covers the whole of the multi-faith religious education as well as Church education materials. Open 9.00am-5.00pm Mondays - Fridays. Contact can also be made with the Secretary, tel: 0248-382956.

York Religious Education Centre

York RE Centre
University College of Ripon and York St John
Lord Mayor's Walk
York Y03 7EX
Tel: 0904-616958/7
Fax: 0904-612512
Contact: Mary Hayward and Revd Dr Peter Doble
Office: Deputy Director and Director
York RE Centre offers one of the foremost collections of RE resources in Britain. The Centre specialises in RE Inset and its staff are always willing to respond to requests for courses. It is open daily (Monday-Friday) and its loan facilities are available to the general public; its computerised retrieval system enables a quick response to all enquiries.

THE SHAP WORKING PARTY ON WORLD RELIGIONS IN EDUCATION

Each year the SHAP Working party publishes its Calendar of Religious Festivals. This includes a detailed listing of the dates for the religious festivals of the world's religions, with notes on each festival, an index to them and a separate wall chart calendar. The 1993-94 SHAP calendar covers the period from August 1993 to December 1994.

The SHAP Working Party has also produced a separate book of nearly 300 pages, which is available in both hardback and softback, containing a wealth of useful and detailed information on festivals in all the major religions.

SHAP Calendar of Religious Festivals: £1.50 (inc. p&p)

Festivals in World's Religions, edited by Alan Brown:
Hardback   £13.35   (inc. p&p)
Softback   £10.15   (inc. p&p)

The SHAP Working Party also produces a variety of other publications, including an annual journal which explores a different issue or theme each year and includes an extensive resources review section. Back issues of these are available. Other publications deal with the teaching of world religions in school. Full details of all SHAP publications can be obtained from the address below.

SHAP Working Party Publications
c/o The National Society's RE Centre
23 Kensington Square
London W8 5HN
Tel: 071 937 7229
Fax: 071 938 2004

Cheques payable to SHAP Working Party
Postage and packing charges are deducted from orders collected from the Centre.

LOCAL GUIDE

To index every organisation in the directory would require an extremely large index. National organisations can be straightforwardly looked up by alphabetical order of organisational name within the national listings for each religion. Listing large numbers of local organisational names and page numbers would not necessarily assist the user, since many organisations have the same name. Therefore, instead of a comprehensive organisational index, this "Local Guide" is included to assist use of the local listings according to the general rules and exceptions in the chapter "Using the Directory" (pp 17-19).

The local listings sections of the directory are organised into the nations of the UK and regions of England. Local organisations are then listed by alphabetical order of place and, where there is more than one organisation in a given place, also by alphabetical order of organisational name. This structure means that when you know the county in which a place is located, the entries for that place can be found directly by looking up the appropriate region and the place name in alphabetical order.

In those cases where you are not sure in which county or region the place has been located within this directory, then this "Local Guide" lists all the places where local organisations contained in the directory are to be found as well as the region within which each place is located.

At the foot of this list, the "Local Guide" includes a Table of Page Numbers for each regional section cross-referenced with each religion covered by the directory. Having located a place and its region, you can use this Table to turn to the appropriate pages of the directory to find what you are looking for. Therefore, to use this guide when you do not know the location of a place:

● Look down the alphabetical list for the place name you want (eg Ambleside).

● Note the region in which it is located within the directory (in the case of Ambleside, this is North West England).

● Go to the Table of Page Numbers for regional sections at the foot of the Place Name Index.

● Look for the cross-reference between the North West region and the religion you are looking for (in the case of Baha'is in North West England the pages would be 62-63).

● Finally, you can turn to those pages within the local listings and see whether there are any organisations of that religion in the place you are concerned with and, if so, you will find their contact details.

Borehamwood, South East England (North)
Bournemouth, South West England
Bradford, Yorkshire and Humberside
Brentwood, South East England (South)
Brierfield, North East England
Brighton, South East England (South)
Bristol, South West England
Brixham, South West England
Broadford, Scotland
Bromley, South East England (South)
Buckie, Scotland
Buckingham, South East England (North)
Burnley, North West England
Burton-on-Trent, English West Midlands
Bury, North West England
Bury St Edmunds, East Anglia
Bushey, South East England (North)
Buxton, English East Midlands
Builth Wells, Wales
Caernarfon, Wales
Caerphilly, Wales
Calne South, West England
Camberley, South East England (South)
Cambridge, East Anglia
Campbletown, Scotland
Canterbury, South East England (South)
Cardiff, Wales
Carlisle, North West England
Carnoustie, Scotland
Chandler's Ford South East England (South)
Chatham, South East England (South)
Cheadle, North West England
Chelmsford, South East England (North)
Cheltenham, South West England
Chesham, South East England (North)
Chester, North West England
Chesterfield, English East Midlands
Chichester, South East England (South)
Chigwell, South East England (North)
Chippenham, South West England
Christchurch, South West England
Clithero, North West England
Colchester, South East England (North)
Coleraine, Northern Ireland
Colne, North West England
Colwyn Bay, Wales
Corwen, Wales
Coventry, English West Midlands
Cowes, South East England (South)
Cranfield, South East England (North)
Cranley, South East England (South)
Cranmore, South West England
Crawley, South East England (South)
Crayford, South East England (South)
Crewe, North West England
Crossgar, Northern Ireland
Crowborough, South East England (South)

Croxley Green, South East England (North)
Croydon, South East England (South)
Cwmbran, Wales
Dalrymple, Scotland
Darlaston, English West Midlands
Darlington, North East England
Darwen, North West England
Derby, English East Midlands
Dewsbury, Yorkshire and Humberside
Dollar, Scotland
Doncaster, Yorkshire and Humberside
Dowlais, Wales
Douglas, North West England
Dublin, Ireland (Republic)
Dudley, English West Midlands
Dumfries, Scotland
Dundee, Scotland
Dunfermline, Scotland
Dunstable, South East England (North)
Durham City, North East England
East Barnet, South East England (North)
East Croydon, South East England (South)
Eastbourne, South East England (South)
Eastcote, South East England (North)
East Dereham, East Anglia
Eccles, North West England
Edgware, South East England (North)
Edinburgh, Scotland
Egham, South East England (South)
Elgin, Scotland
Ely East, Anglia
Emsworth, South East England (South)
Enfield, South East England (North)
Esher, South East England (South)
Eskdaelmuir, Scotland
Exeter, South West England
Falkirk, Scotland
Farnborough, South East England (South)
Farnworth, North West England
Felixstowe, East Anglia
Fife, Scotland
Finstown, Scotland
Firstown, Scotland
Fishguard, Wales
Folkeston, South East England (South)
Fort William, Scotland
Frazerburgh, Scotland
Gainsborough, East Anglia
Galashiels, Scotland
Galston, Scotland
Gateshead, North East England
Gatley, North West England
Gillingham, South East England (South)
Glan Conwy, Wales
Glasgow, Scotland
Glenluce, Scotland
Gloucester, South West England

Godalming, South East England (South)
Gravesend, South East England (South)
Great Moulton, East Anglia
Greenford, South East England (North)
Greenlaw, Scotland
Greenock, Scotland
Griminish, Scotland
Grimsby, Yorkshire and Humberside
Guildford, South East England (South)
Guisborough, North East England
Hale Barns, North West England
Halesowen, English West Midlands
Halifax, Yorkshire and Humberside
Hamilton, Scotland
Hanley, English West Midlands
Hanwell, South East England (North)
Harlow, South East England (North)
Harold Hill, South East England (North)
Harrogate, Yorkshire and Humberside
Harrow, South East England (North)
Hartlepool, North East England
Haslemere, South East England (South)
Hastings, South East England (South)
Hatchend, South West England
Hatfield, South East England (North)
Hawick, Scotland
Hayes, South East England (North)
Hayle, South West England
Hay-on-Wye, South West England
Haywards Heath, South East England (South)
Haverford West, Wales
Heckmondwicke, Yorkshire and Humberside
Hemel Hempstead, South East England (North)
Hereford, English West Midlands
Hexham, North East England
Highworth, South West England
High Wycombe, South East England (North)
Hildenborough, South East England (South)
Hinckley, English East Midlands
Hitchin, South East England (North)
Holywood, Northern Ireland
Honiton, South West England
Hornchurch, South East England (North)
Hounslow, South East England (North)
Hounslow West, South East England (North)
Hove, South East England (South)
Huddersfield, Yorkshire and Humberside
Hull, Yorkshire and Humberside
Ilford, South East England (North)
Invergordon, Scotland
Inverness, Scotland
Ipswich, East Anglia
Isle of Lewis, Scotland
Isleworth, South East England (North)
Keighley, Yorkshire and Humberside
Kempston, South East England (North)
Kendal, North West England

Kenton, South East England (North)
Kettering, English East Midlands
Kidderminster, English West Midlands
Kilbirnie, Scotland
Kingston-upon-Thames, SE England (South)
Kingwiniford, English West Midlands
Kirkcudbright, Scotland
Kirkwall, Scotland
Knaresborough, Yorkshire and Humberside
Lairg, Scotland
Lancaster, North West England
Launceston, South West England
Leamington Spa, English West Midlands
Leatherhead, South East England (South)
Leavesen, South East England (North)
Leeds, Yorkshire and Humberside
Leicester, English East Midlands
Leigh-on-Sea, South East England (North)
Lerwick, Scotland
Lesmahagow, Scotland
Lewes, South East England (South)
Lichfield, English West Midlands
Lincoln, English East Midlands
Lisburn, Northern Ireland
Liverpool, North West England
Liversedge, Yorkshire and Humberside
Llandaff, Wales
Llangollen, Wales
Llanidloes, Wales
Llanwrtyd Wells, Wales
Locharron, Scotland
Lochmaddy, Scotland
London (see postcode areas)
Londonderry, Northern Ireland
Long Ditton, South East England (South)
Lostwithiel, South West England
Loughborough, English East Midlands
Loughton, South East England (North)
Lowestoft, East Anglia
Ludlow, English West Midlands
Luton, South East England (North)
Macclesfield, North West England
Machynlleth, Wales
Maidenhead, South East England (North)
Maidstone, South East England (South)
Malmesbury, South West England
Manchester, North West England
Margate, South East England (South)
Marlow, South East England (South)
Meigle, Scotland
Melksham, South West England
Melton Mowbray, English East Midlands
Middlesborough, North East England
Middleton Stoney, South East England (South)
Milton Keynes, South East England (North)
Mitcham, South East England (South)
Mold, Wales

Monkton, Scotland
Montrose, Scotland
Mossley, North West England
Motherwell, Scotland
Nelson, North West England
Nethy Bridge, Scotland
New Barnet, South East England (North)
Newark, English East Midlands
Newbury, South East England (North)
Newbury Park, South East England (North)
Newcastle-under-Lyme, English West Midlands
Newcastle-upon-Tyne, North East England
Newport, English West Midlands
Newport, South East England (South)
Newport, Wales
Newport Pagnell, South East English (North)
Newton Abbot, South West England
Newton Le Willows, North West England
Newtown Abbey, Northern Ireland
Newtownards, Northern Ireland
New Malden, South East England (South)
Northampton, English East Midlands
Northaw, South East England (North)
Northolt, South East England (North)
Northwood, South East England (North)
North Harrow, South East England (North)
North Hillingdon, South East England (North)
North Wembley, South East England (North)
Norton-Sub-Hamdon, South West England
Norwich, East Anglia
Nottingham, English East Midlands
Nuneaton, English West Midlands
Oakham, English East Midlands
Oban, Scotland
Old Cowyn, Wales
Oldham, North West England
Overy Tracey, South West England
Oxford, South East England (North)
Paignton, South West England
Paisley, Scotland
Peel, North West England
Penarth, Wales
Penicuik, Scotland
Penygroes, Wales
Penzance, South West England
Perth, Scotland
Peterborough, East Anglia
Peterhead, Scotland
Petersfield, South East England (South)
Pilton, South West England
Pinner, South East England (North)
Plymouth, South West England
Plympton, South West England
Poole, South West England
Port Charlotte, Scotland
Port Talbot, Wales
Portsmouth, South East England (South)

Preston, North West England
Pwelheli, Wales
Radcliffe, North West England
Radlett, South East England (North)
Raglan, Wales
Rainham, South East England (South)
Ramsgate, South East England (South)
Randalstown, Northern Ireland
Rawdon, Yorkshire and Humberside
Rawtenstall, North West England
Rayner's Lane, South East England (North)
Reading, South East England (North)
Redbridge, South East England (North)
Redditch, English West Midlands
Redhill, South East England (South)
Reigate, South East England (South)
Rhos-on-Sea, Wales
Richmond-upon-Thames, SE England (South)
Risca, Wales
Rochdale, North West England
Rochester, South East England (South)
Rossendale, North West England
Romford, South East England (North)
Ross-on-Wye, English West Midlands
Rotherham, Yorkshire and Humberside
Rothesay, Scotland
Rowley Regis, English West Midlands
Royal Tunbridge Wells, SE England (South)
Rugby, English West Midlands
Rugeley, English West Midlands
Ruislip, South East England (North)
Ruislip Manor, South East England (North)
Ryde, South East England (South)
St Alban's, South East England (North)
St Andrews, Scotland
St Anne's-on-Sea, North West England
St Asaph, Wales
St Brelade, South East England (South)
St Leonard's-on-Sea, South East England (South)
St Mellons, Wales
St Monans, Scotland
St Peter Port, South East England (South)
Saffron Walden South East England (North)
Sale, North West England
Salford, North West England
Salisbury, South West England
Saltash, South West England
Saltcoats, Scotland
Sandall, Yorkshire and Humberside
Sanquar, Scotland
Saxmundham, East Anglia
Scalloway, Scotland
Scunthorpe, Yorkshire and Humberside
Selsden, South East England (South)
Sevenoaks, South East England (South)
Sheffield, Yorkshire and Humberside
Shipley, Yorkshire and Humberside

Shrewsbury, English West Midlands
Shrivenham, South East England (North)
Sidestrand, East Anglia
Skene, Scotland
Skipton, Yorkshire and Humberside
Sleaford, English East Midlands
Slough, South East England (North)
Solihull, English West Midlands
Southall, South East England (North)
Southampton, South East England (South)
Southend-on-Sea, South East England (North)
Southport, North West England
Southwell, English East Midlands
Southwick, South East England (South)
South Hornchurch, South East England (North)
South Shields, North East England
Spennymoor, North East England
Stafford, English West Midlands
Staines, South East England (South)
Stalybridge, North West England
Stanmore, South East England (North)
Stevenage, South East England (North)
Stirling, Scotland
Stockport, North West England
Stockton-on-Tees, North East England
Stoke-on-Trent, English West Midlands
Stornoway, Scotland
Stourbridge, English West Midlands
Stowmarket, East Anglia
Stranraer, Scotland
Stroud, English West Midlands
Sudbury, South East England (North)
Sunderland, North East England
Surbiton, South East England (South)
Sutton, South East England (South)
Swindon, South West England
Swansea, Wales
Tain, Scotland
Talgarth, Wales
Tattysallagh, Northern Ireland
Taunton, South West England
Teddington, South East England (North)
Telford, English West Midlands
Thornton Heath, South East England (South)
Thurles, Ireland (Republic)
Timperley, North West England
Todmorden, North West England
Tipton, English West Midlands
Tonyrefail, Wales
Toomebridge, Northern Ireland
Torquay, South East England (South)
Truro, South West England
Tuam, Ireland (Republic)
Tunbridge, South East England (South)
Uckfield, South East England (South)
Umberleigh, South West England

Uplands, South West England
Wakefield, Yorkshire and Humberside
Wallasey, North West England
Walsall, English West Midlands
Warley, West Midlands
Warrington, North West England
Warslow, English East Midlands
Warwick, English West Midlands
Waterlooville, South East England (South)
Watford, South East England (North)
Watlington, South East England (North)
Watten, Scotland
Wednesbury, English West Midlands
Welling, South East England (South)
Wellingborough, English East Midlands
Wellington, South West England
Wells, South West England
Welwyn Garden City, South East England (North)
Wembley, South East England (North)
Wembley Park, South East England (North)
Westcliff-on-Sea, South East England (North)
Weston, North West England
West Bromwich, English West Midlands
West Croydon, South East England (South)
West Wycombe, South East England (South)
Weybridge, South East England (South)
Weymouth, South West England
Whitchmore, South East England (South)
Whitchurch, West Midlands
Whitchurch, South East England (South)
Whitefield, North West England
Whitley Bay, North East England
Whitstable, South East England (South)
Wickford, South East England (North)
Wigan, North West England
Wigton, North West England
Wilmslow, North West England
Wimbourne, South West England
Winchester, South East England (South)
Windsor, South East England (North)
Winscombe, South West England
Wirral, North West England
Wishaw, Scotland
Woking, South East England (South)
Woldingham, South East England (South)
Wolverhampton, English West Midlands
Woodford Green, South East England (North)
Worcester, South West England
Workington, North West England
Worthing, South East England (South)
Wrexham, Wales
York, Yorkshire and Humberside

Table of Page Numbers for Regional Sections Within the Local Listings

	Scotland	Wales	N Ireland	NE England	Yorks
Baha'i	58–59	59–60	60–61	61	61–62
Buddhist	93–96	96–98	98	98–100	101–103
Christian	185–191	191–194	194–195	195–197	197–199
Hindu	245–246	246	246	246–247	247–248
Jain	–	–	–	306	–
Jewish	340–342	342	342–343	343–344	344–347
Muslim	411–414	414–416	416	416–418	418–432
Sikh	538–539	539	–	539	539–542
Zoroastrian	–	–	–	581	–
Inter-Faith	611–612	612	–	612	612–613

	NW England	East Midlands	West Midlands	East Anglia	SE (North)
Baha'i	62–63	63–64	64	64–65	65–67
Buddhist	103–107	107–109	109–111	111–114	114–118
Christian	199–202	203–205	205–208	208–210	210–212
Hindu	248–252	252–260	260–264	264	264–273
Jain	306	306–307	307	–	307–308
Jewish	347–353	353–354	354–355	355–356	356–363
Muslim	432–449	450–456	456–473	473–474	474–485
Sikh	542–543	543–546	546–554	554	554–559
Zoroastrian	581–582	–	582	–	582
Inter-Faith	613–614	614–615	615–616	616	617–618

	London (E)	London (N)	London (NW)	London (E)	London (SW)
Baha'i	67	67	67	67	68
Buddhist	118	119	119–120	120	121–122
Christian	★	★	★	★	★
Hindu	273–275	275	275–277	277–278	278–279
Jain	–	308	308	–	309
Jewish	363–365	365–369	369–372	372	372
Muslim	485–489	489–491	491–492	493–494	494–497
Sikh	559	559	–	560	560
Zoroastrian	582	582	–	–	582
Inter-Faith	618	–	618	–	618–619

	London (W)	London (WC)	SE (South)	SW England
Baha'i	68	–	68–71	71–72
Buddhist	122–123	123	123–127	127–132
Christian	★	★	215–217	217–220
Hindu	279–280	280	280–282	282–283
Jain	–	–	309–310	–
Jewish	372–374	–	374–377	377–378
Muslim	497–498	498	498–504	504–506
Sikh	560	–	560–563	563
Zoroastrian	–	–	582	–
Inter-Faith	619	–	619–620	620

★ Because they are entries on regional rather than a local basis, the Christian regional listings for London are not divided into postcode areas but can be found on pp 212-215.

TOPIC INDEX

The "Topic Index" lists the page references within the general introductory chapters and the Introductions to each religious community where you can find paragraphs of material on particular items. The items appearing in bold are the standard sub-section titles (see section on "Introductory Materials" on pp 16-17 in chapter on "Using the Directory") which appear in the Introductions to each religion.

If a word which you are looking for does not appear in this index, you can also search for it in the "Keyword Index" which gives individual page references for each word which is italicised in the text. Generally, these are Romanisations of words in languages other than English, or are English language words with a specific meaning within the religion concerned (see section on "Religions and Languages" on p23 in the chapter on "Using the Directory"). Alternatively, the word you are looking for might be found in the Keys to Organisational Listings in the chapters on each religion.

KEYWORD INDEX

The "Keyword Index" lists, in alphabetical order, the page references for each word which is italicised in the text. Generally speaking, these are Romanisations of words which are either in languages other than English, or are English language words with a highly specific meaning within the religion concerned. The names of religious festivals are also included here.

If a word which you are looking for does not appear in this index, then you can search for it either in the various Keys to Organisational Titles (see pp 19-20 in "Using the Directory") which are set out in alphabetical order within most of the Introductory sections on each religion. Alternatively, consult the "Topic Index" which indexes more generally descriptive paragraphs within the general introductory chapters and the Introductions to each religious community.

A

Aaronic Priesthood, 587
Abdu'l-Baha, 48, 49, 53, 54
Acaranga Sutra, 297
Acharyas, 297, 300
Acts of the Apostles, 144, 149
Adar, 572, 576
Adar mah, 578
Adar roj, 578
Adar roj nu Parab, 578
Adi Granth, 526, 527, 588
Administrative Order, 50
Adur, 576
Advaita, 230, 231, 232, 233
Advaita-Vedanta, 232
Advaitins, 232
Advent, 155
Afrinagan, 572
Afrins, 572
Agamas, 297
Agape, 145
Aggadah, 316
Agha Khanis, 391
Ahimsa, 31, 36, 299, 300
Ahl-e-Hadith, 391, 396
Ahuna Vairya, 575
Ahunavaiti Gatha, 572
Ahunavar, 575
Airyana Vaeja, 572
Aiwisruthrim, 575
Ajiva, 298
Akal Takhat, 28
Akhand Path, 532
Al-khulafa ar-rashidun, 387

Al-Kitab al Aqdas, 49
Ala, 53
All hallows e'en, 157
All Saints' Day, 155, 157
Allah, 389
Altar, 153
Ambedkarite, 76, 84
Amesha Spentas, 573, 576, 577, 578
Amrit, 529, 533
Amrit Pahul, 528, 529
Amritdhari, 529
Anand Karaj, 530
Anand Sahib, 531
Anandpur Sahib, 530
Anatman, 79
Anatta, 78, 81
Anavil Brahmins, 234
Anekantavada, 297
Angabahya, 297
Angas, 297
Anglican, 28, 141, 144, 146, 147, 148, 149, 151, 152, 153, 159, 163, 164
Anglo-Catholic, 148
Anicca, 78, 81
Anniversary of the Ascension of Baha'u'llah, 52
Anniversary of the Birth of Baha'u'llah, 53
Anniversary of the Birth of the Bab, 52
Anniversary of the Declaration of the Bab, 52
Anno Domini, 154
Anniversary of the Blessed Virgin Mary, 156
Antaraya, 298
Anuvratas, 299, 300
Aparigraha, 299, 300
Apostolic Succession, 147
Aql, 389
Apostolicity, 147
Aranyakas, 229
Arati, 300
Aravot, 324
Arba Kanfot, 323
Archbishop, 140, 164
Ardas, 532
Ardhamagadhi, 297
Area Superintendent, 161, 163
Areas, 161
Arhat, 298
Arihanta, 298
Aron Kodesh, 322
Artha, 233
Arti, 33, 236
Arya Astangika Magga, 81
As salaam-u-`alaikum, 34
Asalha Puja, 84
Asatru, 590
Ascension, 157
Ascension Day, 156
Ascension of Abdu'l-Baha, 53
Ash Wednesday, 156
Asha, 575, 576